389-364
124-127
372-373

Edward L. ACREE
911 Goodman Rd.
323-7391

TEXTBOOK OF
BIOCHEMISTRY

EIGHTH EDITION

BENJAMIN HARROW, Ph.D.

Professor Emeritus of Chemistry
City College, City University of New York

ABRAHAM MAZUR, Ph.D.

Professor of Chemistry
City College, City University of New York

W. B. SAUNDERS COMPANY

Philadelphia • London • 1962

PREFACE

WHAT WE have said in the preface to the last edition applies equally at this time: "The accelerated development of biochemistry shows no abatement, and we believe that this new edition is evidence for such a statement." Several chapters, representing rapid advances, have been considerably altered. We have, however, been careful to retain the essential character of the book: a readable and thoroughly up-to-date volume.

For help in various directions, our thanks are due to Dr. D. Cavallini and Professor Rossi Fanelli (University of Rome); Professor J. E. Jorpes (University of Stockholm); Professor M. Karshan and Professor A. Krasna (Columbia University); Professor Allan H. Roush (Illinois Institute of Technology).

Our thanks are also due to our publishers, W. B. Saunders Company, for help in innumerable ways.

BENJAMIN HARROW
ABRAHAM MAZUR

CONTENTS

Chapter 1   INTRODUCTION   1

Chapter 2   CARBOHYDRATES   5

Chapter 3   THE LIPIDS   42

Chapter 4   PROTEINS   68

Chapter 5   NUCLEOPROTEINS AND NUCLEIC ACIDS   112

Chapter 6   ENZYMES   128

Chapter 7   DIGESTION AND ABSORPTION.............   170

Chapter 8   BLOOD   200

Chapter 9   CHEMISTRY OF RESPIRATION............   226

Chapter 10   BIOLOGICAL OXIDATIONS   250

Chapter 11   METABOLISM OF CARBOHYDRATES.........   266

Chapter 12   METABOLISM OF THE LIPIDS.............   298

Chapter 13   METABOLISM OF PROTEINS..............   321

Chapter 14   METABOLISM OF NUCLEOPROTEINS........   359

Chapter 15   ENERGY METABOLISM 378

Chapter 16   INORGANIC METABOLISM 394

Chapter 17   NUTRITION 417

Chapter 18   VITAMINS 442

Chapter 19   CHEMISTRY OF THE TISSUES............. 485

Chapter 20   BIOCHEMISTRY OF THE KIDNEYS—URINE... 511

Chapter 21   HORMONES 535

Chapter 22   METABOLISM OF FOREIGN ORGANIC COM-
POUNDS 585

Chapter 23   IMMUNOCHEMISTRY AND CHEMOTHERAPY.. 600

ABBREVIATIONS OF COMPOUNDS........... 623

APPENDIX 625

INDEX 634

INTRODUCTION

Biochemistry deals with the chemical processes which go on in living matter, ranging from the smallest to the largest—from viruses and bacteria to plants and animals.

One of the earliest workers in the field was Lavoisier (1734–1794), who is often spoken of as the father of modern chemistry. His classic researches into oxidation, and the role played by oxygen in the process, led him to investigate "burning" in the body; and he came to the conclusion that oxygen is consumed in the reaction, that carbon dioxide is eliminated, and that heat is evolved. Later, in the hands of Voit, Pettenkofer and Rubner in Germany, and Atwater, Benedict and DuBois in the United States, animal calorimetry became a science in the modern sense.

The early history of biochemistry is associated with the studies of organic chemists who attempted to isolate and identify a variety of compounds of vegetable and animal origin. Liebig (1803–1873), for example, arrived at the conclusion that "the nutritive materials of all green plants are inorganic substances," and Wöhler (1800–1882) synthesized urea, the principal end-product of nitrogenous metabolism in the body—an achievement which did much to destroy the notion that animal products were endowed with a "vitalism" which made them fundamentally different from "lifeless" substances.

The work of Chevreul (1786–1889) on the chemical constitution of fats, and the researches of Kossel (1853–1927) on nucleoproteins and proteins, and of Emil Fischer (1852–1919) on carbohydrates and proteins, gradually led to an understanding of the chemical composition of foods and, to a limited extent, of the chemical composition of the cell.

Nor must the influence of the illustrious Pasteur (1822–1895) be overlooked. His extensive researches into the nature of fermentation led Buchner (1860–1917) to our modern concept of enzymes, the cellular

1

catalysts which are responsible for many of the activities within the body.

Researches by such pioneers as Arrhenius, van't Hoff and Ostwald on electrolytic dissociation and osmotic pressure led physical chemists (as well as organic chemists) to turn their attention to biological phenomena. Sörensen developed our concept of pH; Loeb studied the colloidal behavior of proteins and their effect on the cell; Henderson and Van Slyke developed their ideas concerning body neutrality; Michaelis evolved the concept of chemical compound formation between enzyme and substrate; and Stanley showed that viruses were nucleoproteins. Important in this and neighboring fields were the invention of several instruments—the Barcroft-Warburg manometric apparatus, the Van Slyke blood gas apparatus, the ultracentrifuge of Svedberg, the electrophoresis apparatus of Tiselius; the use of isotopes in biological and chemical research (Urey, Hevesy, Schoenheimer and Rittenberg); and, more recently, the application of paper chromatography, as developed by Martin and Synge.

Nor can we overlook the impetus to further work given by the founding, in 1879, of the first journal devoted to biochemistry, the *Zeitschrift für physiologische Chemie*. In 1906 three other journals were started: the *Journal of Biological Chemistry* in the United States, the *Biochemical Journal* in England, and the *Biochemische Zeitschrift* in Germany.

Modern biochemistry may be said to have started with the demonstration by Meyerhof and Hill that a correlation exists between lactic acid production in contracting muscle and oxygen consumption and heat evolution. This was one of the early attempts to relate a chemical reaction with a particular physiological function. Isolation of substrates and their enzymes from muscle extracts made it possible to reconstruct a sequence of chemical reactions intermediate between glycogen (or glucose) and lactic acid. The fundamental importance of these reactions (glycolysis) became evident when they were also demonstrated in animal tissues other than muscle as well as in yeast and bacteria (fermentation).

The researches of Warburg, Wieland, Keilin and Theorell led to the discovery of enzymes and cofactors involved in cellular oxidation. There now arose the concept of several steps for each oxidation reaction involving hydrogen and electron transfer, thus making it possible to liberate the energy of oxidation in small packets. The recognition that ADP was converted to ATP during aerobic oxidation, and Lipmann's observation on the significance of the terminal pyrophosphate linkages of ATP as an energy storage reservoir, led to the establishment of a fundamental principle of biochemistry—that radiant energy of the sun, utilized by the green plant for the synthesis of foodstuffs, is converted in the animal cell into the terminal pyrophosphate groups of ATP during the hydrogen and electron steps of oxidation. This stored energy can be transferred for purposes of reactions which are needed by the living cell, e.g., synthesis of proteins, nucleic acids, acetylcholine (nerve impulse transmission) and muscle contraction.

As a result of the studies of Szent-Györgi and of Krebs, the fate of lactate (or pyruvate) during aerobic oxidation was elucidated, leading to the sequence of reactions known as the Krebs or tricarboxylic acid cycle. The importance of this metabolic pathway was further enhanced when it was shown that fatty acids and amino acids are oxidized to yield intermediates identical with those in the Krebs cycle, thus providing a common mechanism for the liberation of energy from all foodstuffs. These enzymes and cofactors were located in the mitochondrial particles of the cell and in this way the physiological function of these bodies was identified.

Biochemistry has advanced in recent years on several fronts. Perhaps the most significant advance is represented by a clarification of the structure of the cellular macromolecules, proteins and nucleic acids. The primary polypeptide structure of proteins, first proposed by Emil Fischer, has been confirmed by the brilliant researches of Sanger who established the complete amino acid sequence of the protein hormone insulin, and by the work of Du Vigneaud who proved the structure of the hormone octapeptides of the posterior pituitary by direct synthesis. In large measure, these accomplishments have been aided by newly developed techniques. Among these are paper and column chromatography, ion exchange resins, and the coupling of these with automatic collecting and analyzing devices. These have made possible the Herculean task of a complete quantitative analysis of the amino acids in mg. quantities of protein (Stein and Moore). The studies of Pauling and Corey led to the concept of a secondary structure of protein molecules in the form of the helix. Similar studies have confirmed a similar kind of structure for the nucleic acids. Watson and Crick proposed that a double-stranded DNA molecule could be made by involving bases on adjacent strands in hydrogen bonding. This base-pairing hypothesis was confirmed by the quantitative data in the literature and was soon followed by the enzymatic synthesis of RNA by Ochoa and of DNA by Kornberg. These synthetic macromolecules have properties which suit the Watson-Crick hypothesis. Finally, the problem of protein synthesis is well on its way to a solution with the identification of several important steps in this complex reaction, involving RNA molecules as carriers of individual amino acids (transfer RNA) and ribonucleoprotein molecules in the microsomes as the receivers and builders of the final protein molecule.

The field of biochemistry which has stimulated lively interest and shows great promise for the future is that of biochemical genetics. DNA is the bearer of the genes of chromosomes. This genetic role for DNA has steadily developed, starting with the early observations of Avery that one type of bacteria could be transformed into another by exposing the organism to the DNA isolated from the latter type of bacteria. This was followed by the observation of a sexual type of reproduction in some bacteria (Lederberg) involving the passage of DNA from one organism to the other. Jacob and Wollman have shown that the transfer of genetic information is a sequential one, suggesting that the gene represents one segment of the DNA molecule which occupies a specific site with reference to another gene. The effects of x-irradiation, discovered by Muller and extended by Beadle and Tatum to the effects of irradiation on specific enzymes, have firmly established the concept that DNA is coded with respect to its abilities (genes) to direct the synthesis of specific proteins; and that a loss of such synthetic ability by a cell is associated with some alteration of that portion of the DNA molecule which carries that specific gene.

❊   ❊   ❊   ❊   ❊

Professorships of biochemistry are of comparatively recent origin. In Germany the pioneers were professors of chemistry or of physiology. At present there are many professorships of biochemistry, as well as separate departments of biochemistry.

In France, Claude Bernard, though a professor of physiology, did fundamental work in biochemistry; later, Gabriel Bertrand occupied the first chair of biochemistry. In England, one of the first chairs of biochemistry was occupied by Hopkins in 1914. In the United States, there was already an active laboratory of biochemistry at the beginning of the present century. Chittenden was its founder at Yale. One of his pupils, Mendel, succeeded him; and another, Gies, became professor of the subject at Columbia. Folin was appointed to a chair of biochemistry at Harvard in 1907. The guiding spirits in the medical schools quickly recognized the importance of the subject, and chairs of biochemistry sprang up all over the country. Today, biochemistry is a part of the curricula of the undergraduate and graduate departments of chemistry and biology in most colleges and universities.

❊   ❊   ❊   ❊   ❊

REFERENCES

Chittenden: The First Twenty-Five Years of the American Society of Biological Chemists. 1945; *Von Meyer:* History of Chemistry. 1891; *Lieben:* Geschichte der Physiologischen Chemie. 1935; *Borek:* The Atoms within Us, 1961; *Moore:* The Coil of Life, 1961.

CARBOHYDRATES

CHAPTER TWO

PHOTOSYNTHESIS

Carbohydrates (and, for that matter, countless organic compounds) originate in the green plants. Here, in the presence of light (hence photosynthesis) and in the presence of chlorophyll, a green pigment found in the chloroplasts, carbohydrates are synthesized. In the course

TABLE 1. SYNTHESIS OF ORGANIC COMPOUNDS IN GREEN PLANTS

Raw materials	Primary products	The more important secondary substances	
		(a) *Molecular weight less than 1000*	(b) *Materials of high molecular weight*
CO_2	Sugars	Polyene pigments	Cellulose
		Aliphatic acids, alcohols	Hemicelluloses,
H_2O	Amino acids	Terpenes	gums, pectins
	Sunlight on chloroplast pigments	Sterols	
		Waxes	Resins
Inorganic nitrogen compounds		Phosphatides (e.g., lecithin)	Rubber
		Inositol	
	Reserve materials	Aromatic hydroxy acids	Tannins
		Hydroxy compounds as glucosides (phenols, complex alcohols)	Lignins
			Nucleic acids
	Proteins, fats and oils	Volatile aldehydes, alcohols, esters, ethers (in essential oils with terpenes)	
		Alkaloids	
	Polysaccharides (e.g., starch), hemicelluloses	Pyrrole pigments	
		Anthocyan pigments	

(From Conant: Chemistry of Organic Compounds. By permission of The Macmillan Company, Publishers.)

of their formation, some of the simpler units needed to build these carbohydrates take part in various side reactions, by combining with other elements such as nitrogen, phosphorus and sulfur, to form lipids and proteins, etc. In fact, starting with the photosynthetic reaction, there are numerous syntheses for which the plant is responsible (Table 1).

When sugar is metabolized energy is released; but for the synthesis of sugar a source of energy is required. This energy is obtained from sunlight and is absorbed by chlorophyll. It is used to build carbohydrate molecules from carbon dioxide and water. The chemical reactions by which this transformation takes place will be discussed later in some detail (p. 293). But at this point suffice it to say that there appear to be two methods by which carbon dioxide is fixed by photosynthetic cells. In the conventional reaction carbon dioxide and water combine to form sugars which are then transformed into other cellular constituents, including fats, amino acids and proteins. Actually carbon dioxide is combined with a sugar phosphate, ribulose diphosphate, and the resulting complex splits and forms the 6-carbon sugar, fructose. From this sugar the higher plants build carbohydrates, which are then converted to other components. In another type of reaction photosynthetic bacteria, in the presence of light, convert carbon dioxide directly to amino acids and proteins without intermediate formation of sugars.

CHLOROPHYLL

When seedlings are germinated and grown in the dark, one finds a yellowish-green pigment. It has been called "protochlorophyll." Upon illuminating the seedlings, the yellowish-green pigment disappears and is replaced by the green chlorophyll. Protochlorophyll contains two less hydrogens than chlorophyll, which indicates that the transformation from the one to the other involves a process of reduction.

Chlorophyll consists of two modifications, *a* and *b*. In a mixture of petroleum ether and methyl alcohol, component *a* is found in the former and component *b* in the latter. An analysis of these two substances yields the following:

Chlorophyll *a*, $C_{55}H_{72}N_4O_5Mg$
Chlorophyll *b*, $C_{55}H_{70}N_4O_6Mg$

Reduction and oxidation of chlorophyll pigments yield pyrrole compounds, such as hemopyrrole, which suggests the pyrrole nature of chlorophyll itself. Incidentally, a similar series of pyrrole compounds is obtained from hemoglobin.

Drastic alkaline treatment of chlorophyll (and hemoglobin) yields porphyrins (red compounds with characteristic absorption spectra) containing four pyrrole nuclei; their structure as suggested by Küster is:

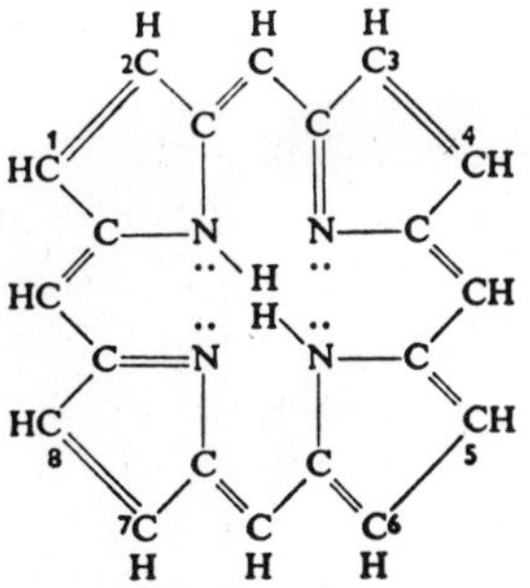

Porphin nucleus

The unsubstituted nucleus is known as *porphin*. The synthesis of a porphyrin having the characteristic spectrum of the porphyrins was first accomplished by Hans Fischer in 1926. More recently, Woodward has succeeded in synthesizing chlorophyll *a*.

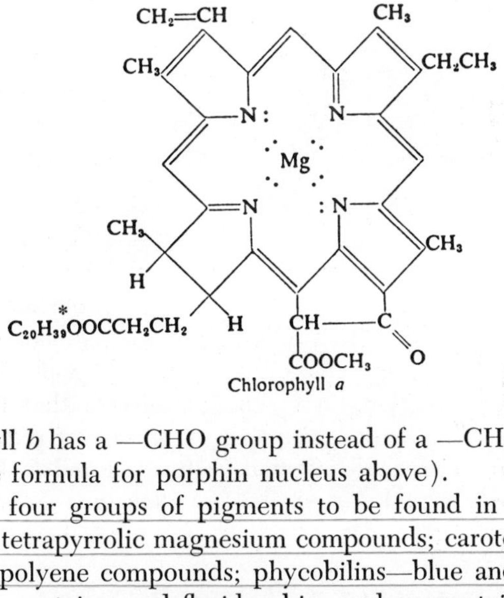

Chlorophyll *a*

Chlorophyll *b* has a —CHO group instead of a —CH₃ group at position no. 3 (see formula for porphin nucleus above).

There are four groups of pigments to be found in plants: chlorophylls—green, tetrapyrrolic magnesium compounds; carotenoids—yellow, orange or red polyene compounds; phycobilins—blue and red pigments associated with proteins; and floridorubin—red nonprotein material, but containing nitrogen.

Although the mechanism of photosynthesis is still incompletely understood, we may present a general picture of the role of chlorophyll in the primary biochemical reaction. Chlorophyll is found to be concentrated in green leaves in granules, called *grana*, contained in disk-shaped structures called *chloroplasts* (Plate 1). These chloroplasts are capable of carrying out the complete process of green plant photosynthesis and have proved to be useful materials for research.

° $C_{20}H_{39}$ = phytyl.

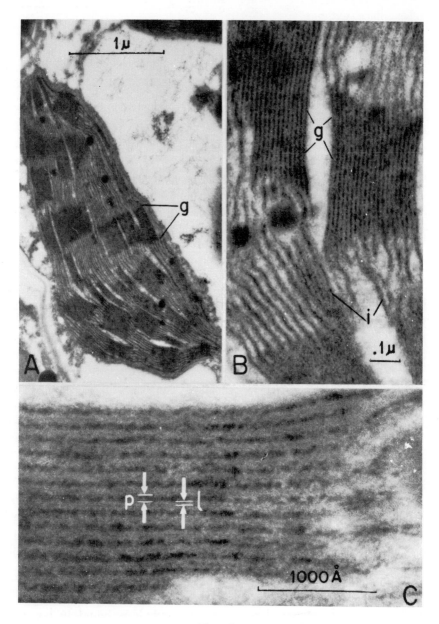

Plate 1

A, Chloroplast of a mesophil cell of corn showing numerous grana (g). × 30,000.

B, Higher magnification of a portion of a chloroplast showing two grana (g); i, composed lamellae between the grana. × 105,000.

C, Higher magnification of a portion of one grana; p, protein lamellae; l, lipid. × 370,000. (Courtesy of A. J. Hodge.)

(From De Robertis, Nowinski and Saez: General Cytology.)

The conversion of CO_2 and water to carbohydrate and oxygen takes place without any outside supply of energy other than visible light. Chlorophyll participates in the primary photochemical reaction involving light energy. The role of chlorophyll is that of reacting with a photon (a quantum unit) of light,* resulting in excitation of an electron to an energy sufficient to remove it from the molecule. In the absence of any electron acceptor chlorophyll would recombine with the electron and dissipate its energy in the form of fluorescence. During photosynthesis, however, compounds called *cofactors* are present which capture the electron. In green plants chlorophyll derives its external electron supply from water. The OH^- ions derived from water are converted to OH radicals which combine to form water and O_2. The photosynthetic evolution of O_2 is called the Hill reaction and accounts for the origin of O_2 from water molecules. In the meantime the electron derived from chlorophyll is utilized to convert the H^+ of water to H atoms which participate in the reduction of the cofactor.

Figure 1 illustrates this scheme in a general way and will be discussed in greater detail later (see p. 293).

The chemical reactions which involve the electron transmitted by chlorophyll finally culminate in a reaction whereby its energy is utilized to synthesize the compound adenosine triphosphate, ATP. This compound, as we shall see, is the storehouse for energy in all living cells and is used to drive the synthetic reactions which produce carbohydrates, proteins, nucleic acids, and other organic compounds. The scheme shown in Figure 1 is applicable to many forms of cells other than those of higher plants. It is known that many bacteria contain pigments (bacteriochlorophylls) which enable these cells to carry out photochemical reactions without the liberation of O_2. Here, instead of the electron donor being water, the donor source may be H_2 gas, sulfur compounds (H_2S or thiosulfate) or certain organic compounds (acids or alcohols).

---

* The photon represents a bundle of energy constituting light. The amount of energy possessed by a photon is inversely proportional to the wave length of light.

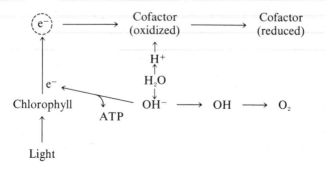

Figure 1. General scheme for photosynthesis in green leaves. ATP = adenosine triphosphate. (Adapted from Arnon: Scientific American, *203*:105, 1960.)

CARBOHYDRATES

These substances supply the largest source of energy to the cell.

CLASSIFICATION

The more important of these carbohydrates may be classified as follows:

MONOSACCHARIDES

Triose, $C_3H_6O_3$ (e.g., glyceraldehyde)

Tetrose, $C_4H_8O_4$ (e.g., erythrose)

Pentose, $C_5H_{10}O_5$ (e.g., ribose, deoxyribose, ribulose, xylose, arabinose)

Hexose, $C_6H_{12}O_6$ [e.g., glucose (dextrose), fructose (levulose), galactose, mannose]

Heptose, $C_7H_{14}O_7$ (e.g., sedoheptulose)

OLIGOSACCHARIDES*

Disaccharides, $C_{12}H_{22}O_{11}$ [e.g., sucrose (cane sugar), lactose (milk sugar), maltose]

Trisaccharides, $C_{18}H_{32}O_{16}$ (e.g., raffinose)

POLYSACCHARIDES

$(C_6H_{10}O_5)_x$ (e.g., starch, glycogen, dextrins, gum, mucilage, inulin, cellulose)

The monosaccharides cannot be hydrolyzed to simpler sugars. By the use of the appropriate acid or enzyme, the higher saccharides can be hydrolyzed:

$$C_{12}H_{22}O_{11} + H_2O \longrightarrow C_6H_{12}O_6 + C_6H_{12}O_6$$

Sucrose	$\longrightarrow$	Glucose + Fructose
Maltose	$\longrightarrow$	Glucose + Glucose
Lactose	$\longrightarrow$	Glucose + Galactose

$$C_{18}H_{32}O_{16} + 2H_2O \longrightarrow C_6H_{12}O_6 + C_6H_{12}O_6 + C_6H_{12}O_6$$

| Raffinose | $\longrightarrow$ | Fructose + Glucose + Galactose |

A number of the polysaccharides, upon complete hydrolysis, yield glucose as the end-product (for example, glycogen, starch, dextrin, cellulose); some yield fructose (for example, inulin); and some yield galactose (for example, certain gums).

MONOSACCHARIDES

STRUCTURE OF GLUCOSE

The somewhat exceptional position occupied by glucose in carbohydrate metabolism (Chap. 11) and the impossibility, owing to limita-

---

* This term is used for compounds made up of two or more molecules of hexose monosaccharides.

tions of space, of discussing the structure of each sugar individually make it desirable to describe glucose in some detail. Much of this discussion holds for other sugars.

A qualitative analysis of a purified sample of glucose shows the presence of the elements carbon and hydrogen; a quantitative analysis reveals the presence of oxygen also. The elements are in such proportion to one another that the formula (CH_2O) can be assigned to the compound. A molecular weight determination (by the freezing point depression method, for example) reveals that the formula assigned should be $(CH_2O)_6$, or $C_6H_{12}O_6$.

Glucose forms an oxime with hydroxylamine (p. 28), an osazone with phenylhydrazine (p. 28), and reduces Benedict's solution (p. 26); all of these reactions point to the presence of a $>C{=}O$ group, and this group may represent an aldehyde or a ketone.

Glucose forms a penta-acetyl derivative with acetic anhydride, indicating the presence of five free hydroxyl groups. It is reduced by means of sodium amalgam to an alcohol, hexahydroxyhexane, $CH_2OH.(CHOH)_4.CH_2OH$, which is sorbitol; the latter compound, when treated with hydrogen iodide, is converted to a derivative of *normal* hexane, $CH_3.(CH_2)_3.CHI.CH_3$. With hydrogen cyanide, glucose forms an addition compound which, when hydrolyzed, gives a straight-chain 7-carbon acid. All these facts point to a straight-chain compound, with the $>C{=}O$ at one end (a compound containing the aldehydic group):

1. CHO
   |
2. CHOH
   |
3. CHOH
   |
4. CHOH
   |
5. CHOH
   |
6. CH₂OH

ISOMERS OF GLUCOSE

An examination of the formula reveals that the compound has four asymmetric carbon atoms (at positions 2, 3, 4, and 5), each carbon being attached to four different atoms or groups of atoms. For example, the carbon at position 2 may be shown thus:

$$\text{H—C—OH}$$

with R above and R¹ below the carbon.

where R stands for the CHO group and R¹ for everything below carbon 2. According to van't Hoff, the number of possible isomers is given by the formula, $I = 2^n$, where n represents the number of asymmetric carbon atoms. Since glucose has four such asymmetric carbon atoms, the number of isomers should equal 16 (2^4).

THE SPATIAL ARRANGEMENT OF THE ISOMERS OF GLUCOSE

The exact proof for the stereochemical configuration of each isomer of glucose is beyond the scope of this book. Noller and also Fieser and Fieser give accounts of this phase of the work. All that can be said at this point is that the isomers are traced back to some simple compound, the constitution of which is beyond question. We may, for example, regard these isomers as being derived from glyceraldehyde:

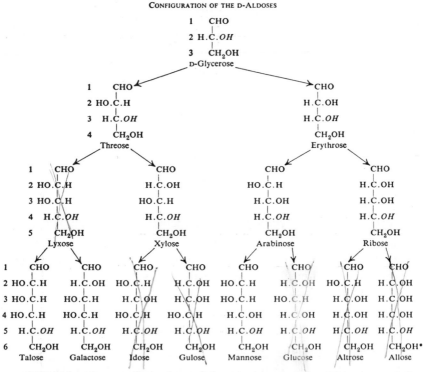

From each isomer of this aldehyde there are derived eight isomers of glucose. For example, the accompanying chart shows the derivation and configuration of eight aldohexoses:

* These hexoses are all members of the D-series, since the OH group at C-5 is derived from D-glyceraldehyde.

Using the notation that

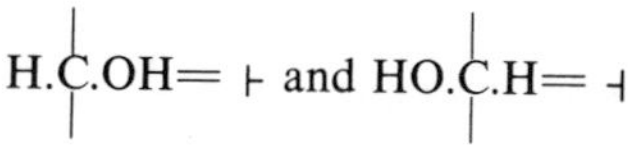

$$H.\overset{|}{\underset{|}{C}}.OH= \vdash \quad \text{and} \quad HO.\overset{|}{\underset{|}{C}}.H= \dashv$$

then D-glucose,*

```
        CHO
         |
     H.C.OH
         |
    HO.C.H
         |
     H.C.OH
         |
     H.C.OH
         |
        CH₂OH
```

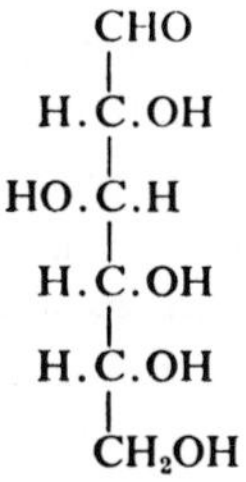

can be represented in shorthand form as

and L-glucose,

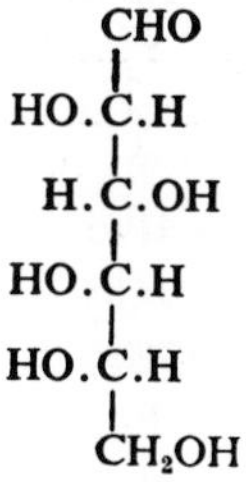

```
        CHO
         |
    HO.C.H
         |
     H.C.OH
         |
    HO.C.H
         |
    HO.C.H
         |
        CH₂OH
```

can be represented as

The two end-carbon combinations are ignored in this notation. We can represent the sixteen possible isomers as follows:

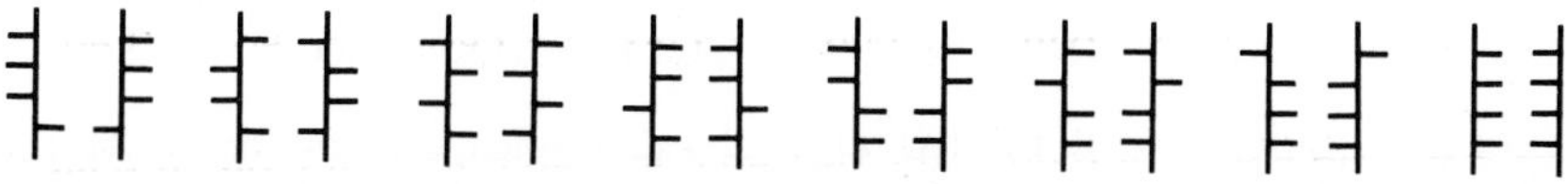

The first of each pair represents the D-series (related to D-glucose and D-glyceraldehyde), and the second, the L-series.

In this D-series, the hydroxyl group next to the primary alcohol

* The symbols D- and L- refer to *configuration*, whereas dextro (+) and levo (−) refer to *sign of rotation*. D- and L- are always pronounced "dee" and "ell," *never* "dextro" and "levo."

group is written to the right; whereas the reverse is true with the L-series.

THE CYCLIC STRUCTURE FOR GLUCOSE

The above formula for glucose still does not explain all the facts. To begin with, glucose, which is pictured as an aldehyde, falls somewhat short of certain common aldehydic properties. For example, glucose fails to give a Schiff's test (the formation of a reddish-violet color with magenta solution which has been decolorized with SO_2), nor does it form a stable addition compound with sodium bisulfite. Hydroxy acids of the γ- or δ-variety, similar in general structure to glucose, form lactones very readily, and these are cyclic in structure; for example, γ-hydroxybutyric acid, $CH_2OH.CH_2.CH_2.COOH$, is changed to γ-butyrolactone,

$$\overset{\displaystyle \lceil\text{———}O\text{———}\rceil}{CH_2.CH_2.CH_2.CO}$$

MUTAROTATION

Even more important is the property of mutarotation or "change of rotation." A freshly crystallized sample of glucose has a specific rotation (in water) of $111°$ ($[\alpha]_D = 111°$); upon standing, this changes to $52°$. Since the specific rotation of any compound is, as a rule, characteristic of the optically active compound in question (just as melting and boiling points are usually characteristic criteria), a change in rotation suggests a change in the structure of the substance. This appears all the more probable when it is shown that the compound with the rotation $111°$ (now known as α-glucose) can be dissolved in boiling pyridine and crystallized from this solvent to give an isomer with the specific rotation of $19°$ (now known as β-glucose), which, upon standing, also changes slowly to $52°$. The β-form is the more stable one at temperatures near $100°$ C.

Another fact has to be recorded now. When an aldehyde is treated with methyl alcohol (using an acid to catalyze the reaction), an acetal is formed.

$$R.CHO + 2CH_3OH \longrightarrow R.CH(OCH_3)_2 + H_2O$$

Here two molecules of methyl alcohol react with one molecule of the aldehyde. When, however, glucose is treated similarly, the sugar combines with but *one* molecule of methyl alcohol:

$$C_6H_{12}O_6 + CH_3OH \longrightarrow C_7H_{14}O_6 + H_2O$$

The methyl glucoside which is formed can be resolved into two modifications: an α-methyl glucoside (rotation $159°$) and a β-methyl glucoside (rotation 34°). The enzyme α-glucosidase (yeast) hydrolyzes the former initially to α-glucose, and the enzyme emulsin (β-glucosidase) hydrolyzes the latter initially to β-glucose, followed by mutarotation to give an equilibrium mixture of both forms of glucose.

The two modifications each of D-glucose and the corresponding methyl glucoside suggest the presence of an additional asymmetric carbon atom in the molecule, which can be shown if we assume a cyclic structure:

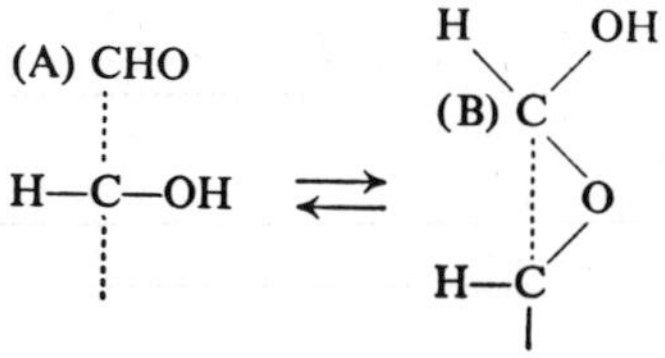

$$(A) \; \text{CHO} \qquad \qquad \overset{\text{H}\qquad\text{OH}}{\underset{\;}{(B) \; \text{C}}}$$

$$\text{H}-\text{C}-\text{OH} \; \rightleftarrows \qquad \overset{\big|}{\underset{\text{H}-\text{C}}{\big/}} \text{O}$$

Here the carbon atom at (A), part of an ordinary aldehydic group, has been converted into an asymmetric carbon atom (B); so that now in glucose we have the possibility not of 16 ($= 2^4$), but of 32 ($= 2^5$) isomeric aldohexoses.

In the accompanying formulas the structures and relationships of the compounds just discussed are given (the evidence for the oxygen bridge in the 1:5 position will be taken up presently).

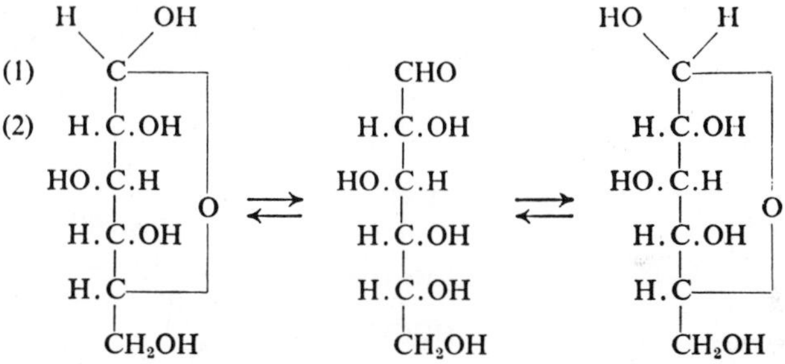

(1) (2)

H.C.OH	CHO	H.C.OH
HO.C.H	H.C.OH	HO.C.H
H.C.OH	HO.C.H	H.C.OH
H.C	H.C.OH	H.C
CH₂OH	H.C.OH	CH₂OH
	CH₂OH	

α-D-Glucose   D-Glucose   β-D-Glucose

The two methyl glucosides would therefore be

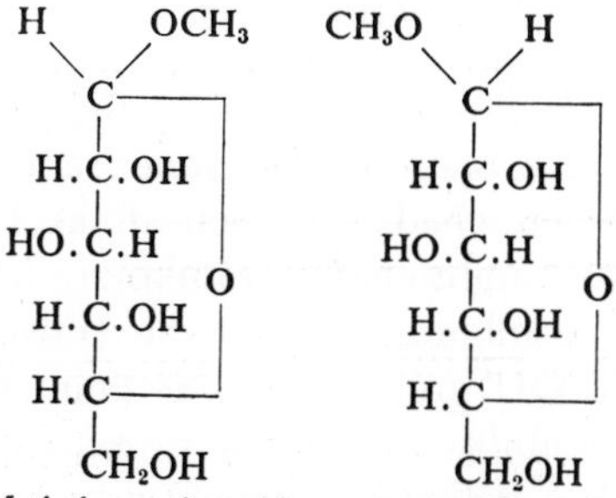

H.C.OH	H.C.OH
HO.C.H	HO.C.H
H.C.OH	H.C.OH
H.C	H.C
CH₂OH	CH₂OH

Methyl-α-D-glucoside   Methyl-β-D-glucoside

It might be pointed out that there are reasons for writing the H and OH positions at carbon (1) in α- and β-glucose as shown. For example, α-glucose combines very readily with boric acid:

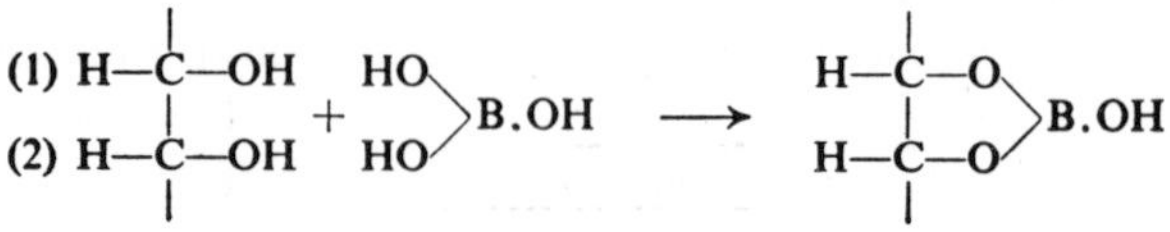

suggesting that the two OH groups in (1) and (2) are in the same plane. The β-form, however, does not combine so readily with boric acid until mutarotation has given some α-form.

Assuming, for the time being, a $1:5$ oxygen bridge, glucose may be pictured as a derivative of pyran: hexapyranose:

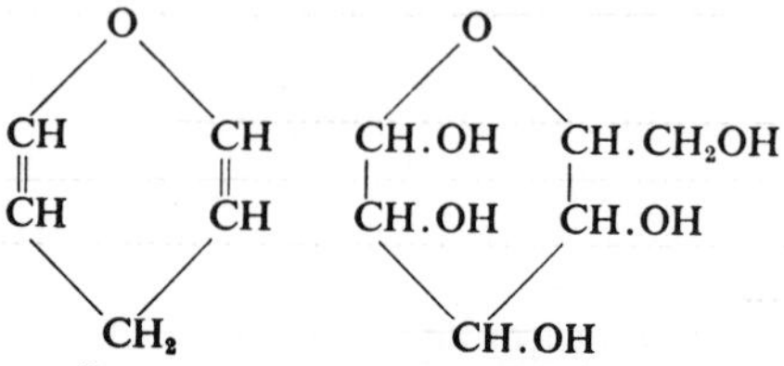

Pyran   Hexapyranose

One such hexapyranose, glucose, can therefore be called glucopyranose.

Haworth shows this model in perspective, with the H and the OH groups above or below the plane of the ring:

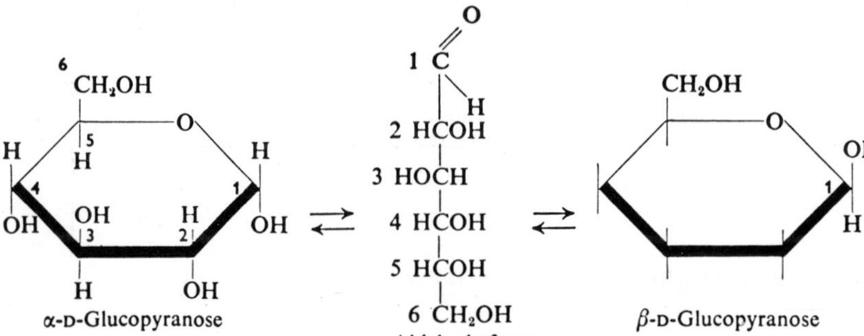

α-D-Glucopyranose   Aldehyde form β-D-Glucopyranose

The ring is at right angles to the plane of the paper. The thin bonds of the ring are behind the plane of the paper, and the thick bonds in front of it. (H and OH attached to carbon atoms 1, 2, 3, 4, which are on the *right* side of the straight-chain formula, are here on the *bottom*.) Note that the α and β configurations (in the Haworth representation) depend on whether the OH group at C-1 is pointing down (α) or up (β). Also, note that the ability of a sugar to reduce Benedict's solution (p. 26) is dependent on a potential carbonyl group at C-1.

METHYLATION STUDIES; EVIDENCE FOR THE 1:5 OXYGEN BRIDGE

It has been assumed so far that the oxygen is attached to carbons 1 and 5.

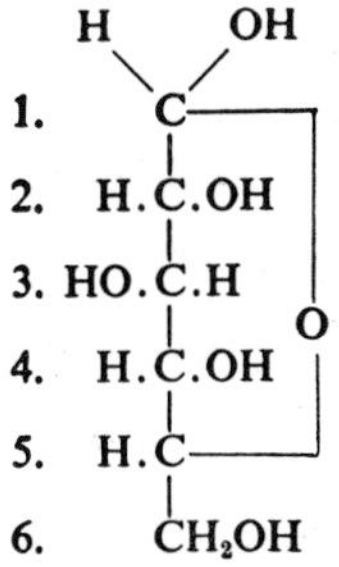

There are obviously several other possible attachments. As a matter of fact, but two forms have been isolated: the 1:5 and the 1:4. Of these, the 1:5 is the more stable and the commoner.

After the methyl glucoside has been formed (with $CH_3OH + HCl$), the product is next treated with dimethyl sulfate. This results in complete methylation of the OH groups. Without using the stereochemical formulas, and still assuming the 1:5 oxygen bridge, the reactions are:

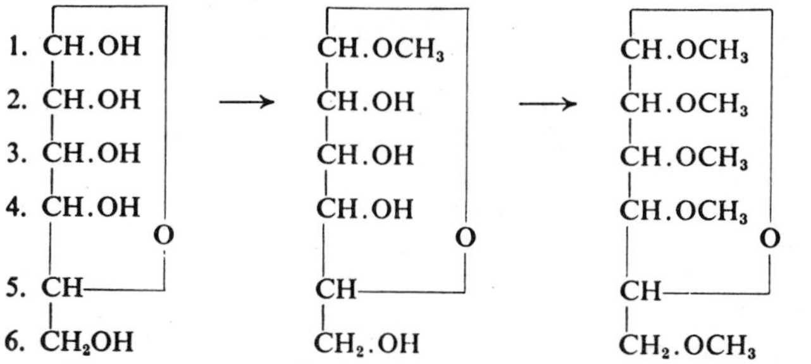

Methyl glucoside

Tetramethyl methyl glucoside

The glucosidic methoxyl group can be easily hydrolyzed, whereas the other methoxyls cannot—behaving, indeed, as true ethers. If, then, we hydrolyze the completely methylated compound, we get

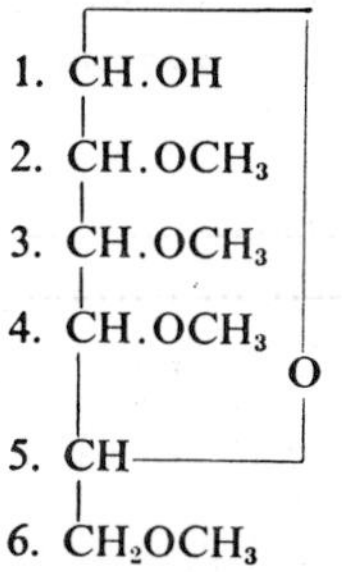

Tetramethyl α-D-glucose

which, upon oxidation with nitric acid, yields a trimethoxy derivative of glutaric acid:

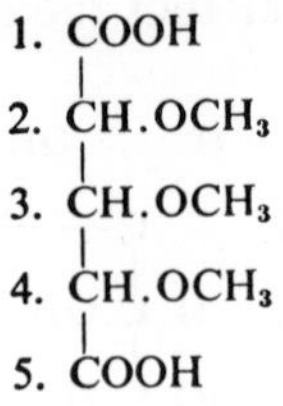

1. COOH
2. CH.OCH₃
3. CH.OCH₃
4. CH.OCH₃
5. COOH

which indicates that the oxygen was attached to carbon atom 5 in the glucoside.

1:4 OXYGEN BRIDGE

Ordinarily, in the formation of methyl glucosides, hot alcoholic HCl is used. This forms the 1:5 oxygen bridge linkage, as we have already seen. If, however, cold alcoholic HCl is used, a far less stable compound is formed, differing from the more stable form by having a 1:4 linkage. Complete methylation and final oxidation with nitric acid lead to the production of a succinic acid derivative:

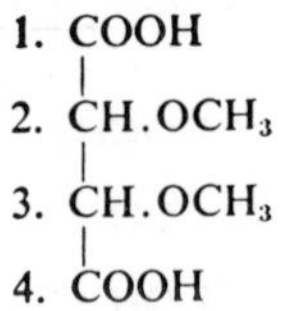

1. COOH
2. CH.OCH₃
3. CH.OCH₃
4. COOH

showing that this methyl glucoside has the structure

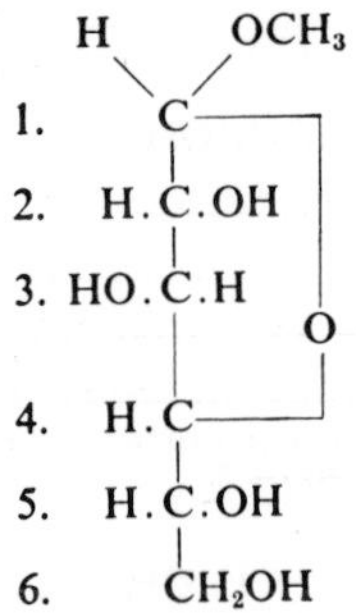

```
        H      OCH₃
         \    /
   1.      C ──────┐
           |       │
   2.   H.C.OH     │
           |       │
   3.  HO.C.H      │
           |       O
   4.   H.C ───────┘
           |
   5.   H.C.OH
           |
   6.      CH₂OH
```

or a 1:4 oxygen bridge.

Just as the parent substance of the 1:5 sugars is pyran, so the parent compound of the 1:4 sugars is furan:

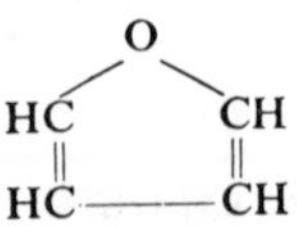

```
            O
          /   \
      HC        CH
      ‖         ‖
      HC ────── CH
          Furan
```

and the sugars derived from it are furanose sugars.

THE STRUCTURE OF FRUCTOSE

From the physiological point of view, glucose, fructose, and galactose are the three important hexoses.

Fructose, a naturally occurring sugar, is levorotatory. Despite this fact, the sugar is known as D-fructose because it is related structurally to D-glucose.[*] It has the same molecular formula as glucose ($C_6H_{12}O_6$), forms a penta-acetyl derivative, and has the properties of a carbonyl

($\overset{|}{C}$=O) compound. When fructose is treated with HCN it forms an

addition compound, which upon hydrolysis and subsequent reduction with HI gives methylbutylacetic acid:

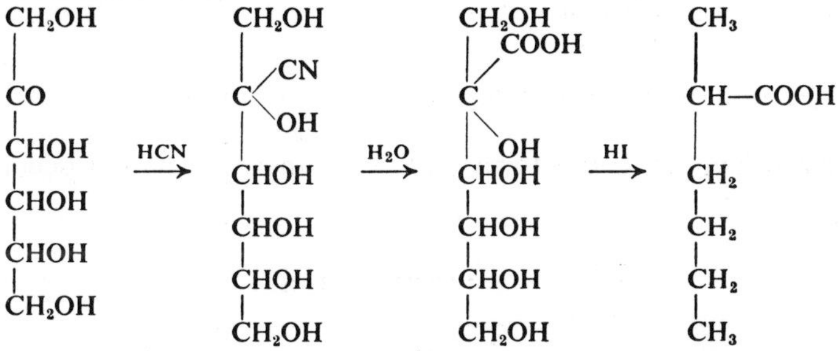

CH₂OH		CH₂OH		CH₂OH		CH₃
CO	HCN	C⟨CN OH	H₂O	C⟨COOH OH	HI	CH—COOH
CHOH	⟶	CHOH	⟶	CHOH	⟶	CH₂
CHOH		CHOH		CHOH		CH₂
CHOH		CHOH		CHOH		CH₂
CH₂OH		CH₂OH		CH₂OH		CH₃
Fructose						Methylbutyl- acetic acid

and this means that fructose is a ketone and not an aldehyde. (Under similar conditions, glucose yields a 7-carbon straight-chain and not a branched-chain compound.)

The oxidation of fructose [with HgO and Ba(OH)₂] yields glycollic acid, $CH_2OH.COOH$, and trihydroxybutyric acid, $CH_2OH.(CHOH)_2.COOH$, indicating a splitting of the compound between carbons 2 and 3.

Both glucose and fructose give the same osazone (p. 29), and this, as we shall see, points to the fact that, in fructose, the groups at 3, 4, and 5 must be the same as those in glucose:

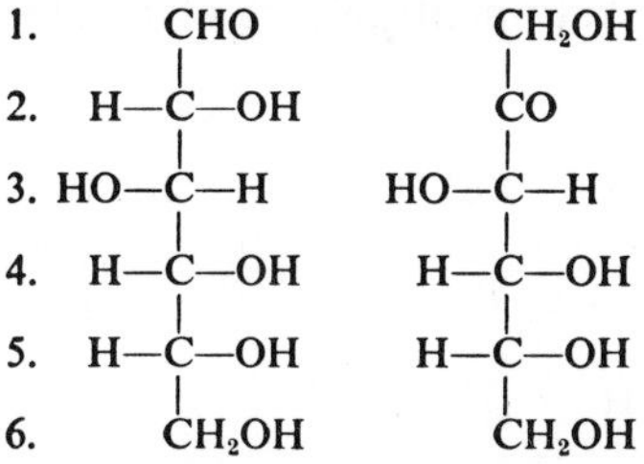

	Glucose	Fructose
1.	CHO	CH₂OH
2.	H—C—OH	CO
3.	HO—C—H	HO—C—H
4.	H—C—OH	H—C—OH
5.	H—C—OH	H—C—OH
6.	CH₂OH	CH₂OH

---

[*] D glucose is related structurally to D fructose, for both give the same osazone (p. 29), but glucose rotates the plane of polarized light to the right, and fructose, to the left. The mirror images of these compounds are referred to as the L-series, regardless of whether the compounds are dextro- or levorotatory.

Like glucose, fructose exhibits the property of mutarotation, and normally forms a 2:6 oxygen bridge linkage, giving a fructopyranose. These structures may be summarized as follows:

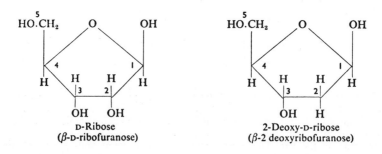

| β-Fructose | Ketone formula of fructose | α-Fructose | α-D-Fructopyranose |

GALACTOSE

Mutarotation (β- and α-forms) with pyranose formation occurs here too.

Galactose   or   α-D-Galactopyranose

Note that in galactose the position of the OH group at C-4 differs from that in glucose (p. 16).

PENTOSE SUGARS

Several aldo- and keto-pentoses are of biochemical importance:

D-Ribose
(β-D-ribofuranose)

2-Deoxy-D-ribose
(β-2 deoxyribofuranose)

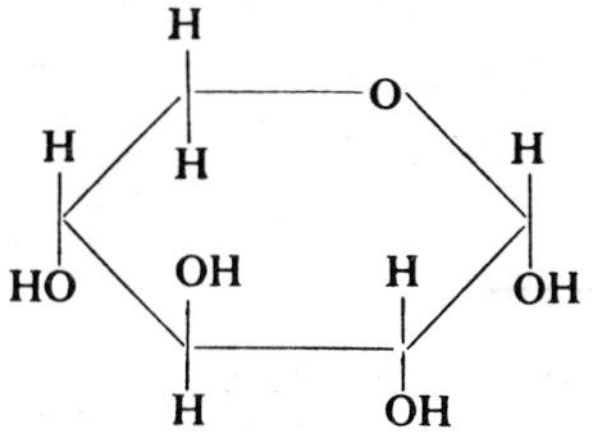

α-D-Xylose 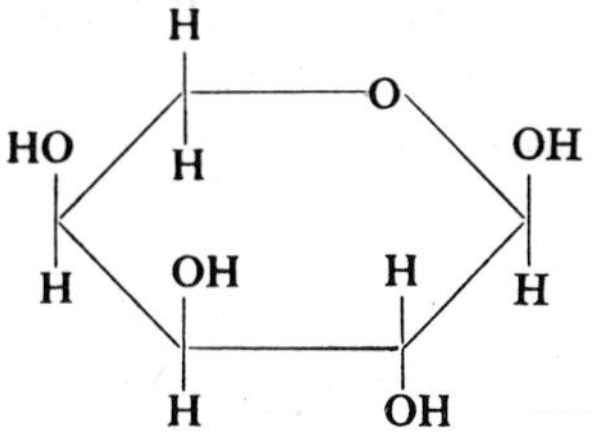   β-L-Arabinose

Examples of a ketopentose (D-ribulose) and of a ketoheptose (sedo-heptulose) are shown below:

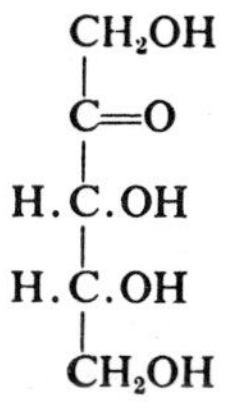

$$CH_2OH$$
$$C=O$$
$$H.C.OH$$
$$H.C.OH$$
$$CH_2OH$$
D -Ribulose

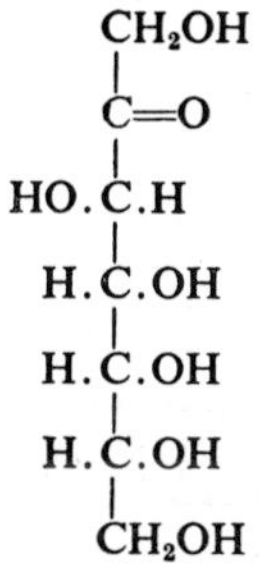

$$CH_2OH$$
$$C=O$$
$$HO.C.H$$
$$H.C.OH$$
$$H.C.OH$$
$$H.C.OH$$
$$CH_2OH$$
Sedoheptulose

AMINO SUGARS

A number of sugars occur in nature in which a hydroxyl group of the aldose has been replaced by an amino or acetylamino group. The structures of several are shown below:

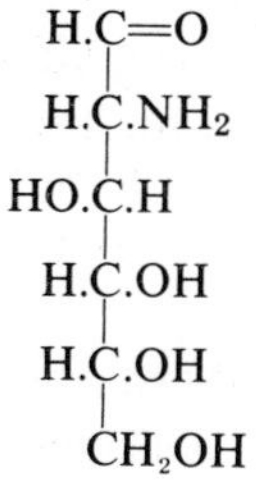

$$H.C=O$$
$$H.C.NH_2$$
$$HO.C.H$$
$$H.C.OH$$
$$H.C.OH$$
$$CH_2OH$$
D-Glucosamine

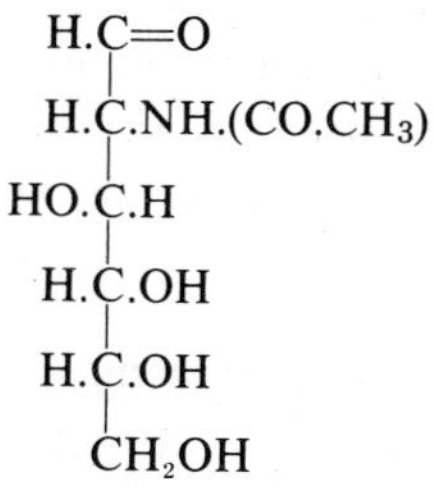

$$H.C=O$$
$$H.C.NH.(CO.CH_3)$$
$$HO.C.H$$
$$H.C.OH$$
$$H.C.OH$$
$$CH_2OH$$
D-Acetyl glucosamine

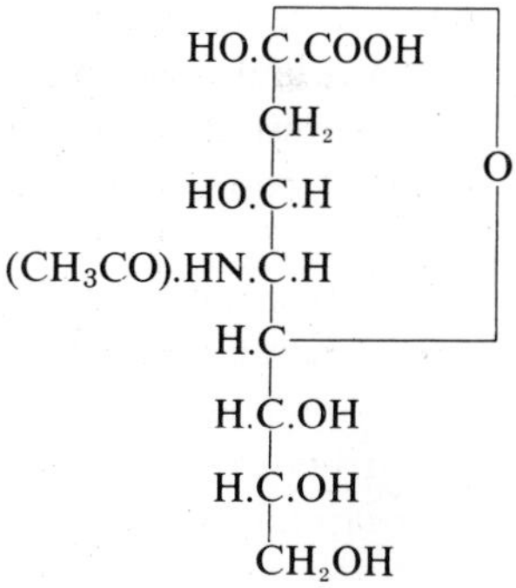

$$HO.C.COOH$$
$$CH_2$$
$$HO.C.H$$
$$(CH_3CO).HN.C.H$$
$$H.C$$
$$H.C.OH$$
$$H.C.OH$$
$$CH_2OH$$
N-Acetylneuraminic acid

Glucosamine is found as a constituent of chitin (p. 36), hyaluronic acid (p. 36), heparin (p. 222), mucopolysaccharides (p. 131) and bacterial polysaccharides. Galactosamine is found in chondroitin (Chap. 19). The neuraminic acids are N- and O- acyl derivatives of a deoxy-amino sugar called sialic acid. They are found as constituents of lipids, poly-saccharides and mucoproteins in a variety of tissues.

DISACCHARIDES

The disaccharides may be regarded as glycosides of the form:

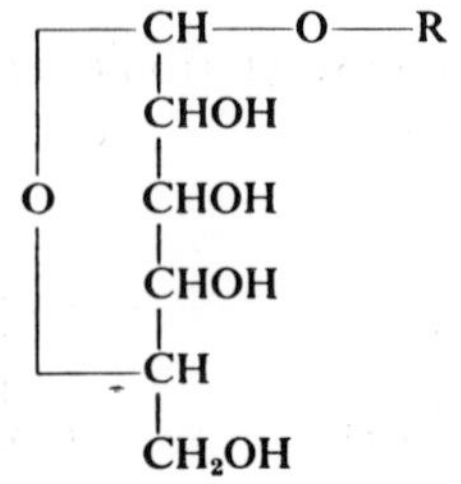

$$
\begin{array}{ccc}
 & \text{—CH——O——R} \\
 & \text{|} \\
 & \text{CHOH} \\
 & \text{|} \\
\text{O} & \text{CHOH} \\
 & \text{|} \\
 & \text{CHOH} \\
 & \text{|} \\
 & \text{—CH} \\
 & \text{|} \\
 & \text{CH}_2\text{OH}
\end{array}
$$

where R is a monosaccharide which (1) has a potential free aldehydic group (as in maltose and lactose), or (2) has no such reducing group (see Sucrose, p. 24).

Where R is CH_3, we have the methyl glycoside which has already been discussed. In nature, important glycosides are known where R is a nonsugar, often of complex structure. For example, phlorhizin (also spelled *phloridzin* and *phlorizin*), found in the bark of Rosaceae, is a combination of glucose and phloretin; amygdalin, present in the seed of the bitter almond, is a combination of glucose and mandelonitrile; digi-tonin, found in the leaves and seeds of digitalis, is a combination of glucose, galactose, and digitogenin. In the cardiac glycosides (found in certain plants and possessing a characteristic action on the heart), the R is represented by a steroid. (*Glycoside* is the general name for this group of compounds, irrespective of the sugar present; *glucoside* is the more specific name for those glycosides which contain glucose as the sugar constituent.)

As has already been pointed out, maltose, lactose, and sucrose, the three common disaccharides, are easily hydrolyzed to monosaccharides. The structures of these disaccharides, in turn, are dependent upon the monosaccharides they yield.

MALTOSE

This yields two molecules of glucose when hydrolyzed. Upon methylation and subsequent hydrolysis, we get 2,3,4,6-tetramethylglucose and 2,3,6-trimethylglucose. While these results lead to two possible struc-tures, the following has been selected as more in accord with the facts:

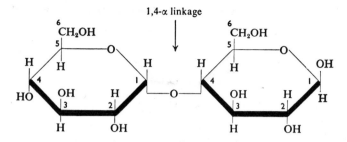

β-Maltose
4-*O*-(α-D-Glucopyranosyl)-β-D-glucopyranose

LACTOSE

Glucose and galactose are formed on hydrolysis of lactose. When the lactose is methylated and then hydrolyzed, we get 2,3,6-trimethylglucose and 2,3,4,6-tetramethylgalactose, leading to the formula:

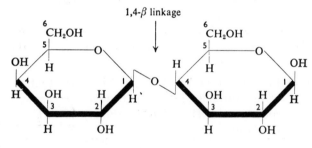

β-Lactose
4-*O*-(β-D-Galactopyranosyl)-β-D-glucopyranose

(galactose)   (glucose)

Both lactose and maltose reduce Benedict's solution, owing to the free OH group at C-1.

SUCROSE

Unlike maltose and lactose, sucrose does not reduce Benedict's solution; it is a nonreducing sugar. When hydrolyzed it yields glucose and fructose. Methylation and subsequent hydrolysis convert sucrose into a tetramethyl glucose and a tetramethyl fructose.

Sucrose has a pyranose structure for the glucose part, and a furanose structure for the fructose part. It is, therefore, a glucosido-fructofuranoside.

In the free form fructose itself exists as a stable six-membered pyranose compound; but in the sucrose molecule the fructose exists as the more unstable five-membered furanose compound:

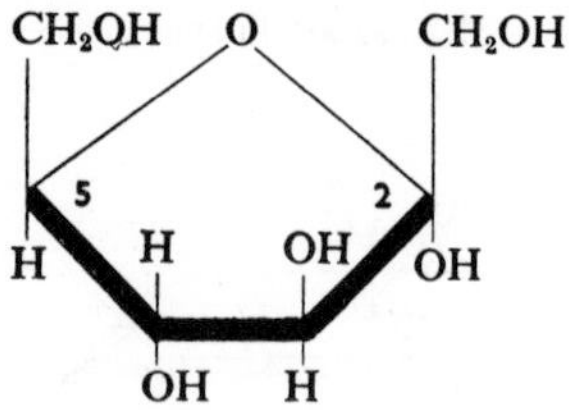

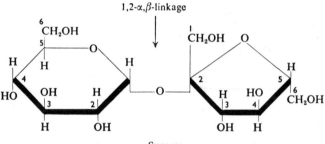

α-D-Fructofuranose

The Haworth representation for sucrose would be

Sucrose
α-D-Glucopyranosyl-β-D-fructofuranose

Note that sucrose has a 1,2- linkage. Note also that the Haworth formula for β-D-fructofuranose has been turned over as well as upside down (with respect to the H and OH groups) in order to show the 1,2- linkage more simply.

SOME GENERAL PROPERTIES OF THE MONO-
AND DISACCHARIDES

These substances are crystalline, soluble in water, and moderately soluble in dilute alcohol. They are practically insoluble in absolute alcohol, ether, and the usual organic solvents.

THE ACTION OF NONOXIDIZING ACIDS

Certain acids (like HCl) hydrolyze the disaccharides. (They also hydrolyze tri- and polysaccharides.) Their action on the monosaccharides is negligible if the acid is dilute. In higher concentrations, and at the boiling point, such acids act on monosaccharides largely by dehydrating them, forming furfural derivatives. The pentoses form furfural:

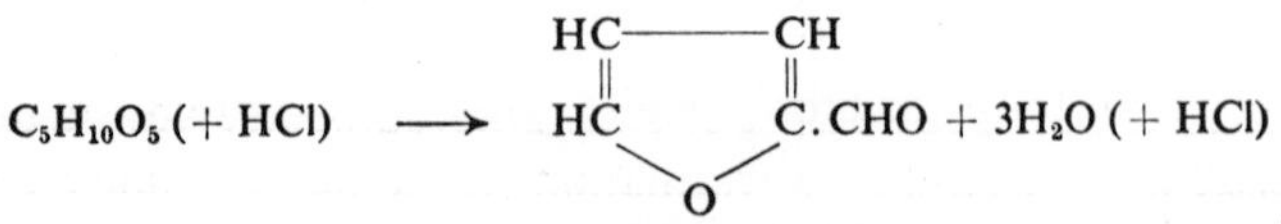

$$C_5H_{10}O_5\ (+ HCl) \longrightarrow$$

$$
\begin{array}{c}
HC\!\!-\!\!\!-\!\!\!-\!\!CH \\
\parallel \qquad \parallel \\
HC \qquad\ C.CHO + 3H_2O\ (+ HCl) \\
\diagdown\ \ \diagup \\
O
\end{array}
$$

Furfural

The hexoses yield varying quantities of hydroxymethylfurfural:

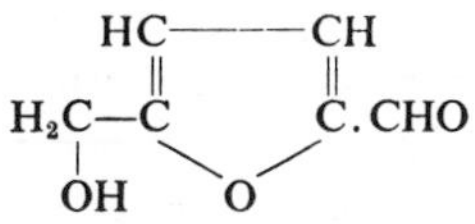

$$HC\text{------}CH$$
$$H_2C-C \quad\quad C.CHO$$
$$OH \quad O$$

Hydroxymethylfurfural

The formation of such furfurals is the basis for a number of tests. One of the commonest is the *Molisch test:* The sugar mixed with

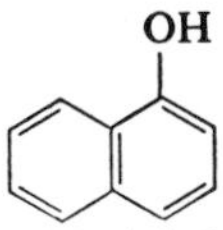

OH

α-Naphthol

α-naphthol and concentrated sulfuric acid gives a violet color. It is presumed that the concentrated sulfuric acid acts as a dehydrating agent, acting on the sugar to form furfural derivatives, which then combine with α-naphthol to form colored products of uncertain constitution. This is a very general test for carbohydrates.

Another very general test for carbohydrates is known as the *anthrone test.* Anthrone itself has the formula:

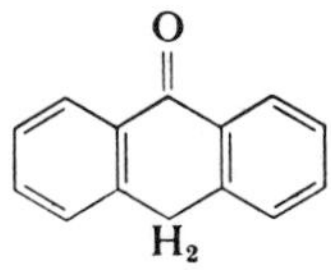

O

H₂
Anthrone

and, when mixed with concentrated sulfuric acid and the carbohydrate, it forms a blue or green color.

A more specific test is the *Selivanoff test,* involving the action of

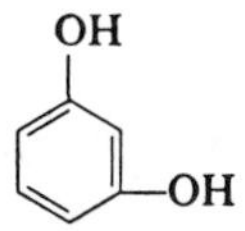

OH

—OH
Resorcinol

resorcinol and HCl on the sugar. Here a red color is developed rapidly in the presence of a ketose sugar, such as fructose. The explanation of the test lies in the formation, first, of hydroxymethylfurfural and the condensation of this substance with resorcinol to form the colored product or products.

Two tests for pentoses, *Tollens' phloroglucinol test* and *Tollens' orcinol test,* are based on the formation of similar intermediate furfural products and ultimate condensations to yield colored substances:

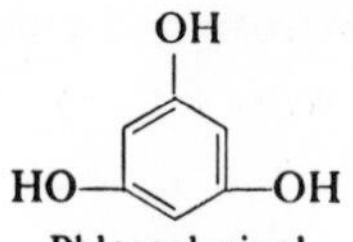

OH

HO—⬡—OH
Phloroglucinol

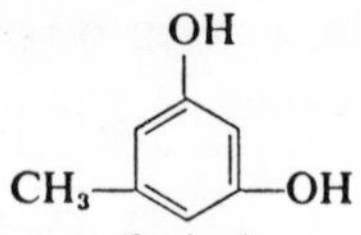

OH

CH₃—⬡—OH
Orcinol

A test for deoxyribose is to mix the sugar with diphenylamine, glacial acetic acid and sulfuric acid, yielding a blue color (Dische). It is used to detect deoxyribose in nucleic acids, where the sugar is linked to a purine.

OXIDATION

Alkaline copper solutions readily oxidize the disaccharides (with the exception of sucrose) and the monosaccharides. The oxidation products are numerous, and not all of them have been identified. From a practical point of view, however, this reaction is important because with the oxidation of the sugar there is a simultaneous reduction of the cupric to insoluble, red cuprous oxide, which can be identified easily. The best-known reagents are *Fehling's solution* [an alkaline (NaOH) copper sulfate solution, with potassium sodium tartrate to keep the cupric oxide in solution] and *Benedict's solution* [an alkaline (Na₂CO₃) copper sulfate solution in the presence of sodium citrate]. An acid copper solution (copper acetate in acetic acid), known as *Barfoed's reagent,* is often used, though not always satisfactorily, to distinguish mono- from disaccharides. Under identical conditions the monosaccharides are more rapidly oxidized.

With bromine water as the oxidizing agent glucose forms gluconic acid:

$$\text{COOH}$$
$$|$$
$$\text{(CHOH)}_4$$
$$|$$
$$\text{CH}_2\text{OH}$$
Gluconic acid

and with nitric acid, saccharic acid is formed:

$$\text{COOH}$$
$$|$$
$$\text{(CHOH)}_4$$
$$|$$
$$\text{COOH}$$
Saccharic acid

With galactose, nitric acid yields an isomer, *mucic acid,* which, unlike saccharic, is highly insoluble. This mucic acid test is used to identify galactose (or lactose, which hydrolyzes to form galactose as one of the products).

When saccharic acid is heated, it forms the corresponding lactone, which can be reduced to *glucuronic acid* with sodium amalgam:

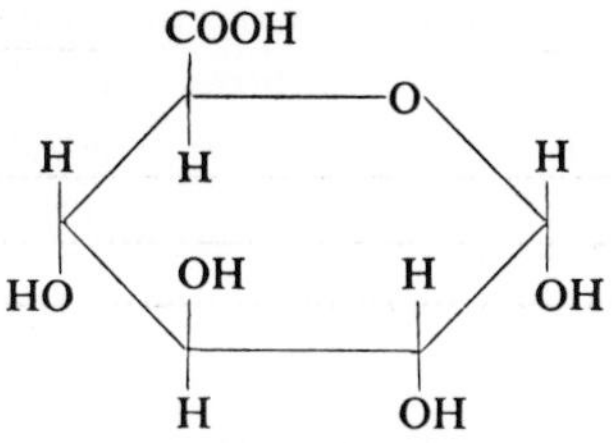

$$
\begin{array}{c}
\text{COOH} \\
\text{H} \quad \text{H} \quad \quad \text{O} \quad \text{H} \\
\text{HO} \quad \text{OH} \quad \text{H} \quad \text{OH} \\
\text{H} \quad \quad \text{OH}
\end{array}
$$

Glucuronic acid

This oxidation product of glucose is a physiologically important substance. It occurs in glucosidic linkage with many compounds. For example, the female hormones are found in the urine as glucuronides (see Chap. 21).

Examples of other derivatives of glucuronic acid found in the body are heparin, the blood anticoagulant, and chondroitin sulfate, a constituent of cartilage.

REDUCTION

Reduction (with sodium amalgam) converts the monosaccharides to the corresponding alcohols. Glucose, for example, gives sorbitol:

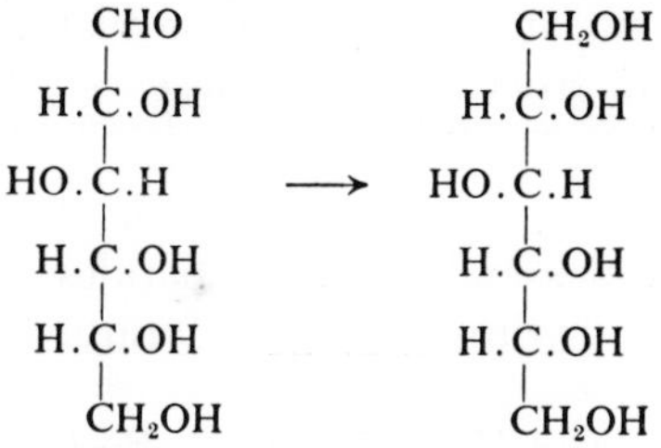

$$
\begin{array}{ccc}
\text{CHO} & & \text{CH}_2\text{OH} \\
\text{H.C.OH} & & \text{H.C.OH} \\
\text{HO.C.H} & \longrightarrow & \text{HO.C.H} \\
\text{H.C.OH} & & \text{H.C.OH} \\
\text{H.C.OH} & & \text{H.C.OH} \\
\text{CH}_2\text{OH} & & \text{CH}_2\text{OH} \\
\text{Glucose} & & \text{Sorbitol}
\end{array}
$$

Fructose yields a mixture of sorbitol and mannitol, since the carbon of the ketonic group now becomes asymmetric:

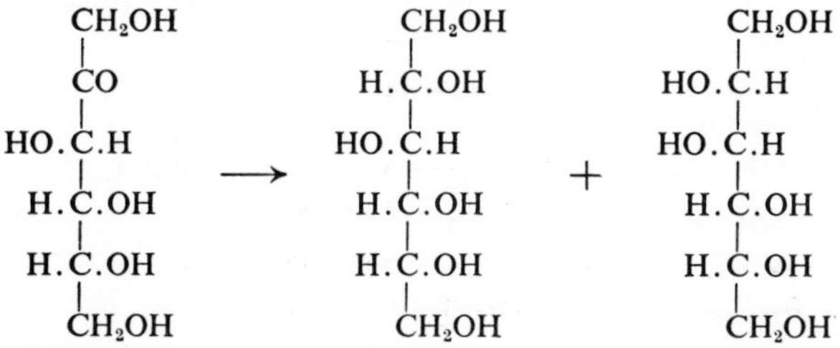

$$
\begin{array}{ccccc}
\text{CH}_2\text{OH} & & \text{CH}_2\text{OH} & & \text{CH}_2\text{OH} \\
\text{CO} & & \text{H.C.OH} & & \text{HO.C.H} \\
\text{HO.C.H} & & \text{HO.C.H} & & \text{HO.C.H} \\
\text{H.C.OH} & \longrightarrow & \text{H.C.OH} & + & \text{H.C.OH} \\
\text{H.C.OH} & & \text{H.C.OH} & & \text{H.C.OH} \\
\text{CH}_2\text{OH} & & \text{CH}_2\text{OH} & & \text{CH}_2\text{OH} \\
\text{Fructose} & & \text{Sorbitol} & & \text{Mannitol}
\end{array}
$$

THE ACTION OF WEAK ALKALI

Using a saturated solution of barium hydroxide, and allowing the mixture to stand for some time, we can transform glucose into an equilibrium mixture of glucose, mannose, and fructose. The same holds true if instead of glucose we begin with fructose or mannose. This has been explained on the assumption that a reactive "intermediate" (enol) compound is formed:

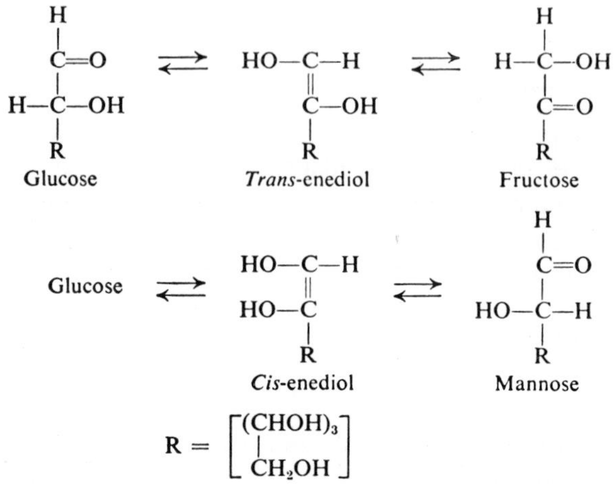

$$
\begin{array}{ccc}
\text{H} & & \text{H} \\
| & & | \\
\text{C}\!=\!\text{O} & \text{HO}-\text{C}-\text{H} & \text{H}-\text{C}-\text{OH} \\
| \rightleftharpoons & \| \rightleftharpoons & | \\
\text{H}-\text{C}-\text{OH} & \text{C}-\text{OH} & \text{C}\!=\!\text{O} \\
| & | & | \\
\text{R} & \text{R} & \text{R} \\
\text{Glucose} & \textit{Trans}\text{-enediol} & \text{Fructose}
\end{array}
$$

$$
\begin{array}{ccc}
& \text{HO}-\text{C}-\text{H} & \text{C}\!=\!\text{O} \\
\text{Glucose} \rightleftharpoons & \| \rightleftharpoons & | \\
& \text{HO}-\text{C} & \text{HO}-\text{C}-\text{H} \\
& | & | \\
& \text{R} & \text{R} \\
& \textit{Cis}\text{-enediol} & \text{Mannose}
\end{array}
$$

$$
R = \left[\begin{array}{c} \text{(CHOH)}_3 \\ | \\ \text{CH}_2\text{OH} \end{array} \right]
$$

By the use of 1-deuterioglucose (glucose in which a hydrogen is replaced by deuterium), it has been shown that the deuterium is transferred from glucose to fructose to mannose.

OSAZONES

The monosaccharides and the disaccharides (with the exception of sucrose) combine with hydroxylamine to form oximes:

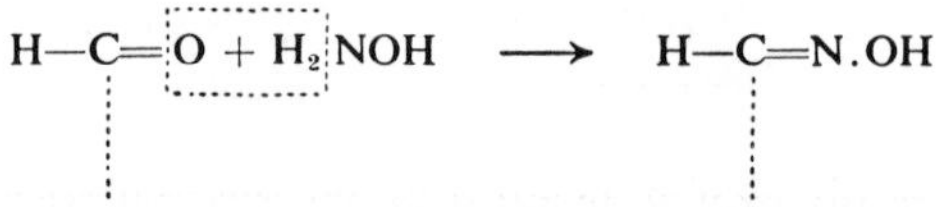

$$
\text{H}-\text{C}\!=\!\text{O} + \text{H}_2\text{NOH} \longrightarrow \text{H}-\text{C}\!=\!\text{N.OH}
$$

but from a practical standpoint, the more important reaction is the formation of osazones with phenylhydrazine, $C_6H_5NHNH_2$. First, one molecule of the sugar combines with one molecule of the phenylhydrazine to form a hydrazone:

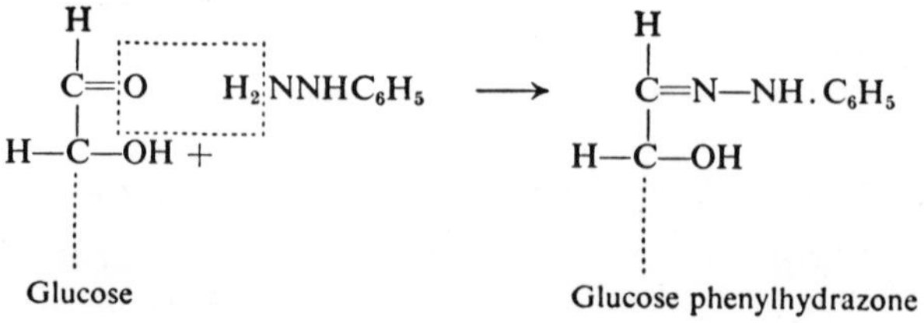

$$
\begin{array}{ccc}
\text{H} & & \text{H} \\
| & & | \\
\text{C}\!=\!\text{O} & \text{H}_2\text{NNHC}_6\text{H}_5 \longrightarrow & \text{C}\!=\!\text{N}-\text{NH.C}_6\text{H}_5 \\
| & & | \\
\text{H}-\text{C}-\text{OH} + & & \text{H}-\text{C}-\text{OH} \\
\\
\text{Glucose} & & \text{Glucose phenylhydrazone}
\end{array}
$$

Next, in the presence of an excess of phenylhydrazine, another molecule of this reagent reacts with the sugar:

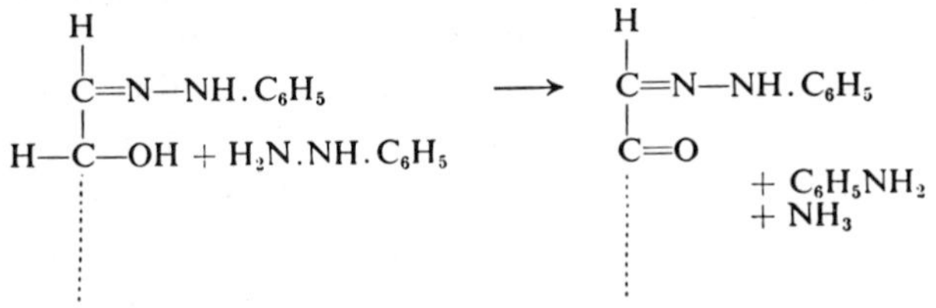

$$
\begin{array}{l}
\text{H} \\
| \\
\text{C=N—NH.C}_6\text{H}_5 \\
| \\
\text{H—C—OH} + \text{H}_2\text{N.NH.C}_6\text{H}_5
\end{array}
\longrightarrow
\begin{array}{l}
\text{H} \\
| \\
\text{C=N—NH.C}_6\text{H}_5 \\
| \\
\text{C=O} \\
\qquad + \text{C}_6\text{H}_5\text{NH}_2 \\
\qquad + \text{NH}_3
\end{array}
$$

converting the secondary alcohol group of the hydrazone into a ketone; and, finally, a third molecule of the reagent enters the reaction, giving an osazone:

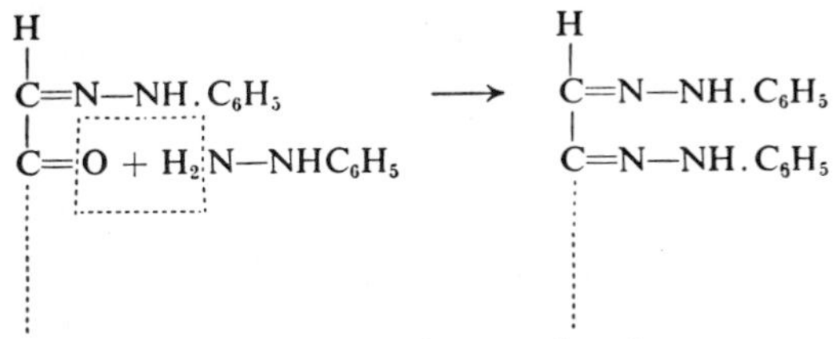

$$
\begin{array}{l}
\text{H} \\
| \\
\text{C=N—NH.C}_6\text{H}_5 \\
| \\
\text{C=O} + \text{H}_2\text{N—NHC}_6\text{H}_5
\end{array}
\longrightarrow
\begin{array}{l}
\text{H} \\
| \\
\text{C=N—NH.C}_6\text{H}_5 \\
| \\
\text{C=N—NH.C}_6\text{H}_5
\end{array}
$$

Glucose phenylosazone

These osazones are yellow, water-insoluble, crystalline compounds fairly characteristic in form (and other properties) for each individual sugar, so that the osazone test becomes an important one for purposes of identification.

Glucose and fructose give the same osazone. This must mean that such sugars differ only in the first two carbon loadings:

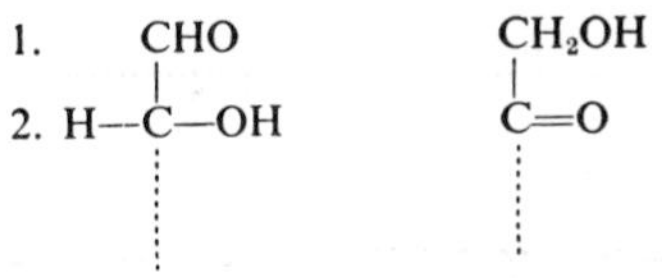

$$
\begin{array}{ll}
1. \quad \text{CHO} & \text{CH}_2\text{OH} \\
\qquad \quad | & | \\
2. \text{ H—C—OH} & \text{C=O}
\end{array}
$$

Glucose   Fructose

With fructose the first molecule of the phenylhydrazine reacts with the carbonyl group; the second molecule is involved in the reaction which oxidizes the primary alcoholic group (next to the carbonyl group) to an aldehyde; and the third molecule of the reagent reacts with this aldehydic group to form the osazone.

DESCRIPTIONS OF SOME MONO- AND DISACCHARIDES

GLUCOSE ($C_6H_{12}O_6$)

Glucose is also called *dextrose* and *grape sugar*. It occurs with fructose in sweet fruits. It is the normal sugar present in blood. In diabetes the amount in the blood increases and very often a considerable quantity of this sugar appears in the urine. Its preparation from corn-starch by acid hydrolysis is a commercial process. Glucose is surpassed in sweetness only by fructose and sucrose.

FRUCTOSE ($C_6H_{12}O_6$)

Fructose is also called *levulose* and *fruit sugar,* and is present in sweet fruits, together with glucose. It is now obtained on a commercial scale by the hydrolysis of inulin, a polysaccharide found in the Jeru-salem artichoke.

GALACTOSE ($C_6H_{12}O_6$)

Galactose is obtained when agar (an Asiatic seaweed) or lactose is hydrolyzed. It is found in combination in nerve tissue.

MANNOSE ($C_6H_{12}O_6$)

An aldohexose, mannose occurs in combination in mannans (found, for example, in the ivory nut from which buttons are made). While glucose, galactose, and fructose are common foodstuffs, mannose plays a minor role.

MALTOSE ($C_{12}H_{22}O_{11}$)

This is also called *malt sugar* and is obtained when starch is hy-drolyzed by an enzyme (diastase or amylase) found in sprouting barley or malt. It is also a product formed when the enzyme in saliva (ptyalin or salivary amylase) acts on starch. When hydrolyzed (by acid or by the enzyme maltase of the small intestine), glucose is formed. For each molecule of maltose we obtain two molecules of glucose.

LACTOSE ($C_{12}H_{22}O_{11}$)

Lactose, or *milk sugar,* is the sugar present in milk. It is sometimes found in the urine of women during lactation. When hydrolyzed (by acid or by the enzyme lactase of the small intestine), a mixture of glucose and galactose is obtained.

SUCROSE ($C_{12}H_{22}O_{11}$)

Sucrose is also called *cane sugar* or *saccharose.* It occurs in abun-dance in sugar cane and sugar beets and is the sugar commonly used for sweetening purposes. When hydrolyzed (by acid, by the enzyme invertase of yeast, or by the enzyme sucrase of the intestine), a mixture of glucose and fructose is obtained. This mixture is known as *invert sugar* because the sucrose is dextrorotatory, whereas the product ob-tained is levorotatory. The fructose molecule turns the plane of polarized light to the left more than the glucose molecule does to the right.

POLYSACCHARIDES $(C_6H_{10}O_5)_x$

STARCH

Starch, which occurs abundantly in grains, tubers and fruits, is the greatest source of carbohydrates for man. It consists of two types of molecules: a linear or nonbranched polymer of glucose (amylose) and a branched polymer of glucose (amylopectin). One method of separating the amylose from the amylopectin is to allow starch grains, soaked in water, to swell. The temperature should be 60 to 80° C. The amylose diffuses into the water. The residue, containing the amylopectin, is separated by centrifugation. The amylose may be represented as:

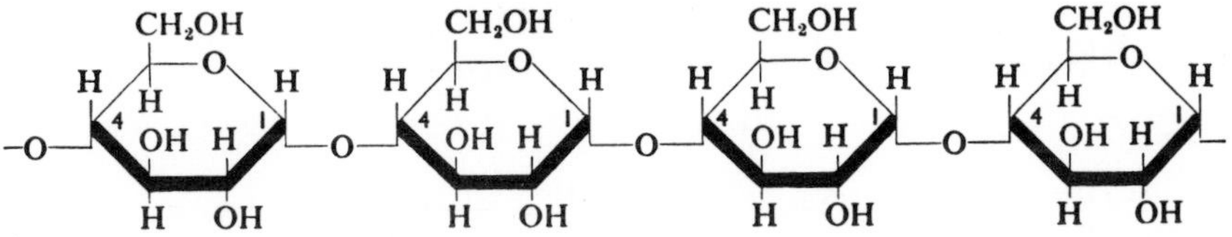

which shows linear chains of glucopyranose units joined by the first and fourth carbon atoms (a 1,4- linkage). Amylopectin, the branched type, shows joining of branches at 1,6- glucosidic linkages (compare the numbering on page 16 for formula for glucose):

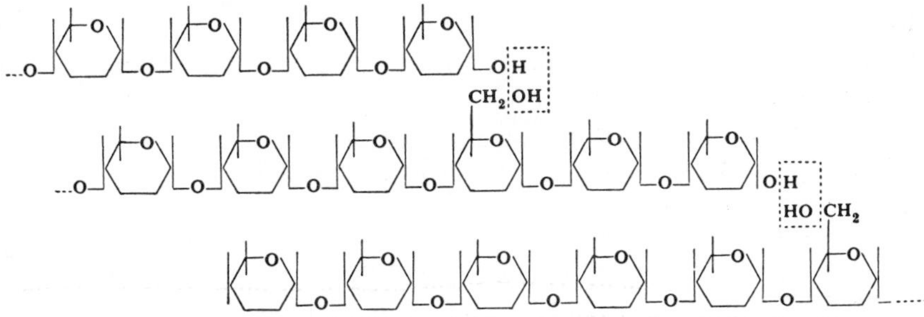

Structure of Starch. Some evidence for the formulas of amylose and amylopectin is the following:

A. METHYLATION STUDIES. When starch is methylated and then hydrolyzed, a study of the products so obtained gives a clue to the structure of the original polysaccharide. The main product is 2,3,6-trimethyl-D-glucose. This is an indication of the presence of long chains of glucose units belonging to the amylose type. In addition, smaller amounts of 2,3,4,6-tetramethyl-D-glucose and 2,3-dimethylglucose are also formed. The former would arise from the nonreducing chain which exists in amylopectin. The relative amounts of each of these two methylated sugars indicate the number of such chains in the molecule.

In amylopectin there are some 26 to 30 anhydroglucopyranosidic units for one "nonreducing end," whereas in amylose there are 300 to 350 such units.

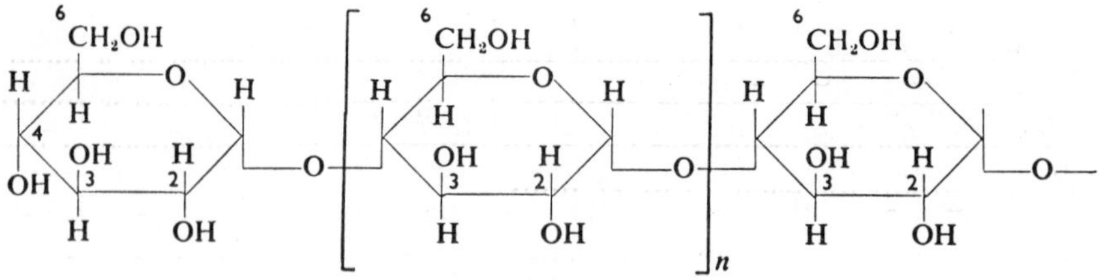

Amylose type chain
(Yields 2,3,6-trimethylglucose and a small
amount of 2,3,4,6-tetramethylglucose.)

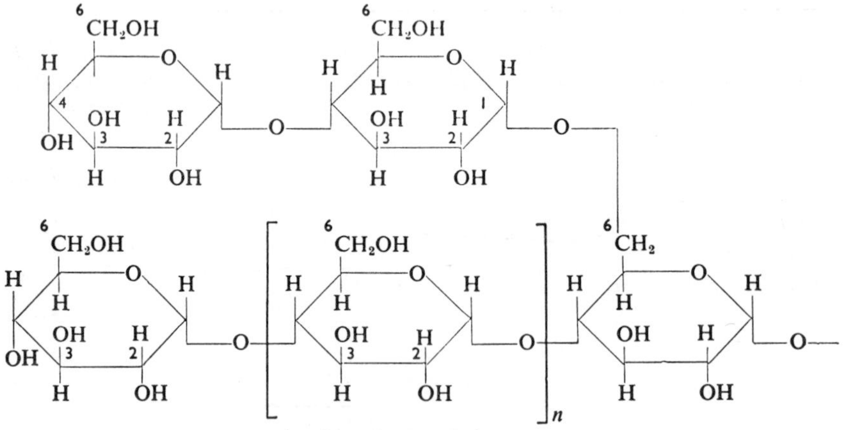

Amylopectin type chain
(Yields 2,3,6-trimethylglucose and more 2,3,4,6-
tetramethylglucose, as well as 2,3-dimethylglucose.)

B. PERIODIC ACID OXIDATION. End-group determinations have been made in which the amount of formic acid produced by the oxidation of a polysaccharide with periodic acid is measured. Each nonreducing end-group forms one mole of formic acid (A, in the formula), whereas each reducing end-group forms 2 moles of formic acid (B, in the formula below). The glucopyranosidic units within the chains do not form formic acid.

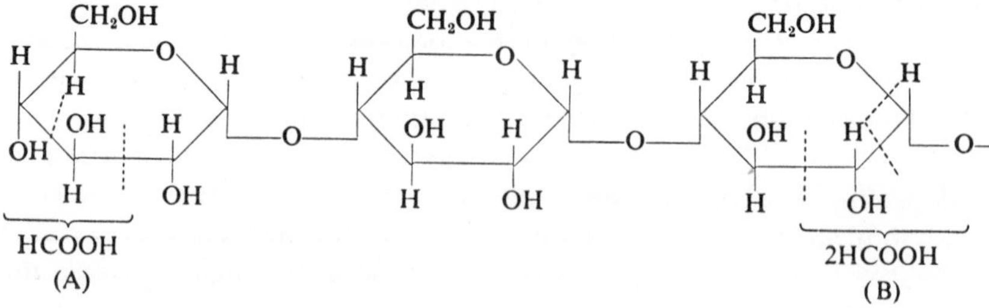

A linear molecule like amylose will form 3 moles of formic acid. For branched molecules of large molecular weight, the amount of formic acid produced by the reducing end-group is an inconsequential part of the whole; so that it may be assumed that all the formic acid arises from nonreducing end-groups, of which there will be many more in a molecule like amylopectin than in amylose. By this method amylose is found to contain one end-group per 250 to 980 units, whereas amylopectin has one end-group for each 25 to 27 units.

Action of Enzymes on Starch. Plant enzymes called *amylases* split starch into smaller units. One of these, β-amylase (which has been crystallized), acts on amylose and hydrolyzes it to maltose. When β-amylase acts on whole starch, only some 60 to 70 per cent of the theoretical yield of maltose is obtained; the unhydrolyzed residue is called the "β-amylase limit dextrin." Apparently, the enzyme cannot hydrolyze the amylopectin molecule beyond some branch in the chain.

In contradistinction to the β-variety, α-amylase is more vigorous in its hydrolysis of starch; it hydrolyzes starch into fragments of 6 to 7 units.

Salivary and pancreatic amylases (Chap. 7) are similar to the plant amylases in their action.

In addition to the amylases, plants contain a *phosphorylase* which can split the 1,4- glucosidic bond in starch with the help of phosphoric acid (phosphate ion) instead of water, as with the amylases:

$$\text{Starch} + \text{PO}_4 \overset{\text{phosphorylase}}{\rightleftharpoons} \alpha\text{-D-glucose-1-phosphate}$$

The process is called "phosphorolysis" (instead of hydrolysis).

Phosphorylase can degrade amylose completely; but if amylopectin is the substrate, a "phosphorylase-resistant dextrin" is obtained, owing to the branches in the amylopectin molecule at the 1,6- positions.

The action of phosphorylase is reversible *in vitro:* it converts glucose-1-phosphate into a linear amylose molecule, releasing inorganic phosphate. When purified phosphorylase is used, this action is a slow one—a long induction period is required; but the reaction can be accelerated by the addition of small amounts of starch or oligosaccharide fragments ("activators," "primers"). Maximum activation is obtained when primers contain 4–5 glucose residues.

For the synthesis of amylopectin, an additional enzyme (for branching) is required; this is the "Q enzyme." This enzyme (found, together with phosphorylase, in the potato, among other places), together with phosphorylase and α-D-glucose-1-phosphate, will give rise to a branched amylopectin–like polysaccharide.

The Q enzyme can act on amylose to produce amylopectin, without the help of inorganic phosphate; it is not, therefore, a phosphorylase but rather a transglucosidase because it can cleave the 1,4- linkage and simultaneously produce the 1,6- linkage.

GLYCOGEN

Animal starch, or glycogen, is found in liver and muscle. It is soluble in water (unlike starch), and gives a red color with iodine (starch gives a blue color). It is hydrolyzed *in vivo* to glucose, and when hydrolyzed *in vitro* by acid, glucose is again the only product. Like starch it fails to reduce Benedict's solution or to form an osazone.

A substance resembling glycogen has been found in lower plants (fungi, yeasts, and bacteria). Glycogen, in addition to starch, has been isolated from the seed of the sweet corn. The isolation of glycogen from corn is important because it has always been assumed that this poly-saccharide is a typical animal product, whereas now it is shown to be present in one of the higher plants as well.

By use of methods similar to those for starch it can be shown that glycogen possesses a structure similar to that of amylopectin: 1,4-glucose units which branch at 1,6- positions. Glycogen differs from amylopectin by having shorter and more frequent branches. One preparation of this glycogen indicates a molecular weight of five million, which makes it one of the largest molecules of the naturally occurring water-soluble variety.

Animal tissues, such as liver and muscle, contain a phosphorylase capable of the following reaction:

$$\text{Glycogen} + \text{PO}_4 \equiv \quad \longrightarrow \quad \text{glucose-1-phosphate}$$

It differs from the phosphorylase of plants in that it requires a *co-enzyme* in the shape of adenine-ribose-5-phosphate, also called adenylic acid.

Phosphorylase splits the 1,4- linkages between glucose residues. When it reaches the 1,6- branching point, the enzyme ceases to act, and another enzyme, amylo-1,6-glucosidase, now attacks the branching points, thereby allowing phosphorylase to continue its action.

The enzyme amylo-1,6-glucosidase does not require inorganic phosphate for its action, which means that hydrolysis (rather than phosphorolysis) occurs and free glucose is formed. The glycogen is characterized by determining the ratio of glucose-phosphate to free glucose formed after treatment with phosphorylase and amylo-1,6-glucosidase.

Analysis of glycogen by this technique is illustrated in Figure 2.

DEXTRAN

This is a polysaccharide of a molecular weight of approximately 50,000, closely related to starch and glycogen. It is synthesized from sucrose by certain bacteria and is a polymer of D-glucopyranose units.

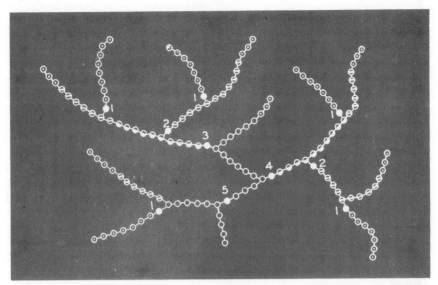

Figure 2. Model of segment of muscle glycogen based on results obtained by stepwise enzymatic degradation. ⊙, ⊖, and ◖ glucose residues removed by first, second, and third degradation with phosphorylase, respectively. ●, glucose residues removed by amylo-1,6-glucosidase. Of five tiers three were degraded, corresponding to 122 out of 150 glucose residues. (From Larner, Illingworth, Cori and Cori: J. Biol. Chem., *199*:641.)

The dextrans comprise chains of α1,6- linked units with α1,4- branching points. It may be recalled (p. 31) that starch and glycogen consist of α1,4- linked units with α1,6- branching points.

DEXTRINS

Dextrins, such as erythrodextrin (which gives a reddish color with iodine) and achroodextrin (which does not give a color with iodine), are formed in the early stages of the hydrolysis of starch. They have the general formula $(C_6H_{10}O_5)_x$.

CELLULOSE

The constituent of the cell walls of plants, cellulose is a highly insoluble substance. It can be dissolved in Schweitzer's reagent (ammoniacal cupric hydroxide), in an acid (HCl) solution of zinc chloride and in a solution of sodium hydroxide and carbon disulfide, the last forming *viscose*, from which rayon is made. It is hydrolyzed with difficulty, the product formed being glucose. Unlike starch, glycogen, and the dextrins, which are readily digested, cellulose passes through the human digestive tract without being attacked by any of the digestive enzymes, though some bacterial decomposition probably takes place in the large intestine. In herbivorous animals, microorganisms (bacteria, yeasts, protozoa) in the digestive tract attack cellulose to form, among other products, lower fatty acids which the animal utilizes for energy purposes.

When hydrolyzed with acids, cellulose is converted to β-D-glucose (p. 15). The cellulose molecules appear to consist of unbranched chains of glucopyranose.[*]

INULIN

This is present in the Jerusalem artichoke, is soluble in hot water, gives a negative iodine test, and yields fructose on hydrolysis. It has been suggested that the molecule of this polysaccharide consists of thirty fructose units and has a molecular weight of about 5000.

When inulin is injected, it is excreted through the glomeruli of the kidney. The substance has been used as a test for kidney function.

CHITIN

The organic constituent of the skeletal material of the Insecta and Crustacea is chitin, which yields glucosamine on hydrolysis.

Glucosamine is also obtained when the mucin of saliva and the mucoids of connective tissues are hydrolyzed.

One of the constituents of the molecule of streptomycin is glucosamine.

HYALURONIC ACID

This polysaccharide—present in animal tissues—yields, when hydrolyzed, a hexosamine (glucosamine) and a uronic acid (glucuronic acid). The substance has been prepared from umbilical cord, skin, vitreous humor, synovial fluid, tumors, and hemolytic streptococci.

PENTOSANS

The pentosans are polysaccharides which yield pentoses on hydrolysis. Examples of pentosans are found in gum arabic, from which arabinose is obtained, and in oat hulls and corn cobs, which yield xylose.

---

[*] Cellulose is very widely distributed. Cotton, linen, and wood are rich in this substance. By changing the physical form of cotton (there are several methods available), rayon, known for a time as artificial silk, is produced. Cellulose acetate forms the basis for motion picture films and shatter-proof glass. From cellulose nitrate a number of important industrial products are also obtained; for example, guncotton, celluloid, collodion, and lacquers.

More than 80 per cent of the rayon manufactured is made by the viscose process. Spruce pulp or cotton linters are soaked in caustic soda, treated with carbon disulfide (to form viscose) and forced through fine holes into an acid bath, thereby forming filaments of regenerated cellulose (rayon). These filaments can then be twisted to form threads.

GALACTANS

The galactans, such as agar-agar, another common plant product, yield galactose on hydrolysis.

PECTINS

The pectins, present in apples, lemons, etc., and which form fruit gels with sugar, give on hydrolysis some galactose and arabinose, but galacturonic acid—resembling glucuronic acid (p. 27)—is the principal product.

AGAR

A complex carbohydrate obtained from seaweed, agar may be mentioned here because of its wide use in bacteriological technique. Bacteria can be grown in agar because most of them neither digest nor liquefy this medium. Agar dissolves in boiling water and does not set until body temperature is reached.

FERMENTATION

It has been known for many years that various plants "respire" in the dark, using oxygen and giving off carbon dioxide. This "dark reaction" is the opposite of photosynthesis in which carbon dioxide is utilized and oxygen is liberated.

In addition to this respiratory type of metabolism, cells are known (anaerobic cells) which in the absence of air can still obtain energy for life. This is true of yeasts, for example; this cell will continue to perform its metabolic functions in the complete absence of free oxygen. Such a process is called *fermentation* or *glycolysis* and is found to occur in higher plants and in many animal cells.

In the fermentation of yeast the starting compound is a sugar ("organic" source) such as glucose, mannose or fructose. One molecule of the hexose gives rise to two molecules of ethyl alcohol and two molecules of carbon dioxide:

$$C_6H_{12}O_6 \longrightarrow 2C_2H_5OH + 2CO_2$$

If the sugar is a disaccharide, such as sucrose, it must first be hydrolyzed by an enzyme, invertase (found in yeast).

In animal tissues, the glycogen is first split to glucose-1-phosphate by means of phosphorylase.

In the early stages of the investigation of fermentation, it was believed that the conversion of glucose to alcohol and carbon dioxide was due to the action of just one enzyme; and this enzyme was called *zymase*. This zymase we know today is in reality a mixture of many enzymes, and many are the intermediate compounds formed during the conversion of glucose to carbon dioxide.

A closer analysis of the process of fermentation in yeast ultimately led to the isolation of a number of phosphoric acid esters of the sugars, which were later found to be present in animal cells as well. These discoveries led to the view that the metabolic processes in plants and animals have much in common.

Some examples of these esters of phosphoric acid and sugars are:

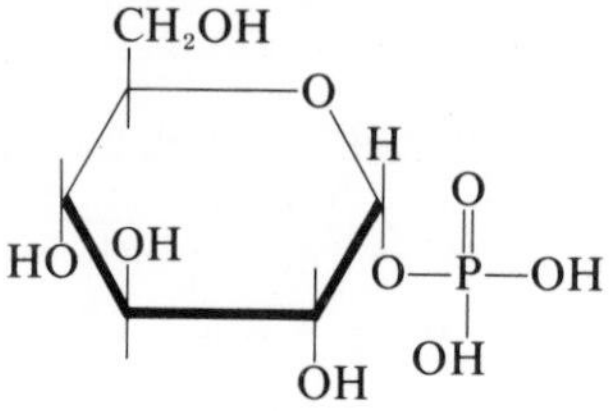

Glucose-1-PO$_4$ 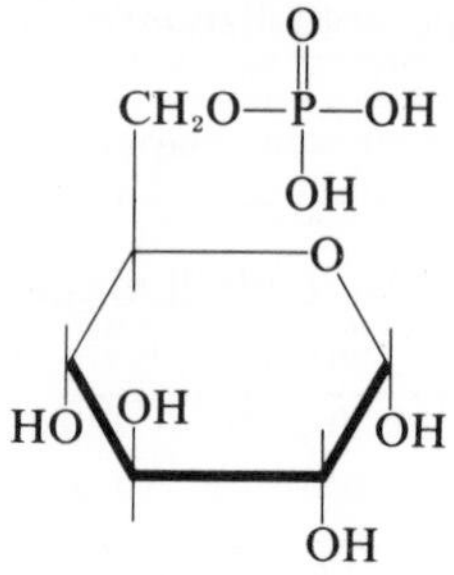   Glucose-6-PO$_4$

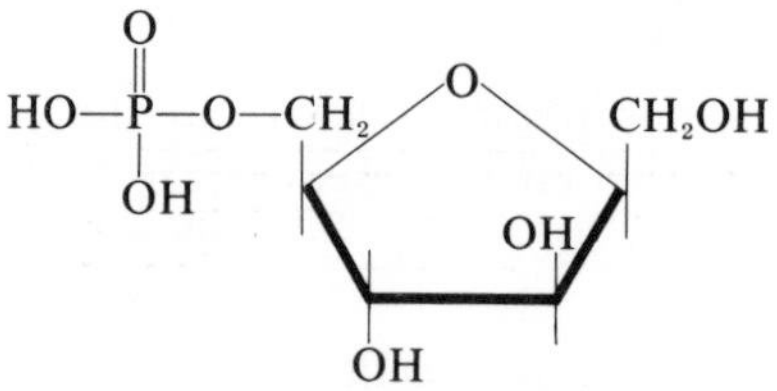

Fructose-6-PO$_4$ 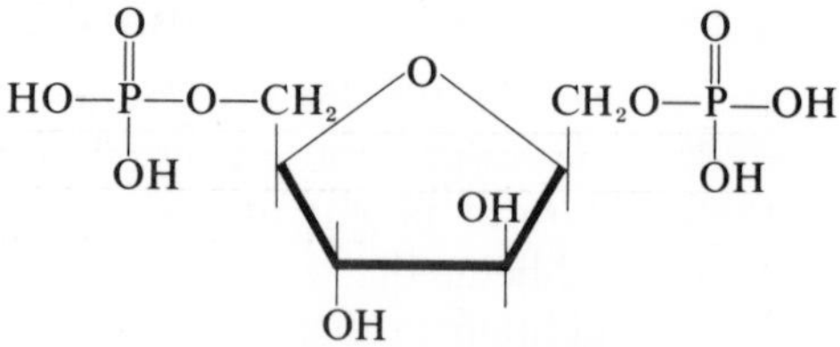   Fructose-1,6-diphosphate

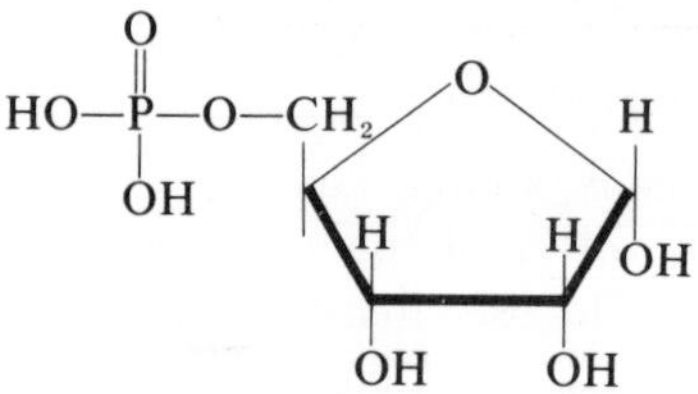

Ribose-5-PO$_4$

It should be stressed at this point that the end-product of all fermentation reactions is not necessarily ethyl alcohol; it may be some other alcohol, or an acid such as lactic acid.

PAPER PARTITION CHROMATOGRAPHY

A very ingenious method for the separation and identification of small quantities of biochemically important compounds was developed by Martin, Consden and Gordon. It has been used for the separation of mixtures of sugars, amino acids, purines, etc.

The method is based on the partition of a compound between water (bound by the cellulose of the filter paper) and the solvent (which may be phenol, collidine, butyl alcohol, etc.).

A small quantity of the mixture in solution is placed as a spot near the top of a strip of filter paper. The paper is hung vertically from a trough containing the solvent in such a way that the edge is immersed in the solvent. The whole is enclosed in a jar whose atmosphere is kept saturated with respect to both the water and the solvent.

As the solvent moves down the paper, a sharp solvent front can be seen. When this "front" has traveled a sufficient distance, it is marked with a pencil, the paper removed, dried and sprayed with a reagent which will produce a colored spot at those points along the paper where the individual compounds are present. The R_F value for each spot is now measured as the ratio of the distance moved by the compound to the distance moved by the advancing solvent front.

The distance moved by the compound is related to its partition coefficient between water and the solvent—to the water bound by a unit area of filter paper and the volume of water-saturated solvent held per unit area of filter paper. The R_F values are compared with the R_F values of known compounds similarly treated.

In the separation of reducing sugars by this method (Fig. 3), the paper is sprayed with a solution of silver nitrate and a large excess of ammonia. Metallic silver is precipitated in the region occupied by the reducing sugar; and this shows itself in the form of a brown or black spot.

A one-dimensional strip may not be sufficient for an unknown containing a relatively large number of sugars. For this reason, the unknown is often placed near one corner of a filter paper square, and is chroma-

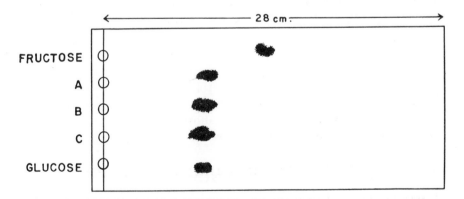

Figure 3. Chromatogram of an extract of egg white in aqueous ethanol. A, extract treated with Zeo Karb 215 and Deacidite. B, extract treated with Zeo Karb only. C, untreated extract. The chromatogram was run 18 hr. in phenol-1% NH₃. (From Partridge: Biochem. J., 42:238.)

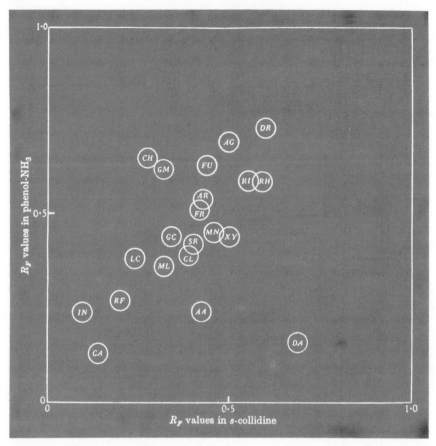

Figure 4. Illustrating the separation obtainable by use of two solvents. The R_F values in phenol-1% NH_3 and *s*-collidine are plotted at right angles. *AA*, ascorbic acid; *AG*, acetylglucosamine; *AR*, arabinose; *CH*, chondrosamine; *DA*, dehydroascorbic acid; *DR*, deoxyribose; *FR*, fructose; *FU*, fucose; *GA*, galacturonic acid; *GC*, galactose; *GL*, glucose; *GM*, glucosamine; *IN*, inositol; *LC*, lactose; *ML*, maltose; *MN*, mannose; *RF*, raffinose; *RH*, rhamnose; *RI*, ribose; *SR*, sorbose; *XY*, xylose. (From Partridge: Biochem. J., *42*:238.)

tographed first in one direction in one solvent, and then at right angles to it in another solvent (Fig. 4). Since the R_F value of any one solute varies with the solvent, a better separation is achieved.

Various modifications of this technique have been suggested.

REFERENCES

Pigman: The Carbohydrates, 1957. On the subject of photosynthesis, see *Jagendorf* in the Federation Proceedings, *18*:974, 1959. See also, *Arnon, Whatley* and *Allen:* Science, *127*:106, 1958; *Warburg:* Ibid., 128:69, 1958; *Daniels:* Borden's Review of Nutritional Research, *15*: Nov.–Dec., 1954; *Calvin:* J. Chemical Society, June, 1956, p. 1895; *Arnon, D. I.:* Fed. Proc., *18*:974, 1959.

A suggestive article dealing with chemical evolution and the origin of life is by *Calvin:* American Scientist, *44:*248, 1956.

For a discussion of sugar configurations, see *Abernathy:* J. Chem. Educ., *33:*88, 1956.

Reviews of yearly progress are summarized in the Ann. Rev. Biochem., of which the first volume appeared in 1932. See, for example, *Whelan: 29:*105, 1960.

The use of the anthrone reagent is discussed by *Seifter, Dayton, Novic,* and *Muntwyler:* Arch. Biochem., *25:*191, 1950; and by *Graff, McElroy,* and *Mooney:* J. Biol. Chem., *195:*351, 1952. *Devor:* J. Am. Chem. Soc., *72:*2008, 1950, describes a modified Molisch reaction.

A suggestive article on the origin of optical activity will be found in the paper by *Wald:* Annals N. Y. Acad. Sciences, *69:*352, 1957.

Chromatography is reviewed by *Keller, Stewart* and *Giddings:* Ann. Rev. Phys. Chem., *11:*347, 1960.

See also Recent Advances in the Chemistry of Cellulose and Starch, edited by *Honeyman,* 1959.

See also Chemistry and Biology of Mucopolysaccharides, A Ciba Foundation Symposium, edited by *Wolsterholm* and *O'Conner,* 1958.

A suggestive article by Fox on how life began will be found in Science *132:*200, 1960.

THE LIPIDS

Lipid is a term used to describe a group of fats and fat-like substances which constitute a major class of tissue components and an important foodstuff. Although we include in this group compounds which are quite unrelated in their structure, they are nevertheless treated together because of their similar solubility characteristics. They are generally soluble in any of a group of organic solvents and insoluble in water. Because of the many difficulties inherent in the separation of the lipids by classical chemical procedures, our knowledge as to their exact chemical constitution is fairly recent. In this chapter we shall deal with the following classes of lipids: *neutral fats, waxes and sterols, phospholipids, cerebrosides* and *lipoproteins*. In addition to the compounds included in the above classification, there are other componds which may be properly listed as lipids. Among these are carotenoids, the vitamins A, D, E and K, as well as the steroids in general. However, these will be considered when their metabolism is discussed.

NEUTRAL FATS

The neutral fats are esters of the trihydroxyalcohol, glycerol, and long-chain fatty acids. The very large number of different fats which are found in nature may be accounted for by the fact that individual species of plant and animal have characteristically different fats, and the fat of one tissue may be quite different from that of another tissue in the same individual. Finally, because there are a large number of different fatty acids, and since glycerol may be esterified with three different fatty acids, the number of different fats increases appreciably.

The structural formulas for several fats (triglycerides) are shown below. The carbon atoms of glycerol may be identified by α, β, α_1 as well as by the corresponding numbers for each C atom: 1, 2 and 3.

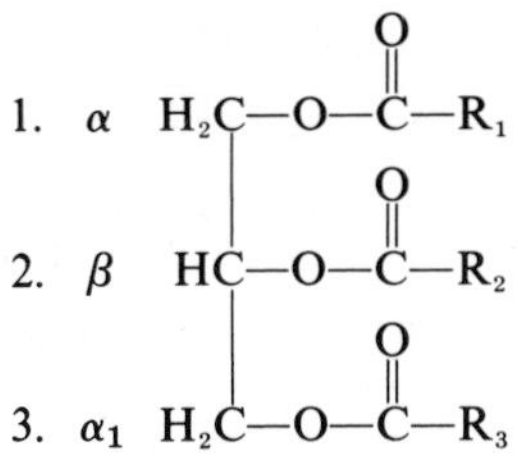

$$
\begin{array}{lll}
\text{1.} & \alpha & H_2C-O-\overset{\overset{\displaystyle O}{\|}}{C}-R_1 \\
\text{2.} & \beta & HC-O-\overset{\overset{\displaystyle O}{\|}}{C}-R_2 \\
\text{3.} & \alpha_1 & H_2C-O-\overset{\overset{\displaystyle O}{\|}}{C}-R_3
\end{array}
$$

If $R_1 = R_2 = R_3$, then we have a simple glyceride; for example,

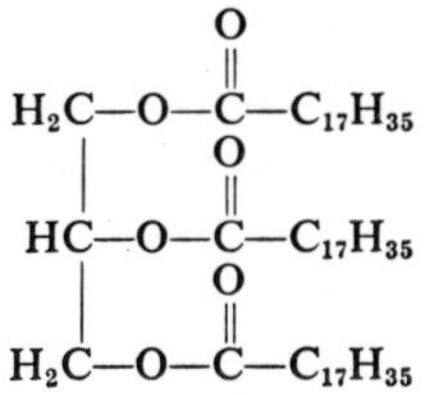

$$
\begin{array}{l}
H_2C-O-\overset{\overset{\displaystyle O}{\|}}{C}-C_{17}H_{35} \\
HC-O-\overset{\overset{\displaystyle O}{\|}}{C}-C_{17}H_{35} \\
H_2C-O-\overset{\overset{\displaystyle O}{\|}}{C}-C_{17}H_{35}
\end{array}
$$

Tristearin
($C_{17}H_{35}COOH$ = stearic acid)

If the R's are unequal, then we get a mixed glyceride; for example,

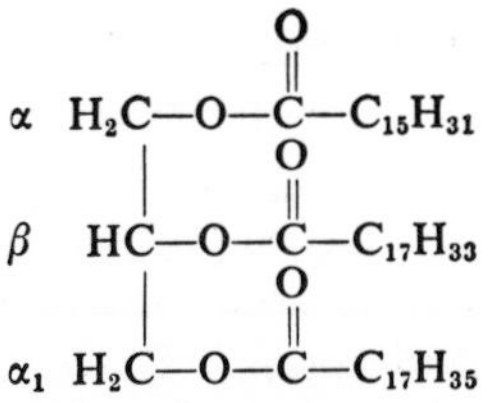

$$
\begin{array}{ll}
\alpha & H_2C-O-\overset{\overset{\displaystyle O}{\|}}{C}-C_{15}H_{31} \\
\beta & HC-O-\overset{\overset{\displaystyle O}{\|}}{C}-C_{17}H_{33} \\
\alpha_1 & H_2C-O-\overset{\overset{\displaystyle O}{\|}}{C}-C_{17}H_{35}
\end{array}
$$

β-Oleo-α-α_1-palmitostearin
($C_{15}H_{31}COOH$ = palmitic acid)
($C_{17}H_{33}COOH$ = oleic acid)
($C_{17}H_{35}COOH$ = stearic acid)

Neutral fats are largely mixed triglycerides. Diglycerides and mono-glycerides are also found in nature. The α,β-diglycerides are precursors of the phosphatides.

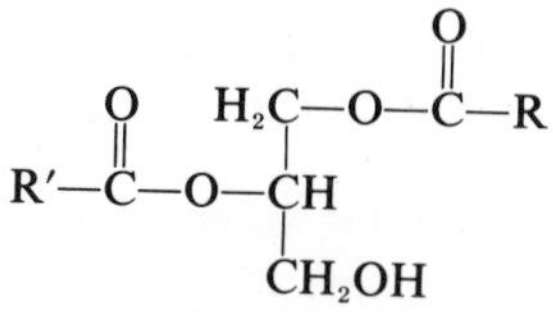

$$
\begin{array}{l}
\qquad\qquad\quad H_2C-O-\overset{\overset{\displaystyle O}{\|}}{C}-R \\
R'-\overset{\overset{\displaystyle O}{\|}}{C}-O-CH \\
\qquad\qquad\quad CH_2OH
\end{array}
$$

L-α,β-Diglyceride

The glycerides constitute over 98 per cent of the lipids of adipose tissue of the mammal, but only 30 per cent of plasma or liver lipids, and less than 10 per cent of erythrocyte lipids.

Since they are esters, fats are readily hydrolyzed:

$$
\begin{array}{c}
\underset{\text{Tripalmitin}}{
\begin{array}{l}
\text{H}_2\text{C}-\text{O}-\overset{\text{O}}{\overset{\|}{\text{C}}}-\text{C}_{15}\text{H}_{31} \\
\text{HC}-\text{O}-\overset{\text{O}}{\overset{\|}{\text{C}}}-\text{C}_{15}\text{H}_{31} + 3\text{H}_2\text{O} \\
\text{H}_2\text{C}-\text{O}-\overset{\text{O}}{\overset{\|}{\text{C}}}-\text{C}_{15}\text{H}_{31}
\end{array}
}
\longrightarrow
\underset{\text{Glycerol}}{
3\text{C}_{15}\text{H}_{31}\text{COOH} +
\begin{array}{l}
\text{CH}_2\text{OH} \\
\text{CHOH} \\
\text{CH}_2\text{OH}
\end{array}
}
\end{array}
$$

This hydrolysis can be accomplished by using acid, alkali, super-heated steam, or the appropriate enzyme (lipase of the pancreas, for example). When acid is used, the free fatty acid is liberated. When alkali is used, a soap is formed, and the process is known as *saponification:*

$$
\underset{\text{Stearin}}{\text{C}_3\text{H}_5(\text{O}.\text{CO}.\text{C}_{17}\text{H}_{35})_3} + 3\text{NaOH} \longrightarrow \underset{\substack{\text{Sodium stearate} \\ \text{(A soap)}}}{3\text{C}_{17}\text{H}_{35}\text{COONa}} + \underset{\text{Glycerol}}{\text{C}_3\text{H}_5(\text{OH})_3}
$$

Fats and oils* are, as a rule, more complex than mere mixtures of the triglycerides (stearin, palmitin, olein). The composition of a number of fats is given in Table 2.

The fats we eat—the edible fats—are glycerides of *even-numbered* fatty acids, ranging from butyric (C_4) to lignoceric (C_{24}) and probably higher.

TABLE **2.**   FATTY ACID CONTENT OF FATS OF REPRESENTATIVE SPECIES

Source	Saturated acids			Unsaturated acids			
	C_{14}	C_{16}	C_{18}	C_{14}	C_{16}	Oleic	Linoleic
Rat	1.8	24.4	4.4	0.3	4.8	44.3	18.6[a]
Carp	3.7	14.6	1.9	1.0	17.8	45.8	15.2
Linseed oil (flax)	8.3	8.3	—	—	—	17.3	21.8[a]
Pistachio Nut	0.6	8.2	1.6	—	—	73.8	7.7
Daphnia (zooplankton)	3.5	13.0	1.7	3.0	21.1	45.0	12.0

[a] The rat has, in addition, 1.4% of a C_{20} unsaturated fatty acid, and linseed oil has 46.5% of this fatty acid. All values are in weight per cent. (Abstracted from Deuel: The Lipids, Vol. 1, 1951.)

The composition of butter fat is as follows, the numbers representing the per cent of glyceryl ester: butyric acid, 3.0; caproic acid, 1.4; caprylic acid, 1.8; capric acid, 1.8; lauric acid, 6.9; myristic acid, 22.6; palmitic acid, 22.6; stearic acid, 11.4; oleic acid, 27.4.

Simple and mixed glycerides have also been prepared synthetically. From 60 to 65 per cent of the total fat and oil production in the

* Oils are liquid at room temperature.

United States is used as food. These fats include butter, lard, cottonseed oil, and soybean oil. Fats and oils used in products other than foods are inedible tallow greases, and the oils of coconut, palm, linseed, tung, fish, soybean, and castor bean.

THE FATTY ACIDS

Table 3 lists some of the fatty acids found in fats which occur more or less commonly. Those found in nature have almost invariably an even number of carbon atoms.

TABLE **3.** COMMON FATTY ACIDS

		Occurrence
I. *Saturated fatty acids*		
Acetic	CH_3COOH	Vinegar
Butyric	C_3H_7COOH	Butter
Caproic	$C_5H_{11}COOH$	Butter, etc.
Caprylic	$C_7H_{15}COOH$	Butter, etc.
Capric	$C_9H_{19}COOH$	Coconut oil, butter, etc.
Lauric	$C_{11}H_{23}COOH$	Spermaceti, coconut oil, etc.
Myristic	$C_{13}H_{27}COOH$	Nutmeg butter, coconut oil, etc.
Palmitic	$C_{15}H_{31}COOH$	Animal and vegetable fats
Stearic	$C_{17}H_{35}COOH$	Animal and vegetable fats
Arachidic	$C_{19}H_{39}COOH$	Peanut oil
Lignoceric	$C_{23}H_{47}COOH$	Arachis oil; cerebrosides
Carnaubic	$C_{23}H_{47}COOH$	Carnauba wax
Cerotic	$C_{25}H_{51}COOH$	Beeswax, wool fat, etc.
II. *Unsaturated fatty acids*		
(*a*) One double bond		
Oleic	$C_{17}H_{33}COOH$	Animal and vegetable fats
Erucic	$C_{21}H_{41}COOH$	Rapeseed oil; etc.
(*b*) Two double bonds		
Linoleic	$C_{17}H_{31}COOH$	Linseed oil, cottonseed oil, etc.
(*c*) Three double bonds		
Linolenic	$C_{17}H_{29}COOH$	Linseed oil
(*d*) Four double bonds		
Arachidonic	$C_{19}H_{31}COOH$	Lecithin, cephalin
III. *Saturated monohydroxy acids*		
Cerebronic	$C_{24}H_{48}O_3$	Cerebron
IV. *Unsaturated monohydroxy acids*		
Ricinoleic	$C_{18}H_{34}O_3$	Castor oil
V. *Cyclic acids*		
Chaulmoogric	$C_{18}H_{32}O_2$	Chaulmoogra oil

(Reprinted by permission from Bull: The Biochemisty of the Lipids, John Wiley & Sons, Inc.)

The following list shows the position of the double bonds in other unsaturated fatty acids:

Erucic, $CH_3(CH_2)_7CH=CHCH_2)_{11}COOH$
Linoleic, $CH_3(CH_2)_4CH=CHCH_2CH=CH(CH_2)_7COOH$
Palmitoleic, $CH_3(CH_2)_5CH=CH(CH_2)_7COOH$
Linolenic, $CH_3CH_2CH=CHCH_2CH=CHCH_2CH=CH(CH_2)_7COOH$
Ricinoleic, $CH_3(CH_2)_5CHOHCH_2CH=CH(CH_2)_7COOH$

Animal fats differ from vegetable fats in containing a larger variety of fatty acids. In addition to the usual saturated C_{16} and C_{18} acids, animal fats have both saturated and unsaturated fatty acids of the C_{20}, C_{22} and C_{24} variety. Vegetable fats, however, contain a larger proportion of linoleic acid, which is present only in small amounts in animal fats. Such an unsaturated fatty acid is essential for good animal nutrition.

The type of fat which is deposited in an animal can be altered by the feeding of specific kinds of fat. As much as 27.6 per cent of the fatty acids in rats and 11.4 per cent in the pig can be changed to linolenic acid if this fatty acid is fed.

Table 4 gives a typical analysis of the fatty acids in human fat.

TABLE 4. FATTY ACID CONTENT OF HUMAN FAT (PER CENT BY WEIGHT)

Lauric	0.9	Hexadecenoic	7.6
Myristic	3.9	Oleic	46.6
Palmitic	25.7	Linoleic	8.7
Stearic	5.2	Arachidonic	0.6
Tetradecenoic	0.5	Other C_{20}	0.3

(Adapted from Cramer, D. L., and Brown, J. B.: J. Biol. Chem., *151*:428, 1943.)

Physical Properties.

A. MELTING POINT. The melting point of a fatty acid is influenced by chain length and by the degree of unsaturation. With an increase in the number of carbon atoms in the chain, the melting point increases. This is also true of the corresponding glycerides. An odd numbered fatty acid with a carbon chain of $x + 1$ has a lower melting point than an even numbered acid with a carbon chain x. The melting point is considerably decreased with the introduction of a double bond in the molecule. In fact, the more double bonds the lower the melting point.

B. SOLUBILITY. Biochemical reactions take place in an aqueous medium, and most, but not all, biochemically important compounds are water-soluble. The soaps, which are the sodium and potassium salts of fatty acids, are freely soluble, but neither the free acids nor the glycerides are soluble. Solubility is a relative term. Even the higher fatty acids are soluble to *some* extent; and it is probable that due to this slight solubility they can take part in chemical reactions.

In a general way, it may be said that as the chain length is in-

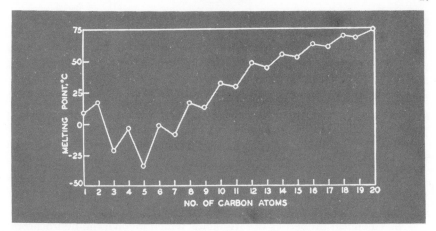

Figure 5. Melting points of normal carboxylic acids. (From Noller: Chemistry of Organic Compounds.)

creased, the solubility of the acid decreases. However, the introduction of hydroxyl groups markedly increases the solubility.

Associated closely with the problem of the solubility of fatty acids is their property of spreading (to form a thin and uniform layer) when placed on the surface of the water. Langmuir explains this behavior on the basis that these compounds contain, first, a hydrophilic or polar carboxyl group which dissolves in water; and second, a hydrophobic or nonpolar hydrocarbon chain which forms a layer on the surface and is anchored to its water-soluble carboxyl group. The layer so formed has the thickness of a molecule (a monomolecular layer), and the hydrocarbon chains of the fatty acids align themselves parallel to each other but perpendicular to the surface of the water. X-ray analysis suggests the arrangement and distances of the atoms:*

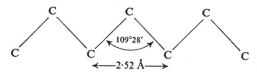

Chemical Properties. These may be conveniently subdivided into (a) those properties involving the carboxyl group and (b) those involving the hydrocarbon chain.

a. Fatty acids form salts (soaps) with metallic ions because of the presence of a terminal carboxyl group. The soaps containing sodium and potassium are soluble in water; those containing calcium and magnesium are insoluble. "Hard" waters are those containing calcium

* See *Bull:* Biochemistry of the Lipids. The symbol Å is the Angstrom. One Å equals 1×10^{-8} cm.

and magnesium salts: the latter combine with soap to form insoluble soaps, which are useless for washing purposes.

Fatty acids react with alcohols to form esters. When the alcohol is glycerol, the ester is a triglyceride (a fat). Aside from such fats, which are common in the animal (and plant) organism, esters of fatty acids and alcohols other than glycerol are known. For example, the alcohol cholesterol combines with fatty acids to form esters which are found in the blood.

The body has the ability, apparently, to reduce a carboxyl group to its corresponding aldehyde, alcohol, or even hydrocarbon. Fatty aldehydes have been reported to be present in the brain. Fatty alcohols are components of waxes. The carotenoids of plants and squalene of liver are examples of long-chain hydrocarbons.

b. Chemical properties of fatty acids which involve the hydrocarbon chain are confined to hydrogenation and oxidation reactions.

Unsaturated fatty acids react with hydrogen (in the presence of metal catalysts such as platinum, palladium, nickel and copper) to form the corresponding saturated acids. This is the basis for a method to determine the number of double bonds in a fatty acid or triglyceride.

Vegetable fats which are hydrogenated yield solid products which can be used in cooking and which are not subject to rancidity changes.

A typical hydrogenation is the conversion of oleic to stearic acid:

$$CH_3(CH_2)_7CH{=}CH(CH_2)_7\ COOH \xrightarrow{\ 2H\ } CH_3(CH_2)_{16}COOH$$

In addition to hydrogenation, fats (or fatty acids) are susceptible to oxidation because of the presence of double bonds. Combination with oxygen results in the formation of peroxides together with a mixture of volatile aldehydes, ketones and acids. Oxidation with $KMnO_4$ cleaves the double bond:

$$CH_3(CH_2)_7CH{=}CH(CH_2)_7COOH \longrightarrow CH_3(CH_2)_7COOH + HOOC(CH_2)_7COOH$$

$$\text{Oleic acid} \qquad\qquad \text{Pelargonic} \qquad \text{Azelaic acid}$$
$$\text{acid}$$

As has already been mentioned, the fatty acids form soaps with metal ions and esters with alcohols. In the organism they undergo an extensive series of transformations, their ultimate oxidation being related to the oxidation of carbohydrate.

A number of the unsaturated fatty acids contain eighteen carbon atoms. They undergo oxidation when exposed to the air and become brown in color. Mild oxidation gives hydroxy acids. For example,

$$CH_3(CH_2)_7CH{=}CH(CH_2)_7COOH + O + H_2O \longrightarrow$$
$$\text{Oleic acid}$$

$$CH_3(CH_2)_7CHOHCHOH(CH_2)_7COOH$$
$$\text{9,10-Dihydroxystearic acid}$$

Somewhat associated with the process of rancidity are the changes undergone by certain oils when exposed to the air. These oils, of which linseed and tung oils are the most important, form a solid surface that is strong and waterproof when exposed to the air. The oils are apparently oxidized and polymerized. Such "drying" oils have an iodine number greater than 130 and contain large percentages of highly unsaturated fatty acids. For example, linseed oil contains nearly 50 per cent of linoleic acid and more than 30 per cent of linolenic acid.

Separation and Determination of Fatty Acids. Several methods which have been used for the separation and quantitative estimation of the fatty acids are listed below:

A. CHEMICAL SEPARATION. Although this method will not yield quantitative data, it is useful for a preliminary separation of the fatty acids into different groups and serves to give us an idea of their properties. The fat is saponified with alcoholic potassium hydroxide and extracted with ether. The ether-insoluble materials, the soaps, are acidified to form the free fatty acids, and distilled with steam. To each fraction, volatile and nonvolatile, hot alcohol and an alcoholic solution of lead chloride are added. The soluble lead salts are mostly unsaturated fatty acids (liquid), and the insoluble lead salts are, for the most part, saturated fatty acids (solid).

The lead salts are changed to their free acids by the addition of hydrochloric acid, extracted with ether and converted to their methyl esters for fractional vacuum distillation, in order to separate the esters.

B. COUNTERCURRENT DISTRIBUTION. The fatty acids can also be separated by the method of *countercurrent* distribution. The name originates from a consideration of the distribution of a solute between two immiscible solvents as each phase (upper and lower) is moved in opposite directions after equilibration with fresh solvent. The solute distributes itself between the two immiscible solvents according to its partition ratio. Craig, the originator of the method, uses in actual practice some 220 specially designed "separatory funnels."

The choice of solvents depends upon the partition coefficients of the compounds to be separated in these solvents. Knowing such data, it is possible to calculate the degree of separation to be attained, and the numbers of the tubes in which to find the free fatty acids (Fig. 6). (K values represent partition coefficients in the solvent system which has been used.)

To amplify the meaning of "partition coefficient," let us imagine substance A dissolved in two solvents that are immiscible, but in contact with each other, after having been shaken to achieve complete equilibrium. The solute A is now distributed between two solvents, and, for slightly soluble substances, the ratio of the concentrations of the solute in each of the two solvents is equal to the ratio of the solubilities of the solute in each solvent. For example, the solubility of iodine in water is

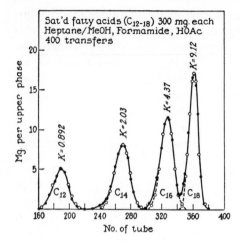

Figure 6. Separation by countercurrent distribution of a mixture of saturated fatty acids (solid line curve) as compared with a theoretically calculated separation (dotted line curve) based on the partition coefficients (*K*) of the acids. (From Ahrens and Craig: J. Biol. Chem., *195*:299, 1952.)

0.10 gm. per liter, whereas its solubility in carbon tetrachloride is 8.5 gm. per liter.

$$\frac{8.5}{0.1} = 85.0 = K$$

where *K* is the "partition coefficient."

    This method has proved of value in the separation not only of fatty acids but of a mixture of other compounds of similar chemical composition (amino acids, etc.).

    C. SILICA GEL CHROMATOGRAPHY. The use of chromatographic columns using silica gel has been successfully applied to the separation of fats and fatty acids.

    D. LIQUID-GAS CHROMATOGRAPHY. In this method the mixed fatty acids are converted into their methyl esters and carried through a long tube by an inert gas. The tube is filled with a finely divided inert solid which is coated with a nonvolatile oil. Separation is achieved by virtue of the fact that each component migrates at a rate determined by its solubility in the oil as well as by its vapor pressure. As the components leave the tube they are detected by the method of thermal conductance.* The results are then compared with those obtained using a mixture of known fatty acids. This is by far the most efficient technique for the quantitative determination of small quantities of acids in a mixture.

FAT ANALYSIS

    Aside from physical methods (melting point, index of refraction, etc.), the usual analysis of a fat depends upon determining certain chemical constants. Among these are the following:

---

   * The quantity of heat passing through a unit area (one cubic centimeter) in a unit time when the opposite faces of the cube differ by one degree centigrade.

1. Saponification Number. This represents the number of milligrams of KOH needed to saponify completely 1 gm. of fat (or oil). Roughly speaking, this number varies inversely with the molecular weight of the fat. For example,

	M. W.	Saponif. No.
Tributyrin	302.2	557.0
Tricaprin	554.4	303.6
Tripalmitin	806.8	208.6
Tristearin	890.9	188.9
Triolein	884.8	190.2

2. Reichert-Meissl Number. This is the number of milliliters of 0.1 N alkali required to neutralize the soluble volatile fatty acids from 5 gm. of fat. Butterfat has a particularly high Reichert-Meissl number.

Volatile fatty acids represent the acids which volatilize on steam distillation. They are confined, approximately, to the series ranging from butyric (C_4) to lauric (C_{12}) and are divided into two groups: those soluble in water and those insoluble in water. Butterfat and coconut and palm oils have a relatively high "volatile fatty acid" content; the reverse is true of most of the fats.

3. Acetyl Number. This is the number of milligrams of KOH required to neutralize the acetic acid resulting from the hydrolysis of 1 gm. of the acetylated fat. A fatty acid containing a hydroxyl group will react with acetic anhydride to form the acetylated compound. Castor oil, for example, which contains the unsaturated hydroxy acid, ricinoleic acid, gives a high acetyl number (142 to 150); the common fats containing smaller quantities of hydroxy fatty acids yield a considerably smaller number (2.5 to 20).

4. Iodine Number. The number of grams of iodine absorbed by 100 gm. of fat is the iodine number. From what has already been said, it is obvious that the iodine number will depend upon the extent of un-

TABLE **5.**   SAPONIFICATION AND IODINE NUMBERS OF SOME OF THE COMMON FATS

Fat	Saponif. No.	Iodine No.
Butter	220–241	22– 38
Lard	193–203	54– 70
Mutton tallow	192–195	32– 50
Coconut oil	246–265	8– 10
Cottonseed oil	191–195	104–114
Linseed oil	190–196	170–202
Olive oil	190–195	74– 95
Peanut oil	186–189	83–105
Soybean oil	190–197	116–145

(From Winton and Winton: Analysis of Foods.)

saturation in the molecule of fat. To accelerate the absorption process, "halogenating agents" are added; iodine monobromide (*Hanus'* method) or iodine monochloride (*Wijs'* method). A list of some iodine numbers of several fats and oils is given (Table 5).

DISTRIBUTION OF FATTY ACIDS IN TRIGLYCERIDES

There appears to be some degree of specificity with respect to the position occupied by the saturated and unsaturated fatty acids in naturally occurring triglycerides. This may be determined by utilizing enzymes which act on specific ester linkages, i.e. α-, β- or γ-, which will be designated 1-, 2- and 3-, respectively. First the enzyme phosphatidase D (p. 59) is allowed to act on the phosphatide lecithin (p. 59) and the phosphorylcholine group removed from the 3- position, giving rise to a 2,3-diglyceride (α,β-diglyceride). This diglyceride is then treated with pancreatic lipase which will split the ester linkage on carbon atom 1:

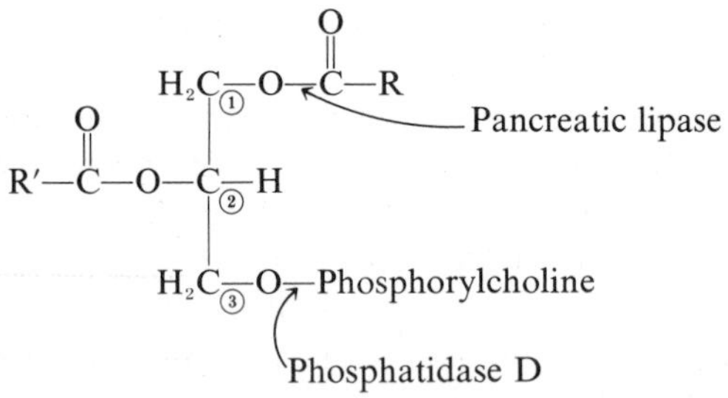

$$
\begin{array}{c}
 \overset{O}{\overset{\|}{H_2C-O-C-R}} \text{\underline{\hspace{1cm}} Pancreatic lipase} \\[2pt]
\overset{O}{\overset{\|}{R'-C-O-}}\underset{②}{C}-H \\[2pt]
H_2\underset{③}{C}-O-\text{Phosphorylcholine} \\[2pt]
\text{Phosphatidase D}
\end{array}
$$

Table 6 shows the distribution of saturated and unsaturated fatty acids in the original lecithin, the diglyceride obtained by phosphatidase D action, the fatty acids liberated after lipase action on the diglyceride, and the monoglyceride which remains. The results demonstrate that no

TABLE 6.   FATTY ACID COMPOSITION OF PRODUCTS OF LIPASE ACTION ON DIGLYCERIDE DERIVED FROM EGG LECITHIN BY THE ACTION OF PHOSPHATIDASE D

	Saturated acids	Unsaturated acids
	moles per cent	
Lecithin	48	51
Diglyceride	49	50
Fatty acids	97	3
Monoglyceride	1	99

(From Hanahan et al.: J. Biol. Chem., *235*:1917, 1960.)

perceptible change in distribution of fatty acids occurs when phosphatidase acts on lecithin, confirming the hydrolysis of the phosphorylcholine group at C-3 of glycerol. The diglyceride therefore has the same distribution as the original lecithin. After lipase has acted on the diglyceride, the fatty acids which are liberated are of the saturated variety, whereas the monoglyceride, which remains, has all of the unsaturated acids. These results prove that the diglyceride has unsaturated fatty acids at C-2 and saturated fatty acids at C-1. We shall see later that phospholipids as well as triglycerides are synthesized in the body from a similar diglyceride; and we might therefore conclude that the distribution of saturated and unsaturated acids in lecithin is the same as for the triglycerides. There remains the problem of the kind of fatty acids attached to C-3 in triglycerides. This can be solved by allowing pancreatic lipase to act on triglycerides, hydrolyzing the ester bonds at both C-1 and C-3. This is illustrated in Table 7.

TABLE 7. FATTY ACID DISTRIBUTION OF PRODUCTS OF LIPASE ACTION ON RAT LIVER TRIGLYCERIDES

	Saturated acids	Unsaturated acids
	moles per cent	
Triglycerides..........................	20	80
Diglycerides..........................	19	77
Monoglycerides......................	3	97
Fatty acids..........................	47	54

The data in Table 7 show that the monoglyceride formed from the triglyceride has exclusively unsaturated fatty acids, confirming the association of unsaturated acids with C-2 of glycerol. The diglyceride has a distribution of acids similar to that which existed in the triglyceride; and the free fatty acids, which are removed by lipase action, are almost equally distributed between saturated and unsaturated, suggesting that the acids attached to C-3 are also unsaturated. These conclusions would be consistent with the following formula for triglycerides:

$$
\begin{array}{c}
\qquad\qquad\qquad \overset{\displaystyle O}{\underset{\displaystyle \|}{}} \\
H_2C-O-C-R \qquad \text{(saturated)} \\[1em]
\overset{\displaystyle O}{\underset{\displaystyle \|}{}} \\
\text{(unsaturated)} \quad R'-C-O-C-H \\[1em]
\qquad\qquad\qquad \overset{\displaystyle O}{\underset{\displaystyle \|}{}} \\
H_2C-O-C-R'' \qquad \text{(unsaturated)}
\end{array}
$$

GLYCERYL ETHERS

Although such compounds are not common among land animals, glyceryl ethers have a widespread distribution among marine animals. Several have also been reported in bone marrow of the cow, spleen of the pig, and the arteriosclerotic aortas of humans. The ether linkages involve the alcohol group of glycerol and that belonging to three fatty alcohols: palmityl, stearyl and oleyl, which are known in the combined form as chimyl, batyl and selachyl alcohol, respectively. These alcohols are attached to C-1 (α) of glycerol:

$$\begin{array}{c} H_2C\!-\!O\!-\!R \\ H\!-\!C\!-\!OH \\ CH_2OH \end{array}$$

Because the second carbon atom is asymmetric, D- and L- forms are possible. In nature, the D- form appears to predominate.

WAXES AND STEROLS

Waxes may be defined as esters of monoatomic alcohols of high molecular weight, in which the fatty acids are palmitic, stearic and oleic. Cholesterol esters of fatty acids may therefore be listed as waxes, since cholesterol is an alcohol of high molecular weight. A number of common waxes (and the degree of unsaturation of their fatty acids) are given in Table 8.

TABLE 8.   A NUMBER OF COMMON WAXES

Wax	Iodine number
Sperm oil	81–90
Carnauba wax	13
Wool wax	30–35
Beeswax	8
Spermaceti	0–4
Chinese wax	0–1.4

Industrially, waxes are used in the manufacture of lubricants (sperm oil), polishes (carnauba wax), ointments (lanolin, which contains wool wax), candles (spermaceti), etc. In the body, waxes occur as cholesterol esters, in which the fatty acid is joined to the alcohol cholesterol. Anderson has shown that the tubercle bacillus contains a complex wax.

Aside from cholesterol, the common alcohols found in waxes are cetyl alcohol, $C_{16}H_{33}OH$, ceryl alcohol, $C_{26}H_{53}OH$, and myricyl alcohol, $C_{30}H_{61}OH$.

CHOLESTEROL

The best known of the steroids* is cholesterol. It is present in all animal cells and is particularly abundant in nervous tissue. Varying quantities of this sterol are found admixed in animal, but not in vegetable, fats. Cholesterol has the following structure:

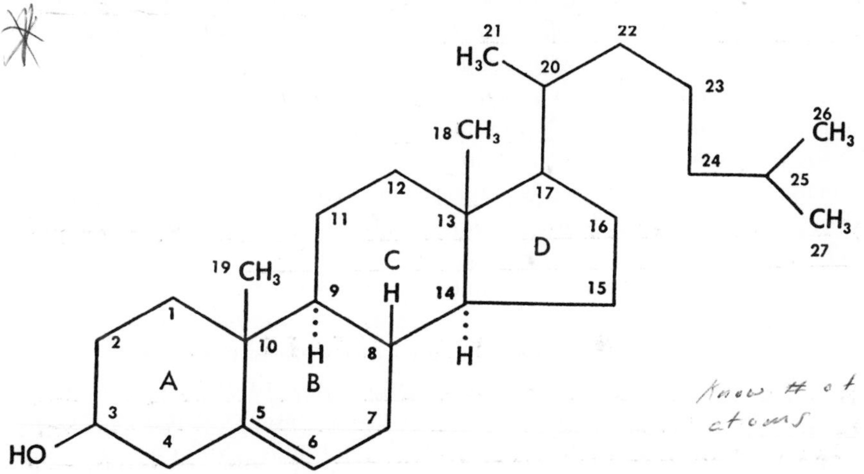

Figure 7. Cholesterol. The four rings are labeled with letters, and the 27 carbons with numbers. The solid lines indicate bonds that project above the plane of the molecule; the dotted lines indicate atoms projecting below the plane.

Cholesterol belongs to one of a group of steroids, compounds which have in common the basic phenanthrene derivative:

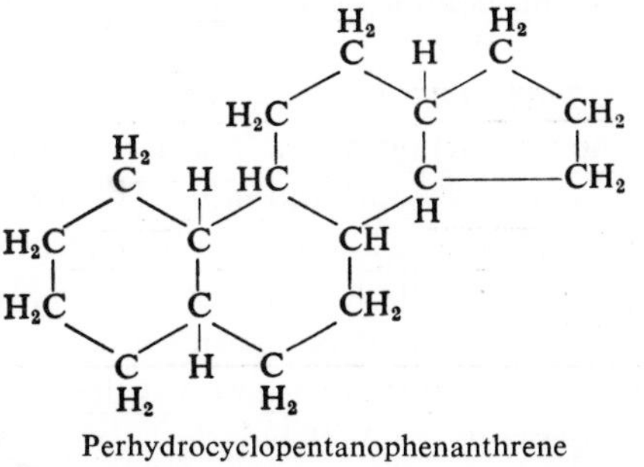

Perhydrocyclopentanophenanthrene

In the cholesterol nucleus there are eight centers of asymmetry, and, theoretically, something like 240 isomers are possible. Fortunately,

* *Steroids* is the general name for a group of compounds related in structure. *Sterols* represent one such group; *bile acids*, another, etc.

but two carbon centers seem to be involved in naturally occurring sterols, those at position 3 and position 5.

Cholesterol can be prepared from brain tissue, or, even better, from gallstones. In either case, the essential point in the method is to extract the cholesterol with ether and, after evaporation of the ether, to recrystallize the sterol from hot alcohol. Unlike the fats or the phospholipids, cholesterol and other sterols cannot be saponified. They represent part of the "unsaponified fraction."

Cholesterol gives a number of characteristic color tests. One of these is the *Liebermann-Burchard* test, in which a chloroform solution of the sterol is treated with acetic anhydride and concentrated sulfuric acid. The bluish-green to green color obtained varies in intensity with the amount of cholesterol present, and this color test is therefore the basis of a quantitative estimation. Another common test is the one developed by *Salkowski*, which consists in mixing the sterol with chloroform and concentrated sulfuric acid to give a bluish-red to purple color. These tests are not confined to cholesterol, but are given by a number of the sterols. However, in animal tissues one finds comparatively small quantities of sterols other than cholesterol. Saturated sterols (like dihydrocholesterol and coprosterol) fail to give these color tests.

Another test of importance is precipitation with *digitonin*, $C_{56}H_{92}O_2$, (a glycoside belonging to the saponin group and occurring in digitalis leaves and seeds), forming cholesterol digitonide. Not only is this a qualitative test, but it has been made the basis for a quantitative determination. The combination with digitonin is possible only if the hydroxyl group in position 3 remains free. Cholesteryl acetate, for example, does not give the test. Certain vegetable sterols, such as stigmasterol, sitosterol, and ergosterol, are also precipitated with digitonin.

STEROL NOMENCLATURE

The most important center of asymmetry in cholesterol is at C_3, whereas derivatives of cholesterol in which the double bond is missing have a second asymmetric center at C_5. In plant sterols (phytosterols) C_{24} is also an asymmetric carbon atom. The two classes of stereoisomers which involve C_5 are called *normal* and *allo-*. This can best be illustrated with the hydrogenated forms of cholesterol, coprosterol and dihydrocholesterol (coprostanol and cholestanol respectively). Coprosterol belongs to the *normal* whereas dihydrocholesterol belongs to the *allo* series. Windaus suggested that this type of isomerism involved the relationship of rings A and B; in coprosterol A/B have a *cis*-relationship, that of two "bed" forms, whereas in dihydrocholesterol A/B is *trans*, that of two "chair" forms. This may be better shown by considering the relationship of the H atom at C_5 to the angular methyl group at C_{10}. In the *normal* series H/CH_3 is *cis* whereas in the *allo* series H/CH_3 is *trans*. In addition there now exists another relationship, that of the OH group at C_3 to the methyl group at C_{10}, which gives rise to two more isomers one of which is designated with the prefix *epi-*. These relationships are illustrated in the following formulas:

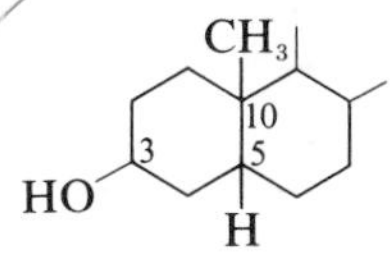

Coprosterol 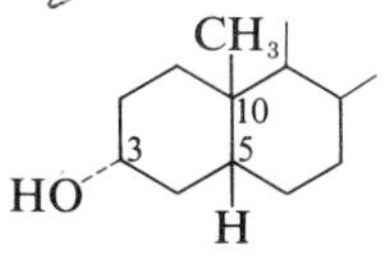   Epicoprosterol

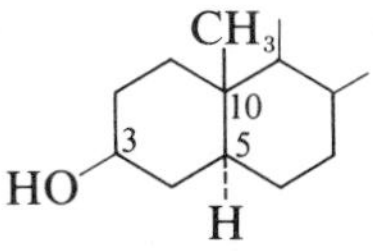

Dihydrocholesterol 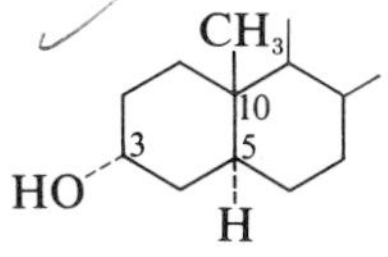   Epidihydrocholesterol

It should be noted that the methyl group at C_{10} becomes the reference point for all other groups. Digitonin will precipitate all *cis-* derivatives whereas *epi-* forms will not be precipitated. Still another prefix *etio-* refers to the final degradation product of a more complex molecule, but one which still retains the essential characteristics of the original compound. This is illustrated below:

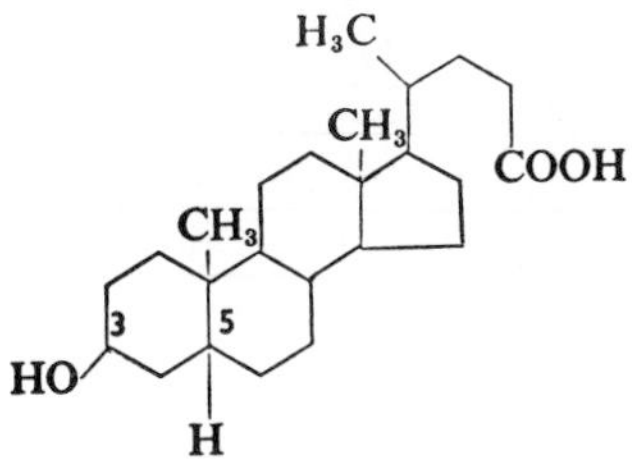

Cholanic Acid 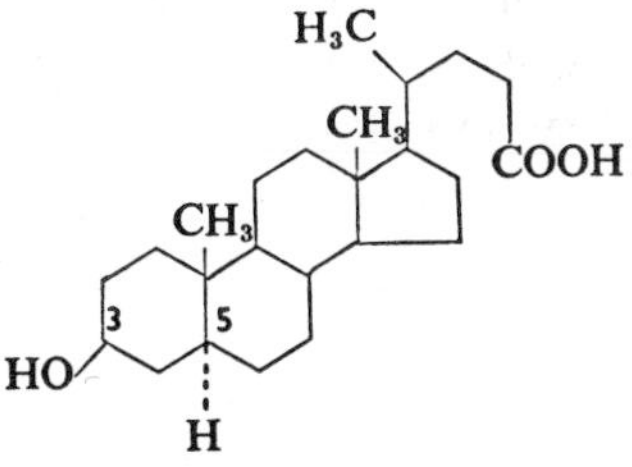   Allocholanic acid

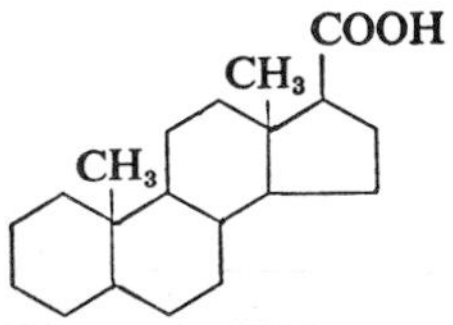

Etiocholanic acid

The prefix *deoxy-* means that the parent molecule has lost an atom of oxygen; *dehydro-*, that it has lost 2 hydrogen atoms; *dihydro-*, that it has gained 2 hydrogen atoms:

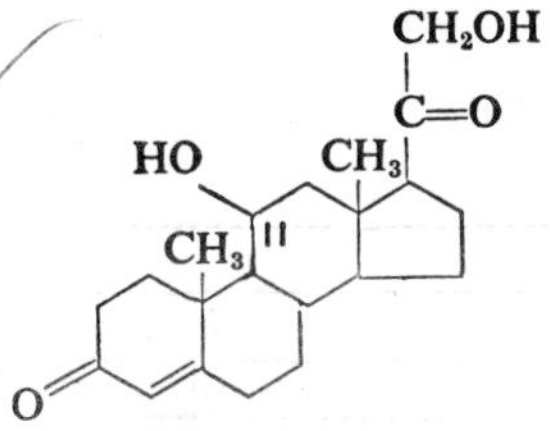

Corticosterone 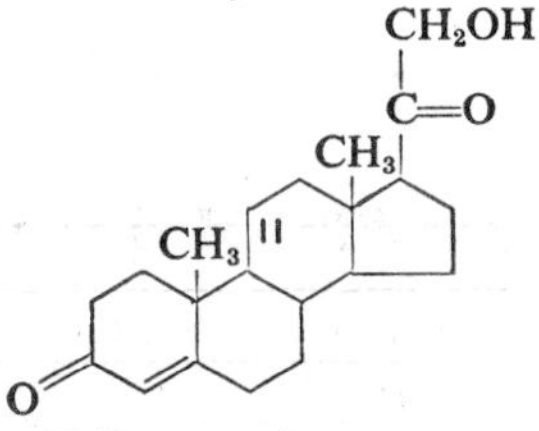   11-Deoxycorticosterone 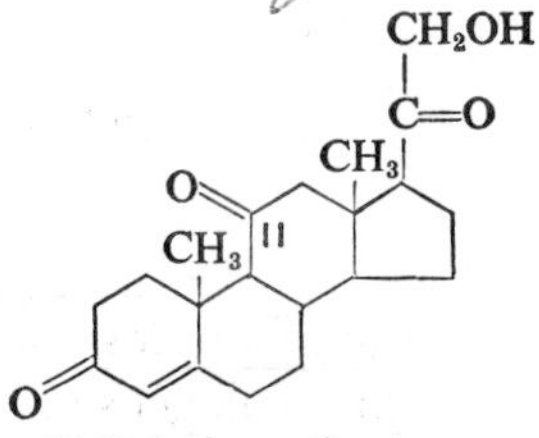   11-Dehydrocorticosterone

There are several specific suffixes used for sterols for the purpose of identifying important chemical groups: *-one* for a ketone, *-ol* for an alcohol, *-ane* for a saturated hydrocarbon and *-ene* for an unsaturated hydrocarbon.

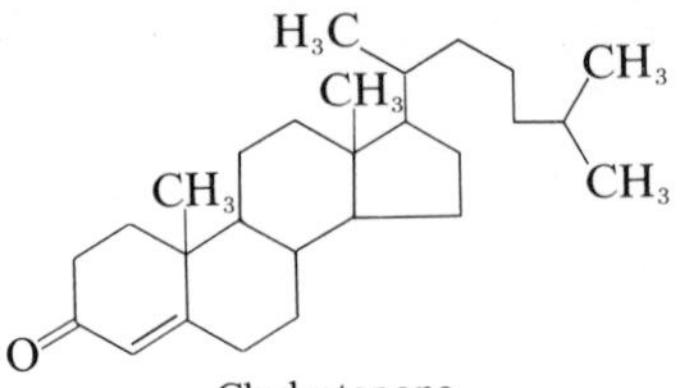

Cholestenone

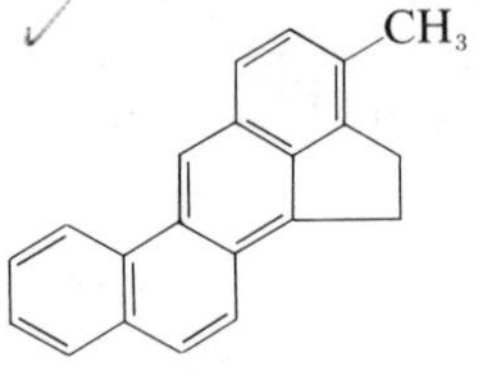

Methylcholanthrene

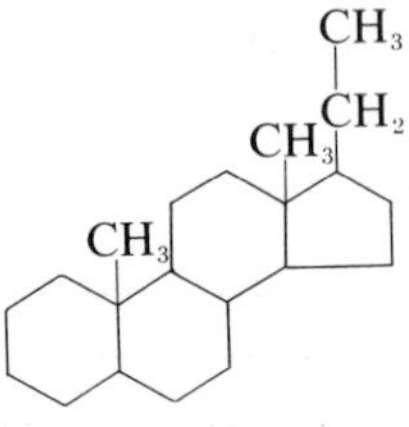

Pregnane

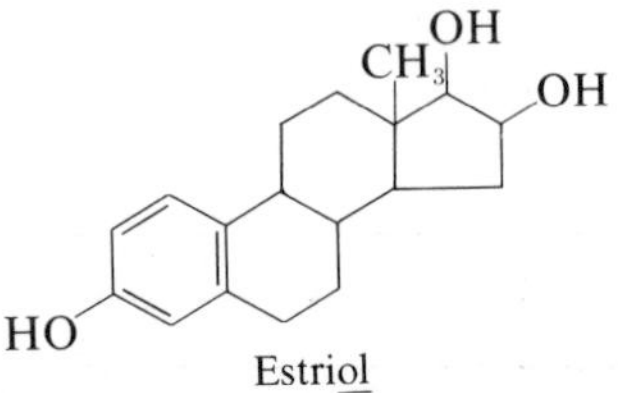

Estriol

Among the animal sterols other than cholesterol there are: 7-dehydrocholesterol, which is a precursor of vitamin D_3; dihydrocholesterol, which is found together with cholesterol in tissues; and coprosterol, which occurs in feces. Among the plant sterols (phytosterols), the two most important are sitosterol and several isomers of stigmasterol:

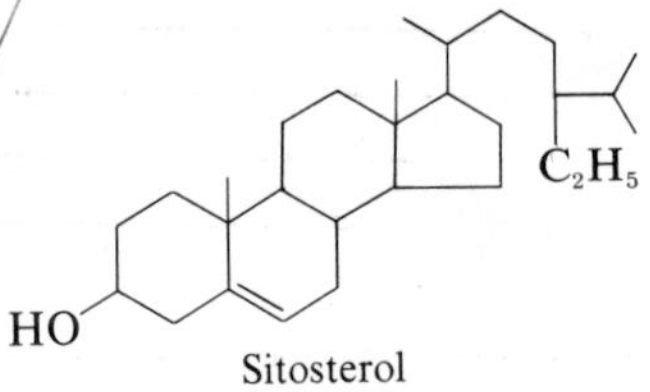

Sitosterol

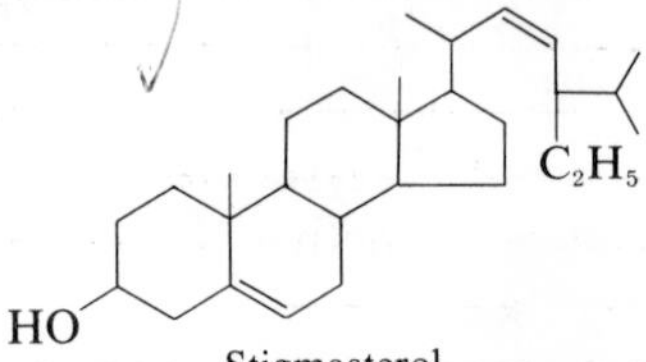

Stigmasterol

In the above formulas, note the abbreviated version of the side chain.

The sterols in cryptogams (mycosterols) include ergosterol, which is a precursor of vitamin D_2, and fucosterol, which is found in algae:

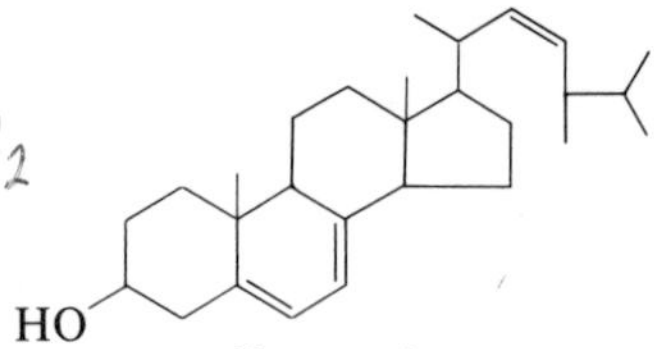

Ergosterol

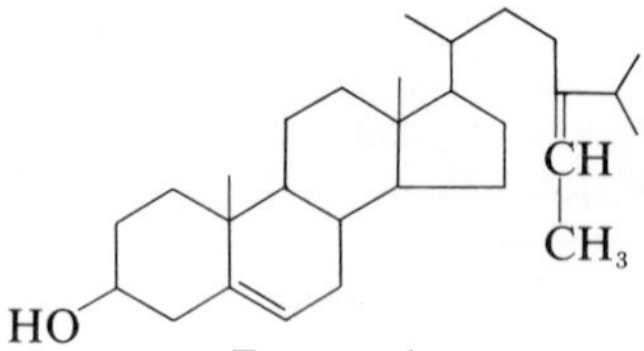

Fucosterol

PHOSPHOLIPIDS

The phospholipids include the *phosphoglycerides* (lecithins, cephalins and plasmalogens), the *phosphoinositides*, and the *sphingolipids* (sphingomyelins).

PHOSPHOGLYCERIDES

A. *Lecithins.* This term describes a group of compounds which are glyceryl esters of two fatty acid molecules and esterified at its third C atom with phosphoric acid, which in turn is bound by ester linkage to a nitrogeneous base, choline:

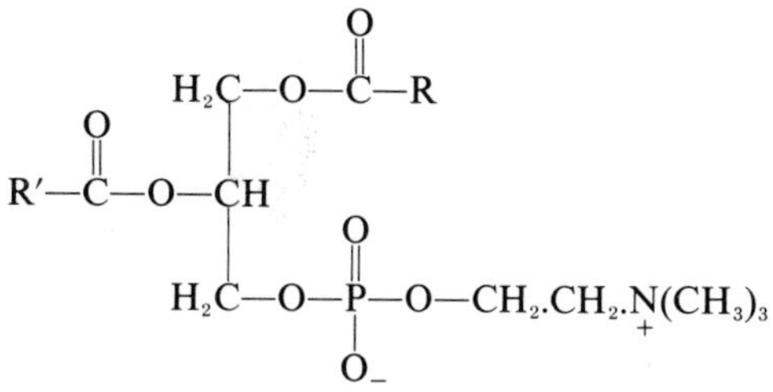

$$
\begin{array}{c}
\hspace{3em} \overset{\displaystyle O}{\overset{\|}{}} \\
\text{H}_2\text{C}-\text{O}-\text{C}-\text{R} \\
\overset{\displaystyle O}{\overset{\|}{}} \hspace{2em} | \\
\text{R}'-\text{C}-\text{O}-\text{CH} \\
\hspace{4em} \overset{\displaystyle O}{\overset{\|}{}} \\
\text{H}_2\text{C}-\text{O}-\text{P}-\text{O}-\text{CH}_2.\text{CH}_2.\underset{+}{\text{N}}(\text{CH}_3)_3 \\
\hspace{3em} | \\
\hspace{3em} \text{O}_-
\end{array}
$$

L-α-Lecithin

Although theoretically the phosphorylcholine group may also be attached to the β-carbon of glycerol, it has been shown that the lecithins in nature are of the α- variety. Also, since C-2 of glycerol is asymmetric there are two possible isomers, although the lecithins found in nature appear to be of the L- variety.

Many different lecithins are possible because of the wide variety of fatty acids which may be attached to the glycerol moiety. They are found in relatively large quantities in egg yolk and liver and constitute most of the phospholipid fraction of dog or human plasma.

Lecithin is a waxy colorless solid, which turns yellow and then brown on exposure to air and light. It is extremely hygroscopic and can be prepared in crystalline form at very low temperatures. It is insoluble in acetone or methyl acetate and dissolves in an aqueous medium if bile salts are present.

PHOSPHATIDASES. These enzymes act on the lecithin molecule or on compounds similar to, or derived from, lecithin and hydrolyze specific ester linkages. Although there has been some question in the past concerning the specific site of action of these enzymes, the following diagram summarizes the action of the phosphatidases:

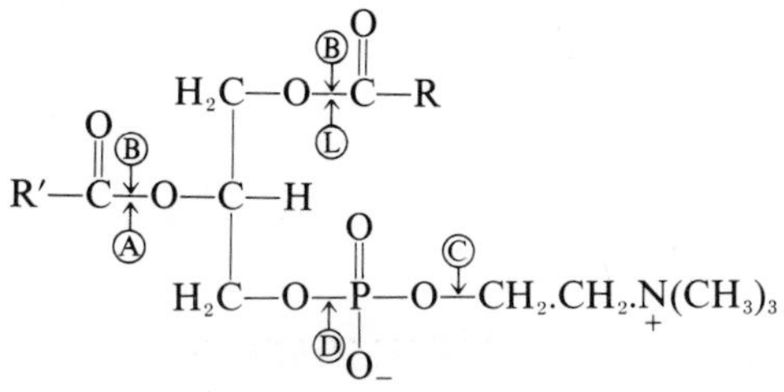

$$
\begin{array}{c}
\hspace{3em} \overset{\text{Ⓑ}}{\overset{\displaystyle O}{\overset{\|}{}}} \\
\text{H}_2\text{C}-\text{O}\text{Ⓛ}\text{C}-\text{R} \\
\overset{\text{Ⓑ}}{\overset{\displaystyle O}{\overset{\|}{}}} \hspace{2em} | \\
\text{R}'-\text{C}\text{Ⓐ}\text{O}-\text{C}-\text{H} \\
\hspace{5em} \overset{\displaystyle O}{\overset{\|}{}} \hspace{1em} \text{Ⓒ} \\
\text{H}_2\text{C}-\text{O}\text{Ⓓ}\text{P}-\text{O}\text{CH}_2.\text{CH}_2.\underset{+}{\text{N}}(\text{CH}_3)_3 \\
\hspace{3em} | \\
\hspace{3em} \text{O}_-
\end{array}
$$

The letters A, B, C and D refer to the respective phosphatidases, whereas L refers to lysophosphatidase, which acts on lysolecithin to yield one mole of fatty acid, in contrast to B, which splits two moles of fatty acid from a mole of lecithin. Formulas for the various hydrolytic products are given below:

$$
\begin{array}{c}
\text{H}_2\text{C}-\text{O}-\overset{\displaystyle\text{O}}{\overset{\|}{\text{C}}}-\text{R} \\[4pt]
\text{HO}-\text{C}-\text{H} \\[4pt]
\text{H}_2\text{C}-\text{O}-\overset{\displaystyle\text{O}}{\overset{\|}{\text{P}}}-\text{O}-\text{CH}_2.\text{CH}_2.\overset{+}{\text{N}}(\text{CH}_3)_3 \\[4pt]
\text{O}_-
\end{array}
$$

L-α-Lysolecithin

$$
\begin{array}{c}
\text{HO}-\overset{\displaystyle\text{O}}{\overset{\|}{\text{P}}}-\text{O}-\text{CH}_2.\text{CH}_2.\overset{+}{\text{N}}(\text{CH}_3)_3 \\[4pt]
\text{O}_-
\end{array}
$$

Phosphorylcholine

$$
\begin{array}{c}
\text{H}_2\text{C}-\text{OH} \\[4pt]
\text{HO}-\text{C}-\text{H} \\[4pt]
\text{H}_2\text{C}-\text{O}-\overset{\displaystyle\text{O}}{\overset{\|}{\text{P}}}-\text{O}-\text{CH}_2.\text{CH}_2.\overset{+}{\text{N}}(\text{CH}_3)_3 \\[4pt]
\text{O}_-
\end{array}
$$

L-α-Glycerylphosphorylcholine

$$
\begin{array}{c}
\text{H}_2\text{C}-\text{O}-\overset{\displaystyle\text{O}}{\overset{\|}{\text{C}}}-\text{R} \\[4pt]
\text{R}'-\overset{\displaystyle\text{O}}{\overset{\|}{\text{C}}}-\text{O}-\text{C}-\text{H} \\[4pt]
\text{H}_2\text{C}-\text{O}-\overset{\displaystyle\text{O}}{\overset{\|}{\text{P}}}-\text{OH} \\[4pt]
\text{OH}
\end{array}
$$

L-α-Phosphatidic acid

FATTY ACIDS OF LECITHIN. The fatty acids found in lecithin include both the saturated (stearic and palmitic) as well as the unsaturated acids (oleic, linoleic, linolenic and arachidonic). Although there is some variability in composition among lecithins, there appears to be a pattern with respect to the type of acids attached to the α- or β- carbon atom of glycerol. Determination of specific distribution depends on identification of the acids liberated when lecithin is treated with phosphatidase A. Since this enzyme is now believed to hydrolyze the ester bond at the β- carbon of glycerol, we may now determine the exact distribution of fatty acids in the molecule. As a result of these studies it has been concluded that the α- carbon atom of glycerol contains saturated acids, whereas the β- carbon atom is attached to unsaturated acids:

$$
\begin{array}{c}
\text{H}_2\text{C}-\text{O}-\overset{\displaystyle\text{O}}{\overset{\|}{\text{C}}}-\text{R} \quad (\text{saturated}) \\[4pt]
(\text{unsaturated})\ \ \text{R}-\overset{\displaystyle\text{O}}{\overset{\|}{\text{C}}}-\text{O}-\text{C}-\text{H} \\[4pt]
\text{H}_2\text{C}-\text{O}-\overset{\displaystyle\text{O}}{\overset{\|}{\text{P}}}-\text{O}-\text{CH}_2.\text{CH}_2.\overset{+}{\text{N}}(\text{CH}_3)_3 \\[4pt]
\text{O}
\end{array}
$$

Table 9 gives the data of an experiment in which lecithin obtained from egg yolk, as well as fully hydrogenated lecithin, was treated with phosphatidase A and the distribution of fatty acids determined.

TABLE 9. FATTY ACIDS RELEASED FROM EGG LECITHIN BY THE ACTION OF PHOSPHATIDASE A

	Egg lecithin (native)	Egg lecithin (hydrogenated)
Relative Distribution (moles %)		
Saturated	4	100
Unsaturated	96	0
Specific Distribution (moles %)		
Saturated		
C_{16}	3	
C_{18}	1	91
C_{20}		9
Unsaturated*		
C'_{16}	0.5	
C'_{18}	51	
C''_{18}	35	
C'''_{18}	0.5	
C'''_{20}	1	
C''''_{20}	8	

* The number of prime marks indicates the number of double bonds.
(From Hanahan et al.: J. Biol. Chem., *235*:1917, 1960.)

When radioactive palmitic acid is fed to rats, more than 90 per cent of the label in the liver lecithins is found in the α- position. When labeled unsaturated acids are fed, they are found attached to the β- position. These results suggest that all of the ester groups of a phosphoglyceride may not be equally reactive *in vivo*.

CHOLINE. This compound is an essential component of the diet of mammals and is therefore included among the vitamins. It is a quaternary ammonium compound with very strong basic properties. Its absence from the diet leads to a fatty infiltration of the liver. In addition to its importance as a part of the lecithin molecule, choline is required for the synthesis of acetylcholine, a compound released at the parasympathetic nerve endings when they are stimulated. Acetylcholine is responsible for transmission of the nerve impulse.

$$HO.CH_2.CH_2.\overset{+}{N}(CH_3)_3$$

Choline

$$CH_3-\overset{O}{\overset{\|}{C}}-O-CH_2.CH_2.\overset{+}{N}(CH_3)_3$$

Acetylcholine

B. Cephalins. These compounds differ from the lecithins in the nature of the nitrogenous component esterified with phosphoric acid.

A. PHOSPHATIDYLETHANOLAMINE. Next to the lecithins, this phosphatide is the most widely distributed in nature. It contains more unsaturated fatty acids than lecithin and belongs to the L-α- configuration:

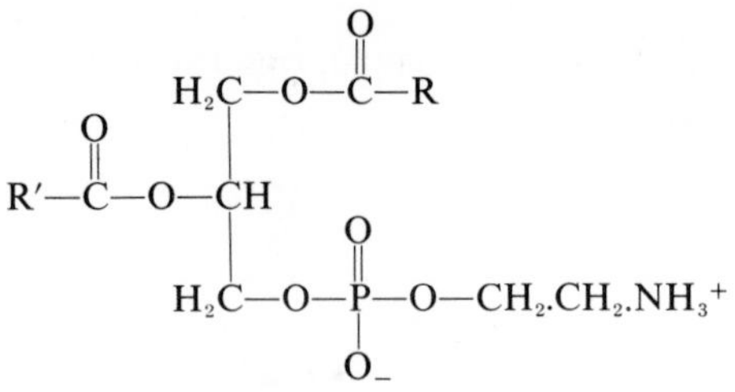

$$H_2C-O-\overset{\overset{\displaystyle O}{\|}}{C}-R$$
$$R'-\overset{\overset{\displaystyle O}{\|}}{C}-O-CH$$
$$H_2C-O-\overset{\overset{\displaystyle O}{\|}}{P}-O-CH_2.CH_2.NH_3{}^+$$
$$\underset{O_-}{}$$

L-α-Phosphatidylethanolamine

It is most conveniently prepared from brain, liver and yeast. The distribution of fatty acids in phosphatidylethanolamine reveals an almost equal division between saturated and unsaturated acids. Most of the unsaturated acids have been shown to be associated with the β- (C-2) position in much the same manner as has been found for the lecithins.

B. PHOSPHATIDYLSERINE. This compound has been prepared from brain and also appears to belong to the L-α- configuration:

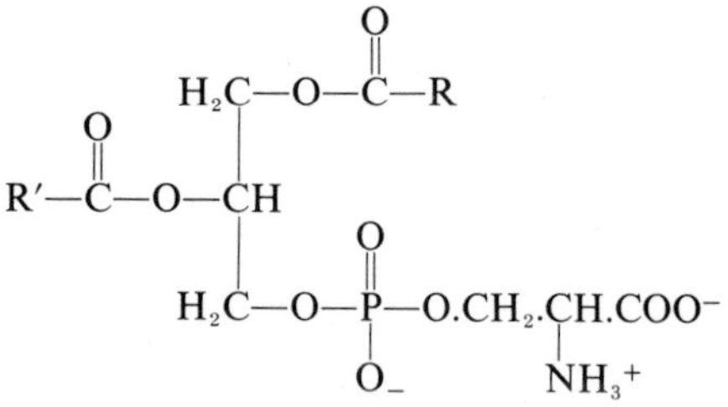

$$H_2C-O-\overset{\overset{\displaystyle O}{\|}}{C}-R$$
$$R'-\overset{\overset{\displaystyle O}{\|}}{C}-O-CH$$
$$H_2C-O-\overset{\overset{\displaystyle O}{\|}}{P}-O.CH_2.CH.COO^-$$
$$\underset{O_-}{} \qquad \underset{NH_3{}^+}{}$$

L-α-Phosphatidylserine

C. PLASMALOGENS. These compounds contain a fatty acid residue, an aldehydogenic unit (as a vinyl ether), together with glycerylphosphorylethanolamine or choline. They are widely distributed in nature in animal tissues. Brain and nerve myelin have relatively large quantities of this lipid. It is also present in heart muscle, skeletal muscle and in semen. It is now known that the vinyl ether is linked to glycerol at the α- position.

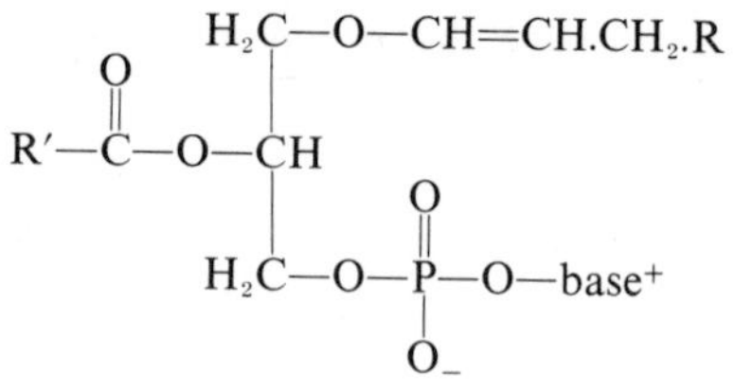

$$H_2C-O-CH=CH.CH_2.R$$
$$R'-\overset{\overset{\displaystyle O}{\|}}{C}-O-CH$$
$$H_2C-O-\overset{\overset{\displaystyle O}{\|}}{P}-O-base^+$$
$$\underset{O_-}{}$$

Plasmalogen

PHOSPHOINOSITIDES

Inositol, as a component of the phospholipids, has been known for some time but it is only in recent years that the specific structure of the inositides has been clarified. Inositol is a hexahydroxycyclohexane of which there are 9 possible stereochemical forms. The most important of these that is present in lipids is the optically inactive *myo-inositol:*

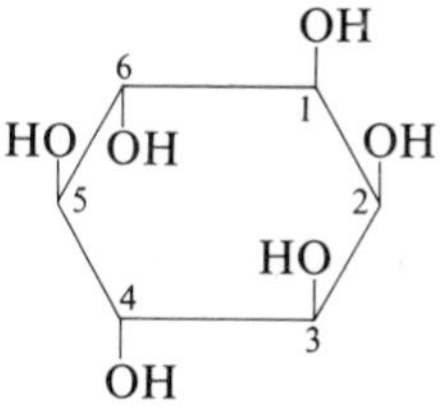

Myo-inositol

Two forms of inositol phospholipids are known: inositol mono-phosphate (monophosphoinositide), which is widely distributed, and inositol diphosphate (diphosphoinositide), which has been found only in brain:

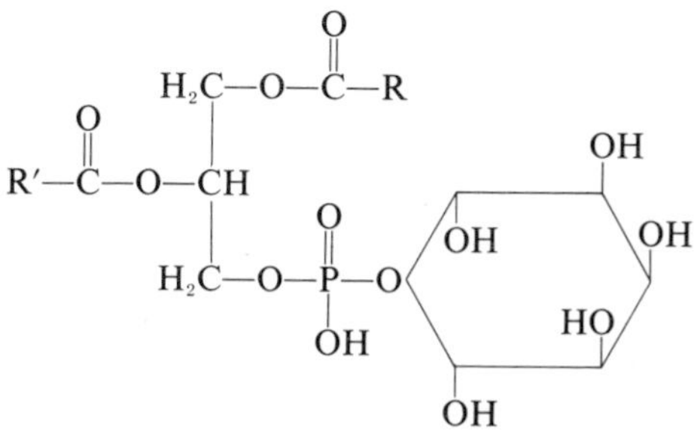

Monophosphoinositide

It is noteworthy that in liver the phosphoinositides contain a high proportion of stearic acid. There is no information available as yet which would allow us to assign a specific structure for the diphosphoinositides which yield 2 moles of phosphoric acid on hydrolysis.

SPHINGOLIPIDS

These phospholipids contain a long-chain alcohol, sphingosine. Re-cently several additional alcohols have been discovered: dihydrosphingo-sine, phytosphingosine and dehydrophytosphingosine—the latter two in plant tissues only. The sphingolipids occur in particularly high concen-trations in brain and nerve tissue. In the disease *lipidosis*, these com-pounds accumulate in various organs.

In sphingomyelin, sphingosine, or a related base, is bound by amide linkage to a long-chain fatty acid and by ester linkage to phosphoryl-choline. The fatty acids may be stearic, lignoceric or nervonic in brain sphingomyelins, or palmitic or lignoceric in sphingomyelins from lung and spleen.

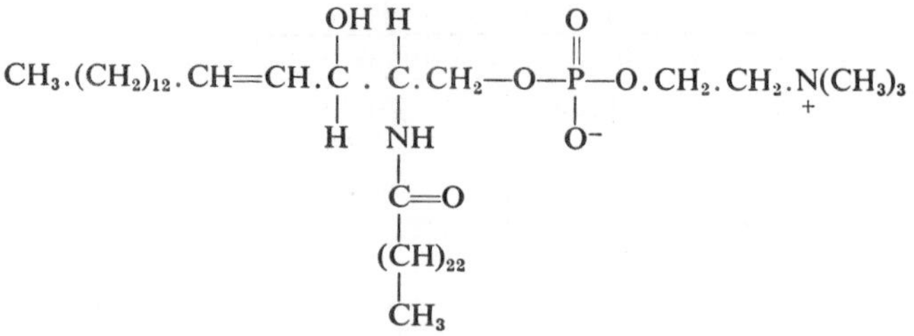

$$\underset{\text{H}}{\overset{\text{OH}}{\underset{|}{\overset{|}{\text{C}}}}} \quad \underset{\text{NH}}{\overset{\text{H}}{\underset{|}{\overset{|}{\text{C}}}}}$$

CH$_3$.(CH$_2$)$_{12}$.CH=CH.C . C.CH$_2$—O—P—O.CH$_2$.CH$_2$.N(CH$_3$)$_3$

$$\begin{array}{c}\text{C=O}\\|\\(\text{CH})_{22}\\|\\\text{CH}_3\end{array}$$

Sphingomyelin

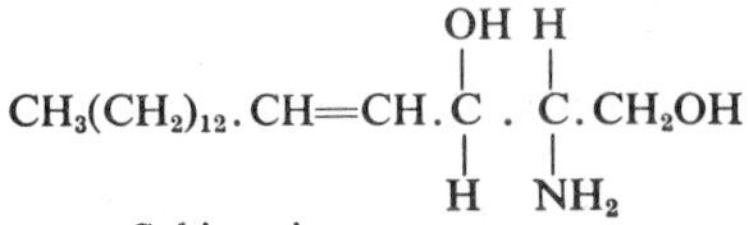

OH H

CH$_3$(CH$_2$)$_{12}$.CH=CH.C . C.CH$_2$OH   CH$_3$(CH$_2$)$_{22}$.COOH

H NH$_2$

Sphingosine   Lignoceric acid

Phytosphingosine is C$_{14}$H$_{29}$.CHOH.CHOH.CHNH$_2$.CH$_2$OH.

CEREBROSIDES (GLYCOLIPIDS)

These compounds consist of a nitrogenous base, sphingosine or dihydro-sphingosine, a long-chain fatty acid and a sugar. There are at least four cerebrosides: phrenosin, kerasin (cerasin), nervone and oxynervone. They occur in brain, adrenals, kidney, spleen, liver, leukocytes, thymus, lung, retina, egg yolk and fish sperm. In Gaucher's disease they occur in relatively large quantities in the liver and especially in the spleen.

Phrenosin yields a characteristic hydroxy acid, cerebronic acid, to which the formula CH$_3$(CH$_2$)$_7$CH$_2$CH$_2$(CH$_2$)$_{12}$CHOHCOOH has been assigned. Cerasin contains lignoceric acid, CH$_3$(CH$_2$)$_7$CH$_2$CH$_2$(CH$_2$)$_{12}$-CH$_2$COOH. The acid in *nervone* is nervonic acid, CH$_3$(CH$_2$)$_7$CH=CH(CH$_2$)$_{12}$CH$_2$COOCH, which is an unsaturated lignoceric acid. Oxynervonic acid, CH$_3$(CH$_2$)$_7$CH=CH(CH$_2$)$_{12}$CHOHCOOH, an un-saturated hydroxy lignoceric acid, is the acid which characterizes *oxynervone*.

The general formula for a cerebroside is

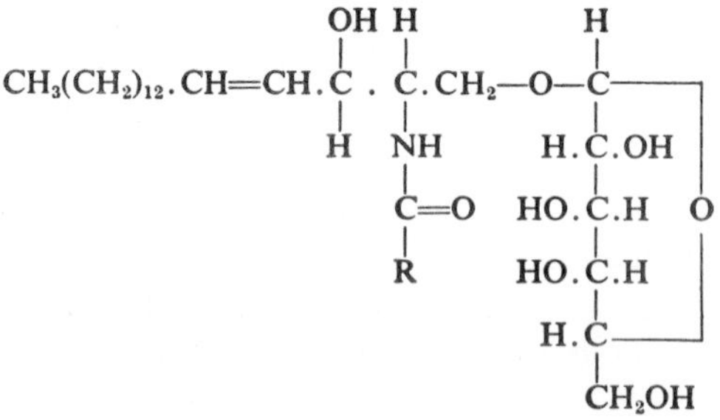

CH$_3$(CH$_2$)$_{12}$.CH=CH.C . C.CH$_2$—O—C

with OH, H, NH, C=O, R substituents on the sphingosine chain and the sugar ring: H.C.OH, HO.C.H, HO.C.H, H.C, CH$_2$OH.

RCOOH = lignoceric acid in cerasin
cerebronic acid in phrenosin
nervonic acid in nervone
oxynervonic acid in oxynervone

Cerebrosides that are found in animal brain contain galactose whereas that found in spleen in Gaucher's disease contains glucose.

LIPOPROTEINS

The fact that lipids are often found associated with proteins in various tissues has led to a search for the complexes in which these two classes of compounds are associated. Lipoproteins have the solubility characteristics of proteins (water-soluble), although complexes have been isolated from tissues such as brain which have the solubility characteristics of lipids (fat-soluble) and have been named *proteolipids*. Lipoproteins occur in the plasma, where they are concerned with the transport of lipids in a soluble form; in tissues at cell surfaces, maintaining the integrity of the cell; and in intracellular particles such as the mitochondrion and microsome. In the latter particles, the lipoprotein complex, which contains much phospholipid, appears to hold together the various enzymes in a structural unit in a particular sequence. Removal of the lipid moiety, e.g., by extraction with a lipid solvent, leads to a separation of enzymes from each other.

The method by which lipid and protein molecules are held together in a complex is not certain, although it is agreed that the bonds

TABLE 10. COMPOSITION OF THE MAJOR HUMAN PLASMA LIPOPROTEINS (%)

Concentration in plasma (mg./100 ml.)	Peptide	Phospholipid	Cholesterol Alcohol Ester		Triglyceride
Chylomicrons					
100–250	2	7	2	6	83
Lipoproteins, density = 0.98					
130–200	9	18	7	15	50
Lipoproteins, density = 1.035					
210–400	21	22	8	38	10
Lipoproteins, density = 1.09					
50–130	33	29	7	23	8
Lipoproteins, density = 1.14					
290–400	57	21	3	14	5

(From Hanahan: Lipide Chemistry, John Wiley and Sons, 1960; values taken from Oncley, The Lipoproteins, ed. by Homburger and Bernfeld, S. Karger, 1958.)

are not covalent. It is likely that the association of these two different types of structures involves attractive forces between nonpolar groups of the fatty acid moiety of the lipid (and similar groups which occur in several of the amino acids) and between polar groups in the two compounds. The lipoprotein complexes are affected by agents which influence the integrity of the proteins (heat, pH) or the lipids (air oxidation and peroxide formation).

TABLE 11. AVERAGE COMPOSITION OF PHOSPHOLIPIDS IN PLASMA LIPOPROTEIN FRACTIONS

Phospholipid	Density <1.019	Density <1.063	Density >1.063
	(micromoles per liter of serum)		
"Cephalin" *	0.032	0.056	0.088
Lecithin	0.40	0.91	1.15
Sphingomyelin	0.15	0.35	0.23
Lysolecithin	0.032	0.056	0.18

* The cephalin fraction consisted mostly of phosphatidylethanolamine, the lecithin fraction yielded only choline.
(From Phillips: J. Clin. Invest., *38:*489, 1959.)

The lipids present in plasma are almost entirely associated with proteins. By the Cohn fractionation procedure (p. 213) two main groups of lipoproteins are found: α_1-lipoprotein in fraction IV-1 and β_1-lipoprotein in fraction III-O. These may also be obtained by ultracentrifugation, in which case they move to the surface of the plasma (flotation) because of their low density. Better separations are obtained by using a medium of specific density or by using a medium consisting of a density gradient. In the latter case the less dense solution is layered over the more dense one and the lipoproteins separate during ultracentrifugation according to their respective densities. Table 10 lists the various lipid and lipoprotein fractions together with their composition.

TABLE 12. LIPID COMPOSITION OF RAT LIVER CELL FRACTIONS

		Per Cent of Total Lipid		
Fraction	Per Cent Total Lipid	Phospholipid	Cholesterol	Neutral Fat
Nuclei	16	93	4.5	2.5
Mitochondria	21	93	5.5	1.4
Microsomes	32	94	5.8	0
Supernatant	7	28	3.9	68

(From Spiro and McKibbin: J. Biol. Chem., *219:*643, 1956.)

Table 11 shows the distribution of the various phospholipids among three plasma lipoprotein fractions.

Lipoproteins which are found in tissues may best be described by the composition of rat liver cell fractions shown in Table 12.

REFERENCES

A standard reference work is by *Hanahan:* Lipide Chemistry, 1960; see *Deuel:* The Lipids, Vol. 1, 1951; Vol. 2, 1955. A good introduction is by *Lovern:* The Chemistry of Lipids of Biochemical Significance, 1957.

For general reviews: *Law:* Ann. Rev. Biochem., 29:131, 1960 (glycolipids); *Klenk* and *Debuch:* Ibid., 28:39, 1959 (lipids).

An excellent review on the phosphatids will be found in the Federation Proceedings, 16:816, 1957.

For the chemistry of cephalin, see *Folch:* J. Biol. Chem. 177:495, 505, 1949; and *Hutt:* Nature, 165:314, 1950. *Baer, Maurakas,* and *Russell:* J. Am. Chem. Soc., 74:152, 1952, describe the synthesis of cephalin.

For the structure of cerebrosides, see *Carter* and *Greenwood:* J. Biol. Chem., 199:283, 1952; *Carter* and *Fujino:* J. Biol. Chem., 221:879, 1956.

For other phospholipid fractions (plasmalogens) see *Rapport et al.:* J. Organic Chem., 23:1241, 1958.

Goffman: Circulation, 2:161, 1950, describes the lipoproteins; and *Folch* and *Lees:* J. Biol. Chem., 191:807, 1951, discuss the proteolipids.

The many ramifications of the steroids are discussed by *Fieser* in Scientific American, p. 52 (Jan.) 1955. *Mason:* J. Clinical Endocrinology, 8:190, 1948, outlines the system used for steroid nomenclature.

The use of paper chromatography for the detection of steroids is applied by *Kritchevsky* and *Kirk:* Arch. Biochem., 35:346, 1952.

For the synthesis of cholesterol see *Woodward, Sondheimer, Taub, Heusler,* and *McLamore:* J. Am. Chem. Soc., 74:4223, 1952.

For gas chromatography see *Jones:* Endeavour, 15:73, 1956; *Lipsky* and *Landowne,* Ann. Rev. Biochem., 27:649, 1960.

PROTEINS

CHAPTER FOUR

PROTEINS IN THE CELL

Some 15 per cent by weight of the total animal body is made up of protein. The membrane of animal cells represents an insoluble protein complex; the protoplasm contains soluble proteins and cytoplasmic bodies, which are, to a large extent, insoluble proteins such as are found associated with mitochondria and microsomes, though microsomes also contain soluble proteins. Insoluble and soluble proteins are found in the nucleus.

Proteins are found in all living cells—in single-celled algae and bacteria and in multicelled man—and in substances known as "viruses," which may well represent the borderline between the living and the lifeless.

These proteins have many functions: they include maintaining osmotic integrity; storage for some particular element; enzymes, to catalyze biochemical reactions; hormones to regulate metabolic processes (e.g., insulin); carriage of molecular oxygen (e.g., hemoglobin); the transportation of lipids (e.g., lipoproteins).

The complexity of proteins is illustrated by their molecular weights: Whereas the molecular weight of glucose, a typical carbohydrate, is 180, that of a protein may vary anywhere from 10,000 to 10,000,-000. From the point of view of elementary composition these proteins contain the elements carbon, hydrogen, oxygen, nitrogen and sulfur; but their molecules are so large that the possible arrangements of their atoms in space are very great.

CHEMICAL NATURE OF THE PROTEINS

Using the traditional methods of the organic chemist, it can be shown that proteins yield a mixture of amino acids when hydrolyzed by acid, alkali or enzymes. Most proteins yield some 19 different amino acids. They are alpha (α-) amino acids, or α-imino acids, and, with the exception of glycine (which contains no asymmetric atom), they all belong to the L- series with reference to the α- carbon atom.

$$\begin{array}{c} COOH \\ | \\ H_2N-C-H \\ | \\ R \end{array}$$

The structure of a typical amino acid is given above. R represents some group which determines the particular kind of amino acid in question.

In the original protein molecule, these amino acids are joined together by bonds between the carboxyl group of one amino acid and the amino group of another, with the splitting off of water:

$$\begin{array}{ccccc} H & H & & H & H \\ | & | & & | & | \\ R-C-CO|OH + H|NH-C-R^1 & \longrightarrow & R-C-CO-NH-C-R^1 \\ | & | & & | & | \\ NH_2 & COOH & & NH_2 & COOH \end{array}$$

The bond between two amino acids, —CO—NH— is called the *peptide* bond. When just two amino acids are involved, the resulting compound is called a *dipeptide.* The availability of an amino and a carboxyl group in the dipeptide makes further combinations with other (or the same) amino acids possible, so that we can build tripeptides, tetrapeptides, and so on; that is to say, we build *polypeptides.* The large synthetic *straight-chain* polypeptides begin to resemble proteins in both their chemical and their physical properties.

This polypeptide theory of the structure of proteins—due in large measure to Emil Fischer—is, however, only a partial explanation. The evidence which has accumulated more recently is for the existence, within the protein molecule, of large *ring* systems made up of many amino acids. As an illustration of this, one may cite Du Vigneaud's work on oxytocin and vasopressin, two polypeptide hormones found in the posterior lobe of the pituitary. Du Vigneaud and his co-workers have isolated, analyzed and synthesized them. Oxytocin and vasopressin are polypeptides which form large rings owing to the presence of cystine, a sulfur-containing amino acid. The disulfide bridge in cystine (p. 76) contributes to the bridge in the hormone molecule.

The following gives an abbreviated version[*] of the structure of beef oxytocin:

$$\begin{array}{l} Cy-Tyr\!\!-\!\!-Ileu \\ | \qquad\qquad\quad | \\ S \qquad\qquad\quad | \\ | \qquad\qquad\quad | \\ S \qquad\qquad\quad | \\ | \qquad\qquad\quad | \\ Cy-Asp\!\!-\!\!-Glu.NH_2 \\ | \qquad NH_2 \\ Pro-Leu-Gly.NH_2 \end{array}$$

(See pages 74 to 76 for the structures of these amino acids.)

[*] See page 623 for a list of the abbreviations employed here.

Insulin, another hormone belonging to the group of proteins, has a similar ring structure (p. 107).

The Hydrogen Bond. In addition to the peptide and disulfide bonds which are involved in bridging polypeptide chains, another type of bond is of importance to protein structure: the *hydrogen bond.*

An electrovalent bond results when two atoms exchange electrons to form charged atoms (ions). This type of bond is involved in proteins, since the amino and carboxyl groups can be charged. The covalent bond is formed as a result of a sharing of electron pairs between two elements.

The term *bond energy* represents that energy which must be absorbed, under standard conditions of temperature and pressure, in order to break the bond of a gas molecule and produce neutral gas atoms. It represents the heat content of the bond. Thus the energy of the O—H bond in water is 110.2 kcal.* and the bond energy in the C=O bond is 152 kcal.; whereas that for the N—H bond is 83.7 kcal.

The hydrogen bond results from the attraction of electronegative atoms for a proton. Such hydrogen bonds occur among the fatty acids and among water molecules:

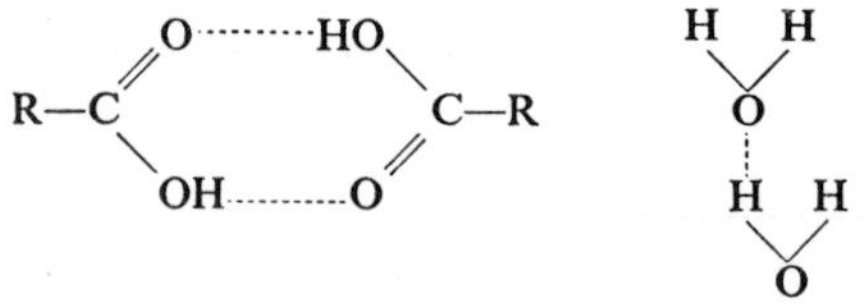

They also occur among polypeptide chains in proteins, and they can be detected by spectroscopic (infrared) analysis. Hydrogen bonds have bond energies of only 5 kcal., which explains why they are so easily broken at normal temperatures or by changes in pH. They may be represented as:

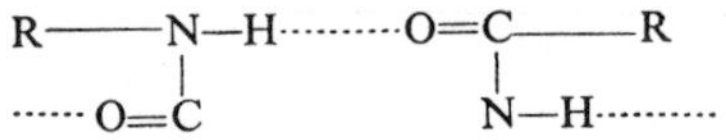

These bonds serve to hold together large polypeptide units (aggregation). To break these bonds will cause disaggregation into smaller polypeptide units (or unfolding of the coiled polypeptide chain). Bull terms these bonds "zippers," since they bring together long chain molecules. We shall see that the process of denaturation involves the breaking of hydrogen bonds, and the "unzippering" of proteins. The function of hydrogen bonding in terms of the living cell may be important, since the process of aggregation or disaggregation of proteins is accompanied by changes in physical properties such as viscosity and osmotic activity.

* Kcal. = one large Calorie = 1000 small calories.

CLASSIFICATION OF PROTEINS

I. ACCORDING TO GROSS STRUCTURE

A. *Fibrous Proteins.* These are largely insoluble in ordinary aqueous media (salt solutions, acids, bases, or aqueous alcohol). Their molecular weight is high, though this has not been definitely determined. They consist of fibers made up of long linear molecules arranged (roughly) parallel to the fiber axis. They are amorphous (that is, noncrystalline) and are capable of being stretched and then released to contract again. Their function is largely one of structure or support. Formerly they were given such names as albuminoids and sclerins. Examples of individual members are collagen (from cartilage); myosin (muscle); keratin (hair); fibrin (clot of blood). These proteins are difficult to purify.

B. *Globular Proteins.* These are soluble in aqueous salt solutions, acids, etc. They have been crystallized and have definite molecular weights. They are characterized by their ability to become "denatured" (p. 102), which is a molecular disorganization, with accompanying changes in physical and physiological properties. Among these proteins are many showing specific physiological activities (such as enzymes and hormones).

II. ACCORDING TO SOLUBILITIES

A. *Albumins* are characterized by being soluble in water and coagulated on heating. Examples are egg albumin, serum albumin, lactalbumin (from milk), and leucosin (from wheat).

B. *Globulins* are insoluble in water, coagulated by heating, soluble in dilute salt solutions and precipitated when the salt concentration is increased. NaCl, $MgSO_4$, and $(NH_4)_2SO_4$ are salts often used. Examples are myosinogen (from muscle), edestin (from hemp seed), ovoglobulin (from egg yolk), serum globulin, amandin (from almonds), legumin (from peas), and excelsin (from Brazil nuts).

C. *Glutelins* are insoluble in neutral solvents but soluble in dilute acids and alkalies. Examples are glutenin (from wheat) and oryzenin (from rice).

D. *Alcohol-soluble Proteins* (*Prolamins or Gliadins*) are soluble in 70 to 80 per cent alcohol and insoluble in water and in absolute alcohol. Examples are gliadin (from wheat), hordain (from barley), and zein (from corn).

E. *Fibrous Proteins.* (See above.)

F. *Histones* are soluble in water and insoluble in dilute ammonia. Solutions of other proteins precipitate histones. The coagulum formed on heating is soluble in dilute acids. Examples are globin (from hemoglobin), thymus histone, and scombrone (from mackerel).

G. **Protamines** are polypeptides which are less complex than the proteins so far considered, but are still more complex than proteoses and peptones (p. 73). They are soluble in water, are not coagulated by heating, precipitate other proteins from their aqueous solutions (for example, the insulin-protamine complex, Chap. 21), possess strong basic properties and form stable salts with strong mineral acids. The few amino acids which are obtained from the protamines on hydrolysis are largely basic in character. Examples are salmine (from salmon), sturine (from sturgeon), clupeine (from herring), scombrine (from mackerel), and cyprinine (from carp).

III. ACCORDING TO CONTENT OF NONPROTEIN CONSTITUENTS

Conjugated Proteins. These are substances made up of proteins combined with some other compound or compounds.

1. NUCLEOPROTEINS are combinations of proteins with nucleic acid. Examples are found in products obtained from glandular tissue and from the germ of grain.

2. GLYCOPROTEINS are combinations of proteins with carbohydrate groups. Such groups may include hexoses, hexosamines, and hexuronic acids. Examples are mucin (from saliva), osseomucoid (from bone), and tendomucoid (from tendon).

3. PHOSPHOPROTEINS are combinations of protein with phosphorus-containing substances other than nucleic acid or lecithin. Examples are casein (from milk) and vitellin (from egg yolk).

4. CHROMOPROTEINS are combinations of protein with various pigments. Examples are hemoglobin, the blood pigment, which is an iron pyrrole complex joined to protein; ferritin, an iron protein compound found in the liver and spleen; catalase, peroxidase and cytochrome *c*, iron-protein enzymes which play a part in biological oxidations; hemocyanin, a protein containing copper and found in lower invertebrates; laccase and tyrosinase, also enzymes containing copper, which are important in biological oxidations.

5. LIPOPROTEINS are combinations of proteins with lipids. They occur in cell nuclei, blood, egg yolk, milk, serum, etc. These complexes, rather ill defined, are believed to be present in the thromboplastic factor, some viruses, and bacterial antigens.

IV. ACCORDING TO STATE OF DEGRADATION   *not important*

A. **Native Proteins.** These are presumably proteins in the state in which they exist in the intact cell.

B. **Derived Proteins.** These include the products of protein degradation, the first step of which is "denaturation" (p. 102).

They are ill defined substances, divided into (1) *primary protein derivatives* (proteans, metaproteins, and coagulated proteins) and (2) *secondary protein derivatives* (proteoses, peptones, and peptides). Primary protein derivatives represent a comparatively slight hydrolytic change in the protein molecule; secondary protein derivatives represent a more extensive hydrolysis of the protein.

1. PROTEANS are insoluble products resulting probably from the action (for a comparatively short time) of water, dilute acids or enzymes. Examples are myosan (from myosin), edestan (from edestin).

2. METAPROTEINS (infraproteins) are products of the further action of acids and alkalies and are soluble in dilute acids and alkalies, but insoluble in solutions of neutral salts. Examples are acid metaprotein or acid albuminate and alkali metaprotein or alkali albuminate.

3. COAGULATED PROTEINS are insoluble products resulting either from the action of heat or of alcohol.

4. PROTEOSES are soluble in water and cannot be coagulated on heating. They can be precipitated by saturating their solutions with ammonium sulfate.

5. PEPTONES are also soluble in water, are not coagulated on heating, and they are not precipitated by saturating their solutions with ammonium sulfate. Certain alkaloidal reagents—phosphotungstic acid, for example—do precipitate them.

6. PEPTIDES are combinations of two or more amino acids, the carboxyl group of one amino acid being joined to the amino group of another (p. 69).

V. ACCORDING TO FUNCTION

Some examples are:

A. *Structural.* Myosin of muscle
B. *Storage.* Ferritin (in the liver) stores iron
C. *Enzymes.* Pepsin of the stomach, which hydrolyzes proteins
D. *Hormones.* Insulin, vasopressin
E. *Antibodies.*
F. *Toxins.* Proteins with toxic properties
G. *Special Purpose.* Hemoglobin to carry molecular oxygen; rhodopsin in the visual process; viruses

AMINO ACIDS

The following amino acids occur in most proteins. They are classified according to their functional groups.

I. ALIPHATIC AMINO ACIDS (MONOAMINO-MONOCARBOXYLIC ACIDS)

Glycine. The simplest of the amino acids, is also called glycocoll or aminoacetic acid. It is the only amino acid without an asymmetric carbon atom and therefore does not have an optical isomer.

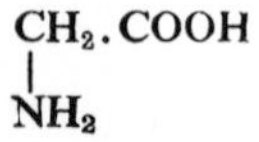

$$\begin{array}{c} CH_2.COOH \\ | \\ NH_2 \end{array}$$

Alanine, or α-aminopropionic acid. Silk fibroin contains 25 per cent of alanine.

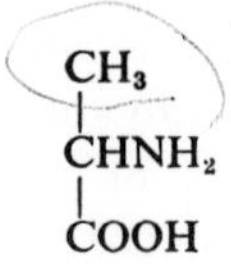

$$\begin{array}{c} CH_3 \\ | \\ CHNH_2 \\ | \\ COOH \end{array}$$

Valine, or α-aminoisovaleric acid:

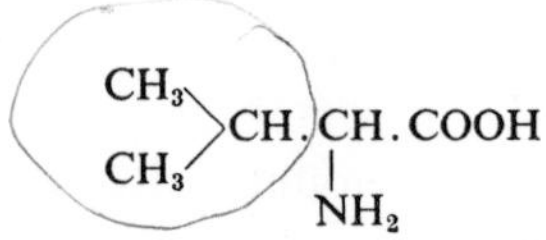

$$\begin{array}{c} CH_3 \\ \diagdown CH.CH.COOH \\ CH_3 \diagup \qquad | \\ NH_2 \end{array}$$

Leucine, or α-aminoisocaproic acid:

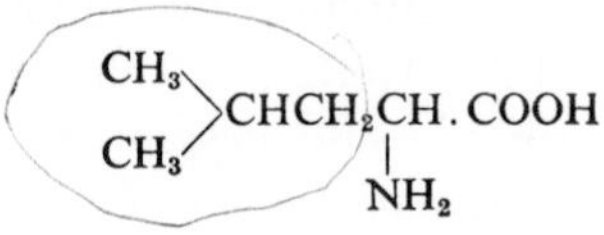

$$\begin{array}{c} CH_3 \\ \diagdown CHCH_2CH.COOH \\ CH_3 \diagup \qquad | \\ NH_2 \end{array}$$

Isoleucine, or α-amino-β-methyl-β-ethylpropionic acid:

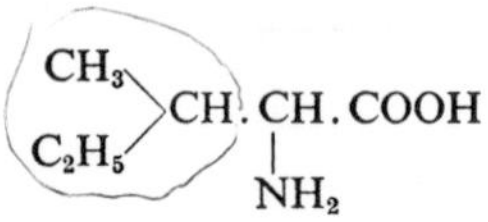

$$\begin{array}{c} CH_3 \\ \diagdown CH.CH.COOH \\ C_2H_5 \diagup \qquad | \\ NH_2 \end{array}$$

II. AROMATIC AMINO ACIDS

Phenylalanine, or β-phenyl-α-aminopropionic acid:

$$\bigcirc\!\!-CH_2\!\!-\!CH.COOH$$
$$\qquad\qquad\quad | $$
$$\qquad\qquad\quad NH_2$$

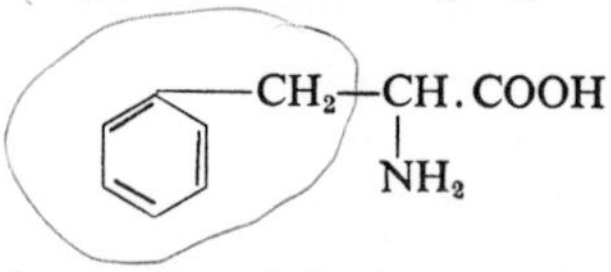

Tyrosine, or p-hydroxyphenylalanine, or β,p-hydroxyphenyl-α-amino-propionic acid:

$$\bigcirc\!\!-CH_2\!\!-\!CH.COOH$$
$$\qquad\qquad\quad | $$
$$\qquad\qquad\quad NH_2$$
$$OH$$

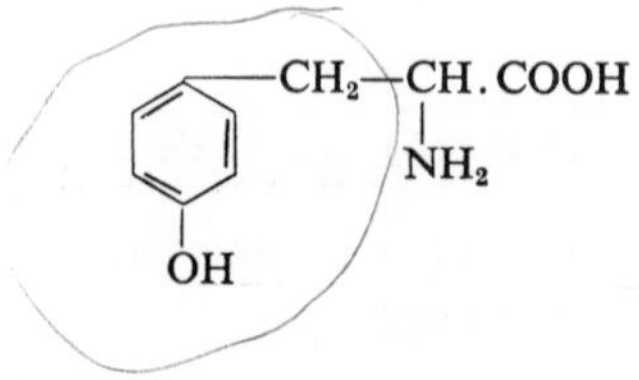

Tryptophan, or α-amino-β-3-indolepropionic acid:

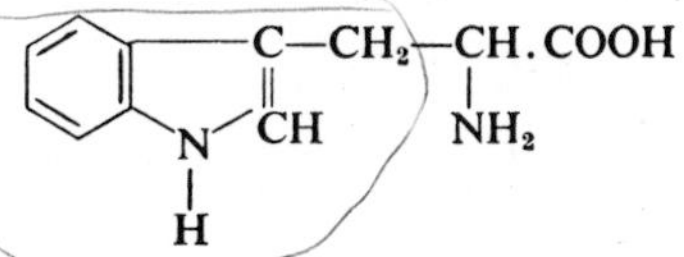

$$\begin{array}{c} \text{C---CH}_2\text{---CH.COOH} \\ \| \quad | \\ \text{N} \quad \text{CH} \quad \text{NH}_2 \\ | \\ \text{H} \end{array}$$

III. HYDROXYAMINO ACIDS

Serine, or β-hydroxy-α-aminopropionic acid:

$$\begin{array}{c} \text{CH}_2.\text{CH.COOH} \\ | \quad | \\ \text{OH} \quad \text{NH}_2 \end{array}$$

Threonine, or β-hydroxy-α-aminobutyric acid:

$$\begin{array}{c} \text{CH}_3.\text{CH.CH.COOH} \\ | \quad | \\ \text{OH} \quad \text{NH}_2 \end{array}$$

IV. ACIDIC AMINO ACIDS

Aspartic acid, or α-aminosuccinic acid:

$$\begin{array}{c} \text{CH}_2.\text{COOH} \\ | \\ \text{CHNH}_2 \\ | \\ \text{COOH} \end{array}$$

Glutamic acid, or α-aminoglutaric acid:

$$\begin{array}{c} \text{CH}_2.\text{COOH} \\ | \\ \text{CH}_2 \\ | \\ \text{CHNH}_2 \\ | \\ \text{COOH} \end{array}$$

Glutamic and aspartic acids are present, to some extent, in proteins in the form of their amides:

$$\begin{array}{c} \text{CH}_2\text{CONH}_2 \\ | \\ \text{CH}_2 \\ | \\ \text{CHNH}_2 \\ | \\ \text{COOH} \\ \text{Glutamine} \end{array} \qquad \begin{array}{c} \text{CH}_2.\text{CONH}_2 \\ | \\ \text{CHNH}_2 \\ | \\ \text{COOH} \\ \text{Asparagine} \end{array}$$

V. BASIC AMINO ACIDS (DIAMINO-MONOCARBOXYLIC ACIDS)

Lysine, or α,ε-diaminocaproic acid:

$$\begin{array}{c} \text{CH}_2.\text{CH}_2.\text{CH}_2.\text{CH}_2.\text{CH.COOH} \\ | \qquad\qquad\qquad | \\ \text{NH}_2 \qquad\qquad\quad \text{NH}_2 \end{array}$$

Arginine, or δ-guanidyl-α-aminovaleric acid:

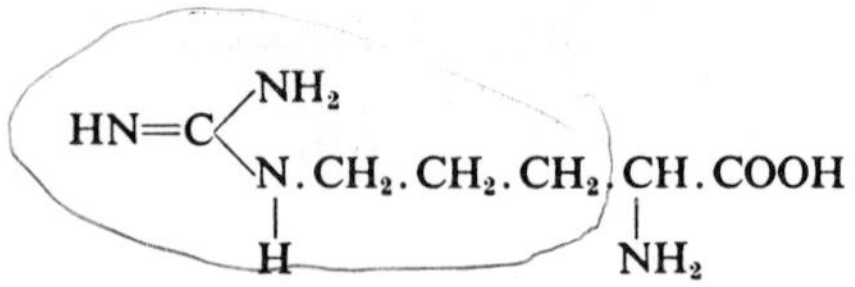

$$HN=C\begin{matrix} NH_2 \\ N.CH_2.CH_2.CH_2.CH.COOH \\ | \qquad\qquad\qquad | \\ H \qquad\qquad\qquad NH_2 \end{matrix}$$

Histidine, or β-4-imidazolylalanine:

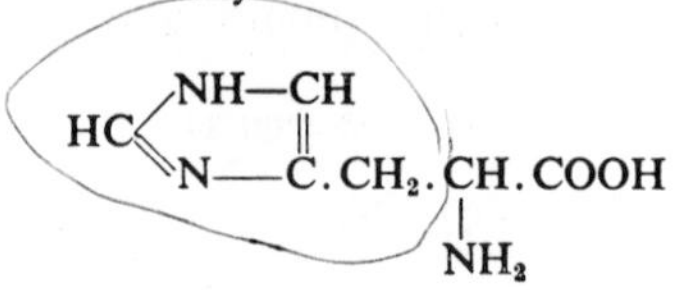

$$HC\begin{matrix} NH—CH \\ \| \\ N—C.CH_2.CH.COOH \\ | \\ NH_2 \end{matrix}$$

VI. SULFUR AMINO ACIDS

Cystine, or di-(β-thio-α-aminopropionic) acid:

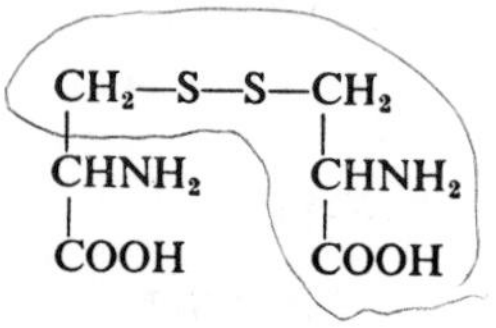

$$\begin{matrix} CH_2—S—S—CH_2 \\ | \qquad\qquad | \\ CHNH_2 \qquad CHNH_2 \\ | \qquad\qquad | \\ COOH \qquad COOH \end{matrix}$$

It also occurs as the reduced *cysteine:*

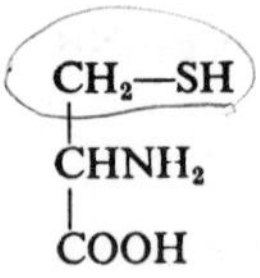

$$\begin{matrix} CH_2—SH \\ | \\ CHNH_2 \\ | \\ COOH \end{matrix}$$

Methionine, or γ-methylthiol-α-aminobutyric acid:

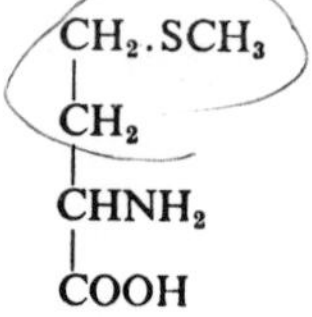

$$\begin{matrix} CH_2.SCH_3 \\ | \\ CH_2 \\ | \\ CHNH_2 \\ | \\ COOH \end{matrix}$$

VII. IMINO ACIDS

Proline, or pyrrolidine-α-carboxylic acid:

$$\begin{matrix} CH_2——CH_2 \\ | \qquad\quad | \\ CH_2 \quad CH—COOH \\ \diagdown N \diagup \\ | \\ H \end{matrix}$$

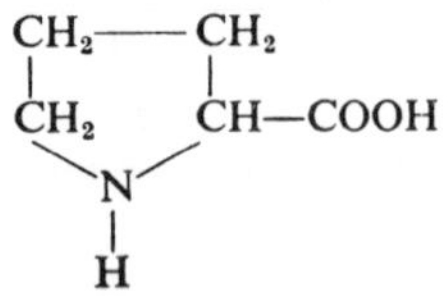

Hydroxyproline, or γ-hydroxypyrrolidine-α-carboxylic acid, is present in gelatin and in the collagens to the extent of 14 per cent.

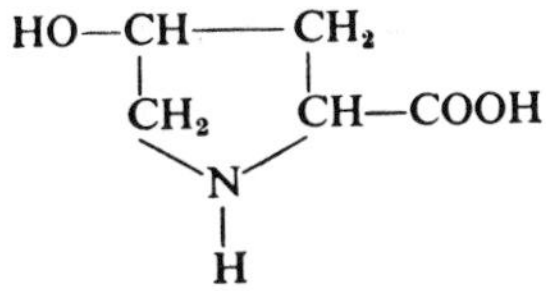

$$HO-CH{-\!\!-\!\!-}CH_2$$

(structure: HO—CH——CH₂, with CH₂ and CH—COOH below, joined to N—H)

The following amino acids do not represent the usual hydrolytic products obtained from proteins:

β-**Alanine,** a constituent of carnosine and anserine from muscle, is also part of the pantothenic acid molecule.

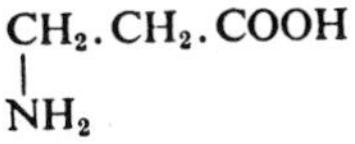

$$CH_2.CH_2.COOH$$
$$\overset{|}{NH_2}$$

Phosphoserine, obtained by partial hydrolysis of casein with dilute HCl.

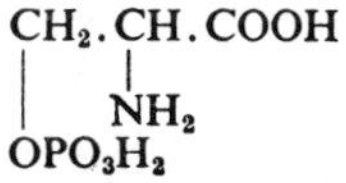

$$CH_2.CH.COOH$$
$$\overset{|}{OPO_3H_2} \quad \overset{|}{NH_2}$$

Ergothioneine, found in ergot and blood, is the betaine of thiolhistidine.

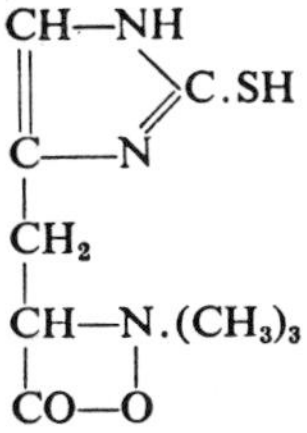

$$CH-NH$$
$$\qquad \diagdown C.SH$$
$$C-N$$
$$\overset{|}{CH_2}$$
$$CH-N.(CH_3)_3$$
$$\overset{|}{CO-O}$$

Hydroxylysine (α,ϵ-diamino-δ-hydroxycaproic acid), present in gelatin and as a phosphoric ester in the calf embryo.

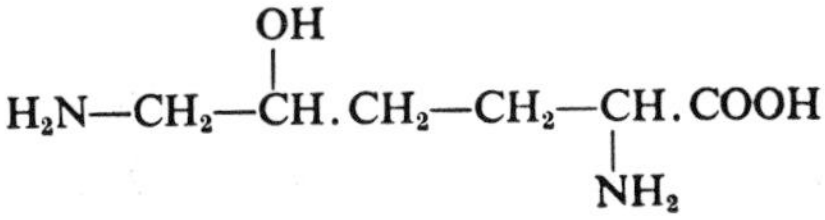

$$OH$$
$$H_2N-CH_2-\overset{|}{CH}.CH_2-CH_2-CH.COOH$$
$$\overset{|}{NH_2}$$

Ornithine (α,δ-diaminovaleric acid), plays an important role in urea synthesis. It is produced from arginine by enzymatic or alkaline hydrolysis.

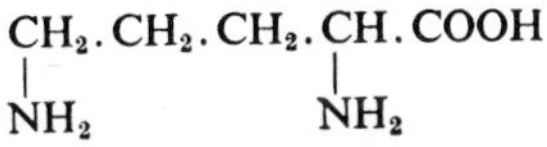

$$CH_2.CH_2.CH_2.CH.COOH$$
$$\overset{|}{NH_2} \qquad \overset{|}{NH_2}$$

Citrulline (δ-carbamido-α-aminovaleric acid), important in urea formation in the mammalian organism:

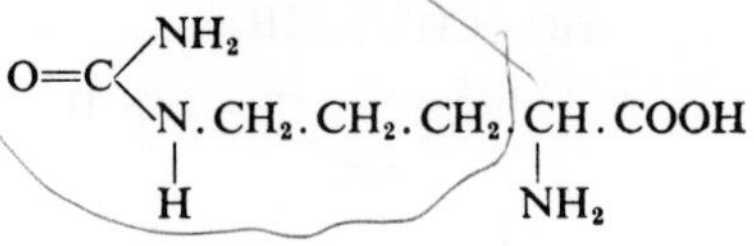

$$O=C{<}^{NH_2}_{N.CH_2.CH_2.CH_2.CH.COOH}$$
$$\underset{H}{|} \qquad \underset{NH_2}{|}$$

Homocysteine, the next higher homologue of cysteine, is converted to methionine in the body.

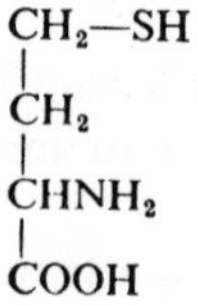

$$CH_2—SH$$
$$|$$
$$CH_2$$
$$|$$
$$CHNH_2$$
$$|$$
$$COOH$$

3,5-Dibromotyrosine, found in the skeletal proteins of certain coral:

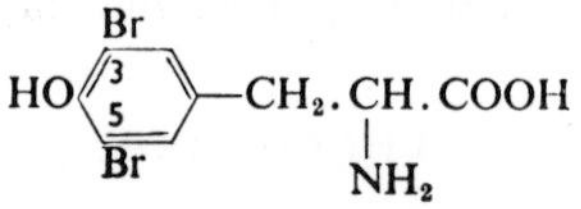

$$HO{\overset{Br}{\underset{Br}{\bigcirc}}}—CH_2.CH.COOH$$
$$\underset{NH_2}{|}$$

3-Iodotyrosine, a constituent of the thyroid gland:

$$HO{\overset{I}{\bigcirc}}—CH_2.CH.COOH$$
$$\underset{NH_2}{|}$$

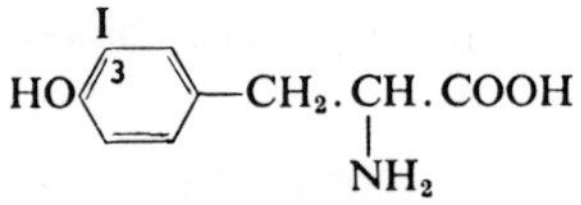

3,5-Diiodotyrosine, also a constituent of the thyroid gland:

$$HO{\overset{I}{\underset{I}{\bigcirc}}}—CH_2.CH.COOH$$
$$\underset{NH_2}{|}$$

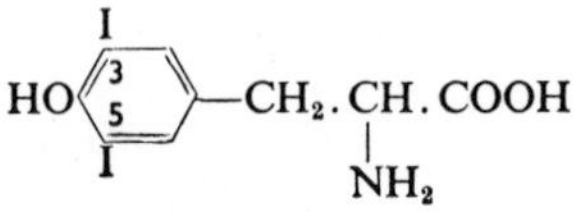

3,5,3′-Triiodothyronine, an active hormone found in the thyroid gland:

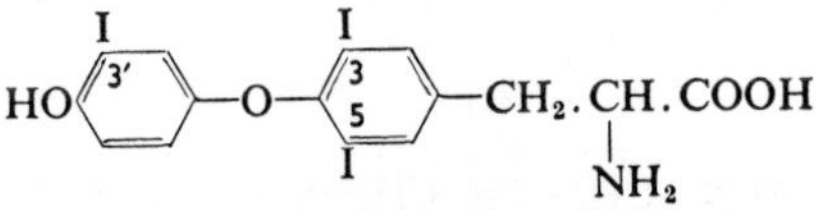

$$HO{\overset{I}{\bigcirc}}—O—{\overset{I}{\underset{I}{\bigcirc}}}—CH_2.CH.COOH$$
$$\underset{NH_2}{|}$$

Thyroxine [3,5-diiodo-4-(3′,5′-diiodo-4-hydroxyphenoxy) phenylalanine], an active hormone in the thyroid: *hormone*

$$HO{\overset{I}{\underset{I}{\bigcirc}}}—O—{\overset{I}{\underset{I}{\bigcirc}}}—CH_2.CH.COOH$$
$$\underset{NH_2}{|}$$

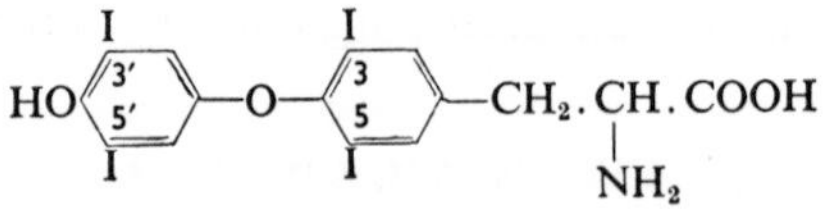

γ-Aminobutyric acid, found in bacteria, green plants, yeast and the brain:

$$H_2N—CH_2—CH_2—CH_2—COOH$$

Dihydroxyphenylalanine (3,4-dihydroxyphenylalanine), important in the formation of melanin pigments:

$$HO\underset{\underset{NH_2}{|}}{\overset{HO}{\diagup}}\diagdown CH_2.CH.COOH$$

In addition to those listed above, there are still others. To mention a few: *octopine* (octopus), *djenkolic acid* (djenkel nut), *canavanine* (soy bean, jack bean). There are also a number of "unnatural" stereoisomers (D- series), which occur in natural products.* Among these are D-*phenylalanine* (gramicidin S and tyrocidine), D-*leucine* and D-*valine* (gramicidin D), D-*β-thiolvaline* (penicillins), D-*alanine* (*Lactobacillus arabinosus*), D-*glutamic acid* (capsular substance of *Bacillus anthracis* and *L. arabinosus*), and D-*proline* (ergot alkaloids).

HYDROLYSIS OF PROTEINS AND SEPARATION OF THE AMINO ACIDS

Hydrolysis of a protein is brought about by boiling with acid, or by allowing a proteolytic enzyme such as trypsin to act on the protein. Alkali is practically never used (except in the Folin method of estimating tryptophan), since it racemizes the amino acids and destroys arginine and cystine. Sulfuric acid is often favored as the hydrolytic agent because, after the necessary heating (from 15 to 20 hours), the excess acid is conveniently removed with barium hydroxide. Hydrochloric acid is found more useful when the ultimate goal is the isolation of the monoamino acids.

The separation and the isolation of the various amino acids in the mixture after hydrolysis is briefly outlined below.

Usually, an attempt is made first to separate the amino acids into groups, such as the monoamino acids, the basic (two amino groups) acids and the dicarboxylic (two carboxyl groups) acids. Butyl alcohol will extract many of the monoamino acids. The dicarboxylic acids can be separated as their calcium salts, insoluble in alcohol (the calcium salts of the other amino acids are soluble). The basic amino acids are precipitated with phosphotungstic acid. Sometimes the separation into groups is accomplished by electrodialysis. Here the basic amino acids tend to migrate to the cathode, the dicarboxylic acids tend to proceed to the anode. The separation of individual amino acids, particularly in quantitative amounts, is difficult. Some of the monoamino acids can be separated by the fractional distillation of their methyl esters. Tyrosine and cystine may often be obtained directly from a protein hydrolysate,

* The naturally occurring amino acids belong to the L- series of configurationally related compounds.

owing to their comparative insolubility. Tryptophan may be precipitated as the mercury salt, histidine as a silver salt, arginine as a flavianate, glycine as a double salt with potassium trioxalatochromiate.

COLOR REACTIONS OF PROTEINS

The fact that proteins yield α-amino acids on hydrolysis characterizes them quite well, but to carry out such an operation, and to identify the products, is a time-consuming procedure. For a preliminary survey, the protein color tests are extremely useful.

BIURET REACTION

This consists in mixing the protein with sodium hydroxide solution and a very weak solution of copper sulfate. A violet color is obtained. The test depends upon the presence of two or more of the following groups (peptide linkages) in the protein molecule: $-CONH_2$ with another $-CONH_2$, or one of the following groups in place of $-CONH_2$: $-CSNH_2$, $-C(NH)NH_2$, $-CH_2NH_2$, $-CRHNH_2$, $-CHOHCH_2NH_2$, $-CHNH_2CH_2OH$, $-CHNH_2CHOH$. Such simple compounds as oxamide, $CONH_2$, and biuret, $H_2N-CO-NH-CO-NH_2$ (from which

$$| $$
$$CONH_2$$

the test takes its name), give positive biuret reactions.

MILLON'S REACTION

When a protein is heated with Millon's reagent (a solution of mercuric nitrite and mercuric nitrate in a mixture of nitric and nitrous acids), a red color or precipitate is obtained. The test is due to the presence in the protein molecule of a phenolic group:

OH
Phenolic group

The specific compound with this structure present in proteins is tyrosine.

HOPKINS-COLE (GLYOXYLIC ACID) REACTION

A violet ring is obtained when concentrated sulfuric acid is added to a mixture containing the protein and glyoxylic acid, CHO.COOH. The tryptophan molecule containing the indole nucleus, present in proteins, is responsible for this test. It is believed that tryptophan condenses with the aldehyde to form the colored product. Gelatin gives a negative test;

hydrolysis of gelatin fails to yield any appreciable quantity of tryptophan among its hydrolytic products.

XANTHOPROTEIC REACTION

A yellow color is obtained when nitric acid and a protein are heated. The yellow color is changed to orange on the addition of alkali. The benzene ring is responsible for the test. Compounds containing the benzene ring give yellow products on nitration. Among the amino acids, tyrosine and tryptophan give the test.

NINHYDRIN (TRIKETOHYDRINDENE HYDRATE) REACTION

Amino acid solutions when heated with ninhydrin yield a blue colored complex, carbon dioxide and an aldehyde corresponding to the amino acid.

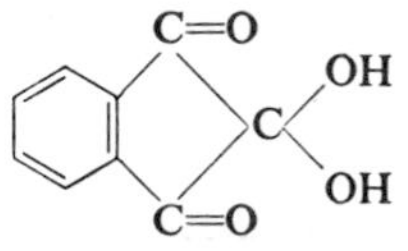

Ninhydrin

(Peptides and proteins also give colored complexes, but no carbon dioxide is evolved.) This reaction is due to α-amino acid groups in the protein molecule. Individual α-amino acids give a positive test, the color varying from blue and purple for most amino acids to red for proline and hydroxyproline.

THE QUANTITATIVE ESTIMATION OF AMINO ACIDS

Brief outlines are given for several methods in use.

COLORIMETRIC METHODS

Specific color reactions for some amino acids can be utilized for their quantitative estimation. Tyrosine, for example, is determined by the application of the Millon's reaction (p. 80).

MICROBIOLOGICAL METHODS

Many bacteria grow in a solution which includes adequate amounts of amino acids, vitamins, salts, purines and pyrimidines (p. 116). Some bacteria grow at a decreased rate when one of the amino acids is present in concentrations below the optimum. A set of growth rates may thus be determined experimentally for these bacteria in the presence of varying but known quantities of some particular amino acid. The sample of protein to be analyzed is hydrolyzed so as to yield a mixture of its amino acids. The bacteria are now suspended in a series of identical solutions complete in all respects for bacterial growth but lacking the amino acid to be determined. To each such suspension is now added a definite but varying quantity of the protein hydrolysate. By comparing the growth rate of the bacteria in these tubes with the growth rates of bacteria in the solutions containing known quantities of the amino acid, one can determine the quantity of the amino acid present in the protein hydrolysate, and thus in the original protein.

The growth rate of the bacterial suspension may be determined by measuring increased turbidity, or by the determination of some characteristic end-product of its metabolism (such as the production of lactic acid from lactobacilli).

The bread mold, *Neurospora*, may here be included. (For further details concerning this bread mold, see Chap. 18.) Irradiation of the wild variety of the mold produces mutant strains which have lost their ability to synthesize some particular compound. One such variety may now need choline for growth, which gives the basis for the determination of choline in an unknown mixture. This method has been used for the determination of some vitamins, purines and pyrimidines.

Microbiological methods have the advantage, whenever they can be used, in that the amount of protein needed to run a determination is extremely small.

ISOTOPE DILUTION METHOD

This is the most accurate method for the quantitative determination of amino acids in protein hydrolysates. It necessitates special equipment for the determination of the concentration of isotopes. The principle involved is that a compound which has an abnormal isotope content is inseparable by the usual laboratory procedures from its normal analogue. If, for example, the isotope-containing glycine is added to a hydrolytic mixture of normal amino acids, and then glycine is isolated, this will be a representative sample of the mixture of the added isotope-containing glycine and the glycine originally present.

From the amount of glycine added (x) and its content of N^{15} (C_0), as well as the N^{15} content of the isolated glycine (C), the amount (y) of glycine originally present in the mixture can be calculated from the equation

$$y = \left(\frac{C_0}{C} - 1\right)x$$

The importance of this technique lies in the fact that a quantitative yield of the amino acid is not necessary. What is important is that the sample which is isolated should be pure.

CHROMATOGRAPHIC ANALYSIS

Tswett wrote (in 1906): "Like the light radiation in the spectrum, so is a mixture of pigments systematically separated on the calcium carbonate column into its constituents, which can then be qualitatively and quantitatively determined." Since then Tswett's method has been widely applied. The principle—as the above quotation makes clear—is the differential adsorption of a mixture on a column of adsorbing material.

The name "chromatography" originated because it was used to separate colored compounds; but the method has been extended so that colorless compounds can also be handled. Here the position on the adsorbing column can be determined by the use of reagents yielding characteristic color reactions.

By a judicious use of solvents, the separate bands on the column can be made to flow down into a receiver and be recovered.

Stein and Moore have applied this technique for the analysis of the amino acids in a protein hydrolysate. Not more than 2.5 mg. of protein is needed for the entire analysis.

A column partially filled with an adsorbent such as starch or an ion-exchange resin is used. The substance to be analyzed (protein hydrolysate) is placed at the top of the column and slowly developed with a variety of solvents. Equal volumes of the effluent are collected in separate tubes and analyzed for amino acid content by reaction with ninhydrin (see p. 81) and estimated colorimetrically. Figure 8 illustrates the analysis of 2.5 mg. of bovine serum albumin by this method. The identity of the amino acids in each tube is determined by comparison with an analysis of a known mixture of amino acids run under identical conditions. The actual amount of each amino acid present is determined from the area under the individual curve.

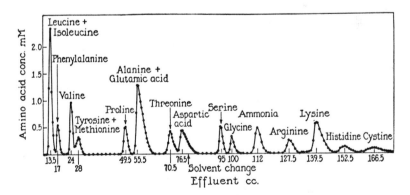

Figure 8. Chromatographic fractionation of a hydrolysate of bovine serum albumin. Solvents, 1:2:1 *n*-butyl alcohol–*n*-propyl alcohol–0.1 N HCl and 2:1 *n*-propyl alcohol–0.5 N HCl. Column dimensions, 0.9 × 30 cm. Sample, an amount of hydrolysate corresponding to about 2.5 mg. of protein. (Stein and Moore: J. Biol. Chem. *178:*79.)

DETERMINATION OF "END-GROUPS" IN PROTEINS; COMPLETE PROTEIN STRUCTURAL ANALYSIS

A most important technique which has been devised for the study of the specific arrangement of amino acids in a protein is that of "end-group" analysis. In any polypeptide chain, there are two terminal amino acids, the N-terminal and the C-terminal amino acid unless the polypeptide is cyclic in nature. The N-terminal amino acid is that amino acid whose α-carboxyl group is involved in peptide linkage with the α-amino group of the adjoining amino acid, thus leaving the α-amino group of the N-terminal amino acid free. On the other hand, the C-terminal amino acid is that amino acid whose α-amino group is involved in peptide linkage with an adjoining amino acid and therefore has a free α-carboxyl group.

Since a number of polypeptide units may be connected by means of disulfide bridges, a protein may have several N-terminal and C-terminal amino acids. These may all be the same, they may all be different, or there may be a few different and several similar amino acids occupying the terminal positions. The identity of the C-terminal amino acids is determined by treating the protein with the enzyme carboxypeptidase, which specifically hydrolyzes a peptide bond adjacent to a free α-carboxyl group. The C-terminal amino acid can then be identified by paper chromatography (p. 38).

A method which has proved itself to be of great importance is one which identifies the N-terminal amino acids. This method, devised by Sanger, is based on the reaction of a protein with the reagent, 2,4-dinitrofluorobenzene (DNFB) at room temperature and in the presence of sodium bicarbonate. The reaction involves the coupling of the free α-amino group of the N-terminal amino acid with DNFB to form dinitrophenyl protein (DNP protein):

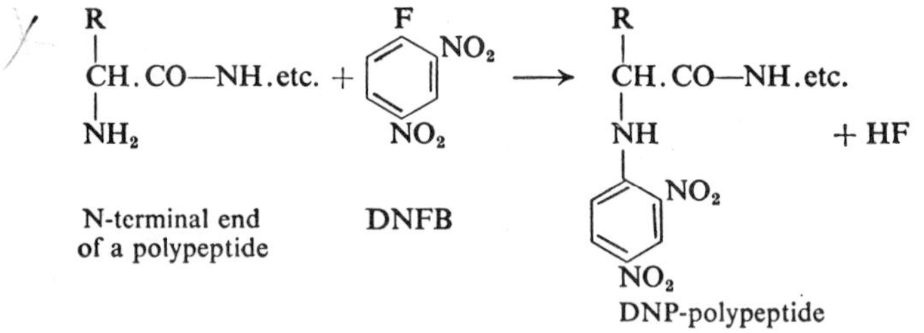

N-terminal end of a polypeptide   DNFB   DNP-polypeptide

In this way, the N-terminal amino acid of a protein is tagged with the DNP grouping. In addition, DNFB will also react with any other free amino group along the polypeptide chain, e.g., the ϵ-amino group of lysine, which is not involved in peptide linkage. When the DNP protein is hydrolyzed with HCl, a mixture of free amino acids and DNP amino acids results. Since the DNP amino acids are yellow in color, they may be separated and identified by means of chromatography. The possibilities are as follows:

a. The DNP amino acid isolated is ϵ-DNP lysine. This amino acid occurs along the peptide chain.
b. The DNP amino acid is α,ϵ-di-DNP lysine. This amino acid occurs as an N-terminal amino acid.
c. A mixture of any other DNP amino acids. These amino acids occupy N-terminal positions on the several polypeptide chains.

In order to determine the number of different polypeptide units in a protein molecule, the protein is treated with performic acid, which oxidizes the disulfide bridges holding the polypeptide units together, resulting in a mixture of polypeptide units which may be separated by means of the Stein-Moore method of ion exchange chromatography (p. 125).

By applying the DNFB reaction to each of the resulting oxidized polypeptides, one can now identify the association of each N-terminal amino acid to its specific polypeptide unit. For example, Sanger showed that insulin contains two amino acids in the N-terminal position: glycine and phenylalanine. After oxidation of insulin with performic acid, he found two oxidized polypeptides, one of which had glycine at the N-terminal position, the other of which had phenylalanine at the N-terminal position. Thus the basic unit of insulin contains two polypeptides cross-linked by means of cystine disulfide bridges, with glycine and phenylalanine at each N-terminal end.

Sanger found it possible to determine the complete amino acid sequence of each of these two polypeptides by applying several other techniques. Partial hydrolysis of each of the polypeptides gives rise to a mixture of smaller polypeptide units. The N-terminal and C-terminal position of each of these may now be determined. By continuing this type of study, sequences of amino acids in such peptides will soon fit together to give the complete sequence. Stein and Moore have used partial hydrolysis by pepsin, trypsin and chymotrypsin, together with the DNFB reaction, for an analysis of the crystalline enzyme ribonuclease. Using these methods, we can now write the exact formulas, complicated as they are, for some proteins.

SYNTHESIS OF AMINO ACIDS

A great variety of methods has been used. Several are listed below. An example is given in each case.

A. USE OF HALOGENATED ACIDS

This method is particularly useful when the need is to prepare an amino acid containing the N^{15} isotope, because $N^{15}H_3$ is readily available.

$$CH_2Cl + NH_3 \longrightarrow \underset{\text{Glycine}}{CH_2NH_2 | COOH} + HCl$$

B. MALONIC ESTER SYNTHESIS

This involves a direct condensation of a halide with malonic ester.

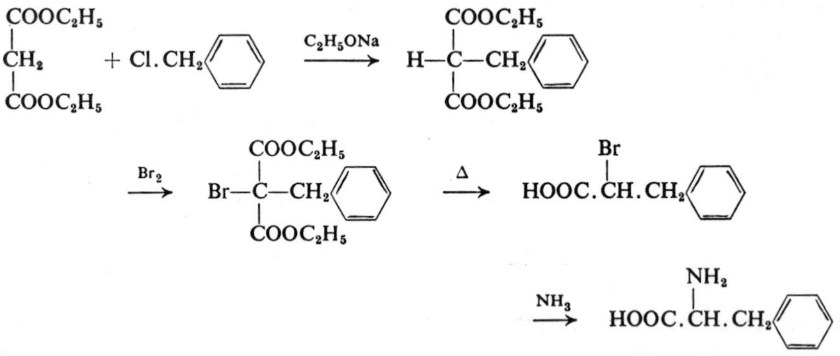

$$\underset{COOC_2H_5}{CH_2} + Cl.CH_2\text{—}\bigcirc \xrightarrow{C_2H_5ONa} H\text{—}\underset{COOC_2H_5}{\overset{COOC_2H_5}{C}}\text{—}CH_2\text{—}\bigcirc$$

$$\xrightarrow{Br_2} Br\text{—}\underset{COOC_2H_5}{\overset{COOC_2H_5}{C}}\text{—}CH_2\text{—}\bigcirc \xrightarrow{\Delta} HOOC.\underset{Br}{CH}.CH_2\text{—}\bigcirc$$

$$\xrightarrow{NH_3} HOOC.\underset{NH_2}{CH}.CH_2\text{—}\bigcirc$$

Phenylalanine

C. STRECKER SYNTHESIS

The addition of hydrogen cyanide and ammonia to an aldehyde gives the corresponding amino nitrile, which may then be hydrolyzed to the amino acid.

$$\underset{CHO}{CH_3} + HCN + NH_3 \longrightarrow \underset{CN}{\overset{CH_3}{CHNH_2}} + H_2O$$

$$\underset{CN}{\overset{CH_3}{CHNH_2}} + 2H_2O \longrightarrow \underset{COOH}{\overset{CH_3}{CHNH_2}} + NH_3$$

Alanine

SYNTHESIS OF POLYPEPTIDES

Examples of several methods are shown.

A. ACYL CHLORIDE METHOD

Fischer devised a method for "coupling" two or more amino acids.

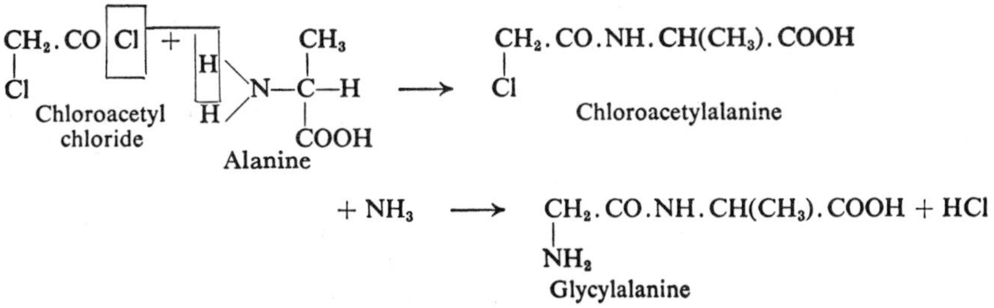

$$CH_2.CO\boxed{Cl} + \boxed{H} \underset{\substack{|}}{\overset{\substack{|}}{}} \quad \begin{matrix} CH_3 \\ | \\ N-C-H \\ | \\ COOH \end{matrix} \longrightarrow \begin{matrix} CH_2.CO.NH.CH(CH_3).COOH \\ | \\ Cl \end{matrix}$$

Chloroacetyl chloride   Alanine   Chloroacetylalanine

$$+ NH_3 \longrightarrow \begin{matrix} CH_2.CO.NH.CH(CH_3).COOH + HCl \\ | \\ NH_2 \end{matrix}$$

Glycylalanine

B. CARBOBENZOXY METHOD (BERGMANN)

The key to this method is the selection of the group used to "block" the amino group. The one selected is known as the "carbobenzoxy" group. Benzyl alcohol may be made to combine with phosgene to form the carbobenzoxy derivative:

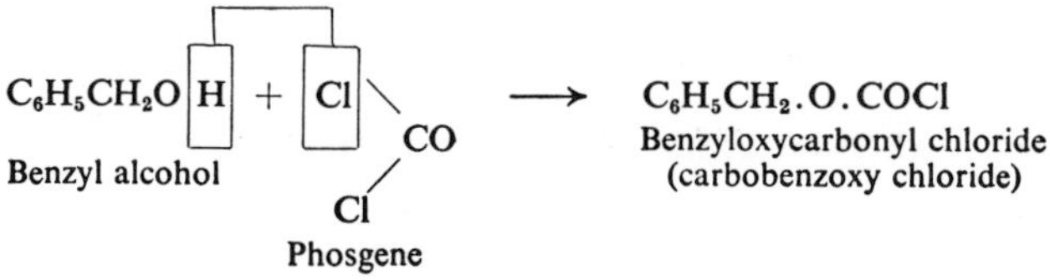

$$C_6H_5CH_2O\boxed{H} + \boxed{Cl} \underset{\substack{}}{\overset{}{}} \begin{matrix} CO \\ Cl \end{matrix} \longrightarrow C_6H_5CH_2.O.COCl$$

Benzyl alcohol   Phosgene   Benzyloxycarbonyl chloride (carbobenzoxy chloride)

which combines with an amino acid thus:

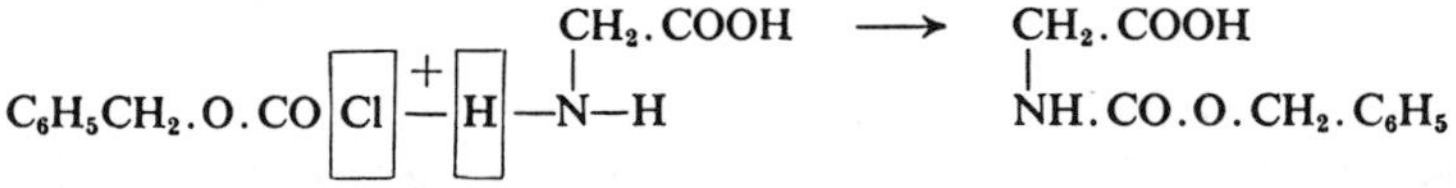

$$C_6H_5CH_2.O.CO\boxed{Cl} - \boxed{H}-N-H \quad \begin{matrix} CH_2.COOH \\ | \\ \end{matrix} \longrightarrow \begin{matrix} CH_2.COOH \\ | \\ NH.CO.O.CH_2.C_6H_5 \end{matrix}$$

and this can be transformed into the corresponding acid chloride with phosphorus pentachloride:

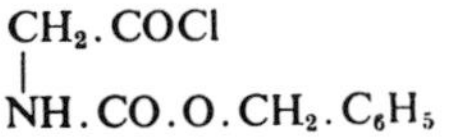

$$\begin{matrix} CH_2.COCl \\ | \\ NH.CO.O.CH_2.C_6H_5 \end{matrix}$$

The resulting compound can now be combined with an amino acid:

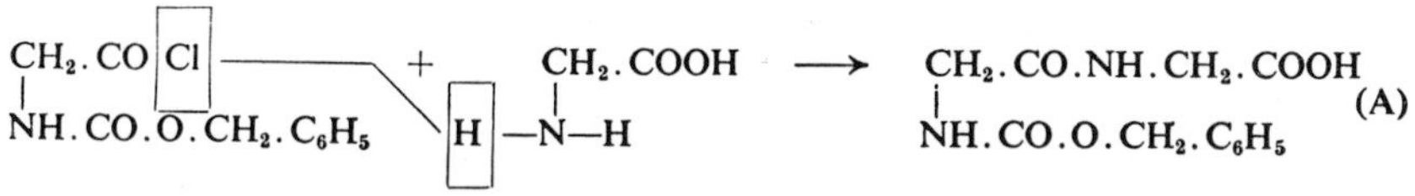

$$\begin{matrix} CH_2.CO\boxed{Cl} \\ | \\ NH.CO.O.CH_2.C_6H_5 \end{matrix} + \boxed{H}-N-H \quad \begin{matrix} CH_2.COOH \\ | \\ \end{matrix} \longrightarrow \begin{matrix} CH_2.CO.NH.CH_2.COOH \\ | \\ NH.CO.O.CH_2.C_6H_5 \end{matrix} \quad (A)$$

The carbobenzoxy group can be eliminated by treatment with hydrogen (in the presence of palladium black). The free peptide is formed by the removal of toluene and carbon dioxide:

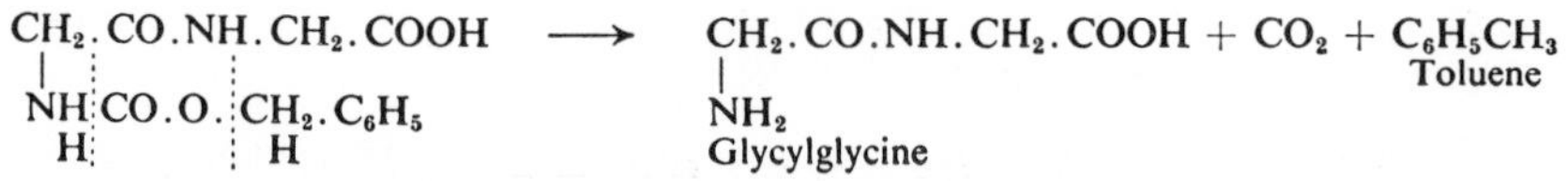

$$CH_2.CO.NH.CH_2.COOH \longrightarrow CH_2.CO.NH.CH_2.COOH + CO_2 + C_6H_5CH_3$$

$$\underset{H}{NH}\underset{H}{|CO.O.|CH_2.C_6H_5} \qquad \underset{Glycylglycine}{NH_2} \qquad Toluene$$

Here no hydrolytic agent is needed to split off the carbobenzoxy group —a procedure which also tends to split the peptide linkage itself.

If a tripeptide is required, (A) is halogenated and coupled with another amino acid:

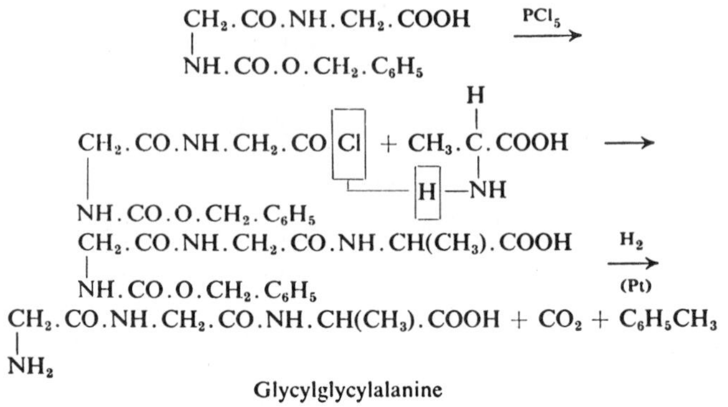

$$CH_2.CO.NH.CH_2.COOH \xrightarrow{PCl_5}$$
$$|$$
$$NH.CO.O.CH_2.C_6H_5$$

$$CH_2.CO.NH.CH_2.CO\boxed{Cl} + CH_3.\overset{H}{\underset{|}{C}}.COOH \longrightarrow$$
$$| \qquad\qquad\qquad\boxed{H}-NH$$
$$NH.CO.O.CH_2.C_6H_5$$

$$CH_2.CO.NH.CH_2.CO.NH.CH(CH_3).COOH \xrightarrow{H_2}$$
$$| \qquad\qquad\qquad\qquad\qquad\qquad (Pt)$$
$$NH.CO.O.CH_2.C_6H_5$$

$$CH_2.CO.NH.CH_2.CO.NH.CH(CH_3).COOH + CO_2 + C_6H_5CH_3$$
$$|$$
$$NH_2$$

Glycylglycylalanine

AMINO ACIDS AS ACIDS AND BASES

ACIDS AND BASES: A REVIEW

An acid is a compound which dissociates to furnish protons (H^+). A base is a substance which combines with protons.

An acid, HA, for example, dissociates thus:

$$HA \rightleftharpoons H^+ + A^-$$

which means that HA is an acid because it furnishes a proton. It also means that A^- is a base because it can unite with a proton to form HA.

$$\underset{(acid)}{HA} \rightleftharpoons \underset{(proton)}{H^+} + \underset{(base)}{A^-}$$

Applying this concept to acetic and carbonic acids, we have

$$\underset{(acid)}{CH_3COOH} \rightleftharpoons H^+ + \underset{\substack{(base;\ the\\ acetate\ ion)}}{CH_3COO^-}$$

$$\underset{(acid)}{H_2CO_3} \rightleftharpoons H^+ + \underset{\substack{(base;\ the\\ bicarbonate\ ion)}}{HCO_3^-}$$

These definitions of acids and bases apply for all solvents, including water.

In water, HA dissociates to furnish a hydrated hydrogen ion, known as the hydronium ion and written as H_3O^+:

$$H_2O + HA \rightleftharpoons H_3O^+ + A^-$$

Or, to bring out the acid-base relation, we can write

$$\underset{\text{(base)}}{H_2O} + \underset{\text{(acid)}}{HA} \rightleftharpoons \underset{\text{(acid)}}{H_3O^+} + \underset{\text{(base)}}{A^-}$$

Now, water may act as a base because it can combine with a proton:

$$H_2O + H^+ \rightleftharpoons H_3O^+$$

and it may act as an acid because it can furnish a proton:

$$H_2O \rightleftharpoons H^+ + OH^-$$

Such a substance, which may act either as an acid or as a base is called an *amphoteric* substance. (See also p. 92, under a discussion of *buffers*.)

To derive the dissociation constant for water, we shall simplify the discussion by using H^+ in the place of the hydronium ion:

$$H_2O \rightleftharpoons H^+ + OH^-$$

Applying the law of mass action, we have

$$K = \frac{[H^+][OH^-]}{[H_2O]}$$

where [ ] indicates concentration in moles per liter.

Since the concentration of undissociated H_2O is constant, we may rewrite the equation

$$K_w = [H^+][OH^-]$$

where K_w is an expression for the dissociation constant for water.

The value for this constant (at 25° C.) is 1×10^{-14}. Since

$$[H^+] = [OH^-],$$
$$[H^+] = 1 \times 10^{-7} \text{ moles per liter}$$

If water be regarded as a "neutral" substance, any solution whose $[H^+]$ is equal to 10^{-7} moles per liter is a neutral solution. On this basis, an "acid" solution is one whose $[H^+]$ is greater than 10^{-7} (for example, 10^{-3}); and a "basic" solution is one whose $[H^+]$ is less than 10^{-7} (for example, 10^{-9}).

To avoid the use of negative exponents, Sørensen introduced the concept of *pH*, which he defined as follows:

$$pH = \log \frac{1}{[H^+]}$$

A solution, then, whose [H$^+$] is 1×10^{-7} moles per liter, would have a pH of log $\frac{1}{10^{-7}}$, or log 10^{-7}, or $7 \times$ log 10, or 7×1, or 7.0

A neutral solution is one whose pH is 7.0. The pH of an acid solution would be lower than 7.0, and the pH of a basic solution would be higher than 7.0.

The terms *weak* and *strong* acids have reference to relative concentrations of H$^+$, which, in turn, will depend upon the degree of dissociation. Similar considerations hold for *weak* and *strong* bases.

Table 13 gives the pH and [H$^+$] for several acids and bases:

TABLE 13. pH AND HYDROGEN ION CONCENTRATIONS FOR SOME ACIDS AND BASES

			pH	[H$^+$]
1	*N*	HCl	0.0	1.0
0.1	*N*	HCl	1.0	1×10^{-1}
0.01	*N*	HCl	2.0	1×10^{-2}
1	*N*	CH$_3$COOH	2.3	4.3×10^{-3}
0.1	*N*	CH$_3$COOH	2.8	1.3×10^{-3}
1	*N*	NaOH	14.0	1×10^{-14}
0.1	*N*	NaOH	13.0	1×10^{-13}
1	*N*	NH$_4$OH	11.7	1.7×10^{-12}
0.1	*N*	NH$_4$OH	11.2	5.4×10^{-12}

Figures 9, 10, 11 show the results of titrating different kinds of acids and bases, as expressed by a plot of the pH of the solution when different quantities of the one were mixed with a constant quantity of the other.

Dissociation of a Weak Acid in the Presence of Its Salt. With the exception of the hydrochloric acid in the stomach, the acids and bases of biochemical importance are *weak* acids and bases. Examples of these acids are H_2CO_3 and NaH_2PO_4, and of bases, $NaHCO_3$ and Na_2HPO_4.

A weak acid (HA) dissociates:

$$HA \rightleftharpoons H^+ + A^-$$

$$K = \frac{[H^+][A^-]}{[HA]}$$

$$\text{or} \quad [H^+] = K\frac{[HA]}{[A^-]}$$

If in addition to the acid (HA) in solution we also have its corresponding salt (BA) present, then the concentration of A$^-$ will be approximately equal to the concentration of BA, because the concentration

Figure 9.   Figure 10.

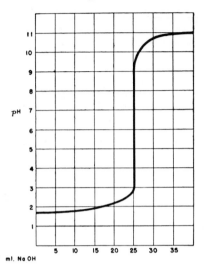

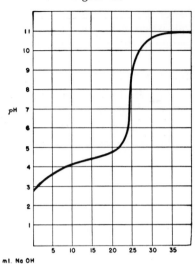

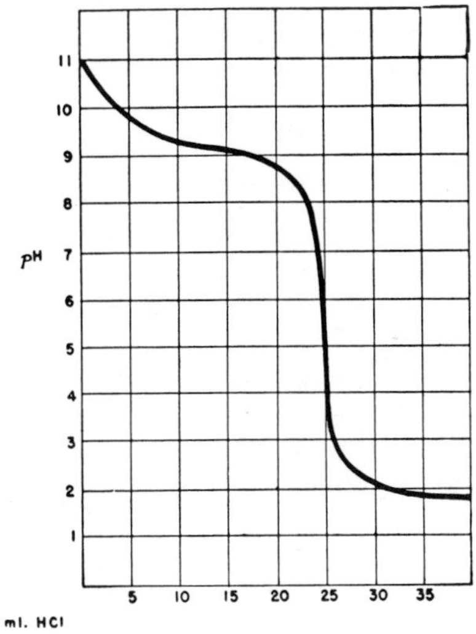

Figure 11.

Figure 9. Titration of 25 ml. of 0.1 N hydrochloric acid with 0.1 N sodium hydroxide.

Figure 10. Titration of 25 ml. of 0.1 N acetic acid with 0.1 N sodium hydroxide.

Figure 11. Titration of 25 ml. of 0.1 N ammonium hydroxide with 0.1 N hydrochloric acid.

of A⁻ derived from the weak acid is negligible compared to that of A⁻ derived from the salt BA. So that we may rewrite the equation thus:

$$[H^+] = Ka \frac{[HA]}{[BA]}$$

Converting both sides to their respective negative logarithms, we have

$$pH = pK_a + \log \frac{[BA]}{[HA]}$$

(When BA and HA are present in equal concentration, pH = pK$_a$.)

Using this equation as the basis for numerical calculations, it can be shown that a mixture of a weak acid and its salt acts as a *buffer* system; that when acids or bases are added to such a system, the resulting change in the pH of the solution is very much minimized.

AMINO ACIDS AS ACIDS AND BASES

Within its molecule the amino acid contains a potentially acidic (carboxyl) group and a basic (amino) group, which suggests that such a compound would act as a buffer.

With glycine for our example, we can write the formula of an amino acid in its fully dissociated state thus:

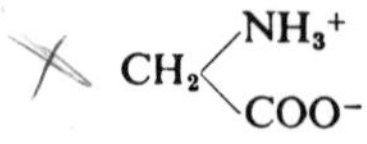

$$CH_2 \begin{matrix} NH_3^+ \\ COO^- \end{matrix}$$

This form of an amino acid is called a *zwitterion* (meaning "hybrid") or dipolar ion.

Glycine exists in this zwitterion form at a pH of 6.1. The reason this state does not correspond to a pH of 7.0 is that the carboxyl group dissociates to a greater extent than the amino group.

Glycine may act as an acid by liberating a proton:

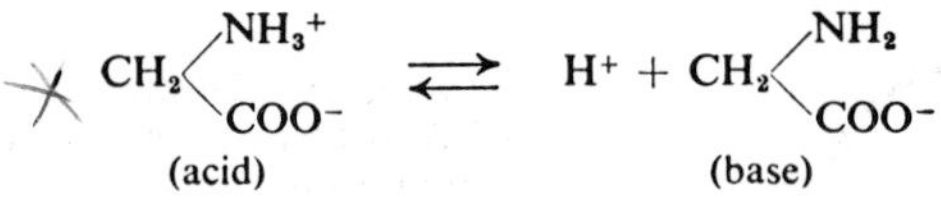

$$CH_2 \begin{matrix} NH_3^+ \\ COO^- \end{matrix} \rightleftarrows H^+ + CH_2 \begin{matrix} NH_2 \\ COO^- \end{matrix}$$

(acid)   (base)

or it may act as a base by combining with a proton:

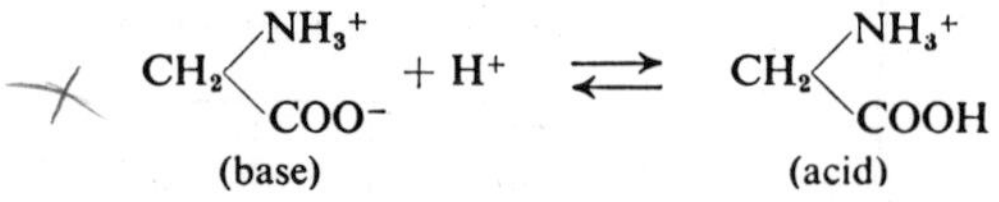

$$CH_2 \begin{matrix} NH_3^+ \\ COO^- \end{matrix} + H^+ \rightleftarrows CH_2 \begin{matrix} NH_3^+ \\ COOH \end{matrix}$$

(base)   (acid)

When a base or an acid is added to an amino acid, we would then get the following:

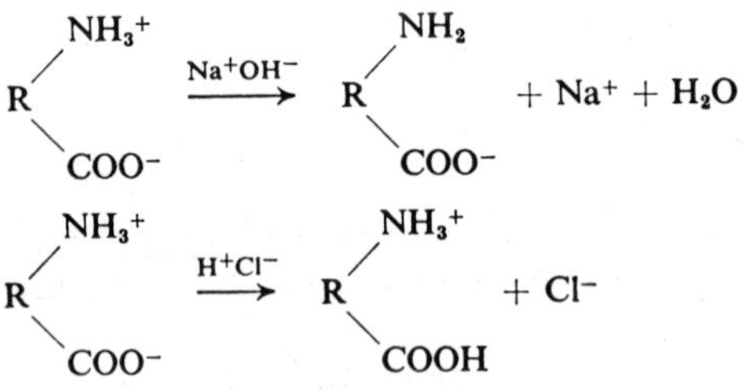

$$R \begin{matrix} NH_3^+ \\ COO^- \end{matrix} \xrightarrow{Na^+OH^-} R \begin{matrix} NH_2 \\ COO^- \end{matrix} + Na^+ + H_2O$$

$$R \begin{matrix} NH_3^+ \\ COO^- \end{matrix} \xrightarrow{H^+Cl^-} R \begin{matrix} NH_3^+ \\ COOH \end{matrix} + Cl^-$$

When the amino acid is in the zwitterion state, it will not migrate to either electrode in an electrical field. However, when an acid is added to the amino acid, the latter assumes its positively charged form and moves towards the cathode; and when a base is added to the amino acid, the latter assumes its negatively charged form and moves towards the anode. The pH at which the amino acid has no tendency to move to either the positive or negative electrode is called its *isoelectric point*.

To derive the dissociation constants for the amino and carboxyl groups of amino acids, a series of titrations of the amino acid, first with acid and then with base, are performed, and the pH is observed after the addition of small amounts of the acid and the base.

To derive expressions for these dissociation constants, let us take as our example glycine and consider the dissociation of this amino acid as an acid. When sodium hydroxide is added to a solution of glycine in water, we can represent the reaction as

$$CH_2\underset{COO^-}{\overset{NH_3^+}{\diagup}} \rightleftharpoons H^+ + CH_2\underset{COO^-}{\overset{NH_2}{\diagup}}$$

This expression is in the form of $HA \rightleftharpoons H^+ + A^-$. To determine the dissociation constant of the amino group, we have

$$K_b = \frac{[H^+]\left[CH_2\underset{COO^-}{\overset{NH_2}{\diagup}}\right]}{\left[CH_2\underset{COO^-}{\overset{NH_3^+}{\diagup}}\right]}$$

$$\text{or} \quad [H^+] = \frac{K_b\left[CH_2\underset{COO^-}{\overset{NH_3^+}{\diagup}}\right]}{\left[CH_2\underset{COO^-}{\overset{NH_2}{\diagup}}\right]}$$

$$\text{or} \quad pH = pK_b + \log\frac{\left[CH_2\underset{COO^-}{\overset{NH_2}{\diagup}}\right]}{\left[CH_2\underset{COO^-}{\overset{NH_3^+}{\diagup}}\right]}$$

pK_b, the dissociation constant of the amino group, can now be determined by remembering that when the ratio of the two ions is equal to 1, pK_b becomes equal to the pH (for the log of 1 is 0).

In a similar manner an expression for the dissociation constant of the carboxyl group can be derived, for when glycine combines with a proton we get

$$CH_2\underset{COOH}{\overset{NH_3^+}{\diagup}} \rightleftharpoons CH_2\underset{COO^-}{\overset{NH_3^+}{\diagup}} + H^+$$

then

$$K_a = \frac{[H^+]\left[CH_2\underset{COO^-}{\overset{NH_3^+}{\diagup}}\right]}{\left[CH_2\underset{COOH}{\overset{NH_3^+}{\diagup}}\right]} \quad \text{and} \quad [H^+] = K_a\frac{\left[CH_2\underset{COOH}{\overset{NH_3^+}{\diagup}}\right]}{\left[CH_2\underset{COO^-}{\overset{NH_3^+}{\diagup}}\right]}$$

so that

$$pH = pK_a + \log \frac{\left[CH_2 \begin{matrix} NH_3^+ \\ COO^- \end{matrix} \right]}{\left[CH_2 \begin{matrix} NH_3^+ \\ COOH \end{matrix} \right]}$$

The values pK_a and pK_b are now largely replaced by pK_1 and pK_2 since in more complicated amino acids containing several acid or basic groups there will be other pK values for them, and also because we may determine the pK value for a group during a titration without sometimes knowing which group it actually is. The pK values with subnumerals 1, 2, 3, and so on, are listed in order of increasing values of pK. Table 14 lists the pK values for the dissociating groups of some typical amino acids, as well as their isoelectric points (IEP).

TABLE 14. pK AND IEP VALUES

Amino Acid	pK_1	pK_2	pK_3	IEP
Glycine	2.35 (COOH)	9.78 (NH₃⁺)	—	6.1
Aspartic acid	2.09 (COOH)	3.87 (COOH)	9.82 (NH₃⁺)	3.0
Glutamic acid	2.19 (COOH)	4.28 (COOH)	.9.66 (NH₃⁺)	3.2
Tyrosine	2.20 (COOH)	9.11 (NH₃⁺)	10.1 (OH)	5.7
Cysteine	1.96 (COOH)	8.18 (NH₃⁺)	10.28 (SH)	5.07
Arginine	2.02 (COOH)	9.04 (NH₃⁺)	12.48 (guanido)	10.8
Lysine	2.18 (COOH)	8.95 (α NH₃⁺)	10.53 (ε NH₃⁺)	9.7
Histidine	1.77 (COOH)	6.10 (imidazole)	9.18 (NH₃⁺)	7.6

Titration of Amino Acids: The Formol Titration. The buffering action of an amino acid is best illustrated by titrating an aqueous solu-

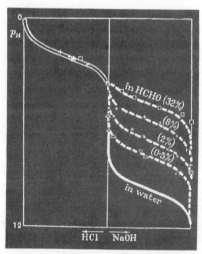

Figure 12. Titration curves of glycine in presence of increasing concentrations of HCHO. (From Harris: Biochem. J., *24*: 1080.)

tion of an amino acid with acid and base. Figure 12 illustrates such a titration curve for glycine. The portions of the curve where the addition of acid or base causes the least change in pH are the buffering regions and denote the presence of the appropriate amino acid ion: $R(NH_2)COO^-$ in the alkaline region and $R(COOH)NH_3^+$ in the acid region.

Figure 12 illustrates the results of the titration of an amino acid like glycine with acid and with alkali in the absence and in the presence of formaldehyde. The reactions of amino acids with formaldehyde yield a series of ill-defined compounds which are unstable but are best illustrated by the following:

$$R\overset{COO^-}{\underset{NH_3^+}{\diagup\diagdown}} \rightleftarrows R\overset{COO^-}{\underset{NH_2}{\diagup\diagdown}} + HCHO \rightleftarrows R\overset{COO^-}{\underset{NH.CH_2OH}{\diagup\diagdown}}$$
(Methylol)

$$R\overset{COO^-}{\underset{NH_2}{\diagup\diagdown}} + 2HCHO \rightleftarrows R\overset{COO^-}{\underset{N.(CH_2OH)_2}{\diagup\diagdown}} .$$
(Dimethylol)

From the above it can be seen that formaldehyde reacts only with the —NH$_2$ group and not with the —NH$_3^+$ group. As we titrate the amino acid in the presence of formaldehyde, only that portion of the curve which represents the reaction of alkali with the protons of the —NH$_3^+$ group is altered when compared to the titration with alkali in the absence of formaldehyde. Thus, in the presence of formaldehyde, the concentration of R.COO$^-$.NH$_2$ is diminished and the action of the alkali remains that of stripping protons from the R.COO$^-$.NH$_3^+$ molecule, but the titration curve is displaced from its normal position towards lower values of pH, the greater the concentration of formaldehyde. These

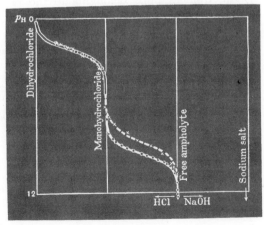

Figure 13. Titration of arginine in water and HCHO. ○, in water. ✕, in HCHO (0.25%). (From Harris: Biochem. J., *24:* 1087.)

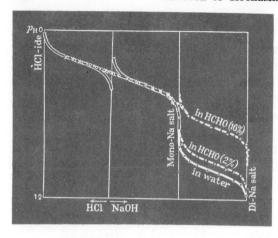

Figure 14. Titration of aspartic acid in water and HCHO. ○, in water. ×, in HCHO (2%). +, in HCHO (16%). (From Harris: Biochem. J., 24: 1089.)

results confirm the hypothesis that HCl reacts essentially with the —COO⁻ group, whereas NaOH reacts with the —NH₃⁺ group. Similar conclusions can be drawn from the titration of dicarboxylic and diamino acids (see Figs. 13 and 14).

PROTEINS

PROTEINS AS ACIDS AND BASES

Since proteins may be considered as chains of amino acids, it must be clear that these substances also contain charged groups. The number of such charged groups will vary with the pH. The titration curve of a protein will represent the composite of the effects of the various groups as they are able to combine with acids and bases. From a knowledge of the pK values for these groups, we can gather at what point in our titration the particular group is reacting with acid or base.

The charged groups of proteins are:

a. Amino groups belonging to the N-terminal amino acid of each polypeptide chain (amino end-groups).

b. Carboxyl groups belonging to the C-terminal amino acid of each polypeptide chain (carboxyl end-groups).

c. Groups due to basic amino acids not involved in peptide linkage: the ε-amino group of lysine; the imidazole group of histidine; and the guanido group of arginine.

d. Groups due to acidic amino acids not involved in peptide linkage: glutamic and aspartic acids.

e. Phenolic groups due to tyrosine.

f. Sulfhydryl groups due to cysteine.

Proteins behave as charged colloidal particles. The properties of proteins are largely due to the charged groups in the protein molecule, and to the changes they undergo with changes in pH.

MIGRATION IN AN ELECTRICAL FIELD: ELECTROPHORESIS

A protein molecule, it is clear, contains electrically charged groups. These, in turn, are dependent upon the amino acid content of the protein molecule, and upon the pH. At a pH alkaline to its isoelectric point, the protein will contain an excess of —COO⁻ groups and will behave as a negative ion, sodium⁺ proteinate⁻. At a pH acid to its isoelectric point, the protein will contain an excess of —NH₃⁺ groups and will behave as a positive ion, protein⁺ chloride⁻. At a pH acid to its isoelectric point, a protein migrates towards the cathode; and when the pH is alkaline to the isoelectric point, it migrates to the anode. This migration in an electrical field is the basis for separating proteins from one another. The method is known as *electrophoresis*. (It should be noted here that at a pH corresponding to its isoelectric point, the protein will have a net charge density of zero and will show no tendency to migrate.)

Assuming that the protein is impure and has for its impurity one other protein, at some particular pH (not, of course, their isoelectric points) these proteins will move at different speeds, because of the difference in net charge of the two species of molecules at that pH. In a suitable apparatus, the presence of an accompanying protein may thus be detected.

The results obtained by the electrophoretic method are best illustrated by Figure 15 which gives the actual pictures obtained during the electrophoretic separation of the proteins from normal human plasma. The ability to get a picture of the separated protein fractions is based on the fact that there exists a difference in refractive index between the buffer solution acting as solvent and the protein solution. Using a suitable optical system these differences are photographed after a suitable time interval during which an electric current has been passed through the solution contained in a special U-tube electrophoretic glass cell. In this way one obtains information regarding the number of electrophoretically different proteins in the mixture as well as the relative concentration of each protein fraction in the mixture.

In Figure 15 the rising boundary picture refers to the separation of proteins in that portion of the U-tube where the protein molecules are moving upwards towards one of the electrodes. The descending pattern is obtained from that limb of the U-tube containing the proteins which migrate downwards towards the same electrode. The area under each curve corresponds to the relative concentration of that protein fraction. One soon learns that in a complex mixture of proteins such as is present in plasma, each individual protein cannot be separated by this method; even those curves which look uniform can be further separated by removing the protein mixture from the cell and repeating the electrophoresis again. Fraction A corresponds to the albumin fraction, α to the mixture of α-globulins, β to the mixture of β-globulins, φ

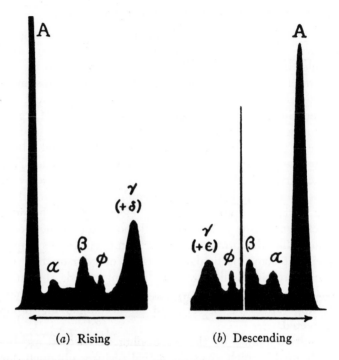

(a) Rising   (b) Descending

Figure 15. Electrophoretic pattern of normal blood plasma. (From Longsworth, Shedlovsky, and MacInnes, J. Exp. Med., *70*:399.)

to fibrinogen, γ to the mixture of γ-globulins and δ and ϵ represent salt boundary anomalies caused by an accumulation of salts during electrophoresis.

Where a single molecular species of protein is present, it would appear as a single sharp boundary throughout the period of electrophoresis and also when run at various values of pH, assuming that the pH itself does not cause a splitting of the protein molecule into several fragments.

SEDIMENTATION IN THE ULTRACENTRIFUGE

We owe to Svedberg the development of an apparatus, the ultracentrifuge, which is capable of giving rise to centrifugal forces 500,000 times those of gravity. This centrifugal force is capable of sedimenting protein molecules in solution. Since the sedimentation rate is a function, among other things, of the size of the molecule, the molecular weight of the protein may be determined. Here, too, a protein impurity can be detected because its molecular weight will be different.

The molecular weights and the isoelectric points of several proteins are here given:

Protein	Molecular Weight	Isoelectric Point
Egg albumin......................	42,000	4.9
Hemoglobin.......................	67,000	6.7
Serum albumin...................	70,000	4.88
Apoferritin.......................	465,000	4.4

CONSTANT SOLUBILITY

A sensitive test for the presence of a protein impurity is one based on the constant solubility of a protein regardless of the amount of substance present in the solid phase. Actually, one equilibrates increasing amounts of the protein under test with the same amount of solvent (which may be water or some salt solution), and measures the amount

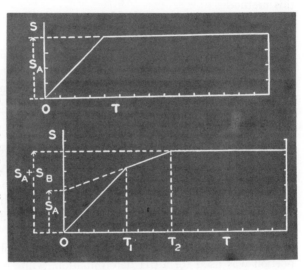

Figure 16. Ideal relation between the solubility of one homogeneous substance (upper figure) and the total amount, T, of solid phase used per unit of solution. Lower curve same for a mixture of two substances that are not in solid solution. (From Clark: Topics in Physical Chemistry, 1948, p. 326.)

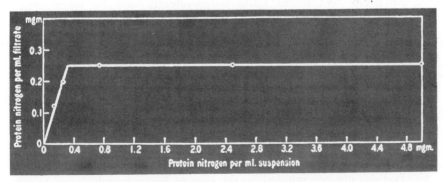

Figure 17. Solubility of crystalline trypsin in saturated magnesium sulfate solution at pH 4.0 and 10° C., showing constant solubility in presence of increasing quantities of solid phase. (After Northrop, Crystalline Enzymes, 1939.)

of protein which has been dissolved. By plotting the amount of dissolved protein against the total protein, it becomes apparent whether we are dealing with one or more molecular species.

Figure 16 illustrates the theoretical curves obtained during the solubility test for purity of proteins. The lower curve indicates what would happen if two proteins, A and B, were present in a solid mixture; S = total solid dissolved, S_A = solubility of A, S_B = solubility of B, T = total of A and B added to the whole system.

Figure 17 illustrates an experimental demonstration of the use of the constant solubility test to show the purity of crystalline trypsin. The curve corresponds to a theoretical curve for a single molecular species. A smooth curve indicates a solid solution which cannot be analyzed by this method.

COMPOSITION OF PROTEINS

The composition of some proteins in terms of their amino acids is given in Table 15. An amino acid residue refers to the amino acid as it exists in peptide linkage in a protein. In the formation of this bond, a molecule of water has been removed.

FORMATION OF COMPOUNDS WITH PROTEINS

A consequence of charged groups in proteins is the ability of proteins to form complexes with other compounds. An example of this behavior is the experiment by Jacques Loeb, who placed a number of samples of gelatin in contact with nitric acid at different concentrations. After pouring off the acid and washing the gelatin, each sample was added to a solution of silver nitrate in the dark. The gelatin was next filtered, washed, dissolved, brought to a known volume, and an adequate portion was used for a pH determination, while another was exposed to sunlight. After a time all solutions with a pH higher than 4.7 turned brown or black, while those of pH less than 4.7 remained colorless.

Michaelis had found quite independently and by other means (migrations in an electrical field) that the isoelectric point of gelatin is. at a pH of 4.7. Loeb assumed that at pH greater than 4.7, gelatin combines with silver to form a salt of the type of silver gelatinate (which darkens on exposure); whereas below pH 4.7, gelatin combines with acid to form gelatin nitrate which does not react with silver salts; hence there is no change in color on exposure.

Using potassium ferrocyanide in the place of silver nitrate, where now the tendency would be to form combinations with the ferrocyanide ion, such combinations took place only below, but not above, pH 4.7; again presenting evidence in favor of Loeb's point of view.

Proteins are precipitated by the salts of heavy metals (such as copper sulfate, lead acetate, mercuric nitrate, etc.). These precipitates are metal proteinates (such as lead proteinate), formed on the alkaline side

TABLE 15. AMINO ACID COMPOSITION OF SOME REPRESENTATIVE PROTEINS

Amino acid	Human Serum Albumin		Horse Hemoglobin		β-Lacto-globulin		Salmine		Insulin (Ox)		Ribo-nuclease		Pepsin		Keratin (Wool)		Gelatin*	
	A	B	A	B	A	B	A	B	A	B	A	B	A	B	A	C	A	C
Alanine	...	...	7.40	54	7.07	30	1.12	1	4.5	6	...	...	...	...	4.14	46.4	9.3	104.6
Glycine	1.60	15	5.60	48	1.50	7	2.95	3	4.3	7	1.3	3	6.4	29	6.53	87.0	26.9	359.0
Valine	7.70	45	9.10	50	5.67	18	3.14	2	7.75	8	7.3	9	7.1	21	4.64	39.7	3.3	28.2
Leucine	11.00	58	15.40	75	15.48	44	0	0	13.2	12	0	0	10.4	27	11.3	86.3	3.4	26.2
Isoleucine	1.70	9	0	0	5.88	17	1.64	1	2.77	1	3.1	4	10.8	28	...	...	1.8	13.8
Proline	5.10	31	3.90	22	5.27	17	5.80	4	2.9	2-3	3.6	5	5.0	15	9.5	82.6	14.8	129.
Phenylalanine	7.80	33	7.70	30	3.86	9	0	0	8.14	6	3.6	3	6.4	13	3.65	22.1	2.55	15.5
Tyrosine	4.70	18	3.03	11	3.69	8	0	0	12.5	8	7.93	7	8.5	16	4.65	25.7	1.0	5.5
Trytophan	0.20	1	1.70	5	1.92	3	0	0	0	0	0	0	2.4	4	1.8	8.8	0	0
Serine	3.34	22	5.80	35	4.07	14	9.1	7	5.23	6	12.0	17	12.2	40	10.01	95.4	3.18	30.3
Threonine	4.60	27	4.36	24	5.15	16	0	0	2.08	2	9.0	11	9.6	28	6.42	53.9	2.2	18.5
Cystine/2	5.60	32	0.45	2.5	2.29	7	0	0	12.5	12	6.51	8	1.64	4	11.9	98.9	0	0
Cysteine	0.70	4	0.56	3	1.10	3	0	0	0	0	0.6	0.7	0.5	2	0	0	0	0
Methionine	1.30	6	1.0	4.5	3.21	8	0	0	0	0	4.43	5	1.7	4	0.7	4.7	0.9	6.1
Arginine	6.20	25	3.65	14	2.88	6	85.2	40	3.07	2	5.16	5	1.0	2	10.4	59.7	8.55	49.2
Histidine	3.50	16	8.71	36	1.60	4	0	0	5.21	4	4.22	4	0.9	2	1.1	6.83	0.73	4.71
Lysine	12.30	58	8.51	38	11.30	29	0	0	2.51	2	10.4	11	0.9	2	2.76	18.9	4.60	31.5
Aspartic acid	8.95	46	10.60	51	11.46	32	0	0	6.80	6	14.2	16	16.0	41	7.2	54.1	6.7	50.6
Glutamic acid	17.0	80	8.50	38	19.10	48	0	0	18.60	15	13.0	13	11.9	28	14.1	96.0	11.2	76.1
Amide N	0.88	44	0.87	36	1.07	28	0	0	1.39	12	2.05	22	1.32	32	1.17	83.2	0.07	5.3

A = grams of amino acid in 100 grams of protein; B = residues of amino acid per molecule; C = residues of amino acid per 10^5 grams of protein.

* Gelatin contains also hydroxyproline, A = 14.5; B = 110.8, as well as hydroxylysine, A = 1.2; B = 7.4.

(Compiled from G. R. Tristram, in H. Neurath and K. Bailey (Editors): The Proteins, Vol. I, part A, Academic Press, New York, 1953.)

of the isoelectric point (p. 145) of the protein. Proteins are also precipitated by alkaloidal reagents (such as picric acid, phosphotungstic acid, and tannic acid). This precipitation represents combinations on the acid side of the isoelectric point of the protein. Neutral salts (such as ammonium sulfate, sodium sulfate, and sodium chloride) are also used to precipitate or "salt out" proteins. Here, some believe, precipitation may be due to dehydration of molecular aggregates in solution. This may also explain precipitation with a dehydrating agent such as alcohol. However, on standing with alcohol at room temperature, proteins undergo other changes (denaturation) which affect their solubility. Other examples of compounds formed with proteins are: the complex lipoproteins (p. 65), the nucleoproteins (p. 112), the phosphoproteins, the glycoproteins (p. 72), and the whole series of enzymes which contain coenzymes attached to the protein molecule.

PROTEIN DENATURATION

When a solution of ovalbumin is heated, it coagulates and resembles the process of heating an egg until it becomes hardboiled.

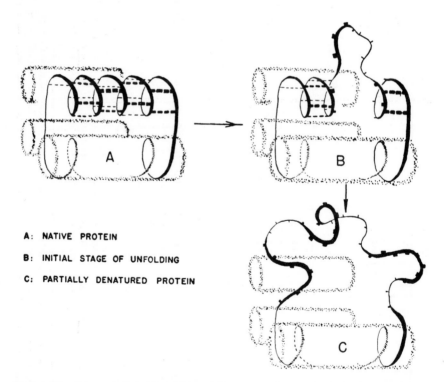

A: NATIVE PROTEIN

B: INITIAL STAGE OF UNFOLDING

C: PARTIALLY DENATURED PROTEIN

Figure 18. Denaturation. (From Kauzmann, in McElroy and Glass: The Mechanism of Enzyme Action, Baltimore, The Johns Hopkins Press.)

Should the ovalbumin solution first be brought to a pH alkaline to its isoelectric point, no coagulation takes place on warming; however, when the solution is then brought to its isoelectric point, a precipitate is formed.

Heating brings about a disorganization (denaturation) of the native protein molecule. Sometimes this is followed by coagulation (loss of solubility); sometimes it is not.

This disorganization of the native protein molecule involves the change from the regular arrangement of a rigid structure to an irregular, diffuse arrangement (see Figs. 18 and 19).

There are two kinds of denaturation: an unfolding of the peptide chains, such as takes place when urea acts on albumin; and a dissociation of the protein into smaller units, which may or may not unfold, as in the case of the action of urea on the tobacco mosaic virus molecule (p. 113). These two kinds of denaturation are dependent upon the nature of the proteins themselves: in the one case we are dealing with one continuous polypeptide chain; in the other we have a series of subunits held together by secondary intramolecular bonds.

The bonds which are affected by the denaturation process include (a) hydrogen bonds (p. 70); (b) hydrophobic bonds, due to amino acids like leucine, valine, phenylalanine, tryptophan and proline, which adhere to each other forming a "micelle," and which do not mix well with water; (c) salt bridges or ionic bonds between groups which are positively and negatively charged; and (d) intramolecular bonds, such as are found in cross linkages due to the disulfide groups of cystine (p. 85).

An example of a denaturation agent is one which has already been

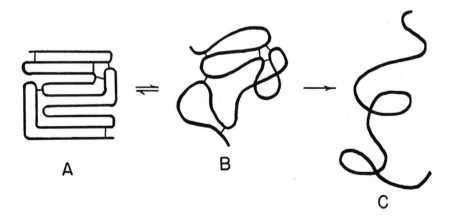

Figure 19. Denaturation. (From Kauzmann, in McElroy and Glass: The Mechanism of Enzyme Action, Baltimore, The Johns Hopkins Press.)

mentioned, urea. This compound breaks hydrogen bonds in the protein, presumably by forming hydrogen bonds of its own (due to its peptide character). Other means of denaturation employ heat, organic solvents, acid, alkali, radiation, enzymes, and detergents (with surface-active properties).

That denaturation represents an unfolding appears established by experiments which show that the denatured protein gives more intense reactions when tested for certain groups, such as —SH, —S—S— and the phenolic group of tyrosine. Presumably, many of these groups fail to react when the protein is in the native state because they are "buried" within the folded molecule.

Denaturation may, in some cases, be partly or wholly reversed, with a recovery of all or most of the native properties. Whereas ovalbumin is irreversibly denatured by urea, serum albumin can be brought back to its native state by removing the urea. One explanation involves the extent of disulfide cross linkage in these two proteins. Ovalbumin has but two such cystine residues, whereas serum albumin has 18 per molecule. In the case of serum albumin, after removal of the urea the molecule can find its way back to the native state because of the intact disulfide cross linkages; whereas in ovalbumin this cannot happen. If, however, one treats serum albumin with an excess of cysteine at pH 10, the denaturation is irreversible. The cross linkages have been broken and, in the process of re-forming, linkages of a haphazard nature take place, resulting in a molecule totally different from the native one. A situation similar to this occurs with the protein hormone insulin, which contains a relatively large quantity of cystine. If insulin is treated with an excess of cysteine and then oxidized to re-form disulfide linkages, the resulting protein has lost its hormonal properties; for example, it will not lower the blood sugar after injection.

DONNAN'S THEORY OF MEMBRANE EQUILIBRIA

Loeb developed his theory of the colloidal behavior of proteins from two principles: one, that proteins are amphoteric substances (this subject has already been discussed); the other, that Donnan's theory of membrane equilibria (which is about to be discussed) furnishes an explanation of the influence of electrolytes on osmotic pressure and membrane potentials. Colloidal properties of proteins, according to Loeb, are associated with the presence of a nondiffusible ion.

Donnan's experiments and formulation of his theory have made a great contribution to our understanding of biochemical phenomena which were difficult to understand otherwise. His theory has helped to describe the important role of proteins as cellular constituents, aside from their more specific action as enzymes. It explains how the cell finds it possible to maintain a difference in concentration of diffusible ions across a membrane; how by this mechanism water may be made to flow into or out of a cell; and even how an electric potential is created across a membrane.

Assume a membrane permeable to inorganic ions but impermeable to protein ions. Place inside of this membrane (1) a solution of a protein (in the form of its chloride) together with a definite quantity of HCl. On the outside of the membrane place an equal quantity of HCl (2). The situation at the beginning of the experiment will be:

$$
\begin{array}{c|c}
\begin{aligned}
H^+ &= y \\
Pr^+ &= x \\
Cl^- &= x + y
\end{aligned}
&
\begin{aligned}
H^+ &= y \\
Cl^- &= y
\end{aligned}
\\
\hline
\text{M}
\end{array}
$$

$$\qquad (1) \qquad\qquad (2)$$

There will now be a movement of H^+ and Cl^- so that at equilibrium n moles of HCl will have been moved from (1) to (2) and the concentration of the various ions will now be:

$$
\begin{array}{c|c}
\begin{aligned}
H^+ &= y - n \\
Pr^+ &= x \\
Cl^- &= x + y - n
\end{aligned}
&
\begin{aligned}
H^+ &= y + n \\
Cl^- &= y + n
\end{aligned}
\\
\hline
\text{M}
\end{array}
$$

$$\qquad (1) \qquad\qquad (2)$$

The free energy required to transfer one mole of H^+ from (2) to (1) reversibly at constant temperature and pressure is:

$$\Delta F = RT \ln \frac{[H^+]_1}{[H^+]_2}$$

where R is the gas constant, T is the temperature, and the concentration of ions is denoted by brackets. In the same way for the movement of the Cl^- ion:

$$\Delta F = RT \ln \frac{[Cl^-]_1}{[Cl^-]_2}$$

By definition, at equilibrium the total change in free energy is zero; so that

$$RT \ln \frac{[H^+]_1}{[H^+]_2} + RT \ln \frac{[Cl^-]_1}{[Cl^-]_2} = 0$$

Therefore $\qquad \dfrac{[H^+]_2}{[H^+]_1} = \dfrac{[Cl^-]_1}{[Cl^-]_2} \qquad$ or $\qquad [H^+]_2[Cl^-]_2 = [H^+]_1[Cl^-]_1$

Since $\qquad [Cl^-]_2 = [H^+]_2 \qquad$ and $\qquad [H^+]_1 + [Pr^+]_1 = [Cl^-]_1$

we get

$$[H^+]_2[H^+]_2 = [H^+]_1[[H^+]_1 + [Pt^+]_1] \qquad \text{or} \qquad [H^+]_1^2 + [H^+]_1[Pr^+]_1 = [H^+]_2^2$$

and $\qquad\qquad [Cl^-]_1^2 - [Cl^-]_1[Pr^+]_1 = [Cl^-]_2^2$

from which it follows that, at equilibrium,

$$[H^+]_1 \text{ is less than } [H^+]_2 \quad \text{and} \quad [Cl^-]_1 \text{ is greater than } [Cl^-]_2$$

PROTEIN STRUCTURE

a. Chemical Methods. Much progress has been made in elucidating the exact amino acid sequence in several proteins. This is true of the proteins insulin and ribonuclease, and of the polypeptides of the posterior lobe of the pituitary (p. 69).

One of the pioneers in this field is Sanger, of Cambridge, England, who has given us a complete picture of the sequence of amino acids in insulin. This protein consists of 16 different amino acids, in the form of aggregates of a basic unit with a molecular weight of 6000. In water and at neutral pH, insulin exists as a dimer, with a molecular weight of 12,000, which some investigators believe to be the hormone itself. Using the "end-group method" of analysis (p. 84), Sanger showed that there were present one mole of glycine and one mole of phenylalanine per mole of the unit with a molecular weight of 6000; and that these amino acids were situated at the N-terminal end of the polypeptide chains. This meant that there were two such chains in the molecule: a glycyl chain and a phenylalanyl chain.

By the action of performic acid, Sanger split apart these two chains, and at the same time oxidized disulfide bonds—an indication that these bonds held together (by cross linkage) the two original chains. One chain that had been split—fraction A—had a molecular weight of 2900 (20 amino acid residues), and the other—fraction B—had a molecular weight of 3800 (30 amino acid residues).

Sanger next determined the C-terminal amino acids by subjecting the peptides to the action of the enzyme carboxypeptidase (an enzyme which hydrolyzes the amino acid peptide linkage at the C-terminal end of the chain). He isolated alanine as a constituent of the phenylalanine chain and asparagine (aspartic acid amide) as a constituent of the phenylalanyl chain.

The chains were subjected to partial hydrolysis, the peptides were separated and the sequence of their amino acids determined. Partial hydrolysis of the original protein gave Sanger residues in which the disulfide linkages were intact, and this enabled him to identify their positions.

Figure 20 shows the formula for beef insulin, the first such formula of a protein ever written.

It is of interest from the point of view of comparative biochemistry to note that the sequence alanine-serine-valine in the "A" chain of beef insulin is replaced by threonine-serine-leucine in swine insulin, alanine-glycine-valine in sheep insulin, threonine-glycine-isoleucine in horse insulin, threonine-serine-isoleucine in whale insulin.

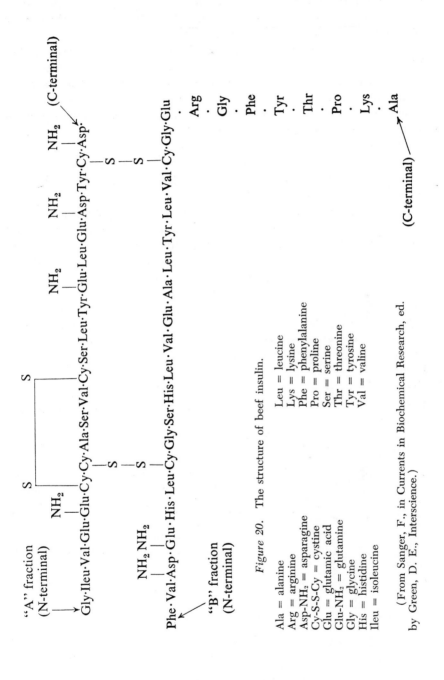

Figure 20. The structure of beef insulin.

Ala = alanine
Arg = arginine
Asp-NH₂ = asparagine
Cy-S-S-Cy = cystine
Glu = glutamic acid
Glu-NH₂ = glutamine
Gly = glycine
His = histidine
Ileu = isoleucine

Leu = leucine
Lys = lysine
Phe = phenylalanine
Pro = proline
Ser = serine
Thr = threonine
Tyr = tyrosine
Val = valine

(From Sanger, F., in Currents in Biochemical Research, ed. by Green, D. E., Interscience.)

b. Physical Methods. These include x-ray diffraction, infrared spectrophotometry and electron microscopy. As a result, some theories of protein structure have been postulated.

One class of fibrous proteins, the keratin-myosin-fibrinogen group, gives an x-ray diffraction pattern which closely resembles unstretched mammalian hair (α-keratin). When soaked in hot water or in dilute alkali the α-keratin can be stretched to yield the β-keratin. When released the β-keratin returns to the α-keratin. (Some natural proteins occur in the "stretched" form; for example, silk fibroin and feather keratin.)

The second class of fibrous proteins—the collagen group—do not stretch at all but contract when treated with hot water. The diffraction pattern here is different from that of the first group.

The question of the orientation in space of the polypeptide chains in proteins has been widely discussed in recent years. One theory which has received much attention and which appears to satisfy the experimental data to a great extent is that proposed by Pauling and Corey,

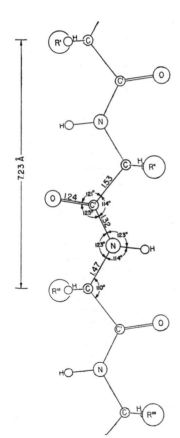

Figure 21. Fully extended *trans* polypeptide chain configuration with chain residue bond lengths and bond angles. (From Corey, R. B., and Pauling, L.: Proc. Roy. Soc. [London], s. B., *141*:10, 1953.)

often referred to as the *helix theory*. The polypeptide chain, on the basis of physical measurements, must have certain dimensions and bond angles. Figure 21 illustrates such a fully extended polypeptide chain with correct bond lengths and angles. The arrangement in space of the polypeptide chain, as proposed by these researchers, is that of a spiral form, made by the polypeptide chain as if it were being wound about a regular cylinder, yielding the helical configuration. This form appears to satisfy the many requirements laid down for such chains, including a maximum of opportunity for hydrogen bonding. This is illustrated in Figure 22. It is presumed that several such helical polypeptide chains may become associated to give a cable effect, such chains held together by cross linking via disulfide bonds (Fig. 23).

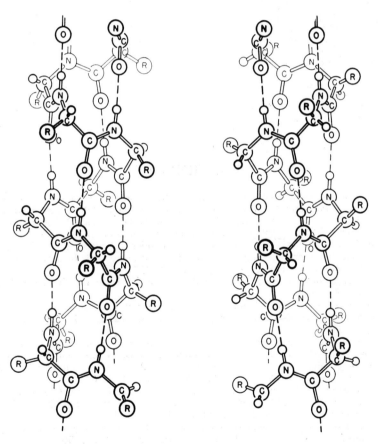

Figure 22. Drawings of the left-handed and right-handed α-helices. The R and H groups on the α-carbon atom arise in the correct position corresponding to the known configuration of the L-amino acids in proteins. (By Pauling, L., and Corey, R. B., from Low, B. W., and Edsall, J. T.: Aspects of Protein Structure, in Currents in Biochemical Research, edited by Green, D. E., New York, Interscience Publishers, Inc.)

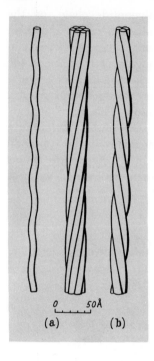

Figure 23. The compound a-helix strands giving (a) the AB₆-cable and (b) the D₃-rope. (From Springall, H. D.: The Structural Chemistry of Proteins, 1954. Published by Academic Press, Inc.)

REFERENCES

A standard work is by *Neurath* and *Bailey:* The Proteins. Two volumes, 1953–1954. *Anson, Bailey* and *Edsall* are the editors of a series of volumes on Advances in Protein Chemistry (Vol. 11, 1956). See also *Perlmann* and *Diringer:* Ann. Rev. Biochem. *29:*151, 1960; *Hill, Kimmel* and *Smith:* Ibid., *28:*97, 1959; *Schwyzer:* Ibid., *29:*183, 1960 (amino acids and peptides); *Edman:* Ibid., *28:*69, 1959 (amino acids and peptides); *Haurowitz:* Chemistry and Biology of Proteins, 1950; and Federation Proceedings, *16:*774, 1957.

Bull: Physical Biochemistry, 1951, should be consulted for details concerning the physical chemistry of proteins.

For nomenclature of natural amino acids and related substances, see Chem. Eng. News, *30:*4522, 1952; *Vickery:* J. Biol. Chem., *169:*237, 1947; Science, *113:* 324, 1951.

Methods of preparing alanine and serine are given in Biochemical Preparations, Vol. 1, p. 9, 1949. Several other amino acids whose preparation is described in these volumes include aspartic acid (Vol. 2, p. 71); glutamic acid (Vol. 2, p. 69); glutamine (Vol. 1, p. 44); lysine (Vol. 1, p. 63).

Methods employed in amino acid syntheses are described by *Fugate* in Interchemical Review (Interchem. Corp.), p. 3, spring, 1946. For the synthesis of polypeptides, see Ann. Rev. Biochem., *25:*319, 1956.

Stein, in Essays in Biochemistry, edited by *Graff,* has an illuminating article on determining the chemical structure of proteins (p. 270, 1956).

For the elucidation of the structure of insulin, see *Brown, Sanger* and *Kitai:* Biochem. J., *60:*557, 1955. See also, *Fraenkel-Conrat:* Ann. Rev. Biochem., *25:*308, 1956; *Sanger* in *Green's* Currents in Biochemical Research, 1956, and in Science, *129:*1340, 1959.

For the application of physical methods to the structure of proteins, see *Pauling, Corey* and *Branson:* Proc. Nat. Acad. Sci. U. S., *37:*235, 1951; *Pauling, Corey* and *Hayward:* Scientific American, July, 1954, p. 51; *Springall:* The Structural Chemistry of Proteins, 1954; *Low* and *Edsall,* in Currents in Biochemistry, 1956, edited by *Green;* and Biological Science, a Study Program, 1959, edited by *Oncley.*

For the structure of ribonuclease see *Hirs, Moore,* and *Stein:* J. Biol. Chem., *235:* 633, 1960.

Details regarding paper chromatography may be found in *Block, Durrum* and *Zweig:* Paper Chromatography, 1955.

NUCLEOPROTEINS
AND
NUCLEIC
ACIDS

CHAPTER FIVE

NUCLEOPROTEIN

Working with cell nuclei, Miescher extracted an acidic substance which was soluble in alkali and insoluble in acids; it contained phosphorus in an organically bound form and was comparatively free of protein. This was nucleic acid, a substance with a high molecular weight. Nucleoprotein is nucleic acid bound to a protein.

The protein in nucleoprotein is attached to the nucleic acid by bonds which are sometimes relatively easy to break (neutral salt solutions in the cold) and sometimes require stronger chemical treatment (alkali). The method of preparing a nucleic acid determines its physical properties. Gentle treatment yields material of high molecular weight (six million), showing an intense streaming birefringence and viscosity in solution—properties due to a great extent to the high degree of asymmetry of the molecule. Treatment with alkali leads to a depolymerization with a consequent loss of viscosity and an apparent lower molecular weight.

The name *nucleoproteins* suggests that these substances are found only in the cell nucleus. This is not so; they are to be found in all living cells, ranging from bacteria and single-celled plants to the most highly developed animal cells. Nucleoproteins appear to be the sole chemical constituents of viruses and are found in high concentration in chromosomes located in the nucleus of the cell. In fact, it appears that the genes themselves, the carriers of hereditary characteristics, are nucleo-proteins.

VIRUSES

Viruses are infectious agents (for man, animals, plants, insects and bacteria). Originally, the name was given to the substance which could pass through fine porcelain filters, even though the filters could retain bacteria. What passed through the filter was given the name *filtrable viruses* and proved to be highly infectious substances.

The viruses can perpetuate themselves by reproduction within, and only within, certain specific living cells. They give rise to such diseases as smallpox, yellow fever, poliomyelitis, measles, mumps, influenza, virus pneumonia and the common cold, as well as several mosaic and yellow diseases of plants.

In 1935 the virus causing the tobacco mosaic disease was isolated by Stanley, who showed the substance to be a nucleoprotein containing some 5 per cent of nucleic acid. Since that time a number of other viruses have been purified and crystallized. For example, there is the "bushy stunt" virus, with 17 per cent of nucleic acid, and the "ring spot" virus, with 40 per cent of the acid.

Of interest are the virus molecules which infect bacteria and which are known as bacteriophages. Some of these have striking shapes when viewed under the electron microscope; in one case the "body" and the "tail" can be distinguished. The phage molecules attach themselves to the bacterium and some of the phage material is "injected" into the bacterium, giving rise to the lysis (or disintegration) of the bacterium. Here the duplication of the phage particles takes place within the bacterial cell (p. 376).

Unlike bacteria, viruses cannot be grown in a nutrient solution. They can be grown, however, *in vitro* in tissue culture. They need specific cells as hosts. Tobacco mosaic virus will grow in certain plant cells; yellow fever virus will grow in the cells of man, monkey and the mouse; rabbit papilloma virus will grow in certain cells of rabbits; and so on.

Stanley emphasizes the similarity in properties between viruses and genes. In size[*] and in composition both resemble each other. Both reproduce within certain living cells. Both may undergo mutations, spontaneously or as a result of irradiation, changes which are reproduced in subsequent generations. But so far, unlike viruses, it has not been possible to isolate and study genes *in vitro*.

A chart showing relative sizes of viruses, is given in Figure 24.

---

[*] Viruses range in size from about 10 mμ—slightly smaller than some protein molecules—to about 300 mμ, which is somewhat larger than certain accepted living organisms.

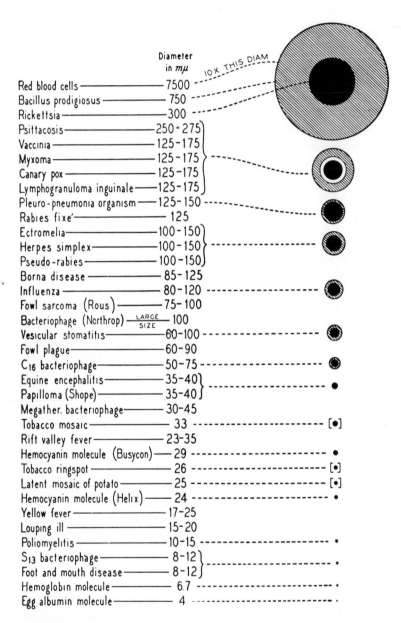

Figure 24. A chart showing the relative sizes of several selected viruses including bacteriophages, as compared with those of the red blood cells, *Bacillus prodigiosus*, rickettsia, pleuropneumonia organism, and protein molecules. (From Stanley: American Naturalist, 72:112.)

NUCLEIC ACIDS

Two types of nucleic acids were at first identified. One type, prepared from yeast and called yeast nucleic acid, gave, on hydrolysis, adenine, guanine, cytosine, uracil, ribose and phosphoric acid. The other, isolated from the thymus gland, yielded, on hydrolysis, adenine, guanine, cytosine, thymine, deoxyribose and phosphoric acid. In addition, small amounts of 5-methyl cytosine were also present. These two types are now called ribonucleic acid, or RNA, and deoxyribonucleic acid, or DNA, respectively. The term pentosenucleic acid (PNA) is also used in place of RNA.

The notion that nucleic acids are confined to the nucleus of the cell gradually gave way when it was discovered that the cytoplasm also contains these substances. By means of the Feulgen test (red color with fuchsin sulfurous acid), a specific test for DNA, it was shown that this substance was present almost exclusively in the cell nucleus, though small amounts of RNA were also present. Most of the RNA is found in the cytoplasm.

The determination of the DNA content of a tissue permits an estimation of the number of cells in that tissue, because the DNA content of the nucleus is generally quite constant. The relative quantities of RNA and DNA present in a cell vary among species; rat liver contains four times as much RNA as DNA, whereas calf thymus presents the reverse picture.

An extensive study of the composition of the nucleic acids isolated from various sources makes it clear that there are many different varieties of DNA and RNA, for the proportion of bases in them varies markedly.

The hydrolytic breakdown of the nucleic acids may be represented thus:

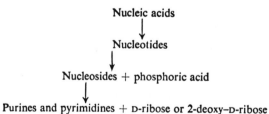

Nucleic acids may be considered to be polynucleotides, each nucleotide consisting of a combination of phosphoric acid, a sugar and a purine or pyrimidine. The nucleoside, then, is the nucleotide minus phosphoric acid.

THE PURINE AND PYRIMIDINE BASES

Aside from the pentoses (D-ribose and the 2-deoxy-D-ribose), the characteristic substances present in nucleic acids are the purine and pyrimidine bases.

The purines are derivatives of the mother substance, *purine:*

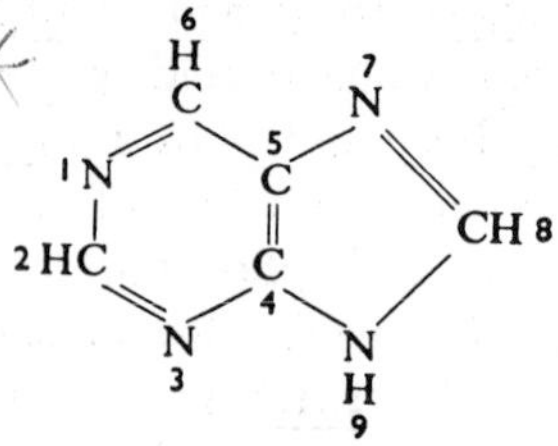

Purine

Two purines, adenine and guanine, are common constituents of nucleic acids:

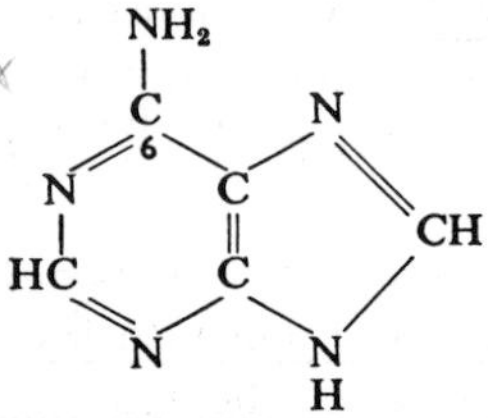

Adenine
(6-Aminopurine)

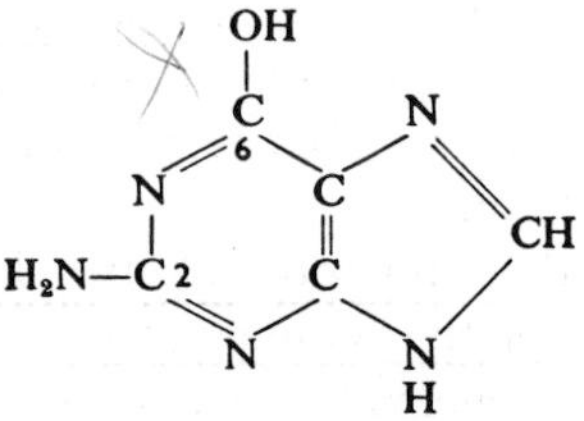

Guanine
(2-Amino-6-oxypurine)

The pyrimidines are derived from *pyrimidine:*

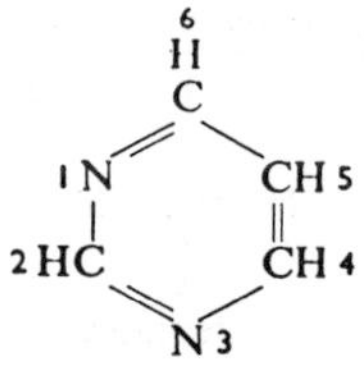

Pyrimidine

The following five pyrimidines have been isolated from nucleic acids:

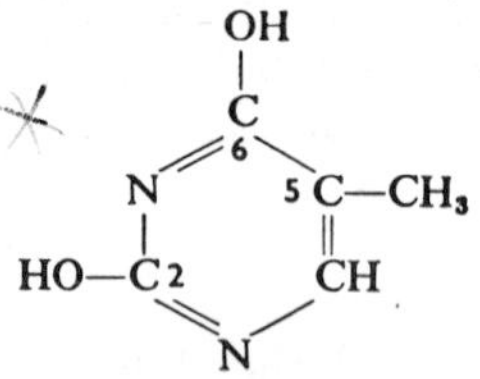

Thymine
(2,6-dihydroxy–5–
methylpyrimidine)

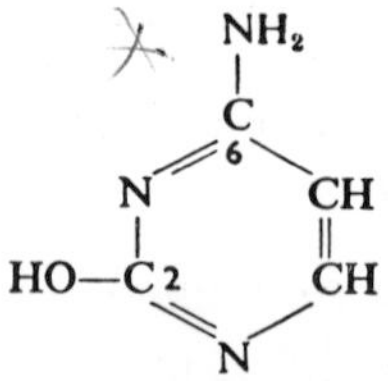

Cytosine
(2-hydroxy–6-amino-
pyrimidine)

Uracil
(2,6-dihydroxypyrimidine)

5-Methylcytosine

5-Hydroxymethylcytosine

Many other purines and pyrimidines are found as products of metabolism; among these are hypoxanthine, xanthine, uric acid, uridine and uracil-4-carboxylic acid, orotic acid.

For identification purposes purines and pyrimidines are often characterized by their ultraviolet absorption spectra and by their dissociation constants. Nucleic acids generally have a maximum ultraviolet ab-

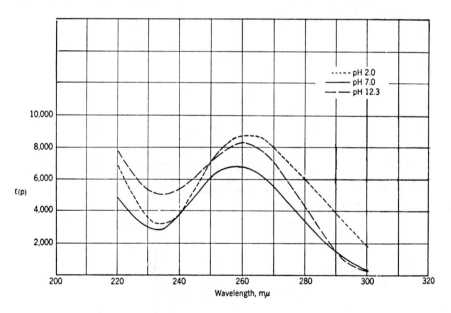

Figure 25. Absorption spectra of calf thymus DNA. (From Shack and Thompsett, in Beaven, G. H., Holiday, E. R., and Johnson, E. A.: The Nucleic Acids, Vol. I, edited by Chargaff, E. and Davidson, J. N., New York, Academic Press, Inc.)

sorption in the region of 260 mμ (which is due to absorption by the bases). This property helps to identify nucleoproteins, nucleic acids and various individual bases (Fig. 25). The dissociation constants of the acidic and basic groups of the purines and pyrimidines are listed below:

DISSOCIATION CONSTANTS OF ACIDIC AND BASIC GROUPS OF PURINES AND PYRIMIDINES

	pK_{a1}	pK_{a2}	
Adenine	4.15	9.80	
Guanine	3.3	9.2	$(pK_{a_2} = 12.3)$
Hypoxanthine	8.8	12.0	
Xanthine	7.53	11.63	
Uric acid	5.4	10.6	
Cytosine	4.60	12.16	
5-Methylcytosine	4.6	12.4	
Uracil	9.5	13	
Thymine	9.5	13	
Orotic acid	2.8	9.45	

NUCLEOSIDES

Nucleosides are ribose derivatives of purine and pyrimidine bases. Several examples are:

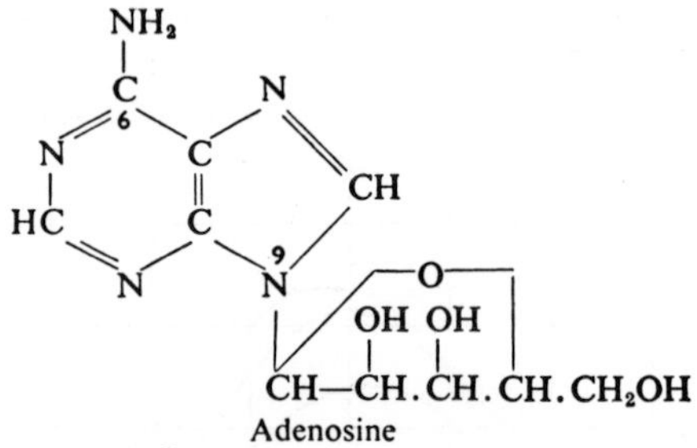

Adenosine
(9-β-D-ribofuranosidoadenine)

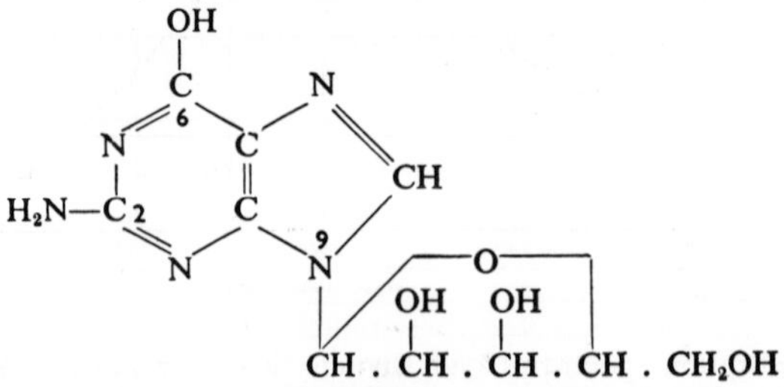

Guanosine
(9-β-D-ribofuranosidoguanine)

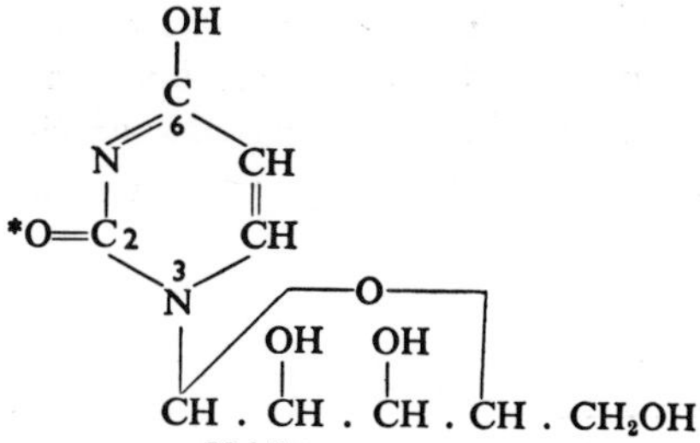

OH
|
C
N⁼⁶ CH
‖
*O=C₂ CH
|₃
N
| OH OH
CH . CH . CH . CH . CH₂OH
Uridine
(3-β-ribofuranosidouracil)

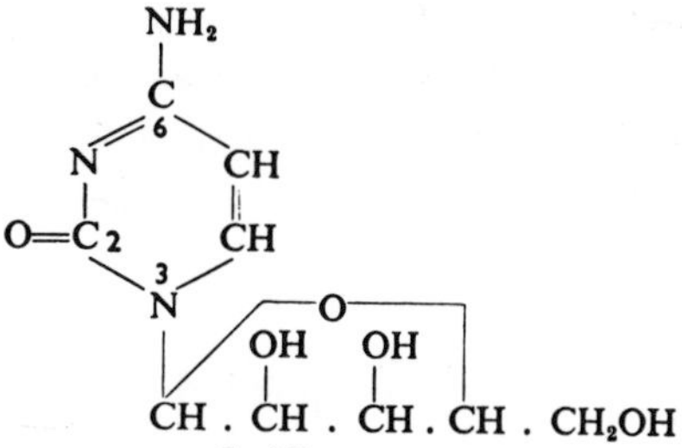

NH₂
|
C
N⁼⁶ CH
‖
O=C₂ CH
|₃
N
| OH OH
CH . CH . CH . CH . CH₂OH
Cytidine
(3-β-D-ribofuranosidocytosine)

By partial hydrolysis of DNA we also get two purine and two pyrimidine derivatives, with differences due to the structure of the sugar:

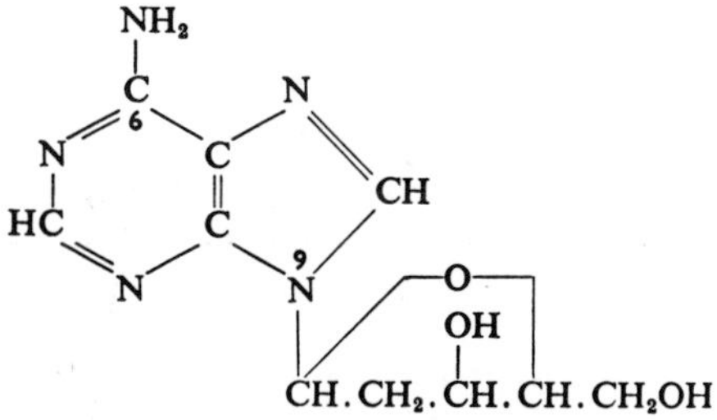

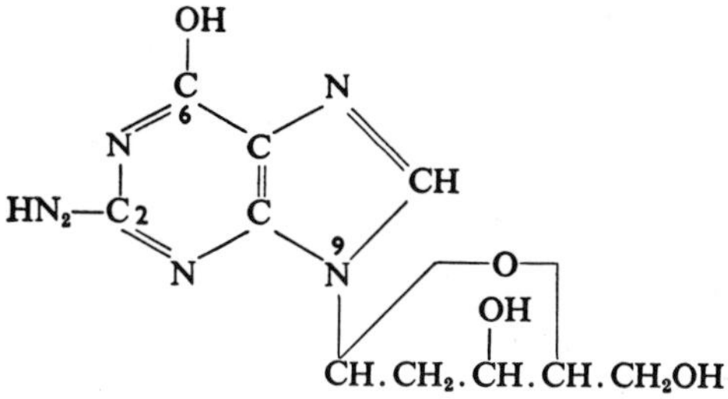

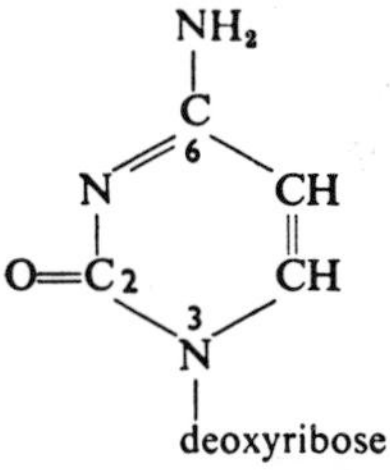

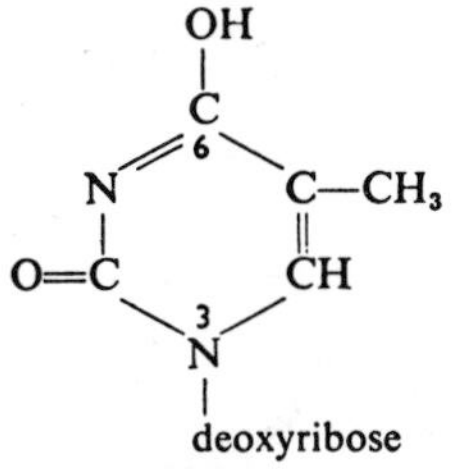

NH₂
|
C
N⁼⁶ C N
HC C ⟩CH
N C N⁹
| OH
CH.CH₂.CH.CH.CH₂OH

OH
|
C
N⁼⁶ C N
HN₂—C₂ C ⟩CH
N N⁹
| OH
CH.CH₂.CH.CH.CH₂OH

NH₂
|
C
N⁼⁶ CH
‖
O=C₂ CH
|₃
N
|
deoxyribose

OH
|
C
N⁼⁶ C—CH₃
‖
O=C CH
|₃
N
|
deoxyribose
Thymidine

* The slight change in structure between the uracil on page 117 and the uracil here is explained by the shifting of an enol to a keto form: —N=C → —N—C—
| | ‖
OH   H   O

The partial hydrolysis of nucleic acids yields, in addition, several other nucleosides, such as inosine (hypoxanthine riboside), xanthosine (xanthine riboside), hypoxanthine deoxyriboside and uracil deoxyriboside.

NUCLEOTIDES

As has been pointed out, the nucleotides are phosphoric esters of nucleosides and can be isolated by employing enzymes for the hydrolysis of nucleic acids (p. 131). Several of these nucleotides will now be shown:

Muscle Adenylic Acid.

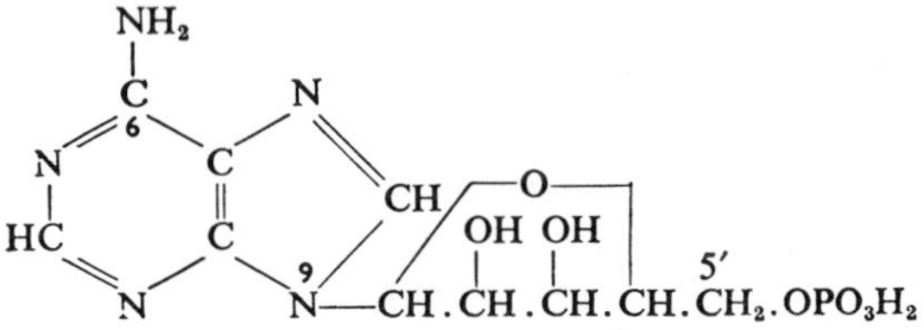

Muscle adenylic acid (AMP)
(adenosine-5'-phosphate)

This substance is known as 9-adenine-5-phosphoribofuranoside and was first isolated from muscle. It is also known as adenosine monophosphate or AMP.

Closely related to muscle adenylic acid are adenosine diphosphate (ADP) and adenosine triphosphate (ATP). These two compounds take part in important metabolic reactions. ATP itself can be isolated directly from muscle.

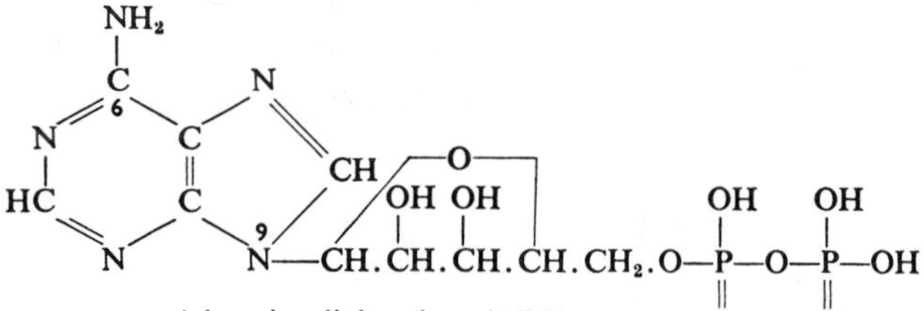

Adenosine diphosphate (ADP)

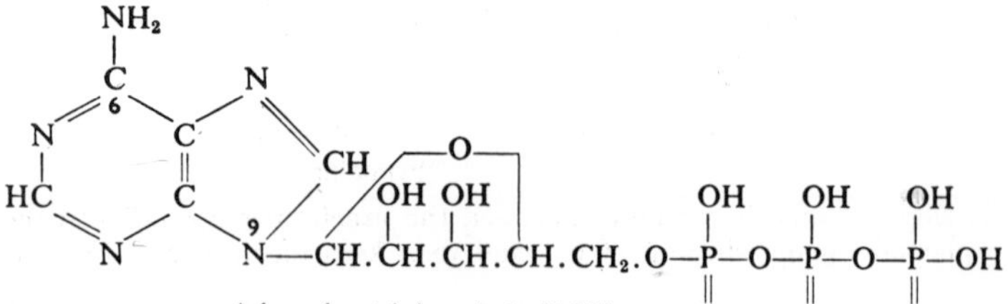

Adenosine triphosphate (ATP)

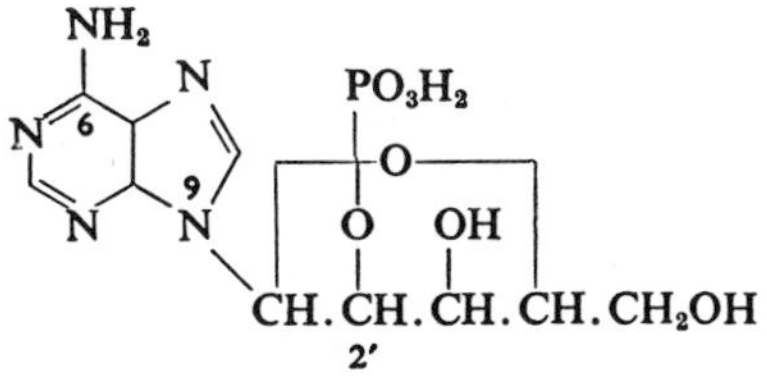

Adenosine-2′-phosphate
(adenylic acid *a*)

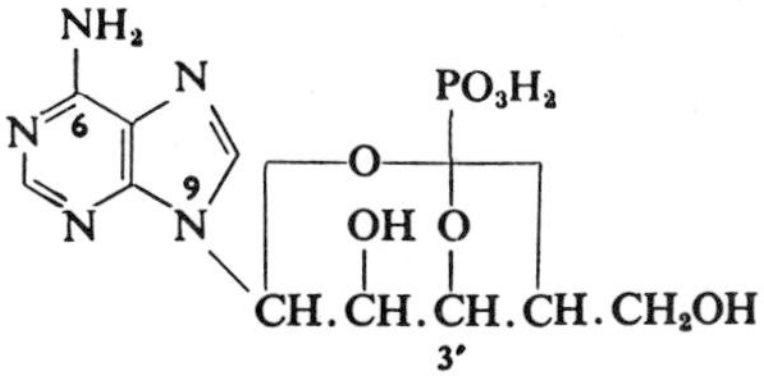

Adenosine-3-phosphate
(adenylic acid *b*)

The last two compounds are the result of alkaline hydrolysis of RNA.

Muscle Inosinic Acid. This nucleotide occupies an important position in the metabolic route of nucleic acid synthesis. It consists of hypoxanthine linked to ribose and phosphoric acid.

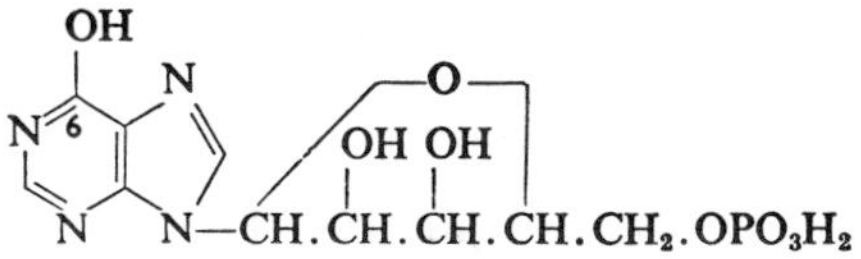

Muscle inosinic acid (IMP)

Pyridine Nucleotides. Diphosphopyridine nucleotide (DPN) and triphosphopyridine nucleotide (TPN) function as coenzymes (p. 263) in biological oxidation reactions.

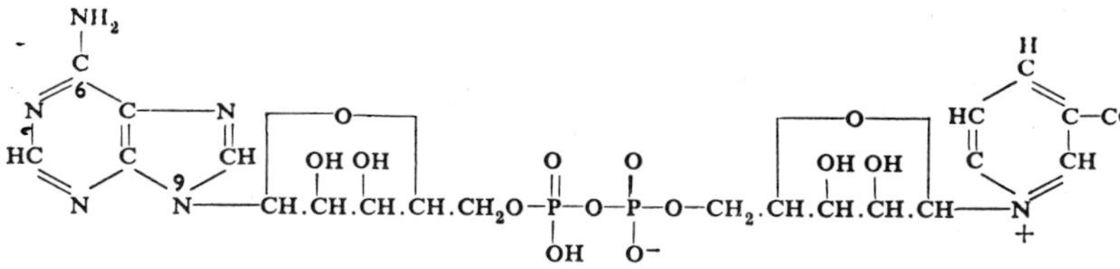

Diphosphopyridine nucleotide (DPN)

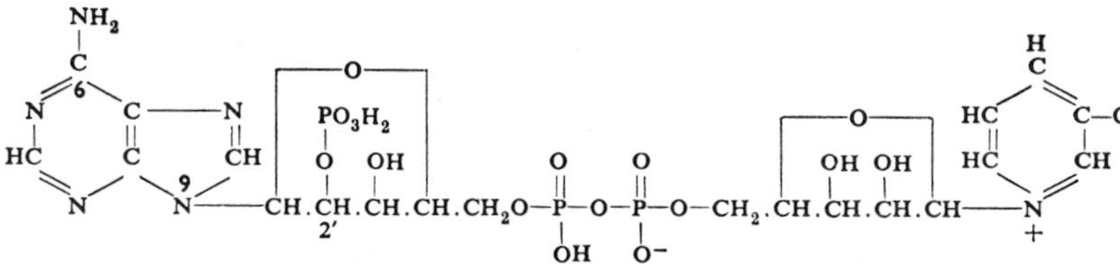

Triphosphopyridine nucleotide (TPN)

Flavin Nucleotides. These too act as coenzymes (p. 263) in biological oxidations. One of them, flavin mononucleotide (FMN), is a combination of isoalloxazine, ribose and phosphoric acid. (Another name for the combination of isoalloxazine and ribose is riboflavin, which is one of a number of B vitamins.)

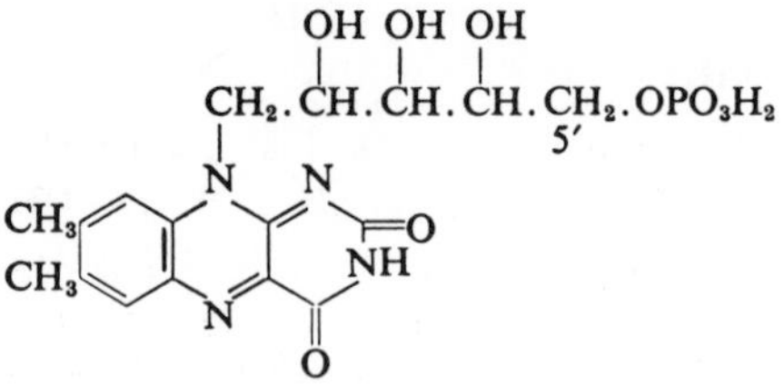

$$\begin{array}{ccc} \text{OH} & \text{OH} & \text{OH} \\ | & | & | \end{array}$$
$$\text{CH}_2.\text{CH}.\text{CH}.\text{CH}.\text{CH}_2.\text{OPO}_3\text{H}_2$$

Flavin mononucleotide (FMN)
(riboflavin-5'-phosphate)

The other flavin nucleotide is flavin adenine dinucleotide (FAD), which contains riboflavin and, in addition, adenine.

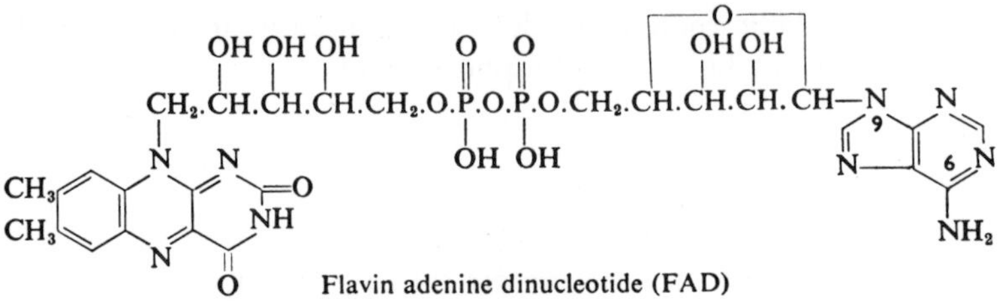

Flavin adenine dinucleotide (FAD)

Coenzyme A. One of the most important of the coenzymes, CoA, is a complex of adenine, ribose, phosphoric acid, pantothenic acid and mercaptoethanolamine.

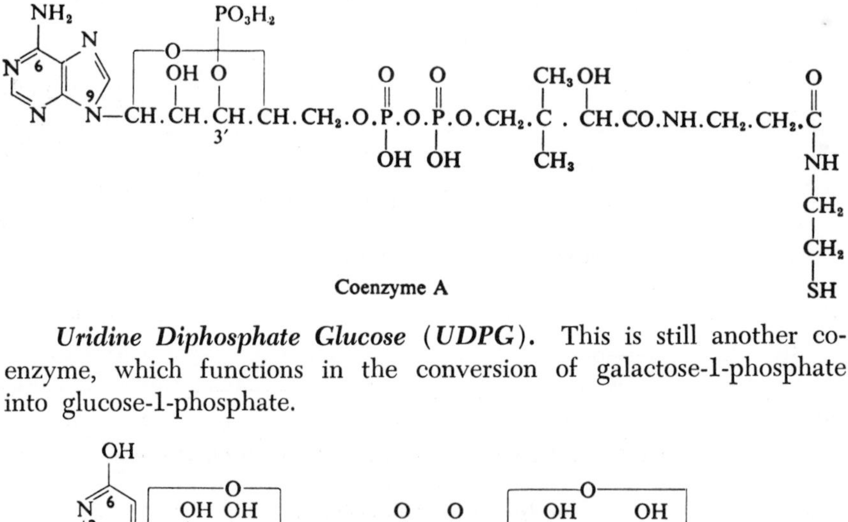

Coenzyme A

Uridine Diphosphate Glucose (UDPG). This is still another co-enzyme, which functions in the conversion of galactose-1-phosphate into glucose-1-phosphate.

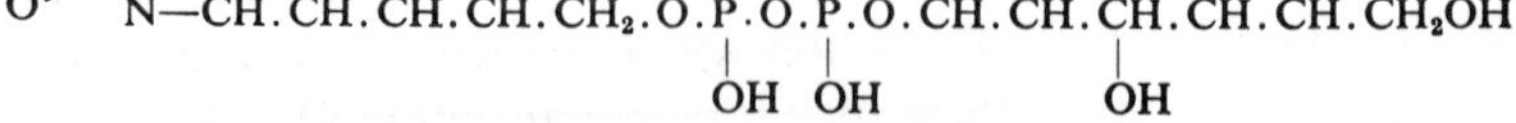

Uridine diphosphate glucose (UDPG)

Uridine triphosphate (UTP) and guanosine triphosphate (GTP) have been isolated from the muscle of the rabbit.

DEOXYRIBONUCLEIC ACIDS (DNA)

The nucleic acid chain is composed of mononucleotides varying in number from 2500 to 15,000. The number of possible isomers becomes extremely large. An enzyme, DNA-ase, splits DNA into smaller but still highly polymerized units, which are sometimes called the polynucleotide "core." The chief connecting links between the mononucleotides are the 3'- and 5'-phosphate bridges; the prime numbers refer to the C atoms of the sugar residue:

$$\begin{array}{ccccc}
\text{base} & & \text{base} & & \text{base} \\
| & O & | & O & | \\
C_{3'}\!\!-\!O\!-\!\overset{\|}{P}\!-\!O\!-\!C_{3'}\!\!-\!O\!-\!\overset{\|}{P}\!-\!O\!-\!C_{3'} & & & & \\
| & | & | & | & | \\
C_{5'} & OH & C_{5'} & OH & C_{5'}
\end{array}$$

RIBONUCLEIC ACIDS (RNA)

Whereas DNA is found largely in the nucleus, RNA is found distributed in both the nucleus and the cytoplasm. The nuclear RNA accounts for about one tenth of the total RNA of the cell. The major portion of the cytoplasmic RNA is part of the "particulate matter," mostly in the microsome fraction, which consists of lipid, protein and RNA.

An enzyme, RNA-ase, splits RNA into smaller polynucleotides.

STRUCTURE OF NUCLEIC ACIDS

With the development of improved methods of analysis, especially that of chromatography, it became clear that nucleic acids did not contain equimolar quantities of each of the nitrogenous bases adenine, thymine, guanine and cytosine (tetranucleotide theory). Instead, there existed another relationship among these bases: (1) the sum of the purine bases is generally equal to the sum of the pyrimidine bases; and (2) the molar ratios of adenine:thymine and of guanine:cytosine + 5-methyl cytosine are equal to unity. These facts suggest the existence of a "pairing" of specific bases, with the result that the total 6-NH_2 groups are equal to the total 6-keto groups. These relationships are illustrated in Table 16 and Figure 26.

Two principal groups of deoxypentose nucleic acids appear, namely the AT type, in which adenine and thymine predominate, and the GC type, in which guanine and cytosine are the major constituents. All preparations from animal sources belong to the AT type, whereas the GC type is encountered among microorganisms and in some insect viruses. As can be seen in Table 16, the ratio of adenine + thymine to guanine + cytosine is greater than one in nucleic acids of the AT type and less than one in those of the GC type. An intermediate group, with a ratio of one, is illustrated among the E. coli.

TABLE **16.** SELECTED DATA ON PURINE AND PYRIMIDINE CONTENT OF SODIUM DEOXYPENTOSE NUCLEATE PREPARATIONS FROM BOVINE TISSUES AND BACTERIA

	Liver	Pancreas	Kidney	E. coli (K12)	Mb. tuber- culosis (avian)
Adenine	28.8	27.8	28.3	26.0	15.1
Guanine	21.0	21.9	22.6	24.9	34.9
Cytosine	21.1	21.7	20.9	25.2	35.4
Thymine	29.0	28.5	28.2	23.9	14.6
Total purine	49.8	49.7	50.9	50.9	49.9
Total pyrimidine	50.1	50.2	50.1	49.1	50.0
$\dfrac{\text{Adenine}}{\text{Thymine}}$	0.99	0.98	1.00	1.09	0.94
$\dfrac{\text{Guanine}}{\text{Cytosine}}$	1.00	1.01	1.08	0.99	0.99
$\dfrac{\text{Adenine} + \text{thymine}}{\text{Guanine} + \text{cytosine}}$	1.37	1.29	1.30	1.00	0.42

Values are expressed as moles of nitrogenous constituent per 100 g.-atoms of phosphorus in hydrolysate. (Compiled from Chargaff and Davidson: The Nucleic Acids, Vol. I, Academic Press, N.Y., 1955.)

The composition of RNA isolated from animal, yeast and bacteria also shows certain regularities. Both yeast RNA and cytoplasm of animal cells contain purine and pyrimidine nucleotides in nearly equimolar quantities. In animal RNA, guanylic acid and cytidylic acid predominate, while in yeast RNA, the four nucleotides are present in nearly equimolar concentrations.

In addition to the four nitrogenous bases listed above, at least two others occur naturally. These are 5-methyl cytosine, which substitutes for part of the cytosine (as in DNA isolated from wheat germ), and 5-hydroxymethyl cytosine, which replaces cytosine entirely in certain bacteriophages. In certain circumstances the synthetic compounds, 5-bromouracil or 5-iodouracil, will take the place of thymine.

Based on the regularities of purine and pyrimidine content, illustrated above, and on x-ray analyses by Wilkins, Watson and Crick postulated a molecular structure for DNA which involves a helical dyad, a double-stranded helix. The two strands are held together by hydrogen bonding between specific base pairs, which show the unity relationships mentioned above. This is demonstrated in Figure 26. The accuracy of this elegant hypothesis is supported by the synthesis of DNA by Kornberg.

The double-stranded DNA may be separated into single strands by denaturing DNA at 100° C. On slow cooling, the strands recombine to form a helix of "renatured" DNA. If the denatured material is cooled quickly, the single strands fail to combine and remain undamaged. In

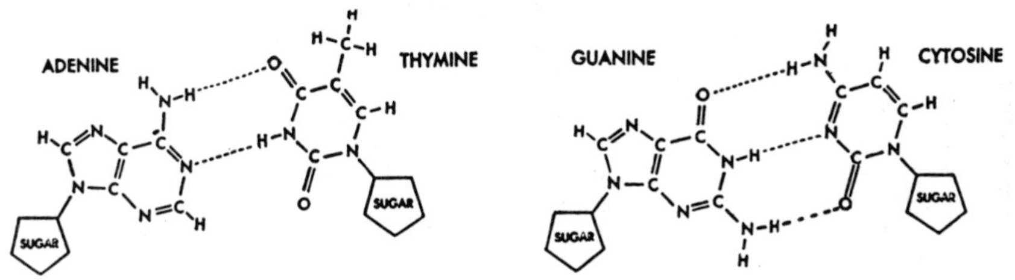

Figure 26. Hydrogen bonding of bases. (From A. Kornberg: Science *131*:1503, 1960.)

this way, hybrid DNA molecules have been prepared, using single-stranded DNA from two different strains of bacteria, or from two different bacterial species. The biological activity of the "renatured" DNA remains intact.

A mixture of DNA was prepared from a wild strain of *Diplococcus pneumoniae,* which has no resistance to the antibiotic streptomycin, and from a strain of the organism which had become resistant to streptomycin. This mixture was denatured and then "renatured." The wild culture incorporated the resulting hybrid DNA bringing about a resistance to streptomycin. This process is called *bacterial transformation.* It is suggested, therefore, that the genetic information in DNA is carried independently by each strand.

USE OF ION-EXCHANGE RESINS FOR SEPARATION OF NUCLEIC ACID CONSTITUENTS

The use of ion-exchange materials for the separation of dissolved solutes in solution dates from the use of zeolites (clays) for the removal of Ca^{++} and Mg^{++} from "hard" water, thus converting it to "soft" water, useful for washing or for hot water boilers. With the manufacture of synthetic resins and an understanding of their structure and properties, a wide variety of ion-exchange compounds of this variety became available.

Although a complete discussion of the theory and practice of ion-exchange chromatography is outside the scope of this book, a few simple principles and illustrations of their use in separating nucleic acid constituents will be of help in understanding their application. Ion-exchange resins can be divided into the anionic and cationic exchangers. For example, Dowex-50, containing the strong sulfonic acid grouping, and Amberlite-IRC-50, containing a weak carboxylic acid grouping, are among the cationic exchangers. On the other hand, Dowex-1 or Amberlite-IRA-400 are anionic exchangers containing the strongly basic quaternary ammonium groups.

Illustrating their application, Figure 27 shows the use of Dowex-50

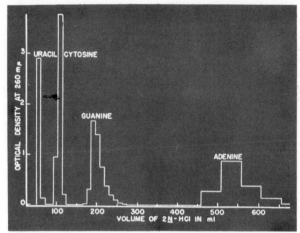

Figure 27. Separation of purine and pyrimidine bases by cation exchange in an acid system.

Exchanger: Dowex-50-H⁺, ca. 300 mesh, 8.1 cm. × 0.74 cm.

Solution: 2 normal HCl, 0.6 ml./min.

Sorbed material: 0.5–1.0 mg. of each base in 7.5 ml. 2 normal HCl. (Larger volumes of more dilute acid may be used.)

(From Cohn: The Nucleic Acids, Vol. I, edited by Chargaff and Davidson.)

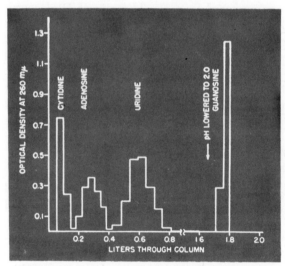

Figure 28. Separation of ribonucleosides by anion exchange in a chloride system with borate present.

Exchanger: Dowex-1-chloride, 200–400 mesh, 11 cm. × 0.85 cm.

Solution. 0.03 M KCL + 0.02 M $K_2B_4O_7$.

Sorbed material: ca. 2 mg. of each nucleoside in 10 ml. 0.01 molar $K_2B_4O_7$.

(From Cohn: The Nucleic Acids, Vol. I, edited by Chargaff and Davidson.)

to separate purine and pyrimidine bases from a mixture. The resin is placed as a wet slurry into a narrow and long column and washed with hydrochloric acid solution, never allowing air bubbles to enter the resin column. This treatment converts the resin to the H⁺ cycle. We might write its general formula as $R.SO_3^-H^+$. The mixture of bases is now poured onto the column and allowed to move slowly down the column by continuously adding HCl to it, and the effluent is collected in definite aliquots in separate containers. Portions of these solutions are now analyzed by determining their optical density at a wave length of 260 mμ, the region of maximum absorption of these compounds. Figure 27 shows a plot of the results, and by running suitable controls, using authentic specimens of these compounds under identical conditions, the position of each of these compounds can be identified. The results are similar to those obtained with amino acid mixtures (see p. 83). In acid solution the amino groups of guanine, adenine and cytosine are cationic, with pK values which increase in that order. Uracil has no amino group and is not adsorbed to an appreciable degree by this resin. Thus the order of elution is uracil (least cationic), followed by cytosine, guanine and adenine, in order of decreasing pK values.

Figure 28 shows the use of an anionic exchanger, Dowex-1, as the chloride ($R'.NR_3^+Cl^-$) for the separation of the ribonucleosides.

REFERENCES

For a general review of the nucleic acids, see *Chargaff* and *Davidson:* The Nucleic Acids. 2 vols., 1955. A well written introductory volume is by *Davidson:* The Biochemistry of the Nucleic Acids, 1950. Recent reviews are by *Dekker:* Ann. Rev. Biochem., 29:453, 1960; *Hartman* and *Buchanan:* Ibid., 28:365, 1959.

See also *Pauling* and *Corey:* Proc. Nat. Acad. Sci. U. S., 39:84, 1953; *Grunberg-Manago, Ortiz* and *Ochoa:* Science, 122:907, 1955 (Enzymic Synthesis of Nucleic Acid-Like Polynucleotides).

The relationship of the genes and nucleoproteins is brought out in the articles by *Mirsky:* Scientific American, Feb. 1953, p. 47; *Beadle:* Ibid., Sept., 1948, p. 30; *Beadle:* Cold Spring Harbor Symposia, 16:143, 1951; *Zamenhoff:* in Essays in Biochemistry (edited by Graff), p. 322, 1956.

For the structure of nucleic acid, see *Crick:* Scientific American, Sept., 1957; *Watson* and *Crick:* Nature, 171:737, 1953.

For nucleoproteins and viruses see *Smith* and *Lauffer:* Advances in Virus Research, Vol. 3, 1955; *Kozloff:* Ann. Rev. Biochem., 29:475, 1960. See also *Franklin:* Nature, 175:379, 1955 (Structure of Tobacco Mosaic Virus); *Fraenkel-Conrat* and *Williams:* Proc. Nat. Acad. Sci. U. S., 41:690, 1955 (Reconstitution of Active Tobacco Mosaic Virus for Its Inactive Protein and Nucleic Acid Components); *Cooper* and *Loring:* J. Biol. Chem., 211:505, 1954 (Purine and Pyrimidine Composition of Tobacco Mosaic Virus); *Pollard:* Scientific American, Dec., 1954, p. 63 (The Physics of Viruses); *Lwoff:* Ibid., March, 1954, p. 33 (The Life Cycle of a Virus); *Siegel* and *Wildman:* Ann. Rev. Plant Physiol., 11:277, 1960 (tobacco mosaic virus).

Bacteriophages (bacterial viruses) are described by *Price:* Scientific Monthly, 67:124, 1948; and by *Evans,* in *Graff's* Essays in Biochemistry, p. 94, 1956.

As examples of methods of preparation, see Biochemical Preparations, Vol. 1, pp. 1, 5, 1949 (Adenosine Diphosphate; Adenosine Triphosphate).

An excellent book on chromosomes, genes, etc., is by *Dunn* and *Dobzhansky:* Heredity, Race and Society, 1946.

See also *Stanley:* Federation Proceedings, 15:812, 1956 (Virus Composition and Structure); *Horowitz:* Ibid., 15:818 (Chemical Concepts of Genetic Phenomena); *Brown:* Ibid., 15:823 (Chemical Pathways of Nucleic Acid Biosynthesis); *Evans:* Ibid., 15:827 Bacteriophage as Nucleoprotein); *Ochoa:* Ibid., 15:832 (Enzymic Synthesis of Ribonucleic Acid-Like Polynucleotides); *Moore, Hirs* and *Stein:* Ibid., 15:840 (Structure of Ribonuclease).

Further interesting articles and reviews are by *Overend* and *Peacocke:* Endeavour (Imperial Chem. Industries), 16:90, 1957 (The Molecular Basis of Heredity); *Darlington:* The Listener (England), March 14, 1957, p. 419 (On Being Descended from a Molecule); Ibid., March 21, 1957, p. 473 (gene and virus); *Gale:* Ibid., Feb. 28, 1957, p. 344 (The Problem of Protein Synthesis); *Todd:* Chemistry and Industry, 1956, p. 802 (Phosphates in Vital Processes); *Fraenkel-Conrat:* Federation Proceedings, 16:810, 1957 (Degradation and Structure of Tobacco Mosaic Virus); *Glass* (editor): The Chemical Basis of Heredity, 1956.

ENZYMES

Enzymes are catalysts produced as a result of cellular activity "but in-dependent of the presence of living cells in their operation" (Wald-schmidt-Leitz). The first use of the name "enzyme" (from the Greek, "in leaven"; "in yeast") was associated with the discovery of fermentation.

THE ACTION OF CATALYSTS ON EQUILIBRIUM REACTIONS

A chemical reaction which is reversible will attain a state of equilib-rium when the velocity of the forward reaction is equal to the velocity of the reverse reaction. The factors which influence the equilibrium state are temperature, pressure (when gases are present), concentration of the reacting substances and the presence of a catalyst. The catalyst speeds up both the forward and backward reactions and thus allows the system to attain a state of equilibrium in a shorter time. A catalyst will not make a reaction proceed unless that reaction can proceed of its own accord, no matter how slowly. As an example, ethyl acetate in water will hydrolyze very slowly to produce acetic acid and ethyl alcohol. The reverse reaction will also take place, but at a slow rate. However, the addition of acid speeds up both reactions and the equilibrium is achieved in a short time.

It should be stressed that at equilibrium the concentrations of the various compounds are not necessarily equal. The equilibrium may be entirely in favor of the reacting substances or of the products of the reaction.

Enzymes are catalysts which are proteins. They act on biochemically important substances. Figure 29 shows an example of the catalysis by hog pancreatic lipase of the hydrolysis of n-butyl butyrate. At equilib-rium, approached from either side, the composition is the same for the final reaction mixture. For the synthetic reaction one would start with butyl alcohol and butyric acid; for hydrolysis, with butyl butyrate.

Here one essential difference must be stressed: inorganic catalysts,

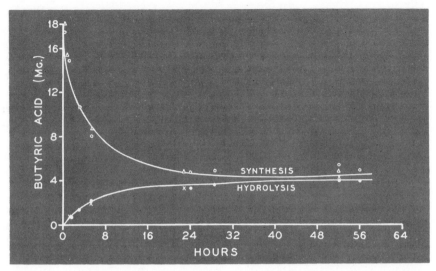

Figure 29. Synthesis and hydrolysis of *n*-butyl-*n*-butyrate by hog pancreatic lipase. (Adapted from Rona and Ammon: Biochem. Z., 249:446, 1932.)

like platinum, catalyze many chemical reactions; enzymes are extremely specific.

It is well known that most chemical reactions do not proceed entirely in one direction. Several reactions of the substrate (compound acted upon by the enzyme) are possible, depending upon the nature of the enzyme. Because of its specificity, the enzyme catalyzes only one of these reactions. For example, glucose-6-phosphate can yield (*a*) glucose + phosphate, (*b*) phosphogluconic acid, or (*c*) fructose-6-phosphate. The product formed will depend upon the enzyme used.

CHEMICAL NATURE OF ENZYMES

Pasteur believed that the fermentation reaction required the presence of living organisms (yeast cells). He showed that killing the organisms by heat (pasteurization), followed by subsequent incubation under sterile conditions, prevented the fermentation reaction. He was only partly correct in his interpretation. Buchner ground the yeast cells and extracted a clear solution which allowed the fermentation reaction to proceed even in the absence of live organisms. The mixture of enzymes in this extract was called *zymase*. Pasteur had not only killed the yeast cell but in doing so he had also denatured and inactivated the enzymes involved in fermentation.

The chemical properties of enzymes, as well as their stability and solubility characteristics, are closely related to those of proteins. As more and more enzymes have been isolated in a crystalline form and have proved to be single components (by a variety of tests), it has become more certain that enzymes are indeed proteins. So far, no enzyme has been isolated which is not a protein. It is also true, however, that, in many instances, for an enzyme to be active, some cofactor of a nonprotein nature is required. Thus inorganic ions such as Ca^{++}, Mg^{++}, or Mn^{++} may be necessary, or organic compounds may be attached to the enzyme protein ("prosthetic groups"). The enzyme amino acid oxidase, for example, requires for its prosthetic group the compound flavin adenine dinucleotide (p. 122). The enzyme (protein) without its prosthetic group is referred to as the "apoenzyme."

CLASSIFICATION OF ENZYMES

As in the case of proteins, classification of enzymes can be made on the basis of several criteria. In the following classification we shall emphasize, first, the kind of chemical reaction catalyzed by the enzymes, and second, a description of a number of enzymes belonging to those grouped according to their catalytic actions. Sumner and Somers classify enzymes as follows:

I. Addition or removal of water
  A. Hydrolases
  B. Hydrases
II. Transfer of electrons
  A. Oxidases
  B. Dehydrogenases
III. Transfer of a radical
  A. Transglycosidase (of a monosaccharide)
  B. Transphosphorylases and phosphomutases (of a phosphate group)
  C. Transaminase (of an amino group)
  D. Transmethylase (of a methyl group)
  E. Transacetylase (of an acetyl group)
IV. Splitting or forming a C—C bond
  A. Desmolases

In the following outline we shall list some of the most important enzymes which belong to the above classes:

ENZYMES INVOLVED IN THE ADDITION OR REMOVAL OF WATER

I. Hydrolases
  A. Esterases
    1. Acetylcholinesterase: Catalyzes the hydrolysis of acetylcholine to acetic acid and choline. (It is important in the transmission of nerve impulses.)
    2. Cholesterol esterases: Hydrolyze fatty acid esters of cholesterol.
    3. Phospholipases: Lecithinase, phosphatidases.

4. Lipases: Such as pancreatic lipase, which splits a neutral fat into glycerol and fatty acid.

5. Sulfatases: Phenolsulfatase and glucosulfatase, for example, hydrolyze sulfuric acid esters.

6. Phosphatases: Representing a large group of enzymes, such as phosphomonoesterases, phosphodiesterases, pyrophosphatases, metaphosphatases, adenosinetriphosphatase (ATP-ase), glycerophosphatase.

B. Carbohydrases

1. Glucosidase: Such as α-glucosidase, maltase, and β-glucosidase.

2. Galactosidase: Such as β-galactosidase, which is also called lactase.

3. Glucuronidase: Splits glucuronides of many compounds.

4. Fructosidase: Also called invertase.

5. Amylases: Also called diastase.

6. Amylo-1,6-glucosidase: See page 34.

7. Cellulase: Present in seeds, bacteria, molds and certain invertebrates, and hydrolyzes cellulose to cellobiose (β-D-glucoside-D-glucose).

8. Hyaluronidase: Hydrolyzes hyaluronic acid to oligosaccharides and some 3-β-D-glucurono-N-acetyl-D-glucosamine.

9. Lysozyme: Present in egg white, tears, nasal mucosa and spleen, and hydrolyzes mucopolysaccharides of the bacterial cell wall.

C. Nucleases

1. Depolymerizing enzymes: Responsible for the depolymerization of the high molecular weight nucleic acids, such as ribonuclease and deoxyribonuclease.

2. Nucleotidases, nucleophosphatases: Split mononucleotides into phosphoric acid and nucleosides.

3. Nucleosidases: Split nucleosides into purine or pyrimidine bases and a pentose sugar.

D. Nuclein Deaminases: Examples are adenase, which converts adenine to hypoxanthine; and adenosine deaminase, which converts adenosine to hypoxanthine riboside (inosine).

E. Amidases: Examples are arginase which converts arginine to urea and ornithine (p. 77); urease which converts urea to ammonia and CO_2.

F. Proteolytic Enzymes: These may be further classified according to Bergmann:

1. Endopeptidases: Act on large protein molecules, although small synthetic molecules are hydrolyzed. Examples are:

a. Pepsin: Present in the gastric mucosa in the form of the inactive precursor pepsinogen. The conversion from enzymatically inactive to active pepsin is caused by the action of acid. The conversion is accompanied by the splitting off of peptides. The molecular weight of pepsinogen, which is 42,500, falls to 34,500 in pepsin.

b. Trypsin: Secreted by the pancreas in the form of the enzymatically inactive trypsinogen. It is converted to trypsin by the action of enterokinase, a substance which has never been well characterized. The conversion is accompanied by the splitting of a peptide residue.

c. Chymotrypsin: Found in the pancreatic secretion in the form of inactive chymotrypsinogen, which is converted to chymotrypsin by the action of trypsin. This change is brought about by the opening of peptide linkages and the removal of a polypeptide with a molecular weight of 1000 to 1500.

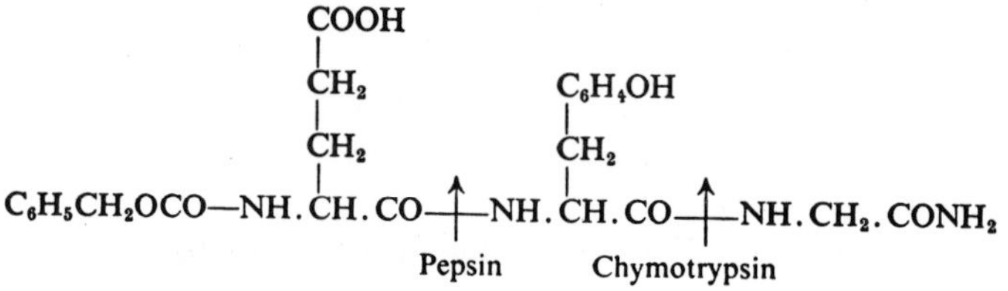

$$C_6H_5CH_2OCO-NH.\overset{\overset{\displaystyle COOH}{|}\overset{\displaystyle CH_2}{|}\overset{\displaystyle CH_2}{|}}{CH}.CO\underset{\text{Pepsin}}{-\!\!\uparrow\!\!-}NH.\overset{\overset{\displaystyle C_6H_4OH}{|}\overset{\displaystyle CH_2}{|}}{CH}.CO\underset{\text{Chymotrypsin}}{-\!\!\uparrow\!\!-}NH.CH_2.CONH_2$$

d. Cathepsins: A group of intracellular enzymes which are activated by cyanide, ascorbic acid, cysteine or glutathione are shown below:

INTRACELLULAR PROTEOLYTIC ENZYMES OF ANIMAL TISSUES

Name	Typical Substrate
Cathepsin A	Carbobenzoxy-L-glutamyl-L-tyrosine
Cathepsin B	Benzoyl-L-argininamide
Cathepsin C	Glycyl-L-phenylalaninamide
Leucine aminopeptidase*	L-Leucinamide
Carboxypeptidase*	Carbobenzoxyglycyl-L-phenylalanine
Tripeptidase*	Glycylglycylglycine

* Exopeptidases.
(From Tallan, Jones, and Fruton: J. Biol. Chem., *194*:793, 1952.)

e. Papain: Found in the milky juice of *Carica papaya*, pineapples, wheat and certain beans. It hydrolyzes most of the proteins and many of the proteoses and peptones. It is activated by HCN, H_2S and other reducing substances.

With regard to the *specificity* of these proteinases, some observations may be made.

Pepsin: An aromatic ring in the side-chain is particularly favorable for hydrolysis by pepsin. This is shown by substances in which the bond that is split involves the amino group of tyrosine or phenylalanine, or in which the link involves the carboxyl group of an aromatic amino acid, and in which both residues involved are aromatic. Exceptions to these rules occur; for example, the splitting of a leucyl-valine linkage in insulin.

Trypsin: This enzyme hydrolyzes linkages involving the carboxyl group of the basic amino acids, lysine and arginine. Amides and esters are also split, even more readily than peptides.

Chymotrypsin: Like trypsin, chymotrypsin also hydrolyzes amides and esters as well as peptides. Unlike trypsin, however, it shows a marked preference for linkages involving aromatic amino acid residues.

Cathepsin C: Like pepsin and chymotrypsin, it acts particularly on compounds containing aromatic amino acids. Unlike these, however, it requires a free alpha-amino group. The enzyme also behaves as an aminopeptidase, which splits off dipeptides from the N-terminal end.

Papain: This enzyme hydrolyzes amides and esters, particularly those of basic amino acids, therefore resembling trypsin. Some glycine and leucine derivatives are also hydrolyzed.

  2. Exopeptidases: This term was used by Bergmann to indicate an enzyme attacking a peptide linkage adjacent to a free polar group.
      a. Dipeptidase: Splits dipeptides only. For example, there is present in many animal tissues a dipeptidase which specifically splits glycylglycine. The enzyme is activated by Co^{++}.
      b. Carboxypeptidases: These split acylated dipeptides where the amino group has been blocked and the carboxyl group is free. An example is pancreatic carboxypeptidase which splits chloracetyl-L-tyrosine. It requires Zn^{++} for its activity.
      c. Aminopeptidases: These split dipeptides, dipeptide amides or amino acid amides requiring a free α-amino group. An example is leucine aminopeptidase from the intestinal mucosa, which splits L-leucylglycine and leucylamide.
      d. Tripeptidases: These split tripeptides. An example is the tripeptidase from calf thymus, which splits glycylglycylglycine, alanylglycylglycine and leucylglycylglycine.
II. Hydrases: These enzymes catalyze a reaction which results in the incorporation of the elements of water. Several examples are:
  A. Fumarase: Converts fumaric acid to malic acid.
  B. Enolase: Converts 2-phosphoglyceric acid to enol-phosphopyruvic acid.
  C. Aconitase: Converts citric acid to *cis*-aconitic acid and then to iso-citric acid.
  D. Carbonic Anhydrase: Present in the red cell and catalyzes the conversion of CO_2 to carbonic acid.

OXIDIZING ENZYMES

I. Oxidases: These enzymes catalyze the reaction of substrates with molecular oxygen. They may be further subdivided into:

   A. Iron Oxidases: Catalase, peroxidase, cytochrome oxidase.

   B. Copper Oxidases: Tyrosinase, ascorbic acid oxidase.

II. Dehydrogenases: During the action of these enzymes, hydrogen is removed from the substrate (bringing about its oxidation) and the hydrogen is carried by a coenzyme (p. 263) attached to the enzyme protein (apoenzyme). These may be divided into:

   A. Riboflavin Dehydrogenases: The coenzymes are FMN or FAD (p. 122).

   B. Pyridine Nucleotide Dehydrogenases: Containing DPN or TPN (p. 121) as the coenzymes.

   C. Cytochrome *C* Reducing Enzymes: Examples are succinic dehydrogenase, which converts succinic to fumaric acid, and the DPN and TPN cytochrome *c* reductases, which have as prosthetic groups the riboflavin coenzymes.

MISCELLANEOUS OXIDIZING ENZYMES

Among these are uricase, luciferase (responsible for light production in the firefly) and hydrogenase, an enzyme found in bacteria, which catalyzes the oxidation of molecular hydrogen.

TRANFERASES

These enzymes are involved in the transfer of radicals. Examples are given below:

I. Transglycosidase: Phosphorylase is an example (p. 33).

II. Transphosphorylase or Phosphomutase: Represents the kind of enzyme involved in the transfer of phosphoryl groups from one molecule to another. The enzyme hexokinase is an example. Involved in this transphosphorylation is the "high-energy" bond of ATP (p. 120). The reaction may be written:

$$\text{Hexose} + \text{ATP} \rightleftarrows \text{hexose monophosphate} + \text{ADP}$$

Another example, this time of a transfer of a phosphoryl group not involving high-energy bonds, is phosphoglucomutase, which catalyzes the conversion of glucose-1-phosphate to glucose-6-phosphate by means of a reaction involving the presence of small amounts of glucose-1,6-diphosphate.

III. Transaminase: The reaction catalyzed by these enzymes involves the reaction between an α-amino acid and an α-keto acid to produce a new amino acid and a new keto acid. An example is the reaction between glutamic acid and oxalacetic acid to produce α-ketoglutaric acid and aspartic acid.

IV. Transmethylase: The enzyme involved in the transfer of a methyl group from one compound to another. An example is the transfer of the methyl group of methionine to guanidoacetic acid to form homocysteine and creatine.

V. Transacetylase: These enzymes involve the action of the coenzyme A, which forms a compound with the acetyl group called acetyl CoA. The transacetylation, therefore, is performed by the coenzyme molecule. An example is the transfer of the acetyl group from acetyl CoA to choline, forming CoA and acetylcholine.

ENZYMES INVOLVED IN SPLITTING A C—C BOND

I. Desmolases are enzymes involved in the splitting of the C—C bond. Examples are:
   A. Aldolase: Which splits fructose-1,6-diphosphate into dihydroxyacetone phosphate and phosphoglyceraldehyde.
   B. Amino Acid Decarboxylase: Which catalyzes the splitting off of CO_2 from amino acids, forming the corresponding amines.

SEVERAL ENZYMES NOT INCLUDED IN THIS CLASSIFICATION

I. Rhodanese: Which converts cyanide to thiocyanate.

$$HCN + Na_2S_2O_3 \longrightarrow NaSCN + NaHSO_3$$

II. Phosphohexose Isomerase: Which converts glucose-6-phosphate to fructose-6-phosphate.

III. Cysteine Desulfhydrase: Which converts cysteine to pyruvic acid, with the evolution of H_2S and ammonia.

ENZYME ACTIVITY

INTACT ORGANISM

Using the whole organism made it difficult, and in many cases impossible, to follow the numerous steps in the metabolic transformations of compounds. Unphysiological compounds such as Knoop's phenyl derivatives of fatty acids (p. 300) were also used in the attempt to identify the products formed in the organism. Such methods, in any case, revealed little about the enzymes involved or about the intermediates of the reactions.

PERFUSED ORGANS

In order to eliminate the complications of a multi-organ system, a technique was perfected whereby an isolated organ was perfused with a solution whose contents approximated those of blood. The substance to be studied (some compound of physiological importance) was introduced into the circulation, and from time to time samples for analysis were withdrawn. This method is, of course, less physiological than using the intact organism.

TISSUE SLICES

Using a technique developed by Barcroft and by Warburg, very thin tissue slices of the organ—surrounded by a suitable salt solution (see Table 17) at optimum pH and at optimum temperature, and with

TABLE 17.   COMPARISON OF THE KREBS MEDIUM AND MAMMALIAN SERUM

	Mammalian Serum*	Krebs Solution*
Na^+	320	327
K^+	22	23
Ca^{++}	10	10
Mg^{++}	2.5	2.9
Cl^-	370	454
$PO_4^=$	10	11
$SO_4^=$	11	11.4
HCO_3^-	54 vols. %	54 vols. %
CO_2	2.5 vols. %	2.5 vols. %
pH	7.4	7.4

* All concentrations are in milligrams per 100 ml., excepting bicarbonate and CO_2, which are expressed as milliliters of CO_2 per 100 ml. Glucose (0.2 per cent final concentration) is sometimes added.

(From Baldwin: Dynamic Aspects of Biochemistry.)

a plentiful supply of oxygen—are used. The substance whose metabolism is to be studied is dissolved in the solution surrounding the slices. The apparatus is of such a kind that tissue respiration (oxygen uptake and carbon dioxide output) can be measured, and the chemical change undergone by the substrate—the substance whose metabolism is being studied—may be determined by suitable means.

One difficulty with this method is that even with the thinnest of tissue slices, the cells which make them up contain not one enzyme but a multi-enzyme system, which increases the difficulty of isolating and identifying intermediate products. However, it does represent the simplest system for the study of metabolic reactions by intact cells with organized enzyme systems.

TISSUE HOMOGENATES

This technique involves the mechanical breakdown of the cell wall, liberating the enzymes in solution or suspension. The problem of the passage of a compound across the intact cell wall is thus eliminated, and more data can be obtained concerning the specificity of enzymes and the effects of various agents on their activity. However, since the cellular enzymes are disorganized, co-factors needed for the complete functioning of many of the enzymes (such as ATP, for example) are rapidly destroyed; and it often becomes necessary to add such factors.

CELL-FREE EXTRACTS

By use of a suitable extracting medium, and the employment of differential high speed centrifugation, cell-free extracts can be obtained from a tissue. Such an extract may serve as the starting point for the isolation and characterization of individual enzymes. Extracts can also be used for the identification of intermediate reaction products.

This type of extract is represented by Buchner's yeast extract, and by Meyerhof's muscle extract with which he studied the reactions of fermentation. A drawback to this technique is that some enzymes are present in an insoluble form and are not found in the extract. Some of these insoluble enzymes have, to be sure, been brought into solution by suitable chemical treatment. In any case, in the intact cell, many enzymes appear to exist in association with insoluble particles.

MEASURING ENZYME ACTIVITY

Among the measurements which are important to an understanding of the over-all activity of enzymes within the living cell (tissue slices, bacteria, yeasts, etc.), are the following:

a. Oxygen Consumption. This is expressed as Q_{O_2}, the number of μl. O_2 consumed per hour per mg. of dry weight tissue, usually at 37° C. In addition, one can also determine the value for the Q_{CO_2}, the number of μl. CO_2 produced by the tissue in an oxygen atmosphere. These two

TABLE 18.   RESPIRATION AND GLYCOLYSIS IN RAT TISSUES

Tissue	Q_{O_2}	$Q_G^{O_2}$	$Q_G^{N_2}$	R.Q.
Retina	25	31	88	1.00
Kidney	21	0	3	0.84
Yolk-sac	14	2	18	1.01
Brain cortex	12	1.5	18	0.99
Liver	11	1	3	0.75
Embryo	11	3	12	0.98
Testis	10	3	8	0.90
Intestinal mucosa	10	13	14	0.90

(Adapted from Dickens, in Sumner and Myrbäck: The Enzymes: Chemistry and Mechanism of Action. Academic Press, 1951, Vol. 2, Part 1, p. 675.)

values yield the R.Q., or respiratory quotient, which is expressed as the ratio Q_{CO_2}/O_{O_2} (Table 18).

b. Fermentation or Glycolysis. Certain metabolic reactions which are catalyzed by enzymes produce acids as end-products. Examples are the fermentation reaction of lactic acid bacteria, and the fermentation reaction (glycolysis) of animal tissues which also produce lactic acid to a large extent. The production of acid by such cells or organizations of cells is also measured in the respirometer. The medium contains bicarbonate which liberates one mole of CO_2 per mole of lactic acid formed. Acid production (fermentation or glycolysis) is expressed quantitatively as $Q_G^{O_2}$ or Q_G; the G refers to glycolysis, and the O_2 and N_2 refer to the fact that acid production is being measured either in an atmosphere of oxygen or in that of nitrogen. In both cases carbon dioxide is measured; so that these terms refer to μl. CO_2 produced per hour per mg. dry weight tissue, and represent, respectively, aerobic or anaerobic glycolysis.

c. Spectrophotometry. Measurement of the rate of disappearance of the substrate, accumulation of the end-product, or disappearance of a coenzyme is sometimes accomplished by taking advantage of the fact that compounds may absorb light at specific wave lengths, either in the visible or ultraviolet regions of the light spectrum. By choosing an appropriate wave length, this method may be used with success. An example is its application during the course of enzymatic reactions where the coenzymes DPN or TPN are reduced to DPNH or TPNH. Since DPNH and TPNH have an absorption band at 340 mμ, whereas the oxidized forms of the coenzymes do not, measurement of the activities of many dehydrogenases is possible. In a similar fashion one may apply this technique to the flavoprotein enzymes whose oxidized forms absorb at 450 mμ, whereas the reduced forms absorb very much less at this wave length.

This method of measuring enzyme activity is often used, despite the absence of an oxidizable or reducible coenzyme. In such a case one adds to the reaction mixture another enzyme which acts on the product formed in the first reaction in such a way as to cause an observable change in the spectrophotometer; for example, the product can be oxidized by use of an enzyme whose coenzyme is DPN or TPN.

d. Thunberg Method. This method has been used in studies of the dehydrogenases. A special tube is employed which can be evacuated so that all oxygen is removed. A dye, such as methylene blue, is placed in the hollow stopper and mixed with enzyme and substrate at the start of the experiment. Usually one measures the time required for decolorization (reduction) of the dye, which replaces oxygen as the terminal electron acceptor. Some tubes are so constructed that they can be placed in a photocolorimeter, allowing for measurement of the rate at which the color disappears. One advantage of this method is the fact that the substrate concentration during the course of the experiment remains essentially constant, since so little substrate is used up in the reaction.

e. Chemical Estimation. Samples of the reaction mixture are analyzed at various intervals for substrate or product. Thus, during the course of hydrolysis of an organic phosphate (glucose-6-phosphate) by phosphatase, one needs only to determine the quantity of inorganic phosphate formed. Compounds such as acyl phosphates can be estimated by addition of hydroxylamine, producing a hydroxamic acid, which yields a purple color on addition of ferric salts.

f. Other Methods. (1) If an enzyme acts on an optically active substrate converting it to an inactive product, the change can be followed by means of a polarimeter. (2) If an acid is produced during the course of the enzyme reaction, one can follow the reaction by means of a pH meter, adding alkali to maintain the pH constant. The reaction velocity is taken as the quantity of alkali needed per unit time to maintain a constant pH. (3) During the study of an oxidizing enzyme, a change in potential of a solution containing a mixture of reduced and oxidized cofactor can be measured by means of a platinum electrode. (4) When other methods fail, the product can be identified by chromatographic means.

RELATIVE ACTIVITY OF ENZYMES (TURNOVER NUMBER)

There are any number of ways in which one may express the activity of an enzyme, and several of these have already been mentioned. When the enzyme has been purified, one usually expresses the activity in terms of the number of substrate molecules which react per minute per molecule of enzyme. The values for several enzymes are: α-amylase, 19,000; β-amylase, 250,000; fumarase, 100,000; catalase, 5,000,000; acetylcholinesterase, 20,000,000. These values do not take into account the fact that enzymes may contain more than one active group per molecule. For example, the enzyme catalase is known to contain four heme groups per molecule, each of which is concerned with the reaction of a molecule of the substrate. A better measure of the activity of this enzyme would be one fourth of five million. This value is termed the "turnover number" of the enzyme.

ISOTOPES

In the evolution of techniques for the study of enzymes, the pendulum has swung back again to the use of the intact organism. One great defect in this method as used earlier has been overcome. Instead of labeling compounds with unphysiological groups—as Knoop's *phenyl* fatty acids, p. 300—for identification purposes, isotopically labeled compounds can now be prepared which are chemically indistinguishable by the organism from the nonisotopic compounds. An additional advantage is that relatively small quantities of the compound to be studied need to be administered.

The compound in question is so prepared that one or more of its elements contains either a radioactive isotope of that element, or a greater than normal abundance of a stable isotope. (Table 19 lists some of the stable and radioactive isotopes of importance in biochemistry.)

TABLE 19.   ISOTOPES OF IMPORTANCE IN BIOCHEMISTRY

| | *Stable Isotopes* | | |
Element	*Atomic No.*	*Mass No.*	*Relative Abundance*
Hydrogen	1	1	99.99
Deuterium	1	2	0.003
Carbon	6	12	99.3
Carbon	6	13	0.7
Nitrogen	7	14	99.86
Nitrogen	7	15	0.14
Oxygen	8	16	99.81
Oxygen	8	17	0.16

| | *Radioactive Isotopes* | |
Isotope	*Half-Life*	*Type of Radiation**
H^3	31 yrs.	β^-
C^{11}	20.35 min.	β^+
C^{14}	10^4 yrs.	β^-
Na^{24}	14.8 hrs.	β^-, γ
P^{32}	14.3 days	β^-
S^{35}	87.1 days	β^-
Cl^{38}	37 min.	β^-, γ
K^{42}	12.4 hrs.	β^-
Ca^{45}	180 days	β^-, γ
Fe^{59}	47 days	β^-, γ
I^{131}	8 days	β^-, γ

* β^- = negative beta-particles (electrons).
β^+ = positive beta-particles (positrons).
γ = gamma-rays (electromagnetic radiation).
(From Bull: Physical Biochemistry, 2nd ed.)

The use of isotopically-labeled compounds will be illustrated throughout the book. Meanwhile, two examples will be given at this stage. The first (Fig. 30) demonstrates that choline causes an increased rate of incorporation of inorganic phosphate into the plasma phospholipids. In this experiment, P^{32}, in the form of inorganic phosphate, has been used.

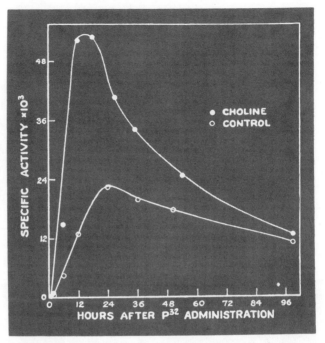

Figure 30. The effect of choline on the extent of incorporation of P³² into plasma phospholipid in the dog. (From Friedlander, Chaikoff and Entenman: J. Biol. Chem. *158*:231, 1945.)

TABLE **20.** LABELED P³² CONTENT OF EGGS

Time Between Administration of Active P and Egg Laying	Per Cent of Labeled P Administered Found in			
	Shell	Albumin	Total Yolk	Yolk Lecithin
5 hrs.	0.24	0.0015	0.0014	0.000
1.0 day	0.052	0.032	0.109	0.014
3.0 "	0.036	0.030	0.42	0.17
4.5 "	0.026	0.027	0.95	0.34
6.5 "	0.022	0.020	0.85	0.35

(From Hevesy: Adv. Enzym., 7:159.)

The second example (Table 20) illustrates the distribution in the egg of administered P³² with time.

LOCALIZATION OF ENZYME ACTIVITY IN THE CELL

The biochemist has always been aware that during a water or saline extraction of ground tissue, much of the formed elements (see Plates 2 and 3) is disorganized and destroyed. To lessen such alterations, Schneider and Hogeboom developed a technique that permits separation of the homogenate into several uniform fractions. The tissue is subjected to mild homogenization in the cold with a solution of isotonic or slightly hypertonic sucrose. The homogenate is next subjected to centrifugation

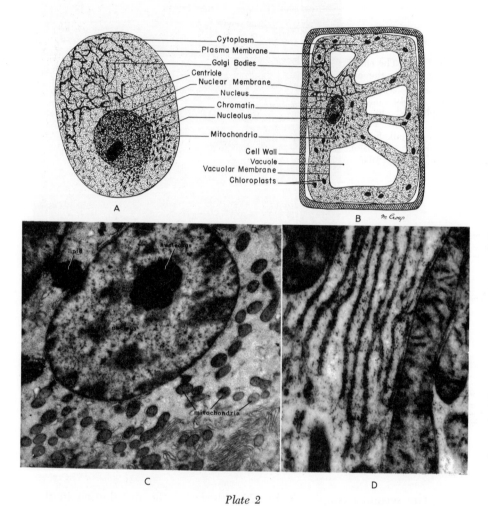

Plate 2

The structure of cells. *A,* Diagram of a typical animal cell. *B,* Diagram of a typical plant cell. *C,* Electron micrograph of the nucleus and surrounding cytoplasm of a frog liver cell. The spaghetti-like strands of the microsomes are visible in the lower right corner. Magnified 16,500 ×. *D,* High power electron micrograph of mitochondria and microsomes within a rat liver cell. Granules of ribonucleoprotein are seen on the strands of microsomes, and structures with double membranes are evident within the mitochondria in the upper left corner and on the right. Magnified 65,000 ×. (Electron micrographs courtesy Dr. Don Fawcett; from Villee: Biology.)

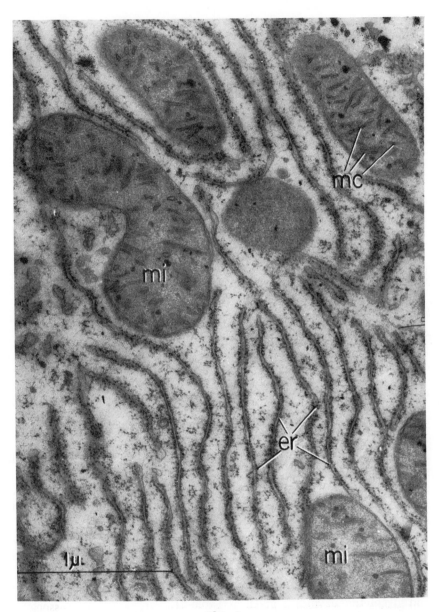

Plate 3

Electron micrograph of a portion of the cytoplasm from a liver cell corresponding to the basophil region. In addition to mitochondria (*mi*) with mitochondrial
crests (*mc*), the ergastoplasm (*er*) shows flattened cisternae with RNP (ribonucleoprotein) granules on the surface. Some regions of the cisternae appear devoid of
these granules. Fixation with osmium tetroxide and staining with lead acetate.
50,000 ×. (Courtesy of K. R. Porter; from De Robertis, Nowinski and Saez: General Cytology.)

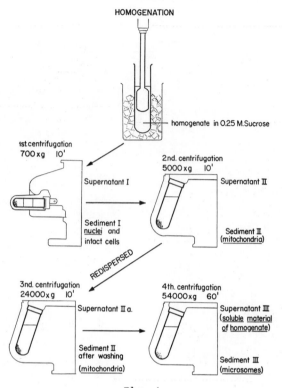

Plate 4

Diagram of a cellular fractionation. (From De Robertis, Nowinski and Saez: General Cytology.)

at varying speeds. Each precipitate so obtained is suspended in fresh sucrose solution and again centrifuged. In this manner one obtains the following fractions (in the order of increasing speed required for their sedimentation: 1, nuclei; 2, mitochondria; 3, microsomes (submicroscopic particles); 4, supernatant (see Plate 4).

When the nuclei and mitochondria are examined microscopically, little change is apparent as compared with their appearance in the intact cell. Nor is any change apparent after staining.

An analysis of the content of such fractions in terms of oxidizing and glycolytic enzymes is given in Table 21.

It may be seen that the oxidizing enzymes appear to be associated with the mitochondrial particles, whereas the glycolytic enzymes are in solution in the supernatant. That cofactors are needed is seen by comparing the enzyme activity of any one fraction with the enzyme activity of the same fraction to which has been added a second fraction. Thus the mitochondria contain 81 per cent of the activity of the original homogenate in so far as its ability to oxidize octanoic acid is concerned;

TABLE 21.   DISTRIBUTION OF ENZYME ACTIVITIES IN LIVER HOMOGENATE
FRACTIONS OBTAINED BY DIFFERENTIAL CENTRIFUGATION

Fraction	Octanoxidase	Oxalacetic Oxidase	Glycolysis
	(per cent of original homogenate activity)		
Nuclei (N)	2.8	10.5	12.6
Mitochondria (M)	81	44.5	0
Submicroscopic particles (P)	0	0	2.7
Supernatant (S)	0	0.5	52.7
M + P	95.0	81.5	
M + S		62.0	68.6
P + S			94.9

(From Schneider: J. Biol. Chem., *176*:259, 1948; LePage and Schneider: Ibid., *176*:1021, 1948; Schneider and Potter: Ibid., *177*:893, 1949.)

the submicroscopic particles show no activity at all. When the two fractions are mixed, the activity increases to 95 per cent.

PURIFICATION OF ENZYMES

The techniques involved in the isolation and crystallization of enzymes are the same as those used for proteins. With enzymes there is the added advantage that the extent of purification can be followed by a quantitative estimation of enzyme activity. Again, the criteria of purity for enzymes are the same as those used for proteins: homogeneity upon sedimentation, electrophoresis, and solubility (pp. 97–100).

Table 22 lists molecular weights and isoelectric points for a number of enzymes.

TABLE 22.   MOLECULAR WEIGHT AND ISOELECTRIC POINT OF SOME ENZYMES

Enzyme	Molecular Weight	Isoelectric Point
Catalase	248,000	5.58
Pepsin	37,000	2.85
Trypsin	34,000	7.50
Urease	483,000	5.09

(From Sumner and Myrbäck: The Enzymes. Article by Moelwyn-Hughes, Vol. 1, Part 1, p. 28.)

KINETICS OF ENZYME ACTION

The equilibrium point of a chemical reaction is more rapidly reached in the presence of an enzyme capable of influencing the particular reaction. The enzyme is apparently unchanged at the end of the reaction and contributes no measurable energy to it. This may involve heterogeneous as well as homogeneous reactions; it may involve adsorption phenomena as well as reactions in solution. The enzymes are often inhibited in their activity by increasing the quantity of substrate—a phenomenon which has led to various theories of intermediate enzyme-substrate formation. The enzymes are further inhibited in their activity by the accumulation of the products of the reaction. They are very sensitive to changes in temperature and to pH changes; and they may be "poisoned" by heavy metals, sulfhydryl inhibitors, cyanide, or carbon monoxide.

MEASURING THE VELOCITY OF AN ENZYME REACTION; EFFECT OF ENZYME CONCENTRATION

In measuring the velocity of an enzyme reaction, the general procedure involves mixing enzyme and substrate at "zero" time, followed by measurement, at various time intervals, of some evidence of the reaction. Such evidence may mean the disappearance of the substrate, appearance of the end-product, or, in other cases, the uptake or release of some gas (e.g., oxygen and carbon dioxide). The kinetics (rate measurement) of such reactions will depend on many factors: the nature of the reacting molecules, the concentration of the substrate and the enzyme, temperature, pH and the nature of the medium (kind of salts and buffers).

When the rate of a reaction is proportional to the concentration of a molecular species undergoing a chemical change, we may express this situation in the form of an equation, which is called "first order"

$$Velocity = -\frac{dC}{dt} = kC$$

where C is the concentration of the substrate, t is the time and k is a proportionality constant. If we designate x as the amount of substrate that has undergone change in time t, a as the quantity of substrate present initially ($t = 0$), then

$$v = \frac{dx}{dt} = k(a - x)$$

and k becomes the velocity constant for the reaction. The value of $(a - x)$ is therefore the prevailing concentration of the substrate. Figure 31 shows a graphic plot of $(a - x)$ against t, resulting in a curve which decreases with time but never quite reaches a value of zero for $(a - x)$. A more useful plot is obtained if we integrate the above expression, leading to:

$$kt = 2.3 \log \frac{a}{a - x}$$

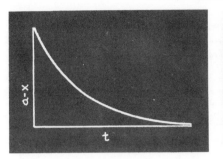 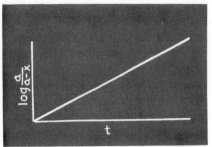

Figure 31   Figure 32

Figures 31 and 32. (From Hitchcock: Physical Chemistry for Students of Biology and Medicine. 2nd Ed. Charles C Thomas.)

or,

$$\frac{k}{2.3} = \frac{\log \frac{a}{a-x}}{t}$$

If we now plot $\log a/a - x$ against t, we get a straight line whose slope is equal to $k/2.3$, from which the value of k can be obtained (Fig. 32). If twice the amount of enzyme were to result in the same degree of reaction in one-half the time, then k would be directly proportional to the enzyme concentration.

TABLE 23. REACTION COURSE OF CANE SUGAR INVERSION BY H IONS

Time (t), Minutes	Angle of Rotation, Degrees	$K = \dfrac{1}{t} \log_{10} \dfrac{a}{a-x}$
0	+46.75	
45	+38.25	0.001 34
120	+26.00	0.001 38
240	+11.50	0.001 40
450	− 4.50	0.001 47
630	−10.00	0.001 39
∞	−18.70	. . . .

(From Wilhelm.)

A simple example is the inversion of cane sugar by acid:

$$C_{12}H_{22}O_{11} + H_2O \longrightarrow C_6H_{12}O_6 + C_6H_{12}O_6$$

The acid in the reaction is the catalyst. The results of an experiment are given in Table 23.

By substituting an enzyme for the acid, we get results shown in Table 24.

TABLE 24. SACCHARASE QUANTITY AND REACTION VELOCITY

Relative Saccharase Concentration	Time, Minutes	Transformation (per cent) with Initial Concentration of Sugar of		
		4.55 per cent	9.09 per cent	27.3 per cent
2.00	15	73.2	45.3	11.2
1.50	20	73.2	44.8	11.2
1.00	30	72.9	45.3	11.5
0.50	60	72.9	45.2	11.4
0.25	120	73.1	45.2	10.9

(From Hudson.)

In this case, the table shows the proportionality between the concentration of enzyme and the reaction velocity.

EFFECT OF CONCENTRATION OF SUBSTRATE

Table 24 shows very clearly how the reaction velocity is influenced by the concentration of the substrate. Within a given time, a definite amount of saccharase (invertase) will hydrolyze a larger percentage of sucrose when the solution is dilute than when it is concentrated. This is illustrated in Figure 33.

To explain such retardation, Bayliss introduced his adsorption theory, wherein the colloidal enzyme particles become "saturated" and "a further increase in concentration will not result in more adsorption and therefore in no increase in the rate of reaction." Today we assume chemical bond formation between enzyme and substrate.

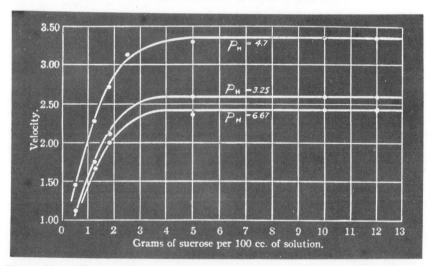

Figure 33. Effect of substrate concentration on reaction velocity, illustrating the limiting or saturation value at higher concentrations. Experiments with sucrose and invertase. (Nelson and Bloomfield: J. Am. Chem. Soc., 46:1027.)

In at least one instance, that of pepsin, Northrop explains enzymic peculiarities on the basis that the reaction is between the ionized protein and the free enzyme. In the presence of acid the protein forms an ionized protein salt which varies by an amount depending upon the pH of the solution. The pepsin, on the other hand, is present as free pepsin, negatively charged, and as pepsin in combination with the products of hydrolysis of the protein.

EFFECT OF HYDROGEN ION CONCENTRATION

As has already been intimated, the activity of the enzyme is very much dependent upon the hydrogen ion concentration of the solution. Another curve of this type we owe to Michaelis and Davidsohn (Fig. 34). Here we are dealing with the action of invertase (saccharase) on sucrose. The optimum pH is at 4.5. Both on the acid and alkaline side there is a rapid decrease in activity. Betweeen pH 4.5 and 9 the shape of the curve resembles the ionization curve of a weak acid, which suggests that invertase itself might be such a weak acid (within these pH limits), dissociating thus:

$$\text{Invertase (acid)} \underset{\text{acid}}{\overset{}{\rightleftarrows}} \text{Invertase (anion)} + H^+$$

and that it is the un-ionized portion which catalyzes the hydrolysis of sucrose. The shape of the curve from pH 2 to 4.5 resembles the ionization curve of a weak base.

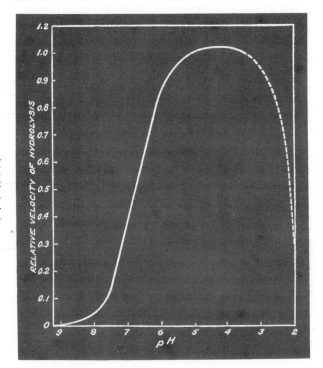

Figure 34. Relationship between the pH and activity of a yeast invertase preparation. (Michaelis and Davidsohn: Biochem. Z., 35: 405.)

Table 25, taken from Waldschmidt-Leitz, gives the pH optimum of a number of enzymes.

TABLE **25.**   pH OPTIMUM FOR SEVERAL ENZYMES

Enzyme	pH optimum
Lipase (pancreas)	8
Lipase (stomach)	4–5
Lipase (castor oil)	4.7
Pepsin	1.5–1.6
Trypsin	7.8–8.7
Urease	7.0
Invertase	4.5
Maltase	6.1–6.8
Amylase (pancreas)	6.7–7.0
Amylase (malt)	4.6–5.2
Catalase	7.0

THE EFFECT OF TEMPERATURE

Enzyme reactions are influenced by temperature changes in much the same way that chemical reactions are influenced by them. Very approximately, for an increase in temperature of 10° C. the velocity of the reaction is doubled or tripled. Between 20° and 30° C., then, the temperature coefficient (Q_{10}, or k_{30}/k_{20}) for many enzymic reactions is between 2 and 3. However, it must be remembered that enzymes are very susceptible to heat, and that temperatures from 50° C. and up for any length of time (and the time factor is very important) very rapidly destroy them. As the temperature is increased beyond body temperature, two forces come into play: the rate of destruction of the enzyme versus the increase in the rate of transformation of the substrate; and at comparatively high temperatures the first completely overshadows the second.

QUANTITATIVE EXPRESSION OF THE ENZYME-SUBSTRATE COMBINATION

Michaelis and Menten proposed that an enzyme first combines with the substrate to form an intermediate complex. Experimental confirmation of this hypothesis has since been obtained by the actual identification of compounds of the enzyme-substrate complex. The enzyme next undergoes dissociation in such a way that the substrate is chemically altered, and the enzyme is liberated:

$$E + S \underset{k_2}{\overset{k_1}{\rightleftarrows}} ES^* \overset{k_3}{\longrightarrow} E + P$$

* Actually there may be several enzyme-substrate intermediate complexes before the final product is formed; for example, $\rightleftarrows ES' \rightleftarrows ES'' \rightleftarrows ES''' \rightleftarrows P$.

where E = enzyme, S = substrate, ES = enzyme-substrate complex and P = products.

If we designate $K_m{}^\circ$ as the dissociation constant of ES, it will be equal to $(E)(S)/(ES)$.

If E_o is the total concentration of enzyme, E is the concentration of free enzyme, and ES is the concentration of bound enzyme, then

$$K_m = \frac{(E_o - ES)(S)}{(ES)}$$

$$K_m(ES) = (E_o)S - (ES)S$$

$$K_m(ES) + (ES)S = (E_o)S$$

$$(ES)(K_m + S) = (E_o)S$$

$$(ES) = \frac{(E_o)S}{K_m + S}$$

The velocity of the reaction, v, is equal to $k_3(ES)$, so that

$$v = \frac{k_3(E_o)(S)}{K_m + S}$$

If the substrate concentration is increased to the point where the enzyme is saturated with the substrate, the maximum velocity of the reaction, V, is equal to $k_3(E_o)$; or v is equal to $(V)(S)/K_m + S$; or, taking reciprocals,

$$\frac{1}{v} = \left(\frac{K_m}{V}\right)\left(\frac{1}{S}\right) + \frac{1}{V}$$

If one plots $1/v$ against $1/S$ from the experimental values, a straight line is obtained whose value for the slope is K_m/V, and whose intercept is $1/V$. The Michaelis constant, K_m, which is the dissociation constant for the enzyme-substrate complex, can thus be evaluated. Actually it is only when k_3 is very much smaller than k_2 that K_m becomes equal to the true dissociation constant of the complex.

MECHANISM OF ENZYME ACTION

Keilin and Mann were among the first to contribute towards the theory of the enzyme-substrate complex by observing spectroscopically that the enzyme peroxidase acting on hydrogen peroxide first combines with it to form a well-defined compound. Similar results were obtained with the enzyme catalase (Fig. 35). Chance studied the kinetics of these intermediate complexes and showed that they were in agreement with the

---

$^\circ$ K_m, calculated from experimental data, may not be the true dissociation constant; it approaches $\dfrac{k_2}{k_1}$ when k_2 is much greater than k_3.

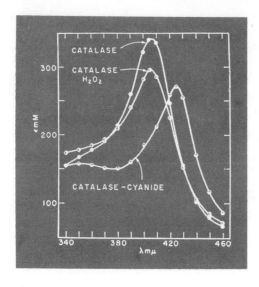

Figure 35. Absorption spectrum of catalase, catalase-peroxide compound, and catalase-cyanide compound. (From Sizer: Science, *125*: 54.)

velocity constants computed on the basis of the formation of an enzyme-substrate complex.

COFACTORS

Many enzymes require additional help from substances so that they may function effectively. These additional substances go under the general name of cofactors. Some examples will explain the part played by some of these compounds (Fig. 36).

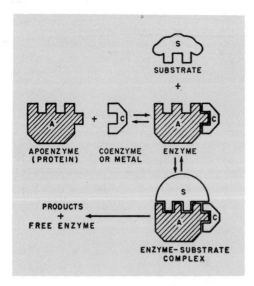

Figure 36. Schematic diagram illustrating the pathway of many enzyme-catalyzed reactions. For some enzymes, the step involving the combination with coenzymes or activating metal is not required (modified from McElroy, Quart. Rev. Biol., *22:*25).

a. Metal Ions. Some proteolytic enzymes need inorganic ions to act as "activators." Aminopeptidase, for example, needs for its complete activity the presence of Mn^{++}. Here it is believed that the Mn^{++} acts as a "bridge" linking the enzyme and the substrate:

Table 26 lists some metallo-enzymes.

TABLE 26.   SPECIFIC METALLO-ENZYMES

Enzyme	Reaction	Metal
Carbonic anhydrase	$CO_2 + H_2O \rightleftarrows H_2CO_3$	Zn
Dehydropeptidase	Glycyldehydrophenylalanine $\rightarrow NH_3$ + penylpyruvic A	Zn
Glycylglycine dipeptidase	Glycylglycine $\rightarrow$ glycine	Zn
Carboxypeptidase	Carbobenzoxyglycyl-L-phenylalanine $\rightarrow$ phenylalanine	Zn
Alcohol dehydrogenase	Ethanol + DPN $\rightleftarrows$ acetaldehyde + DPNH	Zn
Glutamic dehydrogenase	Glutamate + DPN $\rightleftarrows$ ketoglutarate + DPNH + NH_3	Zn
Lactic dehydrogenase	Lactate + DPN $\rightleftarrows$ pyruvate + DPNH	Zn
Inorganic pyrophosphatase	Pyrophosphate + $H_2O \leftarrow PO_4$	Mg
Succinic dehydrogenase	Succinic acid $\rightarrow$ fumaric acid + 2H	Fe
Catalase	$2H_2O_2 \rightarrow 2H_2O + O_2$	Fe
Peroxidase	H_2O_2 oxidation of aromatic amines and other compounds	Fe
Cytochromes	Electron transport	Fe
DPNH-cytochrome c reductase	DPNH + cytochrome c $(Fe^{+++}) \rightarrow$ DPN + cytochrome c (Fe^{++})	Fe
Uricase	Uric acid + $O_2 \rightleftarrows$ allantoin + $H_2O_2 + CO_2$	Cu
Tyrosinase	Tyrosine + $\frac{1}{2}O_2 \rightarrow$ hallochrome + H_2O	Cu
Laccase	Phenols $\rightarrow$ ortho and para quinones + H_2O	Cu
Ascorbic acid oxidase	Ascorbic acid $\rightarrow$ dehydroascorbic A + H_2O	Cu
Prolidase	Glycylproline $\rightarrow$ proline	Mn
Nitrate reductase	$NO_3 + TPNH + H^+ \rightarrow NO_2 + TPN^+ + H_2O$	Mo
Xanthine oxidase	Xanthine + $O_2 \rightarrow H_2O_2$ + uric acid	Mo
Aldehyde oxidase	Acetaldehyde + $O_2 \rightarrow$ acetate + H_2O	Mo

(From McElroy and Nason: Borden's Review of Nutrition Research, *17*:53, 1956.)

b. Dehydrogenase cofactors act as hydrogen acceptors—they "accept" hydrogen—so that the substrate can be oxidized. As an example, ethyl alcohol can be oxidized to acetaldehyde by means of the enzyme alcohol dehydrogenase; but this becomes possible only in the presence of the cofactor DPN, which during the process is reduced to DPNH.

The part of the molecule of DPN which is affected is the nicotinamide, for it is reduced as follows:

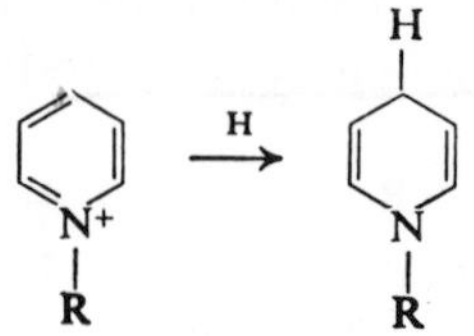

$$
\underset{R}{\overset{}{\text{(pyridinium ring)}}} \xrightarrow{\ H\ } \underset{R}{\overset{H}{\text{(dihydropyridine ring)}}}
$$

The complete reaction can be written:

$$
CH_3.CH_2.OH + DPN^+ \xrightarrow[\text{(dehydrogenase)}]{} CH_3CHO + DPNH + H^+
$$

The hydrogen which is accepted by DPN comes directly from the alcohol (the substrate).

TPN acts similarly to DPN. FMN and FAD also act as hydrogen acceptors. Here the particular group which is reduced is isoalloxazine.

c. Electron-transfer cofactors belong to the iron-protoporphyrin compounds. An example is cytochrome oxidase. During the oxidation of the substrates—in these cases it would be succinate and ferrocytochrome c—the iron gains electrons.

d. Glutathione, a tripeptide of glutamic acid, cysteine and glycine, and abbreviated as GSH, has the formula

$$
\underset{\overset{|}{COOH}}{H_2N.CH}.CH_2.CH_2.CO.NH.\underset{\underset{CO.NH.CH_2.COOH}{|}}{\overset{\overset{CH_2SH}{|}}{CH}}
$$

(GSH = glutathione)

and acts as a coenzyme for the enzyme glyoxalase. Glyoxalase converts methyl glyoxal ($CH_3.CO.CHO$) to lactic acid ($CH_3.CHOH.COOH$). The mechanism of the reaction may be written as follows:

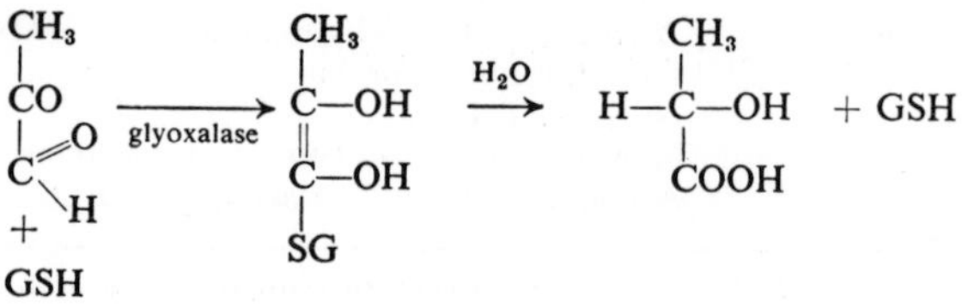

$$
\begin{array}{ccc}
\underset{GSH}{\overset{}{\underset{+}{\overset{\overset{CH_3}{|}}{\overset{CO}{\underset{C}{\Vert}}}}{\overset{}{}}}} & \xrightarrow{\text{glyoxalase}} & \underset{SG}{\overset{\overset{CH_3}{|}}{\underset{\Vert}{\overset{C-OH}{C-OH}}}} \\
\end{array}
\xrightarrow{H_2O}
\underset{COOH}{\overset{\overset{CH_3}{|}}{\overset{}{H-C-OH}}} + GSH
$$

e. Transfer of a Phosphoryl Group. The enzyme phosphoglucomutase catalyzes a reaction whereby glucose-1-phosphate is converted to glucose-6-phosphate. The coenzyme for this reaction is glucose-1,6-diphosphate. By labeling the phosphate group of glucose-1-phosphate with P^{32}, it can be shown that the glucose-6-phosphate is unlabeled. The mechanism of the reaction is illustrated by the following equation:

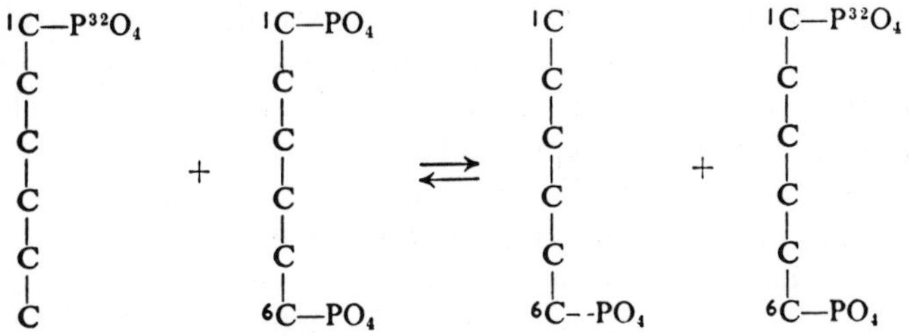

$$
\begin{array}{ccccccc}
{}^1C-P^{32}O_4 & & {}^1C-PO_4 & & {}^1C & & {}^1C-P^{32}O_4 \\
| & & | & & | & & | \\
C & & C & & C & & C \\
| & & | & & | & & | \\
C & & C & & C & & C \\
| & + & | & \rightleftharpoons & | & + & | \\
C & & C & & C & & C \\
| & & | & & | & & | \\
C & & C & & C & & C \\
| & & | & & | & & | \\
C & & {}^6C-PO_4 & & {}^6C--PO_4 & & {}^6C-PO_4
\end{array}
$$

FUNCTION OF THE APOENZYME

As has been stated before, an essential part of the enzyme system is its protein. The protein portion of the molecule is spoken of as the *apoenzyme*. A striking illustration of the importance of the apoenzyme is shown in the cases of catalase and peroxidase, both of which are iron-protoporphyrin-protein complexes. Both decompose H_2O_2, but iron-protoporphyrin (p. 205) itself does not.

That specific groups attached to the enzyme protein are needed for enzymic activity becomes clear when such groups are "blocked" or oxidized, with the result that the activity is lost. For example, it is known that organic arsenicals, such as Lewisite, inactivate the enzyme, "pyruvic acid oxidase."[*] Peters found that Lewisite combines with —SH groups. This action can be prevented, and in fact reversed, by BAL (British Anti-Lewisite):

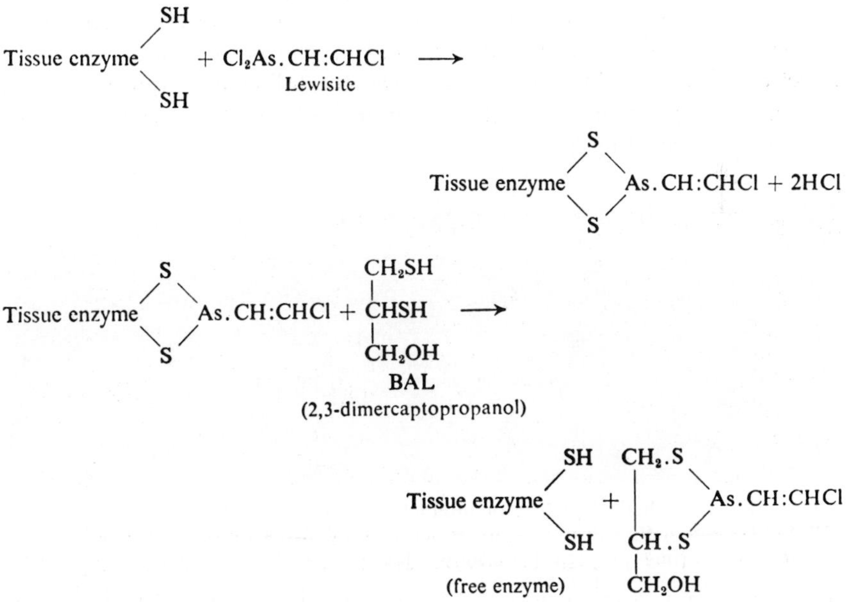

$$
\text{Tissue enzyme}\!\!\begin{array}{c}\nearrow^{\text{SH}}\\ \searrow_{\text{SH}}\end{array} + Cl_2As.CH{:}CHCl \longrightarrow
$$
Lewisite

$$
\text{Tissue enzyme}\!\!\begin{array}{c}\nearrow^{S}\\ \searrow_{S}\end{array}\!\!As.CH{:}CHCl + 2HCl
$$

$$
\text{Tissue enzyme}\!\!\begin{array}{c}\nearrow^{S}\\ \searrow_{S}\end{array}\!\!As.CH{:}CHCl + \begin{array}{c}CH_2SH\\ |\\ CHSH\\ |\\ CH_2OH\end{array} \longrightarrow
$$
BAL
(2,3-dimercaptopropanol)

$$
\text{Tissue enzyme}\!\!\begin{array}{c}\nearrow^{\text{SH}}\\ \searrow_{\text{SH}}\end{array} + \begin{array}{c}CH_2.S\\ |\ \ \ \searrow\\ CH.S\\ |\nearrow\\ CH_2OH\end{array}\!\!As.CH{:}CHCl
$$
(free enzyme)

[*] Inactivation may be due to blocking of SH groups of cofactors (coenzyme A or lipoic acid) rather than those of the enzyme protein.

BAL has also been found to be effective in the treatment of poisoning by a number of heavy metals—mercury, for example. Here the —SH of BAL and the mercury combine to form a relatively undissociated complex which is rapidly eliminated.

Another function of the apoenzyme may be to bind the substrate and coenzyme in a close and specific type of linkage to enable them to interact. An example is the action of the enzyme triose phosphate dehydrogenase on 3-phosphoglyceraldehyde, which requires DPN as a cofactor. The enzyme requires the presence of free —SH groups, since it is inactivated by treatment with the compound p-chloromercuribenzoate:

$$\text{R—SH} + \text{ClHg} \langle \bigcirc \rangle \text{COOH} \longrightarrow \text{R—S.Hg} \langle \bigcirc \rangle \text{COOH} + \text{HCl}$$

Racker has suggested that the following is the reaction that takes place on the surface of the enzyme:

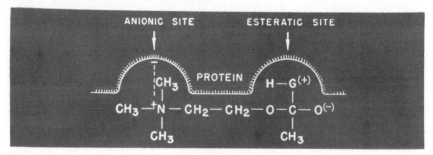

The need for several sites on the enzyme protein is illustrated by the action of the enzyme acetylcholinesterase on acetylcholine. On the basis of the study of the action of this enzyme on a variety of substrates related chemically to acetylcholine—and on the basis of a study of the effect of inhibitors—Wilson has proposed the following requirements for this enzyme, involving two active "centers" or sites: an anionic site and an esteratic site (Fig. 37):

Figure 37. Hypothetical picture of interaction between the active groups of acetylcholinesterase and its substrate. The structure symbolized by G is assumed to have electron-transmitting properties, as shown for example by a conjugate double-bond system. The mechanism is a two-step process involving the simultaneous acylation of the enzyme and the internal elimination of a small molecule followed by the deacylation of the enzyme. (From Wilson: A Symposium on the Mechanism of Enzyme Action. Edited by McElroy and Glass, 1954.)

IDENTIFICATION OF SUBSTRATE BOND CLEAVAGE

An important tool in elucidating the mechanism of action of enzymes which split (or synthesize) O—C or O—P bonds is the isotope O^{18}. Two methods may be used:

1. Hydrolysis of the substrate AOB is carried out in H_2O^{18}. The products AOH and BOH are isolated and analyzed for O^{18}. It is clear that O^{18} will be found in one part of the molecule or the other according to the position at which the break occurs:

$$A+O—B \quad \text{or} \quad A—O+B$$
$$O^{18}H \mid H \qquad\qquad H \mid O^{18}H$$
$$\downarrow \qquad\qquad\qquad \downarrow$$
$$AO^{18}H + BOH \qquad AOH + BO^{18}H$$

2. Ordinary unlabeled water is used together with AOH and $BO^{18}H$. The same enzyme which produces hydrolysis will also cause synthesis to some extent, followed again by hydrolysis. The following reactions will then take place:

$$\underline{AOH + HO^{18}B} \quad \text{or} \quad \underline{AOH + HO^{18}B}$$
$$AO^{18}B \qquad\qquad\qquad AOB$$
$$\downarrow \qquad\qquad\qquad\qquad \downarrow$$
$$AOH + BO^{18}H \qquad\quad AOH + BOH$$

Given sufficient time for the reaction to go up and back several times, in the second case the original $BO^{18}H$ will lose practically all of its O^{18}, but in the first case it will lose none.

Cohn has applied these methods to phosphatases and phosphorylases in order to identify the point of hydrolysis. The results are shown below:

Catalyst	Hydrolysis point
Acid	C$\overset{\downarrow}{—}$O—P
Acid phosphatase	C—O$\overset{\downarrow}{—}$P
Alkaline phosphatase	C—O$\overset{\downarrow}{—}$P
Sucrose transglucosylase	C$\overset{\downarrow}{—}$O—P
Glucosan phosphorylase	C$\overset{\downarrow}{—}$O—P

(From Dixon and Webb: Enzymes, Academic Press, 1958.)

The results suggest that the break comes on that side of the atom which is nearest to the part of the molecule for which the enzyme is specific and as close as possible to the group being transferred.

ACTION OF INHIBITORS

The Michaelis formulation can be extended to provide an explanation for the action of enzyme inhibitors. Here the assumption is made of an enzyme-inhibitor complex,

$$E + S \rightleftarrows ES \longrightarrow E + P$$
$$E + I \rightleftarrows EI$$

where I is the inhibitor.

$$K_m = \frac{(E)(S)}{(ES)} \text{ and } K_I = \frac{(E)(I)}{(EI)}$$

Combining, we get

$$EI = \frac{K_m(ES)(I)}{K_I(S)}$$

since

$$E = E_o - ES - EI$$

we get

$$E = \frac{K_m(ES)}{S} = E_o - ES - \frac{K_m(ES)(I)}{K_I(S)}$$

Substituting $v = k_3(ES)$ and $V = k_3(E_o)$, we have

$$v = \frac{V}{\dfrac{K_m}{S} + 1 + \dfrac{K_m I}{K_I(S)}}$$

and taking the reciprocals,

$$\frac{1}{v} = \left(\frac{K_m}{V}\right)\left(\frac{1}{S}\right)\left(1 + \frac{I}{K_I}\right) + \frac{1}{V}$$

By plotting $1/v$ against $1/S$ one gets a straight line whose slope is $(K_m/V)\left(1 + \dfrac{I}{K_I}\right)$, which represents an increase of the slope over the uninhibited slope of $\left(1 + \dfrac{I}{K_I}\right)$.

For inhibition of the competitive type—which is the example just given—such inhibition can be overcome by increasing the concentration of the substrate. For noncompetitive inhibition where the degree of inhibition is independent of the substrate concentration

$$\frac{1}{v} = \left(1 + \frac{I}{K_I}\right)\left(\frac{1}{V} + \frac{K_m}{VS}\right)$$

If $1/v$ is plotted against $1/S$, both the slope and the intercept are increased by a factor $(1 + I/K_I)$.

Figure 38 gives an example of a plot of the reciprocal of the reaction velocity ($1/v$) against the reciprocal of the substrate concentration ($1/S$) for the enzyme which catalyzes the hydrolysis of acetyl choline to acetate and choline. Where the experimental lines intercept the vertical axis gives the value for $1/V$ whereas the slope of the experimental line gives the value for K/V, thus yielding the value for K, the Michaelis constant. It may be seen that in the case of the inhibitor eserine, the value of $1/V$ is the same as in the absence of inhibitor while the slope is altered upwards. This is an example of competitive inhibition and can be overcome by adding more substrate. In the case of the inhibitor diisopropyl fluorophosphate, the slope remains the same whereas the intercept, or $1/V$, is different. This is an example of noncompetitive inhibition where the experimental results can be interpreted as meaning that a portion of the enzyme is tied up in an inactive form and is unavailable for action on the substrate.

On the basis of the multisite nature of substrate-enzyme complexes which are possible, it becomes a simple matter to picture the nature of the enzyme inhibition which sometimes occurs at high concentration of substrate. Assume that the substrate has two groupings, A and B, which must both combine with corresponding groups A′ and B′ which are

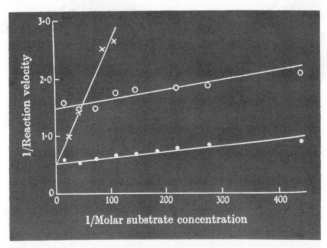

Figure 38. Plot of reciprocal of reaction velocity against reciprocal of substrate concentration for horse serum acetylcholinesterase (ACh esterase) with and without inhibitors. ●—●, control, no inhibitor; ×—×, eserine; ○—○, diisopropyl fluorophosphate (see Chap. 19). (From Mackworth and Webb: Biochem. J., 42:91, 1948.)

present on the enzyme surface in a fixed position:

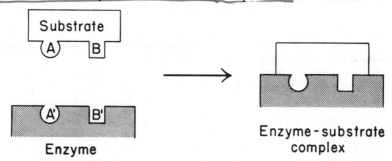

As the concentration of the substrate is increased, the enzyme groups A' and B' will soon be saturated. Now, because of the presence of so many substrate molecules, inhibition of the enzyme may be caused by the following:

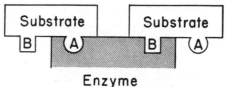

leading to an inactive enzyme-substrate complex.

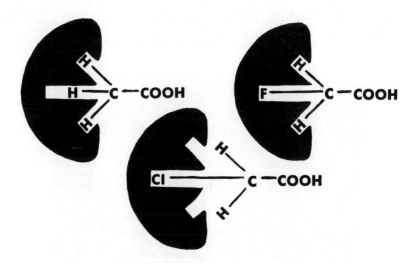

Figure 39. Lock and key theory explains why enzymes are specific to certain compounds and how their action can be inhibited by similar compounds. Here at left acetic acid fits an enzyme (black) and the reaction works. When a fluorine atom is substituted for a hydrogen atom, forming monofluoroacetate, the fit is close enough to occupy the enzyme and to block its reaction with acetic acid. However, when a chlorine atom replaces the fluorine atom (monochloroacetate), the key fits so poorly that the enzyme does not accept it. The compound therefore does not rob acetic acid of its enzyme. (From Pfeiffer: The Physics and Chemistry of Life. Copyright 1955 by Scientific American, Inc. Published by Simon and Schuster, New York.)

Competitive inhibition may be explained as the result of the inhibitor forming a bond with the same enzymatically active sites as does the substrate (Fig. 39). In the case of noncompetitive inhibition, increasing the concentration of the substrate does not make this bond any looser; whereas in the case of competitive inhibition, the increase of substrate concentration can overcome the inhibition on the basis of mass action in a reversible equilibrium.

THE ACTION OF CATALYSTS AS APPLIED TO ENZYMES

With all our knowledge of the mechanism of enzyme action, we have still failed to answer the most important question. Given the structural uniqueness of the enzyme protein, its required groupings, the specific substrate, the required pH, the required cofactor, what happens —when the enzyme-substrate complex is formed—to make this result in a chemical reaction? This question still remains unanswered. However, we might gain a better understanding of the basic question if we were to apply the concepts of the physical chemist, concerning the action of catalysts in general, to the problem of enzymes.

According to the modern concept of catalysis, before molecules can react they must pass through a configuration known as the "activated state." In this state the molecules have an energy greater than that of the normal reactants. This is called the "activation energy."

The normal state of the reactants at an energy level corresponding to A (Fig. 40) is raised first to the activated state at an energy level B before it can go on to a decomposition of the activated complex to form the products at an energy level corresponding to C.

E_1 corresponds to the free energy of activation of the forward reaction, and E_2 corresponds to the free energy of the opposing, or reverse, reaction. The function of the catalyst would appear to be that of

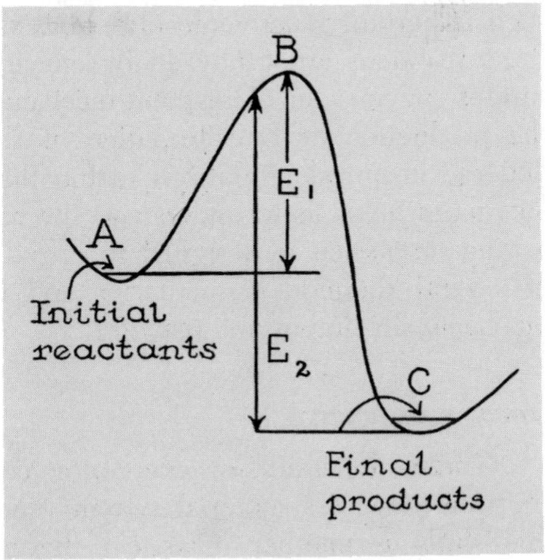

Figure 40. The activation energy of a chemical reaction. (Adapted from Butler: J. Roy. Soc. Arts, Sept. 26, 1947.)

"tunneling" under the energy pass and thus reducing the energy of activation. Table 27, collected by Lineweaver, gives figures to compare the energy of activation, E (Arrhenius), without and with catalysts.

TABLE 27. EXAMPLES OF ACTIVATION ENERGIES WITH VARIOUS CATALYSTS

Reaction	Catalyst	E*
H_2O_2 decomposition	None	18,000
	Colloidal Pt	11,700
	Liver catalase	5,500
Sucrose inversion	H^+	26,000
	Yeast invertase	11,500
Casein hydrolysis	HCl	20,600
	Trypsin	12,000
Ethyl butyrate hydrolysis	H^+	13,200
	Pancreatic lipase	4,200

* From $\ln k = - (E/RT) + C$, where E = Arrhenius' energy of activation, R = the gas constant, T = temperature, C = an integration constant, and k = reaction velocity.

BIOCHEMICAL ENERGETICS

Chemical thermodynamics is a branch of chemistry which explores energy relationships among chemical reactions. Such a study is of great importance to biochemistry, since some of the fundamental questions concerning the living cell relate to the problem of energy transformation from chemical compounds (foodstuffs) to a form which the cell can utilize for its vital functions; e.g., muscular contraction, nerve impulse transmission, and a variety of synthetic reactions required to furnish such important macromolecules as RNA, DNA and proteins. Although these reactions are catalyzed by enzymes, a study of the chemical nature of enzymes, or of reaction mechanisms, yields no information about the production or transformation of the energy of molecules as they undergo chemical alterations within the cell. The study of biochemical energetics helps us to understand the nature of these problems. The following discussion is designed to introduce the student to the meaning of several thermodynamic terms and to describe their application to biochemically important reactions.

CONCEPT OF ENERGY

Thermodynamics, or energetics, considers the rules which govern the transition of a material system (such as a chemical reaction) from one state to another. Classical thermodynamics is completely independent of any concept of molecular structure, but rather concerns itself with the behavior of systems based on facts relating to energy changes under a variety of conditions, when the system passes from one state to another.

The concept of energy arose during a consideration of mechanical phenomena, such as Count Rumford's observation in the eighteenth century of the boring of cannon. He noted that the mechanical work performed was roughly measured by the amount of heat produced. This idea was further developed and led to the determination of the mechanical equivalent of heat. Heat and work could be made equal by the proper choice of units, and heat could be considered as a form of energy.

When a quantity of heat, Q, is added to a system, it will be utilized to raise the internal energy of the system and will be used to perform any external work done by that system as a result of the absorption of heat. If we designate E_A as the internal energy of a system in its initial state, and E_B as the internal energy of the system in its final state, then

$$E_B - E_A = \Delta E \tag{1}$$

where ΔE represents the change in internal energy of the system and depends only on the initial and final states of the system and is independent of the pathway or method used to attain that state. If W is used to designate the work done by the system on its surroundings, then

$$Q = \Delta E + W \tag{2}$$

or
$$\Delta E = Q - W \tag{3}$$

Equation (3) is a statement of the first law of thermodynamics and defines the concept of energy in terms of heat and work, which are directly measurable. The dimension of heat is that of energy and the unit assigned to it is the *calorie*, the work done to raise 1 gram of water 1° C., or more precisely from 15 to 16° C. The *kilocalorie* (kcal.) is equal to 1000 cal.

The work done by the system, W, may be expressed as the energy utilized to effect a change in volume (V) against a pressure (P). In determinations of the calorimetric type it is the pressure which is maintained constant and the volume which is allowed to change. The system which absorbs heat increases its volume, thus performing work. The work done for a change in volume (ΔV) at constant pressure is equal to $P\Delta V$ and equation (2) becomes

$$Q = \Delta E + P\Delta V = \Delta H \tag{4}$$

where the change in heat energy at constant pressure, ΔH, refers to the change in "heat content" or *enthalpy*. If ΔH is negative, heat is evolved and the reaction is *exothermic;* if heat is absorbed, ΔH is positive and the reaction is *endothermic*. ΔH can be determined by using a calorimeter and several values are given for biochemically important compounds:

$$C_6H_{12}O_6(\text{solid}) + 6O_2(\text{gas}) \rightleftarrows 6H_2O(\text{liquid}) + 6CO_2(\text{gas})$$
$$\Delta H = -673 \text{ kcal./mole}$$

Similarly, the corresponding value for a fatty acid, palmitic acid, is −2380, and for an amino acid, glycine, it is −234. These are known as "heats of combustion."

FREE ENERGY

A problem which often arises in a consideration of biochemical reactions is that of the feasibility (spontaneity) of a reaction. For example, once it was proved that a protein molecule consists of amino acids linked together in the form of peptide bonds, it was suggested that the cell might make a protein molecule by a reversal of the process of hydrolysis. This may be illustrated for a dipeptide:

Alanylglycine + H_2O → alanine + glycine

Alanine + glycine → alanylglycine + H_2O

The first law contains within it no criteria for spontaneity. Spontaneity may be likened to the process of diffusion which occurs from a region of high concentration to that of a lower concentration; or to the fact that a hot object cools, but a cool object does not become hot by itself. These are spontaneous processes in which the system approaches a state of equilibrium. For chemical reactions it is important to know in which direction the reaction proceeds spontaneously, since a reaction proceeding spontaneously in a given direction can be made to do work. The useful work that can be obtained from a chemical reaction is called the *free energy change* and is designated ΔF. Its relation to the change in heat content is given below:

$$\Delta F = \Delta H - T\Delta S \tag{5}$$

where S stands for the term *entropy* which is related to the quantity of heat, Q, and the temperature, T. In any spontaneous process the entropy of the system increases. This is a statement of the second law of thermodynamics.

ΔS is a measure of the disorder of a system; the increase in entropy as a system approaches equilibrium is related to the change of a system from a highly ordered state to a more disorganized state. For example, the value of ΔS for the combustion of glucose is +60.7 cal./degree/mole, and the corresponding value for the denaturation of trypsin is +213. The latter value is quite high and is some index of the state of disorganization produced by the denaturation process (p. 102). Entropy can also be considered as a measure of probability. It is more probable that a sample of water will be in the random liquid state than in a highly organized crystalline state (ice). Thus, in any chemical reaction a certain amount of energy, in the form of entropy, is lost, owing to disorder of the system, and is unavailable for useful work. Therefore the change in free energy, ΔF, is more useful than ΔH as a measure of the work available from a chemical reaction, since ΔF also takes into account the energy due to entropy ($T\Delta S$) that is unavailable for useful work.

A reaction will be spontaneous if energy is produced during the reaction (exergonic); ΔF is negative. If a reaction requires energy in order to proceed (endergonic), ΔF is positive, and the reaction will not proceed spontaneously but must be supplied with energy. When a system is in equilibrium, there is no tendency to proceed in either direction, no work can be done by the system, and therefore $\Delta F = 0$.

FREE ENERGY AND THE EQUILIBRIUM CONSTANT

Consider a reaction where A are the reactants and B the products of the reaction:

$$A \rightarrow B \tag{6}$$

For this reaction ΔF will be the difference in free energies between the products and the reactants, or

$$\Delta F = F_B - F_A \tag{7}$$

The free energies of the products and the reactants are related to their *activities*, as follows:

$$F_A = F_A^\circ + RT \ln a_A \tag{8}$$
$$F_B = F_B^\circ + RT \ln a_B$$

where a_A and a_B are the activities of A and B, which, in dilute solution, are approximately equal to the concentrations of A and B; R = gas constant; T = absolute temperature; and $\ln$ = natural logarithm.

F_A° and F_B° are the free energies of A and B in a standard state where the activities are unity (approximately 1 M concentration). This leads to:

$$\Delta F = F_B - F_A = F_B^\circ - RT \ln a_A - (F_A^\circ - RT \ln a_B)$$
$$\Delta F = F_B^\circ - F_A^\circ + RT \ln \frac{a_B}{a_A}$$
$$\Delta F = \Delta F^\circ + RT \ln \frac{a_B}{a_A} \tag{9}$$

ΔF° is called the *standard free energy change* of the reaction when the activity of the products and reactants are unity. Since at equilibrium $\Delta F = 0$, then substituting in equation (9)

$$0 = \Delta F^\circ + RT \ln \frac{a_B}{a_A}$$

$$\Delta F^\circ = -RT \ln \frac{a_B}{a_A} \tag{10}$$

and since at equilibrium $\frac{a_B}{a_A}$ is equal to the equilibrium constant, K

$$\Delta F^\circ = -RT \ln K \tag{11}$$

This allows us to calculate ΔF° for a reaction from its equilibrium constant and since we now know the value for ΔF°, we can calculate ΔF for any reaction condition. Thus, the free energy of any reaction depends on the standard free energy change and on the concentration of reactants and products. Clearly the value of ΔF for a reaction will be altered by varying the ratio $\frac{a_B}{a_A}$. This suggests that an unfavorable reaction may be driven by increasing the concentration of reactants (A) or by decreasing the concentration of the products (B).

FREE ENERGY AND BIOCHEMICAL REACTIONS

Several examples of enzyme-catalyzed reactions and the calculated values for ΔF° are given below to demonstrate their usefulness.

a. The conversion of fumaric acid to malic acid (p. 284) by the enzyme fumarase is an important reaction in the sequence of oxidations involved in metabolism. For this reaction at 25° C. the equilibrium constant is 4.42. Thus,

$$\Delta F^\circ = -\frac{(1.987 \text{ cal.}}{\text{mol.} \times \text{deg.)}} (298.16 \text{ deg.})(2.303) \log_{10} (4.42)$$
$$= -880 \text{ cal./mole} \tag{12}$$

b. The hydrolysis of ATP may be pictured as follows, and is catalyzed by the enzyme adenosine triphosphatase:

$$ATP^{-4} + H_2O \rightarrow ADP^{-2} + HPO_4^{-2}$$
$$\Delta F^\circ = -7,000 \text{ cal./mole} \tag{13}$$

These reactions can and do occur spontaneously. However, consider the problem of the synthesis of a peptide bond:

$$\text{alanine} + \text{glycine} \rightarrow \text{alanylglycine} + H_2O$$
$$\Delta F^\circ = +4130 \text{ cal./mole} \tag{14}$$

This reaction cannot proceed spontaneously, although the reverse reaction of hydrolysis whose value for ΔF° would be −4130 can and does. It is important to emphasize that just because the value for ΔF° for a reaction is found to be negative, this does not mean that we know this reaction to take place. We must, of course, first show that there is present an enzyme to catalyze the reaction. Also, if a reaction has been shown to be thermodynamically unfeasible, a catalyst will not make the reaction proceed since, as we have pointed out earlier, a catalyst cannot change the point of equilibrium but only changes the *rate* by decreasing the activation energy.

COUPLING OF REACTIONS

Although a chemical reaction may have a value of $\Delta F°$ which is positive, it is possible to drive this reaction by providing energy to the system to overcome the unfavorable $\Delta F°$ value. Thus, one might drive the reaction by removing one or more of the end-products, or one might couple an endergonic reaction with one which is highly exergonic. The following examples will serve to illustrate these points.

a. Creatine phosphate is an important constituent of living cells. Also found in the cell are creatine and inorganic phosphate. Can it be assumed that creatine phosphate is synthesized by an enzyme-catalyzed reaction between creatine and phosphate? Determination of the standard free energy change for this reaction from the known values for each constituent leads to:

$$\text{creatine}^+ + \text{HPO}_4^- \rightarrow \text{creatine.PO}_4 + \text{H}_2\text{O}; \ \Delta F° = +7 \text{ kcal./mole} \quad (15)$$

This reaction does not proceed spontaneously if unassisted. However, it may be coupled with the hydrolysis of the terminal pyrophosphate linkage of ATP (equation 13), a reaction which is exergonic. This coupled reaction, involving the enzyme, creatine transphosphorylase, may be written:

$$\text{creatine} + \text{ATP} \rightarrow \text{ADP} + \text{creatine.PO}_4; \ \Delta F° \cong 0 \quad (16)$$

This reaction will therefore proceed to an appreciable extent. Note that the reverse reaction, the conversion of creatine phosphate to creatine and ATP will also take place, suggesting that creatine phosphate may serve as a source of ATP (high energy potential). It is believed that this is indeed the function of creatine phosphate in nerve and muscle cells.

Again, one should emphasize the fact that knowledge of the values of $\Delta F°$ for these reactions does not mean that by mixing creatine and ATP in a test tube one will get a coupled reaction. Thermodynamics merely tells us that, if there were a mechanism for coupling, the over-all reaction would proceed.

b. Acetyl coenzyme A (acetyl CoA) is an important intermediate in metabolic reactions (p. 285). The cell contains this compound as well as acetate and CoA. Is the synthesis of this compound from acetate and CoA thermodynamically feasible?

$$\text{acetate} + \text{CoA} \rightarrow \text{acetyl CoA}; \ \Delta F° = +7 \text{ kcal./mole} \quad (17)$$

The value of $\Delta F°$ tells us that the synthesis of this compound would require coupling with a highly exergonic reaction. Again, such a reaction could be the hydrolysis of ATP. However, this information does not tell us the mechanism for the coupling. Several such mechanisms are possible:

Mechanism I   acetate $+$ ATP $\rightarrow$ acetyl phosphate $+$ ADP
acetyl phosphate $+$ CoA $\rightarrow$ acetyl CoA $+$ PO_4

Mechanism II   CoA $+$ ATP $\rightarrow$ CoA phosphate $+$ ADP
acetate $+$ CoA phosphate $\rightarrow$ acetyl CoA $+$ PO_4

Mechanism III   acetate $+$ ATP $\rightarrow$ acetyl.AMP $+$ PP(pyrophosphate)
acetyl.AMP $+$ CoA $\rightarrow$ acetyl CoA $+$ PO_4

c. The reverse of reaction (12), the conversion of malate to fumarate, would have a value for $\Delta F°$ of $+880$ kcal./mole and would not proceed spontaneously. However the conversion of fumarate to aspartate is exergonic:

$$\text{fumarate}^{-2} + NH_4^+ \rightarrow \text{aspartate}^{\pm}; \quad \Delta F° = -3720 \text{ kcal./mole}$$

and a coupling of these two reactions serves to bring about:

$$\text{malate}^{-2} + NH_4^+ \rightarrow \text{aspartate}^{\pm} + H_2O; \quad \Delta F° = -2640 \text{ kcal./mole}$$

HIGH-ENERGY BONDS

The observation that there existed a group of organic phosphate esters whose hydrolyses were highly exergonic, whereas other organic phosphate esters had values of $\Delta F°$ much less negative led Lipmann to suggest that compounds such as ATP and creatine phosphate contained a phosphate ester bond of "high energy." This does not mean that the energy resides in that particular bond alone, but rather that the cleavage of this bond involves a release of much energy; that is, a compound is a high-energy compound with respect to the products of the reaction. Another term, suggested by Klotz, is perhaps more descriptive, "high transfer potential." Examples of such compounds are given below, and it should be noted that the anhydride structure is associated with many compounds of high transfer potential:

a. Compounds associated with high transfer potential. ($\Delta F° = -7$ kcal./mole)

acetyl coenzyme A	S-adenosylmethionine
acetyl phosphate	creatine phosphate
adenosine diphosphate	1,3-diphosphoglyceric acid
adenosine triphosphate	phospho-enol pyruvic acid

b. Compounds associated with a low transfer potential ($\Delta F° = -3$ kcal./mole)

glucose-1-phosphate	2-phosphoglyceric acid
glucose-6-phosphate	3-phosphoglyceric acid
glycerol phosphate	

Original estimates for the values of $\Delta F°$ of 10–12 kcal./mole for compounds such as ATP have since been replaced by 7 kcal. after more careful determinations. Despite this revision, this value does represent an important high transfer potential for such compounds, especially when one considers that it has been determined *in vitro* at relatively high concentrations in so far as the quantities present in the cell are concerned, and that the ratio of concentrations will affect the value of $\Delta F°$. The significance of compounds such as ATP, as well as GTP, CTP and UTP, is readily appreciated when we note that these compounds are intimately concerned in enzymatic reactions leading to the synthesis of RNA, DNA and proteins. The role of ATP in muscle contraction (p. 491) and nerve impulse transmission (p. 497) will be discussed.

REFERENCES

Laidler: Introduction to the Chemistry of Enzymes, 1954: *Neilands* and *Stumpf:* Outlines of Enzyme Chemistry, 1955. More advanced texts are by *Sumner* and *Myrbäck:* The Enzymes, 1951; *Sumner* and *Somers:* Chemistry and Methods of Enzymes, 1953; *Colowick* and *Kaplan:* Methods of Enzymology, 1956; *Dixon* and *Webb,* Enzymes, 1958.

A review dealing with the mechanism of enzyme action, published in book form, is edited by *McElroy* and *Glass,* 1954. A symposium dealing with enzymes as units of biologic structure and function, also in book form, is edited by *Gaebler,* 1956.

Reviews of current work may be found in Ann. Rev. Biochem., 29:45, 1960 (proteolytic enzymes by *Hartley*); Ibid., 29:73, 1960 (transferases by *Hoffmann-Ostenhof*); Ibid., 28:527, 1959 (oxygenases and hydroxylases by *Massart* and *Vercauteren*); Ibid., 27:427, 1958 (enzymic metabolism of drugs, etc. by *Brodie, Gillette* and *La Du*); Ibid., 27:489, 1958 (proteolytic enzymes by *Dixon, Neurath* and *Pechère*). See also Advances in Enzymology and Related Subjects of Biochemistry, Vol. 17, 1956, edited by *Nord.*

Two papers by *Sumner* on crystalline urease are in the J. Biol. Chem., 69:435, 1926, and 76:149, 1928. An interesting autobiographical sketch may be found in J. Chem. Educ., 14:255, 1937.

For the isolation and crystallization of enzymes, see *Northrop, Kunitz* and *Herriot:* Crystalline Enzymes, 1948.

Some individual papers of interest are the following: *Kimmel* and *Smith:* J. Biol. Chem., 207:515, 1954 (Crystalline Papain); *Vallee* and *Neurath:* Ibid, 217:253, 1955 (Carboxypeptidase, A Zinc Metalloenzyme); *Green* and *Cori:* Ibid., 151:21, 1943 (Crystalline Muscle Phosphorylase); *McElroy* and *Nason:* Borden's Review of Nutritional Research, 17:47, 1956 (Trace Elements in Nutrition); *Mahler, Hübscher* and *Baum:* J. Biol. Chem., 216:625, 1955 (Uricase, A Cuproprotein); *Moore, Hirs* and *Stein:* Federation Proceedings, 15:840, 1956 (Structure of Ribonuclease); *Anfinsen:* Ibid., 16:783, 1957 (Ribonuclease); *Neurath* and *Dixon:* Ibid., 16:791, 1957 (Trypsinogen and Chymotrypsinogen); *Markert* and *Moller:* Proc. Nat. Acad. Sciences, 45:753 (1959) (Multiple Forms of Enzymes); *Folk* and *Gladner:* J. Biol. Chem., 235:2272, 1960 (Carboxypeptidase).

Biochemical energetics are discussed by *Bray* and *White:* Kinetics and Thermodynamics in Biochemistry, 1957; *Édsall* and *Wyman:* Biophysical Chemistry, 1958; *Klotz:* Energetics in Biochemical Reactions, 1957.

Wellner and *Meister:* J. Biol. Chem., 235:2013, 1960 (L-amino acid oxidase).

See also *Frieden's* article on the elusive enzyme-substrate complex in Wallerstein Labs, August, 1960, p. 107.

DIGESTION
AND
ABSORPTION

CHAPTER SEVEN

DIGESTION

In general foods must be hydrolyzed—that is, simplified chemically—before they can be absorbed by the body. This is true of the carbohydrates other than the monosaccharides, and of the fats and proteins. It is not true of water and many inorganic ions, which pass through the digestive tract and are absorbed in their original form. The simplification of the carbohydrates, fats, and proteins is accomplished by a series of hydrolytic changes brought about by enzymes. These changes are carried on in the digestive tract, which includes the mouth, the esophagus, the stomach, and the small and large intestines (Fig. 41). Secretions from the pancreas and the bile find their way into the small intestine, and, as we shall see, play important roles in the digestive process.

As so much of digestion deals with the activity of enzymes, the reader will do well to reread Chapter 6, which deals with the general properties of enzymes.

SALIVARY DIGESTION

Salivary digestion deals largely with the action of ptyalin, an amylase, on starch. The preliminary mastication, involving the breaking up of food particles by the teeth, is a desirable step. Ptyalin is found in saliva, which represents a mixed secretion from the relatively large salivary glands and from accessory glands. The salivary glands consist of the parotid, the submaxillary, and the sublingual, and through their ducts they pour their secretions into the mouth. The flow of saliva is regulated

170

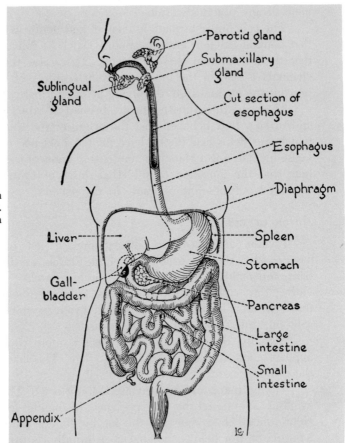

Figure 41. Diagram of the digestive tract. (Etheredge: Health Facts.)

by a reflex stimulation of the secretory nerves. Approximately from 1 to 1½ liters of saliva may be secreted by an individual in the course of 24 hours.

SALIVA

Saliva contains about 99.5 per cent of water. The solid material includes ptyalin, several proteins (of which mucin is the most important) and a number of substances found in blood and urine (such as ammonia, amino acids, urea, uric acid, cholesterol, calcium, sodium, potassium, magnesium, phosphate, chloride and bicarbonate) (see Table 28).

The average pH of unstimulated saliva may vary considerably, although as a rule it is near 6.8.

The fact that saliva contains many of the constituents found in blood has suggested the possibility that the determination of such constituents in saliva may have diagnostic value; but the irregular fluctuations of these constituents, together with a failure to find any constant relationship between the constituents of blood and saliva, have prevented the attainment of any practical results.

The calcium phosphate in enamel and dentin is less soluble in fluids that contain calcium and phosphorus, such as saliva, than it is in fluids that do not contain these elements. Therefore, the presence of these elements is one of the most important features of saliva, because they prevent the enamel from dissolving at the normal pH of saliva.

Traces of thiocyanate ions are present in saliva (as well as in blood and urine). It is believed that the origin of the thiocyanate is cyanides which are detoxified in the liver, in the presence of sulfur compounds (cysteine) to form thiocyanate. In this connection, it is of interest to note that the ingestion of sublethal doses of cyanide gives rise to an increased output of thiocyanate in the urine.

ACTION OF PTYALIN

Ptyalin (also known as salivary amylase) acts on starch,* producing a series of ill-defined products: soluble starch, erythrodextrin, achrodextrins, and maltose. The starch and soluble starch give a blue color with iodine; the erythrodextrin gives a red color; the achrodextrins and maltose give no color. Maltose is the only product which reduces Benedict's solution, unless some glucose is formed.

Actually, the process of hydrolysis is more complex. Some maltose appears even at the erythrodextrin stage. This has been attributed to the complex nature of the starch itself (see p. 31).

The optimum pH for amylase activity is 6.6. The activity of the enzyme is stimulated by the presence of halide ions, particularly the chloride ion. The removal of this ion by dialysis renders ptyalin inactive. At a pH of 4 or below, the enzyme is rapidly destroyed. However, when the food reaches the fundus part of the stomach, salivary digestion may still proceed for 15 to 30 minutes, owing to the slow accumulation of acid and to the partial neutralization of the acid by a temporary combination with the protein of the food.

The ptyalin of the mouth, like the amylase in pancreatic juice, belongs to the group of α-amylases. The primary action of these amylases on starch is liquefaction or lowering of viscosity, the amylose and amylopectin molecules being split by fission of α-1,4- glucosidic linkages into α-dextrins. The second process involves the breakup of 1,4- linkages which had so far escaped attack, yielding α-maltose as the main product, and some glucose.

Pancreatic amylase, which finds its way into the small intestine, continues the hydrolysis of any undigested starch.

In the tissues we find an enzyme, phosphorylase, which can also break down starch and glycogen. This action is not to be confused with

* Ptyalin can also act on glycogen.

TABLE 28. COMPOSITION* OF UNSTIMULATED AND STIMULATED† SALIVA
(Values are in milligrams per 100 ml. except as noted.)

	Unstimulated		Stimulated	
	Range	Average	Range	Average
Calcium	4.6–11.0	6.2	3.5–9.2	5.6
Magnesium	0.2–1.3	0.7		
Sodium	20–55	40	18–88	55
Potassium	50–63	55	57–93	70
Ammonia	6–30		1.4–12	6
Chloride	30–63	55	31–63	42
Fluoride (parts per million)				0.1
Inorganic phosphorus	11–26	17	6–18	12.5
Thiocyanate		15		
pH	6.0–7.4	6.8	7.1–7.8	7.3
CO_2 capacity (cc. per 100 cc.)	5–25	12	8–44	25
Titratable alkalinity‡	50–120	70	80–180	120
Lactic acid		1.5	0.64–2.04	
Total protein	214–525	320	208–565	280
Mucoid (as sodium mucinate)		250	210–290	260
Reducing carbohydrate	11–28		14–30	
Alcohol-ether soluble phosphorus	0.05–1.0	0.24		
Cholesterol	3–15	7.5		
Urea				10
Uric acid		1.5		
Vitamin C				0.25

* These data are from a number of sources.
† Stimulated saliva refers here to the secretion produced while chewing paraffin.
‡ Titratable alkalinity is expressed as cubic centimeters of 0.02N HCl needed to titrate 100 ml. of saliva with methyl orange as indicator.
(From Karshan.)

the action of amylase on starch and glycogen—whether the amylase be ptyalin or pancreatic amylase or amylases which have their origin in the vegetable kingdom. The amylases act by the utilization of water; the phosphorylases utilize phosphate. These two actions may be termed *hydrolysis* and *phosphorolysis,* respectively.

A number of the amylases—including ptyalin—have been isolated in crystalline form.

ESTIMATION OF PTYALIN ACTIVITY

The rate of starch hydrolysis (and the activity of the ptyalin) may be estimated by determining the achromic point—the point at which iodine fails to give a color with the substrate—or by determining the extent of reduction. A more carefully controlled estimation would include the achromic point, the residual polysaccharide, the total reducing power, and the reducing power after the precipitation of the dextrins by alcohol. Using such methods, Glock found that the relative rates of hydrolysis were different with different starches.

MUCIN

Mucin is a *mixture* of proteins and gives to saliva its "ropy" consistency. The mucins have been classified under a number of groups, depending upon their chemical makeup: mucins proper, sulfomucins, chondroproteins and mucoproteins. The mucin of saliva comes under the heading of the mucoproteins—glycoproteins whose prosthetic grouping is of the nature of mucoitin sulfuric acid (glucosamine, glucuronic, acetic, and sulfuric acids).

TOOTH DECAY (DENTAL CARIES)

This disease deals with the disintegration of the enamel, the dentin and the pulp of the tooth. It has been suggested that in addition to its function as a digestive agent, saliva is also important in its influence on the possible development of dental caries. This well-nigh ever-present disease—85–95 per cent of people in civilized countries suffer from it—is of two kinds: in the one, common to young people, caries occurs in the pits and fissures of the crown or near points of contact of adjacent teeth; in the other, prevalent among older people, the smooth surfaces of the crown or exposed roots are attacked. The first variety is the more common, occurring very often during the period of eruption of the teeth.

The various centers of attack, the pits and fissures of the crown and the contact points, are precisely centers where food particles are likely to be deposited. The action of bacteria on such food particles may cause the production of acid. It is believed—and this is advanced as a theory of the origin of dental caries—that first the enamel on the surface of the tooth and then the dentin underneath are dissolved by such acids.

If such a theory is sound, then one might expect a difference between the neutralizing power of saliva derived from a patient suffering with caries and the saliva derived from a caries-free individual, assuming that saliva has some access to the regions where decay occurs. Furthermore, since the enamel is rich in calcium and phosphorus, an analysis of such elements in saliva may prove revealing.

Karshan and Krasnow did find that saliva, stimulated by chewing paraffin and obtained from individuals showing no caries, had a neutralizing power (as revealed by titration with acid), which, in group averages, was 10 per cent greater than that obtained from persons suffering with caries. A much greater difference in mean values between the two groups was found by Hubbell. A difference in neutralizing power between the two groups has also been found in unstimulated saliva.

The bicarbonate in saliva is the main neutralizing substance for acids; it is usually estimated by determining the amount of CO_2 evolved when acid is added. If acid is added, and the amount of carbon dioxide which is evolved is determined, the greater the volume of such gas evolved, the larger the amount of alkali in the fluid. Using many subjects, and taking average values, the results with stimulated saliva were: caries-free, 31 (cubic centimeters of CO_2 per 100 ml. of saliva); arrested caries, 30.2; active caries, 19.5. The H_2CO_3 content is greater in the caries-free group.

Turning next to studies dealing with the content of calcium and phosphorus in saliva, several observers showed that the mean values for total calcium and inorganic phosphate were higher in caries-free than in active-caries groups. This has been denied by others.

There is apparently some correlation between the development of caries and the penetration of enamel, on the one hand, and the composition of saliva, on the other. However, these studies tell us little or nothing at all about possible methods of preventing such tooth decay. Attempts have been made, with indifferent success so far, to change the diet in the hope that it might influence the composition of the saliva. (For the effect of *fluoride* on tooth decay, see Chap. 19.)

SALIVARY CALCULUS

This abnormal concretion—formed on the teeth and sometimes in a salivary duct—contains calcium phosphate as its principal inorganic constituent. The idea has arisen, very naturally, that the concentration of calcium and phosphate in saliva may be related to such deposits. Furthermore, the precipitation of calcium phosphate would be a function of the pH of the medium. Actual experiments indicated that the mean value for the amount of calcium in the calculus-free group was lower than that in the calculus group. To a certain extent this was also true of the content of phosphate, which was lower in the calculus-free group. The studies in pH showed no such clearcut differences.

GASTRIC DIGESTION

Digestion in the stomach involves, primarily, the action of the enzyme pepsin and hydrochloric acid on protein, yielding hydrolytic products such as proteoses and peptones. The enzyme rennin is present in the young; its action is to curdle milk. Some lipase, a fat-splitting enzyme, may also be found. The food, mixed with saliva and formed into a bolus, passes through the pharynx and esophagus into the stomach. There it gradually comes in contact with the pepsin and the acid. For some time, however, considerable starch digestion continues in the fundus part of the stomach.

As early as 1783 Spallanzani detected the acidity of gastric juice and also noted that it had the power of dissolving meat. He introduced food in perforated metal capsules into the stomach and recovered their contents by strings attached to the capsules. In 1833 Beaumont, an American physician, published his "Experiments and Observations on the Gastric Juice and the Physiology of Digestion," in which he described various experiments performed on a patient who, as a result of a gunshot wound, found himself with an opening from the stomach to the exterior. This publication laid the foundation for much of our knowledge of gastric digestion. He described the digestibility of different foods in the stomach, confirmed the presence of hydrochloric acid (first noted by Prout), compared *in vivo* with *in vitro* digestion and made an exhaustive study of the motions of the stomach.

Further contributions on the composition of normal gastric juice were made by Heidenhain, who cut away the fundic or pyloric end of the stomach of an animal and created an opening to the exterior. The secretion of this isolated sac was then studied. The experimental technique was subsequently vastly improved by Pavlov.

GASTRIC JUICE

In the walls of the stomach one finds two types of cells, those at the pyloric end known as the chief cells, and those in the central part of the stomach and elsewhere, consisting of chief cells and parietal (border or oxyntic) cells. These cells secrete what ultimately appears as gastric juice. It is believed by some that the hydrochloric acid is produced by the oxyntic cells, while the chief cells throughout the stomach produce the other constituents.

The flow of gastric juice is controlled by nerve fibers. In one of his classic experiments dealing with "sham feeding," Pavlov divided the esophagus and brought the ends to the skin. The animal ate and discharged its food through this opening, without any of the food finding its way into the stomach. Nevertheless, an abundant flow of gastric juice was induced so long as the vagi were intact; but the flow was interrupted when the nerves were cut.

However, there is apparently a *chemical* as well as a psychical influence. It is possible to extract from the pyloric part of the gastric mucosa a substance to which the name *gastrin* has been given, which when injected into the blood causes a flow of gastric juice. Gastrin plays the role of a hormone. A similar effect is produced by histamine. Both gastrin and histamine stimulate the secretion of hydrochloric acid.

Composition of Gastric Juice. The stomach secretes some 2 to 3 liters of gastric juice in twenty-four hours. The juice, like saliva, usually contains water to the extent of more than 99 per cent. The material consists of mucin; the enzymes pepsin, rennin (in the young), and lipase; hydrochloric acid (around 0.5 per cent); and the chlorides of sodium and potassium, phosphates, etc.

ORIGIN OF HYDROCHLORIC ACID

It is a remarkable fact that a mineral acid of the type of hydrochloric, with a concentration up to 0.5 per cent, should be made in the

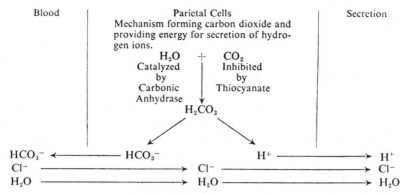

Figure 42. Formation of hydrochloric acid in the stomach. (From Davenport and Fisher: Am. J. Physiol., *131*:165.)

stomach from an approximately neutral fluid. No other secretion manufactured by the body approaches the gastric juice in such high acidity. What is the origin of this hydrochloric acid? It is not hard to assume that the chloride part of the acid has its origin in the chloride of the blood; but no satisfactory explanation has yet been offered for the origin of the comparatively high hydrogen ion concentration. The theories advanced are legion.

In forming the acid secretion, the cells of the gastric mucosa (of dogs) lower the pH from 7.4 (in blood) to pH 1 to 2 (acid secretion).

The chloride ion concentration is increased from 0.11 M in plasma to 0.17 M in the secretion.

A mechanism for the secretion of acid has been suggested by Davenport (Fig. 42). In the parietal cells carbonic acid is formed, which dissociates and is catalyzed in this reaction by the enzyme, carbonic anhydrase. Chloride ions pass from the plasma through the cells and into the secretion. These chloride ions which are removed from the plasma are replaced by the bicarbonate ions formed in the cells at the time when hydrogen ions are formed.

Davies is of the opinion that the reaction of fundamental importance in the production of HCl in gastric mucosa is

$$H_2O \longrightarrow H^+ + OH^-$$

The H^+ ions are secreted and the OH^- ions are neutralized by CO_2 and passed into the blood.

Davies finds that there is a general correlation between acid secretion and the potential difference across the gastric mucosa ("the resistance of the latter and its ability to produce electrical power externally"). This indicates that the formation of HCl is an electrochemical phenomenon.

PEPSIN AND PEPSINOGEN

The active proteolytic enzyme in the gastric juice is pepsin, which, however, is quite inactive except in acid solution.* Langley pointed out many years ago that in the gastric mucosa the enzyme existed in an inactive form which was more resistant to alkali than the pepsin. The inactive form of the enzyme was given the name *pepsinogen,* and the general name *zymogen* was given to an inactive form of an enzyme.

In the meantime both pepsin and pepsinogen have been isolated in crystalline form, and both show the general characteristics of proteins.

Pepsinogen has no proteolytic activity but is converted into active pepsin by H^+ ions or by pepsin itself, making the activation process an autocatalytic one. Pepsinogen has a molecular weight of 42,500, whereas that of pepsin is 34,500. During the activation process six peptides are split off; one is an inhibitor of pepsin with a molecular weight of 3100, and the other five have molecular weights of about 1000. The precursor and the enzyme itself are both single peptide chains. The activation process appears to consist of the "unmasking" of an active site. This site probably involves the tyrosyl residue, since acetylation of these residues with ketene leads to a progressive loss of activity as the degree of the acetylation of tyrosine increases.

For the determination of peptic activity several methods are available, e.g., the use of Van Slyke amino nitrogen determination and the Sørenson formol titration. Northrop introduced two others. One is based on the increase in conductivity as hydrolysis of the protein proceeds, and the other is based on the rate of change in viscosity of gelatin during digestion. A colorimetric method, using hemoglobin as a substrate, which was perfected by Anson and Mirsky, can be used not only for the determination of peptic activity but also for determination of the activity of other proteolytic enzymes, such as trypsin, papain, cathepsin. Denatured hemoglobin is digested by pepsin under standard conditions; the undigested hemoglobin is precipitated with trichloroacetic acid; and the amount of unprecipitated protein-split products (a measure of the amount of pepsin present) is estimated colorimetrically with Folin's phenol reagent—a phosphotungstic-phosphomolybdic acid—which gives a blue color with the tyrosine and tryptophan present in the hydrolyzed extract.

The great advantage of Anson and Mirsky's method is that "hemoglobin, unlike casein and gelatin, is a reproducible substrate. Different batches of hemoglobin are digested at the same rate by a proteinase solution."

The optimum pH for pepsin action in near 2. What is important,

---

* The claim has been made that another proteolytic enzyme, called gastricsin, is present in gastric juice. (Tang, Wolf, Caputto and Trucco: J. Biol. Chem., 234: 1174, 1959).

as Northrop has shown, is the hydrogen ion concentration, and not any particular acid. At equal pH's, the rate of peptic digestion of various proteins is the same in solutions of hydrochloric, nitric, sulfuric, oxalic, citric, and phosphoric acids.

THE PRODUCTS OF PEPTIC HYDROLYSIS

It is probable that during the few hours that the food stays in the stomach peptic hydrolysis of proteins produces the rather ill-defined proteoses and peptones, but that no amino acids are produced. By incubating protein with an artificial pepsin–hydrochloric acid mixture for some 24 hours it is possible to show the production of some amino acids; but this can hardly apply to gastric digestion *in vivo*.

The first product of peptic hydrolysis is said to be "acid-metaprotein," a soluble protein which precipitates on the careful addition of alkali, and which coagulates when the precipitate is heated. Further hydrolysis produces proteoses and peptones. Proteoses are precipitated with ammonium sulfate; one-half saturated ammonium sulfate precipitating the primary proteoses, and the fully saturated solution precipitating the secondary proteoses. In the filtrate we find peptones, which can be precipitated by certain alkaloidal reagents like tannic acid. These ill-defined stages of peptic hydrolysis differ somewhat in their reaction to the biuret reagent: the primary proteins give definite violet colors, whereas peptones mixed with the biuret reagent are rose-red in color.

RENNIN (ALSO KNOWN AS RENNET, OR CHYMOSIN)

Another enzyme probably elaborated by the cells of the gastric mucosa[*] is one which coagulates milk. This enzyme, known as rennin, acts on the casein of the milk. It is believed that the rennin acts on the casein to change it to some soluble product, to which the name *paracasein* has been given. In the presence of calcium, the paracasein becomes the milk clot.

Commercial peptic preparations—and preparations of various proteolytic enzymes—show not only proteolytic properties, but also the property of clotting milk. This had led to a view that pepsin and rennin were one and the same enzyme, and that within the pepsin molecule certain groupings exhibited rennin properties. Tauber and Kleiner were able to separate the rennin from pepsin by a combination of isoelectric and fractional precipitations. This rennin has an activity of $1:4,550,000$ when skim milk and calcium chloride are used as substrates, but shows no peptic activity at pH 2 (using the formol method). Crystalline pepsin, however, has a rennet activity of $1:800,000$. Berridge has obtained a

[*] Probably present in relatively large quantities only in the stomach of young animals.

crystalline product capable of clotting ten million times its weight of milk in ten minutes.

The pH optimum (for the digestion of hemoglobin) of this crystalline rennin is 4, whereas the pH optimum for crystalline pepsin is 1.8.*

LIPASE

This is an enzyme which hydrolyzes fats. Its action at pH 1 to 2, the normal reaction of gastric juice, is very slight, but Willstätter has shown that its optimum pH is about 5, at which acidity hydrolysis becomes more apparent. In any case, it would seem that under normal conditions, gastric lipase is of little physiological importance. As we shall see presently, the important fat-splitting enzyme is released from the pancreas.

GASTRIC ANALYSIS

An analysis of gastric contents is of importance in clinical diagnosis.

The quantity of material found normally in the fasting stomach (interdigestive period) is about 50 ml. An increase above this amount may be due to retention or regurgitation from the duodenum.

Freshly secreted gastric juice is usually colorless. If yellow or green, it may indicate the presence of bile, due to intestinal obstruction. If red or brown, it may mean the presence of blood, which can be confirmed by the benzidine test (p. 223). Such blood may suggest lesions such as carcinoma of the stomach, or peptic ulcer.

Achlorhydria, the absence of free acid, together with the absence of pepsin, may suggest pernicious anemia, carcinoma of the stomach, etc.†

To determine gastric acidity, we measure the number of milliliters of 0.1N NaOH required to neutralize 100 ml. of gastric contents. The *free* HCl may show an average value of 18.5; which means that 18.5 ml. of 0.1N NaOH are needed to neutralize 100 ml. of gastric contents. The free HCl may also be expressed as grams of HCl per 100 ml. of gastric contents; an average value would be 0.0675 gm.

By *total acidity* is meant free HCl, HCl combined with protein, acid salts (phosphates and carbonates), and organic acids (lactic, butyric, etc.). Its value averages 30; that is, 30 ml. of 0.1N NaOH are needed to neutralize 100 ml. of gastric contents, showing the presence of 0.1095 gm. of HCl.

The methods for free and total acidity are identical, except that different indicators are used. For instance, Töpfer's reagent (dimethylaminoazobenzene), an indicator with a pH range of 2.9 to 4, is frequently used for the determination of free HCl; and phenolphthalein,

---

* Commercially, rennin plays its role in the making of cheese and in the preparation of junket.

† *Achylia* connotes the absence of both HCl and the gastric enzymes.

with a pH range of about 8 to 9, is used for determining total acidity.

Stomach contents are withdrawn after stimulation by the introduction of foods (test meals), alcohol, or the injection of histamine.

Hypoacidity (hypochlorhydria) may suggest carcinoma of the stomach, chronic constipation, chronic gastritis (inflammation of the stomach), or chronic appendicitis.

Hyperacidity may suggest gastric ulcer (peptic ulcer), duodenal ulcer, or cholecystitis (inflammation of the gallbladder).

INTESTINAL DIGESTION

After a time, the food in the stomach, now in more or less liquid form (chyme), passes into the small intestine. Here it is attacked by intestinal juice (*succus entericus*), pancreatic juice, and bile. The latter two find their way into the duodenum via the pancreatic and bile ducts, respectively, which open by a common orifice into the small intestine (Fig. 43). For convenience, we shall discuss these three secretions separately.

PANCREATIC ENZYMES

Pancreatic juice is the most important of the digestive juices. It contains enzymes that split proteins, an enzyme that hydrolyzes starch, and another that hydrolyzes fats. As in the case of pepsinogen, the proteolytic enzymes as they first appear are in the inactive, or zymogen, form. One of them, trypsinogen, is activated by a substance present in the intestinal juice and referred to as *enterokinase*. Chymotrypsinogen,

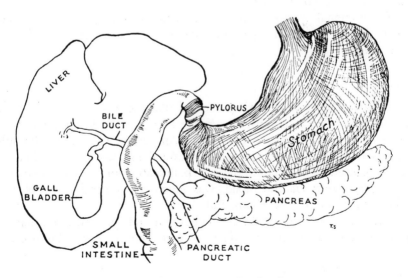

Figure 43. The pancreas and related organs.

another proteolytic enzyme, is activated by trypsin. Carboxypeptidase is also found in pancreatic juice.

There is evidence that the pancreatic juice contains some factor that plays a part in the metabolism of lipids. The blood lipids (cholesterol; free and esterified; phospholipids; and total fatty acids) drop markedly when depancreatized dogs are given insulin and a normal diet. The same result is obtained by completely occluding the pancreatic ducts. The condition can be markedly improved by the administration of pancreatic juice or the addition of pancreas to the diet.

TRYPSIN

Trypsinogen, an inactive precursor of trypsin, is produced in the pancreas. After its secretion it is activated either by trypsin itself or by *enterokinase,* a proteolytic enzyme produced by intestinal secretion. The conversion of trypsinogen to trypsin involves the loss of a hexapeptide. There is also present in the juice a protein that combines with trypsin to form an inactive complex. Trypsin is capable of converting all of the precursor proteolytic enzymes to the active enzymes. If trypsin is added slowly to pancreatic juice, activation of these enzymes does not take place. If, however, the same amount of trypsin is added instantaneously, the whole mechanism is set off and all precursor enzymes are activated.

The process of conversion by enterokinase, Kunitz finds, follows the course of a catalytic unimolecular reaction, "the rate of formation of trypsin being proportional to the concentration of enterokinase added, and the ultimate amount of trypsin formed being independent of the concentration of enterokinase."

By fractional precipitation with ammonium sulfate, using the proper pH conditions, Kunitz has prepared some highly concentrated solutions of enterokinase.

SECRETIN*

In 1902 Bayliss and Starling showed that the stimulation of pancreatic juice was due to a substance in the lining of the intestinal wall, to which they gave the name of *secretin.* An extract containing the substance could be obtained from the intestinal mucosa which, when injected, caused a copious flow of pancreatic juice. This chemical messenger, acting via the blood, was given the general name of *hormone* ("to excite") (see Chap. 21).

The discoverers claimed that the hormone was present in an inactive (prosecretin) condition, and that the acid coming from the stomach

* See also Chapter 21.

converted the inactive into the active (secretin) form. Once produced, this secretin finds its way into the blood and then stimulates the pancreas.

Hammarsten, Ågren, and Wilander isolated secretin, and found it to be a polypeptide with a molecular weight of 5000.

At the time when secretin stimulates pancreatic secretion, the gallbladder empties. This is due to instigation of contraction of the musculature of the gallbladder by a hormone, cholecystokinin.

Ivy, in confirmation of Raper's work, states that there are two hormonal factors controlling the external secretion of the pancreas: one is secretin, which stimulates the production of pancreatic fluid and bicarbonates; and the other is another hormone, to which the name *pancreozymin* has been given, which stimulates enzyme production by the pancreas.

CHYMOTRYPSIN

This proteolytic enzyme is present in several forms as a precursor. One which has been well characterized is chymotrypsin α which is activated by trypsin but not by chymotrypsin. The active chymotrypsins which are formed are many: α, β, γ, δ, ϵ, and π chymotrypsins.

Further hydrolysis is due to a mixture of enzymes—carboxypeptidase, in the pancreatic juice, and aminopeptidase and dipeptidase, mainly in intestinal juice.

PANCREATIC AMYLASE

This enzyme is, in general, similar to the ptyalin of saliva. It has been isolated in crystalline form and is then stable at a pH of 6.9 at 2° C. There is some evidence to point to inositol as a constituent of this enzyme.

LIPASE

This important enzyme hydrolyzes fats into fatty acid and glycerol. Enzyme activity may be estimated by titrating the free fatty acid produced with standard alkali. Using protein-precipitating agents, King has succeeded in purifying a sample sufficiently to regard it as protein.

Apparently the hydrolysis is a step-by-step action, for the triglyceride is first converted to diglyceride, then to monoglyceride, then to glycerol or a derivative (phosphate)—fatty acid being released at each step.

INTESTINAL ENZYMES

The small intestine itself secretes a juice which contains a number of enzymes of importance to digestion. Aminopeptidase and dipeptidase have already been mentioned. Several additional proteolytic enzymes are undoubtedly also present. In addition there are enzymes which hydrolyze three of the disaccharides. Sucrase converts sucrose into glucose and fructose; maltase converts maltose into two molecules of glucose; lactase hydrolyzes lactose into galactose and glucose. Phosphatases—largely alkaline phosphatase—split several of the compounds of phosphorus (nucleotides, hexosephosphate) yielding, as one of the products, inorganic phosphate. Enterokinase, which is an enzyme, though not a digestive one, is also found in intestinal juice. The intestine also contains a lecithinase which hydrolyzes lecithin into fatty acid, glycerol, phosphoric acid, and choline.

BILE

The formation of bile is one of the many activities of the liver. The bile is stored in the gallbladder, which is attached to the liver. During fasting, the bile accumulates in the gallbladder; during digestion, especially after a meal rich in fats, bile leaves the bladder to enter the small intestine (see Figs. 44 and 45). The hormone cholecystokinin instigates the contraction of the gallbladder and, probably, the relaxation of the common duct sphincter.

Bile is alkaline in reaction (pH 7.8 to 8.6) and is composed of bile salts, bile pigments, lecithin, cholesterol, inorganic salts, mucin and other

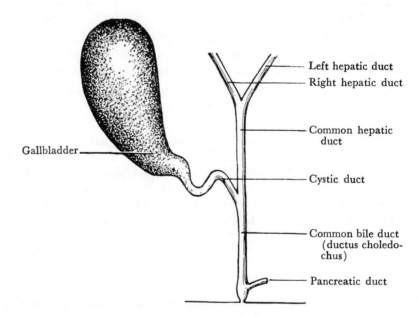

Figure 44. Diagram of bile ducts. (From Pitzman: Fundamentals of Human Anatomy. C. V. Mosby Co.)

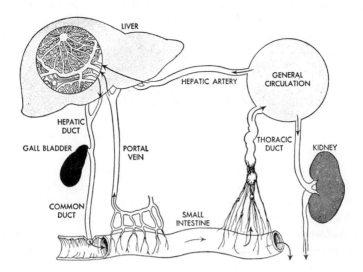

Figure 45. Circulation of bile. Precursors of bile acids are supplied by protein (glycine and taurine) and sterols (cholic acid). Formation of bile acids occurs in the polygonal liver cells. From these cells, the bile acids are secreted into bile canaliculi that lead to the intrahepatic ductal system.

Bile acids are absorbed along with fats. Most enter the portal circulation, are carried to the liver, and again secreted in the bile. Bile acids traverse this cycle repeatedly unless lost through the intestine, kidneys, or from biliary fistula. Some bile acids enter intestinal lymphatics, are carried to the general circulation, and return to the liver in the hepatic arteries. (From Therapeutic Notes, by courtesy of Parke, Davis & Co.)

substances, e.g., urea, alkaline phosphatase. It is, in reality, both a secretion and an excretion, the secretory substances being represented by the bile salts and the excretory ones by the bile pigments, cholesterol, etc.*

BILE SALTS

The value of bile in digestion is largely due to these salts which are formed in the liver. They aid in the digestion and absorption of fat and the absorption of fat-soluble vitamins A, D, E, and K. How this is brought about is now fairly clear. In the first place, mixed with fats, these bile salts lower the surface tension and increase the emulsification of fats, which makes them more easily digested by lipase. In the second place, they combine with fatty acids, produced as a result of lipolytic action, giving rise to a complex which is more soluble and more easily absorbed.

The evidence points to some value of bile salts in promoting in-

---

* There is some evidence that protein stimulates the formation of bile and bile salts.

testinal absorption of fats and fat-soluble vitamins on those occasions when there is a lack of bile in the intestine.*

The bile salts are made up of sodium taurocholate and sodium glycocholate. The former is the sodium salt of taurocholic acid, a combination of taurine and cholic acid. Sodium glycocholate is the sodium salt of glycocholic acid, a combination of glycine and cholic acid.

Taurine, $CH_2.CH_2.SO_3H$, or aminoethylsulfonic acid, is derived
$$\underset{NH_2}{|}$$
from cystine.

Cholic acid is related to cholesterol in structure; the carbon skeleton is similar, but the side-chain is somewhat different, and the relationship of the first two rings, configurationally speaking, is also different. However, Bloch and Rittenberg have shown that the administration to the dog of cholesterol containing heavy hydrogen gives rise to a cholic acid which contains as much of the deuterium as does the cholesterol in the blood and bile.

Besides cholic acid, several other closely related compounds are found in bile, and all of them show a characteristic steroid configuration; examples are deoxycholic acid (of microbial origin) and lithocholic acid.

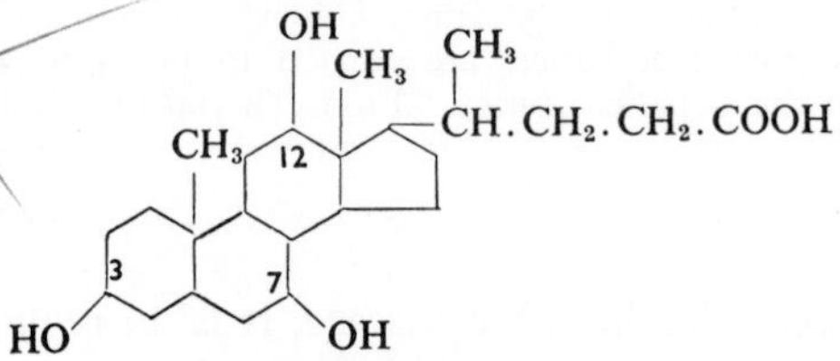

Cholic acid

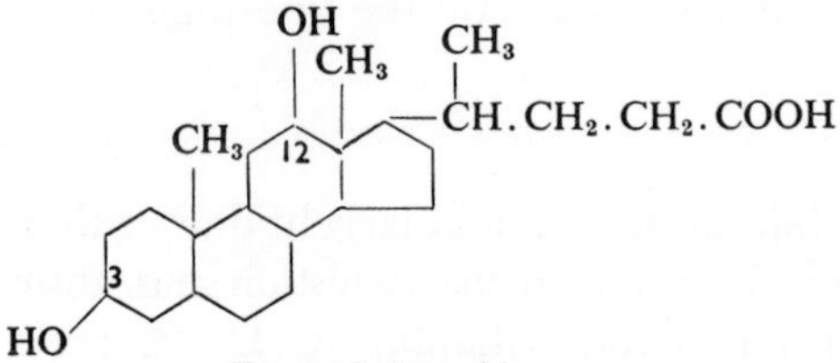

Deoxycholic acid

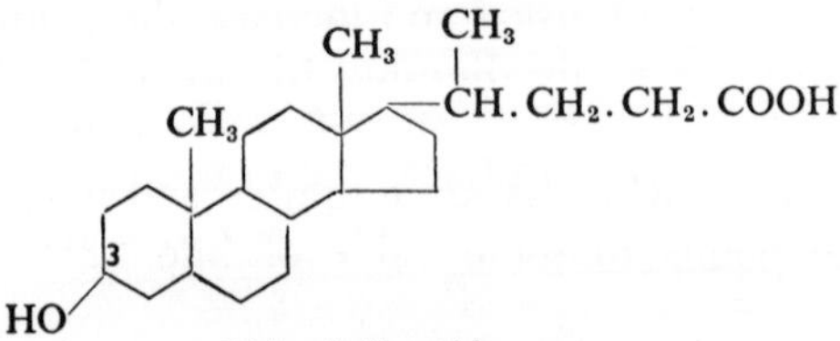

Lithocholic acid

* When bile is excluded from the intestine, excessive amounts of fat appear in the stool (steatorrhea).

Bile acids are synthesized by the animal (from cholesterol). The amount of these acids excreted is less than the total amount formed. Nor do these acids accumulate in the animal body. By studying the fate of cholic acid in the guinea pig, it can be shown that when the acid is injected intravenously it disappears from the body and is not eliminated in the excreta. However, the disappearance is due largely to decomposition within the cecum through the action of bacteria.

BILE PIGMENTS

The bile pigments have their origin for the most part in the decomposition of hemoglobin of the red cell. Possibly the first stage in this decomposition is a compound present to a very small extent inside the red cell, called *choleglobin*, one of a group of altered hemoglobins (*verdoglobins*). The next step in the breakdown of the hemoglobin molecule is the splitting of the iron-protoporphyrin (heme, see p. 205) from the protein, globin, and the opening of the porphyrin ring with a removal of iron. The new structure, a tetrapyrrane, is the basic structure of the bile pigments:

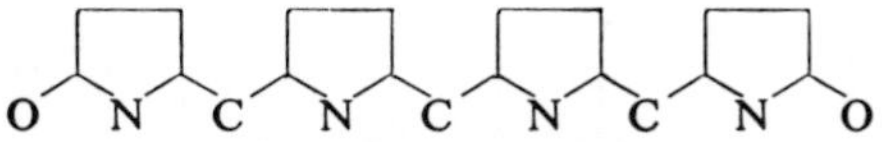

Bile pigment skeleton

The bile pigment most closely resembling the protoporphyrin structure is the green biliverdin:

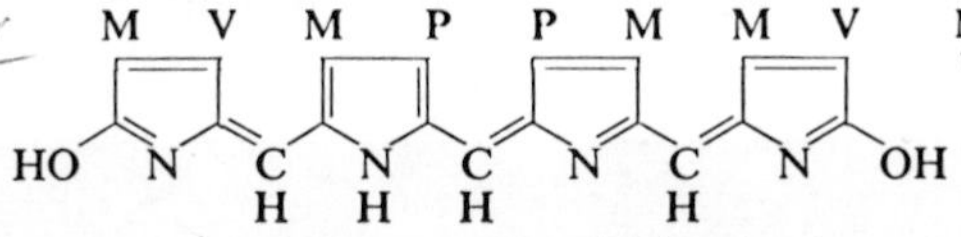

M = methyl (CH₃)
V = vinyl (CH=CH₂)
P = propionic acid
(CH₂CH₂COOH)

Biliverdin

This is presumably converted to bilirubin, the major bile pigment in the blood, where it is largely bound to serum albumin. Bilirubin is orange in color and is a partially reduced form of biliverdin:

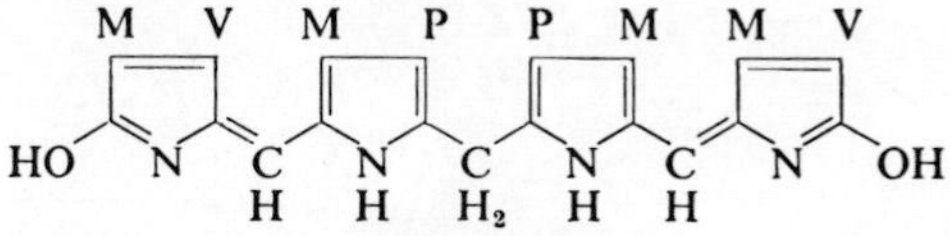

Bilirubin

Reduction of bilirubin yields the colorless mesobilirubinogen:

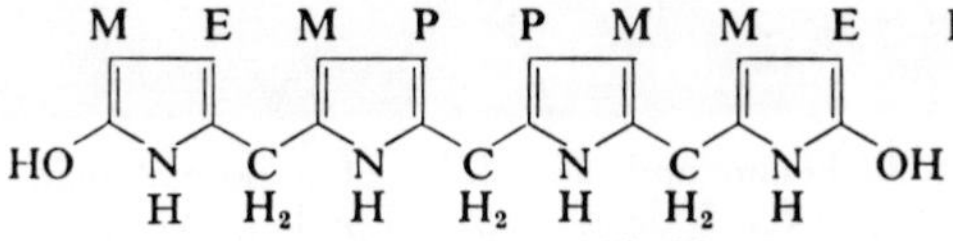

E = ethyl (CH₂CH₃)

Mesobilirubinogen

The action of intestinal bacteria on mesobilirubinogen is presumed to result in the formation of stercobilinogen. Both of these are excreted in feces and urine. Some of each undergoes autoxidation resulting in the formation of stercobilin and urobilin. Stercobilinogen and stercobilin are excreted to the largest extent. Some of the bile pigments are re-absorbed into the circulation where most of it is re-excreted via the bile into the intestinal tract. For analytical purposes the combined bilinogens in the urine are determined and referred to as the "urobilinogen" content.

M   E   M   P   P   M   M   E

HO   N   C   N   C   N   C   N   OH
      H   H₂ H   H   H₂ H

Urobilin

M   E   M   P   P   M   M   E

H
H
OH   N   C   N   C   N   C   N   OH
          H   H₂ H   H₂ H   H₂ H

Stercobilinogen

M   E   M   P   P   M   M   E

H
H
HO   N   C   N   C   N   C   N   OH
          H   H₂ H   H   H₂ H

Stercobilin

Not all of the stercobilin originates from hemoglobin. London fed N^{15}-glycine to a dog and analyzed for the isotope in both the heme of

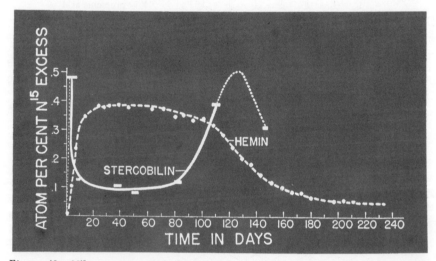

Figure 46. N^{15} concentration in hemin and stercobilin of a normal man after the start of feeding N^{15}-labeled glycine for 2 days. (From London, West, Shemin, and Rittenberg: J. Biol. Chem., *184:*351, 1950.)

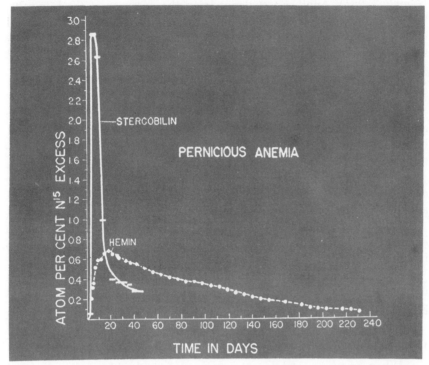

Figure 47. N^{15} concentration in hemin and stercobilin after the start of feeding N^{15}-labeled glycine for 2 days to a patient with pernicious anemia. (From London and West: J. Biol. Chem., *184*:359, 1950.)

the circulating hemoglobin and the stercobilin of the feces. It had been shown by Shemin and Rittenberg that the N of glycine is incorporated into heme and remains inside the circulating red cell during its lifetime. Had all the stercobilin originated from the circulating hemoglobin, the former would not have incorporated the isotopic label during the first six weeks of the administration of glycine (N^{15}), because the life span of the red cell precludes earlier destruction.

Figure 46 shows that N^{15} appears at a very early stage in stercobilin; which means that its predecessor could not have been the hemoglobin of circulating mature red cells.

Whereas, under normal conditions, 11 per cent of the stercobilin is attributable to a nonhemoglobin precursor, in pernicious anemia some 40 per cent is so attributable (Fig. 47).

TESTS FOR BILE

One test depends on the presence of the pigments. With an oxidizing reagent, such as nitric acid, a series of colored products is obtained

(*Gmelin's test*). Another test depends on the presence of the bile salts. With sucrose and concentrated sulfuric acid, a red color is obtained (*Pettenköfer's test*). This is probably not unlike the Molisch test for sugars, involving the intermediate production of furfural.

GALLSTONES

Gallstones (biliary calculi) are found largely in the bile ducts and in the gallbladder in pathological conditions, and they may prevent bile from entering the intestines. They consist of cholesterol or cholesterol mixed with the calcium salts of bilirubin, carbonate, or phosphate.

The calculi in the gallbladder and the bile ducts (cholelithiasis) are often associated with inflammation of the gallbladder (cholecystitis) and of the bile passages (cholangitis).

Gallstones probably originate when the gallbladder is unable to handle the cholesterol reaching it. Mixed gallstones are often due to infection and inflammation of the gallbladder.

Diagnosis of gallbladder disease is often helped by an x-ray examination of the gallbladder after administration of tetraiodophenolphthalein (radio-opaque substance).

JAUNDICE (ICTERUS)

When an excess of bile pigments gets into the blood, the skin and secretions turn yellow. In a common form of the disease, obstructive jaundice, this is due to complete or partial obstruction of the common duct (see Fig. 44). In another form, hemolytic jaundice, the disease is due to an extensive destruction of hemoglobin.

Serum bilirubin content is measured by the *van den Bergh reaction* in which the bilirubin reacts with diazotized sulfanilic acid. Bilirubin glucuronide is water-soluble and gives the test immediately (*"direct" van den Bergh*). To measure *all* of the serum bilirubin, however, the test is inadequate unless ethanol is first added (*"indirect" van den Bergh*) because of the presence of free bilirubin which is very insoluble in water but soluble in alcohol.

INTESTINAL (BACTERIAL) PUTREFACTION

As we shall see presently, most of the absorption of foodstuffs occurs in the small intestine. What is not absorbed passes on to the large intestine, where gradual loss of water occurs by absorption, and the products are evacuated finally as feces.

The normal stool is a mixture of water, undigested food, products of the digestive tract (bile pigments, enzymes, mucus), products of putrefaction (such as indole, skatole, fatty acids, gases), epithelial cells from the walls of the intestine, bacteria, etc.

Probably 25 per cent of the dried feces represents bacteria, mostly of the nonpathogenic variety. Bacterial decomposition of whatever food-stuffs remain in the large intestine is of particular importance to herbivora, for in this way much of their food is utilized. The colon bacillus is the commonest organism found in man, and we have seen how the putrefactive products—toxic substances—are thereby produced. An organism present in much smaller quantity belongs to the aciduric group. Such bacteria produce lactic acid from carbohydrates. The addition of dextrin or lactose to the diet brings about a greater production of the aciduric group, and the acid produced as a result of their metabolic activity tends to establish a medium which is unfavorable to the colon bacillus.

The more favorable medium, containing an optimum of the aciduric organisms, is also supported by a well balanced inorganic diet, particularly by the addition of both calcium and phosphorus.

Despite the fact that with fruits and vegetables, for example, we ingest cellulose, there is little evidence for any digestion of it by man (though it facilitates proper digestion). Herbivorous animals and insects do utilize cellulose. This is due to the action of various microorganisms in their digestive tracts.

From the point of view of nutrition in general, intestinal flora play an important role. Some of these microorganisms have the ability to synthesize a number of vitamins, some amino acids, and possibly even some fatty acids; so that the microflora supply us, to some degree at least, with these nutrients.

In the large intestine active bacterial action takes place. Gases (hydrogen, carbon dioxide, ammonia, hydrogen sulfide, methane), acids (acetic, lactic, butyric), various toxic substances (indole, skatole, phenol, etc.) are formed. The acids are largely products of the bacterial decomposition of carbohydrates. Some special substances, such as choline, neurine, and muscarine, have their source in lecithin.

$$
\begin{array}{ccc}
\underset{CH_3}{\overset{CH_3}{\underset{|}{\underset{CH_3-N^+}{\diagdown}}}}\;CH_2.CH_2OH &
\underset{CH_3}{\overset{CH_3}{\underset{|}{\underset{CH_3-N^+}{\diagdown}}}}\;CH{=}CH_2 &
\underset{CH_3}{\overset{CH_3}{\underset{|}{\underset{CH_3-N^+}{\diagdown}}}}\;CH_2.CHO \\
\text{Choline} & \text{Neurine} & \text{Muscarine}
\end{array}
$$

The most characteristic group of substances are derived from the proteins. After a preliminary hydrolysis into their respective amino acids, the latter undergo a series of reactions involving deamination and decarboxylation. These reactions can be illustrated as follows:

$$R.CH.COOH \quad \xrightarrow[\text{(deamination)}]{-NH_3} \quad R.CH_2.COOH \;(\text{Fatty acid})$$
$$|$$
$$NH_2$$

$$R.CH.COOH \quad \xrightarrow[\text{(decarboxylation)}]{-CO_2} \quad R.CH_2$$
$$| \qquad\qquad\qquad\qquad\qquad\qquad\qquad |$$
$$NH_2 \qquad\qquad\qquad\qquad\qquad\qquad\; NH_2$$
$$(\text{Amine})$$

giving rise in the amines to some highly toxic substances.

To illustrate the process, we will select a number of amino acids which produce characteristic products.

Tryptophan forms, among others, indole and skatole, substances partially responsible for the odor of feces:

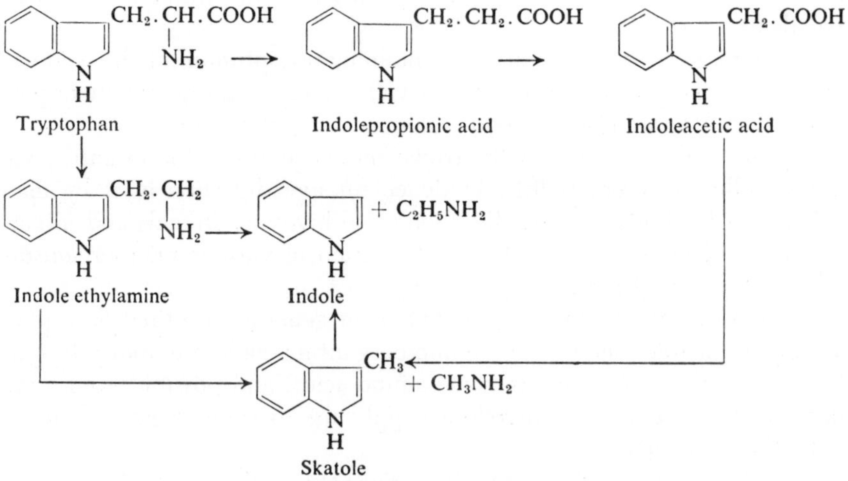

Tryptophan — Indolepropionic acid — Indoleacetic acid — Indole ethylamine — Indole — Skatole

Mercaptans are formed from the sulfur-containing amino acid cystine:

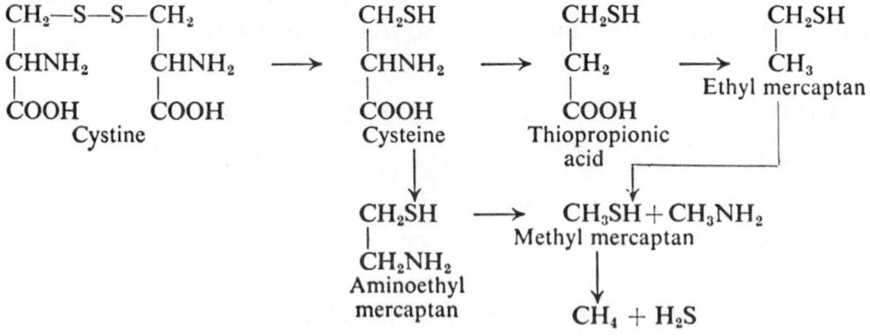

Cystine — Cysteine — Thiopropionic acid — Ethyl mercaptan — Aminoethyl mercaptan — Methyl mercaptan — $CH_4 + H_2S$

The so-called "ptomaines," substances obtained from putrefying flesh, may be formed by the decarboxylation of lysine and arginine, giving rise to cadaverine and putrescine, respectively:

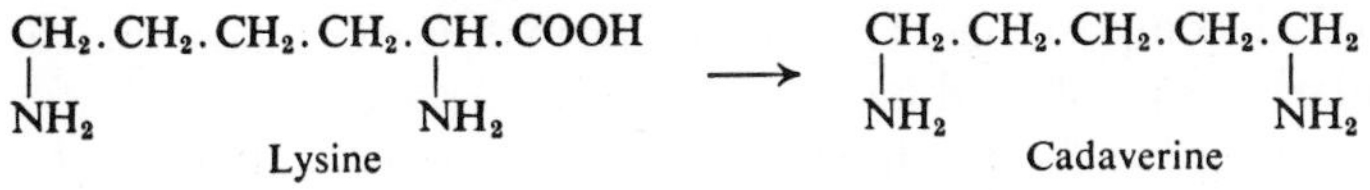

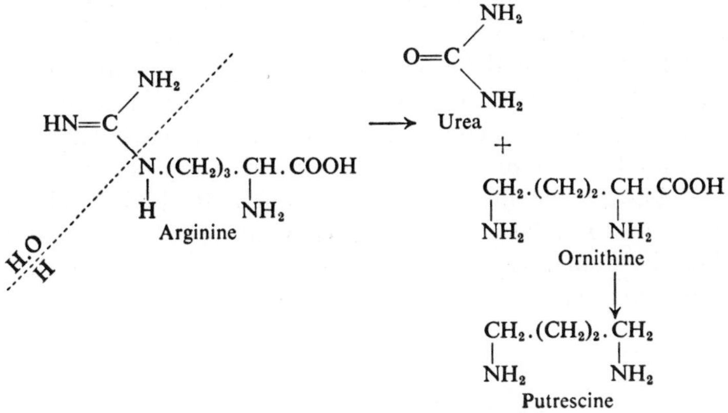

$$CH_2.CH_2.CH_2.CH_2.CH.COOH$$
$$\quad NH_2 \qquad\qquad\qquad NH_2$$
Lysine

$$\longrightarrow$$

$$CH_2.CH_2.CH_2.CH_2.CH_2$$
$$\quad NH_2 \qquad\qquad\qquad NH_2$$
Cadaverine

$$NH_2$$
$$O=C$$
$$\qquad NH_2$$
Urea

$$HN=C$$
$$\qquad NH_2$$
$$N.(CH_2)_3.CH.COOH$$
$$H \qquad NH_2$$
Arginine

$$\longrightarrow$$

$$+$$

$$CH_2.(CH_2)_2.CH.COOH$$
$$\quad NH_2 \qquad\qquad NH_2$$
Ornithine

$$CH_2.(CH_2)_2.CH_2$$
$$\quad NH_2 \qquad\qquad NH_2$$
Putrescine

H_2O

Histamine, obtained from histidine by decarboxylation, is a highly toxic substance when injected, and some have claimed it to be identical with the gastrin of the stomach and also to be responsible for allergic reactions (Chap. 23):

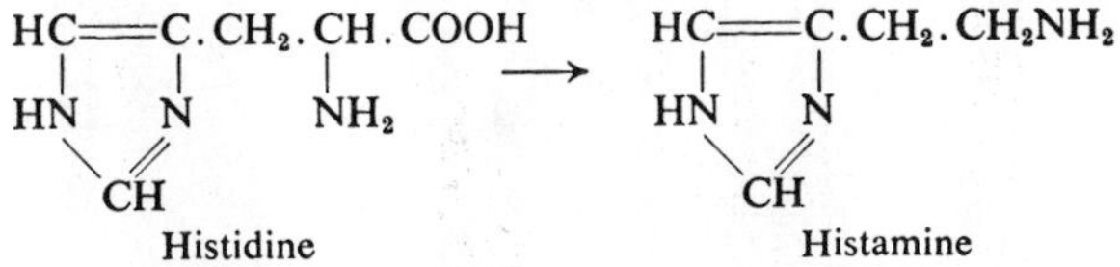

$$HC=C.CH_2.CH.COOH$$
$$HN \quad N \qquad NH_2$$
$$CH$$
Histidine

$$\longrightarrow$$

$$HC=C.CH_2.CH_2NH_2$$
$$HN \quad N$$
$$CH$$
Histamine

Tyramine, obtained from tyrosine, is somewhat similar to epinephrine in raising blood pressure:

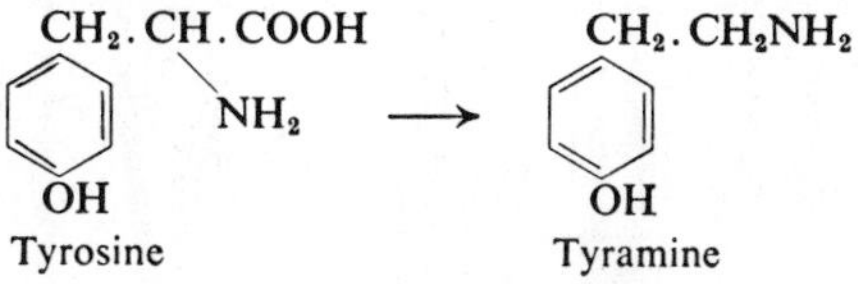

$$CH_2.CH.COOH$$
$$NH_2$$
OH
Tyrosine

$$\longrightarrow$$

$$CH_2.CH_2NH_2$$
OH
Tyramine

ABSORPTION

Before being absorbed, foods must be in a relatively simple (chemically speaking), soluble form. The action of the digestive juices converts much of the foodstuffs into amino acids, hexoses (glucose, fructose, and galactose), glycerol, and fatty acids. If pentosans and mannans are present, pentoses and mannose may be formed. Some pentose is also formed from animal nucleic acid. The cellulose in the diet remains largely unchanged and passes into the large intestine, acting as "roughage." Some bacterial decomposition of cellulose probably does take place. This is particularly true of herbivorous animals.

In general, absorption through the stomach wall is slight. By occluding the pylorus, 99 per cent of sugar can be recovered from the stomach several hours after feeding. Not even water is absorbed to any appreciable extent. In a particular experiment on a dog with a fistula in the duodenum just beyond the pylorus, of 500 ml. of water offered by mouth, 495 ml. appeared through the duodenal fistula in twenty-five minutes. However, experiments involving the use of heavy water suggest that there may be an appreciable change in the water between the time it enters the gastric contents and the time it enters the body fluids.

Alcohol, on the other hand, seems to be absorbed quite readily.

"While the stomach is definitely not an absorptive organ in the sense of the intestine," writes Karel, "and cannot be considered of especial

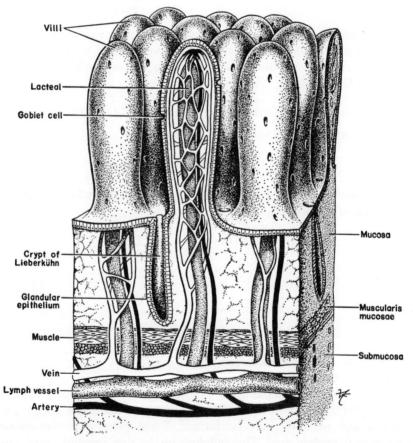

Figure 48. Diagram of villi of human intestine. Lacteals are white and blood vessels are dark. (From Christian: Anatomy for Nurses. C. V. Mosby Co.)

importance in supplying the nutritional needs of the normal organism, its absorptive ability, particluarly as regards substances physiologically active in minute quantities, has been grossly underestimated."

The absorption of food—which includes much, but not all of the water—takes place most readily through the walls of the small intestine. The tube is about 25 feet long, and its surface area is considerably increased by the villi, finger-like projections, approximately 1 mm. in length (Fig. 48). With a fistula at the end of the small intestine, it has been shown that, on the average, 90 per cent of the protein is absorbed. This applies equally well to the carbohydrates and fats. Water is

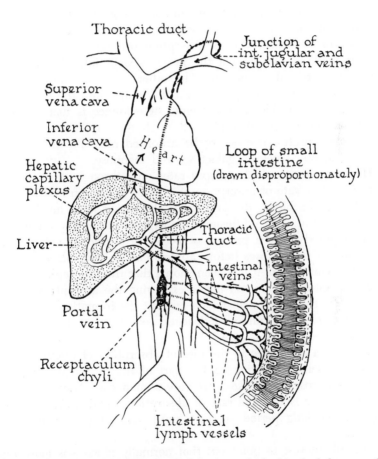

Figure 49. Routes by which the absorbed foods reach the blood of the general circulation. Intestinal veins converging to form, in part, the portal vein, which enters the liver and by repeated branchings assists in the formation of the hepatic capillary plexus; the hepatic veins carrying blood from the liver discharging it into the inferior vena cava; the intestinal lymph vessels converging to discharge their contents, chyle, into the receptaculum chyli, the lower expanded part of the thoracic duct; the thoracic duct discharging lymph and chyle into the blood at the junction of the internal jugular and subclavian veins. (Modified scheme of Bachman.)

absorbed here too, but its loss is apparently made up by diffusion of liquid into the intestine, for the food at the ileocecal valve is still very fluid.

In the large intestine there is considerable absorption of water, resulting in a residue which eventually appears as feces. As we have already seen, bacterial action resulting in putrefactive processes is here very pronounced.

For the general plan of absorption, see Figure 49.

ABSORPTION OF CARBOHYDRATES

The villi of the small intestine contain blood vessels, nerves, and lymphatics, and it is through these villi that absorption takes place. There are two possible paths. One is absorption through the capillaries, the absorbed material passing via the portal system into the liver before entering the general circulation. The other is absorption through the lacteals, the material then passing via the lymph into the thoracic duct and finally into the blood. The weight of evidence is that the absorption of carbohydrates takes place through the capillaries of the villi. These carbohydrates in order to be absorbed must be in the form of hexoses—glucose, fructose, galactose, and mannose.

Hexoses are absorbed at rapid rates only through the living membrane. Since the rate of absorption of glucose is not affected by its concentration in the blood, the process of absorption must involve a force other than that of simple diffusion. One explanation of the source of such energy required for the process of active absorption involves a phosphorylation of the hexoses before absorption can take place.

In this connection, it has been shown that the hexosephosphate content of the intestinal mucosa increases during the absorption of sugars. Furthermore, two substances which prevent the formation of such phosphates *in vitro*, phlorhizin and iodoacetic acid, prevent the absorption of sugars from the small intestine.

There is a difference in the rate of absorption of different hexoses, indicating a selective action on the part of the intestinal mucosa. The order is galactose > glucose > fructose > mannose. Another somewhat puzzling feature is that the rate of absorption remains the same over a comparatively long period—in fact, until most of the sugar has been absorbed.

It is of interest to point out that normally glucose is more rapidly absorbed than a pentose. However, if a dead mucous membrane is used, or if the membrane is first poisoned with iodoacetic acid, the absorption is in the reverse order: first the smaller pentose molecule, and then the hexose. Absorption is, therefore, clearly not a simple diffusion process.

The hexoses are changed largely to glycogen in the liver and stored there as such until needed by the body. Preliminary phosphate combinations are necessary. (The further fate of carbohydrates is discussed under the metabolism of these substances, Chap. 11.)

ABSORPTION OF LIPIDS

ABSORPTION OF FATS (SEE PAGE 298)

It was believed by earlier investigators that, before being absorbed, fats had to be hydrolyzed to free fatty acids and glycerol. More recent studies have shown that complete hydrolysis is not necessary for the absorption of fatty acids, although free fatty acids do appear in the circulation. Fatty acids of chain length greater than ten carbon atoms appear in the lymphatic circulation in the form of triglycerides and to some extent as phospholipids, and then find their way into the blood to the liver. During the process of absorption, incorporation of free fatty acids into fats takes place by enzymatic mechanisms which are still unclear.

How important the bile is in the process involving fat absorption becomes apparent when the bile duct is occluded. Under such conditions, relatively large quantities of undigested fat appear in the feces.

During a meal rich in fat, the lymphatics of the mesentery are filled with fat in a finely emulsified form; this also becomes true of the blood itself. By collecting and estimating the fat absorbed from the intestines through the lacteals—this can be done by means of a cannula inserted into the thoracic duct at the point of its connection with the subclavian and jugular veins—it was shown that some 60 per cent of the fat is absorbed through the lacteals, but, according to Chaikoff, this figure is too low. Even odd-carbon fatty acids, which are rarely present in nature, are absorbed via the lymph to the extent of 84 to 93 per cent.

The fat which finally appears in the blood is either stored (in adipose tissue, etc.) or metabolized. The details will be discussed in the chapter devoted to the metabolism of fats (Chap. 12).

ABSORPTION OF LECITHIN

It is generally believed that lecithin—and phospholipids in general —is hydrolyzed in the small intestine, and that such hydrolysis is necessary before any absorption can take place. Enzymes which can split phospholipids are found in intestinal mucosa and pancreatic juice, among other places. Pancreatic juice, for example, contains an enzyme which partially hydrolyzes lecithins and cephalins, liberating fatty acids; it is believed that this enzyme is not identical with lipase.

Using labeled phospholipids—prepared from the livers of animals after they had been injected with radioactive phosphate—Artom concluded that while part of the phospholipid is split in the small intestine, removing phosphate or glycerophosphate (which is absorbed as such), a portion can also be absorbed as the intact molecule.

ABSORPTION OF CHOLESTEROL

Cholesterol is absorbed to some extent depending upon the amount of fat (the kind of fatty acids?) absorbed at the same time. A factor in the absorption may be the solubility of the cholesterol in bile.

Cholesterol is absorbed through the lacteals. The fact that cholesterol esters have been detected in the chyle suggests that there is esterification of the sterol during absorption. In the blood we find cholesterol as well as cholesterol esters (cholesterol plus fatty acids).

ABSORPTION OF PROTEINS

The proteins are absorbed as amino acids; they, like the hexoses, pass directly into the portal circulation.

Folin and Van Slyke showed that the blood always contains amino acids and that after a meal rich in protein there is a definite increase in the amino acid content of the blood. Abel, using his "vividiffusion" technique, arrived at the same result. Here the blood from the portal vein of a dog was passed through collodion tubes immersed in Ringer's solution, and then the blood was returned to the body. What diffused out through the collodion tubes contained, among other things, amino acids, some of which were actually isolated.

This evidence that the absorption of protein takes place in the form of amino acids is further strengthened by the fact that the injection of foreign protein directly into the blood gives rise to antibodies which can be detected; but no such antibody formation results from the oral ingestion of protein. In fact, there is evidence to point to the view that absorption of even traces of protein through the walls of the intestine may give rise to allergic symptoms.

The amino acids pass into the liver and thence into the general circulation. The further changes which they undergo will be discussed in the chapter on the metabolism of protein (Chap. 13).

A study has been made of the rate of absorption of various D- and L-isomers of amino acids, and in every case the L-isomer disappeared faster than the D-isomer. Since the rates of diffusion of both isomers are the same, a mere diffusion process would not explain this difference in the rates of absorption; it is necessary to assume a specific mechanism for the absorption of the L-amino acids.

ABSORPTION OF SALTS AND WATER

Active absorption of salts and water takes place in the intestine via the blood capillaries. Unlike the three principal foodstuffs, no preliminary treatment would appear to be needed before absorption takes place. However, if one studies the absorption of iron, the evidence that the intestinal mucosa is not just a diffusion membrane but, rather, is made up of actively metabolizing cells which regulate absorption is quite striking.

REFERENCES

A study of the starch-iodine complex we owe to *Ono, Tsuchihashi* and *Takashi:* J. Am. Chem. Soc., *75:*3601, 1953.

An article dealing with *Beaumont* will be found in J. Am. Med. Assoc., *152:*915, 1953, by *Stenn;* and one dealing with *Pavlov,* in the Scientific American, Sept., 1949, p. 44, by *Konorski.* See also *Pavlov's* book, The Work of the Digestive Glands, 1902.

Regarding the origin of HCl in the stomach, see *Conway:* Biochemistry of Gastric Acid Secretion, 1952; and *Hollander:* Federation Proceedings, 11:706, 1952.

For gastric analysis, see *Todd, Sanford* and *Wells:* Clinical Diagnosis by Laboratory Methods, 1953, p. 473.

Proteolytic enzymes are described by *Northrop, Kunitz* and *Herriott:* Crystalline Enzymes, 1948.

Caldwell, Adams, Kung and *Toralballa* describe the preparation of crystalline pancreatic amylase in J. Am. Chem. Soc., 74:4033, 1952.

For absorption, see *Hogben:* Federation Proceedings, 19:864, 1960; *Wilson, Lin, Landau* and *Jorgensen:* Ibid., 19:870, 1960 (sugars and amino acids); *Turner:* Ibid., 19:876, 1960 (fats).

The question as to whether there is more than one pepsin is discussed by *Ryle* and *Porter:* Biochem. J. 73:75, 1959; *Taylor:* Ibid., 71:384, 1959.

For the absorption of fats, see *Mattson:* Food Research, 21:34, 1956; Nutr. Rev., 14:308, 1956; *Reiser* and *Williams:* J. Biol. Chem., 202:815, 1953; *Frazer:* Nature, 175:491, 1955.

The hydrolysis of lecithin is reviewed by *Rimon* and *Schapiro:* Biochem. J., 71:620, 1959.

Zilversmit: Ann. Rev. Biochem., 24:157, 1955, reviews the absorption of phosphatides; see also *Artom:* Ibid., 22:211, 1953.

Two historical papers dealing with the absorption of proteins are by *Folin* and *Denis:* J. Biol. Chem. 12:253, 1912; and *Van Slyke* and *Meyer:* Ibid., 16:213, 1913.

For the absorption of amino acids and proteins, see *Agar, Hird* and *Sidhu:* J. Physiol., 121:251, 1953; *Crane* and *Neuberger:* Biochem. J., 74:313, 1960.

A review of intestinal flora is the work of *Krehl:* Borden's Rev. of Nutrition, 20: Jan.-Feb., 1959.

BLOOD

The products of digestion are carried by the blood to the various tissues of the body. The blood also carries the waste products away from the tissues. The hemoglobin of the blood carries oxygen to the cells and is involved in the elimination of carbon dioxide from the cells. Hormones, the chemical regulators of the body, are also carried by the blood. Transportation within the body, then, is one of the outstanding functions of the blood. (For diagram of the circulation of the blood, see Fig. 50.)

The blood consists of a solution (plasma) in which are suspended cellular components. The suspended materials include the red corpuscles (erythrocytes), the white corpuscles (leukocytes)—of which there are several kinds—and the thrombocytes (blood platelets).* The liquid portion, the plasma, is light yellow, the red color of blood being due to the red corpuscles suspended in it. By centrifuging blood, the corpuscles can be made to separate; and then it can be observed that they occupy about 45 per cent of the total volume (hematocrit).

When the blood is allowed to clot, the clear liquid which separates is the serum. Serum is plasma from which fibrinogen has been removed. If blood is whipped as it is freshly drawn, the fibrin clings to the rod, and a product is obtained which does not clot and which is called "defibrinated blood"; this is, essentially, blood serum together with corpuscles. This defibrinated blood serves quite well for many of the experiments on blood carried out in the laboratory.

FUNCTION

We have already referred to the blood as a transporting medium for food material, waste, gases, and hormones. Blood has a number of other functions of importance. It helps to maintain a delicate osmotic pressure

---

* On the average there are 5 liters of blood in the individual. In each cubic millimeter of blood there are 5,000,000 red cells, 10,000 white cells, and 300,000 thrombocytes.

200

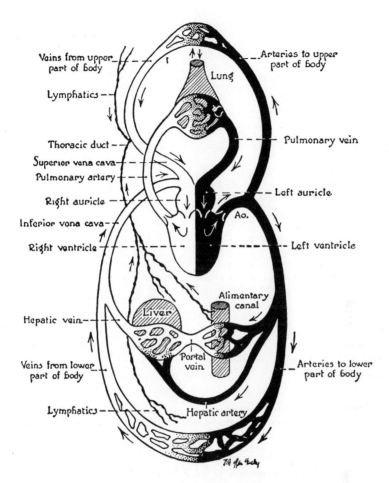

Figure 50. The circulation of the blood. The arterial, or oxygenated, blood is shown in black; the venous blood, in white. The lymphatics are black knotty lines. (From Pettibone: Physiological Chemistry. C. V. Mosby Co.)

relationship with the tissues; it plays a part in the acid-base equilibrium within the body; it aids in regulating the temperature; and, through its white cells and chemical defense mechanisms, it is of importance in immunological reactions (Chap. 23).

CHEMICAL COMPOSITION

The many substances in the blood, with their approximate quantities, are summarized in Table 29. Hemoglobin, fibrinogen, albumin, and globulin are among the chief proteins. Fatty acids (fat), phospholipids, and cholesterol (free and esterified) represent the lipids. The sugar that is nor-

TABLE 29. NORMAL VALUES FOR HUMAN BLOOD AND SPINAL FLUID CONSTITUENTS[1]

Determination[2]	Mean	Units	Standard deviation[3]	Examples of abnormal value[4]
Albumin (S)	5.2	gm./100 ml.	0.25	Low in nephrosis
Amino acids (P)	4.4	mg.N/100 ml.	0.48	High in acute atrophy of liver
Amylase (S)	105	units[5]	26	High in acute pancreatitis
Ascorbic acid (P)	0.75	mg./100 ml.	0.40	Low in scurvy
Bilirubin (S)	0.54	mg./100 ml.	0.25	High in biliary obstruction
Calcium (S)	10.0	mg./100 ml.	0.36	High in hyper-, low in hypoparathyroidism
CO_2 content, venous (S)	28.4	mMol./liter	2.7	Low in diabetic acidosis
Chloride (S)	104	mEq./liter	2.6	Low in pernicious vomiting, diarrhea
Cholesterol, free (S)	26.9	% of total	1.4	High in biliary obstruction
Cholesterol, total (S)	210	mg./100 ml.	50	High in nephrosis
Copper (P)	114	μgm./100 ml.	16	High in anemia of infection
Creatinine (P)	1.0	mg./100 ml.	0.15	High in renal insufficiency
Fat, total (P)	735	mg./100 ml.	216	High in nephrosis
Fat, neutral (P)	225	mg./100 ml.	137	High in nephrosis
Fat, phospholipid (P)	181	mg./100 ml.	71	High in biliary obstruction
Fibrinogen (P)	0.2–0.4	gm./100 ml.	...	Low in severe liver disease
Globulin (S)	2.0	gm./100 ml.	0.27	High in multiple myeloma
Glucose (B)	90	mg./100 ml.	9.6	High in diabetes; low in steatorrhea
Hemoglobin, male (B)	15.9	gm./100 ml.	1.12	High in polycythemia; low in iron deficiency anemia
Hemoglobin, female (B)	13.9	gm./100 ml.	0.86	Same as for male
Iodine, protein-bound (S)	5.0	μgm./100 ml.	0.68	High in hyperthyroidism; low in myxedema
Iron (S)	105	μgm./100 ml.	30	Low in iron deficiency anemia, infection
Iron-binding capacity (S)	200	μgm.Fe/100 ml.	...	High in iron deficiency anemia; low in infection
Ketone bodies, as acetone (B)	0.2–0.7	mg./100 ml.	...	High in diabetes, starvation
Lactic acid (B)	11.5	mg./100 ml.	30	High in exercise
Nitrogen, non-protein (B)	29	mg.N/100 ml.	4.4	High in renal insufficiency
O_2 content, arterial (B)	19.6	ml./100 ml.	1.2	High in polycythemia; low in emphysema
O_2 content, venous (B)	12.6	ml./100 ml.	1.3	Same as for arterial
pH (S)	7.36	pH units	0.034	Low in diabetic acidosis
Phosphatase, acid (S)	2.8	Gutman units[6]	0.6	High in carcinoma of the prostate

Substance[2]	Value	S.D.	Units	Remarks[3][4]
Phosphatase, alk. (S)[7]	2.6	0.59	Bodansky units[8]	High in bone diseases with osteoblastic activity
Proteins, total (S)	7.2	0.35	gm./100 ml.	High in multiple myeloma; low in nephrosis
Phosphorus (S)[7]	3.6	0.42	mg./100 ml.	High in hypoparathyroidism; low in rickets
Potassium (P)	4.26	0.43	mEq./liter	High in adrenal insufficiency
Pyruvic acid (B)	1.04	0.36	mg./100 ml.	High in thiamin deficiency
Sodium (S)	140	1.7	mEq./liter	Low in adrenal insufficiency
Thiamin (B)	3.4	1.2	μgm./100 ml.	
Urea nitrogen (B)	13.6	3.3	mg.N/100 ml.	High in renal insufficiency
Uric acid (S)	4.4	1.1	mg./100 ml.	High in gout
Vitamin A, male (P)	128	29	I.U./100 ml.[9]	Low in vitamin A deficiency
Vitamin A, female (P)	91	22	I.U./100 ml.	Same as in male
Volume, plasma	45.3	5.5	ml./kg.	Low in shock
Volume, RBC	34.8	5.1	ml./kg.	High in polycythemia; low in nutritional edema
Volume, whole blood	80.1	10.5	ml./kg.	Low in dehydration
Spinal Fluid:				
Albumin	17	4.9	mg./100 ml.	See protein
Chloride	709	25	mg./100 ml.	Low in tuberculous meningitis
Globulin, gamma	3.4	1.1	mg./100 ml.	See protein
Glucose	57	13	mg./100 ml.	Low in bacterial meningitis
Protein	37	8	mg./100 ml.	High in brain tumors

[1] Most of these values are taken from a comprehensive table prepared by O. Bodansky, in Bodansky and Bodansky: Biochemistry of Disease (1952). For references to methods see this text. Unless otherwise noted, venous blood was used for the determinations.

[2] S = serum, P = plasma, B = whole blood, RBC = red blood cells.

[3] Bodansky calls a value abnormal when it is different from the mean by 2 to 3 times the standard deviation. It should be remembered that most values will vary depending on the method used.

[4] The degree of alteration will vary with the severity as well as with the stage of the disease. The alteration does not always occur in the disease and there are many other diseases in which it will occur.

[5] Somogyi amylase unit = mg. reducing substance liberated from standard sodium chloride–starch mixture by 100 ml. serum in 30 min. at 40°.

[6] Gutman acid phosphatase unit = mg. phenol liberated at pH 5.0 from standard phenylphosphate-citrate mixture by 100 ml. serum in 1 hr. at 37°.

[7] In children these values are higher.

[8] Bodansky alkaline phosphatase unit = mg. inorganic phosphate liberated at alkaline pH from standard glycerophosphate-Veronal mixture by 100 ml. serum in 1 hr. at 37°.

[9] I. U. = International Units.

mally present is glucose. The nonprotein-nitrogen (NPN) constituents—substances derived from proteins—include urea, uric acid, creatinine, creatine, ammonia, and amino acids. The inorganic material includes chloride, bicarbonate, phosphate, and sulfate ions, together with ionic sodium, potassium, calcium, and magnesium. There may be present small quantities of still other substances such as the acetone bodies, bile pigments, lactic acid, phenol, iodine, etc. All of these substances are kept in some sort of solution in water, which constitutes about 80 per cent by weight of the blood. The pH of the blood is in the neighborhood of 7.4 and its specific gravity is about 1.06.

Clinically, changes in the composition of the blood are of great importance. Being the purveyor of materials to and from the cells, a marked deviation from the normal composition of blood may indicate (a) a subnormal or abnormal supply of foodstuff from the outside, (b) the presence of toxic substances, (c) one or more organs which are diseased.

ERYTHROCYTES

These are the red blood cells. They are biconcave circular disks devoid of a nucleus (human). Normally, there are some 5,000,000 per cubic millimeter. The erythrocyte is made up of membranous material (stroma) which encloses the pigment hemoglobin and other compounds. The pigment accounts for more than three quarters of the total solids.

The mature erythrocyte, after it comes from the bone marrow where it is manufactured, has a life span of some 120 days. At the end of this period the dying erythrocytes are removed from the circulation by the reticuloendothelial cells.

When first formed, the erythrocyte is relatively large and contains a nucleus but no pigment. When finally ready to leave the bone marrow and enter the circulation, the cell has become smaller, it has incorporated the pigment, and has lost its nucleus.

In various types of anemias there is a notable decrease in the red cell count; and under certain conditions—in fevers, at high altitudes, after severe muscular exercise—there may be a marked increase in the number of red blood cells (polycythemia).

If the red cells are injured, hemoglobin may pass out into the surrounding medium. This process is known as hemolysis, or "laking of the blood." A simple experimental procedure accomplishes such a result. Add water (or a solution less concentrated in electrolytes than blood—a hypotonic solution) to blood. Under these conditions, water will pass into the cells, which may burst. By using a solution more concentrated in electrolytes than blood—a hypertonic solution—water will pass out of the erythrocytes and the cells will shrink. By using a solution of sodium chloride containing 0.9 per cent of the salt, no contraction or expansion of the erythrocytes occurs. Such a solution is spoken of as *isotonic:* the osmotic pressure of this solution is equal to the osmotic pressure within the cell.

HEMOGLOBIN

This conjugated protein consists of a protein portion, globin (a histone), linked to the compound iron-protoporphyrin IX. The latter is also called reduced *heme*, since in hemoglobin the valence of iron is 2. The chloride of heme is called *hemin*. It is obtained by crystallization of a solution of blood heated with acetic acid and sodium chloride. This operation can be carried out on a microscope slide and is a very good test for blood, since the crystals of hemin are characteristic.

The structure of iron-protoporphyrin IX is given in Figure 51.

In this structure each ring, with four atoms of carbon and one of nitrogen, is a "pyrrole" ring, and the combination of four pyrrole rings, of which there are two different kinds, makes up the "porphyrin" nucleus. Since there are a large variety of porphyrins possible, the one associated with hemoglobin is given an appropriate Roman numeral. Differences involve different side-chain groups.

Heme forms compounds with many substances other than globin. These are called, generally, hemochromogens. Thus, heme combines with pyridine to give pyridine hemochromogen. These complexes are of value since they have specific absorption spectra which are helpful in the problem of identification. That the same protoporphyrin can form different compounds is illustrated by the occurrence in nature of a variety of different compounds with the same iron-protoporphyrin IX. Among these are myoglobin and catalase. Here the differences are due to different proteins and to differences in the mode of attachment to the protein.

Hemoglobin possesses one of the most unique properties of any compound found in nature—its ability to combine reversibly with

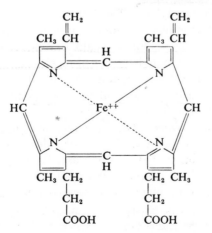

Figure 51. Reduced heme (iron-protoporphyrin IX).

molecular oxygen. It may be mentioned that in arthropods and crustaceans we find the pigment hemocyanin, a protein which also can transport oxygen, but which contains copper instead of iron, and whose prosthetic group is still unknown. Approximately 1 gram of hemoglobin will combine (in solution) with 1.36 cc. of oxygen at standard conditions. Chemical changes in the heme or in the protein portion lead to a loss of this property. Some of these altered forms and their relation to normal hemoglobin are:

a. Oxyhemoglobin: HbO_2 or (globin)(Por:Fe^{++})O_2.

b. Reduced Hemoglobin: Hb or (globin)(Por:Fe^{++}). Obtained by reducing the partial pressure of oxygen in equilibrium with the hemoglobin solution. The reaction may be written:

$$Hb + O_2 \quad \rightleftharpoons \quad HbO_2$$

c. Methemoglobin: MetHb or (globin)(Por:Fe^{+++}). Obtained by the oxidation of oxyhemoglobin or reduced hemoglobin, using ferricyanide as a reagent. This compound has lost its ability to combine with molecular oxygen. It may exist in the blood to some extent owing to the presence in the circulation of some oxidizing agent. There is also a hereditary disease which is characterized by the presence in the blood of MetHb.

d. Carboxyhemoglobin: $HbCO$ or (globin)(Por:Fe^{++})CO. Formed when the animal is exposed to CO gas. It forms a complex which is two hundred times stronger than that formed with O_2.

e. Cyanmethemoglobin: MetHbCN or (globin)(Por:Fe^{+++})CN. Formed by the addition of cyanide to methemoglobin. It is a compound used for the quantitative estimation of methemoglobin. It is important to note that CN^- does not combine with oxyhemoglobin or reduced hemoglobin. Death from cyanide poisoning is *not* due to loss of oxygen-carrying capacity of the blood.

Structure of Hemoglobin. The iron content of hemoglobin is 0.33 to 0.34 per cent. Assuming one atom of iron per molecule, the smallest molecular weight for hemoglobin would be about 16,000. Actually, its molecular weight as estimated by the ultracentrifuge is about 66,800 or some four times this amount. Studies on the structure of hemoglobin suggest that the molecule consists of four polypeptide units, each associated with one iron-protoporphyrin molecule.

Different Hemoglobins. The hemoglobins found in human blood are not necessarily the same kinds of molecules. This was first emphasized as a result of the studies of Itano and Pauling on the hemoglobin present in the blood of people suffering from the disease sickle cell anemia.[*] Since that time many more hemoglobins have been identified

---

[*] In sickle cell anemia the erythrocytes undergo reversible changes in shape as a result of changes of the partial pressure of oxygen. The lowering of the oxygen pressure changes the cells from the normal, biconcave disk to crescent, holly wreath, or similar shapes. The process is known as "sickling." This type of anemia is hereditary.

in a variety of anemias, through use of the technique of electrophoresis combined with paper chromatography (called paper electrophoresis). The term hemoglobin must now be used as a generic one; letters are used to designate the particular types. The normal human hemoglobins are A (adult) and F (fetal), respectively. Others are S (sickle cell), C and D (Figs. 52 and 53). These are all under genetic control. Hemo-

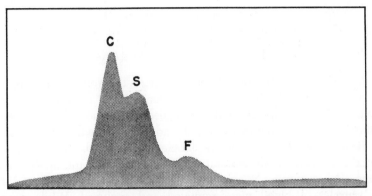

Figure 52. Tiselius electrophoretic pattern of the hemoglobin of a patient with sickle cell–hemoglobin C disease, showing three hemoglobins, C, S and F. Hemoglobin F is identical with fetal hemoglobin and differs from hemoglobin A by its characteristic ultraviolet absorption spectrum and by its resistance to alkali denaturation. (Adapted from Pauling, L.: The Harvey Lectures, Series XLIX, 229, 1953–1954.)

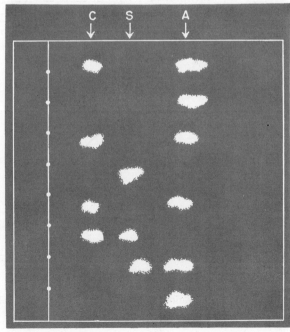

Figure 53. Paper electrophoresis patterns of various human hemoglobins at the end of 4 hours. Migration begins at the dotted line. Hemoglobin A (normal adult) is the fastest moving; hemoglobin S (sickle cell anemia) moves at an intermediate rate; and hemoglobin C (sickle cell anemia) migrates most slowly. (Adapted from Smith, E. W., and Conley, T. L.: Bull. Johns Hopkins Hosp., 93:94.)

globin F is normally present in fetal blood as well as in blood of adults with chronic anemia. Still others have since been reported. Pauling has labeled the occurrence of abnormal hemoglobin as evidence of a "molecular disease."

It is an amazing fact that amino acid sequence analyses have uncovered but one amino acid residue which differs among three of the various hemoglobins (out of a total of about 300 residues):

Hb	Partial structure of the α chain*
A	His—Val—Leuc—Leuc—Thr—Pro—Glu—Glu—Lys
S	His—Val—Leuc—Leuc—Thr—Pro—Val—Glu—Lys
C	His—Val—Leuc—Leuc—Thr—Pro—Lys—Glu—Lys

Biosynthesis of Heme. A discussion of the role of various amino acids in the biosynthesis of proteins in general will be found in Chapter 13. At this stage emphasis will be placed upon the precursors needed for the synthesis of that portion of hemoglobin known as heme. Shemin and Rittenberg fed isotopically labeled compounds to a man, then isolated the heme of the circulating cell hemoglobin and analyzed it for isotope. For example, N^{15}-glycine was administered and from time to time samples of blood were removed and analyzed. While a certain amount of the isotope was incorporated into the globin molecule, a relatively high concentration of N^{15} was found in the heme molecule (Fig. 54).

The hemoglobin of the circulating red cell appears to stay inside the cell for the duration of its lifetime. If, therefore, the concentration of N^{15} in the circulating heme is plotted against time, it becomes possible to calculate the life span of the average red cell. This was found

* See page 623 for list of abbreviations.

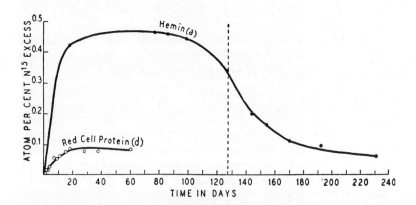

Figure 54. N^{15} concentration in hemin after feeding N^{15}-labeled glycine for 3 days. The dotted line indicates the calculated life span for the average red cell, 127 days. (From Shemin and Rittenberg: J. Biol. Chem., *166*:627, 1946.)

to be 127 days for man—a value which is in good agreement with that
found when other methods are used.

Shemin and co-workers studied the source of the various elements
in the heme molecule in an attempt to account for each of the 4
nitrogen atoms and the 34 carbon atoms of its structure:

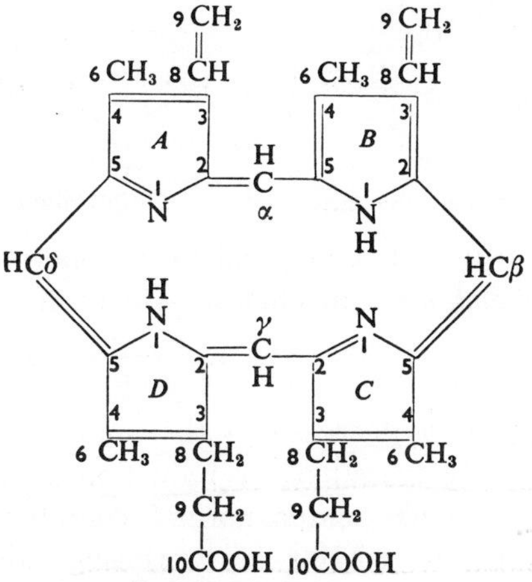

Protoporphyrin IX

These are the conclusions:

a. All four nitrogen atoms are derived from the nitrogen of glycine.

b. All four carbon atoms at position 2 of rings A, B, C and D are
derived from the alpha carbon atoms of glycine. This is also true of the
four methene carbon atoms labeled α, β, γ and δ. The carboxyl carbon
of glycine is not utilized for heme synthesis.

c. The remaining 26 carbon atoms are derived either from methyl
or carboxyl groups of acetate by means of an intermediate 4-carbon
compound arising from the tricarboxylic acid cycle.

This intermediate has been identified by Shemin as the compound,
δ-aminolevulinic acid, which arises metabolically from the condensation
of succinyl coenzyme A and glycine to form a compound which undergoes decarboxylation to yield the levulinic acid; thus:

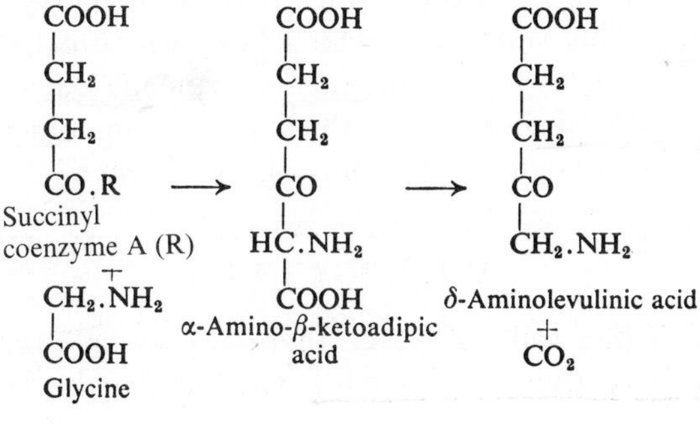

In the presence of a specific enzyme, two molecules of the levulinic acid condense to form the porphyrin intermediate, porphobilinogen:

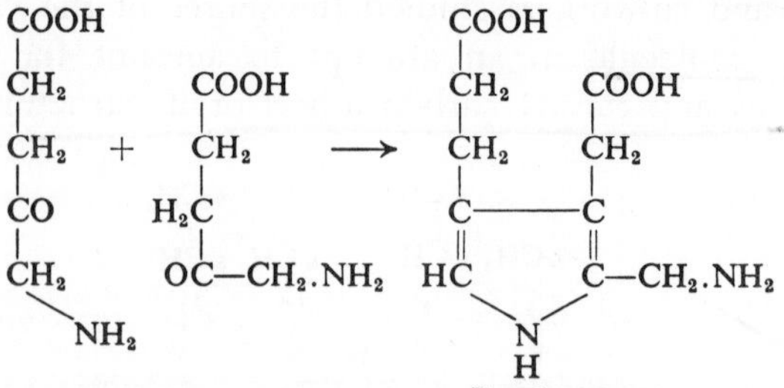

2 Moles δ-aminolevulinic acid   Porphobilinogen

This intermediate, in turn, is converted to protoporphyrin, which reacts with iron—by some unknown mechanism—to form heme.

THE ANEMIAS

In anemia there is a decrease in the amount of hemoglobin per unit volume of blood; this results in a reduction in the oxygen-carrying power of the blood. Since under normal conditions the amount of hemoglobin in the blood remains fairly constant despite the decomposition of the pigment, pigment formation must roughly equal pigment destruction.

The intake depends upon the activity of the marrow in supplying red blood cells. The elimination is brought about by the reticulo-endothelial cells—particularly in the spleen—which remove and decompose the erythrocytes. When this "balance of forces" fails, anemia is likely to result.

The normal amount of hemoglobin in male adult blood is 15.9 gm. per 100 ml. of blood. This is considered 100 per cent. The content within the normal range may decrease to 85 per cent for men and 77 per cent for women. From 70 per cent downwards, the symptoms of anemia usually appear.

Below 4.7 million per cubic millimeter (males) and 4.13 million (females), the red blood cell count indicates abnormality.

A discovery by Shorb that *Lactobacillus lactis* (Dorner) requires a growth factor found in liver extracts led to chemical work to isolate the liver factor. This substance, which has been isolated and contains the element cobalt, is the antipernicious anemia factor. It is called "vitamin B$_{12}$" (see further Chap. 18), and, among other properties, it overcomes the neurological symptoms of the disease.

WHITE CELLS

Leukocytes, or white cells, of which there are several varieties, are, as a rule, larger in size than erythrocytes, and, unlike the latter, possess a nucleus. They also possess the power of ameboid movement, whereby they can wander into surrounding tissues. They may number 10,000 per cubic millimeter.

These leukocytes, being typical cells, are composed of characteristic cellular material—protein, lipid, etc. They act as phagocytes, thereby defending the organism against invading bacteria.

In leukemia, a fatal disease of the blood-forming organs, there is an enormous increase in the number of leukocytes (from 600,000 to 800,000 per cubic millimeter). The leukemic process is considered by many to be a form of malignant tumor. Some small success has attended its treatment with nitrogen mustard, folic acid antagonists, cortisone, etc.

THROMBOCYTES

Blood platelets, or thrombocytes, are believed to be of importance in blood coagulation. They are round oval disks, in diameter about one third that of the erythrocytes, and they may number some 300,000 per cubic millimeter.

BLOOD PLASMA

Plasma is blood from which the corpuscles have been removed. It is, therefore, devoid of hemoglobin, for example, but otherwise contains much of what is found in whole blood. Of the 9 per cent of solids which are present, some 7 per cent is due to proteins.

PLASMA PROTEINS

Aside from fibrinogen, which plays a specific role in blood coagulation, the proteins of the blood (and this applies more particularly to the albumin fraction) maintain the water balance between the blood and tissues. While it is quite true that the osmotic pressure of the plasma proteins is almost negligible when compared with the electrolytes present, nevertheless the latter, unlike the proteins, play a less important role in the distribution of water, owing to the fact that the protein is largely confined to the interior of the cell.

That these proteins—and more particularly the albumin, because it is a smaller molecule and is present in larger quantity*—are important in the distribution of water is evident from the fact that patients with a deficient amount of serum albumin suffer from edema (Fig. 55). In *edema* we find abnormal amounts of fluid in intercellular spaces, which results in swelling. An experimental procedure for producing edema points to a similar conclusion. The procedure is known as *plasmapheresis*. This consists in removing blood from the animal and

---

* About 60 per cent of plasma protein is composed of albumin, "but it is responsible for nearly 80 per cent of the blood's osmotic efficiency" (Cohn).

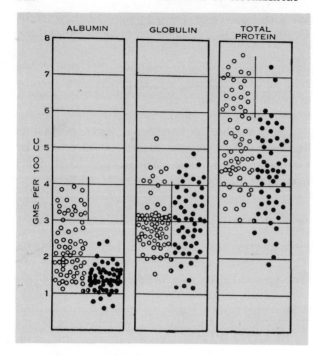

Figure 55. The relation between plasma protein concentration and edema in dogs. Open circles indicate estimations when no edema was present; black circles refer to determinations when edema was present; vertical lines in the middle of each column indicate the range of normal variation. (From Weech: Bull. N. Y. Acad. Med., Feb., 1939, p. 63.)

reinjecting the washed corpuscles bathed in Ringer-Locke solution (a solution of inorganic salts comparable in osmotic pressure to that of the blood itself). The amount of plasma proteins removed in this way will depend upon the amount of blood removed. Leiter found by this method that when the plasma proteins reached a level of less than 3 per cent, edema developed.

What is the mechanism by which edema develops? Fluids, foods, and waste rush through the capillaries, and exchanges occur between the blood and the tissues across the capillary membrane. Unlike the blood plasma, which contains some 7 per cent of protein, the tissue fluids surrounding the capillary membrane contain little protein. This difference in the concentration of protein develops an osmotic pressure, and water attempts to flow from the tissue into the capillary.

This osmotic pressure is approximately the equivalent of 22 mm. of mercury. However, a counterforce, due to blood pressure, tends to equalize the osmotic pressure by attempting to move fluid from the capillary to the tissue.

At the arterial end of the capillary the blood pressure is approximately 35 mm. of mercury, which means that this pressure is greater than the osmotic pressure (22 mm.); and therefore fluid—which includes food material—will pass from the capillary into the tissue, and thence to the cells.

At the venous end of the capillary the blood pressure is only about 12 mm. of mercury; which is considerably less than the osmotic pressure; and therefore fluid—containing the waste products in the tissue and from the cell—will flow back from the tissue into the venous end of the capillary.

Such is the situation under normal conditions. But assume, now, a condition in which the protein of the plasma has been reduced considerably below the normal amount—a result due to loss of protein from the body or due to a decreased intake of protein. The osmotic pressure will drop, and the drop will vary with the drop in protein. Assume that the osmotic pressure instead of 22 mm. is 10 mm. From now on, fluid will flow from the capillary into the tissues not only at the arterial end but at the venous end. The result is an abnormal accumulation of fluid in the tissue, with a development of edema. The blood vessels are squeezed and the blood supply is reduced.

The edema common in nephrosis has been associated with loss of plasma protein, and with a correspondingly lowered osmotic pressure.

Weech has pointed out that edema rarely appears before the albumin is below 2 per cent. Between globulin and edema there is little, if any, correlation (see Fig. 55). Serum albumin is that fraction of the protein of serum which remains in solution after half saturation with ammonium sulfate; the fraction which is precipitated is the globulin. Chemically, these are not very sharp separations.

Of secondary importance is the buffering power of the albumin and globulin. Van Slyke and his co-workers have shown that, among the proteins of the blood, the hemoglobin is the important buffering agent. Nevertheless, the albumin and globulin do help to some extent. The isoelectric point of albumin is given as pH 4.8, and that of globulin, pH 5.5; and since the blood itself is at a pH of 7.4, these proteins are present as anions.

Fractionation of Plasma Proteins. Cohn and his group made a study of the various factors which affect the solubility of proteins. As a result of these studies they formulated methods which can be used for the separation of protein mixtures such as occur in plasma. The factors which are carefully controlled and which may be varied are: pH, ionic strength, temperature, and alcohol concentration. At relatively high concentrations of protein, alcohol at low temperatures (below zero degrees) will not denature most proteins.

Figure 56 illustrates a method used for the separation of the plasma proteins into a number of fractions. Thus, starting with a pH of 7.4 of the original plasma, the pH is raised to 7.8 and alcohol is added to a definite concentration. A precipitate is formed which is separated by centrifugation and is called fraction I. The diagram shows how the separation is continued.

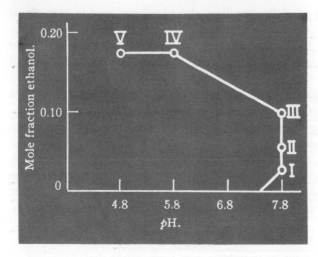

Figure 56. Ethanol concentration and pH for separation of plasma fractions, method 1. (From Cohn, Strong, Hughes, Mulford, Ashworth, Melin, and Taylor: J. Am. Chem. Soc., *68:* 459, 1946.)

Table 30 lists the fractions which have been obtained by this technique. Albumin has been prepared in the crystalline state and fibrinogen has been prepared so that it appears homogeneous electrophoretically. The other fractions have revealed themselves as mixtures. The α- and β-globulins contain the various lipoproteins and many enzymes. The γ-globulins contain a mixture of various antibodies and

TABLE 30. FRACTIONS OBTAINED BY THE COHN FRACTIONATION PROCEDURE

	Gm. Protein per Liter Plasma	*Gm. Protein per Liter of Plasma in Fraction*					*Protein in Fractions*
		I	*II + III*	*IV*	*V*	*VI*	
Protein	60.3	4.3	16.3	9.7	29.6	0.6	60.5
Albumin	33.2	0.2	0.7	1.0	29.0	0.3	31.2
α-globulin	8.4	0.2	1.8	5.4	0.6	0.3	8.3
β-globulin	7.8	0.8	6.2	3.1			10.1
γ-globulin	6.6	0.5	6.0	0.2			6.7
Fibrinogen	4.3	2.6	1.6				4.2

have been used for passive immunization against several diseases. Thus in mixed plasma samples from an adult population, the γ-globulin fraction will contain antibodies to the viruses causing such diseases as poliomyelitis, measles, and mumps.

Origin of Plasma Proteins. These proteins originate in the protein (amino acids) of the food, and their synthesis, to a large extent, occurs in the liver. They are in "dynamic equilibrium" with the amino acids of the body; that is to say, the proteins that are present in plasma and liver are in constant exchange with free amino acids. Feeding rats isotopic amino acids, Schoenheimer confirmed this view; the concentration of isotopic nitrogen in the plasma proteins was slightly lower than that in the liver, but was higher than that in other internal organs. "They demonstrate," he wrote, "the continuous chemical interactions of serum proteins with body proteins and diet."

Protein Deficiency. Plasma protein in amounts below normal (5.5 gm. protein per 100 ml. of blood, or below) (hypoproteinemia) is also an indication of loss of body protein.

The hypoproteinemia may be the result of one or more of the following: insufficient intake of protein; poor utilization; excessive loss of blood, and, therefore, of plasma proteins.

In nephritis there is a marked loss of blood albumin, giving rise to albuminuria.

The hypoproteinemia is often accompanied by edema, which results from an increased interstitial fluid volume, because, with less protein within the blood vessels, less liquid is drawn into them than would normally be the case.

Shock. Physiological shock is a state which results essentially in the reduction of effective circulating volume and blood pressure. It may be brought about by injury, extensive burns, or by blood loss due to hemorrhage. There are two phases in shock which can be characterized by the ability of the animal to respond to blood transfusion. The early state of shock is a reversible one, the blood replacement will bring the circulation of the animal back to normal. After prolonged periods of low blood pressure, due to any of the above states, transfusion of blood is ineffective. During World War II, blood transfusions, especially of plasma, demonstrated the effectiveness of such therapy in the early stages of shock. The need, on a large scale, for "synthetic" blood substitutes or, as they are termed, plasma "expanders," has led to a study of such materials as gelatin, polyvinyl pyrrolidone (PVP) and dextran (p. 34). The action of such compounds is based on their ability to maintain the osmotic pressure in the circulation at such levels as to prevent the movement of water into the tissues (edema).

EXTRACELLULAR FLUID

Surrounding the cell proper, there is the extracellular fluid, which consists of (*a*) the blood plasma and (*b*) the *interstitial fluid*. This interstitial fluid includes the *lymph* (Fig. 57).

Lymph, formed from the plasma of the blood and filling the tissue spaces, acts as a medium between the blood and cells. In composition

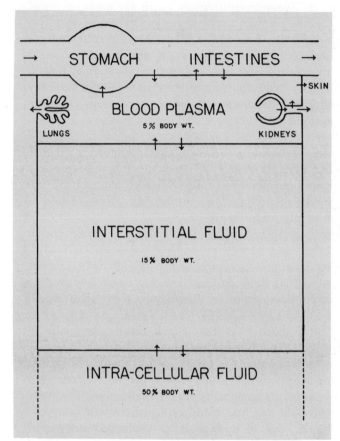

Figure 57. Interstitial fluid (From Gamble: Extracellular Fluid. Harvard Med. School).

it resembles the plasma (Table 31). Lymph capillaries, abounding in the tissue spaces, carry lymph into vessels which become larger and which unite at the thoracic duct, which, in turn, empties into the subclavian vein; so that ultimately the products in the lymph find their way into the general circulation.

Figure 58 describes what Gamble calls the "chemical anatomy" of extracellular fluid (blood plasma and interstitial fluid) as compared with that of sea water and of cell fluid. In this illustration, the values for each component can be read on the left of the ordinates and are expressed in terms of milliequivalents per liter of *water* in the fluid; the space occupied by protein is thus eliminated. The scales on the right of the ordinates refer to the total equivalence (the sum of the values in both columns).

Note the almost identical pattern of plasma and interstitial fluid,

TABLE 31. COMPARISON OF THE CONCENTRATIONS OF SOME OF THE CONSTITUENTS IN PERIPHERAL (CERVICAL) LYMPH AND BLOOD PLASMA OF THE DOG UNDER NORMAL CONDITIONS

| | Protein (Kjeldahl) | NPN | Urea | Uric acid | Creatinine | Sugar | Amino acids | Chlorides as NaCl | Phosphorus | | Calcium |
									Total	Inorganic	
	per cent	mg. per 100 ml.	mg. per 100 ml.	mg. per 100 ml.	mg. per 100 ml.	mg. per 100 ml.	mg. per 100 ml.	mg. per 100 ml.	mg. per 100 ml.	mg. per 100 ml.	mg. per 100 ml.
Plasma:											
Average........	6.18	32.6	21.7	Trace	1.37	123.0	4.90	678	22.0	5.6	11.70
Range........	(5.54–7.23)	(21.1–46.0)	(17.9–28.0)	.....	(1.22–1.54)	(112.0–143.0)	...	(649–721)	(18.3–26.1)	(4.4–6.9)	(10.85–12.95)
Lymph:											
Average........	3.32	34.8	23.5	Trace	1.40	132.2	4.84	711	11.8	5.9	9.84
Range........	(1.38–4.57)	(19.8–45.4)	(19.8–33.0)	.....	(1.28–1.49)	(107.0–144.0)	...	(690–730)	(10.2–13.7)	(4.7–7.3)	(8.93–10.84)

(From Heim: Am. J. Physiol., *103*:553.)

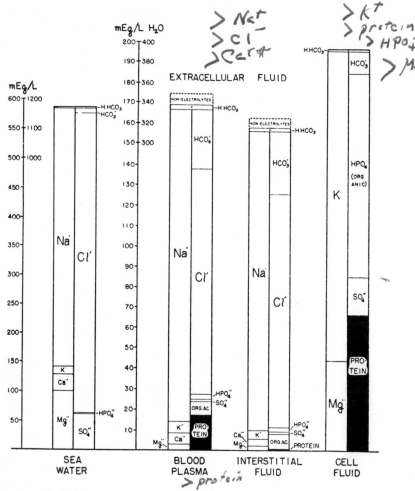

Figure 58. "Chemical anatomy" of extracellular fluid, as compared with that of sea water and cellular fluid. Values for cations (potential base) are in the left hand columns, and values for anions (acid radicals) are in the right hand columns. Figures to the left of the ordinates are used to determine acid-base equivalence. Figures to the right of the ordinates represent the sum of the values in the paired columns. (From Gamble: Extracellular Fluids.)

with the outstanding difference due to the presence of protein in the plasma. In order to maintain osmotic equivalence between these two fluid compartments, the protein of the plasma is replaced in the interstitial fluid by a balanced reduction of cation and increase in diffusible anion. Owing to its multivalency, the chemical equivalent of protein (in terms of osmotic effect) is about eight times its concentration value. Note also the difference in distribution of Na⁺ and K⁺ between the extracellular fluid and the intracellular fluid.

The history of the extracellular fluid is suggested by its resemblance to sea water. Although the absolute concentration of the various ions is much higher in sea water, since the salinity of the sea is known to have increased continuously, workers have suggested that the electrolyte concentration found in the extracellular fluid corresponds to that of sea water at the time of establishment of an internal aqueous environment.

BLOOD COAGULATION

Much work has been and is being done on the mechanism of the clotting of blood. A variety of theories are to be found in the literature but the following is an attempt to outline the main features of the process.

COAGULANT FACTORS

Fibrinogen. When whole blood which is shed is allowed to stand, it clots. The clot consists of an insoluble protein called fibrin, and red cells, which are enmeshed in the clot. If, however, the blood is quickly treated with oxalate or citrate, no clot is formed. On the addition of excess Ca^{++}, the blood will clot.

Prothrombin. If whole blood is treated so as to remove the calcium and the resulting blood is centrifuged, plasma will be obtained. Now treat this plasma with $BaSO_4$ and filter. The filtrate will not clot if an excess of calcium is added. The missing factor, which is adsorbed by the $BaSO_4$, can be recovered and added to the filtrate, which will now clot in the presence of calcium. This adsorbed factor is called prothrombin. The reaction may now be written:

$$\text{Fibrinogen} + \text{prothrombin} + Ca^{++} \longrightarrow \text{fibrin}$$

Thromboplastin. Instead of using plasma or blood one may set up a purified system containing fibrinogen, prothrombin and Ca^{++}. No clot will be formed unless there is added another factor called thromboplastin. This factor is present in tissues, such as lung, but is probably formed from injured platelets in shed blood. We may now write a more complete picture:

$$\text{Fibrinogen} + \text{prothrombin} + \text{thromboplastin} + Ca^{++} \longrightarrow \text{fibrin}$$

It has been shown that thromboplastin acts so as to convert prothrombin to thrombin, which is able now to clot fibrinogen:

$$\left\{ \begin{array}{l} \text{Prothrombin} \xrightarrow[\text{calcium}]{\text{thromboplastic factors (platelets)}} \text{thrombin} \\[2em] \text{Fibrinogen} \xrightarrow{\text{thrombin}} \text{fibrin} \end{array} \right.$$

VELOCITY FACTORS

A somewhat modified theory by Quick is also summarized:

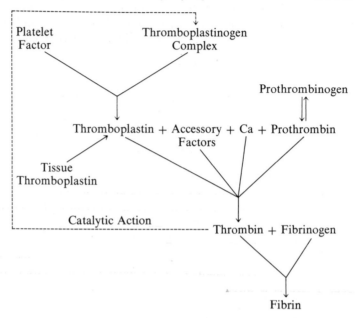

Accelerators. The action of thrombin, a proteinase, on fibrinogen is associated with the release of peptide material and probably removes an active site causing fibrin to clot. These reactions recall the conversion of an inactive enzyme (precursor) to its active form. Indeed, trypsin is capable of converting prothrombin to thrombin and can, therefore, hasten blood coagulation *in vitro*.

In an *in vitro* system containing prothrombin, calcium, thromboplastin (in excess) and fibrinogen, the velocity of clotting is slower than that obtained with plasma. If to this system one adds plasma from which prothrombin has been removed by adsorption with $BaSO_4$, the velocity of clotting is accelerated. This factor in plasma which is responsible for the acceleration of the clotting process, and which has been partially purified, is called the accelerator globulin or *Ac-globulin*. Its specific function is to accelerate the conversion of prothrombin to thrombin.

Inhibitors. There is normally present in the plasma, associated with the albumin fraction, a factor called *antithrombin*. It destroys the thrombin as it is formed.

FIBRINOLYSIN

There is present in the plasma a substance named fibrinolysin which can dissolve (lyse) the fibrin clot. The time for this action varies from a few hours to several weeks. It is present in plasma in an inactive form but can be activated *in vitro* by shaking the plasma with chloroform. Its action is proteolytic since there is a formation of nonprotein nitrogen.

MEASUREMENTS OF CLOTTING

The following are methods used in the measurement of clotting:

A. Clotting Time of Whole Shed Blood.

B. Prothrombin Time. This method measures the time required for enough thrombin to be formed in a given quantity of plasma in order to clot the fibrinogen in that amount of plasma. This time will be low where the velocity of conversion is low due to (*a*) a low concentration of prothrombin or (*b*) a lack of Ac-globulin. The latter compound is labile and disappears from stored blood.

C. The Two Stage Method. This method separates the clotting measurement into two stages: (*a*) fibrinogen to fibrin, and (*b*) prothrombin to thrombin. Plasma is treated so as to remove the fibrinogen either by adding an excess of thrombin, or by heating to 50° C. The plasma is diluted 50 times and Ac-globulin is added. Thromboplastin and calcium are added and, from time to time, aliquots of this mixture are added to a standard quantity of fibrinogen. The clotting time is measured. There is a direct relationship between the concentration of thrombin and the clotting time.

ANTICOAGULANT FACTORS

Many influences can retard or inhibit clotting; such anticoagulant factors include physical agents (cold, dilution, excess salts, protein precipitants, etc.); decalcifying agents (oxalate, citrate, fluoride); lipid solvents; heparin, Dicumarol (*in vivo*).* These anticoagulants may act

---

* *Dicumarol*, the hemorrhagic substance in sweet clover disease, interferes with the formation of prothrombin. It may, therefore, also be looked upon as an antiprothrombin type of substance. However, it is not a compound like heparin which is a normal constituent of the body.

Like heparin, its use has been suggested in the prevention of thromboses. The formula for Dicumarol is:

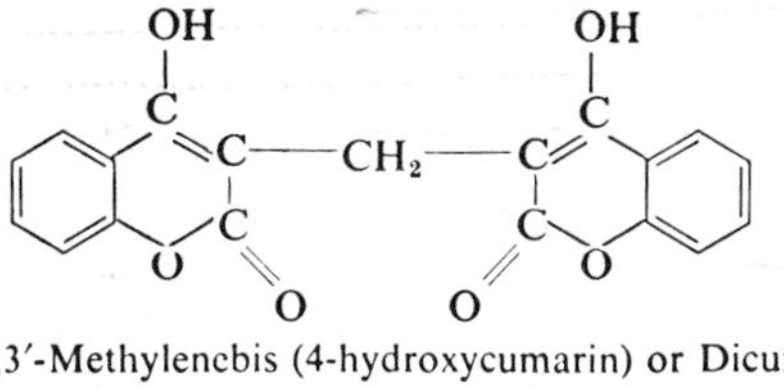

3,3′-Methylenebis (4-hydroxycumarin) or Dicumarol

Cumarin itself has the following structure:

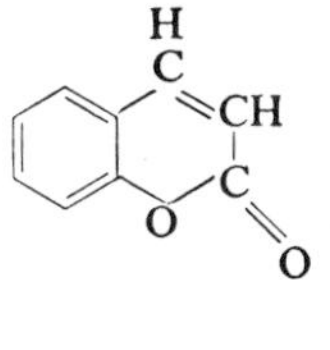

either by preventing thrombin formation or by preventing the reaction between thrombin and fibrinogen.

Heparin: An Antiprothrombin. A substance first obtained by Howell and MacLean, and to which the name "heparin" was given, prevents blood from coagulating. It is the most potent anticoagulant known. Jorpes found it to be a polysulfuric ester of mucoitin (muco-polysaccharide); it contains glucuronic acid, glucosamine, and a large amount of esterified sulfuric acid. It is found in small quantities in normal blood but is present in larger amounts in liver, spleen and lung.

Heparin inhibits the conversion of prothrombin to thrombin. Its action involves the exceedingly strong negative electric charge of its polysaccharide. Significant in this connection is that its anticoagulant activity is abolished by protamines, which are strongly basic proteins.

Heparin, found largely in the liver, is produced and stored in a specific kind of cells (the mast cells of Ehrlich), usually located close to the walls of the finest blood vessels.

The evidence points to different heparins in different species. Thus, the heparin from the dog is 2.5 times stronger than that from cattle; and hog heparin is weaker than that of cattle.

Hirudin: An Antithrombin. Blood-sucking animals (leeches, ticks, etc.) secrete a substance (hirudin) which prevents coagulation. An extract, when mixed with thrombin, will prevent coagulation of fibrinogen.

Synthetic anticoagulants are also known. Two of these substances are the sodium salt of cellulose disulfuric acid $(C_6H_8O_{11}S_2Na_2)_x$ and the potassium salt of polyvinyl sulfuric acid $(C_2H_3O_4SK)_x$. The sulfuric acid esters of the cerebrosides (Chap. 3) also show anticoagulant activity.

VARIATIONS IN THE TIME OF COAGULATION

Normally, of course, blood does not coagulate within the body. However, in certain diseases (arteriosclerosis, varicose veins, etc.), such a coagulation may occur (thrombosis). On the other hand, whereas blood when shed usually coagulates within five minutes or so, in some rare cases the coagulation time is much prolonged, and in a few cases the blood does not clot at all. Here we are dealing with a disease known as *hemophilia*. The disease is a hereditary defect (Fig. 59) occurring in the male but carried by the female—a sex-linked Mendelian recessive. Two types of this disease are known, A and B. Hemophilia A is the classical disease and is characterized by the absence from the plasma of a globulin which is closely associated with fibrinogen. This anti-hemophilic globulin is concerned with the conversion of prothrombin to thrombin. Crude preparations of this globulin increase clotting time in the hemophiliac for some time. Hemophilia B is characterized by

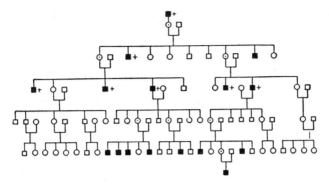

Figure 59. The family tree of the Hawkins-Cooper family. This family has lived in southern Illinois since before the Civil War. The squares represent males: the black squares, those with hemophilia; the black squares with crosses, those who bled to death; the circles, females; the circles with inner dots, transmitters of hemophilia. The chart shows fifteen patients known to have hemophilia and one whose condition is questionable. All eight persons in this generation who have hemophilia have been studied. (From Birch: J. Am. Med. Assoc., 99:1566.)

the absence from the plasma of an unknown factor termed the "Christmas" factor after the first patient.

TESTS FOR BLOOD

Two of the tests depend upon color production, the result of oxidation: the *guaiac test* and the *benzidine test*. The former involves the use of guaiac dissolved in glacial acetic acid, to which are added the blood and hydrogen peroxide; a blue color is formed. The benzidine test involves the use of an acid (glacial acetic) solution of benzidine mixed with blood and hydrogen peroxide. A blue or green color develops.

The best chemical test—a test which definitely indicates the presence of blood, though it does not distinguish human blood from other varieties—is the *hemin test*, to which reference has already been made (p. 223).

The immunological test distinguishes human blood from other varieties. Rabbits are injected with human blood serum over a period of several weeks and in increasing quantities. The rabbit develops antibodies. Blood is withdrawn from the animal and its serum mixed with human serum under examination. A turbidity, gradually changing to a flocculent precipitate, indicates the presence of human blood.

BLOOD ANALYSES

Table 29 (pp. 202–203) gives the composition of the blood. For more specific information with regard to such analyses, more detailed texts must be consulted (see the references at the end of the chapter). However, a few brief remarks at this stage may not be amiss.

The importance of blood analyses as aids in clinical diagnosis has been realized for a long time. To take but a few examples at random: a low hemoglobin content in the anemias, hyperglycemia in diabetes, low phosphorus and increased serum phosphatase in rickets (Chap. 18), decreased plasma prothrombin in obstructive jaundice, increased blood NPN (urea N, creatinine, uric acid, etc.) in renal impairment.

For a long time, progress in blood chemistry was more or less at a standstill, owing to the fact that the methods were not adapted to small quantities. With the introduction of micro methods, more particularly with the introduction of the photoelectric colorimeter, blood chemistry has become an extremely important adjunct to clinical diagnosis.

REFERENCES

For a general review, the chapters in *Ruch* and *Fulton:* Medical Physiology and Biophysics, 1960, are recommended. Clinical factors are stressed in *Bodansky* and *Bodansky:* Biochemistry of Disease, 1952, and by *Guyton:* Medical Physiology, 1961.

For quantitative methods, see *Hawk, Oser,* and *Summerson:* Practical Physiological Chemistry, 1954.

Krebs: Ann. Rev. Biochem., *19*:409, 1950, is the author of an article on the chemical composition of blood plasma and serum.

For some aspects of red cell production and destruction, see *Wintrobe:* Harvey Lectures, 1949–50, p. 87.

Reviews include the following: *Remington:* Ann. Rev. Biochem., *26*:561, 1957 (heme pigments and porphyrins); *Roughton* and *Kendrew:* Haemoglobin, 1949.

As to the origin of heme and the chemistry of prophyrins, see *Granick:* Harvey Lectures, 1948–49, 220 (structures of heme and chlorophyll compared). *Wriston, Lack,* and *Shemin:* J. Biol. Chem., *215*:603, 1955; *Shemin, Russell* and *Abramsky:* Ibid., *215*:613, 1955; *Remington:* Endeavor, *14*:126, 1955; *Laver, Neuberger* and *Udenfriend:* Biochem. J., *70*:4, 1958; *Gibson, Laver* and *Neuberger:* Ibid., *70*:71, 1958.

The plasma proteins are dealt with by *Whipple:* Physiol. Rev. *20*:194, 1940, and by *Sahyun* in Proteins and Amino Acids in Nutrition, 1948, p. 265. See also *Yule, Lampson, Miller,* and *Whipple,* J. Experimental Medicine, *93*:539, 1951; *Roberts* and *White:* J. Biol. Chem., *180*:505, 1949.

For the physiology of edema, see *Krehl* and *Winters:* Borden's Rev. Nutritional Research, *13:* No. 7, Oct., 1952.

On the subject of blood coagulation, see *Seegers:* Harvey Lectures, 1951–52, 180; J. Michigan State Med. Soc., *55*:272, 1956; *Quick:* British Med. J., April 25, 1959, p. 1059.

For an article on blood platelets, see *Zucker:* Scientific American, Feb., 1961, p. 58.

As to hemophilia, see *Quick:* Medical Times, May, 1958; Archives of Internal Medicine, *103*:762, 1959; Blood, 9:265, 1954.

In connection with heparin and anticoagulants in general, *Jorpes* is the author of a book: Heparin, 1946. For a review of the chemistry of heparin and other mucopolysaccharides, see *Jeanloz:* International Congress of Biochemistry, Brussells, 1955, p. 65 (Conferences and Reports).

Link's pioneer work on the anticoagulant from spoiled sweet clover hay (Dicumarol) is described in Harvey Lectures, 1943–44, 162. See also *Spies:* Ann.

Rev. Biochem., *17:*460, 1948; *Allen:* J. Am. Med. Assoc., *134:*323, 1947; *MacMillan:* Science, *108:*416, 1948.

The nature of shock and the involvement, in part, of ferritin is discussed by *Mazur* and *Shorr:* J. Biol. Chem., *176:*771, 1948; *182:*607, 1950; Nutr. Rev., *9:*204, 1951; *Richards:* Merck Report, April, 1952, p. 18; *Page:* Bull. N. Y. Acad. Med., March, 1952, p. 131; *Granick:* Physiol. Rev., *31:*489, 1951 (ferritin).

The sickle cell variety of anemia is discussed by *Pauling, Itano, Singer,* and *Wells:* Science, *110:*543, 1949; Scientific American, August, 1951, p. 56; *Itano:* Science, *117:*89, 1953; *Pauling:* Harvey Lectures, 1953–54, p. 216.

Extended data on the composition and reactions of blood are given by *Albritton:* Standard Values in Blood, 1952.

CHEMISTRY
OF
RESPIRATION

The process of respiration involves the absorption of oxygen through the lungs, the transfer of this oxygen by the blood to the cells, and the uptake of CO_2 by the blood, with its ultimate elimination through the lungs. What causes the oxygen to be taken up by the blood, and in quantity far beyond what can be explained on the grounds of a mere simple solution of the gas? What causes the oxygen to leave the blood and enter the cells? How is the elimination of carbon dioxide brought about? How, with the production of so much acid (not only carbonic but also sulfuric from the oxidation of the sulfur in proteins) is the pH of the blood maintained in the neighborhood of 7.4?

This chapter is an attempt to answer these questions. Closely related problems will be taken up in subsequent chapters. For example, what is the mechanism involving oxidations within the cell (Chap. 10)? What are the energy relations involved in the process (Chap. 15)? What are the intermediate products formed when complex substances are oxidized (Chaps. 11, 12, 13)?

The air we breathe consists, approximately (in volumes per cent dry gas), of oxygen, 20.93; carbon dioxide, 0.04; nitrogen, 79. The air we expire may have the composition: oxygen, 16.02; carbon dioxide, 4.38; and nitrogen, 79. The essential reaction involves a consumption of oxygen and an elimination of carbon dioxide. The nitrogen as such is not utilized. It is true that cellular material contains nitrogen; but it is also true that the needs of the body for this element can be supplied

226

only in the form of certain compounds of nitrogen (proteins, amino acids, lipids, etc.).*

LAWS GOVERNING BEHAVIOR OF GASES

BOYLE'S LAW

At constant temperature, the volume of a gas varies inversely with the pressure. Stated in another way,

$$P \propto 1/V \qquad \text{or} \qquad P = k_1 \times 1/V \qquad \text{or} \qquad PV = k_1$$

where k_1 is a proportionality constant.

CHARLES' LAW

A drop in temperature of 1° C. produces a decrease in volume of a gas (at constant pressure) equal to $\frac{1}{273}$ of its original volume. Using this information, we can construct a thermometer whose scale corresponds to 273+ degrees C., and which can be used for calculations involving changes in the volume of a gas when the temperature changes. This scale is called the *absolute* or Kelvin scale. Using the symbol T for absolute temperature, we have

$$V \propto T \qquad \text{or} \qquad V = k_2 \times T$$

GENERAL GAS LAW

In actual laboratory practice both pressure and temperature will vary from those of a set of standard conditions which we must use in order to compare values obtained from different laboratories. Standard conditions are a temperature of 0° C. and a pressure of 760 mm. Hg. By combining both gas laws we may now calculate the effect of alteration in temperature and pressure on the volume of a gas.

For example, 100 ml. of a gas is measured at 20° C. and 780 mm. pressure. What would be its volume at standard conditions (0° C. and 760 mm. pressure)? The values of 20° C. and 0° C. are converted to the Kelvin scale; these are $273 + 20 = 293°$ K., and $273 + 0 = 273°$ K., respectively. The volume will be affected by this change in temperature as predicted by Charles' law: it will decrease because the temperature is decreasing (from 293° to 273°):

$$V_{(\text{at standard})} = 100 \text{ ml.} \times \frac{273° \text{ K.}}{293° \text{ K.}} = 93.2 \text{ ml.}$$

On the other hand, the change in pressure will also affect the volume of the gas. Since the pressure will drop (from 780 to 760), the volume should increase, or

* Man can continue to exist for weeks without food and for days without water; but without oxygen he dies within a few minutes.

$$V_{(at\ standard)} = 100\ ml. \times \frac{273°\ K.}{293°\ K.} \times \frac{780\ mm.}{760\ mm.} = 95.6\ ml.$$

DRY VS. WET GAS VOLUMES

In practice we generally measure the volume of a gas which has been liberated or collected over water. The water vapor itself will exert a pressure which depends on the temperature. For purposes of comparison we should correct for the presence of water vapor and calculate the volume of the dry gas. This is done by examining tables which tell us the vapor pressure of water (aqueous tension) at the observed temperature. We then subtract this pressure from the observed pressure in the laboratory. Thus, for our problem in the previous section, the vapor pressure of water at 20° C. is 17.4 mm. Therefore,

$$V_{\substack{(at\ standard \\ of\ dry\ gas)}} = 100\ ml. \times \frac{273°\ K.}{293°\ K.} \times \frac{780\ mm. - 17.4\ mm.}{760\ mm.}$$

DALTON'S LAW OF PARTIAL PRESSURES

Each gas in a mixture of gases exerts a partial pressure which it would exert if it existed alone in the same volume, and the total pressure of the mixture is a sum of the partial pressures of each component. This is important in considering the respiratory gases, since we must consider several gases in the mixture we call air, inspired or expired. For example, at sea level (760 mm. Hg) oxygen makes up 20.93 per cent by volume of the air. Its partial pressure in the inspired air would therefore be:

$$760\ mm. \times 0.2093 = 159.1\ mm.$$

However, if we were at an altitude of 18,000 feet, where the atmospheric pressure is half that at sea level, 380 mm., the partial pressure of oxygen would be:

$$380\ mm. \times 0.2093 = 79.6\ mm.$$

GAS EQUILIBRIA

The Le Chatelier principle affects equilibrium reactions involving gases as well as those reactions involving compounds in solution. For example, if we dissolve a gas in water, the quantity of dissolved gas varies directly with the pressure and is independent of other gases mixed with it. Thus,

$$O_{2(gas)} \quad \rightleftarrows \quad O_{2(dissolved)}$$

The effect of increasing the pressure of oxygen gas will be to drive the equilibrium to the right: more oxygen will dissolve. If the pressure is decreased, the equilibrium will shift towards the left: less oxygen will be dissolved. This is known as Henry's law.

The effect of this law on chemical reactions involving gases in equilibrium with an aqueous solution of a compound with which they can react is shown for the reaction of hemoglobin (Hb) with molecular oxygen in solution, to form oxyhemoglobin: HbO_2

$$O_{2(gas)} \rightleftarrows O_{2(dissolved)} + Hb_{(dissolved)} \rightleftarrows HbO_{2(dissolved)}$$

The relative concentration of HbO_2 will depend on the partial pressure of oxygen gas in contact with the solution: increasing the O_2 pressure will drive the equilibrium towards the right; decreasing it will shift the reaction towards the left (less HbO_2 will be present).

MEASUREMENT OF GASES IN BLOOD

The two gases with which we are concerned during respiration are oxygen and carbon dioxide. Methods for their estimation were developed by Van Slyke and his co-workers and resulted in several types of apparatus (Fig. 60). The general principles for the determination of these two gases in blood are outlined below:

Oxygen. The oxygen content of blood is the volume of oxygen present—that which is dissolved physically as well as that which is in the form of oxyhemoglobin. The oxygen capacity of the blood is that volume of oxygen with which all of the hemoglobin in the blood can

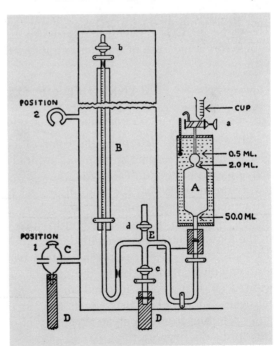

Figure 60. Van Slyke blood-gas analyzer. (From Harrow, et al.: Laboratory Manual of Biochemistry, 4th edition.)

combine. The oxygen capacity of blood is therefore a measure of total hemoglobin. For this determination, blood is saturated with oxygen in the air by rotating a thin film of blood in a separatory funnel in contact with air at atmospheric pressure. A given sample of this equilibrated blood is introduced into the apparatus and treated with an oxidizing agent which liberates the oxygen as a gas. The carbon dioxide which is present is absorbed by alkali; and the volume of the residual gases, oxygen and nitrogen, is read, together with the temperature and barometric pressure. The oxygen capacity of the blood sample is calculated after suitable corrections for nitrogen content (constant quantity) and for temperature, pressure and aqueous tension.

The oxygen content of blood that has not been exposed to the air is determined in much the same manner, except that the blood must be collected under oil and is not exposed to the air before introduction into the apparatus.

Carbon Dioxide. Blood contains carbon dioxide in several forms. These are dissolved CO_2 (as carbonic acid, H_2CO_3), as the bicarbonate ion, HCO_3^-, and as a carbamino compound of hemoglobin (p. 239). Most of the carbon dioxide is present as bicarbonate. Measurement is usually made of the "carbon dioxide capacity" of plasma, which is a measure of all the CO_2 liberated by treating plasma, after equilibration with alveolar air, with a weak acid such as lactic acid. The alveolar air used for equilibration may be supplied by the analyst from his lungs or by use of a 5.5 per cent CO_2–air mixture from a tank. Equilibration is performed in a separatory funnel as outlined above. The value for CO_2 capacity is referred to as the "alkali reserve," which is therefore a measure of the concentration of bicarbonate in the plasma.

TRANSPORT OF OXYGEN

COMPOSITION OF THE ATMOSPHERE AND BLOOD GASES

If we were to determine the composition, in per cent, of the gases (including water vapor) in inspired, expired and alveolar air, we would arrive at the figures in Table 32.

It can be seen that the over-all process of respiration consists of the extraction of oxygen from the atmosphere and a liberation of carbon dioxide. Nitrogen as such is not utilized. A small quantity is dissolved in the plasma, but none is retained or produced in the body. Note, however, the differences in nitrogen content between inspired and expired air. Actually, on a dry basis, the content of nitrogen is greater in the expired air than in the inspired air. This is due not to a liberation of nitrogen, but rather to the reduction in total volume of the respiratory gases resulting from the greater quantity of oxygen absorbed than of the carbon dioxide produced.

TABLE **32.** GAS COMPOSITION OF INSPIRED, EXPIRED AND ALVEOLAR AIR (VOLUMES PER CENT)

	Nitrogen	Oxygen	Carbon dioxide	Water vapor
Inspired air	78.5	20.8	0.04	0.66
Expired air	74.8	15.3	3.8	6.1
Alveolar air*	75.1	13.5	5.3	6.1

* A mixture of inspired air plus air present in the trachea, bronchi, and subdivisions of the lungs spreads to the alveoli and so touches the lung capillaries containing venous blood. This mixture in the alveolar spaces is alveolar air.

We may now calculate the composition of these gases in terms of the pressure exerted by each: their partial pressures. These will be as shown in Table 33.

TABLE **33.** GAS COMPOSITION OF INSPIRED, EXPIRED AND ALVEOLAR AIR (PARTIAL PRESSURES IN MM. HG)

	Nitrogen	Oxygen	Carbon dioxide	Water vapor
Inspired air	596.6	158.1	0.30	5.0
Expired air	568.5	116.3	28.9	46.4
Alveolar air	570.8	102.6	40.3	46.4

The method of computing these figures for the partial pressure of each gas is given by the following example for the oxygen of the inspired air:

$$760 \text{ mm.} \times 0.208 = 158.08 \text{ mm.}$$

When the respiratory gases are measured, the volumes are usually reported in terms of the dry gas (minus the water vapor), although this correction is small.

According to Henry's law, the amount of a gas dissolved in a liquid varies directly with the pressure of that gas and is independent of other gases mixed with it. Thus it has been found that the volume of each gas, measured at 38° C., which is dissolved in 1 ml. of water when the pressure of the gas is 760 mm. over the liquid is:

0.0262 cc. O_2

0.0127 cc. N_2

0.0546 cc. CO_2

These values are referred to as *absorption coefficients*. If we were to calculate how much of each gas can be held in physical solution in 100 ml. of arterial blood in the alveoli of the lungs, we would arrive at the following values:

$$100 \times 0.0127 \times 0.751 = 0.95 \text{ cc. of } N_2$$
$$100 \times 0.0262 \times 0.135 = 0.35 \text{ cc. of } O_2$$
$$100 \times 0.0546 \times 0.053 = 2.89 \text{ cc. of } CO_2$$

In the blood the gases are actually present in the following amounts (volumes per cent, or cubic centimeters of gas per 100 ml. of blood):

	O_2	CO_2	N_2
Arterial blood................	19.45	49.68	1.7
Venous blood	14.04	54.65	1.7

Thus we must account for the much larger quantity of oxygen and carbon dioxide held in solution by blood other than in the physically dissolved state.

OXYGEN IN THE BLOOD

Some time during the development of the animal species a mechanism had to be devised to carry more oxygen than could be obtained by mere solution. In many of the lower animal forms, pigmented proteins in the plasma appeared which had special affinities for molecular oxygen. For example, hemocyanin, a protein-copper complex, is found in the blood of various arthropods (Table 34).

TABLE 34.   OXYGEN CAPACITIES OF SOME DIFFERENT BLOODS

Pigment	Color	Site	Animal	Cubic centimeters oxygen per 100 ml. blood
Hemoglobin	Red	Corpuscles	Mammals	25
			Birds	18.5
			Reptiles	9
			Amphibia	12
			Fishes	9
		Plasma	Annelids	6.5
			Molluscs	1.5
Hemocyanin	Blue	Plasma	Molluscs:	
			Gastropods	2
			Cephalopods	8
			Crustaceans	3
Chlorocruorin	Green	Plasma	Annelids	9

(From Baldwin: Comparative Biochemistry, Cambridge University Press, London.)

It was not until the corpuscle was formed that much larger amounts of oxygen could be carried as a protein-oxygen compound in the form of hemoglobin, without, at the same time, increasing the concentration of the plasma proteins to an extent which would make the blood too viscous for adequate flow.

It is believed by some that the oxygen-carrying power of hemoglobin can be explained on the basis of an iron-porphyrin-protein linkage. The various hemoglobins have been formulated as follows (dotted lines indicate a covalent bond, and solid lines an ionic bond):

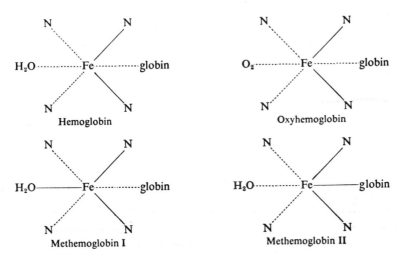

Haurowitz considers these hemoglobins as aqua complexes of iron, with a coordination number of 6. The ferro complexes (hemoglobin and oxyhemoglobin) contain two ionic and four covalent bonds; the ferric (the methemoglobins) contain three ionic and three covalent bonds.

Either by removing hemoglobin from blood and determining its oxygen-combining capacity, or by determining the amount of oxygen evolved from hemoglobin when the pressure is reduced (in vacuo), it can be shown that by far the larger amount of oxygen in the blood is in combination with hemoglobin.

THE OXYGEN DISSOCIATION CURVE

The quantity of oxygen which is carried by hemoglobin is affected by the partial pressure of oxygen, according to the equation:

$$Hb + O_2 \rightleftarrows HbO_2$$

From this equation, which is a simplified way of writing a complex reaction, it is apparent that at high oxygen tensions the degree of saturation of hemoglobin would be greatest. The shape of this curve, which will tell us about the relationship between oxygen saturation and oxygen tension, is found experimentally to agree with this simplified formulation when one uses a dilute solution of purified hemoglobin (Fig. 61).

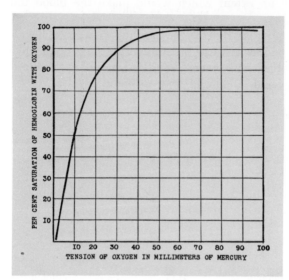

Figure 61. Oxygen dissociation curve of a dilute solution of hemoglobin. (After Barcroft, Best and Taylor: Physiological Basis of Medical Practice, Baltimore, Williams & Wilkins Company.)

However, when one determines the oxygen saturation curve for whole blood, a curve with an S shape is obtained. Obviously then, hemoglobin as it exists *in vivo* does not combine with oxygen according to our simplified equation. We know that each molecule of hemoglobin contains 4 molecules of heme (iron-protoporphyrin) and can therefore combine with a maximum of 8 atoms (4 molecules) of oxygen; or intermediate combinations may occur in which less than this number of oxygen atoms may be involved:

$$(a)\ Hb_4\ + O_2\ \rightleftarrows\ Hb_4O_2$$
$$(b)\ Hb_4O_2 + O_2\ \rightleftarrows\ Hb_4O_4$$
$$(c)\ Hb_4O_4 + O_2\ \rightleftarrows\ Hb_4O_6$$
$$(d)\ Hb_4O_6 + O_2\ \rightleftarrows\ Hb_4O_8$$

If such a series of equilibria were actually to take place, an S-shaped curve would be predicted. The actual curve (Fig. 61) obtained experimentally lies somewhere between reactions (a) and (d).

The shape of the oxygen dissociation curve shown in Figure 61 is a result of the dissociation of human hemoglobin, in dilute solutions, into four approximately equivalent molecules, each with a molecular weight of 17,000. This curve is, therefore, the expression of the combination of one heme unit with oxygen. The sigmoid nature of the oxygen dissociation curve for hemoglobin in blood is due to the fact that an oxygenated heme affects the dissociation constant of the other heme groups of the same molecule, the effect being greatest for the fourth heme group.

EFFECT OF CO₂ OR ACID ON OXYGEN DISSOCIATION CURVE

In Figure 63 we see that the effect of increased CO_2 tension is to shift the oxygen dissociation curve to the right and downwards. The implication of this observation to conditions within the animal organism is of interest. As the blood approaches the tissues, the ability of the hemoglobin to bind oxygen, although essentially unimpaired at high oxygen tensions, decreases markedly at lowered oxygen tensions, since the effect of increased CO_2 tension is to shift the curve downwards and to the right. The same shift of the curve occurs in the presence of lowered pH, such as occurs when lactic acid accumulates during severe muscular activity (Fig. 62). The shift in the dissociation curve is called the Bohr effect and is accounted for by the shift in the equilibrium, since oxyhemoglobin is a stronger acid than hemoglobin. Thus a drop in pH causes a shift in the equilibrium in the direction of the less acid constituent, hemoglobin. The mechanism of change in acidity between hemoglobin and oxyhemoglobin will be discussed under buffers (p. 242).

LIBERATION OF OXYGEN TO THE TISSUES

Since one mole of O_2 at standard conditions occupies 22.4 liters, it can be calculated that 1 gm. of hemoglobin combines with 1.34 cc. of

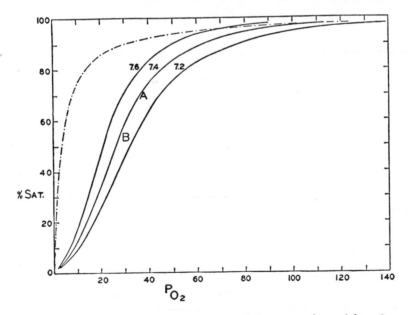

Figure 62. Normal oxygen dissociation curves of the system hemoglobin, O_2, oxyhemoglobin at several values of pH. Also a representative curve for myoglobin (dashed curve) whose molecular weight is about one-fourth of that of hemoglobin. (From Clarke: Topics in Physical Chemistry, 1948, p. 208.)

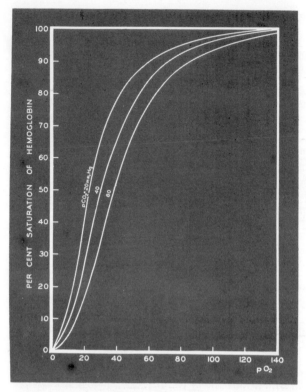

Figure 63. The dissociation curves of hemoglobin at 38° C. and at partial pressures of carbon dioxide equal to 20, 40, and 80 mm. Hg. (From Davenport: The ABC of Acid-Base Chemistry, Univ. of Utah.)

oxygen at body temperature and 1 atmosphere. Since normal human blood contains 15 gm. hemoglobin per 100 ml. of blood, full saturation is 15×1.34, or 20.1 cc. oxygen per 100 ml. blood.

From Table 32 (p. 231) we see that the oxygen tension in alveolar air is 13.5 volumes per cent. At atmospheric pressure the partial pressure of oxygen in contact with the arterial blood in the lungs will be 102.6 mm. (Table 33, p. 231). From the oxygen dissociation curve at 102.6 mm. pO_2 and 40.3 mm. pCO_2, the blood will be saturated to the extent of 98 per cent. Since saturation is equivalent to 20 volumes per cent, the arterial blood at the alveoli would contain

$$\frac{98}{100} \times 0.20 = 19.6 \text{ vols. per cent O}_2$$

To illustrate how the S shape of the dissociation curve operates to unload oxygen at the tissues, let us examine the effect of a drop in O_2 tension of 20 mm. at two different points along the curve—at two different regions of oxygen tension. First, let us go from a pO_2 of oxygen of 100 mm. to 80 mm. From Table 35 we see that the blood of the subject would go from a point where it is 98 per cent saturated to one where it is 96 per cent saturated:

$$\frac{98}{100} \times 0.20 = 19.6 \text{ vols. per cent}$$

$$\frac{96}{100} \times 0.20 = 19.2 \text{ vols. per cent}$$

a drop of only 0.4 cc. of bound oxygen per 100 ml. of blood.

TABLE 35. RELATION OF PARTIAL PRESSURE OF OXYGEN TO OXYGEN CAPACITY IN A HUMAN SUBJECT

pO_2 (mm.)	Saturation (per cent) (O_2 Capacity = 20 vols. per cent)
10	15
20	40
30	60
40	76.5
50	86
60	91
70	94.5
80	96
100	98

(Adapted from Clark: Topics in Physical Chemistry. 2nd Ed. Baltimore, Williams & Wilkins Company, 1952, p. 203.)

Now let us go from a pO_2 of 40 mm. to one of 20 mm. This situation is analogous to that which prevails at the capillaries near the tissues. The corresponding saturations are 77 and 40 per cent, respectively. The amounts of oxygen held at these two points would be:

$$\frac{77}{100} \times 0.20 = 15.4 \text{ vols. per cent}$$

$$\frac{40}{100} \times 0.20 = 8.0 \text{ vols. per cent}$$

a drop of 7.4 cc. of bound oxygen per 100 ml. of blood, and this quantity of oxygen is now delivered to the tissues.

The bulge in the oxygen dissociation curve is of advantage in that high partial pressure of oxygen is maintained when oxygen must be extracted from the atmosphere (alveolar air), while at the tissues, where the partial pressure of oxygen is lower, a relatively great quantity of oxygen can be lost to the tissues. One other factor is also of importance: the venous blood which returns from the tissues has a lower pH than does arterial blood, again helping to release oxygen from oxyhemoglobin.

MYOGLOBIN

Skeletal muscle contains a protein which resembles hemoglobin in its ability to combine reversibly with oxygen. Its oxygen-carrying ability is also due to the presence of protoporphyrin IX linked to a globin which is different from that of globin in hemoglobin. Its molecular weight is 17,500. Whereas the oxyhemoglobin dissociation curve shows a bulge at lower partial pressures of oxygen, that for oxymyoglobin is more rectangular (Fig. 62). Thus, myoglobin can hold a reserve of oxygen when the partial pressure of oxygen is too low for hemoglobin to hold the gas. Further, as the pH of the blood becomes more acid (as in severe exercise), the oxyhemoglobin dissociation curve shifts in the direction of higher partial pressures of oxygen. Thus, when the partial pressure of oxygen is relatively low, and the muscle needs some oxygen, the reserve oxygen of the myoglobin can be unloaded to the tissues.

CARBON DIOXIDE OF BLOOD

FORMS OF CARBON DIOXIDE IN BLOOD

The evolution of CO_2 by the lungs is due to the difference in partial pressure between the CO_2 in the blood and the low tension in the alveoli, a difference brought about by respiration. We may consider this gas to exist in equilibrium among the following forms:

$$HCO_3^- \rightleftharpoons H_2CO_3 \rightleftharpoons CO_2 + H_2O$$

The removal of CO_2 by respiratory activity leads to a shift of the equilibrium to the right. However, this shift can hardly account for all of the CO_2 which is exhaled, since the red cell is present in the lung capillaries but a short period of time.

Two factors contribute to the release of CO_2. One is the presence in the red cell of the enzyme carbonic anhydrase. This enzyme, which is absent from the plasma, is capable of catalyzing the following equilibrium:

$$H_2CO_3 \rightleftharpoons CO_2 + H_2O$$

and since the direction of shift of this equilibrium is affected by the partial pressure of CO_2, a rapid removal of CO_2 takes place in the lungs.* We shall see that when CO_2 is liberated into the plasma at the tissues (Fig. 64), this enzyme is responsible for the rapid removal of CO_2 from the plasma to the red cell where it is incorporated as H_2CO_3 or bicarbonate.

The other factor which contributes to the removal of CO_2 is the

---

* "Without carbonic anhydrase, the release of the amount of CO_2 liberated from the blood during one passage through the lungs would go to within 90 per cent of equilibrium in about 100 seconds. Since erythrocytes spend less than one second in the lung capillaries, enzymic catalysis of the reaction is required." (Davenport.)

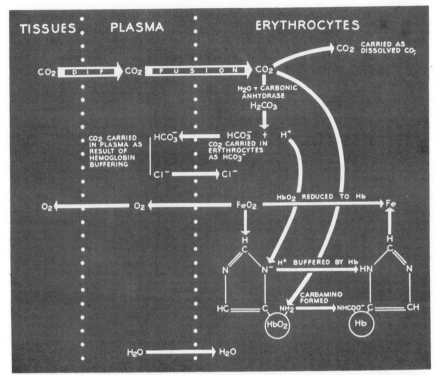

Figure 64. Processes occurring when CO_2 passes from the tissues into the erythrocytes. (From Davenport: The ABC of Acid-Base Chemistry, Univ. of Utah.)

presence in the red cell of some CO_2 bound to hemoglobin in the form of a carbamino compound:

$$\text{Protein}.NH_2 + CO_2 \;\rightleftarrows\; \text{protein}.NH.COOH \;\rightleftarrows\; \text{protein}.NH.COO^- + H^+$$

This reaction achieves the binding of CO_2 without passing through the stage of carbonic acid. It is estimated that some 2 to 10 per cent of the total CO_2 in the blood is in direct combination with hemoglobin as a carbamino compound. It is of some interest that reduced hemoglobin carries more CO_2 in this form than does oxyhemoglobin.

In addition, some 5 per cent of the total CO_2 is physically dissolved in the blood. The remainder is present as bicarbonate.

TRANSPORT OF CARBON DIOXIDE

The pCO_2 in arterial blood is 40 mm., and in tissues it is increased to some 50 to 70 mm. as a result of metabolic activity. The net result is a tendency for CO_2 to pass from the tissues into the blood.

A small amount of carbon dioxide combines with water to form carbonic acid, which ionizes to form bicarbonate ions. Some of the carbon dioxide forms carbamino compounds; some of it passes into the erythrocytes, and some remains in the plasma as dissolved CO_2.

The carbon dioxide which enters the erythrocytes may remain as dissolved CO_2, or form carbamino compounds, or be hydrated in the presence of *carbonic anhydrase* (p. 133). All three reactions take place, but the major reaction is that due to the carbonic anhydrase. Here much of the carbonic acid which is first formed is converted into bicarbonate ions.

As the arterial blood becomes venous and a large amount of bicarbonate appears in the plasma, much of this bicarbonate is drawn to the erythrocytes (where the hemoglobin is a source of temporary combination). What was originally an equilibrium between the bicarbonate of the plasma and that of the cells has now been upset; and to offset this condition, some bicarbonate passes from the cells into the plasma. But this effect upsets electrical neutrality, both in the cells and in the plasma; and the situation can be remedied either by the removal of an equal amount of cation from the cells, or by the substitution of an equal amount of some other anion within the cells. The suitable anion in this case is the chloride ion; so that as the bicarbonate ions leave the cells and enter the plasma, an equivalent quantity of chloride ions leave the plasma and enter the cells. This is known as the *chloride shift* (Fig. 64).

THE BUFFERS OF THE BLOOD

If we remember that the extremes of life range between a pH of blood of 7 to 7.8, then the importance of having an adequate buffering system becomes apparent (Fig. 65).

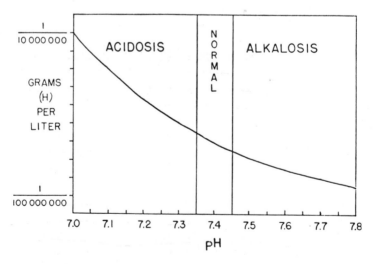

Figure 65. Possible range of pH in blood. (From Gamble: Extracellular Fluid, Harvard Med. School.)

The principal buffers of the blood are

$$\frac{H_2CO_3}{NaHCO_3}, \quad \frac{NaH_2PO_4}{Na_2HPO_4}, \quad \frac{HHbO_2}{NaHbO_2}, \quad \frac{HHb}{NaHb}, \quad \frac{HPr}{NaPr}$$

(Hb = hemoglobin and Pr = protein).

The plasma contains most of the bicarbonate and albumin and globulin, whereas the corpuscles contain the hemoglobin and most of the phosphates.

In a buffer system the pH is related to the concentrations of the components of the buffer by the following expression:

$$pH = pK_a \text{ (or } pK_1) + \log \frac{BA}{HA}$$

where BA stands for the salt of a weak acid (e.g., sodium acetate, sodium bicarbonate, Na_2HPO_4, Protein.COO⁻) and HA stands for the weak acid (e.g., acetic acid, carbonic acid, NaH_2PO_4, Protein.NH_3^+).

Where the salts in question are phosphates—where, in other words, the salts are $Na_2HPO_4 : NaH_2PO_4$, $pK_1 = 6.8$. Where the salts are the carbonates, $NaHCO_3 : H_2CO_3$, $pK_1 = 6.1$.

It is obvious, then, that, knowing the pK_1 and the ratio of salt to acid, the pH can be determined.

When this ratio = 1, and $[H^+] = K_1$, the pH changes least, giving us maximum buffer effects (Fig. 66). In other words, when we have 50 per cent of the CO_2 as $NaHCO_3$, the addition of either acid or alkali causes less change in pH than at any other point on the curve.

With blood at pH 7.4, $NaHCO_3 : H_2CO_3 = 20 : 1$. When $NaHCO_3 :$

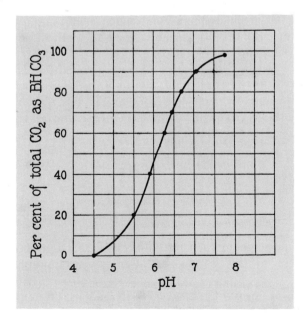

Figure 66. Action of $NaHCO_3 : H_2CO_3$ buffer, showing maximum buffer effect at middle of curve when $NaHCO_3 : H_2CO_3$ ratio = 1. (From Van Slyke: Physiol. Rev., 1:147.)

$H_2CO_3 = 1$, pH $= 6.1$.* With the phosphate, when $Na_2HPO_4 : NaH_2PO_4$ $= 1$, pH $= 6.8$.

If, for any reason, the pH of the blood is lowered (as in acidosis), then these buffers become much more efficient.

In so far as the oxyhemoglobin is concerned, its maximum buffering effect is at pH 7.2, which is appreciably nearer to the normal pH of blood.

THE DISTRIBUTION OF BUFFERING CAPACITIES

That the blood cells are richer in buffering capacity than the plasma has been known for a long time. By determining the CO_2 absorption curves of whole blood and of separated serum, it can be shown that the increase in combined CO_2 in whole blood is more than three times that in serum. The cell buffers are hemoglobin and phosphate, neither of which diffuses into the plasma. Despite this fact, they exert their influence on the plasma.

HEMOGLOBIN-OXYHEMOGLOBIN

Aside from its buffering properties, the change which hemoglobin undergoes when it is converted into oxyhemoglobin (and vice versa) has an important bearing on the transfer and ultimate elimination of the CO_2. At the lungs hemoglobin combines with oxygen to form oxyhemoglobin. In the tissue capillaries, with a lowered oxygen tension, oxygen passes from the blood into the cells. In the meantime, differences in partial pressure of the CO_2 in blood and tissues cause this gas to leave the tissues and enter the blood.

Oxyhemoglobin is a stronger acid than hemoglobin; pK for the former is 6.62 and for the latter, 8.18. Both these substances are present as salts and as free acids.

The buffering action of hemoglobin between pH 7 and 7.8 is due mostly to its content of the amino acid histidine, which is present in comparatively high concentrations in this protein. The behavior of the imidazole group of histidine as a base and as an acid is shown below:

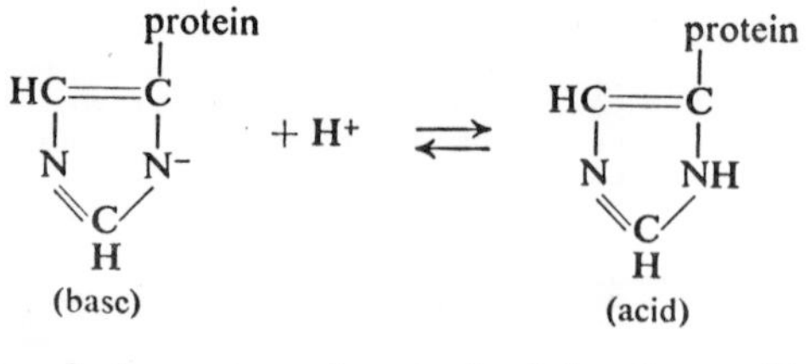

In hemoglobin each iron atom is attached by 6 coordinate bonds, 4 of these to the 4 nitrogen atoms of protoporphyrin IX, and one or

---

* The control of carbon dioxide by the respiratory system makes the carbonic acid–bicarbonate buffering in blood much more effective than in vitro. The bicarbonate system is a most important buffer.

two to the imidazole nitrogen atoms of histidine. When hemoglobin combines with oxygen, one of the bonds between the iron atom and histidine is replaced by oxygen, resulting in the release of protons; the oxyhemoglobin is a stronger acid than reduced hemoglobin. Furthermore, when oxyhemoglobin loses one millimole of O_2, 0.7 millimole of H^+ is taken up by the hemoglobin.

In the tissues the change from oxyhemoglobin to hemoglobin is also accompanied by a release of base which neutralizes some of the carbon dioxide. In the lungs, with the change of hemoglobin to oxyhemoglobin, the latter acts on the bicarbonate to liberate carbon dioxide.

QUANTITATIVE ASPECTS OF CO_2 IN BLOOD

We may write the expression for the buffer system containing CO_2 and bicarbonate as follows:

$$pH = pK_1 + \log \frac{[HCO_3^-]}{[CO_2]}$$

However, although we can measure the pH of the blood, we cannot measure directly either the $[HCO_3^-]$ or $[CO_2 \text{ (dissolved)}]$. We can measure total CO_2 and the partial pressure of CO_2 (pCO_2).

When a gas dissolves in a liquid, the concentration of the gas in the liquid is directly proportional to the partial pressure of the gas. This can be expressed by the following equation:

$$CO_{2(dissolved)} = k_1 \times [pCO_2]$$

where k_1 is a constant and is equal to 0.03. Now we may substitute in the above equation:

$$pH = 6.10 + \log \frac{[HCO_3^-]}{0.03[pCO_2]}$$

The total CO_2 of the plasma is equal to the sum of the bicarbonate and dissolved CO_2.

$$[\text{Total } CO_2] = [CO_2] + [HCO_3^-] \qquad \textbf{or} \qquad [HCO_3^-] = [\text{total } CO_2] - [CO_2]$$

Substituting, we get:

$$[HCO_3^-] = [\text{total } CO_2] - 0.03[pCO_2]$$

and if we substitute in our original equation:

$$pH = 6.10 + \log \frac{[\text{total } CO_2] - 0.03[pCO_2]}{0.03[pCO_2]}$$

we can now determine two of these three unknowns (pH, total CO_2 and pCO_2) and find the third by calculation.

For example, if the pH is 7.40 and the total CO_2 is 30 millimoles per liter, we can calculate that the pCO_2 is 47 mm.

DISTURBANCES IN THE ACID-BASE BALANCE

Peters and Van Slyke consider two broad possibilities as causes of acid-base balance disturbance: one, that it is due to a respiratory disturbance, involving the CO_2 content of the blood; and the other, that it is due to a metabolic disturbance—a disturbed relation between acids and alkalies other than carbonic acid. For a summary of possibilities, see Table 36 and Figure 67.

Acidosis, according to Peters and Van Slyke, should be applied to a condition in which the rate of formation or absorption of acids (hydrogen ions) exceeds that of their neutralization or elimination. It may also at times be due to a loss of a considerable amount of base.

From the equation

$$C_{H^+} = K \frac{[H_2CO_2]}{[BHCO_3]}$$

it follows that the C_{H^+} is increased when either $[H_2CO_3]$ is increased or $[BHCO_3]$ is decreased.

After the ingestion of 10 gm. of NH_4Cl, the pH of the blood of a subject decreased from 7.45 to 7.23, the HCO_3^- decreased from 25.2 to 14.0 millimoles per liter, and the pCO_2 increased from 37 to 45 mm. The values returned to normal in four hours. The nitrogen atom of NH_4Cl was converted to urea, the protons were absorbed by the buffers, and the Cl^- then had to draw upon cations, resulting in acidosis.

Alkalosis is defined by Cantarow as a state in which either excessive amounts of acid (hydrogen ions) are lost from the body without a

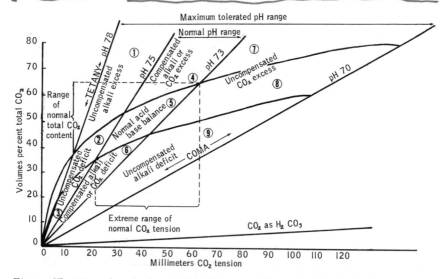

Figure 67. Normal and abnormal variations of the $BHCO_3$, H_2CO_3, CO_2 tension and pH in oxygenated human whole blood drawn from resting subjects at sea level. (Van Slyke.)

TABLE **36.** DISTURBANCES OF ACID-BASE EQUILIBRIUM OF BLOOD

Area	Acid-Base Balance	Conditions	Associated Symptoms	Compensatory Mechanisms
1 Uncompensated alkali excess.	[BHCO₃] increased without proportionate rise in [H₂CO₃], therefore pH increased.	Overdosage of NaHCO₃. Excessive vomiting (pyloric obstruction) or gastric lavage (loss of HCl). X-ray or radium treatment.	If marked, tetany.	Diminished respiration (rise in alveolar CO_2) to hold back CO_2. Diuresis and increased NaHCO₃ excretion.
2–3 Uncompensated CO_2 deficit.	[H₂CO₃] decreased without proportionate fall in [BHCO₃], therefore pH increased.	Hyperpnea, voluntary or induced (oxygen want, e.g., at high altitudes). Fever. Hot baths.	If marked, tetany.	Retention of acid metabolites (low NH₃ and titratable acidity of urine). Excretion of NaHCO₃.
4 Compensated alkali or CO_2 excess.	[BHCO₃] (or [H₂CO₃]) increased but balanced by proportionate rise in [H₂CO₃] (or [BHCO₃]), therefore pH normal.	*Alkali excess.* NaHCO₃ therapy, with slow absorption. *CO_2 excess.* Retarded gas exchange (e.g., emphysema) with CO_2 tension chronically increased.	Cyanosis due to deficient oxygen exchange.	CO_2 retention. BHCO₃ retention.
5 Normal.	[BHCO₃] and [H₂CO₃] normal at ordinary altitudes.			
6 Compensated alkali or CO_2 deficit.	[BHCO₃] (or [H₂CO₃]) decreased but balanced by proportionate fall in [H₂CO₃] (or [BHCO₃]), therefore pH normal.	*Alkali deficit.* Accelerated production (e.g., diabetes) or retarded elimination (e.g., nephritis) of nonvolatile acids. Experimental acid intoxication. Diarrheal acidosis of infancy (marasmus). *CO_2 deficit.* Overventilation at high altitudes (oxygen want).	Hyperpnea.	Increased respiration ("blowing off CO_2"). Accelerated NH₃ formation and acid excretion. Same as in Areas 2 and 3.
7–8 Uncompensated CO_2 excess.	[H₂CO₃] increased without proportionate rise in [BHCO₃], therefore pH decreased.	Retarded respiration as in pneumonia (physical obstruction) or morphine narcosis (deadening of respiratory center). Experimental rebreathing. Cardiac decompensation.	Dyspnea.	Increased respiration. Accelerated NH₃ formation and acid excretion. Probable shift of acid from blood to tissue.
9 Uncompensated alkali deficit.	[BHCO₃] decreased without proportionate fall in [H₂CO₃], therefore pH decreased.	Terminal stages of nephritic acidosis, and diabetic acidosis (compensated by insulin therapy). Deep ether anesthesia. Certain cardiac cases. Eclampsia.	Dyspnea.	Increased respiration. Increased acid excretion and NH₃ formation (except probably in nephritis).

(From Hawk, Oser, and Summerson: Practical Physiological Chemistry, The Blakiston Co., p. 622.)

comparable loss of alkali, or alkali is formed in or supplied to the body at a rate exceeding that of its neutralization or elimination. Thus alkalosis may result from a decrease in $[H_2CO_3]$ of the blood, or an increase in $[NaHCO_3]$.

In one particular case, 20 gm. of $NaHCO_3$ was ingested by a subject. The blood pH rose from 7.35 to 7.39, the HCO_3^- rose from 23.5 to 29 millimoles per liter, and the pCO_2 rose slightly from 44 to 49 mm. Here there is an excess of cations with a resulting alkalosis (Shock and Hastings).

Ketosis is concerned with abnormal amounts of the "acetone bodies" —β-hydroxybutyric acid, acetoacetic acid, and acetone. Acetone is, in reality, a by-product of acetoacetic acid. These substances are involved in the metabolism of fats. The two acids are eliminated in the form of their salts, which means that sodium ion in the body is used for the formation of these salts and is eventually lost. This may give rise to the acidosis seen in diabetes. However, many cases of acidosis are possible without any corresponding ketosis.

CONTROL OF RESPIRATION

It is known that a certain region of the brain can control the respiratory rate. This center is under neurogenic control. The rate can also be affected by chemical compounds. As a simple example, variation in the partial pressure of O_2 and of CO_2 will affect respiratory rate. Figure 68 shows the effect of increased CO_2 tension on the increase in respiratory rate. Figure 69 shows the effect of increased O_2 tension on ventilation.

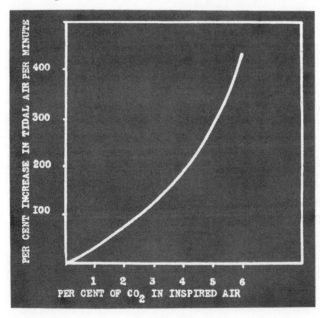

Figure 68. Effect of CO_2 on pulmonary ventilation of decerebrate cat. (After Scott, in Best and Taylor: Physiological Basis of Medical Practice. Baltimore, Williams & Wilkins Company.)

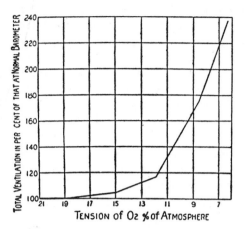

Figure 69. Effect of oxygen lack upon pulmonary ventilation in human subject. (After Means, in Best and Taylor: Physiological Basis of Medical Practice. Baltimore, Williams & Wilkins Company.)

The action of CO_2 and of acids such as lactic acid in the blood probably is to raise the hydrogen ion concentration and to excite the respiratory center directly. In the case of a lack of oxygen the mechanism is probably via the carotid sinus. (This is a slight enlargement of the common carotid artery where it divides to form the internal and external carotids.) It also plays an important part in the regulation of cardiac rate and arterial blood pressure. Initially, a decrease in oxygen tension causes an increase in respiratory rate, but ultimately the center is damaged by the decrease and its activity is depressed. An excess of CO_2 increases chiefly the depth of breathing.

RESPIRATION CHEMISTRY AT HIGH ALTITUDES

Several scientific expeditions have been made to study the specific effects of high altitudes and the accompanying lowered oxygen tension on the chemistry and physiology of man. Table 37 lists the partial pressure of oxygen at various heights above sea level. The first signs of oxygen deprivation in an unacclimatized person appear at an altitude of approximately 10,000 feet. With training and suitable periods of ad-

TABLE 37. PARTIAL PRESSURE OF OXYGEN IN THE ATMOSPHERE

Altitude	Partial Pressure of Oxygen in the Atmosphere	
(ft.)	*(per cent of sea level)*	*(mm. Hg)*
0	100	159
5,000	83	132
10,000	70	111
18,000	50	79.5
33,500	25	39.7
40,000 *	18.4	29.2

* Approximate limit of flying without pressurized equipment.
(From Berger and Davenport: Bureau of Mines Information Circular No. 7575.)

justment, a person can reach heights of from 23,000 to 25,000 feet, although mountain climbers have gone higher. In the conquest of Mt. Everest by Hillary and Tensing, oxygen was used for the final assault.

At an altitude of 14,200 feet the barometric pressure is 450 mm. and the partial pressure is 95 mm. The arterial blood is from 85 to 88 per cent saturated with oxygen. However, the lowered oxygen tension causes an increase in respiratory rate, so that the alveolar tension of CO_2 is lower than at sea level (by 23 to 29 mm.).

After a period at great heights people become capable of exercising in a normal manner. In the Peruvian Andes near Lima natives work and live near the silver mines at heights of about 18,000 feet. Analysis of the blood taken from people who have become acclimatized to such altitudes demonstrates that there has taken place an increase in the number of circulating red cells, so that the hemoglobin content ranges from 20 to 25 gm. per 100 ml., or higher. This greater quantity of circulating hemoglobin raises the oxygen capacity of the blood, tending to counteract its lowered saturation because of the lowered oxygen tension. In addition, because of the larger number of red cells, smaller amounts of oxygen need to be given up as it passes through the tissue capillaries. Consequently, the saturation and oxygen tension of the venous blood are maintained at a higher level than could otherwise be possible; and this venous blood combines with less oxygen in the lungs.

Another change which results from acclimatization is caused by the lowering of the alveolar CO_2, which brings about a decrease in the pCO_2 in the arterial blood. The ratio, $H_2CO_3/NaHCO_3$, which would tend to be altered by the loss of CO_2 (H_2CO_3), is counteracted by a decrease in the excretion of acid and ammonia and a lowering of the "alkali reserve." The O_2 dissociation curve of hemoglobin shifts to the left, and O_2 is bound more tightly, presumably because of the increased alkalinity inside the red cell.

EFFECT OF CARBON MONOXIDE

The lethal effect of carbon monoxide is due to its ability to combine with hemoglobin to form carboxyhemoglobin, a complex which is 200 times less dissociated than the corresponding complex formed by oxygen with hemoglobin. In this manner carbon monoxide effectively competes with oxygen and removes a portion of the hemoglobin capable of carrying oxygen to the tissues.

EFFECT OF CYANIDE

In contrast to the effect of carbon monoxide, cyanide does not affect the oxygen-carrying capacity of hemoglobin. In fact, in cyanide poisoning the venous blood contains enough oxygen so that the arteriovenous difference in oxygen content is lower than normal. The lethal effect of cyanide is due to the inability of the tissue cells to utilize the oxygen. Cyanide has been shown to form a highly undissociable complex with cytochrome oxidase, an enzyme concerned with cellular oxidations. This complex results in a loss of activity of the cytochrome oxidase. Normally, compounds are present in the cell which undergo oxidation by the method of a coupled reaction which involves the simultaneous reduction of cytochrome c, as follows:

Compound + cytochrome c (ox.) $\longrightarrow$ oxid. compound + cytochrome c (red.)

The hydrogen (proton) which is removed can eventually be made to combine with molecular oxygen to form water, if the reduced form of cytochrome c is re-oxidized. This re-oxidation is normally catalyzed by the enzyme, cytochrome oxidase:

$$\text{Cytochrome } c \text{ (red.)} \xrightarrow{\text{cytochrome oxidase}} \text{cytochrome } c \text{ (oxid.)}$$

$$2H^+ + \tfrac{1}{2}O_2 \longrightarrow H_2O$$

Since cyanide forms an inactive complex with the enzyme, the utilization of oxygen for this important metabolic reaction is prevented.

Methemoglobin competes with cytochrome oxidase for the cyanide, since the former forms a tighter complex with cyanide (cyanmethemoglobin). This results in the liberation of active cytochrome oxidase. Thus, it is possible to prevent cyanide poisoning if some of the hemoglobin in the circulation is converted to methemoglobin in such quantities as not to interfere with the oxygen-carrying capacity of the blood, since methemoglobin is incapable of combining with oxygen. Some compounds which convert hemoglobin to methemoglobin *in vivo* are amyl nitrite and p-aminopropiophenone.

REFERENCES

For composition of the blood gases, etc., see *Best* and *Taylor:* Physiological Basis of Medical Practice, 1955.

A fine introduction to the subject will be found in *Davenport:* The ABC of Acid-Base Chemistry, 1947. See also *Guyton:* Medical Physiology, 1956, pages 448–471.

Material pertaining to this chapter will be found in *Gamble:* Extracellular Fluid (Harvard Medical School, 4th Ed.).

See also *Roughton* and *Kendrew:* Haemoglobin, 1949, Chap. 2 (reversible reactions with O_2 and CO) and Chap. 8 (comparative biochemistry and physiology of oxygen carriers).

The work on the CO_2 transport by the blood is reviewed by *Roughton:* Harvey Lectures, 1943–44, p. 96.

A fascinating book by a pioneer in this field is *Henderson:* Blood: A Study in General Physiology, 1928.

For the work on carbonic anhydrase, see *Meldrum* and *Roughton:* J. Physiol., *80:* 113, 1933; *Krebs* and *Roughton:* Ibid., 43:550, 1948 (enzyme to study reactions involving H_2CO_3, CO_2, and HCO^{3-}); *Roughton* and *Booth:* Ibid., 40:319, 1946 (pH and enzyme activity).

For the structure of myoglobulin, see *Kendrew:* Federation Proceedings, *18:*740, 1959.

Acidosis and Alkalosis are discussed by *Cecil* and *Loeb:* A Textbook of Medicine, 1959, pp. 669, 674.

BIOLOGICAL
OXIDATIONS

In this chapter we will consider the mechanism by which molecular oxygen brought to the cell is able to oxidize substances (*metabolites*) in the cell.

That molecular oxygen by itself is incapable of such oxidations has been proved in many experiments. For example—to take a very simple case—hypoxanthine in contact with an extract of liver is easily oxidized to xanthine in the presence of oxygen; yet in the absence of the enzyme from liver, molecular oxygen has no such effect. In fact, hypoxanthine can be boiled with nitric acid without any appreciable change. The liver contains the enzyme xanthine oxidase, which enables the oxygen to carry out the oxidation.

That tissues contain such oxidases can be readily shown in the very simple experiment of treating a solution of guaiac with an aqueous extract of the potato. The guaiac contains a phenolic derivative which, when oxidized, changes to a blue color (guaiac blue). The blue color is very readily obtained when the tissue extract and the guaiac solutions are mixed in the presence of oxygen.*

The mere knowledge that there are enzymes—to which the general name "oxidases" has been given—which catalyze oxidative reactions within the cell brings with it more questions than answers. Are we dealing with one oxidase or with many oxidases? What is their chemical composition? What is the mechanism involved in their reaction with metabolites?

---

* Catechol is very often used in place of guaiac. With the oxidase the catechol goes through a series of color changes: green, yellow, brown, black.

250

OXIDATION AND REDUCTION

The term "oxidation," and its companion, "reduction," first originated with the early chemists who were concerned with reactions involving molecular oxygen; for example, the combination of a metal with oxygen:

$$\text{Metal} + O_2 \longrightarrow \text{metal oxide}$$

The formation of the oxide was called oxidation. Reduction was associated with the idea of taking away of oxygen:

$$\text{Metal oxide} + C \longrightarrow \text{metal} + CO_2$$

In this way one could oxidize ferrous oxide to ferric oxide by the addition of more oxygen. When ferrous oxide and ferric oxide are separately dissolved in hydrochloric acid, ferrous chloride and ferric chloride, respectively, are formed. With the discovery of ionization it became apparent that the essential difference between these two forms of ionic iron was that of a unit electric charge, the electron. Oxidation now could mean the loss of an electron:

$$Fe^{++} - 1\,e \longrightarrow Fe^{+++}$$

In dealing with organic reactions, chemists looked upon oxidation as an instance of the removal of hydrogen, and reduction as the addition of hydrogen. Our definitions for oxidation and reduction have multiplied, and to cover all cases, we can now define oxidation as the addition of oxygen, the loss of hydrogen or the loss of electrons. Reduction would therefore be defined as the removal of oxygen, the addition of hydrogen or the gain of electrons. It is useful to consider the similarity in approach of the modern definitions of acids and bases, and of oxidation and reduction, as written below:

$$\text{Acid} \rightleftarrows \text{base} + (+)$$
$$\text{Reductant} \rightleftarrows \text{oxidant} + (-)$$

THE PROBLEM OF CELLULAR OXIDATION

We have already seen how molecular oxygen is transported from the atmosphere to the lungs and (via hemoglobin) to the tissues, where, with a lowered oxygen tension, the oxygen is released. We know that the living cell, in the course of complex chemical reactions, rapidly consumes this molecular oxygen. (The nature of these complex reactions will be considered in the chapters in which the intermediary metabolism of carbohydrates, lipids and proteins is discussed.)

Our concern here is to inquire into the mechanism whereby the metabolites of the cell utilize molecular oxygen.

The oxidation of metabolites results in the splitting of chemical bonds and the liberation of energy. It is this energy which the cell needs in order to carry out those functions associated with living matter. And yet it could get no such cellular energy if the mechanism were merely that whereby metabolites and oxygen would combine directly, for then all the energy would be liberated as heat.

OXIDATION CATALYSTS: RESPIRATORY ENZYMES

The idea that living cells contain a catalyst for the oxidation of metabolites was proposed by Otto Warburg. He noted that many oxidation reactions involving organic compounds are catalyzed by metallic ions, especially iron. Ferric iron could act as an oxidizing agent and be reduced to the ferrous state, which could be reoxidized by molecular oxygen. In 1927 he reported the presence in tissue of a respiratory enzyme, the "atmungsferment," which contained organically bound iron in the form of a heme-protein complex. The mechanism by which this enzyme acted is suggested in the following equation:

$$\text{Metabolite} + \text{enzyme.Fe}^{+++} \longrightarrow \text{oxidized metabolite} + \text{enzyme.Fe}^{++} + \text{H}^{+}$$

The reoxidation of the reduced enzyme takes place by reaction with molecular oxygen:

$$\text{Enzyme.Fe}^{++} + \text{O}_2 \longrightarrow \text{enzyme.Fe}^{++}.\text{O}_2$$
$$\text{(activated complex)}$$
$$\text{Enzyme.Fe}^{++}.\text{O}_2 + 2\text{H}^{+} \longrightarrow \text{enzyme.Fe}^{+++} + \text{H}_2\text{O (or H}_2\text{O}_2)$$

The oxidized form of the enzyme can now continue to oxidize the metabolite. Inherent in this theory is the formation of an activated complex, that is, the activation of oxygen.

Another approach to the problem of cellular oxidations is that of Wieland. He suggested that oxidation be looked upon as a loss of hydrogen—a dehydrogenation process. An example of such a reaction is the oxidation of acetaldehyde by finely divided platinum or palladium black:

$$\text{CH}_3.\text{CHO} \xrightarrow{\text{H}_2\text{O}} \text{CH}_3.\text{C}\!\!\begin{array}{c} \nearrow\text{H} \\ -\text{OH} \\ \searrow\text{OH} \end{array} \xrightarrow{\text{Pd}} \text{CH}_3\text{COOH} + \text{Pd.H}_2$$

The loss of hydrogen, as illustrated above, emphasizes the activation of hydrogen. In order to regenerate the catalyst, the hydrogen could be removed by transferring it to a compound which acts as a "hydrogen acceptor." Such an acceptor is the dye methylene blue:

$$Pd.H_2 + Me.blue \longrightarrow Pd + Me.blue.2H$$
(oxidized
dye—blue)
(reduced dye—
colorless)

In order for the reaction to continue the reduced form of methylene blue is oxidized by oxygen. Here molecular oxygen acts as the "terminal hydrogen acceptor." It should be noted that Wieland stressed the need for intermediate hydrogen carriers, with oxygen needed only to re-oxidize the carriers, whereas Warburg stressed the presence of a metal ion and the direct action of molecular oxygen. We shall see that both are correct, and that cells have both types of enzymes: oxidases which act by virtue of their content of metal ions and involve direct reaction with oxygen; and dehydrogenases, which bring about the transfer of hydrogen from the substrate to some carrier compound.

Warburg's "atmungsferment" is identical with the enzyme called cytochrome oxidase, which contains iron. Cytochrome oxidase and sev-eral other enzymes containing metal ions as prosthetic groups make up the oxidases. The dehydrogenase enzymes have as carriers the com-pounds DPN, TPN, FMN or FAD.

Before we explore the role of these oxidative enzymes in cellular metabolism we must first review our knowledge of their action in purified systems.

OXIDASES

Cytochrome Oxidase. This is the enzyme which is identical with Warburg's "atmungsferment" and Keilin's "indophenol oxidase." When it was discovered that the substrate for the enzyme in the living cell was cytochrome c, the present name, cytochrome oxidase, was assigned to the enzyme. Cytochrome oxidase has not yet been isolated in pure form because it is present in the cell as insoluble particles or part of insoluble particles. It can be obtained in a soluble state by treatment with deoxycholic acid. It contains a special heme molecule, as well as Cu.

Keilin found that living cells contain a series of pigmented com-pounds which all contain heme-protein linkages, and which differ in their light absorption spectra. These are called the cytochromes. Cyto-chrome oxidase, the enzyme, belongs to this group and is believed to be identical with cytochrome a_3 because the spectra are identical. The only cytochrome thus far obtained in a pure state is cytochrome c, which occurs in animal cells, together with cytochromes a_3, a, b and b_1. Cytochromes c and a_3 are found in all cells. Cytochrome b is found in heart muscle, and b_1 in kidney tissue. Cytochrome b_1 is also found in bacteria, and b_2 in yeast.

The porphyrin of cytochrome c differs from that found in hemo-globin in that the two vinyl side-chains are reduced and linked

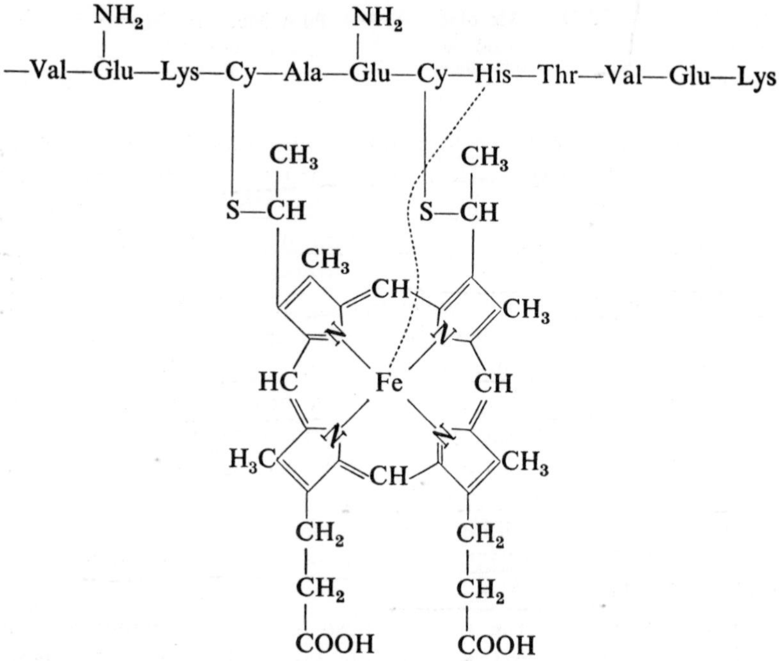

Figure 70. Structure of cytochrome *c*, showing the sequence of amino acids in the immediate vicinity of the prosthetic group. (From Theorell, in Green: Currents in Biochemical Research, 1956. New York, Interscience Publishers, p. 279.)

to cystine residues of the protein. It is attached to the protein moiety by the S atoms of cystine, as well as to the imidazole N atoms of histidine (Fig. 70).

It is of some interest that cytochrome *c* is present in tissues to an extent roughly proportional to the oxygen consumption of the tissues, thereby emphasizing the importance of this cytochrome for aerobic cellular respiration. We shall see that during the oxidation of metabolites, reduced compounds are formed (reduced cytochrome *c* among them). Cytochrome oxidase catalyzes the oxidation of reduced cytochrome *c*, and in the presence of a proton (formed during the reduction of cytochrome) and molecular oxygen, it produces water:

$$Fe^{++}.\text{cytochrome } c + 2 H^+ + 1/2 O_2 \xrightarrow[\text{oxidase}]{\text{cytochrome}} Fe^{+++}.\text{cytochrome } c + H_2O$$

Hydroperoxidases. These enzymes are essentially oxidases which act on hydrogen peroxide (catalase) or organic peroxides (peroxidases). Catalase is a heme-protein enzyme which catalyzes the decomposition of H_2O_2. It is present in animal tissues (it has been crystallized from liver and red cells), which may indicate that H_2O_2 is present in tissues, though there is no direct evidence for the presence of peroxide. In animal tissues there are some enzymes which yield, *in vitro*, H_2O_2 as an end-product (for example, xanthine oxidase and amino acid oxidases). Catalase may be considered as a special member of the peroxidases, whose action on H_2O_2 can be formulated as follows (one molecule of peroxide is the substrate and the other is the acceptor):

$$H_2O_2 + \begin{array}{c} HO \\ | \\ HO \end{array} \longrightarrow O_2 + 2H_2O$$

Peroxidases are widely distributed in plants and animals. Their action can be shown as follows (the acceptor is an organic compound, in this case a dihydroxyphenol):

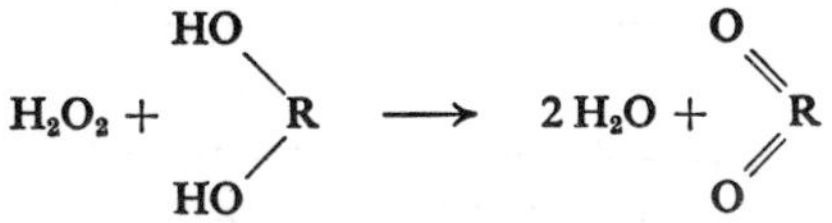

$$H_2O_2 + \begin{array}{c} HO \\ \diagdown \\ \diagup \\ HO \end{array} R \longrightarrow 2H_2O + \begin{array}{c} O \\ \diagdown \\ \diagup \\ O \end{array} R$$

where R is an organic radical, such as C_6H_4—.

Tyrosinase and Ascorbic Acid Oxidase. Both of these enzymes contain copper as part of the enzyme molecule. Removing the copper, or binding it tightly with specific copper-chelating agents, results in the inactivation of the enzymes. Compounds which form chelates with metal ions are ones which form coordinate bonds with the unpaired electrons of the metal and so form a ring structure with great stability (8-hydroxyquinoline is such a compound and is quite specific for copper ions). This must not be taken as meaning that a chelate structure will always result in the inactivation of the metal ion for catalytic purposes. Indeed, it is highly probable that by such a chelate structure the metal ion, which is part of the active site of an enzyme, may be bound to the enzyme with groups of the enzyme protein. It is also highly probable, on the basis of studies with these enzymes and others, that the metal ion undergoes reversible oxidation and reduction during its function as a coenzyme.

Tyrosinase catalyzes the oxidation of tyrosine to its corresponding dihydroxyphenol, then to the quinone. Finally, the quinone is converted to a series of ill-defined pigments called melanins:

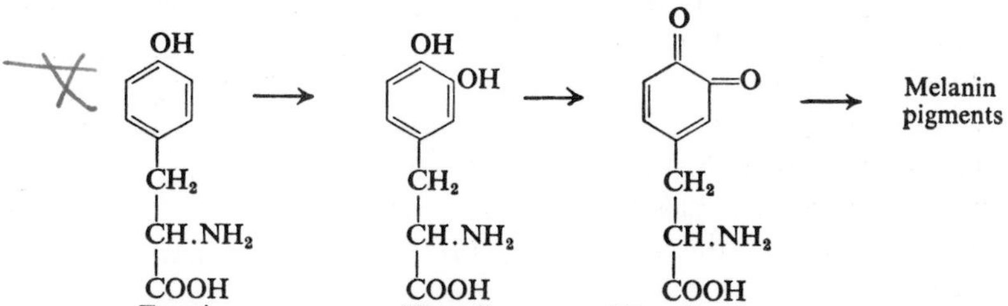

Ascorbic acid oxidase catalyzes the oxidation of ascorbic acid to dehydroascorbic acid:

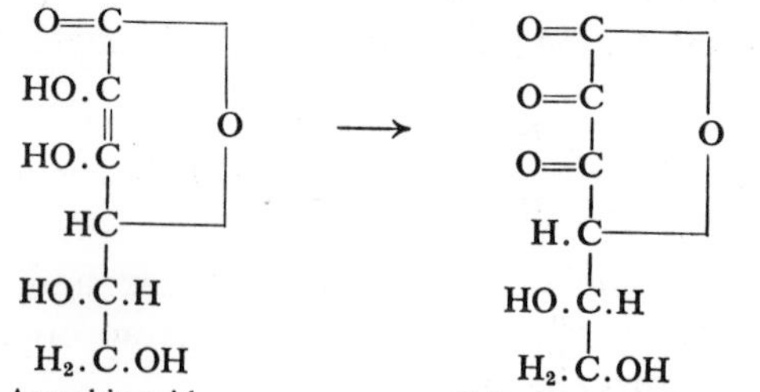

Ascorbic acid   Dehydroascorbic acid

DEHYDROGENASES

These are a group of enzymes which catalyze the oxidation of their substrates by virtue of the presence of a coenzyme which participates in the removal of hydrogen from the substrate. The coenzymes are DPN, TPN, FMN and FAD. The dehydrogenases may be further subdivided into two classes: (a) the aerobic dehydrogenases, and (b) the anaerobic dehydrogenases.

Aerobic Dehydrogenases. These are called "aerobic" because, although the prosthetic group (FMN or FAD) acts as an H acceptor, the reduced flavin nucleotide reacts directly with molecular oxygen without the intervention of further H carriers. An example is xanthine dehydrogenase (also called xanthine oxidase), which catalyzes the oxidation of hypoxanthine to xanthine, and of xanthine to uric acid. The mechanism of this reaction, in the presence of oxygen, is as follows:

$$\text{Xanthine} + \text{enz.FAD} \longrightarrow \text{uric acid} + \text{enz.FADH}_2$$
$$\text{Enz.FADH}_2 + \text{O}_2 \longrightarrow \text{enz.FAD} + \text{H}_2\text{O}_2$$

Thus molecular oxygen is the acceptor. However, it is of interest to note that although xanthine dehydrogenase is not active anaerobically, it can be made so by the presence of a suitable electron acceptor, such as methylene blue or ferricytochrome *c*.

$$\text{Enz.FADH}_2 + 2\,\text{Fe}^{+++}.\text{cyt } c \longrightarrow \text{enz.FAD} + 2\,\text{Fe}^{++}.\text{cyt } c + 2\,\text{H}^+$$

It is possible that this double type of action of the enzyme may have metabolic significance, since the addition of an electron acceptor to xanthine dehydrogenase acting aerobically, stimulates its catalytic activity. Another point of interest with regard to this enzyme is the presence, in addition to FAD, of molybdenum and iron. This makes it an enzyme with three possible prosthetic groups.

Other enzymes of the same type are D-amino acid and L-amino acid oxidases.

Anaerobic Dehydrogenases. These enzymes, although called "anaerobic," can act aerobically since the hydrogen carriers associated with them will be reduced and cease to function until they are reoxidized. The terminal electron acceptor, molecular oxygen, will therefore be needed. However, these enzymes are anaerobic dehydrogenases since they are capable of acting on their substrates in the complete absence of oxygen, provided that there is a sufficient supply of the oxidized hydrogen acceptor. Examples are as follows:

A. GLUCOSE-6-PHOSPHATE DEHYDROGENASE (also called "zwischenferment"). In this reaction glucose-6-phosphate (G-6-P) is oxidized to 6-phosphogluconic acid (6-PGA). The prosthetic group attached to the enzyme is FMN and it requires, in addition, TPN. The first steps in the reaction sequence are:

$$\text{G-6-P} + \text{TPN}^+ \longrightarrow \text{6-PGA} + \text{TPNH} + \text{H}^+$$
$$\text{TPNH} + \text{enz.FMN} + \text{H}^+ \longrightarrow \text{TPN}^+ + \text{enz.FMNH}_2$$

Now the oxidized TPN can act again. However, enz.FMNH$_2$ must be reoxidized in order to continue its activity. This is accomplished by means of the cytochrome c–cytochrome oxidase system in the presence of oxygen:

$$\text{Enz.FMNH}_2 + 2\,\text{Fe}^{+++}.\text{cyt } c \longrightarrow \text{enz.FMN} + 2\,\text{Fe}^{++}.\text{cyt } c + 2\,\text{H}^+$$
$$2\,\text{Fe}^{++}.\text{cyt } c + 2\,\text{H}^+ + \tfrac{1}{2}\text{O}_2 \xrightarrow[\text{oxidase}]{\text{cytochrome}} 2\,\text{Fe}^{+++}.\text{cyt } c + \text{H}_2\text{O}$$

B. LACTIC ACID DEHYDROGENASE. The reactions involved here are:

$$\text{Lactic acid} + \text{enz.DPN}^+ \longrightarrow \text{pyruvic acid} + \text{enz.DPNH}$$
$$\text{Enz.DPNH} + 2\,\text{Fe}^{+++}.\text{cyt } c \longrightarrow \text{enz.DPN}^+ + 2\,\text{Fe}^{++}.\text{cyt } c + \text{H}^+$$
$$2\,\text{Fe}^{++}.\text{cyt } c + 2\,\text{H}^+ + \tfrac{1}{2}\text{O}_2 \longrightarrow 2\,\text{Fe}^{+++}.\text{cyt } c + \text{H}_2\text{O}$$

In this case the reduced enz.DPNH is reoxidized by the cytochrome system. Note that the importance of cytochrome oxidase is to restore the reduced cytochrome c to the oxidized state; it is in this reaction that the molecular oxygen is coupled with H$^+$ to form water.

C. CYTOCHROME C REDUCTASES. These are a group of flavoprotein enzymes which reduce ferricytochrome c. Cytochrome c is the substrate reduced, and the reduced form of the coenzyme DPNH or TPNH is oxidized:

$$2\,\text{Fe}^{+++}.\text{cyt } c + \text{TPNH} \longrightarrow 2\,\text{Fe}^{++}.\text{cyt } c + \text{TPN}^+ + \text{H}^+$$

MECHANISM OF OXIDATION-REDUCTION OF THE COENZYMES

The experiments of Vennesland and Westheimer are illuminating with respect to the mechanism of hydrogen transfer which occurs with the pyridine nucleotides. They added the enzyme alcohol dehydrogenase and DPN to ethanol, which had been "labeled" with the isotope of hydrogen, deuterium (D), in the alpha position. The reduced DPN which was isolated was found to contain all of its extra hydrogen as deuterium; none of it had come from the medium (water). This can be illustrated as follows:

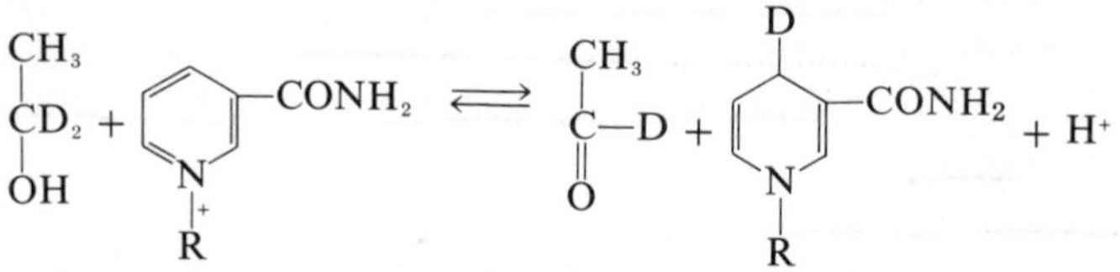

$$\underset{\substack{\mathrm{CH_3}\\|\\\mathrm{CD_2}\\|\\\mathrm{OH}}}{}+\underset{R}{\bigodot}\text{—CONH}_2 \rightleftarrows \underset{\substack{\mathrm{CH_3}\\|\\\mathrm{C—D}\\||\\\mathrm{O}}}{}+\underset{R}{\bigodot}\text{—CONH}_2 + \mathrm{H^+}$$

Further, it was also shown that when the reduced DPN, which contained deuterium, was reoxidized enzymatically and acetaldehyde was reduced, the deuterium was now removed rather than any of its hydrogen atoms. This result would strongly suggest a stereospecificity for the attachment of the coenzyme to the apoenzyme during its activity.

The reduction of the flavin coenzyme involves the riboflavin grouping, isoalloxazine:

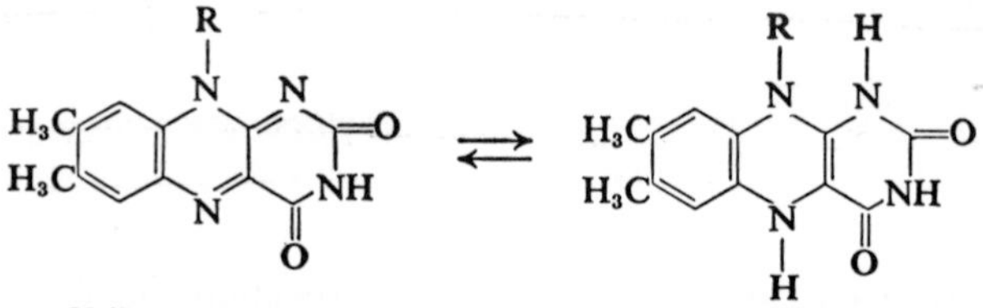

Yellow oxidized state   Colorless reduced state

GLUTATHIONE AND ASCORBIC ACID

It is believed that glutathione and ascorbic acid are both concerned with some biological system of oxidation.

Glutathione is a tripeptide of cysteine, glutamic acid, and glycine.

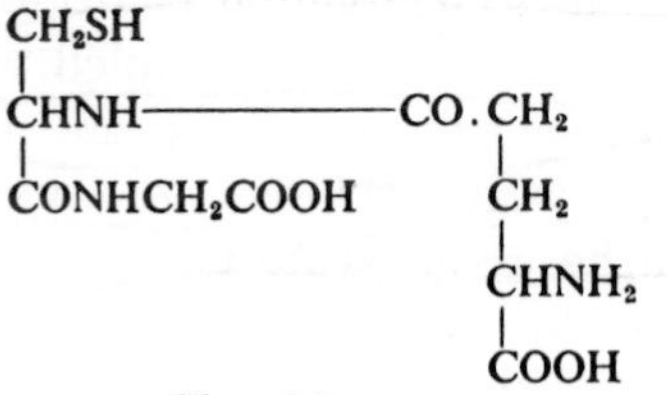

$$\begin{array}{l}\mathrm{CH_2SH}\\|\\\mathrm{CHNH}\text{————————}\mathrm{CO.CH_2}\\|\qquad\qquad\qquad\qquad|\\\mathrm{CONHCH_2COOH}\qquad\mathrm{CH_2}\\\qquad\qquad\qquad\qquad\qquad|\\\qquad\qquad\qquad\qquad\quad\mathrm{CHNH_2}\\\qquad\qquad\qquad\qquad\qquad|\\\qquad\qquad\qquad\qquad\quad\mathrm{COOH}\end{array}$$

Glutathione

It was isolated from tissues by Hopkins in the form of its cuprous salt. The oxidized form, which may be written as G—S—S—G (where G and G stand for oxidized glutathione minus its two sulfur atoms), is readily reduced by tissues to the sulfhydryl form, G.SH; and the latter, in presence of traces of metal ions, gives up its hydrogen to molecular oxygen, becoming oxidized in turn.

Barron suggested that glutathione maintains enzymes active by keeping their —SH groups (and many possess them) in this reduced form.

Ascorbic acid, the antiscorbutic vitamin (Chap. 18), is a very active reducing agent and may have a role in reactions involving oxidations and reductions in the tissue. It may, in other words, be a carrier; but our information, at present, is meager.

Hopkins believed that ascorbic acid may be a coenzyme for the oxidation of glutathione. He found that the oxidation of ascorbic acid by oxygen and the ascorbic acid oxidase—obtained from cauliflower— is prevented by the addition of glutathione. He believed that the oxidized ascorbic acid reacts with glutathione, forming ascorbic acid and oxidized glutathione, and that this reaction proceeds faster than the oxidation of ascorbic acid.

An enzyme, glutathione reductase, is present in yeast as well as in animal tissues. It catalyzes the reduction of oxidized glutathione by TPN as follows:

$$G—S—S—G + TPNH + H^+ \longrightarrow TPN^+ + 2\,GSH$$

The enzyme is highly specific and will not act on cystine, nor will it act when DPN is substituted for TPN. Its significance lies in the fact that it may serve as a hydrogen carrier for all enzymes which require TPN as a prosthetic group. Further, reduced glutathione can be oxidized by dehydroascorbic acid, forming ascorbic acid. The latter will undergo oxidation directly by molecular oxygen in the presence of ascorbic acid oxidase, to complete the transfer of hydrogen to molecular oxygen.

ENERGY AND OXIDATION REACTIONS

The cell converts energy derived from the oxidation of chemical compounds into a form which can be utilized to perform those functions characteristic of the living cell. Johnson has calculated the energy that would result from the oxidation of one mole of lactic acid to pyruvic acid (the hydrogen being transferred through a carrier coenzyme to cytochrome c). This energy would be sufficient, if it were completely utilized, to light a 100-watt bulb for a period of 14 minutes. The energy which is produced as a result of this type of biochemical oxidation, and the extent of its utilization, will be explored in later chapters. In the meantime we shall discuss the oxidation-reduction potentials of systems involved in oxidation reactions and see how the oxidation of a substrate is accomplished.

MEANING OF OXIDATION-REDUCTION POTENTIAL

Let us construct two electrical half cells, one containing equal concentrations of Fe^{++} and Fe^{+++} ions, the other, gaseous hydrogen circulating over a platinum electrode which dips into a solution of 1 N H^+. If we place an electrode into the solution of iron salts, we may consider that in this cell there is a potential flow of electrons—electrons escaping from the solution to the electrode. Similarly, this is also possible in the case of the hydrogen electrode. A comparison of the extent of this tendency for these two cells can be observed by completing a circuit between them; that is, by placing the ends of a salt bridge into each solution and connecting the two electrodes by a potentiometer. An electric current is developed, the proportion of Fe^{++} ions increases, and so does the concentration of H^+. The reaction can be illustrated as follows:

$$Fe^{+++} + 1e \rightleftarrows Fe^{++}$$
$$H° - 1e \rightleftarrows H^+$$

If we arbitrarily define the potential of the hydrogen half cell as equal to zero, the observed potential of the ferrous-ferric system is $+0.75$ volts. The potential of the Fe^{++}-Fe^{+++} system is shown to be higher than that of the hydrogen electrode, and this is indicated by a positive sign. As the ratio of Fe^{++}/Fe^{+++} is increased, the potential becomes less positive (for example, $+0.69$ volts). When the ratio is altered in the opposite direction, the potential becomes more positive.

The expression for the observed difference in potential is given by the equation:

$$E_h = E_o + \frac{RT}{n\bar{f}} \ln \frac{\text{(oxidized form)}}{\text{(reduced form)}}$$

where R is the gas constant, T is the absolute temperature, n is the number of electrons transferred per gram equivalent and f is the Faraday electrochemical equivalent, the quantity of electricity needed to liberate one gram equivalent of a univalent element during electrolysis. Where $n = 1$, and at $30°$ C.:

$$E_h = E_o + 0.06 \log \frac{\text{(oxidized form)}}{\text{(reduced form)}}$$

When the ratio of oxidized to reduced forms is unity, $E_h = E_o$ and E_o is therefore the potential established by an oxidation-reduction system when the concentrations (or more correctly, the activities) of the oxidized and reduced forms are equal. Since E_h varies directly with the concentration of H^+, and since physiological pH is near 7.0, the term E_o' is used to denote potentials at a specific pH, usually 7.

INTERACTION OF SYSTEMS WITH DIFFERENT
OXIDATION-REDUCTION POTENTIALS

Figure 71 lists the values for a number of systems of importance in cellular oxidations (columns II and III), as well as for a series of oxidation-reduction dyes which change color when they alternate between the oxidized and reduced state; e.g., methylene blue is deep blue in the oxidized state but is colorless in the reduced state. These

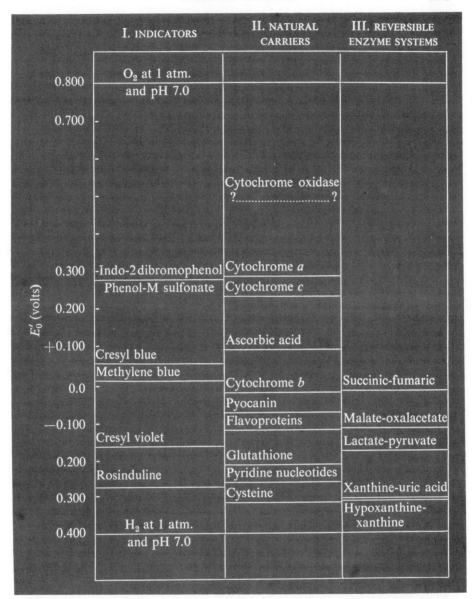

	I. INDICATORS	II. NATURAL CARRIERS	III. REVERSIBLE ENZYME SYSTEMS
0.800	O_2 at 1 atm. and pH 7.0		
0.700			
		Cytochrome oxidase ?...........................?	
0.300	Indo-2 dibromophenol	Cytochrome a	
	Phenol-M sulfonate	Cytochrome c	
0.200			
+0.100	Cresyl blue	Ascorbic acid	
	Methylene blue		
0.0		Cytochrome b	Succinic-fumaric
		Pyocanin	
−0.100	Cresyl violet	Flavoproteins	Malate-oxalacetate
			Lactate-pyruvate
0.200	Rosinduline	Glutathione	
		Pyridine nucleotides	
0.300		Cysteine	Xanthine-uric acid
			Hypoxanthine-xanthine
0.400	H_2 at 1 atm. and pH 7.0		

E'_0 (volts)

Figure 71. E_o' values for biological systems and dye indicators. (Adapted from Stephenson: Biochemical Metabolism.)

are included in our discussion because of their usefulness in studying the oxidation-reduction potentials of biological systems, which cannot, in many cases, be measured directly.

The oxidized form of any substance in column I will, under certain conditions, rapidly oxidize the reduced form of any other substance lying below it on the scale. However, any substance lying above it will not be oxidized. Conversely, the reduced form of any substance will reduce the oxidized form of any substance lying above it, but any substance below it is either not reduced or reduced very slowly. In such cases, for oxidation-reduction to take place, no assistance from any other substance is required. In column II are examples of biochemically important compounds which can behave in a manner essentially the same as that of the dyes. Note, however, that the glutathione and cysteine systems are very sluggish and will not achieve equilibrium easily unless an outside carrier, such as an oxidation-reduction indicator, is added to act as an intermediary.

In column III we have examples of enzyme systems and the substrates which they help to oxidize. If we were to mix hypoxanthine with the oxidized form of methylene blue, unlike our previous examples, it will not be oxidized. If we now add xanthine dehydrogenase and catalyze the transfer of hydrogen to the dye, oxidation takes place. In other words, in the presence of the appropriate enzyme, the oxidized form of any substance in column III will oxidize the reduced form of any substance in column I lying below it, whereas the reduced form of any substance in column III will reduce the oxidized form of any substance in column I lying above it, but none lying below it. This is of practical help in determining the oxidation-reduction systems of a complex such as exists in living cells. For example, B. coli has a lactic dehydrogenase which will reduce the oxidized form of all indicators whose E_o' (at pH 7.0) is more positive than -0.20 (e.g., cresyl violet), whereas the same enzyme, in the presence of pyruvic acid, oxidizes the reduced form of all indicators more negative than rosinduline but none more positive. The potential of an equimolecular mixture of pyruvate and lactate, in the presence of lactic dehydrogenase, lies between -0.167 and -0.281.

In column III itself the situation is different; hypoxanthine will not reduce fumaric acid, even in the presence of both enzyme systems, xanthine dehydrogenase and succinic dehydrogenase. They can be made to interact, however, if one can couple them by means of a compound which will react with a member of each of these two systems. Cresyl violet, in column I, is such an intermediary. Fumarate is thus reduced to succinate because hypoxanthine reduces cresyl violet while it is being oxidized to xanthine:

Hypoxanthine + cresyl violet $\longrightarrow$ xanthine + reduced cresyl violet
Fumarate + reduced cresyl violet $\longrightarrow$ succinate + cresyl violet

This emphasis on the need for a carrier clarifies the role of the compounds listed in column II; these are the cellular carriers which take the place of the dyes. However, do not altogether discount the biological importance of the dyes. Many of them are of plant or animal origin. For instance, pyocyanin occurs in *Bacillus pyocyaneus*, and it was a study of the mechanism of oxidation and reduction of this dye that led Michaelis to postulate his theory of one-electron transfer reactions involving the intermediate formation of semiquinones (free radicals), which is of importance in biochemistry.

FUNCTION OF THE CARRIERS

It can be seen that the coenzymes DPN, TPN, FMN, FAD and the cytochromes are the "dyes" of our cellular oxidation systems. The problem which they appear to solve is the lifting of substrate H from a potential of about -0.42 volt up to a potential of $+0.81$ volt for conversion to water, utilizing molecular oxygen. What is the advantage to the cell of such an intricate mechanism? For one thing, it provides for the liberation of energy in small parcels at each step, without allowing the cell to release all the energy in the form of heat. Another advantage is that, being a ladder with many steps, it allows for a variety of different reactions to "feed" into the reaction sequence, and thus does not limit the type of metabolic reactions which can yield energy to the living cell.

The relation of oxidation-reduction potential to energy is given by the following expression:

$$- \Delta F° = nf\Delta E_o$$

where ΔE_o is the potential difference, $\bar{f}$ is the Faraday, and $-\Delta F°$ is the negative change in free energy, the electrical work capable of being done by the formation of one mole of a product. As an example, the value of E_o' of the lactate-pyruvate system at pH 7.0 is -0.180; for the cytochrome c system it is $+0.262$. When both are in the half-reduced state:

$$\Delta E_o' = 0.444 \text{ volt, and } -\Delta F° = 20,500 \text{ cal.}$$

Now the potential corresponding to one fifth of an atmosphere of oxygen (air) is $+0.81$ volt. The energy obtained if lactate is reduced by cytochrome c and the reduced cytochrome c reacts with atmospheric oxygen can also be calculated. The results indicate that about as much energy is available in the step from cytochrome c to oxygen (24,800 cal.) as from lactate to cytochrome c. Thus we have the liberation of approximately equal amounts of energy at each step, if we can couple these reactions.

In effect, such a coupling raises the oxidation-reduction potential of substrate H by small steps, making use of the hydrogen carriers, first the pyridine nucleotides and then the flavoproteins, and then the single electron acceptors, cytochromes b, c, a and a_3 (cytochrome oxidase) until reaction with molecular oxygen, the terminal electron acceptor, yields water. This can be pictured in the accompanying diagram, which gives the values for the oxidation-reduction potentials for each stage of electron transport:

Stage of electron transport	E_o' (volts)	$\Delta F°$ (per electron pair; kcal./mole)
Reduced substrate (H_2 at 1 atmosphere, pH 7)	-0.42	
Pyridine nucleotides	-0.32	
		$\rightarrow$ -9.2
Flavin nucleotides	-0.12	
		$\rightarrow$ -4.6
Cytochrome b	-0.04	
		$\rightarrow$ -11.6
Cytochrome c	$+0.27$	
		$\rightarrow$ -2.3
Cytochrome a	$+0.25$	
Cytochrome a_3 (oxidase)	?	$\rightarrow$ -23.1
$\frac{1}{2}O_2 + 2H^+ \rightarrow H_2O$	$+0.81$	

(oxidation · electron flow)

The magnitude of the total free energy change during the transfer of two electrons from DPNH to atmospheric oxygen amounts to approximately -50 kcal. per mole. We shall see later that this energy is utilized to drive an endergonic reaction, the reaction of adenosine diphosphate with inorganic phosphate to produce ATP, a process known as oxidative phosphorylation which takes place in the cell mitochondria.

The various stages of electron transport which are listed in the previous section should not be viewed as complete or as the only stages to be found in all living cells. There may be other oxidation-reduction systems in a cell in addition to, or replacing, those which have been listed. Among these are: ascorbic acid–dehydroascorbic acid, reduced glutathione–oxidized glutathione, reduced lipoic acid–oxidized lipoic acid, vitamin K_1, and coenzyme Q, which may exist as dihydroxyphenol or quinone. In addition, cytochrome c_1 has been identified in mitochondria of some cells and is inserted in the electron transport chain between cytochromes b and c.

Another consideration to be kept in mind is that although the electron transport chart suggests that these compounds may react among themselves so that the reduced form of one (pyridine nucleotides) would serve as a good reducing agent for the oxidized form of another (flavin nucleotides or cytochromes), it does not tell us anything about the relative rates of these reactions, since these rates are determined by the nature of the enzymes involved which catalyze the reactions. For example, of the compounds listed above only the flavin nucleotides in the reduced state will react directly with atmospheric oxygen (autoxidation), yet in the intact cell it is the cytochromes which react with atmospheric oxygen. In considering biological oxidations within the organized structure of the living cell, the nature and position of the enzymes and their carriers determine the nature of the over-all reaction. Studies by Green and his group with intact as well as fragmented mitochondria have illustrated these points.

REFERENCES

Reviews of research in the field of biological oxidations will be found in the Ann. Rev. Biochem., *29*:669, 1960 (*Klinkenberg* and *Büchler*); *26*:17, 1957 (*Mahler*).

Theorell in Science, *124*:467, 1956, describes the nature and mode of action of oxidation enzymes.

Keilin and *Slater:* British Medical Bulletin, *9*:89, 1953, review the cytochromes. See also *Keilin* and *Hartree:* Nature, *171*:413, 1953 (Cytochrome Oxidase); *Theorell* in *Green's* Currents in Biochemical Research, 1956 (Structure of Cytochrome *c*); *Stotz, Morrison* and *Marinetti* in *Green's* Enzymes: Units of Biological Structure, 1956, 401 (Cytochrome System).

Mahler and *Green:* Science, *120*:7, 1954, review metallo-flavoproteins and electron transport. See also *Mackler, Mahler* and *Green:* J. Biol. Chem., *210*:149, 1954 (xanthine oxidase, a molybdoflavoprotein).

For discussions dealing with energy relations in biological systems, see *Chance* in *Gaebler's* Enzymes: Units of Biological Structure and Function, 1956; *Stephenson:* Bacterial Metabolism, 1939; *Clark:* Topics in Physical Chemistry, 1948.

The measurement of catalase activity is discussed by *Greenfield* and *Price:* J. Biol. Chem., *209*:355, 363, 1954. The substrate specificity of peroxidase is described by *Fergusson* and *Chance:* Science, *122*:466, 1955.

Electron transfer through phosphorylating mechanisms in photosynthesis is reviewed by *Kandler* in Ann. Rev. Plant Physiol., *11*:37, 1960.

See also *George* and *Rutman:* Progress in Biophysics and Biophysical Chemistry, *10*:1, 1960 (high energy phosphate bond).

METABOLISM
OF
CARBOHYDRATES

Much of contemporary biochemistry includes studies of the transformation of relatively simple compounds—produced during the digestive process—to a variety of intermediate substances until the final end-products are reached. These changes are brought about by enzymes. These studies include the mechanism whereby the energy in the chemical bond, created by photosynthetic activity, is transformed so that it may do the kind of work associated with the living cell. This energy may be associated with heat production, so that enzymic reactions take place at high rates; it may be transformed into mechanical energy, illustrated by muscle contraction; it may be transformed into electrical energy, illustrated by the conduction of nerve impulse; or it may be transformed into light energy, illustrated by the firefly or the luminescent microorganisms of the sea.

Studies of this kind include the isolation of many "intermediate" compounds; hence, in the place of "metabolism," we often speak of "intermediate metabolism" of compounds.

As a result of digestive processes, utilizable carbohydrates are largely in the state of hexoses when absorption begins. Our intention is to discuss what happens to carbohydrate from the point where it is absorbed to the point where it is eliminated in the form of carbon dioxide and water.

The field is a complex one. It deals with the storage of glycogen in liver and in muscle; with the glucose of the blood and the manner in which its amount is controlled; and with the oxidation of carbohydrate, involving a number of enzymes and a number of intermediary products. These topics will be considered in turn.

266

Another aspect of cellular metabolism is that of synthesis—the joining of relatively small molecules to create special compounds needed by the cell for special purposes, such as enzymes, hormones and tissue proteins. These synthetic reactions require energy and it is from oxidation reactions that the cell draws such energy.

At first glance it might appear that synthesis is simply a reversal of degradation reactions, since these reactions are catalyzed by enzymes and are theoretically reversible. Indeed, this is undoubtedly true in a great many cases, but not all. For example, the breakdown of glycogen to form glucose-1-phosphate takes place in the presence of the enzyme phosphorylase and inorganic phosphate. The reverse reaction may also take place. Which it will be depends upon several factors. It may depend upon the action of a hormone, or it may depend upon the relative concentration of inorganic phosphate. This reaction may be viewed as one which can operate in both directions:

$$\text{Glycogen} + PO_4^{\equiv} \underset{\longleftarrow}{\overset{phosphorylase}{\longrightarrow}} \text{glucose-1-phosphate}$$

However, in the cell only the reaction to give glucose-1-phosphate is of importance; the synthesis of glycogen takes place via UDPG (p. 122). There are reactions which, although theoretically reversible, are so far to one side that for all practical purposes they may be considered as irreversible. Thus, glucose is transformed to glucose-6-phosphate by the action of the enzyme hexokinase in the presence of ATP:

$$\text{Glucose} + ATP \overset{hexokinase}{\longrightarrow} \text{glucose-6-phosphate} + ADP$$

This reaction is highly exergonic and essentially irreversible. However, there is present in tissues a different mechanism, a different enzyme to accomplish what is essentially the reverse reaction, although ATP is not resynthesized. The enzyme involved is phosphatase:

$$\text{Glucose-6-phosphate} \overset{phosphatase}{\longrightarrow} \text{glucose} + PO_4^{\equiv}$$

SITES OF CARBOHYDRATE STORAGE
AND UTILIZATION

THE LIVER

This organ is so intimately concerned with the mechanism of carbohydrate metabolism (and of fat and protein metabolism too, as we shall see later) that a few preliminary remarks are necessary.

Aside from the secretion of bile and its property of detoxication—to name but two properties of this organ—a third characteristic of the liver is what concerns us particularly in this chapter: its relation to the utilization of food. The liver stores, manufactures, and regulates food materials.

Some vitamins, vitamin A, for example, are stored to an appreciable degree in the liver; and so is the substance effective in treating pernicious anemia, vitamin B_{12}.

Several syntheses occur in this organ. Heparin, for example, seems to be manufactured here. So are the plasma proteins, fibrinogen and prothrombin—the last with the help of vitamin K.

Various tests have been devised ("liver function tests") to get clinical information. The center of detoxication is considered to be the liver. Here, for example, much of the hippuric acid is synthesized from benzoic acid and glycine. The capacity for such synthesis is considerably reduced in certain liver diseases.

The liver has strong regenerative capacity. As much as 80 per cent of it can be removed and normal size regained within six to eight weeks.

LIVER GLYCOGEN

The French physiologist, Claude Bernard, first prepared and identified liver glycogen by applying chemical methods to the study of physiology. Liver glycogen is the form in which carbohydrate is stored in the body. The organism can obtain energy from this source of carbohydrate when it is not ingesting and digesting food materials. Two series of reactions are of importance: glycogenesis, the synthesis of glycogen, and glycogenolysis, the breakdown of glycogen. The importance of liver glycogen is illustrated by the fact that extirpation of the liver results in a marked lowering of blood glucose and death. In cases of starvation, not all of the liver glycogen disappears.

For glycogenesis, the liver depends on the monosaccharides absorbed from the small intestine and carried by the portal vein to this organ. The digestion and absorption of carbohydrate serves to produce the three monosaccharides, galactose, fructose and glucose; and yet glycogen, on hydrolysis, forms only glucose. The feeding of galactose or fructose, each labeled with C^{14}, results in the incorporation of the isotope into glycogen; the hydrolysis of such glycogen yields glucose containing C^{14}. These results suggest that galactose and fructose can be converted to a form of glucose which is then converted to glycogen; this form is glucose-1-phosphate.

The enzyme hexokinase is present in the liver and is capable of converting the three monosaccharides to the corresponding phosphate esters. Glucose is converted to the 6-phosphate:

$$\text{Glucose} + \text{ATP} \xrightarrow{\text{hexokinase}} \text{glucose-6-phosphate} + \text{ADP}$$

and then, by the action of phosphoglucomutase, to the 1-phosphate:

$$\text{Glucose-6-phosphate} \xrightleftharpoons{\text{phosphoglucomutase}} \text{glucose-1-phosphate}$$

Fructose can be converted to the 6-phosphate by hexokinase or by the action of a fructokinase (in liver) to the 1-phosphate:

$$\text{Fructose} + \text{ATP} \xrightarrow{\text{hexokinase}} \text{fructose-6-phosphate} + \text{ADP}$$
$$\text{Fructose} + \text{ATP} \xrightarrow{\text{fructokinase}} \text{fructose-1-phosphate} + \text{ADP}$$

The 6-phosphate can be converted to the corresponding glucose compound by the enzyme, phosphohexose isomerase:

$$\text{Fructose-6-phosphate} \xrightarrow{\text{phosphohexose isomerase}} \text{glucose-6-phosphate}$$

which, by the action of phosphoglucomutase, is converted to the 1-phosphate. Galactose is converted to the 1-phosphate by the action of galactokinase:

$$\text{Galactose} + \text{ATP} \longrightarrow \text{galactose-1-phosphate} + \text{ADP}$$

There is also an enzyme in the liver which accomplishes the inversion of the OH group on C-4 of galactose to yield glucose. This enzyme requires the coenzyme uridine-diphosphate-glucose (UDPG). The mechanism of the reaction is believed to be:

$$\text{Galactose-1-phosphate} + \text{UDPG} \underset{\text{uridyl transferase}}{\rightleftarrows} \text{glucose-1-PO}_4 + \text{UDP-galactose}$$

and the enzyme is called uridyl transferase. The enzyme galactowaldenase, together with DPN, accomplishes the inversion reaction:

$$\text{UDP-galactose} \rightleftarrows \text{UDP-glucose}$$

and this is followed by the production of the glucose phosphate:

$$\text{UDP-glucose} + \text{pyrophosphate} \rightleftarrows \text{glucose-1-PO}_4 + \text{UTP}$$

The synthesis and breakdown of glycogen are catalyzed *in vitro* by the enzyme phosphorylase acting in conjunction with other enzymes. (The nature of phosphorylase will be discussed under muscle glycogen, p. 271.) The direction of the reversible phosphorylase reaction can be determined by the ratio of inorganic phosphate to glucose-1-phosphate. Since phosphorylase lengthens the outer chains during synthesis of the glucosidic linkages from glucose-1-phosphate, the chain length reaches 8 residues, and can now be acted upon by the "branching" enzyme, called amylo-$(1,4 \rightarrow 1,6)$-transglucosidase. This enzyme is also found in muscle. A transglucosidation reaction takes place in which a number of glucose residues are transferred by exchange of α-1,4- for α-1,6-linkages.

When glycogen is degraded enzymatically, phosphorylase causes the link between C-1 of the terminal glucose residue and C-4 of the adjacent residue to be exchanged for a link to phosphate. The chain thus loses a glucose residue to form glucose-1-phosphate. The process of phosphorolysis stops as the branching point of an outer tier in the glycogen molecule is reached, and cannot bypass this point. This "phosphorylase limit dextrin" is then acted on by the "debranching" enzyme, amylo-1,6-glucosidase, removing free glucose molecules. In this way, if one treats a specimen of glycogen with these enzymes, a mixture of glucose and glucose-1-phosphate will be obtained. Analysis of such a mixture will yield the ratio of glucose to glucose-1-phosphate, which will be a measure of the per cent of branching points in the glycogen sample.

The synthesis of glycogen might be considered to take place by a reversal of the reactions which convert glycogen to glucose-1-phosphate, involving the enzyme phosphorylase and amylo-1,6-glucosidase. However, the ratio of inorganic phosphate to glucose-1-phosphate would have to be very low to make a net synthesis of the polysaccharide possible; conditions in living tissue rarely, if ever, favor this direction of the reaction. Furthermore, activation of the enzyme phosphorylase (p. 272) by various factors such as epinephrine, glucagon and high Na$^+$ concentration leads to an increased breakdown of glycogen (glycogenolysis) rather than to glycogen synthesis (glycogenesis). Studies by Leloir have uncovered a reaction which leads to the net synthesis of polysaccharide, catalyzed by an enzyme isolated from liver and from skeletal and heart muscle. For this reaction a primer polysaccharide is required; glycogen itself is most active. The reaction, which requires UDP-glucose, may be formulated as follows:

$$UDP + ATP \longrightarrow UTP + ADP$$
$$UTP + glucose\text{-}1\text{-}PO_4 \longrightarrow UDP\text{-}glucose + PP$$
$$UDP\text{-}glucose + primer \longrightarrow glucosyl\text{-}\alpha(1 \to 4)\text{-}primer + UDP$$

Under physiological conditions such a system would appear to favor glycogen synthesis rather than glycogen breakdown.

BLOOD GLUCOSE

In addition to the level of ingested carbohydrate, the factors which regulate liver glycogen storage are the ability of the liver to synthesize glycogen from precursors which may arise from noncarbohydrate sources (e.g., amino acids), and the ability of nonhepatic tissues (muscle) to store glucose as glycogen. This will be reflected in the level of circulating glucose in the blood.

The glucose of the blood is remarkably constant under normal conditions. It rarely rises (in the normal human) much above 100 mg. per 100 ml. of blood (the range is about 80 to 120 mg.). The regulatory mechanism consists of a number of factors: the formation of glycogen in the liver and in muscle, and, to a lesser extent, in other tissues; the oxidation of carbohydrate; the conversion of carbohydrate into fat; and the excretion of glucose. The hormones of the pancreas and the pituitary play a dominant role.

In the process of regulating the amount of sugar in the blood, we have discussed a number of factors at work: the amount of liver glycogen transformed to glucose; the amount of glucose itself transformed into muscle glycogen; and, somewhat indirectly, the amount of lactic acid converted into liver glycogen. We have seen that these factors are under the control of hormones. But the amount of glucose in the blood

—as has already been indicated—also depends upon how fast the sugar is oxidized: in active muscular exercise, for example, the rapid breakdown of muscle glycogen would demand a rapid transfer of blood sugar to the muscles, and such sugar would then have to be replaced by the further conversion of liver glycogen into glucose. The amount of sugar in the blood also depends upon how much carbohydrate is converted to body fat: the individual who eats much and exercises little will find this process of considerable importance.

There is, however, still another factor which has not yet been discussed; and this one involves the kidney. Normally, the amount of glucose in the urine is negligible. However, when for any reason one or more of the various regulatory mechanisms become impaired and the amount of glucose in the blood increases appreciably above normal, then the renal threshold is reached and appreciable quantities of glucose begin to appear in the urine.

Normally, the glucose in the blood filters through the glomerular membrane of the kidney and is again reabsorbed in the tubules. But when the sugar in the blood reaches, say, 140 to 160 mg. per 100 ml. and above, the reabsorptive capacity of the tubules may be too highly taxed and sugar may pass into the urine. The renal threshold may, therefore, be defined as "that level of blood glucose beyond which complete tubular reabsorption no longer occurs" (Drabkin).

By using phlorhizin, which prevents the reabsorption of the sugar, glucose readily passes into the urine and experimental glycosuria is established.

MUSCLE GLYCOGEN

The source of muscle glycogen is the glucose of the blood. The enzyme hexokinase, together with ATP, converts glucose to glucose-6-phosphate, which can be further converted to muscle glycogen by the action of phosphoglucomutase, to form glucose-1-phosphate; and the conversion of this compound to UDP-glucose (see p. 270). Although liver and muscle glycogen are essentially the same, liver glycogen is affected quantitatively by the extent of food intake and the nature of the diet, whereas muscle glycogen remains fairly constant except for the depletion which occurs during active muscular contraction. Glycogen now breaks down in a manner similar to that described for the liver, and, as we shall see, furnishes energy for the contraction process. Cori has shown that muscle contraction is associated with a reversible change of phosphorylase—between an active and inactive form. During contraction the active form increases, and during rest it decreases. Actually, two phosphorylases are present in liver and muscle: a and b. The a enzyme is active and has a molecular weight of 495,000, whereas the b enzyme is inactive and has a molecular weight of about one-half (240,000). The inactivation of phosphorylase a involves a cleavage of the molecules into halves. Phosphorylases a and b contain bound pyridoxal phosphate, the removal of which inactivates phosphorylase a. Addition of pyridoxal phosphate reactivates the enzyme. Phosphorylase b is converted to the active phosphorylase a by an enzyme according to the following reaction:

$$4 \text{ ATP} + 2(\text{phosphorylase } b) \rightarrow \text{phosphorylase } a + 4 \text{ ADP}$$

Phosphorylase is present in the liver, mostly in the inactive state.

HORMONES AND GLYCOGEN METABOLISM

Although hormones will be discussed in detail in Chapter 21, we shall discuss here several hormones which affect carbohydrate metabolism. The mechanism involved in the action of these hormones is still not clear.

EPINEPHRINE

This dihydroxyphenol (p. 354) is elaborated by the adrenal medulla and secreted into the blood stream. Injection of epinephrine leads to a rise in blood glucose and a lowered glycogen content in the liver and muscle. Blood lactic acid is also increased, presumably as a result of the breakdown of glycogen (glycolysis, p. 275). The mechanism whereby these effects are achieved is suggested by the fact that when epinephrine is injected into the intact animal, as well as when it is added to tissue slices in vitro, the enzyme phosphorylase is activated. This occurs for both liver and muscle. At the same time, glucose output and lactic acid production are increased. Despite these results, epinephrine does not have similar effects on a cell-free extract of homogenized tissues.

Sutherland and co-workers have isolated and identified a cyclic adenylic acid which is present in liver, heart and skeletal muscle and brain. The compound is 3′,5′-adenylic acid and is concerned in the

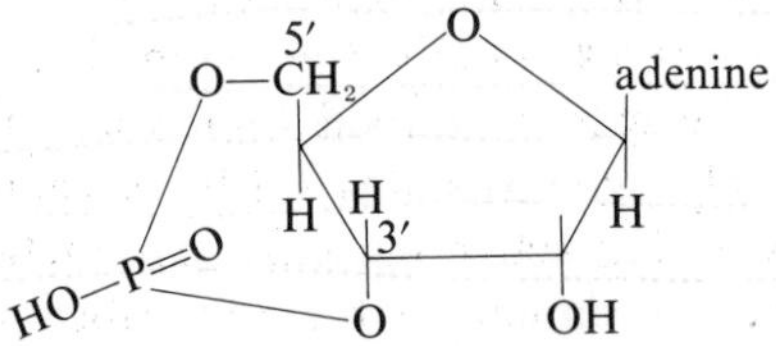

3′,5′-AMP

reactivation of inactive phosphorylase by the action of epinephrine. An enzyme, a diesterase, is present in various tissues which cleaves the cyclic compound to 5′-AMP.

GLUCAGON

In addition to insulin, which is found in the beta cells of the pancreas, another crystalline protein hormone, which is apparently elaborated by the alpha cells, has been isolated from the pancreas. Curiously enough, the injection of glucagon has an effect opposite to that of insulin: it results in a hyperglycemia, a rise in blood glucose. As in the case of epinephrine, glucagon leads to an increased phosphorylase activity of the liver. However, in contrast to epinephrine, glucagon does not cause an increased blood lactic acid, nor does it have any action on the phosphorylase *a* content of the isolated muscle diaphragm. Its action appears to be that of increasing hepatic glycogenolysis by activating liver phosphorylase.

INSULIN

This protein hormone of the pancreas results in a marked hypoglycemia after injection. The exact mechanism by which this occurs is not clear. Several possibilities have been explored:

a. Insulin acts on the transfer of glucose across the cell membrane. When insulin is injected, the diaphragm (the muscular membranous tissue separating the abdomen from the thorax), as well as other muscles, is found to have accumulated an increased quantity of glycogen. When added to diaphragm *in vitro*, in a medium containing glucose, insulin causes an accumulation of free glucose within the cells and is itself bound to them. These experiments favor the transport theory.

b. Insulin affects some enzymatic reaction involved in carbohydrate metabolism. There is evidence that insulin affects the first step in the utilization of glucose; that it accelerates the hexokinase reaction (p. 277) by means of which glucose is converted to glucose-6-phosphate. In diabetes this conversion is inhibited. This would explain the increased glycogen synthesis which occurs in the presence of insulin in the rat diaphragm both *in vivo* and *in vitro*. Furthermore, the activity of glucose-6-phosphatase is greatly enhanced in the liver of the diabetic animal—an effect which is reversed by the administration of insulin. Hexokinase is inhibited by a substance of pituitary origin which is present in the serum of diabetic animals and which disappears after hypophysectomy. Diabetic serum added to the isolated diaphragm results in an inhibition of glucose uptake (glycogen synthesis), which can be counteracted by the addition of insulin. A lipoprotein fraction from the anterior pituitary produces a strong inhibition of glucose uptake, which is reversible by the addition of insulin to the intact diaphragm; but this factor has no effect on cell-free hexokinase preparations. These experiments support the concept that insulin acts on glucose utilization. In the intact animal other hormones also affect carbohydrate metabolism; for example, the adrenal corticosteroids (p. 557).

c. Insulin acts primarily on the peripheral tissues (muscle) with regard to glucose utilization, rather than directly on the liver. Although this question has not been settled, it has been shown that when insulin is injected into diabetic animals the carbohydrate metabolism in the diaphragm is affected within minutes, whereas that in the liver is not affected for some hours. This would suggest that the effects of insulin on the liver are secondary to its action on the muscle, even though insulin does affect metabolism in the normal liver in the course of *in vitro* experiments.

OXIDATION OF GLUCOSE

The early work by Pasteur and others on the fermentation of yeast led to a study of reactions whereby glucose is converted to ethyl alcohol and carbon dioxide. Following the discovery by Buchner of enzymes in cell-free extracts of yeast, much work was done on the enzymes and their substrates in the fermentation mixture. In animal tissues, and in some bacteria, the result of fermentation was shown to give rise to lactic acid, rather than to alcohol and carbon dioxide, as in yeast. Nevertheless, certain similarities were observed in reactions involving fermentations in yeast, muscle and liver.

It was a study of reactions in connection with muscular activity which led to a more detailed picture of the nature of fermentation.

CARBOHYDRATE BREAKDOWN IN MUSCLE

Fletcher and Hopkins (in 1907) observed that less lactic acid was formed in a muscle which contracted aerobically than in one which contracted anaerobically. During anaerobic contraction, lactic acid accumulated until the muscle was fatigued, and then disappeared when the muscle was placed in oxygen, at the same time regaining its ability to contract. Meyerhof showed that the lactic acid had its origin in the glycogen of muscle. There appeared to be a proportionality between the work done, the heat produced, the tension developed and the lactic acid formed. In 1925 Meyerhof succeeded in preparing a cell-free extract from muscle which, *in vitro*, could convert glycogen to lactic acid. Dialysis of such an extract reduced its activity; but this could be restored by the addition to the dialyzed material of a heated extract of muscle ("kochsaft"). The "kochsaft" contained the activators and co-enzymes necessary for full activity.

PHOSPHOCREATINE

In 1927 Fiske and Subbarow isolated phosphocreatine from a tri-chloroacetic acid extract of muscle. Its formula is

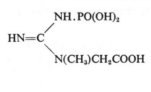

This compound disappeared during muscular activity and was resynthesized when the muscle was at rest. Since the phosphocreatine disappeared more rapidly than did glycogen, it was considered to be the more immediate source of energy for contraction. This idea was strengthened by Lundsgaard's discovery (in 1930) that a muscle poisoned with iodoacetic acid continued to contract before going into rigor, and that during this contraction process no lactic acid was produced. It was shown that in the muscle poisoned with iodoacetic acid, the phosphocreatine broke down while work was being done, and in amounts proportional to the amount of energy expended. After the phosphocreatine had been used up, the muscle went into rigor.

Later it will be seen that the action of iodoacetic acid is to poison one of the enzymes involved in glycolysis, and thereby prevent the formation of lactic acid.

ADENOSINE TRIPHOSPHATE (ATP)*

In addition to phosphocreatine, phosphate esters of glucose and fructose were shown to be present, and finally ATP itself was discovered. Lohman showed that until some ATP hydrolyzed to provide ADP (adenosine diphosphate), there was no decomposition of any phosphocreatine. Apparently, the hydrolysis of ATP preceded that of phosphocreatine; and the former was, therefore, the more immediate source of the energy needed for contraction.

The Lohman reaction, involving phosphocreatine and ATP, is:

$$\text{Phosphocreatine} + \text{ADP} \rightleftharpoons \text{ATP} + \text{creatine}$$

and the enzyme, ATP-creatine transphosphorylase, has been isolated.

GLYCOLYSIS

In yeast, glucose is the starting compound for the reactions involving fermentation; in muscle and liver, it is glycogen.† The intermediate compounds formed in such a reaction are not easy to isolate because their existence is fleeting, and they are quickly used for succeeding reactions. This problem is largely overcome by the knowledge that the change of one intermediate compound to another is brought about by an enzyme: for each step, for each link in the chain, a specific enzyme is necessary; and that the reaction may be stopped at certain points by the introduction of an inhibitor specific for some one enzyme in the group involved. In this way the reaction which would normally remove the intermediate compound is brought to a halt, the compound piles up, and the isolation and identification can be accomplished more readily.

* For the chemistry, see page 120.
† The glucose of the blood does, in fact, enter the reaction sequence via the liver.

The reactions involved in fermentation have been identified, and many of the enzymes have been crystallized and their mode of action determined.

In what follows, the conversion of glycogen (or glucose) to lactic acid is divided into three parts: (A) the conversion of glycogen, or glucose, to glucose-6-phosphate; (B) the conversion of glucose-6-phosphate to pyruvic acid; (C) the conversion of pyruvic acid (under anaerobic conditions) to alcohol in yeast and to lactic acid in liver and muscle. (Under aerobic conditions, the pyruvic acid is oxidized via the "tricarboxylic acid cycle," which will be discussed later [p. 284],—a process which prevents the accumulation of lactic acid.)

The Embden-Meyerhof Pathway of Glycolysis

(A) Formation of Glucose-6-phosphate

Yeast	Muscle	Liver
Glucose	Glycogen	Glycogen

(B) Formation of Pyruvate

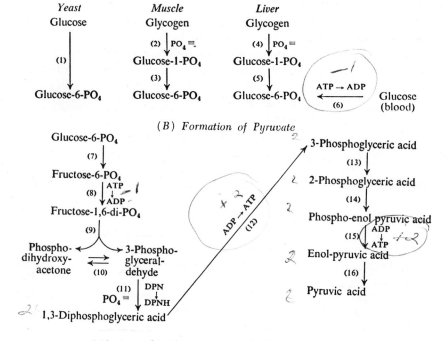

(C) Anaerobic Formation of Alcohol or Lactic Acid

Yeast

Pyruvic acid

(17)

Acetaldehyde + CO_2

(18) DPNH / DPN

Ethyl alcohol

Muscle and Liver

Pyruvic acid

(19) DPNH / DPN

Lactic acid

Enzymes of Glycolysis.

Reaction	Enzyme	Reaction	Enzyme
(1)	Yeast hexokinase	(11)	Triose phosphate dehydrogenase
(2)	Muscle phosphorylase	(12)	Phosphoglycerate kinase
(3)	Phosphoglucomutase	(13)	Phosphoglyceromutase
(4)	Liver phosphorylase	(14)	Enolase
(5)	Phosphoglucomutase	(15)	Pyruvate phosphokinase
(6)	Liver hexokinase	(16)	Spontaneous
(7)	Phosphohexose isomerase	(17)	α-Carboxylase + pyrophospho-
(8)	Phosphohexokinase		thiamine
(9)	Aldolase	(18)	Alcohol dehydrogenase
(10)	Triosephosphate isomerase	(19)	Lactic dehydrogenase

Structures of Intermediates in Glycolysis.

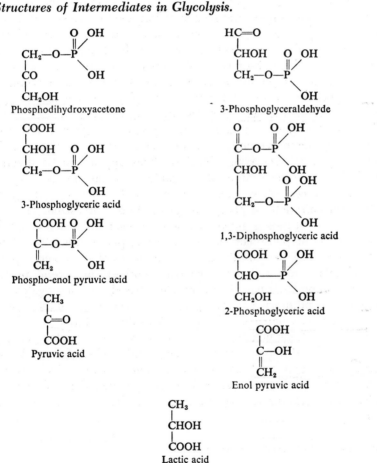

Phosphodihydroxyacetone

3-Phosphoglyceraldehyde

3-Phosphoglyceric acid

1,3-Diphosphoglyceric acid

Phospho-enol pyruvic acid

2-Phosphoglyceric acid

Pyruvic acid

Enol pyruvic acid

Lactic acid

Examples of Inhibitors. Inhibitors of enzymes concerned with glycolysis will restrict the formation of lactic acid. a. Fluoride inhibits the enzyme enolase (no. 14) by forming a complex with Mg^{++} (which is attached to the enzyme) and with phosphate: a protein-magnesium fluorophosphate.

b. Iodoacetate inhibits triose phosphate dehydrogenase (no. 11) by combining with the free sulfhydryl groups on the enzyme.

c. Dialysis inhibits many of these enzymes which require small molecules or ions as activators or coenzymes (e.g., Mg^{++}, DPN).

REVERSIBILITY OF GLYCOLYSIS AND GLYCOGEN SYNTHESIS

Although the reactions on page 276 have been written with a single arrow, the student should keep in mind that the reactions that are given are, to a large extent, reversible. As an example, the equilibrium mixture which results in the reaction catalyzed by phosphoglucomutase contains 94 per cent glucose-6-phosphate and 6 per cent glucose-1-phosphate. In the next reaction, catalyzed by fructose phosphohexose isomerase, glucose-6-phosphate makes up 70 per cent of the equilibrium mixture, fructose-6-phosphate accounts for 30 per cent. However, reaction 8 (the conversion of fructose-6-phosphate to fructose-1,6-diphosphate) is exergonic and irreversible, like the hexokinase reaction.* Glucose-6-phosphate can arise from glycogen or glucose and can be used for glycogen synthesis by a reverse series of reactions via UDP-glucose (p. 270), reversing glycolysis. This appears to be determined largely by the concentration of inorganic phosphate in the cell: in the presence of excess phosphate, glycogen is broken down; in the presence of low concentrations of phosphate, glycogen is synthesized. The process of glycogen synthesis is aided by oxidative reactions which result in the incorporation of phosphate into organic phosphate esters. We shall see later (Chap. 21) that insulin and the hormones of the anterior pituitary and adrenal cortex influence glycogen synthesis in several tissues, *in vivo*. The hypothesis has been suggested, based on some evidence, that the anterior pituitary and adrenal cortex secretions inhibit the hexokinase reaction, whereas insulin can relieve this inhibition. Finally, these reversible reactions which can lead to the synthesis of glycogen explain how so many different types of compounds, when fed, yield added stores of glycogen. Such compounds are amino acids, which, as will be shown, are metabolically altered to compounds identical with those which take part in the reactions of intermediary carbohydrate metabolism.

WHY PHOSPHORYLATED INTERMEDIATES?

Lipmann has established the concept that the chemical energy which is liberated as a result of the breakdown of foodstuffs is transformed

---

* An exergonic reaction is one which results in the release of energy, in contradistinction to an endergonic reaction, which involves the absorption of energy.

(not counting that liberated as heat) into a particular kind of bond before it is utilized by the cell for the performance of special kinds of functions such as mechanical work by the muscle. The particular kind of chemical bond which represents the energy produced as a result of oxidation of foodstuff is that which is stored in the terminal pyrophosphate bonds of ATP. Although determinations of the value for the change in free energy of hydrolysis of this bond are still in doubt, we may accept the value of —7 kcal. (see p. 169).

The very first phase of glucose metabolism may be said to start with the conversion of absorbed glucose (or fructose or galactose) to glycogen. The splitting of the glycosidic bonds of glycogen (or starch in the plant cell) yields energy of the order of 4 kcal. Since the complete oxidation of one 6-carbon unit (glucose) of glycogen to carbon dioxide and water would result in a theoretical yield of 686 kcal., this splitting of the glycosidic bonds yields but 1 per cent of the energy present in the glycogen molecule and may be thought of as yielding heat energy.

The next phase, glycolysis (fermentation), yields some of the chemical bond energy in a utilizable form; as ATP molecules synthesized from ADP. This synthesis involves a coupling reaction between the splitting of an organic phosphate linkage and the transfer of this phosphate to ADP to produce ATP. In this way the energy in the sugar molecules, instead of being liberated entirely in the form of heat, is not lost but is transformed to ATP molecules.

ALTERNATE PATHWAYS FOR GLUCOSE OXIDATION: "THE HEXOSEMONOPHOSPHATE SHUNT"

The reactions of glycolysis are often referred to as "The Embden-Meyerhof Pathway" (p. 276). In addition to this scheme, another has been discovered, based on studies with plants and bacteria and with some mammalian tissues. This series of reactions is referred to as the hexosemonophosphate shunt, the alternate pathway of glucose oxidation, the direct oxidative pathway, or the Warburg-Lipmann-Dickens pathway.

Note that the Embden-Meyerhof scheme (p. 276) requires no molecular oxygen up to lactic acid and is therefore capable of acting anaerobically, using DPN for the oxidation of phosphoglyceraldehyde (reaction no. 11), and the reoxidation of DPNH during the reduction of pyruvic acid to lactic acid (reaction no. 9), or during the reduction of acetaldehyde to ethyl alcohol in yeast (reaction no. 18). In the alternate pathway, TPN is reduced. The following scheme starts with glucose-6-phosphate:

Modified Hexosemonophosphate Shunt

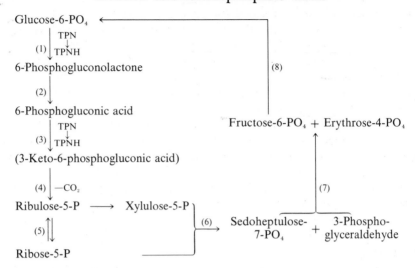

It is important to note (1) that TPNH, which is generated in the hexosemonophosphate shunt reactions, is necessary for the synthesis of fatty acids and steroids, and (2) that the eventual reoxidation of the reduced intermediate cofactor requires molecular oxygen.

Enzymes of Hexosemonophosphate Shunt.

Reaction	Enzyme
(1)	Glucose-6-phosphate dehydrogenase (Zwischenferment)
(2)	6-phosphogluconolactonase
(3, 4)	6-phosphogluconic dehydrogenase
(5)	Phosphopentose isomerase
(6)	Transketolase
(7)	Transaldolase
(8)	Phosphohexose isomerase

The reactions and formulas involved follow:

$$
\begin{array}{cc}
\text{H—C—OH} \\
\text{H—C—OH} \\
\text{HO—C—H} \quad O \\
\text{H—C—OH} \\
\text{H—C—} \\
\text{H}_2\text{C—OPO}_3\text{H}_2
\end{array}
\quad \underset{\rightleftharpoons}{-2\,H}
\quad
\begin{array}{cc}
\text{C=O} \\
\text{H—C—OH} \\
\text{HO—C—H} \quad O \\
\text{H—C—OH} \\
\text{H—C—} \\
\text{H}_2\text{C—OPO}_3\text{H}_2
\end{array}
\quad \overset{\text{glucono-}}{\underset{\text{lactonase}}{\longrightarrow}}
\quad
\begin{array}{cc}
\text{OH} \\
\text{C=O} \\
\text{H—C—OH} \\
\text{HO—C—H} \\
\text{H—C—OH} \\
\text{H—C—OH} \\
\text{H}_2\text{C—OPO}_3\text{H}_2
\end{array}
\quad \overset{}{\underset{-2\,H}{\longrightarrow}}
$$

Glucose 6-phosphate   6-Phosphoglucono-lactone   6-Phosphogluconic acid

$$
\begin{bmatrix}
\text{OH} \\
\text{C}=\text{O} \\
\text{H}-\text{C}-\text{OH} \\
\text{C}=\text{O} \\
\text{H}-\text{C}-\text{OH} \\
\text{H}-\text{C}-\text{OH} \\
\text{H}_2\text{C}-\text{OPO}_3\text{H}_2
\end{bmatrix}
\longrightarrow
\begin{array}{c}
\text{CO}_2 \\
+ \\
\text{H}_2\text{C}-\text{OH} \\
\text{C}=\text{O} \\
\text{H}-\text{C}-\text{OH} \\
\text{H}-\text{C}-\text{OH} \\
\text{H}_2\text{C}-\text{OPO}_3\text{H}_2
\end{array}
\longrightarrow
\begin{array}{c}
\text{H}_2\text{C}-\text{OH} \\
\text{C}=\text{O} \\
\text{HO}-\text{C}-\text{H} \\
\text{H}-\text{C}-\text{OH} \\
\text{CH}_2.\text{OPO}_3\text{H}_2
\end{array}
$$

3-Keto-6-phospho-gluconic acid   Ribulose-5-phosphate   D-Xylulose-5-phosphate

$$
\begin{array}{c}
\boxed{\begin{array}{c}\text{CH}_2\text{OH} \\ \text{C}=\text{O} \\ \text{H O}-\text{C}-\text{H} \\ \text{H}-\text{C}-\text{OH} \\ \text{CH}_2.\text{OPO}_3\text{H}_2\end{array}} \\
\text{Xylulose-5-phosphate*}
\end{array}
\;+\;
\begin{array}{c}
\text{CHO} \\
\text{H}-\text{C}-\text{OH} \\
\text{H}-\text{C}-\text{OH} \\
\text{H}-\text{C}-\text{OH} \\
\text{H}_2\text{C}-\text{OPO}_3\text{H}_2 \\
\text{Ribose-5-phosphate}
\end{array}
\underset{\text{ketolase}}{\overset{\text{Trans-}}{\rightleftharpoons}}
\begin{array}{c}
\text{CH}_2\text{OH} \\
\text{C}=\text{O} \\
\text{HO}-\text{C}-\text{H} \\
\text{H}-\text{C}-\text{OH} \\
\text{H}-\text{C}-\text{OH} \\
\text{H}-\text{C}-\text{OH} \\
\text{H}_2\text{C}-\text{OH} \\
\text{Sedoheptulose-7-phosphate}
\end{array}
+
\begin{array}{c}
\text{CHO} \\
\text{H}-\text{C}-\text{OH} \\
\text{H}_2\text{C}-\text{OPO}_3\text{H}_2 \\
\text{Glyceraldehyde-3-phosphate}
\end{array}
$$

$$
\begin{array}{c}
\boxed{\begin{array}{c}\text{CH}_2\text{OH} \\ \text{C}=\text{O} \\ \text{HO}-\text{C}-\text{H} \\ \text{H}-\text{C}-\text{O}\,\text{H} \\ \text{H}-\text{C}-\text{OH} \\ \text{H}-\text{C}-\text{OH} \\ \text{H}_2\text{C}-\text{OPO}_3\text{H}_2\end{array}} \\
\text{Sedoheptulose-7-PO}_4
\end{array}
+
\begin{array}{c}
\text{CHO} \\
\text{H}-\text{C}-\text{OH} \\
\text{H}_2\text{C}-\text{OPO}_3\text{H}_2 \\
\text{3-Phospho-glyceraldehyde}
\end{array}
\underset{\text{aldolase}}{\overset{\text{Trans-}}{\longrightarrow}}
\begin{array}{c}
\text{CH}_2\text{OH} \\
\text{C}=\text{O} \\
\text{HO}-\text{C}-\text{H} \\
\text{H}-\text{C}-\text{OH} \\
\text{H}-\text{C}-\text{OH} \\
\text{H}_2\text{C}-\text{OPO}_3\text{H}_2 \\
\text{Fructose-6-PO}_4
\end{array}
+
\begin{array}{c}
\text{CHO} \\
\text{H}-\text{C}-\text{OH} \\
\text{H}-\text{C}-\text{OH} \\
\text{H}_2\text{C}-\text{OPO}_3\text{H}_2 \\
\text{Erythrose-4-PO}_4
\end{array}
$$

The presence of a variety of metabolic pathways in tissues of the mammal poses a problem which has been well stated by Barron: "Living organisms . . . have developed multiple schemes for a better utilization of the total energy obtained on oxidation of carbohydrate to CO_2 and water. Thus, the multiple pathways of oxidation . . . are the imprint of the biochemical evolution which has been going on from the moment the cell was created. Direct combination with oxygen . . . was

* Liver contains enzymes which can bring about the conversion of the pentose sugar L-xylulose to D-xylulose via the sugar alcohol xylitol. The D-xylulose is then metabolized via its phosphate to hexose phosphate. Pentosuria is a disease of human beings characterized by the excretion of abnormally large amounts of L-xylulose, suggesting the lack of an enzyme which is concerned with the metabolism of this pentose.

replaced because of its wastefulness by stepwise oxidation and de-carboxylation of hexoses. There are still a number of organisms (molds, some bacteria) which have retained this primitive pathway and even in some mammalian tissues some of its enzymes can be found (e.g., glucose oxidase in the liver). The introduction of the P group repre-sents a great economy, as many largely exergonic reactions became readily reversible. Direct oxidation was then replaced by the stepwise oxidation of the phosphorylated compounds. There are still many cells which retain this pathway; and many more which utilize it when the more elaborate route—fermentation—has been interrupted. Finally came the fermentation pathway with its obligatory phase of pyruvate forma-tion. . . . Of the two kinds of fermentation, alcoholic fermentation is largely confined to the plant kingdom, while lactic acid fermentation is found in animals and bacteria. . . . Pyruvate is the meeting point of these different pathways."

AEROBIC GLYCOLYSIS

Normally, glycolysis—the formation of lactic acid—is restricted to anaerobic conditions, for the presence of oxygen inhibits the formation of lactic acid. This inhibition of glycolysis by oxygen is referred to as the "Pasteur effect." On the other hand, high concentrations of glucose will sometimes inhibit respiration in isolated systems. This phenomenon is called the "Crabtree effect." A theory to explain the "Pasteur effect" has been proposed by Lynen and Johnson. They suggest that during aerobic cellular metabolism much more esterification of inorganic phos-phate takes place than during anaerobic glycolysis. This means that dur-ing aerobic conditions, the concentration of inorganic phosphate in the cell will be lowered considerably as compared to the anaerobic cell. The aerobic conditions will therefore favor glycogen synthesis and will tend to depress glycolysis, the formation of lactic acid.

TABLE 38.   OXYGEN CONSUMPTION OF ASCITES TUMOR CELLS

Cells	Q_{O_2}*	$Q_G^{O_2}$	$Q_G^{N_2}$
Ascites cancer cells	−7	30	70
Earle's cancer cells (high malignancy)	−7	30	70
Earle's cancer cells (low malignancy)	−13	10	25
Chorion of young embryos	−17	0	35

* For an explanation of these symbols, see pages 137, 138.
(From Warburg, O.: On Respiratory Impairment in Cancer Cells. Science, *124*: 269, 1956.)

Some tissues show a high rate of aerobic glycolysis; they do form lactic acid in the presence of oxygen. One of the theories advanced to explain the origin of cancerous tissue is that of Warburg, who many years ago pointed out that cancer tissue had a high rate of aerobic glycolysis as compared with noncancerous tissue. He suggested that cancer tissue had lost its ability to gain energy by the oxidative route (see p. 283) and had increased its ability to perform the reactions of fermentation, thus obtaining enough energy for life. At that time he was limited in his work to tissue which was only partly cancerous in type. Recently, tumor cells which are completely cancerous have become available. These are ascites tumor cells and show a lowered oxygen consumption and a high rate of glycolysis. Table 38 is an illustration.

It is suggested that an "injury" has resulted in the loss of enzymes important in the oxidative mechanism.

AEROBIC OXIDATION

As has been shown, during glycolytic breakdown, DPN is reduced to DPNH; at the same time, 3-phosphoglyceraldehyde is oxidized to 1,3-diphosphoglyceric acid. To conserve this coenzyme, it must be re-oxidized. Under anaerobic conditions this is done when pyruvic acid is converted to lactic acid. In the presence of oxygen, however, DPNH can still be oxidized with the help of the respiratory enzymes (p. 253), reforming DPN; the H is carried by the flavoprotein enzymes and the cytochrome c–cytochrome oxidase system until the H^+ reaches molecular oxygen, with which it combines to form water.

In the anaerobic cycle, glycogen is broken down to lactic acid. In the aerobic, or oxidative cycle, which we are about to discuss, the lactic acid or, rather, its oxidation product, pyruvic acid, is oxidized to carbon dioxide and water.

A great deal of work was done in the study of this mechanism. Szent-Györgyi noticed that the rate of respiration of pigeon breast muscle declined as succinate disappeared, and that respiration was revived when more succinate or fumarate was added. This suggested that the oxidation of carbohydrate was catalyzed by such 4-C acids, and that the path of carbohydrate metabolism would have to include 4-C compounds. Later on, Szent-Györgyi showed that malate and oxaloacetate behaved similarly.

The next step was taken by Krebs. He revealed that citric and α-ketoglutaric acids also act catalytically on minced muscle. This suggested that 6-C and 5-C compounds are also involved. In line with these facts, Krebs suggested that the initial step along the path of oxidation was the combination of pyruvic acid (3-C) and oxaloacetic acid (4-C) to form a compound (7-C) which is broken down to some citric acid derivative (6-C), and then to α-ketoglutaric (5-C), on to the various 4-C dicarboxylic acids. Actually, Krebs showed that when pyruvic acid and oxaloacetate are incubated with minced muscle, citric acid can be isolated as one of the products.

The formation of a hypothetical 7-C compound was a stumbling block to the scheme. From the work of Lipmann, we now know that pyruvate (3-C) is first converted to acetyl coenzyme A (2-C) by oxidative decarboxylation:

$$\begin{array}{c} CH_3 \\ | \\ CO \\ | \\ COOH \end{array} \xrightarrow[+O]{-CO_2} \quad CH_3COOH + CO_2$$

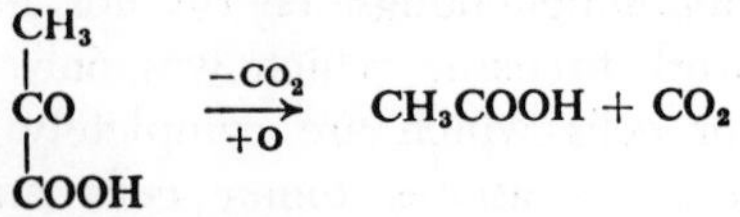

and that it is this compound which combines with oxaloacetate (4-C) to form a 6-C compound (citric acid).

The "Krebs cycle," the "citric acid cycle," or, as it is more commonly known, the "tricarboxylic acid cycle," may be illustrated in the following manner:

Tricarboxylic Acid Cycle

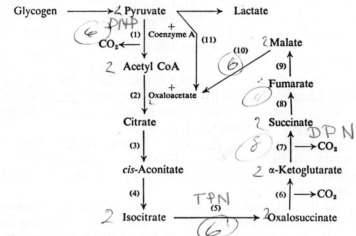

Enzymes of the Tricarboxylic Acid Cycle.

Reaction	Enzyme	Reaction	Enzyme
(1)	Pyruvic acid oxidase (requires DPN)	(8)	Succinic dehydrogenase
(2)	Condensing enzyme	(9)	Fumarase
(3, 4)	Aconitase	(10)	Malic dehydrogenase (requires DPN)
(5)	Isocitric dehydrogenase (requires TPN)	(11)	β-Carboxylase (requires thiamin pyrophosphate and is present in liver but not in muscle)
(6)	Oxalosuccinic decarboxylase		
(7)	Oxidative decarboxylation enzyme (requires DPN)		

The oxidative decarboxylation of pyruvic acid to yield acetyl coenzyme A and CO_2 has been shown to be a complex process involving thiamine (p. 450), lipoic acid (p. 452), coenzyme A (p. 285), DPN+ and Mg++ ions.

Examples of Inhibitors.

a. Arsenite inhibits reaction no. 7.

b. Anaerobiosis inhibits isocitric dehydrogenase (no. 5) since aerobic conditions are necessary in order to reoxidize the reduced TPNH$_2$.

c. Fluoracetate inhibits aconitase (nos. 3 and 4) by forming a fluorotricarboxylic acid which powerfully inhibits the enzyme.

d. Malonate inhibits succinic dehydrogenase (no. 8) by acting as a competitor of succinic acid for combination with the enzyme.

Compounds of the Tricarboxylic Acid Cycle.

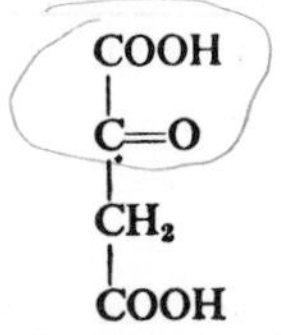

COOH | C=O | CH$_2$ | COOH Oxaloacetic acid	COOH | CH$_2$ | CHOH | COOH Malic acid	COOH | H—C || C—H | COOH Fumaric acid
COOH | CH$_2$ | CH$_2$ | COOH Succinic acid	COOH | C=O | CH$_2$ | CH$_2$ | COOH α-Ketoglutaric acid	COOH | C=O | H—C—COOH | CH$_2$ | COOH Oxalosuccinic acid
COOH | CHOH | H—C—COOH | CH$_2$ | COOH Isocitric acid	COOH | CH || C—COOH | CH$_2$ | COOH cis-Aconitic acid	COOH | CH$_2$ | HO—C—COOH | CH$_2$ | COOH Citric acid

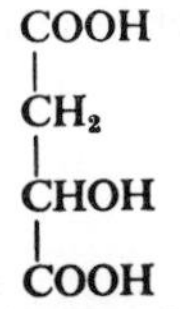

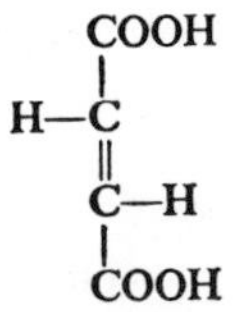

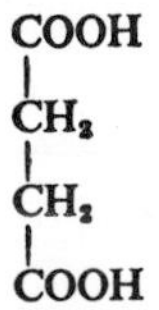

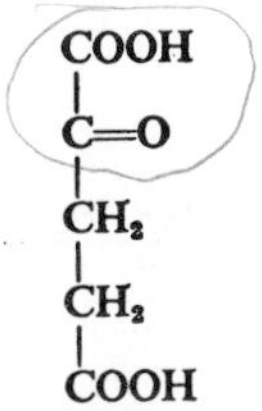

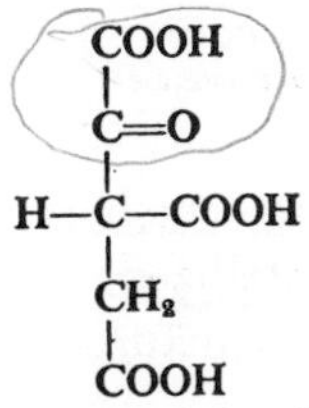

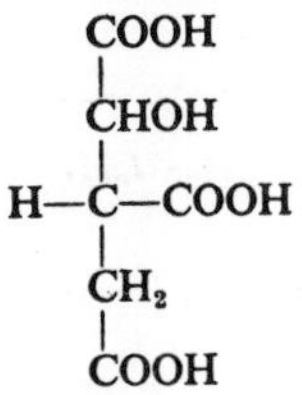

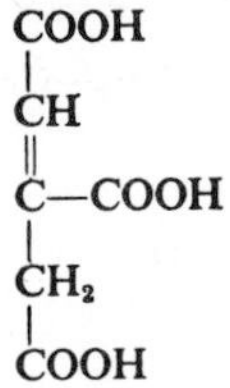

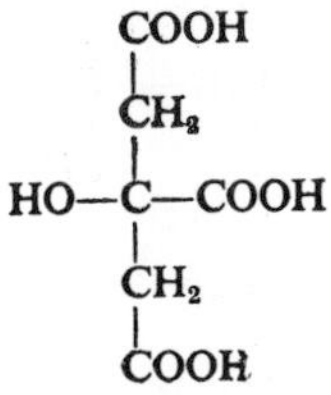

In contrast to the soluble enzymes of the glycolytic cycle, here most of the enzymes are present in an insoluble form, associated with the mitochondrial fraction of homogenized cells. If suitable cofactors are added to such a system, it can perform all the reactions of the cycle.

Coenzyme A. It had been known that acetate as such is not oxidized, and it had been assumed that the acetate is in some "active" form when it condenses with oxaloacetate. Lipmann, working with a bacterial system, showed the presence of acetyl phosphate. The assumption was made that this substance might serve as the "active" acetate. However, while the acetyl phosphate acted as a phosphate donor to form ATP, it failed as an acetyl donor.

In the meantime Lipmann had shown that the liver contains an enzyme system which is capable of acetylating sulfanilamide. A cofactor taking part in this reaction can be removed by dialysis, but acetyl phosphate cannot replace this cofactor. Nachmansohn, who had discovered the enzyme choline acetylase—an enzyme which brings about the acetylation of choline to form acetylcholine—showed that here, too, acetyl phosphate cannot serve as the source of acetyl groups.

Lipmann next showed that the coenzyme needed for the acetylating reaction contains pantothenic acid (p. 459) together with organically bound sulfur. This substance, known as coenzyme A, not only helps in the acetylation of sulfanilamide and in the acetylation of choline, but seems to be a general acetylating agent in the body. Ochoa and Stern, for example, have shown that, in the citric acid cycle, the condensation of acetate and oxaloacetate to form citric acid is brought about as follows:

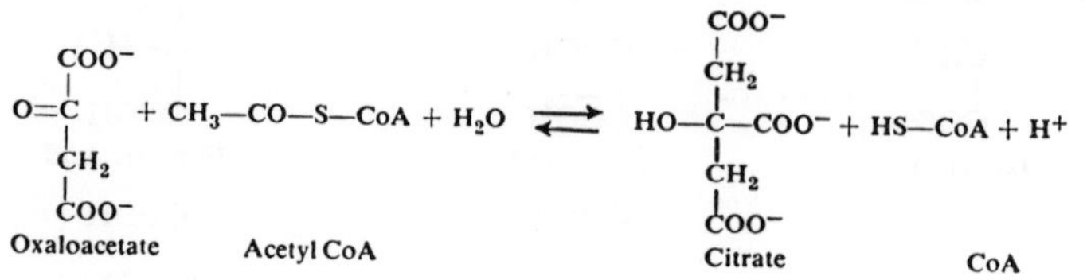

$$
\begin{array}{ccc}
\underset{\text{Oxaloacetate}}{\begin{array}{c} \text{COO}^- \\ | \\ \text{O=C} \\ | \\ \text{CH}_2 \\ | \\ \text{COO}^- \end{array}}
+ \underset{\text{Acetyl CoA}}{\text{CH}_3\text{—CO—S—CoA}} + \text{H}_2\text{O}
\;\rightleftharpoons\;
\underset{\text{Citrate}}{\begin{array}{c} \text{COO}^- \\ | \\ \text{CH}_2 \\ | \\ \text{HO—C—COO}^- \\ | \\ \text{CH}_2 \\ | \\ \text{COO}^- \end{array}}
+ \underset{\text{CoA}}{\text{HS—CoA}} + \text{H}^+
\end{array}
$$

a reaction which is catalyzed by the "condensing enzyme" which has been crystallized.

The structure of coenzyme A is

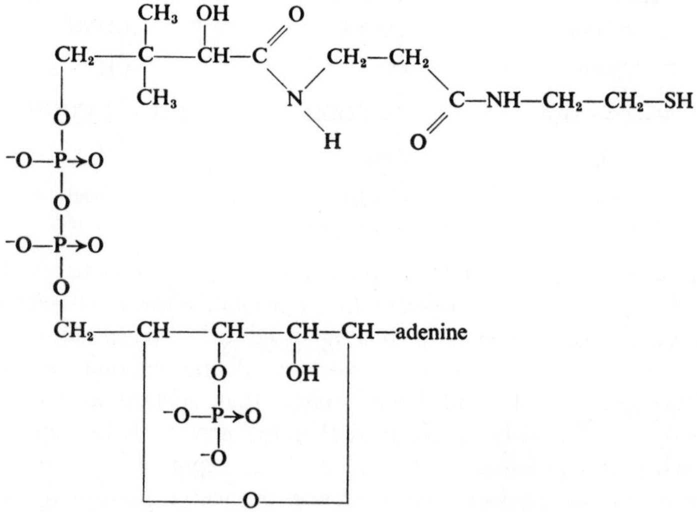

which means that it is composed of thiolethanolamine (top right) joined to pantothenic acid, one of the B vitamins (p. 459), and this is joined in turn, through a pyrophosphate bridge, to adenylic acid (p. 120).

The reaction step between α-ketoglutarate and succinate probably involves the intermediate synthesis of succinyl coenzyme A (see p. 209). This reaction sequence involves lipoic acid (p. 452) and pyrophospho-thiamine (p. 451) as follows:

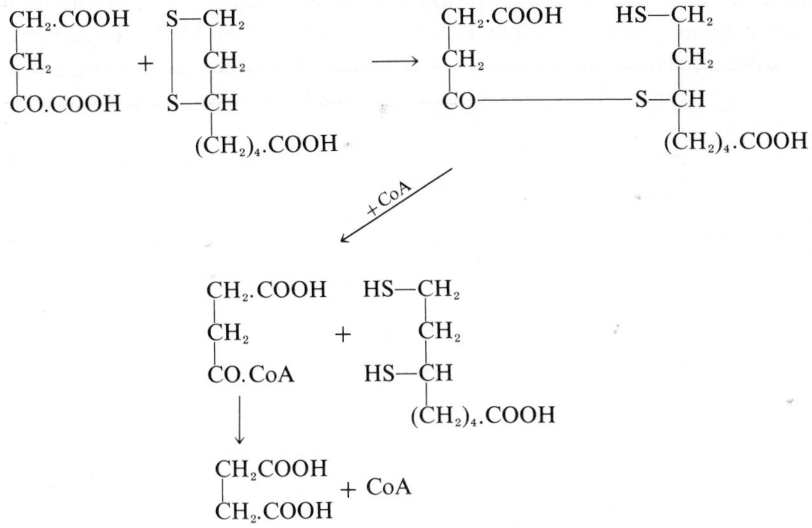

CH₂.COOH ... (chemical structures)

$$CH_2.COOH \quad S{-}CH_2 \qquad CH_2.COOH \quad HS{-}CH_2$$

(chemical structure diagram)

AN ACCOUNTING

It is important at this point that we view the entire sequence of reactions representing the complete oxidation of glucose to carbon dioxide and water.

The over-all reaction may be written:

$$C_6H_{12}O_6 + 6\,O_2 \longrightarrow 6\,CO_2 + 6\,H_2O + 686\ \text{kcal.} \qquad (A)$$

In the following discussion we shall attempt to account for these features of reaction A:

1. Utilization of 6 moles of oxygen
2. Formation of 6 moles of carbon dioxide
3. Formation of 6 moles of water
4. Distribution of the energy released during carbohydrate breakdown between the anaerobic (glycolysis) and aerobic (Krebs cycle) phases
5. Estimate of the proportion of the total energy stored as ATP and which can be used for cellular functions

STOICHIOMETRY OF REACTION A

The over-all reaction during glycolysis can be written as follows:

$$C_6H_{12}O_6 + 2\,DPN^+ \longrightarrow 2\,C_3H_4O_3 + 2\,DPNH + 2\,H^+ \qquad (B)$$

Thus 1 mole of glucose gives rise to 2 moles of pyruvic acid, and in the process 2 moles of diphosphopyridine nucleotide are reduced. The latter takes place during reaction no. 11 (p. 284), in which 3-phosphoglyceraldehyde is oxidized to 1,3-diphosphoglyceric acid. Since 1 mole of glucose gives rise to 2 moles of the triose, 2 moles of DPN are reduced.

During the aerobic phase, the 2 moles of DPNH are reoxidized by molecular oxygen by means of the flavoprotein enzymes and the electron transport system (cytochrome c, etc.):

$$2\,DPNH + 2\,H^+ + O_2 \longrightarrow 2\,DPN^+ + 2\,H_2O \qquad\qquad (C)$$

In addition, the 2 moles of pyruvate formed in reaction B are oxidized to carbon dioxide and water, according to the following:

$$2\,C_3H_4O_3 + 5\,O_2 \longrightarrow 6\,CO_2 + 4\,H_2O \qquad\qquad (D)$$

If we add equations B, C and D, we arrive at the statement of equation A.

We must now account for the stoichiometry of equation D in terms of the individual reactions which are concerned. These are:

Reactions	Moles O_2 used	Moles H_2O formed	Moles CO_2 formed
(1) Pyruvate $\longrightarrow$ acetyl CoA + CO_2 DPNH + H^+ + $\frac{1}{2}O_2$ $\longrightarrow$ DPN$^+$ + H_2O	$\frac{1}{2}$	1	1
(2) Acetyl CoA + oxaloacetate + H_2O $\longrightarrow$ citrate		−1 (used)	
(3) Citrate $\longrightarrow$ cis-aconitate + H_2O		1	
(4) cis-aconitate + H_2O $\longrightarrow$ isocitrate		−1	
(5) Isocitrate $\longrightarrow$ oxalosuccinate TPNH + H^+ + $\frac{1}{2}O_2$ $\longrightarrow$ TPN$^+$ + H_2O	$\frac{1}{2}$	1	
(6) Oxalosuccinate $\longrightarrow$ α-ketoglutarate + CO_2			1
(7) α-Ketoglutarate + H_2O $\longrightarrow$ succinate + CO_2 DPNH + H^+ + $\frac{1}{2}O_2$ $\longrightarrow$ DPN$^+$ + H_2O	$\frac{1}{2}$	−1,1	1
(8) Succinate $\longrightarrow$ fumarate Reduced enzyme + 2 H^+ + $\frac{1}{2}O_2$ $\longrightarrow$ ox. enz + H_2O	$\frac{1}{2}$	1	
(9) Fumarate + H_2O $\longrightarrow$ malate		−1	
(10) Malate $\longrightarrow$ oxaloacetate DPNH + H^+ + $\frac{1}{2}O_2$ $\longrightarrow$ DPN$^+$ + H_2O	$\frac{1}{2}$	1	
	$\overline{2\frac{1}{2}}$	$\overline{2}$	$\overline{3}$

Since 1 mole of glucose gives rise to 2 moles of pyruvate, during the oxidation of these two moles of pyruvate 5 moles of oxygen will be used and 4 moles of water and 6 moles of carbon dioxide will be formed. These values are in accord with equation D. In each oxidation step, the role of the appropriate coenzyme has been shown. In the case of reaction no. 8, the enzyme succinic dehydrogenase has been shown to contain heme-linked iron as well as FAD, whose exact roles in the oxidation-reduction reaction have not been fully explained. In any case the reduced form of this enzyme is reoxidized by coupling with the reduction of ferricytochrome *c*, which in turn is reoxidized by cyto-chrome oxidase and molecular oxygen.

DISTRIBUTION AND STORAGE OF ENERGY

The energy resulting from reaction A is 686 kcal. Of this total, 57 kcal. will be formed as the result of glycolysis and 629 kcal. during the oxidative phase. Glycolysis is therefore a relatively inefficient mechanism for the release of energy during carbohydrate breakdown; over 90 per cent of the energy will result from the aerobic phase of carbohydrate metabolism.

How many moles of ATP are formed during these two phases of metabolism? During glycolysis, the following reactions are involved in the use and formation of ATP:

Reactions	Moles ATP per mole glucose
(1) Glucose ⟶ glycogen, via glucose + ATP ⟶ glucose-1-phosphate	− 1 (used)
(2) Fructose-6-PO₄ ⟶ fructose-1,6-di-PO₄	− 1
(3) 2(1,3-diphosphoglyceric acid) ⟶ 2(3-phosphoglyceric acid)	2
(4) 2(phosphoenolpyruvic acid) ⟶ 2(enolpyruvic acid)	2

DPN → DPNH ✝6 (handwritten)

During the aerobic phase the reactions which involve ATP synthesis are the oxidation reactions. The following shows the number of ATP molecules synthesized during these reactions:

Reactions	Moles ATP per mole glucose
2 Pyruvate ⟶ 2 acetyl CoA	6
2 Isocitrate ⟶ 2 oxalosuccinate	6
2 α-Ketoglutarate ⟶ 2 succinate	8
2 Succinate ⟶ 2 fumarate	4
2 Malate ⟶ 2 oxaloacetate	6
	30

Glycolysis and aerobic oxidation account for 32 moles of ATP per mole of glucose. Assuming the value of −7 kcal. for the $\Delta F°$ of the terminal bond of ATP, we have 32×7 or 224 kcal. This approximate calculation indicates that the energy stored as ATP represents some 33 per cent $(224/686 \times 100)$ of the theoretical energy produced during glucose oxidation.

AEROBIC PHOSPHORYLATION

The appearance of ATP during the operation of the tricarboxylic acid cycle is accompanied by an uptake of molecular oxygen. This coupling of two processes is known as "aerobic phosphorylation." We can see from the data presented that the ratio of phosphorylation to oxygen uptake is 30/10 or 3.0.

The exact mechanism by which oxidation in the cell mitochondrion is coupled with the esterification of ADP by inorganic phosphate to form ATP is still not known. We do know that phosphorylation takes place outside or beyond the substrate level; that is, during the transport of electrons. In rat liver mitochondria, there are at least three phosphorylations between DPNH and oxygen: one between cytochrome c and oxygen, and two between DPNH and cytochrome c. These may be pictured as follows:

$$
\begin{array}{ccccccc}
& \text{ATP} & & \text{ATP} & & \text{ATP} & \\
& \uparrow & & \uparrow & & \uparrow & \\
\text{Substrate} \to \text{DPN} \xrightarrow{} \text{FN} \to \text{Cyt } b & \xrightarrow{} & \text{Cyt } c \to \text{Cyt } a & \xrightarrow{} & \text{Cyt } a_3 \to \text{O}_2 \\
& \uparrow & & \uparrow & & & \\
& \text{Succinate} & & \text{Ascorbic} & & & \\
& & & \text{acid} & & &
\end{array}
$$

in which FN stands for the flavin nucleotides. The scheme also illustrates the points of entry of succinate and ascorbic acid into the electron transport chain.

Oxidation by mitochondria can be "uncoupled" from the phosphorylation of ADP by a number of chemical compounds. These "uncoupling agents" include 2,4-dinitrophenol, Dicumarol, pentachlorophenol, gramicidin, arsenate, methylene blue, Ca^{++} and thyroxine. The last two compounds do not act directly on enzymes involved in oxidative phosphorylation, but act rather on the mitochondrial membrane causing the mitochondrion to swell. Dinitrophenol, on the other hand, accelerates the hydrolytic decomposition of the primary "high energy" phosphate esters. Arsenate competes with phosphate in the phosphorylation reaction. Oxidation-reduction dyes act as artificial electron carriers and thereby by-pass parts of the normal electron transport system. Uncoupling is characterized by continued, or increased, oxygen consumption accompanied by little or no formation of ATP—the energy released during substrate oxidation is "wasted."

The mechanism by which ATP is formed during electron transport is under active investigation. Perhaps the studies of Lehninger are most provocative. It is proposed that at each of the 3 phosphorylation sites in the respiratory chain, coupled electron transfer results in the formation of a "high-energy" $(\sim)$ derivative of an electron carrier with phosphate or some other compound. This intermediate would then donate its $\sim$P to ADP to form ATP, as follows:

(1) Carrier $+ X \to$ Carrier $\sim X$
(2) Carrier $\sim X + P_i \to$ Carrier $+ P \sim X$
(3) $P \sim X + ADP \to X + ATP$

This hypothesis is strengthened by the finding that there exists in mitochondria two different isotopic exchange reactions of ATP which

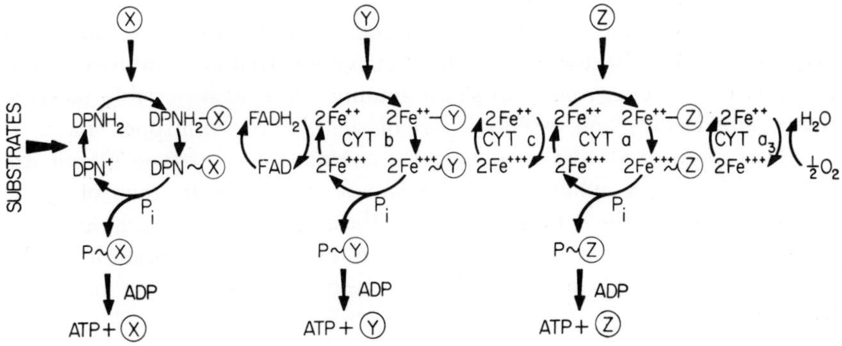

Figure 72. A schematic representation of the energy-coupling at all three sites in the complete respiratory chain.

occur in the complete absence of electron transfer. The first is the ATP–P_i^{32} exchange in which labeled P_i^{32} is rapidly incorporated into the terminal phosphate of ATP. The second is the ATP–ADP exchange in which ADP, labeled with either P^{32} or C^{14}, is incorporated bodily into ATP. Both exchange reactions are inhibited by dinitrophenol, indicating their close relationship to the oxidative phosphorylation process. Furthermore, the enzyme responsible for the ATP–ADP exchange has been separated and purified. X may be an enzyme which is capable of undergoing reversible phosphorylation by ATP (Fig. 72).

COENZYME Q

A group of quinones have been isolated from mitochondria which appear to add one more member to the chain of electron transport carriers. These occur in the lipid of the mitochondria but can be extracted from it by lipid solvents. The basic structure of these compounds, coenzyme Q, is shown below:

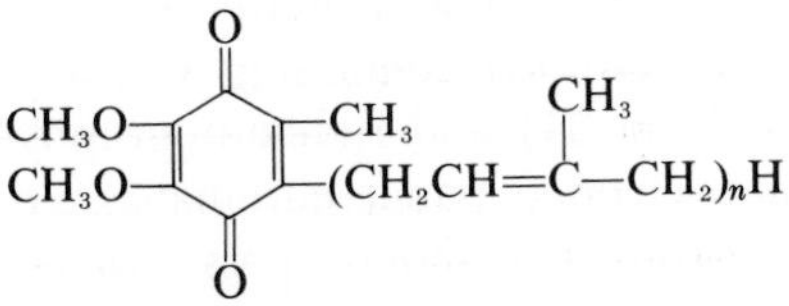

Coenzyme Q

As is indicated by the formula, a number of homologs exist in different species. These have the same quinonoid nucleus but differ in the number of isoprenoid units in the side-chain. In the compound from animal sources, n = 10 and it is therefore called coenzyme Q_{10}. Bacteria contain homologs in which n = less than 10. Coenzyme Q undergoes oxidation-reduction reactions in respiring mitochondria; if the latter are extracted with acetone—removing coenzyme Q—the succin-oxidase and succinic cytochrome c reductase activities of the extracted particles are lost. Restoration of these enzyme activities is brought about by addition of coenzyme Q in small amounts. It is also possible to show that coenzyme Q is an essential part of the electron transport chain.

It is of interest that mycobacteria contain no coenzyme Q but are rich in vitamin K whose structure is not dissimilar to that of Q. It appears that vitamin K fulfills a role in these bacteria comparable to the role of coenzyme Q in electron transport in animal mitochondria. The exact position of Q in the chain of electron transport has not been determined.

PATH OF CARBON DURING PHOTOSYNTHESIS

The chemically important process in photosynthesis is the fixation of carbon dioxide. The reactions which take place include a number of cyclic processes coupled to one another, so that a flow of energy may occur from one cycle to another, resulting in the conversion of light energy to potential chemical bond energy. These reactions are not un-like those that have been discovered for animal tissues, although they are not just the reverse of those that occur during respiratory metab-olism. Evidence has been obtained which suggests that these photo-synthetic reactions may take place in the chloroplast.

The elucidation of the reaction mechanisms that are involved dur-ing photosynthesis is dependent on the use of carbon dioxide labeled with C^{14} and the identification of compounds formed by the plant cell —compounds which contain the isotope as a label. Calvin and his asso-ciates are responsible for much of this phase of the work. They made use of the green alga, *Chlorella,* which is able to convert radiant energy to foodstuffs in the presence of CO_2. The apparatus is so designed that a suspension of this single-celled plant is exposed to $C^{14}O_2$ and illuminated for varying periods of time. Samples can be quickly removed and the enzymes inactivated (e.g., by treatment with alcohol) before the compounds containing C^{14} are identified by filter paper chromatography (p. 38) and radioautography. The latter process involves placing the developed paper chromatogram against a sensitive film; the film is developed and shows spots which correspond to com-pounds containing C^{14}.

An important finding has been that during very short periods of illumination (5 seconds) most of the C^{14} appears in 3-phosphoglyceric acid. With longer periods of illumination other compounds are also labeled with the isotope. The reaction which "fixes" the carbon dioxide involves ribulose-1,5-diphosphate. Important roles are also assigned to TPNH and ATP, which are illustrated in the following cyclic scheme presented by Calvin:

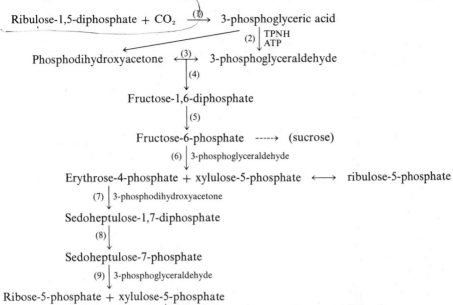

Ribulose-1,5-diphosphate + CO_2 $\xrightarrow{(1)}$ 3-phosphoglyceric acid

(2) $\Big|$ TPNH / ATP

Phosphodihydroxyacetone $\xleftarrow{(3)}$ 3-phosphoglyceraldehyde

(4) $\Big|$

Fructose-1,6-diphosphate

(5) $\Big|$

Fructose-6-phosphate -----> (sucrose)

(6) $\Big|$ 3-phosphoglyceraldehyde

Erythrose-4-phosphate + xylulose-5-phosphate $\longleftrightarrow$ ribulose-5-phosphate

(7) $\Big|$ 3-phosphodihydroxyacetone

Sedoheptulose-1,7-diphosphate

(8) $\Big|$

Sedoheptulose-7-phosphate

(9) $\Big|$ 3-phosphoglyceraldehyde

Ribose-5-phosphate + xylulose-5-phosphate

(10) $\Big|$ ATP

Ribulose-1,5-diphosphate

(For formulas, see p. 281.)

Reaction	Enzyme	Reaction	Enzyme
(1)	Carboxydismutase	(10)	Phosphopentokinase
(2)	Triose phosphate dehydrogenase	(6)	Transketolase
(3)	Phosphotriose isomerase	(7)	Aldolase
(4)	Aldolase	(8)	Phosphatase
(5)	Fructose diphosphatase	(9)	Transketolase

At this point we may refer back to Figure 1, page 9, which illustrates the light reaction that results in the cleavage of water and the generation of "reducing power" which is responsible for the conversion of TPN to TPNH and for the oxidative photophosphorylative synthesis of ATP. Both TPNH and ATP are important ingredients in the reactions listed above.

In summary, CO_2, ATP and TPNH are utilized to form fructose-6-phosphate; as CO_2 feeds into the cycle, fructose-6-phosphate is utilized for the synthesis of more complex sugars. Note that several compounds in the CO_2 fixation scheme can be converted to members of the tricarboxylic acid cycle, and, as we shall see, this provides a mechanism for the synthesis of amino acids and fats.

GLUCURONIC ACID

Glucuronic acid arises from glucose in a reaction in which each of the compounds is bound to uridine diphosphate, and involving the reduction of DPN:

UDP-glucoside + 2 DPN^+ + H_2O → UDP-glucuronide + 2 DPNH + 2 H^+

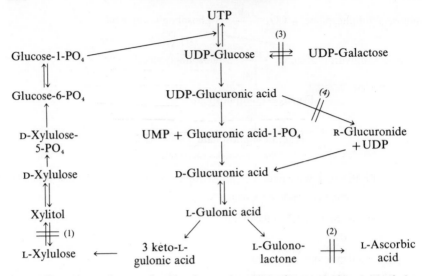

Figure 73. The uridine nucleotide shunt; a cyclic pathway of glucose catabolism via glucuronic acid and ketopentose. From D-Xylulose-5-PO₄ to Glucose-6-PO₄ the reactions are those of the hexosemonophosphate shunt (p. 280). Interrupted reactions indicate congenital enzyme defects: (1) pentosuria, (2) inability to synthesize ascorbic acid, (3) galactosemia, and (4) hyperbilirubinemia. (Adapted from Strominger, Physiol. Rev., *40*:55, 1960.)

The conjugation of many compounds with glucuronic acid in the body (see p. 594) occurs by means of the UDP-glucuronide:

UDP-glucuronide + menthol ⟶ UDP + mentholglucuronide
                (or other
                acceptors)

Figure 73 illustrates the many functions of the uridine nucleotides and the interrelationships among the sugars and glucuronic acid. It is of interest to note that the absence of any of several enzymes results in abnormalities. These diseases, as well as others (see p. 354), are sometimes called "inborn errors of metabolism."

SUMMARY

Liver glycogen represents the stored carbohydrate of the body and is constantly being regenerated by virtue of the reactions involving the absorbed monosaccharides and blood glucose. The regulation of glycogen synthesis and breakdown is effected by several hormones, apparently by controlling the activity of enzymes such as phosphorylase and hexokinase, or by the regulation of glucose transport. The relationship of muscular contraction to liver glycogen and blood glucose is best seen in

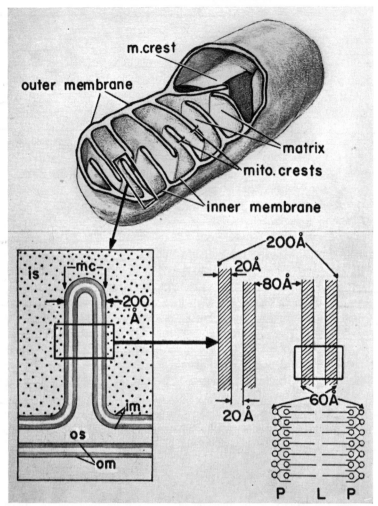

Plate 5

Diagram of the ultrastructure of mitochondria. *Above,* Tridimensional diagram showing outer and inner membranes with the crests and the mitochondrial matrix. *Below left,* At higher magnification, the inset of the previous figure corresponding to a mitochondrial crest. *Below right,* Higher magnification of a molecular diagram interpreting the structure. (From De Robertis, Nowinski and Saez: General Cytology.)

the following diagram, as well as in the fact that some of these hormones also control the synthesis and breakdown of muscle glycogen:

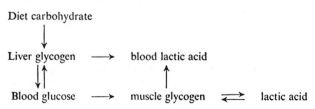

The oxidation of carbohydrate yields energy for cellular purposes and proceeds by a long series of intermediate reactions during which much of this energy is transformed into the terminal phosphate bonds of ATP molecules. The preliminary breakdown of carbohydrate to pyruvic acid (glycolysis or fermentation) requires no molecular oxygen but yields only a small portion of the total potential energy of the carbohydrate molecule. The major source of energy is released during aerobic oxidation in the course of a series of reactions called the tricarboxylic acid cycle. Here oxidation occurs in a stepwise fashion with the intermediate participation of hydrogen carriers (coenzymes), until the final reaction with molecular oxygen (to form water) takes place. This electron chain also serves as a mechanism for the conversion of the chemical bond energy of carbohydrate fragments into ATP. These important reactions are mediated by enzymes present in the mitochondrial particles of the cell cytoplasm (see Plate 5). The reactions of the tricarboxylic acid cycle will have additional significance when we consider the intermediary metabolic reactions of the lipids and proteins, since, as we shall see, these two groups of foodstuffs are eventually converted to compounds which are identical with those of the tricarboxylic acid cycle. This is important because it helps to explain how the three major foodstuffs may be interconvertible. It may explain why, for example, a high protein diet, low in carbohydrate, can yield sufficient energy for metabolic purposes. This places the tricarboxylic acid cycle at the center of all metabolic reaction schemes. Finally, it is of great interest to students of comparative biochemistry that alternate pathways exist in mammalian cells. A study of these pathways in lower forms of plant and animal life yields results which suggest a chemical evolutionary process.

REFERENCES

The chemical evaluations of the function of the liver are reviewed by *Reinhold:* Clinical Chemistry, *1*:351, 1955.

Mayer: J. Nutrition, *45*:3, 1951, is the author of an article on *Claude Bernard.*

Stetten and *Topper:* Am. J. Medicine, *19*:96, 1955, review the metabolism of carbohydrates.

Methods for studying carbohydrate metabolism are illustrated in an article by *Landau, Hastings* and *Nesbett:* J. Biol. Chem., *214*:525, 1955.

Glycogen structure and metabolism is discussed by *Cori:* Harvey Lectures, 1952–1953, p. 145; *Stetten, Katzen* and *Stetten:* J. Biol. Chem., *232*:475, 1958.

In Research Today, Eli Lilly and Co., *10*:58, 1954, there is a description of insulin and glucagon.

A thoughtful article by *Kreb:* Endeavour, *16*:125, 1957, dealing with the control of metabolic processes, should be consulted.

Concepts of diabetes, by *Sherry,* will be found in the Bull. N. Y. Acad. Med., 1953, p. 202.

Beloff-Chain and *Pocchiari:* Ann. Rev. Biochem., *29*:295, 1960, review the subject of carbohydrate metabolism. See also *Krebs* in *Greenberg's* Chemical Pathways of Metabolism, Vol. I, 1954 (tricarboxylic acid cycle).

The enzyme involved in the reaction of ATP and creatine (transphosphorylase) is described by *Kuby, Noda* and *Lardy:* J. Biol. Chem., *209:*191, 1954; *210:*65, 1954.

Pathways of glycolysis (from glucose to pyruvic acid, etc.), are discussed by *Villee:* New England Journal of Medicine, *251:*21, 64, 1954, and by *Stetten* and *Topper:* Amer. J. Medicine, *19:*96, 1955.

A suggestive article by *Warburg* on the origin of cancer cells, involving glycolysis in the process, is to be found in Science, *123:*309, 1956.

The mechanism of the action of the aldolase-catalyzed condensation of dihydroxyacetone phosphate with phosphoglyceraldehyde (and other aldehydes) is discussed by *Bloom* and *Topper:* Science, *124:*982, 1956.

For the formation of acetyl groups from pyruvic acid, see *Weinhouse:* Ann. Rev. Biochem., *23:*132, 1954. See also *Strecker* and *Ochoa:* J. Biol. Chem., *209:*313, 1954.

Articles dealing with coenzyme A are *Lipmann:* Bacteriological Reviews, *17:*1, 1953 (chemistry and function); *Lipmann:* Science, *120:*855, 1954 (the acetylation problem); *Lipmann:* American Scientist, Jan., 1955, p. 37 (coenzyme A and biosynthesis). See also *Lipmann, Kaplan, Novelli, Tuttle* and *Guirard:* J. Biol. Chem., *186:*235, 1950 (isolation of coenzyme A); *Novelli, Schmietz* and *Kaplan:* Ibid., *206:*533, 1954 (degradation and resynthesis).

For an outline of photosynthetic reactions, see *Basham* and *Calvin,* in *Green's* Currents in Biochemical Research, 1956. See, further, *Calvin:* J. Chem. Soc., June, 1956, p. 1895; *Spikes* and *Mayne:* Ann. Rev. Physical Chem., *11:*10, 1960; *Kandler:* Ann. Rev. Plant Physiol., *11:*37, 1960; and *Hill* and *Whittingham:* Photosynthesis, 1955.

Methods of preparing some typical biochemical compounds are given in Biochemical Preparations, *1:*1 (ADP); 5(ATP), 1949; 3:22 (pyruvate); 31 (glucose-6-phosphate); 52 (fructose 1,6-diphosphate).

For a preparation of phosphocreatine, see *Ennor* and *Stocken:* Biochem. J., *43:*190, 1948.

The existence of multiple pathways of carbohydrate metabolism is discussed by *Barron:* Trends in Physiology and Biochemistry, 1952, p. 471.

Galactose metabolism is discussed by *Kalckar:* Science, *125:*105, 1957; Federation Proceedings, *19:*981, 1960. See also *Isselbacher, Anderson, Kurahashi* and *Kalckar:* Science, *123:*635, 1956.

For pathway to pentosuria metabolism, see *Touster:* Federation Proceedings, *19:* 977, 1960.

The use of isotopic carbon in carbohydrate and general intermediary metabolism is discussed by *Buchanan* and *Hastings:* Physiol. Rev., *26:*126, 1946. See also *Greenberg:* Chemical Pathways of Metabolism, Vol. 1, 1954 (carbohydrates and lipids); see also *Kamen:* Isotopic Tracers in Biology, 1957.

For coenzyme Q, see *Green* and *Lester:* Federation Proceedings, *18:*987, 1959.

The interconversion of hexoses is discussed by *Roseman:* Federation Proceedings, *18:*984, 1959.

For oxidative phosphorylation mechanisms, see *Lehninger:* Science, *128:*450, 1958.

Studies of metabolic control by spectrophotometry are discussed by *Chance* and *Hess:* Science, *129:*700, 1959.

For phases of glycogen metabolism, see *Larner:* Federation Proceedings, *19:*971, 1960.

METABOLISM
OF THE
LIPIDS

▰▰▰▰▰▰▰▰▰▰▰▰▰▰▰▰▰▰▰▰▰▰

Animals are provided with nearly all their energy by the oxidation of carbohydrates and fats. Energy is also stored in the body in these two forms. The similarities between these two important foodstuffs are extended to the interrelationships of their metabolic pathways, as will be demonstrated in this chapter.

DIGESTION AND ABSORPTION

Dietary fat is made up largely of triglycerides containing long-chain fatty acids. These are acted upon by enzymes (e.g., lipase from the pancreas) and bile salts in the small intestine and are taken up by the cells of the intestinal mucosa. There the lipids are transformed into particles, *chylomicrons*, which enter the general circulation mostly via the thoracic duct lymph. Almost all of the dietary lipid is normally absorbed.

During digestion the glycerides of the intestine are a mixture of tri-, di- and monoglycerides. About one-half of the fatty acids of dietary lipid is freed during digestion and is absorbed together with the glycerol, of which one-half is still attached to the remaining fatty acids. Pancreatic lipase probably acts slowly on the fatty acid ester bond in the β-position of glycerol.

The long-chain fatty acids (more than 14 C atoms) of both the saturated and unsaturated variety are found in the lymph draining the small intestine and are carried via the thoracic duct to the general

298

circulation. Fatty acids with smaller chain lengths tend to be absorbed into the circulation directly via the portal vein blood.

The distribution of fatty acids found in thoracic duct lymph during fat digestion as well as the composition of chylomicrons is shown in the following:

Lymph Fatty Acid Distribution (%)		Composition of Chylomicrons (%)	
Glyceride	82	Neutral lipids	86
Phospholipid	10	Cholesterol	3
Cholesterol esters	2	Phospholipid	8.5
Nonesterified fatty acids	6	Protein	2
		Carbohydrate	+

Dietary glycerides containing long-chain fatty acids are transported in the thoracic duct lymph in the form of the chylomicrons (low-density lipoproteins), entering the circulation via the jugular vein and, after a meal high in lipid, giving rise to the turbidity of plasma. Injection into the circulation of blood collected from another animal which had been previously injected with heparin results in a rapid clearing of the postalimentary lipemia. This is caused by the presence of an enzyme released by the injection of heparin, and called the "clearing factor." This enzyme is present in blood during postalimentary hyperlipemia in man and rat, and is probably identical with a tissue enzyme, *lipoprotein lipase*. The latter is widely distributed in tissues but is not present in liver. Its action on chylomicrons is to split the lipid to di- and monoglycerides, which are then taken up by the liver, where the components are resynthesized into fat.

NONESTERIFIED FATTY ACIDS IN BLOOD (NEFA)

These free fatty acids are believed to play a role in the transport of fat from the depots to various tissues for oxidation. Some of these fatty acids are removed by the liver to reappear in the circulation as lipid. Injected labeled fatty acids disappear from the blood in man at the rate of 30 per cent per minute. During fasting some of the plasma Nefa arises from depot fat, whereas after glucose and insulin administration the movement of depot fatty acids to blood Nefa decreases. The mechanism of this movement is not clear. Plasma Nefa includes oleic, palmitic, stearic and linoleic acids to the extent of 80 per cent of the total, and these are firmly bound to serum albumin and the lipoproteins.

Glycerides are stored in the body largely as adipose tissue, representing the major storage of energy in higher mammals. Most of the adipose tissue lipid is in the form of triglycerides. Schoenheimer and Rittenberg were the first to show that adipose tissue fat was in a state of dynamic equilibrium; it is constantly renewed. When mice were fed "heavy" water (D_2O) the fatty acids of adipose tissue were rapidly labeled with the isotope. The half-life of the total fatty acids of mice was found to be 2 to 3 days. By use of C^{14}-labeled acetate it has been demonstrated that rat carcass fatty acids have a half-life of 16 to 17 days, the unsaturated ones being synthesized slightly slower than the saturated acids. The fatty acids of rat liver had a half-life of 1 to 2 days.

LIPOLYTIC ENZYMES

Table 39 summarizes the important enzymes involved in the hydrolysis of lipids.

TABLE **39.**   CLASSIFICATION OF LIPOLYTIC ENZYMES

Lipid	Enzyme	Common Substrate	End-Products
Glycerides	Lipase	Triolein	Fatty acids + glycerol
	Clearing factor	Protein-bound neutral fat	Fatty acids + glycerol
Phosphatides	Phosphatidase A	Lecithin	Fatty acid (1 mole) + lyso-lecithin
	Phosphatidase B (Lyso-phosphatidase)	Lysolecithin	Fatty acid (1 mole) + glyc-erylphosphorylcholine
	Phosphatidase C	Lecithin	Phosphatidic acid + choline
	Phosphatidase D	Lecithin	Diglyceride + phosphoryl-choline
Cerebrosides	Cerebrosidase (Galac-tosidase)	Cerebroside	N-acylsphingosine + galac-tose
Sterol esters	Cholesterol esterase	Cholesterol esters	Cholesterol + fatty acid
Vitamin A esters	Vitamin A esterase	Vitamin A acetate	Vitamin A + acetic acid

From Kates, in Lipide Metabolism, edited by Bloch. J. Wiley and Sons, 1960.

FATTY ACID OXIDATION

KNOOP'S "β-OXIDATION" THEORY

In 1904, Knoop performed the first experiment of tagging a compound in order to determine its metabolic fate in the animal body. In those pre-isotope days, he used the phenyl group as a "label," since the animal organism cannot degrade it easily and it therefore remains attached to the compound which is finally eliminated. In a study of the fate of fatty acids, he prepared a homologous series of phenyl fatty acid derivatives, which he fed to the animal, and he isolated the phenyl-labeled compounds in the urine. The simplest phenylated acid is benzoic, which is eliminated in the form of hippuric acid after combination with glycine. The next higher derivative, phenylacetic acid, is eliminated as the corresponding glycine derivative, phenylaceturic acid:

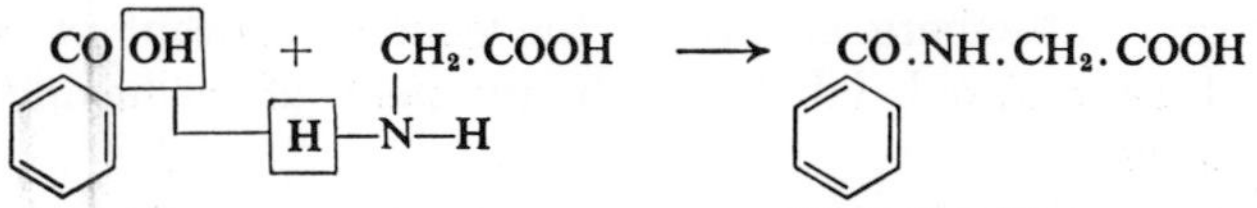

$$CO\boxed{OH} \quad + \quad CH_2.COOH \quad \longrightarrow \quad CO.NH.CH_2.COOH$$

$$\boxed{H}{-}N{-}H \tag{1}$$

Hippuric acid

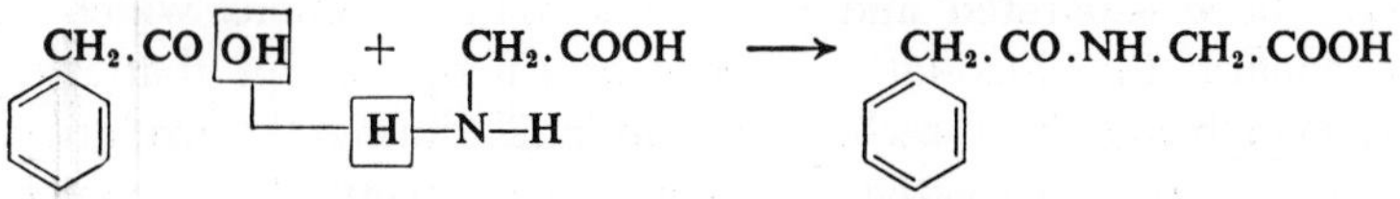

$$CH_2.CO\boxed{OH} \quad + \quad CH_2.COOH \quad \longrightarrow \quad CH_2.CO.NH.CH_2.COOH$$

$$\boxed{H}{-}N{-}H \tag{2}$$

Phenylaceturic acid

With higher fatty acids, the products isolated were either hippuric acid (1) or phenylaceturic acid (2). For example,

> $C_6H_5.CH_2.CH_2.COOH$ yields (1)
> $C_6H_5.CH_2.CH_2.CH_2.COOH$ yields (2)
> $C_6H_5.CH_2.CH_2.CH_2.CH_2.COOH$ yields (1)
> $C_6H_5.CH_2.CH_2.CH_2.CH_2.CH_2.COOH$ yields (2); etc.

From the results he drew the conclusion that oxidation of fatty acids occurred in such a way that at each stage in the degradation process there was a loss of two carbon atoms, due to oxidation at the β-carbon atom. For example,

$$C_6H_5.\overset{\beta}{C}H_2.\overset{\alpha}{C}H_2.COOH \quad \longrightarrow \quad C_6H_5COOH$$

$$C_6H_5.CH_2.\overset{\beta}{C}H_2.\overset{\alpha}{C}H_2.COOH \quad \longrightarrow \quad C_6H_5CH_2COOH$$

$$C_6H_5.CH_2.CH_2.\overset{\beta}{C}H_2.\overset{\alpha}{C}H._2COOH$$

$$\downarrow$$

$$C_6H_5.\overset{\beta}{C}H_2.\overset{\alpha}{C}H_2.COOH$$

$$\downarrow$$

$$C_6H_5.COOH$$

Knoop was of the opinion that acetic acid was split off at each stage of the process, though neither he nor others were able to isolate this acid:

$$\ldots\ CH_2.CH_2.CH_2.\overset{\beta}{C}H_2.\overset{\alpha}{C}H_2.COOH$$

$$\downarrow$$

$$\ldots\ CH_2.CH_2.CH_2.CO \vdots CH_2.COOH$$

$$+\ HO \vdots H$$

$$\downarrow$$

$$\ldots\ CH_2.\overset{\beta}{C}H_2.\overset{\alpha}{C}H_2.COOH + CH_3COOH$$

$$\downarrow$$

$$\ldots\ CH_2.CO. \vdots CH_2.COOH$$

$$HO \vdots H$$

$$\downarrow$$

$$\ldots\ CH_2.COOH + CH_3COOH$$

Schoenheimer and Rittenberg confirmed the general concept of β-oxidation when they isolated labeled palmitic acid after having fed deuterostearic acid.

In recent years the enzymes responsible for the oxidation of fatty acids have been separated and purified and the reactions which they catalyze confirm the β-oxidation theory of Knoop, except that instead of acetic acid being the 2-carbon unit split off during the oxidation, it is the coenzyme A derivative of acetic acid, acetyl CoA, which is formed. Indeed, the secret to the entire series of steps in fatty acid oxidation lies in the very first reaction in which the fatty acid molecule is "activated" by forming a CoA derivative. Since acetyl CoA is formed during fatty acid oxidation, the complete oxidation of this compound would take place via the Krebs cycle. The individual reactions involved follow:

1. Thiokinase. There are three separate enzymes: (a) acetic thiokinase, acting on acetic and propionic acids, (b) fatty acid thiokinase, acting on fatty acids with from 4 to 12 C atoms and on branch-chain acids, phenyl-substituted acids, α,β- or β,γ-unsaturated and β-hydroxylated acids, and (c) long-chain fatty acid thiokinase. The reaction proceeds as follows:

$$R.CH_2.CH_2.COO^- + ATP^- + CoA.SH \xrightarrow{Mg^{++}}$$

$$R.CH_2.CH_2.CO.S.CoA + AMP^- + PP_i^-$$

in which CoA.SH is an abbreviated version of coenzyme A showing its reactive sulfhydryl group, and PP_i is the symbol for inorganic pyrophosphate which is split off from ATP.

2. Acyl Dehydrogenase. Mitochondria, which are the site of fatty acid oxidation in the cell, have two and, in some cases, three flavoprotein enzymes which act in the second step of fatty acid oxidation. These are:

> G(green flavoprotein) = acts on C-4 to C-8 acids
> Y(yellow flavoprotein) = acts mostly on C-8 to C-12 acids
> Y'(yellow flavoprotein) = most active on C-8 to C-18 acids

The reaction catalyzed by these enzymes is:

$$R.CH_2.CH_2.CO.S.CoA + \text{flavoprotein enzyme} \longrightarrow$$

$$R.CH{=}CH.CO.S.CoA + \text{reduced flavoprotein}$$

3. Enol Hydrase. This enzyme acts on all α,β-unsaturated acyl CoA esters from C-4 to C-18, forming the corresponding β-hydroxy compound:

$$R.CH{=}CH.CO.S.CoA + H_2O \rightleftharpoons R.CHOH.CH_2.CO.S.CoA$$

4. β-Hydroxyacyl Dehydrogenase. This enzyme is highly specific for DPN and the chain length is not important. The corresponding β-keto derivative is formed:

$$R.CHOH.CH_2.CO.S.CoA + DPN^+ \rightleftharpoons R.CO.CH_2.CO.S.CoA + DPNH + H^+$$

5. β-Ketoacyl Thiolase. In this reaction a thiolytic cleavage occurs in which the SH group of coenzyme A displaces the $-CH_2.CO.S.CoA$ moiety. The enzyme acts on esters with 4 to 18 C atoms:

$$R.CO.CH_2.CO.S.CoA + CoA.SH \rightleftharpoons R.CO.S.CoA + CH_3.CO.S.CoA$$

The new fatty acyl CoA, two carbon atoms shorter than before, can now be degraded further by a repetition of the five reaction steps, releasing acetyl coenzyme A at the end of each sequence. The over-all conversion of a fatty acid to acetyl CoA can be stated as follows:

$$CH_3(CH_2)_nCOOH + ATP + \frac{n+2}{2}CoA.SH + \frac{n}{2}H_2O \longrightarrow$$

$$\frac{n+2}{2}CH_3CO.S.CoA + 2nH + AMP + PP_i$$

OXIDATION OF FATTY ACIDS WITH AN ODD NUMBER OF CARBON ATOMS

The enzymes which can completely oxidize the naturally occurring fatty acids, containing mostly an even number of carbon atoms, will also oxidize fatty acids with an odd number of carbon atoms. These acids yield acetyl CoA together with propionyl CoA. Liver and kidney mitochondria oxidize propionyl CoA to CO_2 and H_2O by the following mechanism:

$$CH_3.CH_2.CO.S.CoA + CO_2 + ATP \underset{\text{Mg}^{++}}{\overset{\text{biotin}}{\rightleftharpoons}} CH_3.CH(COOH).CO.S.CoA$$
$$\text{methylmalonyl CoA}$$

$$CH_3.CH(COOH).CO.S.CoA \overset{B_{12}\text{ coenzyme}}{\rightleftharpoons} COOH.CH_2.CH_2.CO.S.CoA$$
$$\text{succinyl CoA}$$

Succinyl CoA can then be oxidized via succinate and the Krebs cycle to CO_2 and water. Heart mitochondria cannot oxidize propionyl CoA. The involvement of biotin in the CO_2 fixation reaction is a clear example of the function of this vitamin as a coenzyme. The B_{12} coenzyme active in the second reaction is dimethylbenzimidazole B_{12} and illustrates the coenzyme activity of this vitamin.

ACETOACETATE FORMATION

The plasma of normal individuals contains "ketone" ("acetone") bodies in small amounts. The amount of these compounds, which include acetoacetic acid, β-hydroxybutyric acid and acetone, varies from 0.2 to 0.7 mg. per 100 ml. of blood. Under abnormal conditions—during fasting or in the case of diabetes—these values increase considerably. In order to explain these findings the suggestion was made that during the oxidation of fatty acids the terminal 4-carbon residue was released to the circulation before its oxidation could be completed and, there-fore, acetoacetic acid and its two companion acetone bodies would appear in the blood. However, careful studies with liver showed that more than one mole of acetoacetate was formed per mole of fatty acid oxidized. Liver mitochondria accumulate acetoacetate during fatty acid oxidation, whereas other animal tissues do not. This may be accounted for as follows:

1. Acetoacetyl CoA, which would normally be oxidized further, is condensed with acetyl CoA by the action of enzymes:

a. $CH_3.CO.CH_2.CO.S.CoA + CH_3.CO.S.CoA \longrightarrow$

$$CH_3.\underset{|}{C}(OH).CH_2.COOH + CoA.SH$$
$$CH_2.CO.S.CoA$$

β-hydroxy-β-methylglutaryl CoA

b. $CH_3.\underset{|}{C}(OH).CH_2.COOH \longrightarrow CH_3.CO.CH_2.COOH + CH_3.CO.S.CoA$

$CH_2.CO.S.CoA$

The over-all effect is the conversion of acetoacetyl CoA to acetoacetate.

2. The absence, in liver, of a thiokinase which would normally convert acetoacetate to acetoacetyl CoA.

In the normal animal, the small quantities of acetoacetate which are formed in the liver and released to the circulation are converted to the CoA derivative in other tissues and oxidized completely. During fasting, the low level of glycogen in the liver leads to an accelerated oxidation of fatty acids for purposes of energy production, and a consequent in-crease in ketone bodies. (The situation in diabetes is discussed later.)

The following scheme for the liver serves to summarize the facts and to show the relationship between carbohydrate and fat oxidation, as well as the position occupied by the ketone bodies:

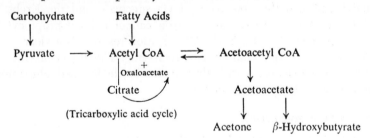

FATTY ACID SYNTHESIS

The synthesis of fatty acids by a reversal of the oxidative pathway would appear to be possible except for the unfavorable K_{eq}. of the thiolase reaction (1.7×10^4), which greatly favors the breakdown of $R.CO.CH_2.CO.S.CoA$ to $R.CO.S.CoA$ and $CH_3.CO.S.CoA$. However, dietary carbohydrate gives rise to tissue fat and labeled acetate is incorporated into fatty acids in the body. Three systems are known which are capable of carrying out the synthesis of fatty acids:

1. *Clostridium kluyverii,* an obligate anaerobe, converts ethyl alcohol to caproic acid and butyric acid. The reaction sequence is:

a. $CH_3.CH_2.OH + DPN^+ \rightleftharpoons CH_3.CHO + DPNH + H^+$

b. $CH_3.CHO + DPN^+ + CoA.SH \rightleftharpoons CH_3.CO.S.CoA + DPNH + H^+$

c. $2\ CH_3.CO.S.CoA \rightleftharpoons CH_3.CO.CH_2.CO.S.CoA + CoA.SH$

d. $CH_3.CO.CH_2.CO.S.CoA + DPNH + H^+ \rightleftharpoons$

$$CH_3.CHOH.CH_2.CO.S.CoA + DPN^+$$
β-hydroxybutyryl CoA

e. $CH_3.CHOH.CH_2.CO.S.CoA \rightleftharpoons CH_3.CH{=}CH.CO.S.CoA + H_2O$

f. $CH_3.CH{=}CH.CO.S.CoA + DPNH + H^+ \rightleftharpoons$

$$CH_3.CH_2.CH_2.CO.S.CoA + DPN^+$$
butyryl CoA

2. *A mitochondrial system* which contains thiolase, β-hydroxyacyl-dehydrogenase, enoyl hydrase, enoyl reductase and TPNH. The reactions are:

$$\text{acetyl CoA + butyryl CoA} \longrightarrow \text{caproyl CoA + CoA}$$
$$\text{acetyl CoA + caproyl CoA} \longrightarrow \text{octanoyl CoA + CoA}$$

3. *A soluble (nonmitochondrial) system* from pigeon liver has been prepared which converts acetyl CoA to a mixture of fatty acids with 12, 14 and 16 carbon atoms in which those with 16 carbon atoms predominate. It requires ATP, biotin, Mg^{++} and TPNH. Malonyl CoA is an intermediate and condenses with acetyl CoA to increase the chain length. Following is the sequence of reactions suggested by the studies of Wakil and Lynen:

a. $ATP + CO_2 + CH_3.CO.S.CoA \xrightarrow{\text{biotin, } Mg^{++}}$

$$ADP + P_i + HOOC.CH_2.CO.S.CoA$$
malonyl CoA

b. $CH_3.CO.S.CoA + HOOC.CH_2.CO.S.CoA \longrightarrow$

$$CH_3.CO.CH(COOH).CO.S.CoA$$
acetylmalonyl CoA

c. $CH_3.CO.CH(COOH).CO.S.CoA \xrightarrow{\text{TPNH}} CH_3.CHOH.CH(COOH).CO.S.CoA$

d. $CH_3.CHOH.CH(COOH).CO.S.CoA \xrightarrow{-H_2O} CH_3.CH{=}C(COOH).CO.S.CoA$

e. $CH_3.CH{=}C(COOH).CO.S.CoA \xrightarrow{\text{TPNH}} CH_3.CH_2.CH(COOH).CO.S.CoA$

f. $CH_3.CH_2.CH(COOH).CO.S.CoA \xrightarrow{-CO_2} CH_3.CH_2.CH_2.CO.S.CoA$, etc.

The role of biotin in CO_2 fixation involves the formation of a complex between the two compounds (which Lynen has isolated). The CO_2 is attached to the ureido group of biotin:

$$
\begin{array}{c}
O \\
\parallel \\
C \\
\end{array}
$$

HN   N—C
HC——CH   O⁻
H₂C   CH.(CH₂)₄.COOH
    S

The series of reactions written above may be summarized for the synthesis of palmitic acid from acetyl CoA as follows:

8 Acetyl CoA + 8 ATP + 16 TPNH $\longrightarrow$

$C_{15}H_{31}COOH$ + 16 TPN⁺ + 16 H⁺ + 8 ADP + 8 P_i + 8 CoA.SH

The need for TPNH in fatty acid synthesis is of interest when one considers the sources of enzyme reactions which are capable of reducing TPN to TPNH. The hexosemonophosphate shunt pathway is an important source for TPNH.

UNSATURATED FATTY ACIDS

Burr showed many years ago that unsaturated fatty acids are essential components of the diet; these are often considered under vitamins. More recently the unsaturated fatty acids have been related to the level of cholesterol in blood. That some unsaturated fatty acids could be formed from their saturated counterparts was shown by Schoenheimer and Rittenberg, who fed the methyl esters of fatty acids which had been obtained from linseed oil after hydrogenation with deuterium (D_2). Unsaturated acids isolated some 7 to 12 days later contained deuterium. Stetten and Schoenheimer prepared deutero-palmitic acid biosynthetically and were able to isolate labeled palmito-leic acid. Later studies with improved techniques have shown that the polyunsaturated acids are not labeled in similar experiments.

Linoleic and linolenic acids cannot be formed in the animal body, whereas arachidonic acid, although not present in the plasma, is a general constituent of animals. If carboxyl-labeled (C^{14}) acetate is given to rats, linoleic acid isolated from the organs and fat depots shows practically no C^{14}, whereas arachidonic acid has considerable radioactivity. Linoleic acid is therefore not formed to an appreciable extent in the animal, while arachidonic acid is synthesized by addition of acetate to an 18-carbon exogenous precursor; since the arachidonic acid had all of its activity essentially in the carboxyl carbon. If carboxyl-labeled linoleic acid is administered one obtains the following distribution of C^{14} (expressed as per cent of the total) in the isolated arachidonic acid:

$$C_{17}H_{35}.CH_2.CH_2.COOH$$

$$\uparrow \quad \uparrow \quad \uparrow \quad \uparrow$$
$$0 \quad 24.5 \quad 0.7 \quad 74.7$$

These results suggest that linoleic acid is incorporated into arachidonic acid unchanged. A possible mechanism for the conversion has been suggested:

$$CH_3.(CH_2)_4.CH{=}CH.CH_2.CH{=}CH.(CH_2)_7.COOH \qquad\qquad \text{Linoleic acid}$$

$$\downarrow$$

$$CH_3.(CH_2)_4.CH{=}CH.CH_2.CH{=}CH.CH_2.CH{=}CH.(CH_2)_4.COOH$$
$$\text{γ-Linolenic acid}$$

$$\downarrow$$

$$CH_3.(CH_2)_4.CH{=}CH.CH_2.CH{=}CH.CH_2.CH{=}CH.(CH_2)_6.COOH$$
$$\text{homo-γ-linolenic acid}$$

$$\downarrow$$

$$CH_3.(CH_2)_4.CH{=}CH.CH_2.CH{=}CH.CH_2.CH{=}CH.CH_2.CH{=}CH.(CH_2)_3.COOH$$
$$\text{Arachidonic acid}$$

If one examines the oleic acid of organ and depot fat of an animal which had been given acetate-1-C^{14} it is found to be labeled. Also, another polyunsaturated acid, 5,8,11-eicosatrienoic acid, is quite radio-active. Examination of the distribution of C^{14} in these two compounds shows the following:

$$\overbrace{}^{39.1} \qquad\qquad \overbrace{}^{60.9}$$

Oleic acid $CH_3.$ $(CH_2)_7.$ $CH{=}CH.$ $(CH_2)_7.$ $COOH$

$$\underbrace{}_{77.9} \qquad\qquad \underbrace{}_{22.1}$$

5,8,11-eicosa-trienoic acid

$$\overbrace{}^{12.8} \qquad\qquad \overbrace{}^{22.9}$$

$$CH_3.(CH_2)_7.CH{=}CH.CH_2.CH{=}CH.CH_2.CH{=}CH.CH_2.CH_2.CH_2.COOH$$

$$\underbrace{}_{27.5} \qquad\qquad \underset{8.2 \;\; 1.8 \;\; 62.5}{\uparrow \;\; \uparrow \;\; \uparrow}$$

It can be seen that the ratio of activity of the 3rd through the 11th carbon atoms of eicosatrienoic acid to that of the remaining 9 carbon atoms at the methyl end of the chain ($22.9/12.8 = 1.8$) is approximately the same as that of the two halves of oleic acid ($60.9/39.1 = 1.6$). Similarly if one compares the ratio of C-3 of eicosatrienoic acid to C-4 through C-20 ($8.2/27.5 = 0.3$) one gets a value similar to that of the ratio of the carboxyl group of oleic acid to the remainder of the chain ($22.1/77.9 = 0.28$). These results strongly suggest that oleic acid is the precursor for eicosatrienoic acid, possibly as follows:

$$CH_3.(CH_2)_7.CH{=}CH.(CH_2)_7.COOH \qquad\qquad \text{Oleic acid}$$

$$\downarrow$$

$$CH_3.(CH_2)_7.CH{=}CH.CH_2.CH{=}CH.(CH_2)_4.COOH$$

$$\downarrow$$

$$CH_3.(CH_2)_7.CH{=}CH.CH_2.CH{=}CH.(CH_2)_6.COOH$$

$$\downarrow$$

$$CH_3.(CH_2)_7.CH{=}CH.CH_2.CH{=}CH.CH_2.CH{=}CH.(CH_2)_3.COOH$$
$$\text{Eicosatrienoic acid}$$

There appear to be three classes of polyunsaturated acids which are not readily interconvertible, since additional double bonds get added, not at the methyl end, but rather at the carboxyl end of the molecule. These are:

a. Linoleic acid-derived with a $CH_3.(CH_2)_4$-terminal grouping; these constitute the principal essential fatty acids.

b. Linolenic acid-derived with a $CH_3.CH_2.$-end, which appear to promote growth but do not behave as essential fatty acids.

c. Oleic acid-derived with the $CH_3.(CH_2)_7$-ending, which are found only in appreciable amounts in fat-deficient animals.

TRIGLYCERIDE SYNTHESIS

Since glycerol can be converted to glucose, one might suggest that a reversal of these reactions would give rise to glycerol which is needed for triglyceride synthesis. Indeed, glycerol may arise from glucose during glycolysis—from dihydroxyacetone phosphate. Enzymes are known which will convert dihydroxyacetone phosphate to L-α-glycerophosphate, which on hydrolysis will give rise to glycerol. It is more likely, however, that L-α-glycerophosphate is used for triglyceride synthesis although glycerol itself can be phosphorylated in the presence of ATP and an enzyme to form the glycerophosphate. These reactions may be illustrated as follows:

1. glucose $\dashrightarrow$ dihydroxyacetone phosphate

2. dihydroxyacetone phosphate $\xrightarrow{\text{DPNH}}$ L-α-glycerophosphate
   or
2a. glycerol + ATP $\longrightarrow$ L-α-glycerophosphate + ADP

L-α-glycerophosphate can be converted by the liver to L-α-phosphatidic acid, a compound which is important in phosphatide synthesis. The insertion of the two fatty acid molecules into L-α-glycerophosphate requires that the fatty acids be present in the form of their activated CoA derivatives. This can be accomplished in the following way:

3a. fatty acid + ATP $\longrightarrow$ fatty acyl adenylate + PP_i
3b. fatty acyl adenylate + CoA $\longrightarrow$ fatty acyl CoA + AMP

Liver also contains an enzyme which synthesizes phosphatidic acid:

4. L-α-glycerophosphate + 2 fatty acyl CoA $\longrightarrow$

L-α-phosphatidic acid + 2 CoA

An enzyme in liver, phosphatidic acid phosphatase, acts to split the phosphate group, giving rise to a diglyceride:

5. L-α-phosphatidic acid $\longrightarrow$ D-α,β-diglyceride + P_i

It is of some interest that D-α,β-diglyceride is a precursor both of phosphatides and of triglyceride. The exact manner in which the diglyceride is converted to a triglyceride is not clear, although its reaction with another molecule of fatty acyl CoA is likely:

6.   D-α,β-diglyceride + fatty acyl CoA $\longrightarrow$ triglyceride + CoA

HORMONES AND FATTY ACID METABOLISM

Although we do not know as yet how any hormone affects metabolic reactions on a molecular level, evidence for the action of hormones on lipid metabolism is abundant. In the following discussion we shall summarize these effects.

INSULIN

Diabetes is associated with alterations in both carbohydrate and fat metabolism, and these are reversed by the administration of insulin. The most important effects of diabetes on fatty acid metabolism are:

1. Increase in plasma Nefa (non-esterified fatty acids).

2. Increase in acetoacetate formation from long-chain fatty acids.

3. Decrease in fatty acid synthesis from glucose, acetate or pyruvate by liver, adipose tissue and mammary gland.

4. Increase in fatty acid oxidation to acetoacetate and CO_2.

The administration of insulin is accompanied by an increased rate of fatty acid synthesis, a decrease in fatty acid oxidation and a decrease in the rate of release of Nefa from adipose tissue.

Fatty acids are transported from adipose tissue to other tissues such as liver in the form of complexes with serum albumin and used by such tissues as a major energy source. After insulin, the fall of plasma Nefa levels results from a decreased rate of release of adipose tissue fatty acids, whereas the rate of utilization of fatty acids by other tissues is not affected. The mechanism for this action is not known.

The conversion of carbohydrate to fatty acids by the normal animal is almost abolished in diabetes. The effect of diabetes on fatty acid synthesis is probably indirect and due to a deficiency in TPNH, which is needed for the synthesis of fatty acids (p. 306). TPNH is generated by the action of the enzymes glucose-6-phosphate dehydrogenase and 6-phosphogluconic dehydrogenase during the pentose phosphate pathway of glucose oxidation (see p. 280). In diabetes there appears to be a marked inhibition in the fraction of glucose oxidized by this pathway in the liver, resulting in a decreased formation of TPNH, and thus limiting the rate of lipogenesis in the diabetic animal.

The accumulation of ketone bodies in the diabetic is due to hepatic production exceeding the capacity of the peripheral tissues to oxidize them. In some way, the curtailment of available carbohydrate results in an overproduction of acetoacetate because of an increase in fatty acid oxidation. This is illustrated in Table 40.

In similar experiments, the administration of short-chain fatty acids

TABLE 40.   OXIDATION OF TRIPALMITIN-1-C^{14} BY RAT LIVER SLICES

	Percentage of Incubated C^{14} Recovered as	
	---	---
	CO_2	Acetoacetate Carboxyl Carbon
Normal	1.3	0.34
Diabetic	2.9	1.25
Insulin-treated diabetic	0.75	0.11

(From Langdon, in Lipide Metabolism, edited by Bloch. J. Wiley and Sons, 1960, from data by Lossow, Brown and Chaikoff: J. Biol. Chem., *220:*839, 1956.)

such as 1-C^{14}-octanoic acid resulted in recovery of identical CO_2 and acetoacetate in livers from diabetic as well as from insulin-treated rats. It is therefore the oxidation of long-chain fatty acids rather than of short-chain acids which is affected. The increase in fatty acid oxidation may be associated with the "uncoupling" of oxidative phosphorylation which has been observed in mitochondria prepared from liver of pancreatectomized cats. Restoration of normal P:O ratios after the administration of insulin was observed. The uncoupling of oxidation from phosphorylation, it has been suggested, is due to the liberation by free fatty acids of a latent "ATPase" in the mitochondria.

ANTERIOR PITUITARY HORMONES

Adrenocorticotropic (ACTH), growth, and perhaps *thyrotropic* hormones produce effects on fatty acid metabolism in a way which is independent of their usual target endocrine gland. Many of the effects are similar for the various hormones and may be illustrated for the *growth* hormone:

1. *Fatty Acid Transport.* Administration of the hormone results in an increase in transport of Nefa from depot fat to the liver, leading to a decrease in depot fat and an increase in hepatic triglycerides.

2. *Ketone Bodies.* The *growth* hormone results in an increase in ketone body production by the liver.

3. *Fatty Acid Synthesis.* The hormones decrease the rate of fatty acid synthesis in normal as well as in pancreatectomized-hypophysectomized animals.

4. The *growth* hormone causes an increase in O_2 consumption and heat production with a decrease in respiratory quotient.

EPINEPHRINE

The effects of epinephrine are:

1. Increase in Nefa of plasma associated with a decrease in fat depots and increase in hepatic triglycerides.

2. Decrease in rate of fatty acid synthesis.

3. Increase in rate of fatty acid oxidation.

The similarity in effects caused by epinephrine and the hormones of the anterior pituitary has suggested that epinephrine might act by stimulating the release of ACTH from the pituitary.

PHOSPHATIDES

Study of the synthesis of phosphatides involves the administration of isotopically tagged precursors in an attempt to define the pathways of synthesis of each of the components in these lipids. In addition to glycerol, we must now account for choline, ethanolamine, serine, etc., which make up the remainder of the various phosphatide molecules.

CHOLINE AND FAT METABOLISM

Normally, the liver contains from 4 to 5 per cent of fat. Under certain abnormal conditions, this figure may increase to as much as 30 per cent, which may mean that almost one half of the total weight of the liver is fat. Such a liver is called a "fatty liver," and this fatty infiltration may lead to fibrotic changes characteristic of the liver disease cirrhosis. In animals a fatty liver may be induced in a variety of ways. Best was among the first to produce fatty livers in experimental animals by feeding them a diet low in protein. Lecithin was soon shown to prevent or abolish this derangement of fat metabolism, and choline proved to be the active "lipotropic" principle in lecithin.

Best also demonstrated that animals supplemented with food rich in protein did not develop fatty livers, although the dietary fat was high. On further study it was shown that cystine exaggerated the condition, whereas methionine was "lipotropic" and prevented the infiltration of fat.

The lipotropic action of methionine is based on its ability to provide the methyl groups needed for choline synthesis.

The following scheme shows the manner in which choline is synthesized in the body. It involves the conversion of serine to ethanolamine which is then converted to choline by the addition of methyl groups. The origin of serine will be discussed with the metabolism of amino acids, but one can see that serine can arise in two ways: (a) from carbohydrate via 3-phosphoglyceric acid or (b) from glycine by the addition of one carbon atom derived from formate or formaldehyde in the form of tetrahydrofolic acid (see p. 467). The active methyl group of methionine is utilized for choline synthesis via s-adenosylmethionine in which the S atom of methionine is bound to the ribose of adenosine in the form of a sulfonium bond:

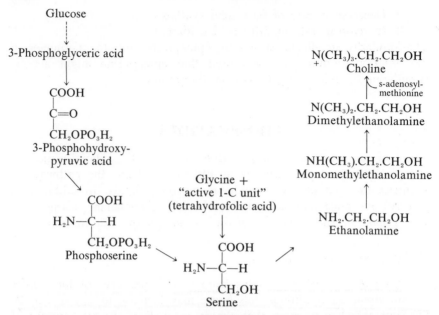

The lipotropic action of choline has usually been interpreted by assuming that fatty acids are carried out from the liver as plasma phospholipids, and that choline acts by enhancing the synthesis of these compounds in the liver. Artom is of the opinion that this lipotropic action of choline may be due to the enhancement of fatty acid oxidation in the liver under the influence of some substances formed from choline.

A compound like betaine can substitute for choline in protecting against fatty liver by being converted in the body to choline.

$$CH_2.COO^-$$
$$|$$
$$N^+(CH_3)_3$$
Betaine

SYNTHESIS OF LECITHIN

Synthesis of this phosphatide involves D-α,β-diglyceride, whose synthesis has been described in a previous section. It also requires choline in the form of a complex with cytidine diphosphate, cytidine diphosphate choline (CDP-choline). This compound is made from choline as follows:

$$\text{choline} + \text{ATP} \longrightarrow \text{ADP} + \text{phosphorylcholine}$$
$$\text{phosphorylcholine} + \text{CTP} \longrightarrow \text{CDP-choline} + \text{PP}_i$$

The choline nucleotide reacts with the diglyceride:

$$\text{CDP-choline} + \text{D-}\alpha,\beta\text{-diglyceride} \longrightarrow \text{L-}\alpha\text{-Lecithin} + \text{CMP}$$

Cytidine triphosphate is regenerated by reaction of CMP with ATP. The formula for CDP-choline is:

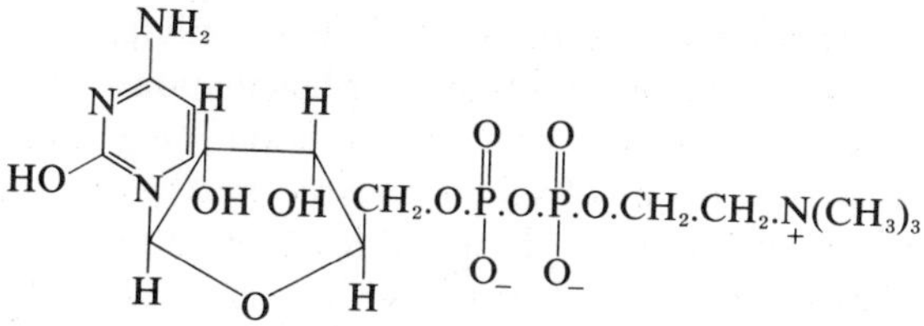

CDP-choline

OTHER PHOSPHATIDES

Little is known concerning the manner of synthesis of phosphatidyl serine. Phosphatidylethanolamine is synthesized in the same manner as lecithin; with the formation of CDP-ethanolamine. Plasmalogen synthesis is stimulated when CTP is added to an incubation mixture suggesting a similar method of synthesis.

SPHINGOMYELIN

Sphingosine originates from the carbon skeleton of the fatty acid, palmitic acid, and the amino acid, serine:

Palmitic acid + ATP + CoA $\longrightarrow$ Palmityl CoA + AMP + PP_i
Palmityl CoA + TPNH + H^+ $\longrightarrow$ Palmitic aldehyde + TPN^+ + CoA
Palmitic aldehyde + Serine $\longrightarrow$ Dihydrosphingosine + CO_2
Dihydrosphingosine + Flavin enzyme $\longrightarrow$ Sphingosine + $Flavin.H_2$ enzyme
Sphingosine + Fatty acyl CoA $\longrightarrow$ N-acyl sphingosine + CoA
(Ceramide)

Sphingomyelin is synthesized from ceramide by reaction with CDP-choline as follows:

N-acyl sphingosine + CDP-choline $\longrightarrow$ Sphingomyelin + CMP

PHOSPHOINOSITIDES

The monophosphoinositides are widespread. It has been suggested that they arise from L-α-phosphatidic acid via a CDP-glyceride.

L-α-phosphatidic acid + CTP $\longrightarrow$ CDP-diglyceride + PP_i
CDP-diglyceride + inositol $\longrightarrow$ inositol phosphatide + CMP

FUNCTIONS OF PHOSPHATIDES

Following are a number of functions with which the phospholipids have been associated:

1. *Structure.* Essential component of the cell membrane. Also constitutes some 70 to 90 per cent of the total lipid of the nuclear, mitochondrial and microsomal fractions of the cell. One-half of the phospholipid is lecithin; 20 to 40 per cent is phosphatidylethanolamine.

2. *Electron Transport.* Treatment of mitochondria with phosphatidase A, known to destroy lecithin, results in the inactivation of the enzymes associated with the Krebs cycle and the electron transport system.

3. Protein Synthesis. Addition of CTP stimulates protein synthesis in special systems whereas addition of phosphatidase A results in its inhibition. Under conditions of protein "secretion" (e.g., pancreatic secretory granules, which are involved in enzyme synthesis) the rate of incorporation of precursors into phosphatides is greatly increased.

4. Ion Transport. Phosphatidyl serine and inositol phosphatide fractions have been isolated from cells with Na^+ and K^+ firmly attached. Lecithin does not bind these ions nor does sphingomyelin. It has been suggested that lecithin is involved in cell permeability.

5. Fat Absorption and Transport. There is an increased phosphatide synthesis associated with fat absorption. Phosphatides are also associated with the plasma lipoproteins.

6. Blood Coagulation. It has been suggested that platelets provide the phosphatides for the formation of thromboplastin.

7. Myelin Components. Sphingomyelin is one of the principal components of the myelin sheath of nerve. Degeneration of a section of peripheral nerve distal to the point of section is associated with a decrease in myelin phosphatides.

8. Atheromatous Deposits. Phosphatides are contained in relatively large amounts in these deposits in the aorta and are formed *in situ* from precursors rather than transported to it.

The pathways used in common for the conversion of glycerol to triglycerides and phospholipids are summarized in the following scheme:

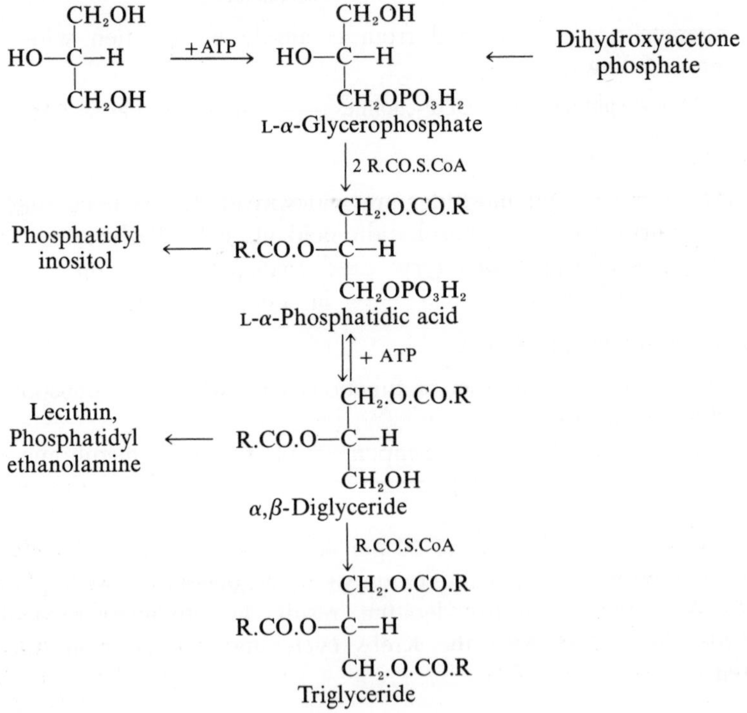

$$
\begin{array}{ccccc}
\text{CH}_2\text{OH} & & \text{CH}_2\text{OH} & & \\
| & & | & & \text{Dihydroxyacetone} \\
\text{HO—C—H} & \xrightarrow{+\text{ATP}} & \text{HO—C—H} & \longleftarrow & \text{phosphate} \\
| & & | & & \\
\text{CH}_2\text{OH} & & \text{CH}_2\text{OPO}_3\text{H}_2 & & \\
& & \text{L-}\alpha\text{-Glycerophosphate} & & \\
\end{array}
$$

L-α-Glycerophosphate   ↓ 2 R.CO.S.CoA

$$
\begin{array}{ccc}
& & \text{CH}_2.\text{O.CO.R} \\
\text{Phosphatidyl} & & | \\
\text{inositol} & \longleftarrow \text{R.CO.O—C—H} \\
& & | \\
& & \text{CH}_2\text{OPO}_3\text{H}_2 \\
& & \text{L-}\alpha\text{-Phosphatidic acid}
\end{array}
$$

↕ + ATP

$$
\begin{array}{ccc}
& & \text{CH}_2.\text{O.CO.R} \\
\text{Lecithin,} & & | \\
\text{Phosphatidyl} & \longleftarrow \text{R.CO.O—C—H} \\
\text{ethanolamine} & & | \\
& & \text{CH}_2\text{OH} \\
& & \alpha,\beta\text{-Diglyceride}
\end{array}
$$

↓ R.CO.S.CoA

$$
\begin{array}{c}
\text{CH}_2.\text{O.CO.R} \\
| \\
\text{R.CO.O—C—H} \\
| \\
\text{CH}_2.\text{O.CO.R} \\
\text{Triglyceride}
\end{array}
$$

BIOSYNTHESIS OF CHOLESTEROL

As early as 1937 Rittenberg and Schoenheimer, using "heavy" water (D_2O), had shown that cholesterol can be synthesized in the animal organism: animals fed D_2O contained deuterium-labeled cholesterol. Later, Bloch and Rittenberg demonstrated that acetate could be incorporated into the cholesterol molecule. It therefore appeared that a molecule as large as cholesterol could be synthesized from small units by condensation reactions.

Bloch and Cornforth have uncovered some of the finer points in this biosynthetic reaction. They fed animals two kinds of C^{14}-labeled acetate, one labeled in the methyl carbon and the other labeled in the carboxyl carbon. Figure 74 shows the results obtained by degradation of the isolated cholesterol and measurement of the radioactivity associated with the carbon atoms of the molecule.

Since acetoacetate is also converted to cholesterol by a pathway which does not include prior cleavage to 2-carbon units, the possibility arose that 4-carbon compounds might lie intermediate between acetate and cholesterol. It was of interest that for cholesterol synthesis isovaleric acid was utilized with greater efficiency than acetate. The relationship of these compounds is shown below:

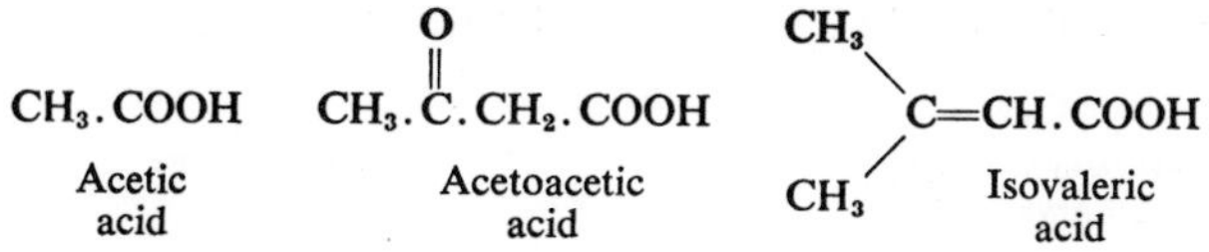

$$CH_3 . COOH \qquad CH_3 . \overset{\overset{\textstyle O}{\|}}{C} . CH_2 . COOH \qquad \overset{\textstyle CH_3}{\underset{\textstyle CH_3}{}}C = CH . COOH$$

| Acetic acid | Acetoacetic acid | Isovaleric acid |

It may be presumed that the 4-carbon intermediate would undergo a type of multiple condensation or polymerization to yield a high molecular weight chain built of isoprene units:

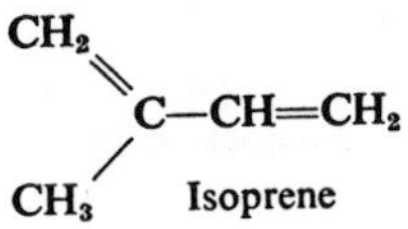

$$\overset{\textstyle CH_2}{\underset{\textstyle CH_3}{}}C—CH = CH_2$$

Isoprene

The search for a polyisoprenoid intermediate yielded a compound in the form of the aliphatic hydrocarbon, squalene. Squalene, hitherto found in shark liver, has been shown to occur in mammalian liver, and labeled squalene is converted to cholesterol. Several of the steps intermediate between acetate and squalene have been clarified. Mevalonic

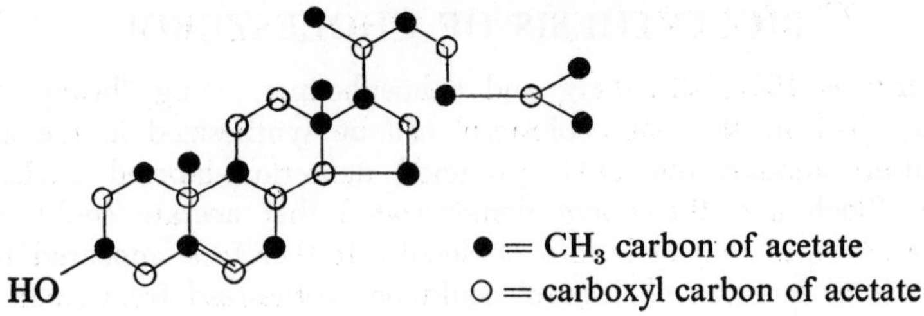

● = CH_3 carbon of acetate
○ = carboxyl carbon of acetate

Figure 74.

acid is readily incorporated into cholesterol. The cyclization of squalene to form the steroid ring system takes place via lanosterol, known to occur in yeast and wool fat and liver. The following is the postulated sequence of reactions:

$$2 \ CH_3.CO.CoA \longrightarrow CH_3.CO.CH_2.CO.CoA \xrightarrow{+ \text{acetyl CoA}}$$

acetyl CoA   acetoacetyl CoA

$$\underset{\overset{|}{CH_3}}{HOOC.CH_2.\overset{\overset{OH}{|}}{C}.CH_2.CO.CoA} \longrightarrow \underset{\overset{|}{CH_3}}{HOOC.CH_2.\overset{\overset{OH}{|}}{C}.CH_2.CH_2.OH} \longrightarrow$$

β-hydroxy-β-methyl-   mevalonic acid
glutaryl CoA

$$\underset{\overset{|}{CH_3}}{HOOC.CH_2.\overset{\overset{OH}{|}}{C}.CH_2.CH_2.O}-\overset{\overset{O}{\|}}{P}-O-\overset{\overset{O}{\|}}{P}-OH \longrightarrow$$

OH   OH

mevalonic acid pyrophosphate

$$\underset{}{CH_3.\overset{\overset{CH_2}{\|}}{C}.CH_2.CH_2.O}-\overset{\overset{O}{\|}}{P}-O-\overset{\overset{O}{\|}}{P}-OH \longrightarrow$$

OH   OH

isopentenyl pyrophosphate

$$\left[\underset{}{CH_3.\overset{\overset{CH_3}{|}}{C}=CH.CH_2} \right]_3 -O-\overset{\overset{O}{\|}}{P}-O-\overset{\overset{O}{\|}}{P}-OH \longrightarrow \text{squalene}$$

OH   OH

farnesyl pyrophosphate

The intermediates between squalene and cholesterol are shown below:

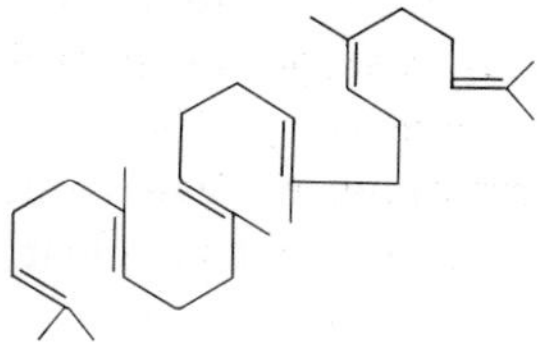

Squalene 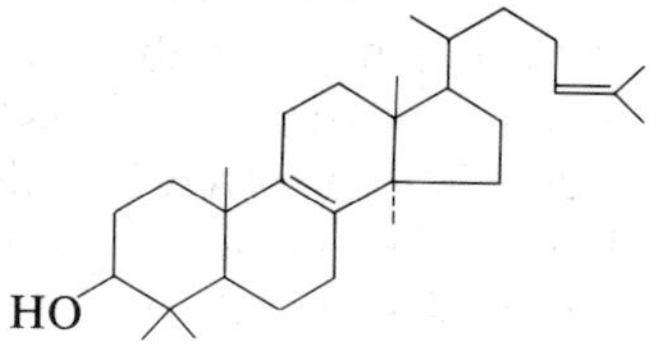   Lanosterol

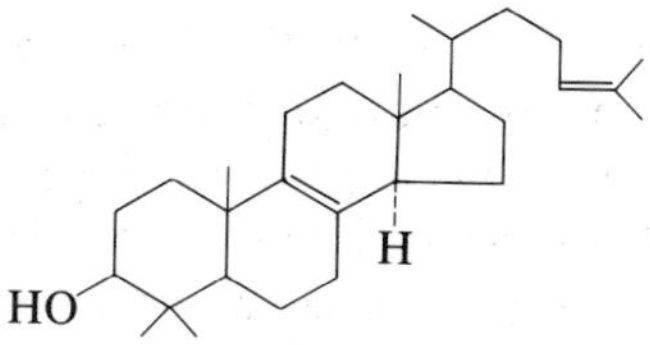

14-Norlanosterol 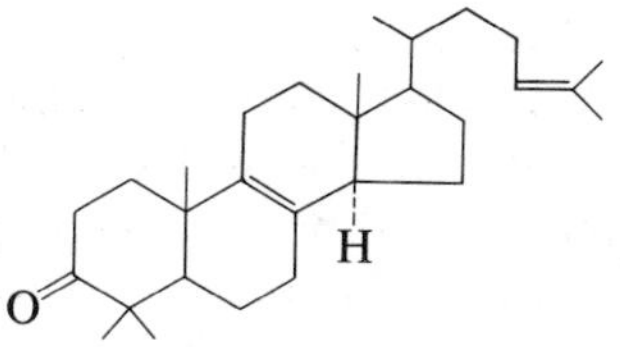   Δ8:24-4,4-dimethyl-cholestadiene-3-one

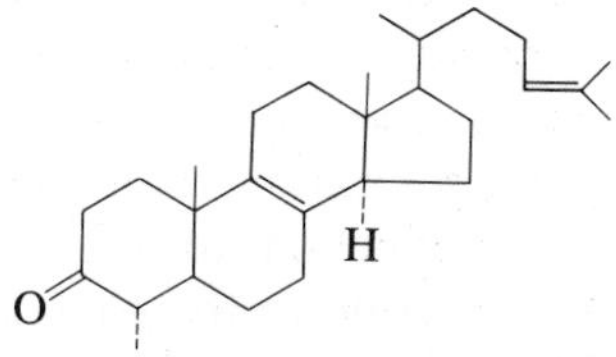

Δ8:24-4α-methyl-cholestadiene-3-one 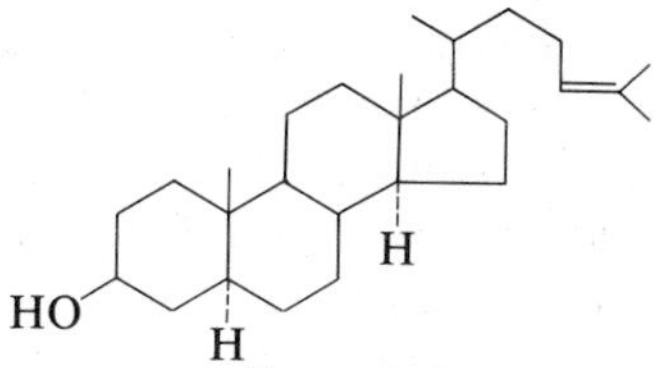   Zymosterol

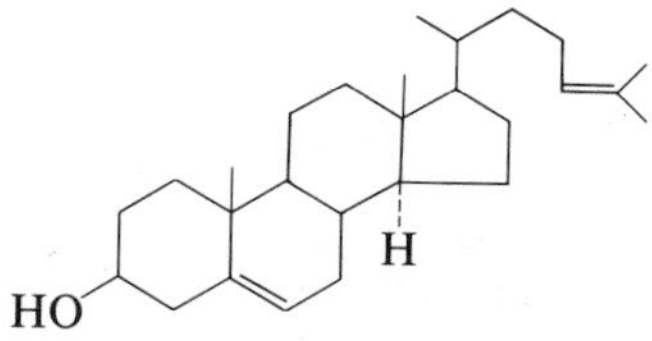

Desmosterol 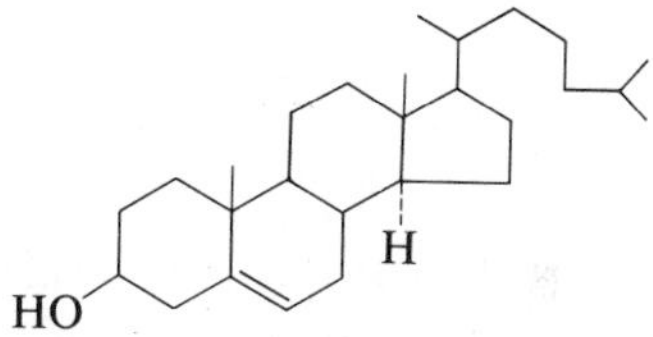   Cholesterol

BILE ACID METABOLISM

The first clear demonstration that cholesterol was the precursor of the bile acids was obtained by Bloch, who showed that labeled cholic acid could be obtained after the administration of deuterium-labeled cholesterol to a dog. This finding was later confirmed with C^{14}-labeled cholesterol. Eighty to 90 per cent of administered cholesterol is ultimately converted to bile acids and the remainder to neutral steroids, which are found in the feces. Among the latter are the two stereoisomeric forms of hydrogenated cholesterol: dihydrocholesterol (cholestanol) and coprosterol (coprostanol) (see page 57 for formulas).

Important in bile acid metabolism are the liver and its enzymes, and the intestinal microorganisms which play an important role in bile acid transformations. Two experimental approaches have been used: (a) action of the liver *in vitro* (slices and homogenates), and (b) direct collection of bile from the animal with a bile fistula. By use of cholesterol and other postulated intermediates labeled with isotopes in specific positions, the transformations involved in bile acid metabolism have been investigated. Although the detailed sequence of reactions is not yet clear, several important conclusions may be listed:

1. The side chain of cholic acid is derived from cholesterol by the direct removal of the 3 terminal carbon atoms.

2. Incubation of rat liver homogenates with $26\text{-}C^{14}$-cholesterol yielded labeled 25-dehydrocholesterol, a steroid aldehyde and acid, suggesting that the oxidation of the side chain of cholesterol proceeds stepwise. In addition, labeled 24-dehydrocholesterol (desmosterol) was also shown to be present. This suggests that this compound may be involved not only in cholesterol synthesis (see p. 317) but also in its conversion to bile acids.

3. Studies with bile-fistula rats demonstrated that the cholesterol nucleus is hydroxylated before oxidation of the side chain is completed. The conversion would therefore involve an epimerization of the hydroxyl group at C-3 from the β- to the α-configuration, saturation of the double bond between C-5 and C-6, and further introduction of α-hydroxyl groups at C-7 and C-12. It is likely that the conversion of the cholesterol 3β-hydroxyl group to the α-variety proceeds via the intermediate formation of a ketone since cholesterol labeled with tritium (T) in its OH group (OT) loses the isotope during its conversion to cholic acid:

TO $\quad\quad\quad\longrightarrow\quad$ O $\quad\quad\quad\longrightarrow\quad$ HO

β-OH $\quad\quad\quad\quad\quad\quad\quad\quad\quad\quad\quad\quad$ α-OH

4. The major bile acids in the rat are cholic acid (80 per cent) and chenodeoxycholic acid. Most of the bile acids in this species are conjugated with taurine, the remainder with glycine. Human gallbladder bile contains cholic, deoxycholic and chenodeoxycholic acids conjugated with glycine and taurine in the ratio of about 3:1 respectively. Deoxycholic acid in man is entirely of microbial origin and cannot be converted to cholic acid by the liver.

An outline of a proposed scheme to show the conversion of cholesterol to the bile acids is presented on the facing page. Human bile also contains traces of lithocholic acid, whose structure corresponds to chenodeoxycholic acid minus the hydroxyl group at C-7.

5. The "pool" size of cholic acid in man is 1.4 g. with a half-life of 2.3 days. Chenodeoxycholic acid accounts for 1.45 g. and deoxycholic for 0.77 g., or a total bile acid pool of 3.6 g. If one subtracts deoxycholic acid because of its microbial origin, it can be estimated that 0.7 g. of cholesterol is degraded daily to bile acids.

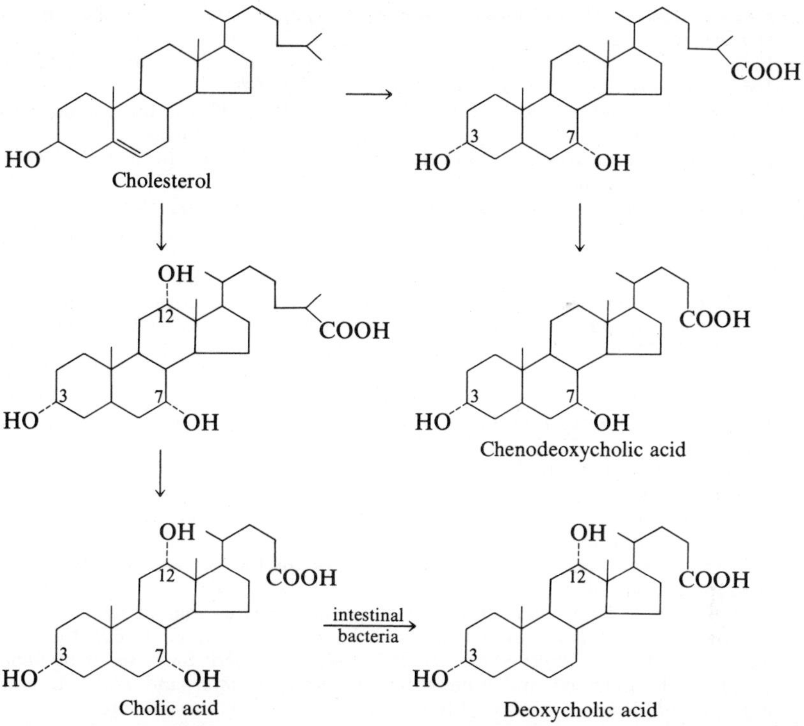

Cholesterol

Chenodeoxycholic acid

Cholic acid

intestinal bacteria

Deoxycholic acid

6. The conjugation of cholic acid with taurine or glycine to form a peptide linkage takes place in the liver microsomes and requires DPN, ATP, Mg^{++} and CoA. The intermediate formation of cholyl CoA has been demonstrated. Conjugated bile acids are not hydrolyzed in the liver but are extensively split by the action of bacteria in the intestine. Normally, free bile acids are found in the feces but if rats are reared in a germ-free environment or given antibiotics they excrete only conjugated bile acids.

REFERENCES

For a general reference, see Lipide Metabolism, edited by Bloch, 1960.

References to fat absorption are by *Frazer:* Nature, *175:*49, 1955. See also Nutr. Rev., *14:*345, 1956; and *Bergström* and *Borgström:* Ann. Rev. Biochem., *25:* 177, 1955.

For the oxidation of fatty acids, see *Green:* Scientific American, Jan., 1954, p. 32; *Green:* Biol. Rev., *29:*330, 1954; *Green:* Clinical Chemistry, *1:*53, 1955; *Gurin:* reprinted from Fat Metabolism, edited by *Najjar,* 1954; *Lehninger:* reprinted from Fat Metabolism, edited by *Najjar.*

See also *Stumpf:* Ann. Rev. Biochem., *29:*261, 1960 (lipid metabolism); *Doisy, Jr., Matschiner* and *Doisy:* Ibid., *28:*259, 1959 (steroids); *Popjak:* Ibid., *27:*533, 1958 (cholesterol biosynthesis); *Kennedy:* Ibid., *26:*119, 1957; *Lynen:* Harvey Lectures, 1952–1953, p. 210 (acetyl coenzyme A and the fatty acid cycle).

Factors involved in the formation and utilization of ketone (or acetone) bodies are discussed by *Weinhouse:* Brookhaven Symposia in Biology No. 5, 1951; *Witter, Cottone* and *Stotz:* J. Biol. Chem., *207:*671, 1954; *Green, Goldman, Mii* and

Reinert: Ibid., *202:*137, 1953; *Brown, Chapman, Matheson, Chaikoff* and *Dauben:* Ibid., *209:*537, 1954; *Stern, Coon* and *Campillo:* Nature, *171:*28, 1953.

The biosynthesis of fatty acids is reviewed by *Artom:* Ann. Rev. Biochem., *22:*212, 1953. See also *Long:* Science Prog., Oct., 1952, p. 671.

Abraham, Chaikoff and *Hassid:* J. Biol. Chem., *195:*567, 1952, are the authors of an article dealing with the conversion of palmitic acid to glucose.

Artom: J. Biol. Chem., *205:*101, 1953 discusses the role of choline in the oxidation of fatty acids by the liver.

For some aspects of the metabolism of lecithin, see *Rodbell* and *Hanahan:* J. Biol. Chem., *214:*595, 607, 1955. See also *Zilversmit:* Ann. Rev. Biochem., *24:*157, 1955.

Bloch's work on cholesterol is summarized up to 1952 in his Harvey Lecture, 1952–1953, p. 68. See also *Langdon* and *Bloch:* J. Biol. Chem., *200:*135, 1953 (squalene); *Woodward* and *Bloch:* J. Am. Chem. Soc., 75:2023, 1953; *Little* and *Bloch:* J. Biol. Chem., *183:*33, 1950 (Acetate → Cholesterol); *Clayton* and *Bloch:* Ibid., *218:*319, 1956 (lanosterol); *Tchen* and *Bloch:* Ibid., *226:*921, 1957 (squalene to lanosterol). See also *Callow* in Annual Reports on the Progress of Chemistry for 1956, p. 307 (biosynthesis of cholesterol); *Blohm* and *MacKenzie:* Arch. Biochem., *85:*245, 1959.

For an excellent review on the biosynthesis of terpenes and sterols, see the *Ciba* Foundation Symposium, 1959.

Bergström and *Borgström:* Ann. Rev. Biochem., *25:*187, 1956, discuss the intermediary metabolism of bile acids.

Oncley: Harvey Lectures, 1954–1955, p. 71, takes up the problem of the lipoproteins of human plasma.

For deranged cholesterol metabolism and its possible relationship to human atherosclerosis, see *Friedman, Rosenman* and *Byers:* J. Gerontol. *10:*60, 1955. See also the Federation Proceedings, *15:*885, 894, 900, 1956, for a series of papers dealing with nutrition and atherosclerosis (*Katz, Stamler* and *Pick; Anfinsen; Stare*); and Research Today (Eli Lilly and Co.), 1953, vol. 9, no. 3.

The biosynthesis of phospholipids is discussed by *Kennedy:* Federation Proceedings, *16:*847, 1957.

For a summary of several mechanisms, see the article on oxidative phosphorylation by *Lehninger:* Federation Proceedings, *19:*952, 1960.

METABOLISM
OF
PROTEINS

The proteins are hydrolyzed in the digestive tract to amino acids. Conjugated proteins give rise to amino acids, but, in addition, produce other substances. For example, casein splits off phosphoric acid; nucleoprotein yields nucleic acid, which hydrolyzes further. But the amino acids are certainly the primary hydrolytic products of the protein molecule.

These amino acids, of which there are some twenty odd, are absorbed through the lumen of the small intestine, pass into the portal system, and thence to the liver. Some of these amino acids proceed to the tissues to form tissue protein; others are utilized for the formation of specific substances (such as glutathione, bile salts, enzymes, and certain hormones); others are deaminated. The deamination—the loss of the amino group—takes place largely in the liver and in the kidney.

As a result of deamination, the amino group, split off as ammonia, contributes to the formation of urea, and the deaminated portion may be oxidized ultimately to carbon dioxide and water; it may form glucose or fatty acid, or it may be resynthesized into an amino acid.

Since the amino acids have, in common, a structure involving the α-amino carboxylic acid, a general reaction for deamination might serve for all of them. The exceptions are the "basic" amino acids with more than one amino group; it is not yet clear whether, in such a case, deamination affects the second amino group.

As a result of these various changes which proteins undergo in the body, not only do we find various end-products of protein catabolism in the urine, but also most of these products first appear in the blood.

These substances include urea, ammonia, creatinine, and amino acids (nonprotein nitrogen, NPN).

The problem of tracing the metabolic fate of ingested food protein may be said to start with the amino acids which after absorption find their way to the liver via the portal vein. One question which deserves further study is the problem of transport of amino acids across the cell membrane, from intestinal lumen to the plasma or from the plasma into the space surrounding the hepatic cell (extracellular fluid). Since the concentration of amino acids in the extracellular fluid is some ten times that inside the cell, transfer of amino acids from the cell against such a concentration gradient requires energy. The nature of such energy is unknown although it is suggested that amino acids need to be combined with some compound before they can be transferred across a cell wall. Pyridoxal, one of the B vitamins, has been implicated as such a compound which can form an amino acid complex and thus penetrate the cell wall against a concentration gradient, being set free after such transfer.

There is some evidence that occasionally small quantities of undigested protein may be absorbed directly into the blood stream. In one experiment a group of guinea pigs were made sensitive by the injection of milk, so that when they were subsequently given milk by mouth, anaphylactic shock resulted in 25 per cent of the animals. This type of experiment may help to explain the sensitivity of certain individuals to specific foods. The ability of some proteins to cross a cell membrane is now accepted as a normal occurrence. As we shall see, much of the plasma proteins is synthesized within the liver cell and passes directly into the plasma. Furthermore, even under normal conditions a small but definite quantity of protein is excreted into the urine.

DYNAMIC STATE OF TISSUE PROTEINS

Of the total nitrogen of the diet, proteins constitute by far the largest proportion. Because of this, the exchange of nitrogen between an animal and its diet may be used as a measure of protein metabolism. On a complete diet, normal animals will excrete an amount of nitrogen equal to their intake; they are in "nitrogen equilibrium" or "nitrogen balance." Positive or negative nitrogen balance results from a shift in equilibrium between the reactions of degradation and synthesis of tissue protein. During starvation an animal goes into negative nitrogen balance, and when fed after such a period, the animal is in a state of positive nitrogen balance for some time.

The earliest concept of protein metabolism was that of Folin, who conceived of two independent fates for ingested protein: one, called *endogenous* metabolism, which utilized the amino acids of ingested protein for the repair and rebuilding of degraded tissue protein; the other, *exogenous* metabolism, which involved an oxidative degradation of dietary amino acids not needed for tissue protein synthesis. He was able to demonstrate that the excretion of urea varied with the dietary intake of protein and was therefore an index of exogenous metabolism, whereas the excretion of creatinine, derived from muscle tissue breakdown, was extremely constant, and was therefore an index of endogenous protein metabolism.

Although the facts are still the same, the first indication that the Folin interpretation was oversimplified came as a result of the classical experiments of Schoenheimer and Rittenberg, who fed to rats in nitrogen equilibrium a diet containing N^{15}-labeled amino acids. The results, in Table 41, showed that although the animals were in no great need of dietary amino acids for the repair of tissue proteins, some 58 per cent of the ingested amino acid nitrogen had been incorporated into the body protein.

TABLE **41.**   BALANCE OF N^{15} AFTER FEEDING N^{15}-LEUCINE

Source of sample	Fraction of N^{15} administered
	(per cent)
Excreta	
Feces	2.1
Urine	27.6
Animal body	
Non-protein N	7.8
Protein N	57.5

(From Schoenheimer, Ratner and Rittenberg: J. Biol. Chem., *130:*703.)

These results were in contradiction with the idea that "excess" dietary proteins would be excreted; rather, the results lent themselves to the view that the nitrogen of the dietary amino acids is constantly being incorporated into the body protein, even at a time when the animal is in nitrogen equilibrium and should not, therefore, demand an extra supply of amino acids for the rebuilding of tissue protein.

Similar results were obtained with other labeled amino acids.

Another experiment involved the N^{15} content of the proteins of the various body tissues (Table 42). Although muscle shows low activity, one must not overlook the fact that it constitutes the largest mass of the animal body, so that it actually represents the highest absolute amount, equivalent to some two thirds of the total nitrogen deposited (one third being represented by the internal organs). The skin is the least active of the tissues.

TABLE 42. DISTRIBUTION OF PROTEINS IN VARIOUS TISSUES OF RATS GIVEN ISOTOPIC LEUCINE

Organ	N^{15} Concentration
	(atom per cent N^{15} excess) *
Plasma	0.108
Red cells	0.019
Liver	0.061
Intestinal wall	0.097
Kidney	0.089
Heart	0.058
Spleen	0.072
Testes	0.050
Skin	0.012
Muscle	0.020
Carcass	0.030

* Glycine containing 10 atoms per cent N^{15} means that the nitrogen of the glycine molecule contains 10 per cent more N^{15} atoms than the normal glycine; or 10.37 per cent of its nitrogen is N^{15}. Valeric acid with 10 atom per cent deuterium means that 10.02 per cent of all of its hydrogen atoms are present as deuterium (D).

In another experiment the proteins of the various tissues were hydrolyzed, and the individual amino acids were isolated for the analysis of N^{15}. Table 43 makes it clear that the labeled nitrogen in the amino acid which was fed was incorporated into all the amino acids isolated, with the notable exception of lysine.

TABLE 43. N^{15} DISTRIBUTION IN PROTEINS FROM RATS FED ISOTOPIC LEUCINE

Protein Constituent	Liver	Intestinal Wall
	(atom per cent excess N^{15})	
Total protein	0.061	0.097
Amide nitrogen	0.051	0.081
Glycine	0.048	0.041
Tyrosine	0.033	0.061
Aspartic acid	0.076	0.150
Glutamic acid	0.121	0.194
Arginine	0.058	0.028
Lysine	0.004	0.005
Leucine	0.518	0.480

Glutamic and aspartic acids are unusual for their high N^{15} content, indicating a rapid incorporation rate. This is also true when, in the place of leucine, other labeled amino acids are given. The amino acids, then, are continually interchanging nitrogen atoms.

In the attempt to explain this interchange of nitrogen, the "transaminase" reaction (p. 328) may be considered. In this reaction "transaminase" enzymes catalyze the reaction of an amino acid with a keto acid whereby an interchange of nitrogen takes place resulting in the

formation of a new keto acid and a new amino acid. Another possibility may be sought for in the "deamination" reaction (p. 326) whereby amino acids are transformed into their corresponding keto acids, and the nitrogen is liberated as ammonia. The ammonia would now contain the N^{15} of the dietary labeled amino acid and could conceivably replace the nitrogen of a protein-bound amino acid. Assuming such a reaction *in vivo*, ammonia itself, as well as any dietary amino acid, should serve as a source of nitrogen.

In an actual experiment, ammonium citrate, labeled with N^{15}, was fed, and the amino acids obtained by hydrolysis of the proteins of tissue were shown to contain the isotope (Table 44).

TABLE 44. N^{15} DISTRIBUTION IN THE PROTEIN CONSTITUENTS OF RATS FED N^{15}-AMMONIUM CITRATE

Protein Constituent	Liver
	(atom per cent N^{15} excess)
Nonprotein nitrogen	0.033
Protein nitrogen	0.022
Amide nitrogen	0.022
Arginine	0.026
Glutamic acid	0.046
Aspartic acid	0.031
Glycine	0.019

(From Rittenberg, Schoenheimer and Keston: J. Biol. Chem., *128:*603.)

Even animals on a diet low in protein—where presumably more body protein is broken down than is replaced by the diet—still continue to incorporate nitrogen from the body pool of ammonia.

The ability of amino acid nitrogen to appear in protein in the form of other amino acids gave rise to another concept—that of the "nitrogen (amino acid) pool." This is illustrated in the following diagram:

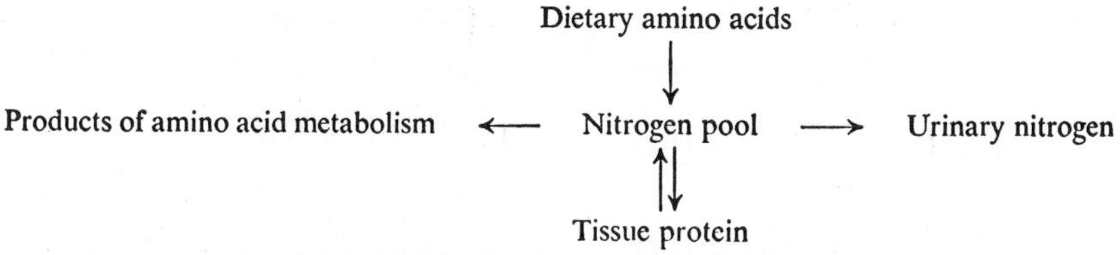

Dietary amino acids
↓

Products of amino acid metabolism ←—— Nitrogen pool ——→ Urinary nitrogen
↑↓

Tissue protein

According to this scheme amino acids which result from tissue degradation become indistinguishable from those which arise from the diet. This pool becomes a central store for amino acids needed for tissue synthesis as well as for the degradation reactions which give rise to a variety of metabolic products. These products vary for each amino acid, and will be studied in greater detail later. During starvation, tissue protein is degraded faster than it can be synthesized, but since the system is in equilibrium, if we then add protein of good quality (see "essential amino acids," p. 422) an increase of tissue protein will result.

We can see that this newer concept is in contradiction, not with the experimental results of Folin, but rather with some of his interpretations. With the introduction of labeled isotopic compounds, one can measure the "turnover rate" of a protein in a particular tissue. This term refers to the percentage of the amount present which is metabolized per unit time. The turnover rates for different tissue proteins vary considerably, from a half-life of 6 days for liver or plasma protein to 180 days for muscle protein to 1000 days for some of the collagen proteins. It is not surprising, in light of the slow turnover rate of muscle protein, that Folin found a constant rate of creatinine excretion; muscle protein would appear to break down irreversibly whereas liver and plasma protein interact rapidly with the nitrogen pool. Some tissue proteins have no "turnover" in the sense of being in dynamic equilibrium with the amino acid pool. Thus the present status appears to be a modified Folin-Schoenheimer concept, with stress on the individuality of the proteins.

METABOLICALLY SIGNIFICANT REACTIONS OF AMINO ACIDS

OXIDATIVE DEAMINATION

In the liver and kidneys are enzymes which are capable of oxidizing amino acids with the production of ammonia. Peculiarly enough, the kidney contains an amino acid oxidase which specifically oxidizes D-amino acids. The D-amino acid oxidase has been purified and shown to contain FAD as a coenzyme. The reaction which it catalyzes takes place in three steps:

$$(1) \quad \underset{\underset{NH_2}{|}}{R.CH.COOH} + O_2 \longrightarrow \underset{\underset{NH}{\parallel}}{R.C.COOH} + H_2O_2$$

$$(2) \quad \underset{\underset{NH}{\parallel}}{R.C.COOH} + H_2O \longrightarrow \underset{\underset{O}{\parallel}}{R.C.COOH} + NH_3$$

$$(3) \quad \underset{\underset{O}{\parallel}}{R.C.COOH} + H_2O_2 \longrightarrow R.COOH + CO_2 + H_2O$$

Only the first of these steps is enzymatic, and evidence for the formation of an imino acid is incomplete. If catalase is present in such a mixture, reaction 3 does not take place and the α-keto acid and ammonia are produced instead.

One L-amino acid oxidase is capable of oxidizing some 13 of the L-amino acids. It requires FMN (riboflavin phosphate) as a coenzyme and functions as follows:

(1) $\underset{\substack{| \\ NH_2 \\ Enz.FMN}}{R.CH.COOH} \xrightarrow[(-2H)]{oxidase} \underset{\substack{\| \\ NH \\ \longrightarrow \quad enz.FMNH_2}}{R.C.COOH}$

(2) $\underset{\substack{\| \\ NH \\ Enz.FMNH_2 + O_2}}{R.CH.COOH} + H_2O \xrightarrow{(non-enzymatic)} \underset{\substack{\| \\ O \\ \longrightarrow \quad enz.FMN + H_2O_2}}{R.C.COOH} + NH_3$

The significance of the D-amino acid oxidases in mammalian tissue is difficult to determine. Certainly our dietary proteins contain L-amino acids. However, there are some compounds in nature that contain D-amino acids as part of their structure, compounds associated with simpler forms of life. Is the D-amino acid oxidase of mammalian tissue of vestigial significance only? To make matters still more uncertain, the L-amino acid oxidase of mammalian tissue generally has a low activity. In contrast to the low activity of mammalian L-amino acid oxidases, venom and certain tissues of the snake exhibit a considerable amount of L-amino acid oxidase activity.

DECARBOXYLATION

A number of animal tissues contain amino acid decarboxylases which convert the L-amino acid to its corresponding amine, with the liberation of carbon dioxide, as follows:

$$R.CH(NH_2).COOH \longrightarrow R.CH_2.NH_2 + CO_2$$

These reactions will be discussed under the metabolism of the individual amino acids. Examples of such reactions are:

Cysteic acid	$\longrightarrow$	taurine
3,4 Dihydroxyphenylalanine	$\longrightarrow$	3,4 dihydroxyphenylethylamine
Glutamic acid	$\longrightarrow$	γ-aminobutyric acid
Histidine	$\longrightarrow$	histamine
Tyrosine	$\longrightarrow$	tyramine

Several of the decarboxylases appear to require pyridoxal phosphate (p. 458) as a coenzyme.

TRANSAMINATION

The incorporation of N^{15} (N^{15}-amino acids fed to animals) into other nonisotopic amino acids of tissue proteins can be explained by the presence of enzymes which catalyze the transamination reaction for a large number of the L-amino acids. It has been known for a long time that α-keto acid analogues of the amino acids can support maximal growth of animals in the absence of the corresponding amino acids. The following are several examples of the transaminase reaction, a reaction which consists of the transfer of α-amino nitrogen from one amino acid to an α-keto acid, resulting in the formation of the corresponding α-keto acid and amino acid analogue:

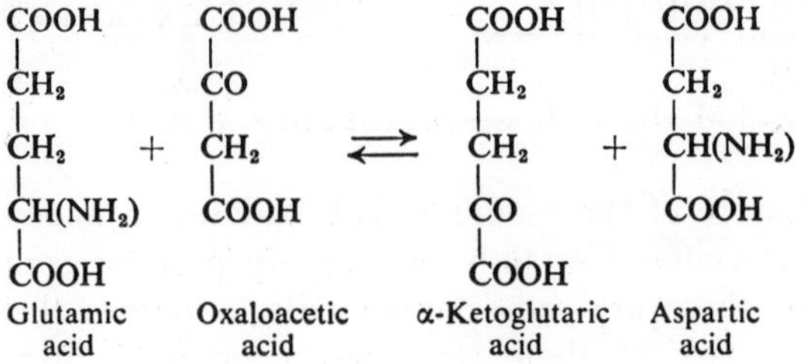

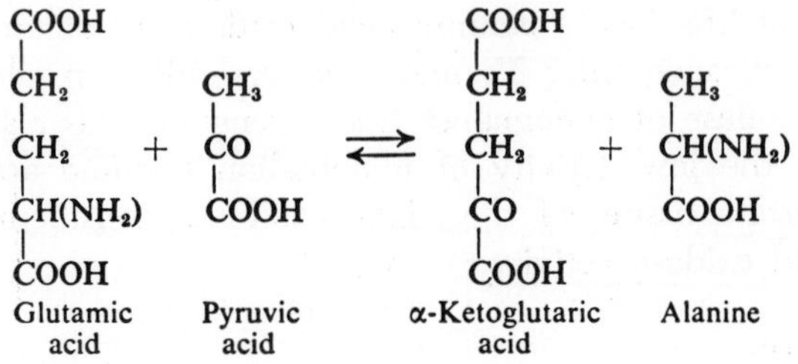

$$
\begin{array}{cccc}
\text{COOH} & \text{COOH} & \text{COOH} & \text{COOH} \\
| & | & | & | \\
\text{CH}_2 & \text{CO} & \text{CH}_2 & \text{CH}_2 \\
| & | & | & | \\
\text{CH}_2 \ + & \text{CH}_2 \rightleftharpoons & \text{CH}_2 \ + & \text{CH(NH}_2) \\
| & | & | & | \\
\text{CH(NH}_2) & \text{COOH} & \text{CO} & \text{COOH} \\
| & & | & \\
\text{COOH} & & \text{COOH} & \\
\text{Glutamic} & \text{Oxaloacetic} & \text{α-Ketoglutaric} & \text{Aspartic} \\
\text{acid} & \text{acid} & \text{acid} & \text{acid}
\end{array}
$$

$$
\begin{array}{cccc}
\text{COOH} & & \text{COOH} & \\
| & & | & \\
\text{CH}_2 & \text{CH}_3 & \text{CH}_2 & \text{CH}_3 \\
| & | & | & | \\
\text{CH}_2 \ + & \text{CO} \rightleftharpoons & \text{CH}_2 \ + & \text{CH(NH}_2) \\
| & | & | & | \\
\text{CH(NH}_2) & \text{COOH} & \text{CO} & \text{COOH} \\
| & & | & \\
\text{COOH} & & \text{COOH} & \\
\text{Glutamic} & \text{Pyruvic} & \text{α-Ketoglutaric} & \text{Alanine} \\
\text{acid} & \text{acid} & \text{acid} &
\end{array}
$$

There is evidence that separate transaminases exist for the separate reactions. These purified enzymes are stimulated by the addition of pyridoxal phosphate (vitamin B_6), for when an animal is placed on a diet deficient in this vitamin, the transaminase content of the tissues decreases. In addition, the amine form of vitamin B_6, pyridoxamine phosphate, is also a stimulant for these enzymes. This has led to the hypothesis that the enzymatic activity involves an interconversion between the two coenzyme factors:

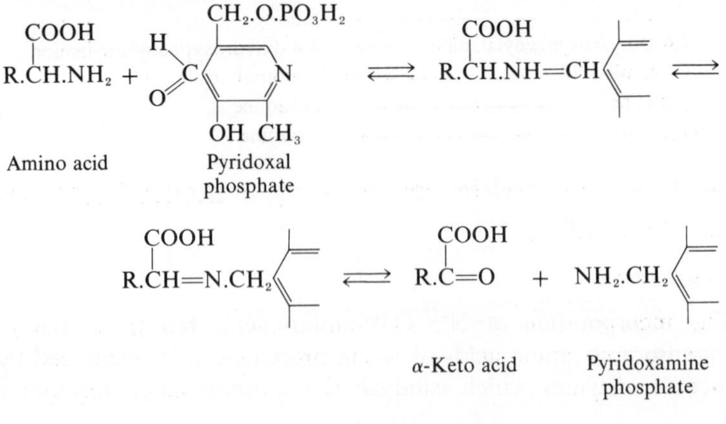

Amino acid　　　Pyridoxal phosphate

α-Keto acid　　　Pyridoxamine phosphate

The pyridoxamine phosphate can now transfer its amino group to another α-keto acid by a reversal of the above equations.

The role of the transaminase reaction in metabolic transformations is a twofold one. First, it provides a mechanism for the interconversion of amino acids via keto acids. Thus one can visualize the synthesis of an important amino acid like glutamic acid from α-ketoglutaric acid, which arises as the result of the oxidation of carbohydrate. In this way, an interrelationship between glutamic acid, aspartic acid, alanine and the tricarboxylic acid cycle intermediates is established. Secondly, transamination provides a mechanism for the oxidation of many L-amino acids, according to the following reactions:

L-Amino acid + α-ketoglutaric acid $\longrightarrow$ α-keto acid + L-glutamic acid

L-Glutamic acid $\xrightarrow{\text{(+DPN)}}$ α-ketoglutaric acid + ammonia

Glutamic acid dehydrogenase, the enzyme involved in the last reaction, is capable of linking the metabolism of amino acids and carbohydrates without the need for oxidative deamination, which, in the mammal, is not quantitatively important.

Finally, transamination is important in the biosynthesis of many amino acids.

FORMATION OF UREA

The average human excretes 30 gm. of urea in 24 hours. This compound has always been regarded as the end-product of nitrogen (protein) metabolism. In some species, urea is replaced by uric acid or ammonia (Table 45).

TABLE 45. END-PRODUCTS OF PROTEIN AND PURINE METABOLISM IN VARIOUS VERTEBRATES, CORRELATED WITH PRESENCE OF LIVER ARGINASE

	End-product of		
	Protein metabolism	Purine metabolism	Liver arginase
Mammalia	Urea	Allantoin*	+
Birds	Uric acid	Uric acid	—
Reptilia:			
Snakes, lizards	Uric acid	Uric acid	—
Turtles	Urea	Allantoin?	+
Amphibia	Urea	Urea	+
Pisces:			
Elasmobranchii (sharks, dogfish, etc.)	Urea	Urea	+
Teleostei (most bony fish)	Ammonia	Urea	+

* Uric acid in man, higher apes and Dalmatian dogs.
(From Baldwin: Comparative Biochemistry.)

Early explanations for the formation of urea in the body, based on liver perfusion experiments, assumed a reaction involving ammonia (obtained by the deamination of amino acids, p. 326) and carbon dioxide, present in blood:

$$2 NH_3 + CO_2 \longrightarrow CO(NH_2)_2 + H_2O$$

Later Krebs and Henseleit, utilizing the tissue slice technique, also showed that ammonium salts could be converted to urea. Of the many substances tested for their possible stimulating effect in this reaction, ornithine and citrulline showed striking activity. It was discovered that the action of ornithine is a catalytic one: only small quantities were needed, and there was no stoichiometric relation between the quantity of ornithine added and the amount of urea formed.

In an attempt at an explanation Krebs assumed the formation of an intermediate compound—by the interaction of ornithine, carbon dioxide and ammonia—which then broke down to form urea. This intermediate compound he showed to be arginine, which, in the presence of the enzyme arginase, is broken down to urea.

In this connection it is important to note that there is a correlation between the ability of a tissue to form urea and its content of arginase. In animals which excrete urea, the arginase occurs chiefly in the liver.

But where does citrulline come into this picture? Here the postulate was made that this compound was doubtless an intermediate in the conversion of ornithine to arginine. Citrulline, originally isolated from the seeds of the watermelon, has since been shown to occur in animals.

The theory by Krebs can now be summarized as follows:

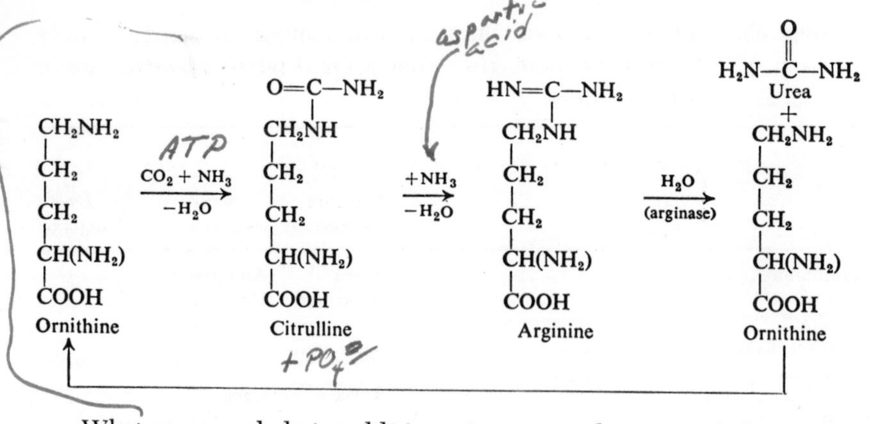

What was needed, in addition, was an explanation of the mechanism of the reactions—the enzymes involved, and the source of energy needed for the production of urea.

The mechanism for the biosynthesis of citrulline from ornithine, carbon dioxide and ammonia involves two enzymatically catalyzed steps. These are:

(a) $ATP + CO_2 + NH_3 \rightleftharpoons$

$$NH_2-\overset{\overset{\displaystyle O}{\|}}{C}-O-\overset{\overset{\displaystyle O}{\|}}{\underset{\underset{\displaystyle OH}{|}}{P}}-OH + ADP$$

Carbamyl phosphate

(b) Carbamyl phosphate + ornithine $\rightleftharpoons$ citrulline + $PO_4^{\equiv}$

In mammalian liver acetyl glutamic acid or related derivatives of glutamic acid are required as cofactors for the synthesis of carbamyl phosphate.

The mechanism of conversion of citrulline to arginine has been clarified by the studies of Ratner, who separated the enzymes required for this conversion and identified the intermediates. The nitrogen donor is not ammonia, but aspartic acid:

$$
\begin{array}{c}
& & \text{COOH} \\
& & | \\
& \text{HN}=\text{C}-\text{NH}.\text{CH} & & \text{HN}=\text{C}-\text{NH}_2 \\
& | \qquad | & & | \\
& \text{CH}_2\text{NH} \quad \text{CH}_2 & & \text{CH}_2\text{NH} \qquad \text{COOH} \\
\text{COOH} & | \qquad | & & | \qquad | \\
| & \text{CH}_2 \quad \text{COOH} & & \text{CH}_2 \qquad \text{CH} \\
\text{CH}_2 & | & & | \qquad \| \\
| & \text{CH}_2 & & \text{CH}_2 \qquad \text{HC} \\
\text{CH(NH}_2) & | & & | \qquad | \\
| & \text{CH(NH}_2) & & \text{CH(NH}_2) + \text{COOH} \\
\text{COOH} & | & & | \\
\text{Aspartate} & \text{COOH} & & \text{COOH} \qquad \text{Fumarate} \\
& \text{Argininosuccinic} & & \text{Arginine} \\
& \text{acid} &
\end{array}
$$

(Aspartate) — + citrulline (ATP, Mg++) → (Argininosuccinic acid) → (Arginine) + (Fumarate)

The picture of urea synthesis, as it emerges from this work, indicates that the classical reaction of ammonia combining with carbon dioxide to yield urea was an oversimplified concept. As a matter of fact, all of the ammonia utilized for urea synthesis does not arise *per se* from oxidative deamination of amino acids. Ammonia is used in the formation of carbamyl phosphate, and some of it is actually supplied in the form of aspartic acid. Of course, aspartic acid can arise in mammalian tissues from ammonia in the following way:

$NH_3 + \alpha$-ketoglutarate $\longrightarrow$ glutamic acid

Glutamic acid + oxalacetic acid $\longrightarrow$ α-ketoglutarate + aspartic acid

Figure 75 indicates the relationship of urea synthesis to the tricarboxylic acid cycle.

From the diagram one can see that two moles of ATP are required for the synthesis of one mole of urea.

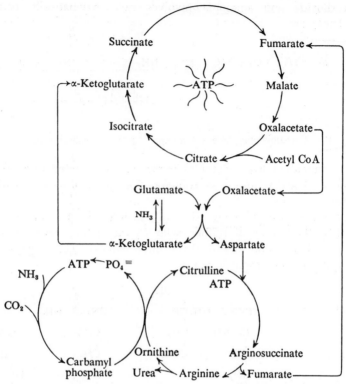

Figure 75. Relationship of urea synthesis to the tricarboxylic acid cycle. (After Ratner, in A Symposium on Amino Acid Metabolism, edited by McElroy and Glass. Baltimore, Johns Hopkins University Press, 1955, p. 249.)

BIOSYNTHESIS OF PROTEINS

The entire mechanism whereby amino acids react to form a complete protein in the living cell is still unknown, although research in this field has produced many suggestive ideas. In the following paragraphs we shall discuss the behavior of the plasma proteins from the point of view of their biosynthesis, and we shall then examine the difficulties which attend the experimental demonstration of protein synthesis in purified systems.

PLASMA PROTEINS

The capacity of the body to synthesize plasma proteins was first studied by Whipple and Weech. Whipple withdrew the plasma proteins from animals by removing whole blood in small quantities and replacing the washed red cells, a process known as *plasmapheresis.* Weech placed the animals on a low-protein diet. In both cases, addition to the diet of various protein foods was followed by measurement of plasma protein regeneration. Beef serum, egg white and casein, in decreasing order of efficiency, were found to be good food proteins for the regeneration of the plasma proteins.

It had been suspected for some time that the liver is the site for plasma protein synthesis, since diseases of the liver, such as cirrhosis, are accompanied by a lowered plasma protein concentration. Similar observations have also implicated the spleen, kidney and intestine. With the advent of isotopically labeled amino acids more concrete results have been obtained. Peters and Anfinsen first demonstrated the ability of cells in surviving liver slices to incorporate the C^{14} of $NaHC^{14}O_3$ into a protein identical with serum albumin. Miller perfused rat livers with whole blood to which he added C^{14}-labeled lysine, together with variable amounts of glucose and other unlabeled amino acids. By following the C^{14} content of the various protein components of the perfused plasma he was able to demonstrate the incorporation of C^{14}-lysine into these proteins, and to show that globulin, albumin and fibrinogen, in decreasing quantities, were synthesized.

In addition to these *in vitro* experiments, the use of labeled amino acids allows for the demonstration of protein synthesis *in vivo*. Here the labeled amino acid is fed or injected into the animal and samples of protein examined at various time intervals for the isotopic label. Generally, there are three types of results which can be expected in such experiments, and these are illustrated in Figure 76. Rate curve A represents a protein with a rapid turnover and is obtained with such tissues as liver, spleen, kidney and glandular material. Curve B represents a slow turnover rate and is obtained with such tissues as muscle, cartilage and skin. Curve C is that which is obtained with a protein which is synthesized and then "protected" from equilibrium reactions with amino acids in the body pool during its lifetime. An example of such a protein would be the globin of hemoglobin in the erythrocyte (which has a finite life span).

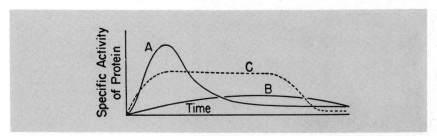

Figure 76. General types of specific activity (S.A.)—time curves obtained following the administration of a single dose of labeled amino acid. Curve A, rapid turnover; curve B, slow turnover; curve C, finite life curve. (From Tarver, H.: The Proteins, Vol. II, Part B, edited by Neurath, H., and Bailey, K. New York, Academic Press, Inc.)

INCORPORATION OF AMINO ACIDS INTO PROTEINS

The ability of tissue slices to incorporate labeled amino acids into their protein has been demonstrated *in vitro*. When the tissue is homogenized the extent of incorporation is reduced; but it may be increased by the addition of suitable compounds, among which are Mg^{++} and ATP. Inhibitors of respiration or of phosphorylation also inhibit the ability of the cell to incorporate amino acids into proteins. When homogenates are subjected to differential centrifugation, one finds the greatest activity residing in the fraction called the "microsomes" (submicroscopic fraction) (see Fig. 77). A point of interest is the fact that the microsome fraction contains the main part of the cytoplasmic ribonucleic acid of the cell, and supports the concept that protein synthesis is tied intimately to the presence of nucleic acids.

EXAMPLES OF PEPTIDE BOND SYNTHESIS

The theoretical difficulty of postulating a simple peptide bond synthesis in the living cell is based on the fact that the equilibrium position for such a reaction is far over on the side of hydrolysis rather than synthesis. $\Delta F°$ for the synthesis of the dipeptide, alanylglycine, is 4000 calories per mole. The equilibrium constant for the reaction of these two amino acids is 1170, and at approximately 0.01 molar concentrations the equilibrium concentration of the dipeptide would be 5×10^{-8} molar. It appears unlikely, therefore, that the mechanism whereby peptides are formed involves equilibrium between the components.

There are a number of ways out of this difficulty. One is to couple the endergonic synthesis of a peptide with an exergonic, energy-yielding, reaction. For example, peptide synthesis might be coupled with the

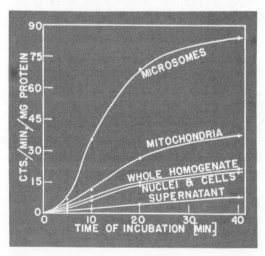

Figure 77. Incorporation of radioactive alanine into the proteins of the various fractions of a rat liver homogenate. (From Siekevitz, P.: J. Biol. Chem., *195*:553.)

hydrolysis of one of the two terminal phosphate bonds of ATP. Another consideration which makes the problem less difficult is the fact that if the amino acid reactants are neutral rather than polar ions, the energy changes are more favorable for synthesis. For example, the value of $\Delta F°$ for the synthesis of benzoylglycine is 2420, whereas that for benzoylglycylglycine is 930 calories per mole. These results suggest that once a small peptide chain is established (by coupling with an energy-yielding reaction), the formation of another peptide bond will require less energy; $\Delta F°$ decreases with increasing separation of the charges on the residue involved. This suggests that the more important problem of (tissue) protein synthesis is one of formation of small peptides. The following are examples of the synthesis of peptide bonds in small molecules by the action of tissue enzymes; a study of the mechanisms involved in these reactions suggests possibilities for protein synthesis:

A. HIPPURIC AND P-AMINO HIPPURIC ACIDS.

$$\text{C}_6\text{H}_5\text{—COOH} + \text{CH}_2\begin{smallmatrix}\text{NH}_2\\ \text{COOH}\end{smallmatrix} \longrightarrow \text{C}_6\text{H}_5\text{—CO.NH.CH}_2.\text{COOH}$$

Benzoic acid   Glycine   Hippuric acid

$$\text{H}_2\text{N—C}_6\text{H}_4\text{—COOH} + \text{CH}_2\begin{smallmatrix}\text{NH}_2\\ \text{COOH}\end{smallmatrix} \longrightarrow \text{H}_2\text{N—C}_6\text{H}_4\text{—CO.NH.CH}_2.\text{COOH}$$

p-Aminobenzoic acid   Glycine   p-Amino hippuric acid

These reactions are catalyzed by enzymes found in the liver and kidney, and represent peptide bond synthesis. ATP is required as an energy source. Coenzyme A is also involved. The mechanism with coenzyme A is as follows (PP is pyrophosphate):

$$\text{Benzoic acid} + \text{ATP} \longrightarrow \text{Benzoyl.AMP} + \text{PP}$$
$$\text{Benzoyl.AMP} + \text{CoA} \longrightarrow \text{Benzoyl.CoA} + \text{AMP}$$
$$\text{Benzoyl.CoA} + \text{glycine} \longrightarrow \text{Benzoylglycine} + \text{CoA}$$

B. ACETYLATION OF AMINES. The discovery of coenzyme A by Lipmann was brought about while he was investigating the liver enzyme which is capable of acetylating sulfanilamide. He found that CoA was a requirement for this synthesis, and Nachmansohn also found that the same coenzyme was required for the synthesis of acetylcholine. These reactions require energy, in the form of ATP, in order to form the acetyl coenzyme A intermediate. The mechanism of the sulfanilamide reaction is given below:

$$\text{Acetate} + \text{ATP} \longrightarrow \text{Acetyl.AMP} + \text{PP}$$
$$\text{Acetyl.AMP} + \text{CoA} \longrightarrow \text{Acetyl.CoA} + \text{AMP}$$
$$\text{Acetyl.CoA} + \text{Sulfa.} \longrightarrow \text{Acetyl Sulfa.} + \text{CoA}$$

where PP is the pyrophosphate derived from ATP.

C. SYNTHESIS OF PEPTIDE DERIVATIVES. Bergmann and Fruton prepared synthetic amino acid derivatives of such a kind as to form insoluble peptides, thereby driving the equilibrium in the direction of peptide synthesis. When, for example, a solution of carbobenzoxyglycine is incubated with activated papain at 40° C. and pH 4.6 in the presence of aniline, carbobenzoxyglycyl anilide is formed.

$$CH_2.COOH \qquad + H_2NC_6H_5 \longrightarrow \qquad CH_2.CO.NHC_6H_5 + H_2O$$
$$| \qquad\qquad\qquad\qquad \text{Aniline} \qquad\qquad\qquad |$$
$$NH.CO.O.CH_2.C_6H_5 \qquad\qquad\qquad\qquad NH.CO.O.CH_2.C_6H_5$$

Carbobenzoxyglycine / Carbobenzoxyglycyl anilide

Such experiments have yielded some important information. For example, they have emphasized the high degree of specificity of the intracellular enzymes. Peptide bond formation occurred only with the L-, or natural, form of the amino acid, and not with the D- form. Bergmann and Fruton defined the configuration of peptides which would enable proteolytic enzymes to act on them.

D. SYNTHESIS OF GLUTATHIONE. The most important contribution to the idea that small peptides can be synthesized by tissue was made by Bloch, who demonstrated the synthesis of the tripeptide glutathione by enzymes present in the liver. Two enzymes are involved: one which catalyzes the reaction of cysteine and glutamic acid to form γ-glutamyl cysteine, and the other which is responsible for the reaction of the dipeptide with glycine. The enzymes require ATP as a source of energy. Coenzyme A is not needed. It is important to stress that the enzyme which couples the dipeptide with glycine is not a hydrolytic enzyme, and thus differs from enzymes which would be postulated to act by simply reversing the reaction of hydrolysis. The reactions are:

$$CH_2.SH \quad COOH \qquad\qquad\qquad CH_2.SH$$
$$| \qquad\qquad | \qquad \xrightarrow{ATP + Mg^{++}} \quad H.C.NH.CO.CH_2.CH_2.CH(NH_2)COOH$$
$$CH(NH_2) + CH_2 \qquad\qquad\qquad\qquad |$$
$$| \qquad\qquad | \qquad\qquad\qquad\qquad\qquad COOH$$
$$COOH \qquad CH_2 \qquad\qquad\qquad\qquad\qquad \gamma\text{-Glutamyl cysteine}$$
$$\qquad\qquad\quad | $$
$$\qquad\qquad CH(NH_2)$$
$$\qquad\qquad\quad |$$
$$\qquad\qquad COOH$$

Cysteine   Glutamic acid

$$\qquad\qquad NH_2 \qquad\qquad\qquad CH_2SH$$
$$\qquad\qquad / \qquad \xrightarrow{ATP + Mg^{++}} \quad H—C—NH.CO.CH_2.CH_2.CH(NH_2)COOH$$
$$+ CH_2 \qquad\qquad\qquad\qquad\qquad |$$
$$\qquad\qquad \backslash COOH \qquad\qquad\qquad CO.NH.CH_2.COOH$$

Glycine   Glutathione

E. GLUTAMYL TRANSFER. Hanes found that kidney and pancreas contain enzymes which catalyze the transfer of the glutamyl group from such compounds as glutathione to a number of different amino acids. Examples of such reactions are:

Glutathione + phenylalanine $\longrightarrow$ glutamylphenylalanine

Glutamylglutamic acid + phenylalanine $\longrightarrow$ glutamylphenylalanine

At present the importance of this' reaction for protein synthesis is somewhat doubtful, since the occurrence of γ-glutamyl peptides is limited in cells to glutathione and polyglutamic acid.

Another type of transfer reaction is one which was originally described by Bergmann working with synthetic substrates. However, since then, more physiological reactions have been shown to be possible. As an example we have the reaction of glycylglycine with methionine to produce glycylmethionine, a reaction catalyzed by an enzyme in cabbage leaves. Another is the reaction of glycylphenylalanine amide with α-glutamic acid amide to form glycylphenylalanyl glutamic acid amide, a reaction catalyzed by cathepsin c, an enzyme in beef spleen. These reactions constitute transfers of amide linkages. Once again, the significance of these reactions for protein synthesis is unknown.

ASSEMBLY OF A PROTEIN MOLECULE

There are several methods which suggest themselves for protein synthesis within the living cell. First, peptide bonds could be formed in a stepwise manner yielding increasingly larger polypeptide chains. One criticism of this hypothesis is the absence of such intermediate polypeptides in actively synthesizing cells. However, they may be present in amounts too small to be isolated and identified. Another hypothesis is that of a single polymerization of a mixture of amino acids to yield the protein molecule. A weakness of this hypothesis is the failure to present a scheme whereby the amino acids could be linked in such a manner as to confer specificity on the protein. A third hypothesis suggests that a protein molecule is built up in a stepwise manner on some surface, such as nucleic acid or protein or both (nucleoprotein). In this way, after the entire protein molecule has been assembled, it would "peel off" from the surface of the template. The template surface would determine the specific arrangement of the amino acids and thus yield a protein with specificity. A similar idea has been suggested to explain the ability of the body to synthesize antibody protein of such structure that it will react specifically with the antigen protein molecules which stimulate its synthesis.

During the past several years we have learned about a method of protein synthesis within the cell which clarifies some of the intermediate steps in the assembly of the amino acids in a protein. These steps have been divided arbitrarily as follows:

1. *Amino acid activation.* In 1953, Lipmann discovered a reaction involving ATP in the synthesis of acetyl coenzyme A in which pyrophosphate (PP) was produced instead of the usual orthophosphate:

$$\text{Acetate} + \text{ATP} + \text{CoA} \longrightarrow \text{AcetylCoA} + \text{AMP} + \text{PP}$$

It was then demonstrated that an intermediate formed in this reaction was an adenylate complex at the carboxyl group:

$$\text{R.COOH} + \text{ATP} \longrightarrow \text{R.CO.AMP} + \text{PP}$$

Workers in other laboratories showed that a similar reaction was catalyzed by enzymes involving the carboxyl group of amino acids:

$$\text{Amino acid (a.a.)} + \text{ATP} + \text{Enzyme (E)} \longrightarrow \text{(a.a.} - \text{AMP)} \, E + \text{PP}$$

There are separate enzymes for each of the amino acids studied and the activated amino acid adenylate remains attached to the enzyme (see Fig. 78).

2. *Preparation of transfer site on soluble RNA.* The activated amino acid-enzyme complex is then transferred to RNA molecules which are characterized by the facts that they are present in the soluble fraction of the cell and are called "soluble" or s-RNA and that they are rather small molecules (molecular weights of 25,000 to 35,000) as compared with other nucleic acids. The terminal sequence of these

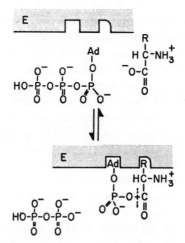

Figure 78. Schematic depiction of amino acid activation. (From Hoagland et al.: *J. Biol. Chem.,* 218:345, 1956.)

s-RNA molecules is always the same: cytidylic-cytidylic-adenylic (C-C-A); this is accomplished as follows:

$$\text{s-RNA} + 2\text{CTP} \longrightarrow \text{s-RNA—C—C} + 2\text{PP}$$
$$\text{s-RNA—C—C} + \text{ATP} \longrightarrow \text{s-RNA—C—C—A} + \text{PP}$$

3. *Esterification of s-RNA.* Addition of the activated amino acid to the prepared site of s-RNA takes place as follows:

$$\text{s-RNA—C—C—A} + (\text{a.a} - \text{AMP})\,\text{E} \longrightarrow \text{s-RNA—C—C—Aa.a} + \text{AMP} + \text{E}$$

The transfer of all amino acids requires CTP. There appear to be separate s-RNA molecules for each amino acid. The enzyme which produces the activated amino acid is also responsible for the transfer of this complex to s-RNA. Because the terminal sequence of s-RNA molecules is the same for all, specificity for a particular amino acid (and the activating enzyme) must reside in a portion of the molecule removed from its terminal sequence. Such a code might concern a unique sequence of purine and pyrimidine bases, hydrogen bonding at specific sites or folding of the chain. The attachment of the amino acid to the terminal adenylate group of s-RNA involves a covalent linkage to the 2' or 3' carbon atom of the ribose moiety.

4. *Sequence determination of amino acids.* The next step appears to involve the transfer of the amino acid together with a portion of its s-RNA molecule to the RNA (ribosomal RNA) present in the microsomes (see Plate 6). This reaction requires the nucleotide triphosphate GTP. The amino acid is attached to a particular site of the ribosomal RNA which cannot be occupied by a different amino acid. Nirenberg has recently reported the existence, in cells, of RNA which is required, in addition to s-RNA and ribosomes, for the incorporation of specific amino acids into the polypeptide chain. It is called "template," or "messenger" RNA, because its assembly (nucleotide sequence) is probably determined by nuclear DNA, and because it appears to be coded specifically for each amino acid. It would therefore be responsible for sending information from DNA to the ribosomes, resulting in the assembly of a specific protein molecule. Synthetic RNA polymers have proved to be active in partially purified systems; polyuridylic acid causes the incorporation only of L-phenylalanine, whereas polycytidylic acid causes the incorporation of L-proline. Ochoa, Nirenberg, and others have prepared a series of copolymers (mixed nucleotides) which have enabled them to determine the nucleotide code for many amino acids.

5. *Polypeptide chain formation.* In a manner which is not understood, adjacent amino acids attached to ribosomal RNA attach themselves by peptide bond formation.

6. *Secondary and tertiary structure of the protein.* Still not understood are the processes involving the "unzippering" of the completed

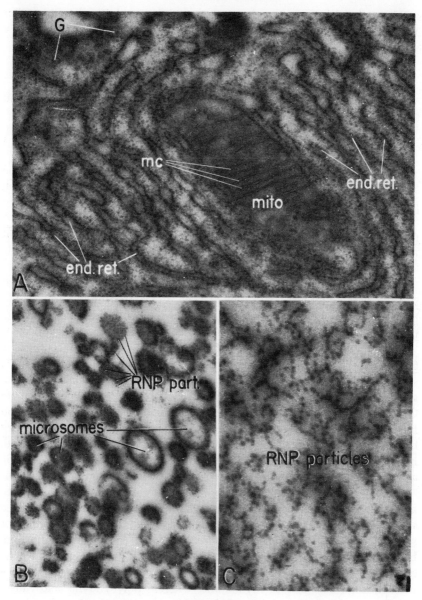

Plate 6

A, Electron micrograph of the basal region of a pancreatic cell showing the ergastoplasm with cisternae and abundant RNP granules: *mito,* mitochondria; *mc,* mitochondrial crests; 47,000×.

B, Microsomic fraction isolated from the pancreas. The microsomes are membranous vesicles with RNP (*RNP part*) granules; 47,000×.

C, Postmicroscopic fraction of RNP particles obtained after solubilization of the membranes by the action of deoxycholate; 80,000×. (Courtesy of G. E. Palade.)

(From De Robertis, Nowinski and Saez: General Cytology.)

polypeptide chain from the surface of the RNA molecule, its orientation in space, and the cross-linking of several polypeptides by disulfide bridges to give the final native protein.

METABOLISM OF INDIVIDUAL AMINO ACIDS

The metabolism of each of the common amino acids will be considered from two aspects: synthesis, and degradation and conversion reactions. If an amino acid is found to be essential for growth (in, for example, rat or man), it cannot be synthesized in the animal organism, although green plants, bacteria, molds or yeasts may be capable of synthesizing it. Only a few of the synthetic pathways due to microorganisms will be considered, for a more extensive examination in this field would bring us into the study of microbiology. If the amino acid is not essential for growth, the animal organism is capable of synthesizing it, and such synthesis will be considered. Certain amino acids will be considered together, because their metabolic pathways are related. It should be understood that in all cases amino acids can arise from protein hydrolysis within the cell and that amino acids are incorporated into the protein molecule; such reactions are common to all amino acids. It should also be noted that much of our present knowledge of amino acid metabolism is a direct result of the use of labeled compounds and of work done with microorganisms.

GLYCINE AND SERINE

Glycine is the simplest of the amino acids. It enters into a great variety of metabolic reactions, though it is not essential in the diet for growth. It arises from serine by several routes:

A. VIA GLYOXYLIC ACID:

$$
\begin{array}{ccccc}
CH_2OH & & CH_2OH & & CH_2OH \\
| & & | & & | \\
CH(NH_2) & \longrightarrow & CH_2 & \longrightarrow & CHO \\
| & & | & & \\
COOH & & NH_2 & & \\
\text{Serine} & & \text{Ethanolamine} & & \text{Glycolaldehyde}
\end{array}
$$

$$
\begin{array}{ccccc}
CH_2OH & & CHO & & CH_2.NH_2 \\
\longrightarrow \quad | & \longrightarrow & | & \longrightarrow & | \\
COOH & & COOH & & COOH \\
\text{Glycolic acid} & & \text{Glyoxylic acid} & & \text{Glycine}
\end{array}
$$

The type of experiment which is carried out to arrive at a scheme like the one above involves the administration of isotopically labeled compounds suspected of being intermediates, together with benzoic acid. After a suitable time interval, hippuric acid (benzoylglycine) is isolated from the urine and assayed for radioactivity.

B. VIA CHOLINE:

$$
\begin{array}{ccc}
\text{Serine} &
\begin{array}{c} CH_2OH \\ | \\ CH_2 \\ | \\ N(CH_3)_3 \\ + \end{array} &
\begin{array}{c} COO^- \\ | \\ CH_2 \\ | \\ N(CH_3)_3 \\ + \end{array} \\
\downarrow & & \\
\text{ethanolamine} \longrightarrow & \text{Choline} \longrightarrow & \text{Betaine}
\end{array}
$$

$$
\longrightarrow
\begin{array}{c} COOH \\ | \\ CH_2 \\ | \\ N(CH_3)_2 \\ \text{Dimethyl-} \\ \text{glycine} \end{array}
\longrightarrow
\begin{array}{c} COOH \\ | \\ CH_2 \\ | \\ NH(CH_3) \\ \text{Monomethyl-} \\ \text{glycine} \\ \text{(sarcosine)} \end{array}
\longrightarrow
\begin{array}{c} COOH \\ | \\ CH_2 \\ | \\ NH_2 \\ \text{Glycine} \end{array}
$$

During the conversion of betaine to dimethylglycine, the methyl group that is lost is utilized for the conversion of homocysteine to methionine (see p. 349). Furthermore, the conversion of dimethylglycine to sarcosine and from sarcosine to glycine involves the loss of one carbon atom in the form of "formate" or some active carrier of formaldehyde or formic acid. This 1-carbon intermediate appears to play the same role as the 2-carbon intermediate which was shown subsequently to be identical to acetyl coenzyme A.

In addition to conversion from serine, glycine may also arise by the oxidation of threonine to glycine and acetate:

$$
\begin{array}{c} CH_3 \\ | \\ CH(OH) \\ | \\ CH(NH_2) \\ | \\ COOH \\ \text{Threonine} \end{array}
\longrightarrow
\begin{array}{c} CH_3 \\ | \\ COOH \\ \text{Acetate} \end{array}
+
\begin{array}{c} CH_2NH_2 \\ | \\ COOH \\ \text{Glycine} \end{array}
$$

Glycine is a precursor of several compounds. Among these are glutathione, glycocholic acid, glyoxylic acid and creatine in muscle:

$$
\begin{array}{c} HN{=}C.NH_2 \\ \text{------|------} \\ NH \\ | \\ (CH_2)_3 \\ | \\ CH(NH_2) \\ | \\ COOH \\ \text{Arginine} \end{array}
+
\begin{array}{c} NH_2 \\ | \\ CH_2 \\ | \\ COOH \\ \text{Glycine} \end{array}
\longrightarrow
\begin{array}{c} HN{=}C.NH_2 \\ | \\ NH \\ | \\ CH_2 \\ | \\ COOH \\ \text{Glycocyamine} \end{array}
\xrightarrow[\text{of methionine}]{CH_3 \text{ group}}
\begin{array}{c} HN{=}C.NH_2 \\ | \\ N.CH_3 \\ | \\ CH_2 \\ | \\ COOH \\ \text{Creatine} \end{array}
$$

Glycine is also a precursor of porphyrins and bile pigments.

Serine is also a nonessential amino acid and can arise either from glycine or from pyruvate. To form serine from glycine requires the addition of one carbon atom (which will become the β-carbon of serine). The one-carbon atom carrier is not formic acid or formaldehyde. Some studies give evidence that this carrier is linked with the vitamin, folic acid (p. 465). Folic acid–deficient rats incorporate C^{14}-formic acid very poorly into the β-carbon of serine. It has been suggested that 5-hydroxymethyltetrahydrofolic acid is the actual intermediate. A compound closely related to this is the "citrovorum factor," found necessary for bacterial growth and capable of replacing folic acid as a bacterial growth factor. The various structures are shown below:

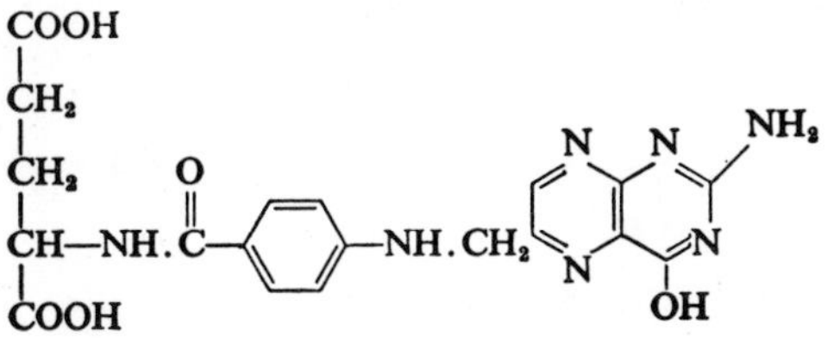

Folic acid

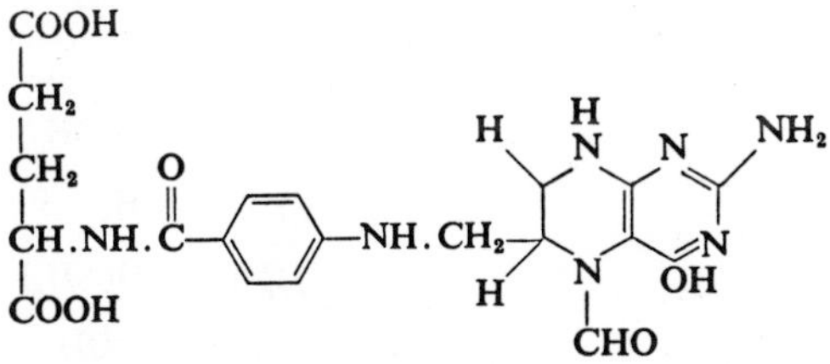

"Citrovorum factor"
(5-formyl-5,6,7,8-tetrahydrofolic acid)

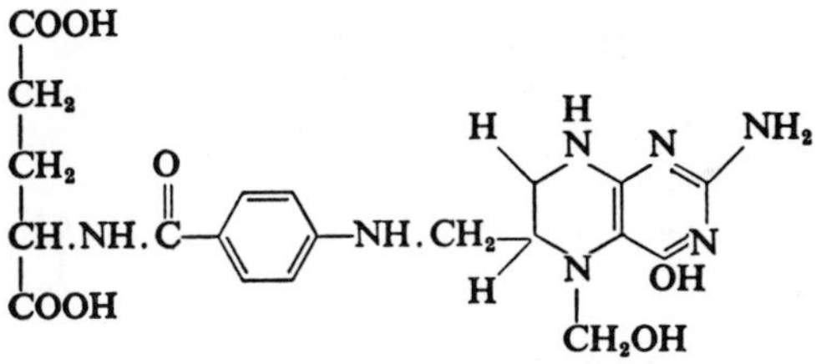

5-Hydroxymethyltetrahydrofolic acid

The interrelationships of these compounds to serine and formaldehyde and formic acid are shown below:

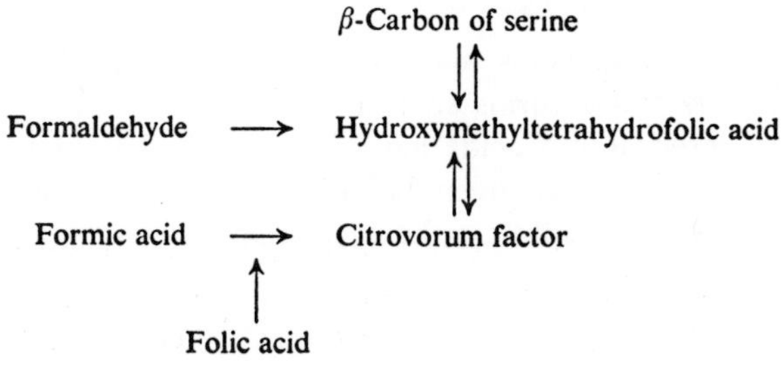

β-Carbon of serine

Formaldehyde $\longrightarrow$ Hydroxymethyltetrahydrofolic acid

Formic acid $\longrightarrow$ Citrovorum factor

Folic acid

ALANINE

This is a nonessential amino acid for animals. It can be made from pyruvate and therefore from carbohydrate. It is degraded to pyruvate (transamination) and then to carbon dioxide and water via the tricarboxylic acid cycle.

THREONINE

This is an essential amino acid and must therefore be taken with the food. It is synthesized by bacteria in the following way:

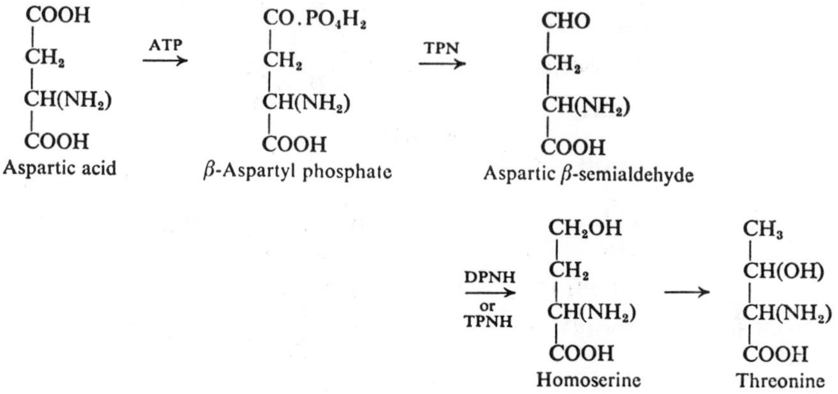

$$
\begin{array}{ccccc}
\text{COOH} & & \text{CO.PO}_4\text{H}_2 & & \text{CHO} \\
| & \xrightarrow{\text{ATP}} & | & \xrightarrow{\text{TPN}} & | \\
\text{CH}_2 & & \text{CH}_2 & & \text{CH}_2 \\
| & & | & & | \\
\text{CH(NH}_2) & & \text{CH(NH}_2) & & \text{CH(NH}_2) \\
| & & | & & | \\
\text{COOH} & & \text{COOH} & & \text{COOH}
\end{array}
$$

Aspartic acid β-Aspartyl phosphate   Aspartic β-semialdehyde

$$
\xrightarrow[\text{TPNH}]{\overset{\text{DPNH}}{\text{or}}}
\begin{array}{c}
\text{CH}_2\text{OH} \\
| \\
\text{CH}_2 \\
| \\
\text{CH(NH}_2) \\
| \\
\text{COOH}
\end{array}
\longrightarrow
\begin{array}{c}
\text{CH}_3 \\
| \\
\text{CH(OH)} \\
| \\
\text{CH(NH}_2) \\
| \\
\text{COOH}
\end{array}
$$

Homoserine   Threonine

Threonine is metabolized in the animal body to form the corresponding keto acid and also gives rise to a new amino acid:

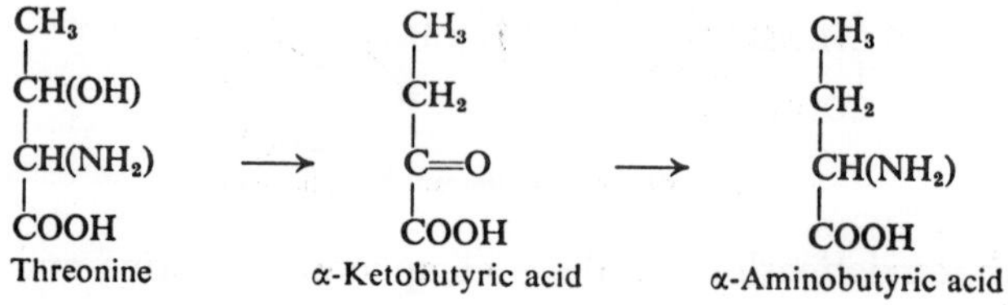

$$
\begin{array}{ccccc}
\text{CH}_3 & & \text{CH}_3 & & \text{CH}_3 \\
| & & | & & | \\
\text{CH(OH)} & & \text{CH}_2 & & \text{CH}_2 \\
| & \longrightarrow & | & \longrightarrow & | \\
\text{CH(NH}_2) & & \text{C=O} & & \text{CH(NH}_2) \\
| & & | & & | \\
\text{COOH} & & \text{COOH} & & \text{COOH}
\end{array}
$$

Threonine α-Ketobutyric acid α-Aminobutyric acid

LEUCINE, ISOLEUCINE AND VALINE

These three amino acids are essential for animal growth and can be synthesized by lower forms such as bacteria. The degradation reactions of these three amino acids have been studied in detail, but only the pathway for leucine is given below; isoleucine and valine are degraded by essentially similar pathways although the end-products are different:

$$
\begin{array}{cccc}
\underset{\text{Leucine}}{\begin{array}{c} CH_3 \quad CH_3 \\ \diagdown \diagup \\ CH \\ | \\ CH_2 \\ | \\ CH(NH_2) \\ | \\ COOH \end{array}}
&
\xrightarrow{}
\underset{\text{α-Keto-isocaproic acid}}{\begin{array}{c} CH_3 \quad CH_3 \\ \diagdown \diagup \\ CH \\ | \\ CH_2 \\ | \\ C{=}O \\ | \\ COOH \end{array}}
&
\xrightarrow{\text{CoA}}
\underset{\text{Isovaleryl-CoA}}{\begin{array}{c} CH_3 \quad CH_3 \\ \diagdown \diagup \\ CH \\ | \\ CH_2 \\ | \\ C{=}O \\ | \\ S\cdot CoA \end{array}}
&
\xrightarrow{}
\underset{\text{Senecioyl-CoA}}{\begin{array}{c} CH_3 \quad CH_3 \\ \diagdown \diagup \\ C \\ \| \\ CH \\ | \\ C{=}O \\ | \\ S\cdot CoA \end{array}}
\end{array}
$$

$$
\xrightarrow{}
\underset{\substack{\text{β-Hydroxy-}\\ \text{isovaleryl-CoA}}}{\begin{array}{c} CH_3 \quad CH_3 \\ \diagdown \diagup \\ C{-}OH \\ | \\ CH_2 \\ | \\ C{=}O \\ | \\ S\cdot CoA \end{array}}
\xrightarrow[CO_2]{ATP}
\underset{\substack{\text{β-Hydroxy-β-}\\ \text{methyglutaryl-CoA}}}{\begin{array}{c} COOH \\ | \\ CH_2 \\ | \\ CH_3{-}C{-}OH \\ | \\ CH_2 \\ | \\ C{=}O \\ | \\ S\cdot CoA \end{array}}
\longrightarrow
\underset{\substack{\text{Acetoacetic}\\ \text{acid}}}{\begin{array}{c} CH_3 \\ | \\ C{=}O \\ | \\ CH_2 \\ | \\ COOH \end{array}}
+
\underset{\text{Acetyl-CoA}}{\begin{array}{c} CH_3 \\ | \\ C{=}O \\ | \\ S\cdot CoA \end{array}}
$$

Thus, one of the end-products of leucine metabolism is the "ketone body," acetoacetic acid, which accounts for the fact that leucine is ketogenic. On the other hand, isoleucine and valine are only weakly ketogenic and actually give rise to other compounds; propionic acid, for example, is an end-product of isoleucine metabolism.

GLUTAMIC ACID, PROLINE, HYDROXYPROLINE, ORNITHINE AND ARGININE

Glutamic acid is an important amino acid, although it is not essential for growth. The relationship between this amino acid and α-ketoglutaric acid indicates its synthetic pathway. That this reaction is reversible is indicated by the fact that the carbon atoms of glutamic acid can be shown to occur in glycogen. In addition, glutamic acid furnishes the carbon skeleton for proline, hydroxyproline, ornithine, arginine, serine, glycine and cysteine. Of special importance is the amide of glutamic acid, γ-glutamine, which is found in brain tissue. It is synthesized from the acid and ammonia in the presence of ATP and an enzyme. The over-all relationships among the amino acids listed above and glutamic acid are given below:

$$
\text{Glutamic acid} \underset{\rightleftarrows}{\rightleftarrows} \quad
\begin{array}{c}
\text{ornithine} \rightleftarrows \text{arginine} \\
\updownarrow \\
\text{proline} \longrightarrow \text{hydroxyproline}
\end{array}
$$

The intermediates which are believed to be involved in these interconversions are:

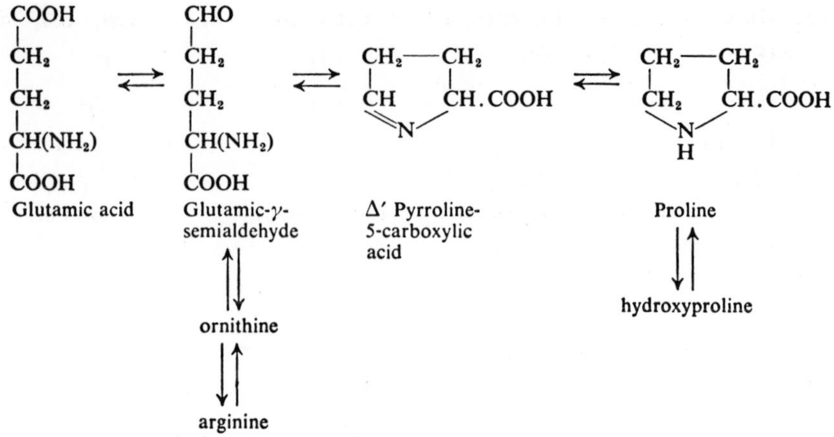

<table>
<tr>
<td>COOH
|
CH$_2$
|
CH$_2$
|
CH(NH$_2$)
|
COOH
Glutamic acid</td>
<td>⇌</td>
<td>CHO
|
CH$_2$
|
CH$_2$
|
CH(NH$_2$)
|
COOH
Glutamic-γ-
semialdehyde</td>
<td>⇌</td>
<td>CH$_2$—CH$_2$
| |
CH CH.COOH
\N/
Δ' Pyrroline-
5-carboxylic
acid</td>
<td>⇌</td>
<td>CH$_2$—CH$_2$
| |
CH$_2$ CH.COOH
\N/
  H
Proline</td>
</tr>
</table>

ornithine

arginine

hydroxyproline

Whereas proline (like other amino acids), when fed, replaces in a few days a fair proportion of the proline in the body proteins, hydroxyproline replaces less than 0.1 per cent of the hydroxyproline in the body proteins in the same time. Part of the answer to this unusual behavior is the fact that much of the body's hydroxyproline is found in collagen, a protein with a very slow rate of turnover. On the other hand, the nitrogen of hydroxyproline appears widely distributed in other amino acids.

HISTIDINE

This amino acid is essential for the growth of rats, although it can be replaced in the diet of rats by imidazole lactic acid or imidazole pyruvic acid (Harrow and Sherwin). It can be synthesized by plants and microorganisms.

Most of the histidine administered to animals is degraded to carbon dioxide. However, conjugated forms of histidine exist in the body, such as ergothionine (blood) and carnosine and anserine (muscle).

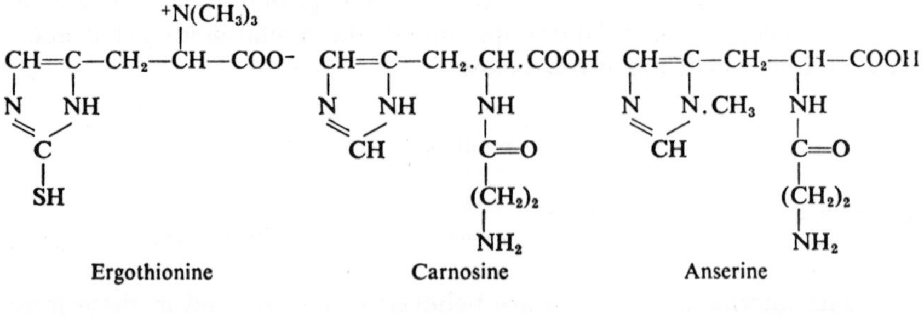

Ergothionine   Carnosine   Anserine

The function of these compounds in the body is not known. Ergothionine is a betaine of thiolhistidine, whereas carnosine is a pseudopeptide of β-alanine and histidine, and anserine is a pseudopeptide of β-alanine and methyl histidine. Melville has shown that animals do not synthesize ergothionine but obtain it from their diet; fungi (Neurospora) do synthesize it.

The degradation of histidine involves several pathways and yields compounds of interest. One of these, histamine, is a powerfully active stimulant of gastric secretion. The destruction of histamine is mediated by the enzyme histaminase, a diamine oxidase, which degrades it to imidazole acetic acid, probably via the aldehyde:

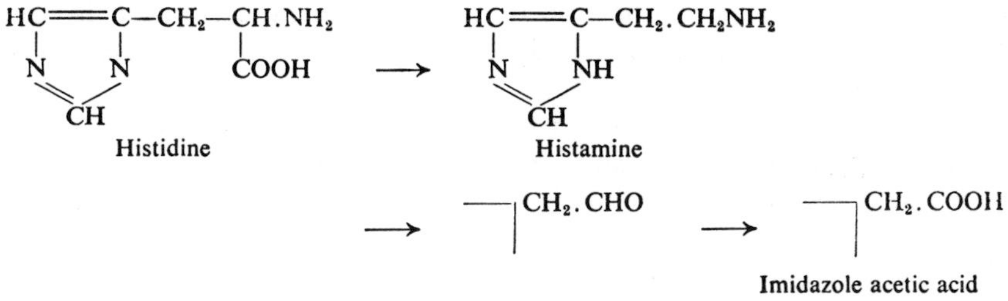

$$HC\!\!=\!\!C-CH_2-CH.NH_2$$
$$\begin{array}{ccc} | & | & \\ N & N & COOH \end{array}$$
$$CH$$
$$\text{Histidine}$$

$\longrightarrow$

$$HC\!\!=\!\!C-CH_2.CH_2NH_2$$
$$\begin{array}{cc} | & | \\ N & NH \end{array}$$
$$CH$$
$$\text{Histamine}$$

$\longrightarrow$ $CH_2.CHO$ $\longrightarrow$ $CH_2.COOH$

Imidazole acetic acid

The main pathway of histidine degradation in animals involves the enzyme histidase, found in the liver, which forms urocanic acid from histidine. This compound, in turn, is converted by urocanase to an intermediate, which on alkaline hydrolysis yields ammonia, formic acid and glutamic acid. Its structure has been shown to correspond to formamidino-L-glutamic acid:

$$CH\!\!=\!\!C.CH_2.CH(NH_2)COOH$$
$$\begin{array}{cc} | & | \\ N & NH \end{array}$$
$$CH$$
$$\text{Histidine}$$

$\longrightarrow$

$$CH\!\!=\!\!C.CH\!\!=\!\!CH.COOH$$
$$\begin{array}{cc} | & | \\ N & NH \end{array}$$
$$CH$$
$$\text{Urocanic acid}$$

$\longrightarrow$

$$O\!\!=\!\!C\!\!-\!\!-\!\!-CH.CH_2.CH_2.COOH$$
$$\begin{array}{cc} | & | \\ N & NH \end{array}$$
$$CH$$
Imidazolonepropionic acid (hypothetical)

$\longrightarrow$

$$CH\!\!=\!\!NH$$
$$|$$
$$NH$$
$$|$$
$$HOOC.CH.CH_2.CH_2.COOH$$
Formamidino-L-glutamic acid

$\longrightarrow$

$$CHO$$
$$|$$
$$NH$$
$$|$$
$$HOOC\!\!-\!\!CH\!\!-\!\!CH_2.CH_2.COOH$$
Formyl-L-glutamic acid
(bacteria only)

$\longrightarrow$

$$NH_2$$
$$|$$
$$HOOC.CH.CH_2.CH_2.COOH + HCOOH$$
Glutamic acid   Formic acid

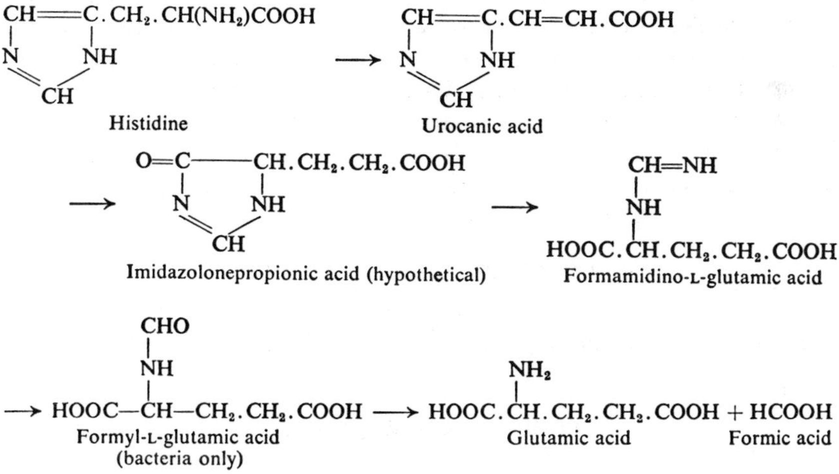

Formamidino-glutamic acid is further metabolized in animals, but the compound formyl-glutamic acid is found only in bacteria. It is of interest to note that formic acid, the one-carbon compound, appears as an end-product. In folic acid–deficient rats, the formamidino-glutamate is excreted (instead of being further metabolized), indicating that normally its metabolism involves the donation of a "formyl" group.

LYSINE

In the diet lysine is indispensable. Among the distinctive features of the metabolism of lysine are the following: replacement of the α-amino group by a keto or hydroxyl group or by an acetyl group makes it nonutilizable for growth; it is not involved in reversible deamination-reamination reactions; neither the L- nor the D- form is attacked by the respective amino acid oxidase; and it is not involved in the transaminase reaction.

An important contribution to knowledge of the metabolism of lysine has been made by Borsook and his associates, using C^{14} as a tracer. The amino acid was synthesized with the isotope in the ϵ position, and resolved into the L- and D-isomers. They found that guinea-pig liver homogenate converts L-lysine into α-aminoadipic acid (* is the position of the labeled carbon):

$$\overset{*}{C}H_2.CH_2.CH_2.CH_2.CH.COOH \longrightarrow \overset{*}{C}OOH.CH_2.CH_2.CH_2.CH.COOH$$
$$\underset{NH_2}{|} \qquad\qquad \underset{NH_2}{|} \qquad\qquad\qquad\qquad\qquad\qquad \underset{NH_2}{|}$$

α-Aminoadipic acid

This is in accordance with the hypothesis that before the α-amino group of lysine is acted upon by animal tissue enzymes, the ϵ-amino group must be masked or removed. Furthermore, it explains why the α-amino group in lysine does not participate in reversible transamination reactions *in vivo;* it must presumably be first transformed into α-aminoadipic acid before the transfer of the α-amino group becomes possible.

In support of this hypothesis, guinea-pig liver homogenate oxidatively deaminizes α-aminoadipic acid to α-ketoadipic acid:

$$\overset{*}{C}OOH.CH_2.CH_2.CH_2.CO.COOH$$

and the latter is oxidatively decarboxylated to glutaric acid:

$$\overset{*}{C}OOH.CH_2.CH_2.CH_2.\overset{*}{C}OOH$$

Additional studies by other workers have uncovered new intermediates, and the following scheme suggests other mechanisms. (The compounds

shown in brackets have not been identified and are therefore hypothetical.)

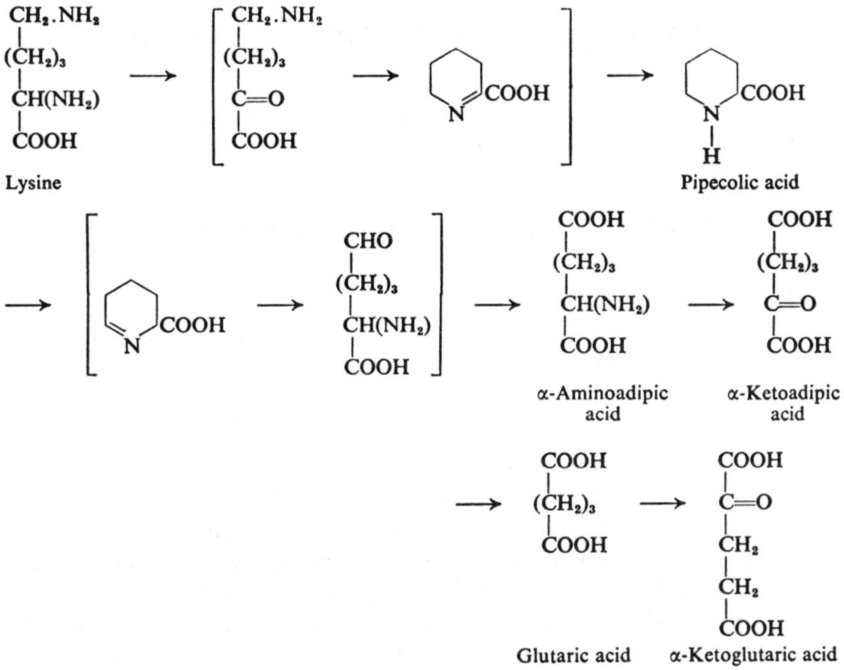

Lysine   Pipecolic acid

α-Aminoadipic   α-Ketoadipic
   acid   acid

Glutaric acid   α-Ketoglutaric acid

CYSTINE AND METHIONINE

Until the discovery of methionine it had always been assumed that
cystine was an indispensable amino acid. It now appears, however, that
whereas methionine can replace cystine in a diet deficient in the latter,
the reverse is not true: cystine cannot replace methionine. By using
methionine containing S^{35}, it can be shown that the S of methionine is
a precursor of the S of cystine. In one of his many experiments, Du
Vigneaud fed methionine containing both S^{35} and C^{13}; the cystine which
was recovered showed S^{35} but no C^{13}, which pointed to the fact that
in the conversion of methionine to cystine, the carbon chain of methionine is not used.

Further developments did show that the methyl group of methionine and the carbon atoms of glycine are utilized by the rat for the
synthesis of cystine. Since glycine is convertible to serine (p. 341), the
pathway to cystine production is probably via serine.

Liver homogenates can convert serine and homocysteine to cysteine.
Here an intermediate compound is formed, cystathionine:

$$HOOC.CH_2.NH_2 \qquad CH_3.S.CH_2.CH_2.CH(NH_2)COOH$$

Glycine Methionine

$$\big\Updownarrow \qquad\qquad\qquad \downarrow$$

$$HOOC.CH(NH_2).CH_2OH + HS.CH_2.CH_2.CH(NH_2)COOH$$

Serine Homocysteine

$$\downarrow$$

$$HOOC.CH(NH_2).CH_2.S.CH_2.CH_2.CH(NH_2)COOH$$

Cystathionine

$$\downarrow$$

$$HOOC.CH(NH_2).CH_2.SH + CH_2OH.CH_2.CH(NH_2).COOH$$

Cysteine Homoserine

$$\downarrow$$

$$CH_3.CH_2.\overset{\|\,O}{C}.COOH + NH_3$$

α-Ketobutyric acid

Enzymes have been purified from liver which catalyze the condensation of serine and homocysteine and the splitting of cystathionine. Both of these require pyridoxal phosphate as coenzyme.

Another important intermediate is the methionine derivative which is responsible for transmethylation reactions. Cantoni has shown that methionine is first converted to S-adenosyl methionine by reaction with an enzyme and ATP, a reaction which results in an "active" methionine since the sulfonium bond is of a high energy type:

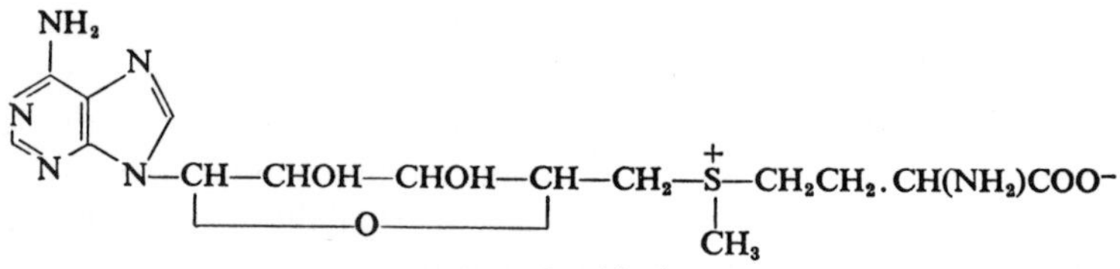

S-Adenosylmethionine

This compound can then act as a methyl donor in transmethylation reactions. Cantoni has also shown that S-adenosylhomocysteine is formed from the corresponding methionine derivative, with the loss of the methyl group. This compound can then accept methyl groups from a variety of donors, such as betaine, to regenerate methionine.

The degradation reactions of methionine and cystine are shown in schematic form below. The oxidation states of the sulfur are shown to the left of the scheme, and the various pathways are illustrated in the main scheme.

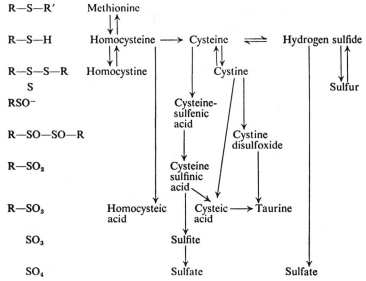

(Fromageot: from Sumner and Myrbäck's The Enzymes, Vol. 2, p. 622.)

The origin of taurine, present in the conjugated bile acids as tauorocholic acid, is illustrated below (together with the structures of the important intermediate oxidation products of cysteine):

$$
\begin{array}{ccc}
CH_2.SH & CH_2.SOH & CH_2.SO_2H \\
| & | & | \\
CH(NH_2) \longrightarrow & CH(NH_2) \longrightarrow & CH(NH_2) \\
| & | & | \\
COOH & COOH & COOH \\
\text{Cysteine} & \text{Cysteine} & \text{Cysteine} \\
 & \text{sulfenic acid} & \text{sulfinic acid}
\end{array}
$$

$$
\begin{array}{cc}
 & CH_2.SO_3H & CH_2.SO_3H \\
 & | & | \\
\longrightarrow & CH(NH_2) \longrightarrow & CH_2.NH_2 \\
 & | & \\
 & COOH & \\
 & \text{Cysteic acid} & \text{Taurine}
\end{array}
$$

Cysteine sulfinic acid also undergoes the transaminase reaction with a variety of keto acids, giving rise to the carbon chain of pyruvic acid. The latter, by reaction with glutamic acid, gives rise to the carbon chain of the amino acid alanine:

$$
\begin{array}{ccccc}
CH_2.SO_2H & COOH & & CH_3 & COOH \\
| & | & & | & | \\
CH(NH_2) & + \quad C{=}O & \longrightarrow & C{=}O & + \quad CH(NH_2) + SO_4{=} \\
| & | & & | & | \\
COOH & CH_2 & & COOH & CH_2 \\
 & | & & & | \\
 & COOH & & & COOH \\
\text{Cysteine} & \text{Oxalo-} & & \text{Pyruvic} & \text{Aspartic} \\
\text{sulfinic acid} & \text{acetate} & & \text{acid} & \text{acid}
\end{array}
$$

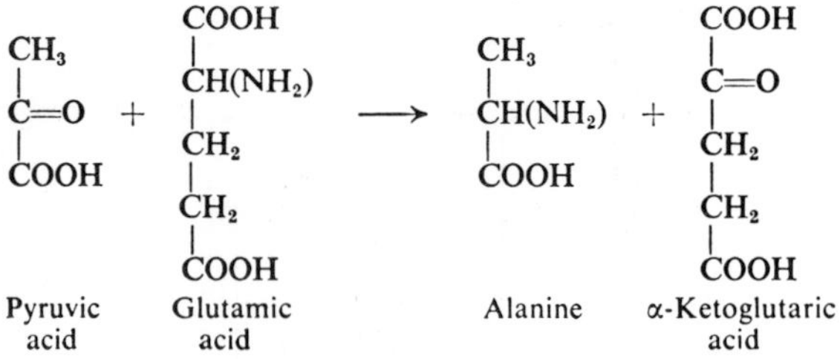

$$
\begin{array}{c}
\text{CH}_3 \\
| \\
\text{C}{=}\text{O} \\
| \\
\text{COOH}
\end{array}
+
\begin{array}{c}
\text{COOH} \\
| \\
\text{CH(NH}_2\text{)} \\
| \\
\text{CH}_2 \\
| \\
\text{CH}_2 \\
| \\
\text{COOH}
\end{array}
\longrightarrow
\begin{array}{c}
\text{CH}_3 \\
| \\
\text{CH(NH}_2\text{)} \\
| \\
\text{COOH}
\end{array}
+
\begin{array}{c}
\text{COOH} \\
| \\
\text{C}{=}\text{O} \\
| \\
\text{CH}_2 \\
| \\
\text{CH}_2 \\
| \\
\text{COOH}
\end{array}
$$

Pyruvic   Glutamic   Alanine   α-Ketoglutaric
acid   acid   acid

PHENYLALANINE AND TYROSINE

Phenylalanine is an indispensable amino acid, whereas tyrosine is not essential. Phenylalanine can be transformed in the animal body to tyrosine, but tyrosine cannot be converted to phenylalanine. The synthesis of the aromatic nucleus is accomplished in plants and microorganisms via the general route:

Acetate $\longrightarrow$ pyruvate $\longrightarrow$ glucose $\longrightarrow$ shikimic acid $\longrightarrow$ phenylalanine and tyrosine

The amino acid precursor, shikimic acid, has the following structure:

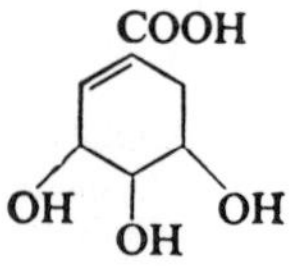

Shikimic acid

This acid is also the precursor for tryptophan and p-aminobenzoic acid.

Most of the phenylalanine and tyrosine in the animal body is converted to acetoacetate. This degradative pathway represents, quantitatively, the most important route. The intermediates are shown below:

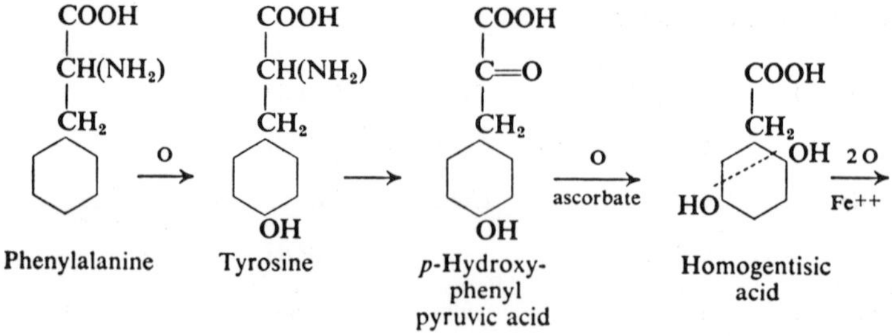

Phenylalanine   Tyrosine   p-Hydroxy-   Homogentisic
                              phenyl   acid
                              pyruvic acid

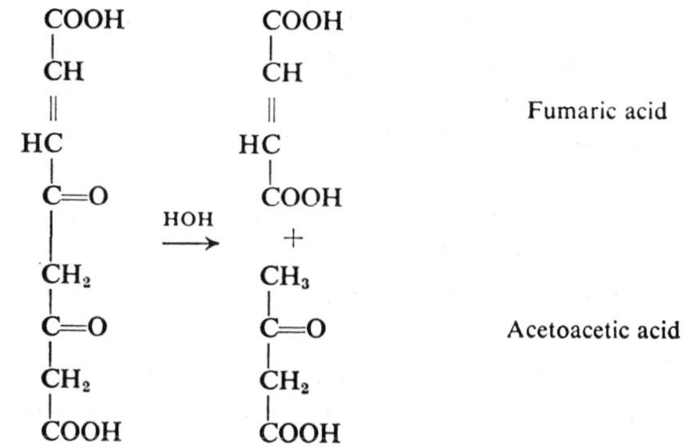

$$
\begin{array}{ccc}
\text{COOH} & \text{COOH} \\
| & | \\
\text{CH} & \text{CH} \\
\| & \| & \text{Fumaric acid} \\
\text{HC} & \text{HC} \\
| & | \\
\text{C=O} & \text{COOH} \\
\quad\;\; \xrightarrow{\text{HOH}} & + \\
\text{CH}_2 & \text{CH}_3 \\
| & | \\
\text{C=O} & \text{C=O} & \text{Acetoacetic acid} \\
| & | \\
\text{CH}_2 & \text{CH}_2 \\
| & | \\
\text{COOH} & \text{COOH} \\
\end{array}
$$

Fumaryl
acetoacetic acid

An odd reaction is the conversion of p-hydroxyphenylpyruvic acid to homogentisic acid, involving a migration of the side-chain. Although the mechanism is unknown, proof of this migration is available from studies in which labeled phenylalanine is given and the label identified in the various carbon atoms of acetoacetic acid.

Another reaction sequence involves the formation of the melanins, compounds responsible for pigmentation of the skin. They are complex molecules which have not been well characterized.

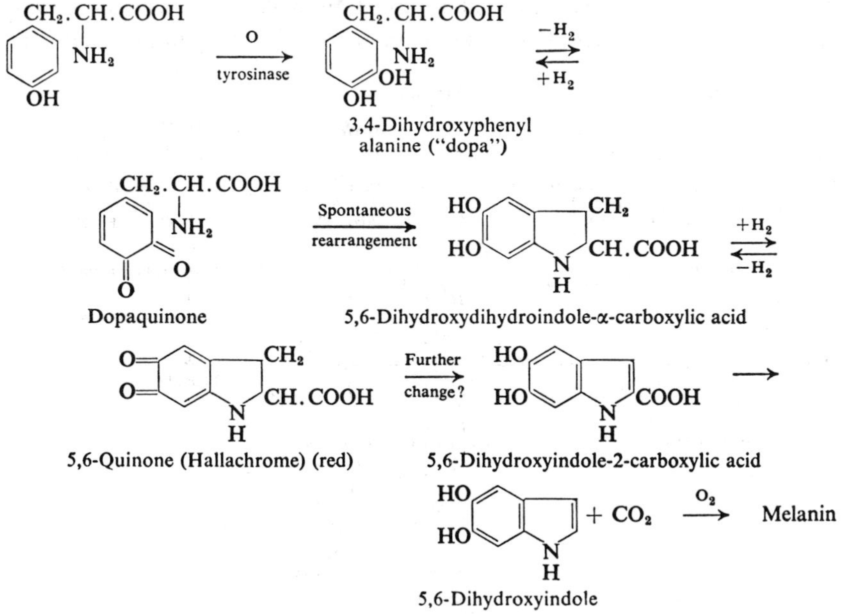

3,4-Dihydroxyphenyl alanine ("dopa")

Dopaquinone — Spontaneous rearrangement → 5,6-Dihydroxydihydroindole-α-carboxylic acid

5,6-Quinone (Hallachrome) (red) — Further change? → 5,6-Dihydroxyindole-2-carboxylic acid

5,6-Dihydroxyindole $+ CO_2 \xrightarrow{O_2}$ Melanin

As with tyrosine, so with dopa: ascorbic acid plays a role in the metabolism of the latter, and this means that the vitamin is an important factor in the formation of the melanin pigment. But dopa, unlike tyrosine, is changed by the kidney, whereas tyrosine is changed by the liver. Kidney slices from normal guinea-pigs readily oxidize dopa, but it is not affected when scorbutic kidney slices are used. When the scorbutic animal is cured with ascorbic acid, its kidney again shows the ability to oxidize dopa.

When dopa is oxidized with an oxidase (either mushroom tyrosinase or melanoma dopa oxidase, obtained from mouse tumor material), spectrophotometric evidence can be obtained for the formation of halla-chrome.

The formulas for tyrosine, epinephrine, and thyroxine suggest that tyrosine may be the mother substance of these two hormones. Evidence for the conversion of tyrosine into epinephrine has been obtained. Epinephrine, containing C^{14} or H^3, has been isolated after the administration of labeled phenylalanine.

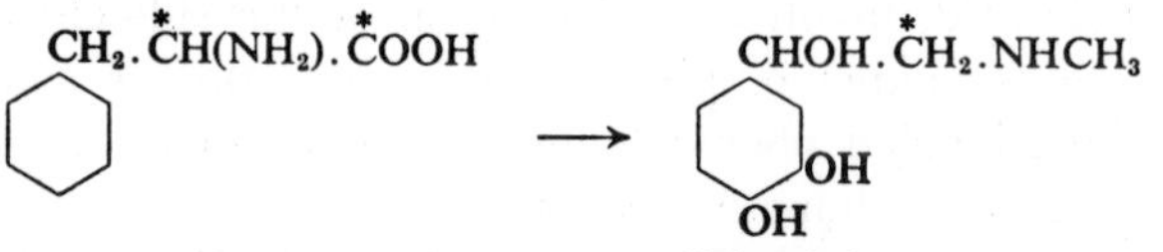

$$CH_2.\overset{*}{C}H(NH_2).\overset{*}{C}OOH \longrightarrow CHOH.\overset{*}{C}H_2.NHCH_3$$

Epinephrine

The metabolic reactions involving phenylalanine and tyrosine offer evidence for the relationship between genes (the carriers of hereditary characteristics) and enzymes. There are four well recognized hereditary diseases which involve the absence of a specific enzyme normally re-

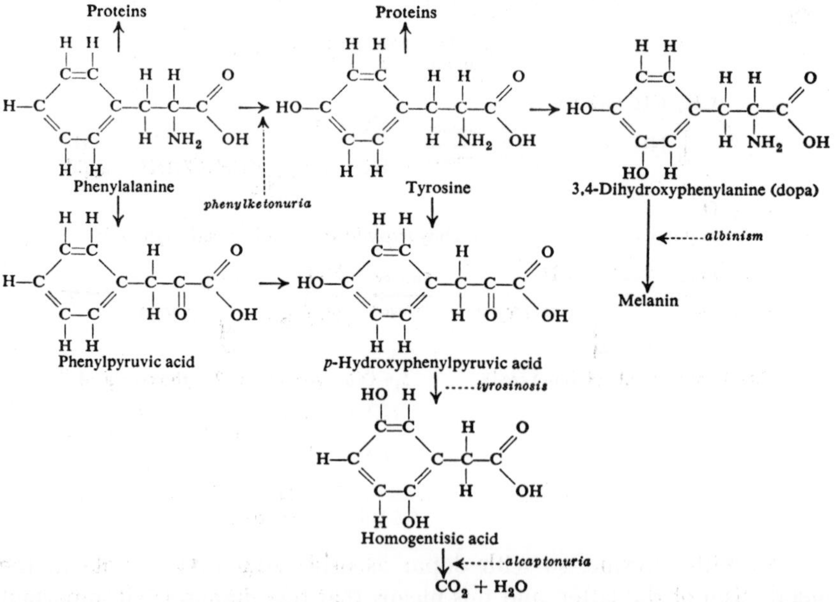

Phenylalanine-tyrosine metabolism in man showing relation of inherited defects to specific chemical reactions. (From Beadle, based on Haldane.)

quired in a sequence of reactions. The absence of one of these enzymes results in the disease *alcaptonuria,* in which there is found in the urine unusually large quantities of homogentisic acid. *Tyrosinosis* is a disease in which *p*-hydroxyphenylpyruvic acid is excreted. *Phenylketonuria* is a disease in which phenylpyruvic acid appears in unusual quantities in the urine. *Albinism* is a disease in which "dopa" fails to be oxidized to the melanin pigments. These may be called "molecular" diseases.

TRYPTOPHAN

This is an unusual amino acid since it is the only one which contains the indole nucleus. It is essential for growth and is synthesized in plants and by microorganisms (via shikimic acid, p. 352).

There are several metabolic pathways for tryptophan metabolism. Of major biological interest is the one which leads to nicotinic acid.

The interrelationship of tryptophan and nicotinic acid (niacin), the conversion of the former into the latter in the animal organism, is brought out by a number of experiments. For example, tryptophan can replace nicotinic acid in the diet of the rat, dog, pig, and rabbit. The amino acid increases the urinary elimination of nicotinic acid derivatives in man, rat, cotton rat, and horse.

Using the carbon isotope, Heidelberger, Abraham, and Lepkovsky have shown how tryptophan is converted into nicotinic acid in the rat.

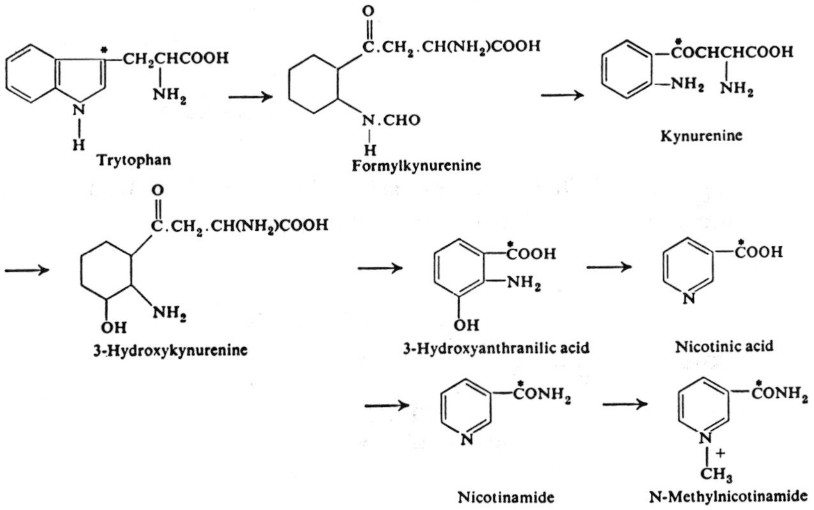

In addition to the pathway just cited, several other possible paths exist. Derivatives of 5-hydroxyindole may also be formed from tryptophan; one such compound, serotonin, is a potent vasoconstrictor. Bufotanin, found in the skin glands of the toad, is also an active pressor agent.

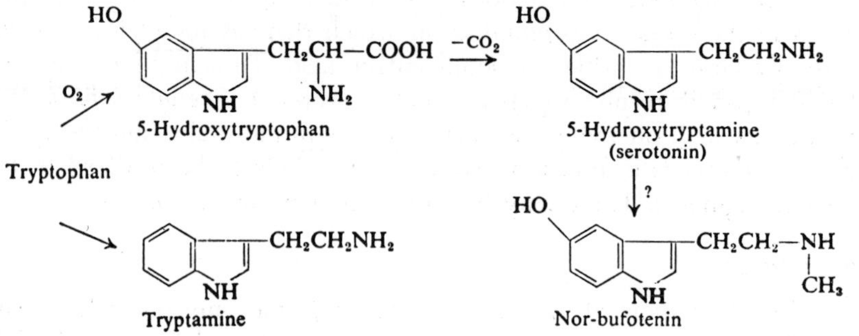

Indolacetic acid, an auxin (a growth hormone in plants, p. 580), may also be derived from tryptophan:

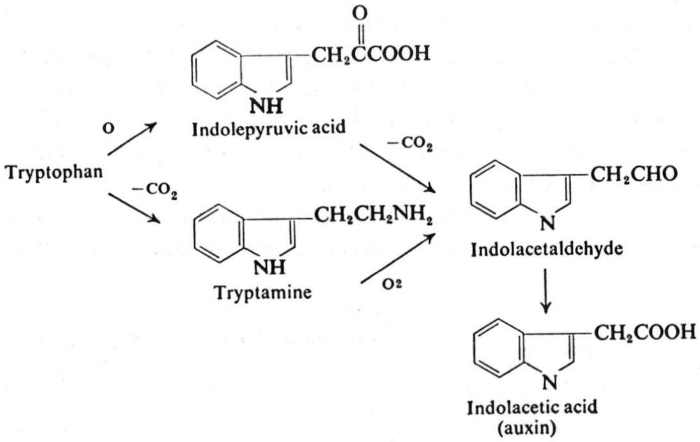

In the urine we find kynurenic acid, which is derived from kynurenine, which, in turn, is derived from tryptophan:

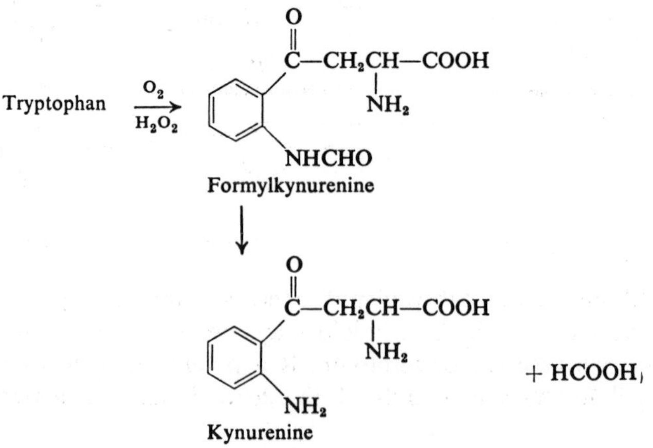

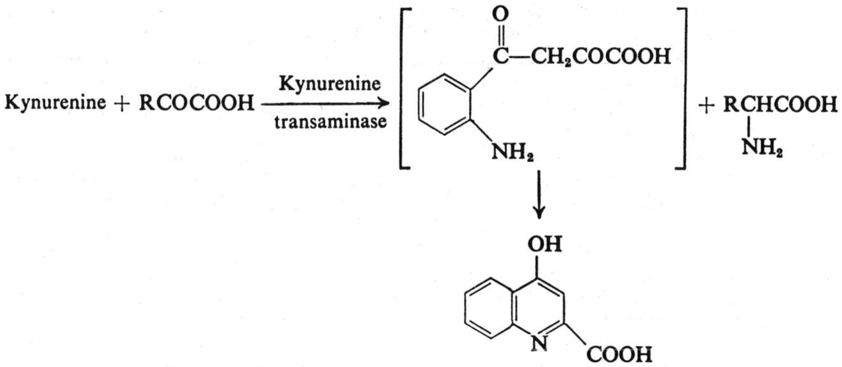

$$\text{Kynurenine} + \text{RCOCOOH} \xrightarrow[\text{transaminase}]{\text{Kynurenine}} \left[\begin{array}{c} \overset{O}{\overset{\|}{C}}-CH_2COCOOH \\ \\ NH_2 \end{array} \right] + \underset{NH_2}{\text{RCHCOOH}}$$

Kynurenic acid

An important contribution to the metabolism of tryptophan has been made by Lepkovsky, who succeeded in isolating a green pigment from the urine of rats suffering from pyridoxine deficiency. This pigment was identified as xanthurenic acid, a quinoline derivative:

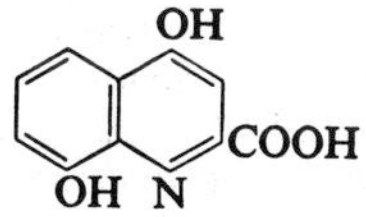

Xanthurenic acid

The substance disappears from the urine when pyridoxine is added to the diet. (Xanthurenic acid represents a further stage in the oxidation of kynurenic acid, but it does not appear to be formed from kynurenic acid in the body.)

REFERENCES

The monographs by *Fischer* (1954) and *Meister* (1957) on protein metabolism are good introductory volumes.

The biosynthesis of proteins is reviewed by *Zamecnik* in the Harvey Lectures, 1960, p. 256.

Vaughan and *Anfinsen:* Science, *124:*389, 1956 (kinetic aspects of assembly and degradation); *Askonas, Campbell, Godin* and *Work:* Biochem. J., *61:*105, 1955 (precursors in the synthesis of casein); *Flavin* and *Anfinsen:* J. Biol. Chem., *211:*375, 1954 (ovalbumin synthesis); *Nirenberg:* Proc. Nat. Acad. Sci., *47:* 1580, 1588, 1961 ("messenger" RNA).

For a review of the metabolism of amino acids, see *Udenfriend, Weissbach* and *Mitoina:* Ann. Rev. Biochem., *29:*207, 1960.

For a discussion of L- and D-amino acid oxidases, see *Meister, Wellner* and *Scott:* J. National Cancer Institute, *24:*31, 1960.

GLYCINE AND SERINE. *Shemin:* Federation Proceedings, *15:*971, 1956 (glycine); *Kisliuk* and *Sakami:* J. Biol. Chem., *214:*47, 1955 (serine biosynthesis); *Nakada, Friedmann* and *Weinhouse:* Ibid., *216:*583, 1955 (glycine); *Alexander* and *Greenberg:* Ibid., *214:*821, 1955; *220:*775, 787, 1956 (serine); *Mackenzie* in *McElroy* and *Glass's* Amino Acid Metabolism. 1955, p. 684 (glycine → serine).

LEUCINE, ISOLEUCINE, AND VALINE. *Adelberg* in *McElroy* and *Glass's* Amino Acid

Metabolism, 1955, p. 419 (isoleucine, valine and leucine); *Kinnory, Takeda, and Greenberg:* J. Biol. Chem., *212*:379, 385, 1955 (valine).

GLUTAMIC ACID, PROLINE, HYDROXYPROLINE, ORNITHINE. *Stetten* in *McElroy* and *Glass's* Amino Acid Metabolism, 1955, p. 227; *Meister:* J. Biol. Chem., *206*:577, 1954 (keto analogues of arginine and ornithine); *Levintow* and *Meister:* Ibid., *209*:265, 1954 (glutamine).

HISTIDINE. *Tabor* in *McElroy* and *Glass's* Amino Acid Metabolism, 1955, p. 373 (degradation of histidine); *Tabor* and *Mehler:* J. Biol. Chem., *210*:559, 1954 (isolation of formyl-L-glutamic acid); *Ames* and *Mitchell:* Ibid., *212*:687, 1955 (biosynthesis); *Levy* and *Coon:* Ibid., *208*:691, 1954 (biosynthesis); *Melville, Horner, Otken* and *Ludwig:* Ibid., *213*:61, 1955 (ergothioneine).

LYSINE. *Schweet, Holden* and *Lowy* in *McElroy* and *Glass's* Amino Acid Metabolism, 1955, p. 496 (α-keto acid of Lysine); *Rothstein* and *Miller:* J. Biol. Chem., *211*:851, 1954 (lysine → pipecolic acid); *Rothstein* and *Miller:* Ibid., *206*:243, 1954 (metabolism); *Schweet, Holden* and *Lowy:* Ibid., *211*:517, 1954 (metabolism in *Neurospora*); *Anon.:* Nutr. Rev., *15*:303, 1957.

CYSTINE AND METHIONINE. *Du Vigneaud:* A Trail of Research in Sulfur Chemistry and Metabolism, 1952; *Cantoni:* Federation Proceedings, *11*:399, 1952.

PHENYLALANINE AND TYROSINE. *Udenfriend* and *Mitoina* in *McElroy* and *Glass's* Amino Acid Metabolism, 1955, p. 876 (phenylalanine → tyrosine); *Dische* and *Rittenberg:* J. Biol. Chem., *211*:199, 1954 (phenylalanine); *Simmonds, Dowling* and *Stone:* Ibid., *208*:701, 1954 (phenylalanine and tyrosine); *Weiss, Gilvarg, Mingioli* and *Davis:* Science, *119*:774, 1954 (phenylalanine); *Jervis:* J. Biol. Chem., *169*:651, 1947 (Phenylpyruvic oligophrenia).

TRYPTOPHAN. *Mehler* in *McElroy* and *Glass's* Amino Acid Metabolism, 1955, p. 882 (metabolism); *Tatum* and *Shemin:* J. Biol. Chem., *209*:671, 1954 (synthesis); *Rafelson:* Ibid., *212*:953, 1955 (acetate → tryptophan).

In connection with the concept of the dynamic state of body proteins, see *Schoenheimer:* The Dynamic State of Body Constituents, 1942; *Borsook:* Physiol. Rev. *30*:206, 1950; *San Pietro* and *Rittenberg:* J. Biol. Chem., *201*:445, 457, 1953.

GLUTATHIONE SYNTHESIS. See, among others, *Snoke, Yanari* and *Bloch:* J. Biol. Chem., *201*:573, 1953 (synthesis of glutathione from γ-glutamylcysteine).

METABOLISM
OF
NUCLEOPROTEINS

The metabolism of nucleoproteins is really the metabolism of nucleic acids, for it is assumed that the protein portion of the nucleoproteins is metabolized in the usual way (see preceding chapter).

As we have seen when discussing the chemistry of the nucleoproteins (p. 112), these substances are of great importance, since they are concerned with the chemical make-up of the nucleus, the chromosomes and the viruses, and since they are concerned with the synthesis of protein. Their metabolism, then, should shed light on these interrelationships.

We shall consider the enzymes that are known to be involved in the decomposition of nucleic acid; the modes of biosynthesis of the pentose, purine and pyrimidine fractions (and their degradation); and some aspects of the metabolic relation of nucleic acids to genes, viruses and protein synthesis.

We should recall at this point that the nucleic acid is a polynucleotide (p. 120); that the nucleotide consists of a combination of phosphoric acid, a sugar (ribose or deoxyribose) and a purine or pyrimidine; and that a nucleoside is a nucleotide from which phosphoric acid has been split off.

ENZYMES AFFECTING THE DEGRADATION OF
NUCLEIC ACIDS

NUCLEODEPOLYMERASES

During the digestive process it is assumed that the protein is split from the nucleic acid and digested to amino acids. Pancreatic juice contains two enzymes, ribonuclease and deoxyribonuclease, which act quite specifically on their corresponding nucleic acids. Ribonuclease will also split some ribonucleotides. This enzyme cleaves the bond between the 3'-pyrimidine nucleoside phosphoryl groups and the 5'-hydroxy group of an adjacent purine or pyrimidine nucleotide group, shown in the diagram below.

In the diagram a purine is indicated by Pu, a pyrimidine indicated by Pyr (each attached to the ribose molecule at C-1), and ribonuclease is indicated by RNA-ase. The ribose molecules are attached by means of phosphate ester groups at the 3' and 5' carbon atoms of the individual sugars. The dotted lines indicate points of cleavage by the enzyme

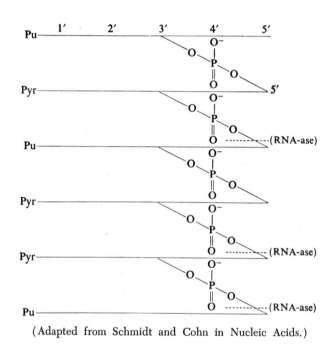

(Adapted from Schmidt and Cohn in Nucleic Acids.)

ribonuclease. After complete digestion, a mixture of nucleotides of various degrees of polymerization is obtained, each containing a terminal pyrimidine nucleotide. These products are mixtures of dialyzable as well as nondialyzable compounds.

Deoxyribonuclease yields di- and trinucleotides as well as oligonucleotides. There is some evidence for several different deoxynucleases.

In addition to these two enzymes, there is in the intestinal mucosa and also in snake venom a nonspecific phosphodiesterase which can split the linkage between carbon 3' and the oxygen atom of the phosphoric acid group in both types of nucleic acids. Alkali splits the linkage between the phosphate group and carbon 5' of the sugar, whereas the enzyme, bone phosphatase, splits the terminal phosphate bonds, yielding inorganic phosphate.

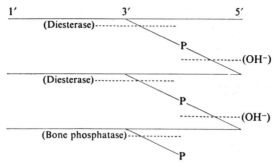

(From Volkin and Cohn: J. Biol. Chem., *205*:767, 1953.)

NUCLEOTIDASES

These enzymes hydrolyze the phosphoryl group of mononucleotides. In addition to the nonspecific phosphatases, such as intestinal, bone, and acid prostatic phosphatase, there are also more specific nucleotidases, one of which, 5'-nucleotidase, occurs in muscle, nerve tissue and bull testicle. Germinating rye grass and germinating barley contain a specific 3'-nucleotidase. The result is the production of nucleosides and inorganic phosphate.

NUCLEOSIDE KINASE

Such an enzyme is found in animal tissues (liver) and is quite specific for adenosine. Its action is illustrated below:

Adenosine	+	ATP	$\longrightarrow$	AMP	+	ADP
(Adenine-ribose)		(Adenine-ribose-P-P-P)		(Adenine-ribose-P or adenylic acid)		(Adenine-ribose-P-P)

This enzyme catalyzes the transfer of the terminal phosphate group of ATP to the nucleoside adenosine, forming a nucleotide, adenylic acid (AMP).

NUCLEODEAMINASES

Among the deaminases which are important in metabolic reactions of the purines and derivatives are adenase, guanase, cytosine deaminase, cytidine deaminase, 5'-adenylate deaminase and ADP deaminase. An example of this group of enzymes is adenosine deaminase, present in most tissues of higher animals. The result of the action of this enzyme is the production of hypoxanthine riboside, also called inosine:

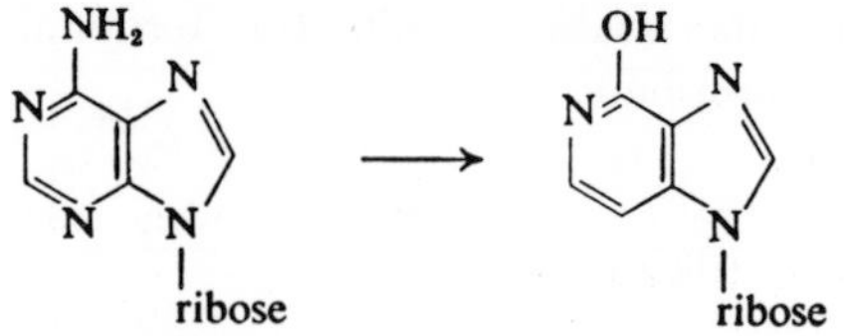

Adenosine → Inosine

Another deaminase, present in striated muscle, is 5'-adenylic acid deaminase. It produces inosinic acid:

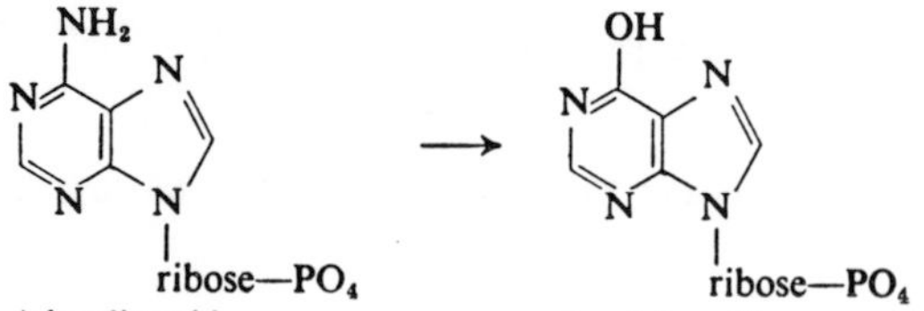

Adenylic acid → Inosinic acid

NUCLEOSIDASES

These enzymes act on the linkages between the basic and the carbohydrate groups of the nucleic acid derivatives. An example is given below for the action of a nucleoside phosphorylase on inosine:

$$\text{Inosine} + PO_4^{\equiv} \longrightarrow \text{hypoxanthine} + \text{ribose-1-phosphate}$$
(hypoxanthine-ribose)

A pyrimidine nucleoside phosphorylase is also known.

XANTHINE OXIDASE

This enzyme is present in most mammals. It is found in the liver, spleen, kidney and small intestine. It is also present in milk. In the purified state it contains, in addition to protein, flavine adenine dinucleotide (FAD), Fe and Mo. It possesses two types of activity. It can act as an oxidase utilizing molecular oxygen for the reoxidation of the reduced FADH-enzyme, or it can utilize other electron acceptors such as ferricytochrome c; in the latter case it acts as a dehydrogenase. The substrates for this enzyme are either hypoxanthine or xanthine, which are converted to uric acid:

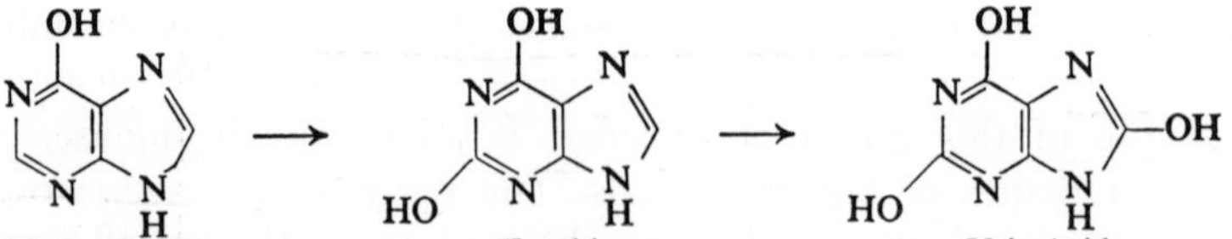

Hypoxanthine → Xanthine → Uric Acid

URICASE

Although man and the higher (anthropoid) apes excrete uric acid as an end-product of purine metabolism, other mammals convert most of their uric acid to allantoin. This is due to the presence in these animals of the enzyme uricase (a cupro-protein), an oxidase which catalyzes the following reaction:

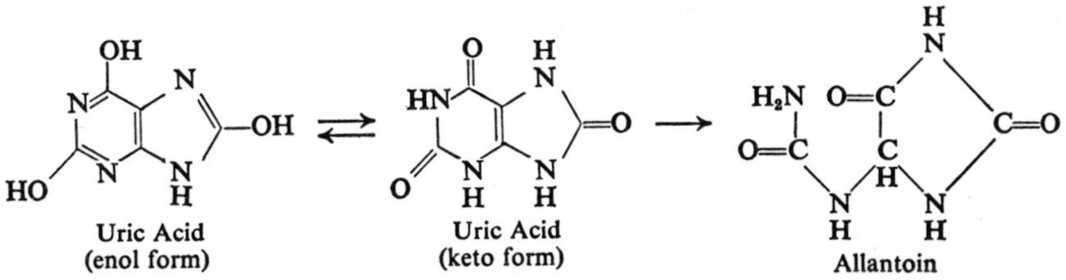

Uric Acid (enol form) ⇌ Uric Acid (keto form) → Allantoin

Among one group of teleosts there is present an enzyme, allantoinase, which degrades allantoin further to allantoic acid. Among amphibia, the enzyme allantoicase degrades allantoic acid to urea; among crustaceans, the enzyme urease breaks down the urea to ammonia.

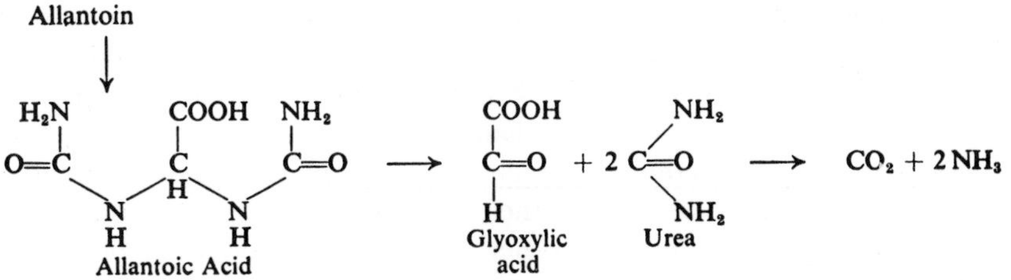

Allantoin → Allantoic Acid → Glyoxylic acid + 2 Urea → $CO_2 + 2 NH_3$

The Dalmatian dog is a curious exception, for it excretes both uric acid and allantoin. This is believed to be due not to a lack of uricase but rather to the inability of the kidney of this dog to reabsorb uric acid from the glomerular filtrate. In birds and reptiles much of the excreta consists of uric acid. Here, however, uric acid represents an end-product of protein metabolism. Although it is suspected that man metabolizes some uric acid, the mechanism of such a reaction is unknown.

NUCLEIC ACID CATABOLISM

The probable metabolic pathway for the degradation of the nucleic acids can best be illustrated in the following scheme, starting with the mononucleotides. The transformation of adenine to hypoxanthine probably does not take place in man because of the absence of the enzyme adenase:

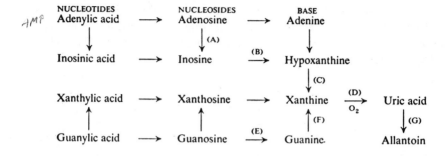

Several examples of the enzymes involved in the specific reactions are: (A), adenosine deaminase; (B) and (E), nucleoside phosphorylase; (C) and (D), xanthine oxidase; (F), guanase; (G), uricase.

BIOSYNTHESIS OF NUCLEIC ACIDS

PENTOSE BIOSYNTHESIS

In contrast to many bacteria, mammalian tissues do not seem to be able to utilize free pentoses. On the other hand, the metabolism of pentose phosphates is definitely known. In man most of the pentose which is ingested is excreted unchanged in the urine and feces. However, there are two pathways which may explain the origin of pentose sugars in animals. One is via the "hexosemonophosphate shunt" described on page 279; and the other is by the condensation of 2- and 3-carbon compounds.

In the alternate pathway of glucose oxidation, D-ribose-5-phosphate is formed by the oxidation of glucose-6-phosphate. The conversion of this 5-carbon sugar phosphate to the pentose in nucleic acids is suggested by the following reactions:

Ribose-5-PO$_4$ $\longrightarrow$ ribose-1-PO$_4$ $\longrightarrow$ ribose nucleoside $\longrightarrow$ ribonucleic acid

To account for the synthesis of deoxyribose, we can make use of the condensation reaction of Racker, who showed that 3-phosphoglyceraldehyde could be converted to deoxyribose phosphate by an enzyme (deoxyribose phosphate aldolase) and acetaldehyde. This enzyme is known to be present in animal tissues as well as in microorganisms:

Glyceraldehyde-3-PO$_4$ + acetaldehyde $\longrightarrow$ deoxyribose-5-PO$_4$

Although acetaldehyde functions actively, it is not, perhaps the natural substrate for this enzyme. There is a belief that in nature the aldehyde is linked to some other compound. The conversion of deoxyribose-5-PO_4 to deoxyribonucleic acid may take place in the same manner as postulated above for the synthesis of RNA.

PURINE BIOSYNTHESIS

It has been known for a long time that purines are synthesized in the animal organism. The work of Schoenheimer with N^{15}-labeled compounds indicated, however, that the nitrogen of arginine, urea, uracil or thymine cannot be incorporated into the purines. Our present knowledge of purine biosynthesis comes from a group of workers using the isotopic labeling technique. Outstanding work with this technique has been done with pigeon liver slices and extracts.

In the bird and man the end-product of purine metabolism is uric acid; in animals such as the rat it is allantoin. One can therefore feed a compound suspected of being a purine precursor and analyze the uric acid or allantoin in the excreta for the isotope. By use of this type of approach, the precursors for all the N and C atoms of the purine skeleton have been elucidated. These are shown in the following structure for uric acid:

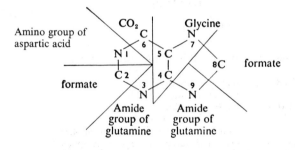

This diagram indicates that both of the carbon atoms and the nitrogen atom of the amino acid glycine are directly incorporated into the purine structure. Carbon atom no. 6 arises from CO_2, that is, from any compound which will give rise to CO_2; and carbon atoms no. 2 and no. 8 arise from formate. Nitrogen atoms no. 3 and 9 have their origin in the amide nitrogen of glutamine; and N-1 arises from the nitrogen of the amino groups of glutamic or aspartic acids. An examination of the purines which occur in polynucleotides (isolated from nucleic acids) shows the same biosynthetic pattern as that shown for uric acid.

Details of the intermediary reactions between the compounds of small molecular weight and the purine skeleton have been accumulating, and are shown in the following scheme (the enzymes involved in this scheme have been separated and partially purified):

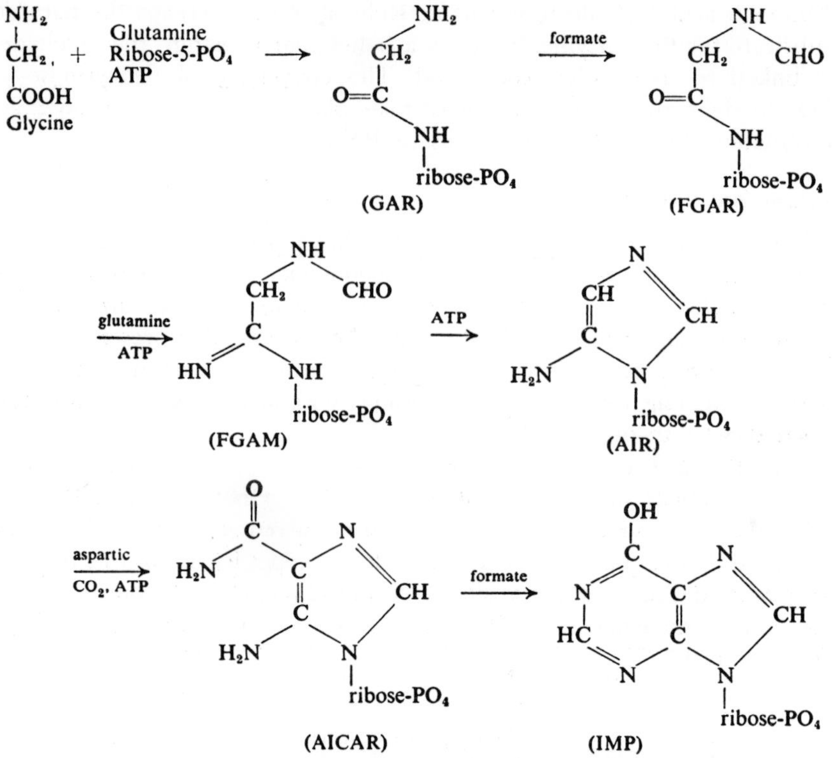

NH$_2$
|
CH$_2$, + Glutamine
| Ribose-5-PO$_4$ $\longrightarrow$
COOH   ATP
Glycine

NH$_2$
|
CH$_2$
|
O=C
    \
     NH
      |
      ribose-PO$_4$
(GAR)

formate $\longrightarrow$

NH
|
CH$_2$ CHO
|
O=C
    \
     NH
      |
      ribose-PO$_4$
(FGAR)

$\xrightarrow[\text{ATP}]{\text{glutamine}}$

NH
|
CH$_2$ CHO
    \   /
     C
    // \
  HN   NH
          |
          ribose-PO$_4$
(FGAM)

$\xrightarrow{\text{ATP}}$

N
||
CH   CH
  \   ‖
   C   CH
  / |
H$_2$N   N
         |
         ribose-PO$_4$
(AIR)

$\xrightarrow[\text{CO}_2, \text{ATP}]{\text{aspartic}}$

O
||
C
|
H$_2$N   C   N
     \ / \\
      C   CH
     / \ |
H$_2$N   C   N
         |
         ribose-PO$_4$
(AICAR)

formate $\longrightarrow$

OH
|
C   N
 \   \\
N   C   CH
 ‖ | ‖
HC   C   N
 \   / \   /
  N   N
         |
         ribose-PO$_4$
(IMP)

The abbreviations refer to the following compounds:

    GAR = glycinamide ribotide
   FGAR = formylglycinamide ribotide
   FGAM = formylglycinamidine ribotide
    AIR = 4-aminoimidazole ribotide
  AICAR = 4-amino-5-imidazolecarboxamide ribotide
    IMP = inosinic acid (hypoxanthine-ribose-phosphate)

INTERCONVERSION OF PURINES

The exact relationship of inosinic acid (IMP) to the other purines is not known. Inosinic acid may occupy a midway position: it may be finally excreted as uric acid, or it may form the purines of nucleic acid.

Among the purines found in nucleic acid, adenine probably plays an important role. The N of adenine is incorporated into the adenine (and guanine) of nucleic acid (largely into the RNA, and little into DNA). With rapidly growing tissues, incorporation into DNA is increased. Of some interest is the fact that adenine itself is better incorporated than adenosine (the riboside) or adenylic acid (the ribotide).

In contrast to adenine, guanine and guanosine are but little incorporated when fed to animals; guanylic acid, however, is much more readily incorporated. An intermediate which is believed to be involved in the conversion of adenine to guanine is 2,6-diaminopurine:

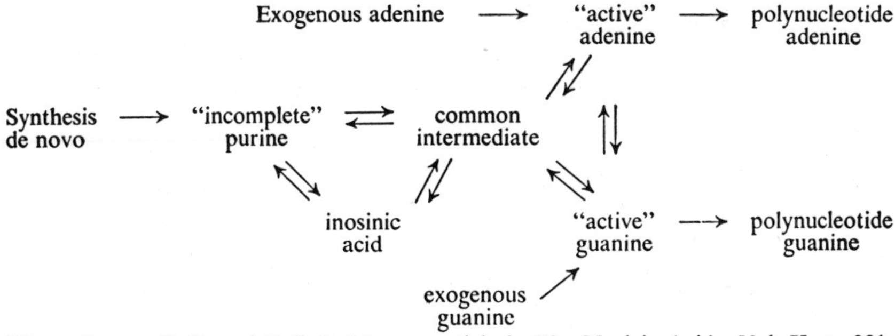

(From Brown, G. B. and Roll, P. M.: an article in The Nucleic Acids, Vol. II, p. 381, edited by Chargaff and Davidson. New York, Academic Press.)

RELATIONSHIP OF PURINE SYNTHESIS TO NUCLEIC ACID METABOLISM

We may now list some facts concerning the pathways which relate the synthesis of purine to nucleic acid synthesis, as well as nucleic acid degradation. Among these facts are:

a. Completion of the purine ring is accomplished *only* after the attachment of ribose and phosphate.

b. The first complete purine, inosinic acid, may not be on the direct pathway of nucleic acid synthesis, but may lie on the pathway of nitrogen excretion, in the form of uric acid.

c. "Active" forms of adenine and guanine are suggested as the forms which are directly incorporated into nucleic acids.

d. Interconversion of the purines can be accounted for by the reversible nature of the reactions.

e. Thus two pathways to account for the origin of uric acid would exist: (1) rapid and direct conversion of biosynthetic purine via inosinic acid, hypoxanthine and xanthine to uric acid, and (2) breakdown of nucleic acids via a common intermediate which would be catabolized to uric acid:

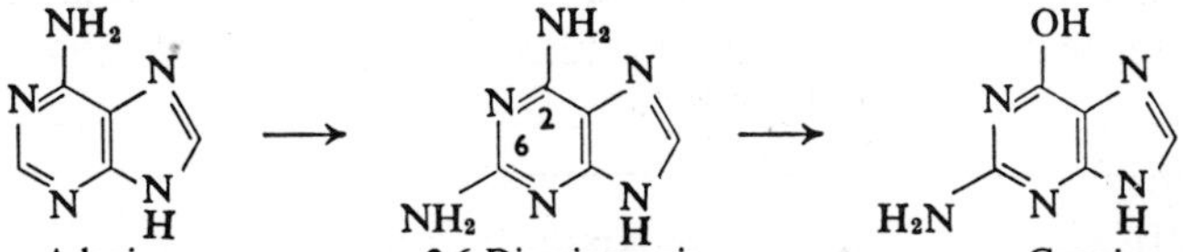

PYRIMIDINE BIOSYNTHESIS

Much less is known concerning the intermediate steps in pyrimidine biosynthesis (as compared with those of the purines). The difficulty lies in the fact that no end-product of pyrimidine metabolism is available which is as specific as uric acid is for purine metabolism. The end-product of pyrimidine metabolism is urea, which is also the end-prod-uct of protein metabolism. Some facts have been collected by studying the incorporation of tagged small molecules into polynucleotide pyrimi-dines. Intact glycine is not utilized *per se*. However, administration of N^{15}-ammonia tags position no. 1, and administration of CO_2 tags posi-tion no. 2 of the pyrimidine nucleus:

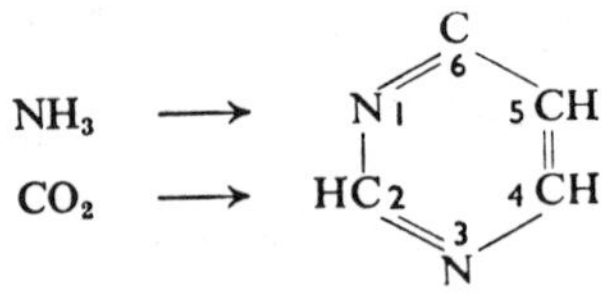

$$NH_3 \longrightarrow$$
$$CO_2 \longrightarrow$$

Some information has been accumulated from studies using *Neuro-spora* and bacteria. Orotic acid (uracil-4-carboxylic acid) is present in milk. It was shown that orotic acid could replace pyrimidines in a medium used for the support of growth of a mutant strain of *Neuro-spora*. It was then shown that in the rat orotic acid was incorporated into polynucleotide pyrimidines in both DNA and RNA.

Another compound which is a precursor of pyrimidines in nucleic acids is ureidosuccinic acid. This compound is incorporated also into orotic acid in liver slices of the rat. The origin of ureidosuccinic acid is aspartic acid together with ammonia (glutamine?) and carbon dioxide.

Finally, Kornberg has demonstrated the reaction of phosphoribosyl pyrophosphate with orotic acid in the synthesis of uridine phosphate. These findings suggest the following scheme for the biosynthesis of pyrimidines:

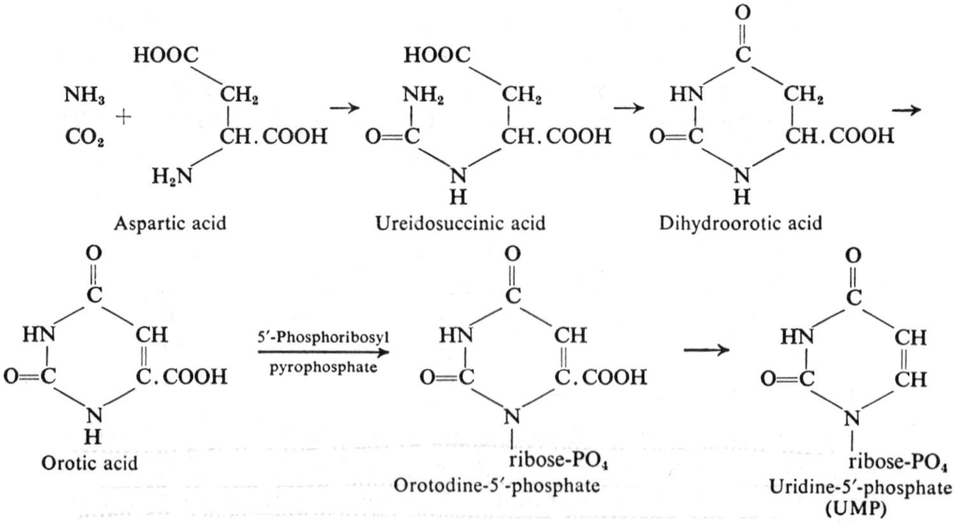

Aspartic acid   Ureidosuccinic acid   Dihydroorotic acid

Orotic acid   5'-Phosphoribosyl pyrophosphate   Orotodine-5'-phosphate   Uridine-5'-phosphate (UMP)

The origin of the phosphoribosyl pyrophosphate and its reaction with orotic acid is shown in the following:

Ribose-5'-phosphate + ATP $\longrightarrow$ 5'-phosphoribosyl pyrophosphate + AMP
(PRPP)

PRPP + orotic acid $\longrightarrow$ orotidine-5'-phosphate + pyrophosphate

Orotidine-5'-phosphate $\longrightarrow$ UMP + CO_2

THE VARIOUS PATHWAYS OF PURINE AND PYRIMIDINE SYNTHESIS

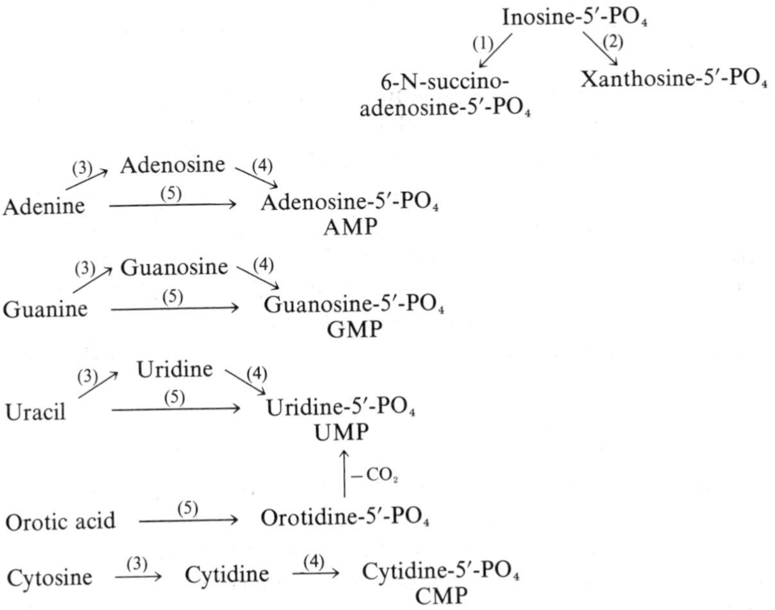

Figure 79. Pathways of purine and pyrimidine synthesis. (1) aspartate + GTP; (2) DPN; (3) ribose-1-PO_4; (4) ATP; (5) phosphoribosyl pyrophosphate. (Adapted from J. L. Strominger, Physiol. Rev., 40:55, 1960.)

VITAMINS AND NUCLEIC ACID SYNTHESIS

Folic acid (p. 465) has been shown to have a specific function in nucleic acid synthesis. Rats on a diet which produces a folic acid deficiency incorporate a decreased amount of formate-C^{14} into the purines in liver nucleic acid. After treatment with folic acid, incorporation returns to normal. The mechanism of this inhibition probably involves a compound structurally related to folic acid. This compound, discovered during work with bacteria, is known as the citrovorum factor (also as leucovorin, folinic acid SF and coenzyme F; see p. 467). It is a derivative of folic acid, N-5-formyl-5,6,7,8-tetrahydrofolic acid, and it promotes the growth of the bacterium Leuconostoc citrovorum—hence its name.

Both folic acid and the coenzyme F (CoF) activate the incorporation of radioactive formate into inosinic acid in the presence of pigeon liver extracts, but CoF is much more active than folic acid.

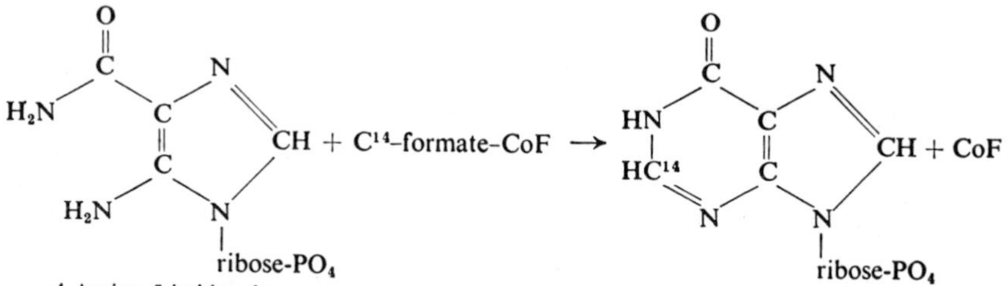

4-Amino-5-imidazole carboxamide ribotide

Inosinic acid

Another vitamin of importance in nucleic acid metabolism is vitamin B_{12} (see p. 470). In rats made deficient in B_{12}, the DNA and RNA of the liver are less than that of normal animals. In addition, there is also a decreased incorporation of glycine N^{15} into nucleic acid. After administration of B_{12} to deficient rats, there is an increase in RNA and DNA of the liver. A clue to the mechanism of this action was obtained from studies with microorganisms, in which it was shown that deoxynucleosides, especially thymidine, can substitute for B_{12}. Thus vitamin B_{12} may function as a coenzyme in the conversion of thymine to thymidine, its deoxyribose.

BIOSYNTHESIS OF RNA

Ochoa and his coworkers have achieved the *in vitro* synthesis of RNA from simpler molecules in the presence of an enzyme purified from *Azotobacter vinelandii* as well as other microorganisms. The enzyme brings about the polymerization of single nucleotides: adenylic acid, guanylic acid, uridylic acid and cytidylic acid to form strands of RNA called poly-A, poly-G, poly-U and poly-C, respectively. Copolymers have also been prepared, such as poly-AU and poly-AGUC. The reaction requires addition of a primer of natural or synthetic RNA. Inorganic phosphate is released. Since the reaction is a reversible phosphorolysis, the enzyme is termed polynucleotide phosphorylase. The synthetic polynucleotides are made up of 5′-mononucleotide units linked to one another through 3′-phosphoribose ester bonds as in natural RNA. The AGUC polymer appears to be indistinguishable from RNA. The nature of the polymerization reaction is:

$$n \; X—R—P—P \; \underset{\text{enzyme}}{\overset{Mg^{++} +}{\rightleftarrows}} \; (X—R—P)_n + n \; P$$

where X is a base, R is ribose, and P–P is pyrophosphate. More recently several groups of workers have uncovered an enzyme (RNA polymerase) which brings about the synthesis of RNA from the four nucleotide triphosphates and requires DNA, which determines the sequence of bases in RNA.

BIOSYNTHESIS OF DNA

Kornberg and his colleagues are responsible for elucidation of the mechanism of DNA synthesis. They have purified an enzyme, polymerase, from *E. coli* which brings about the condensation of the four deoxyribonucleoside-5′-triphosphates in the presence of primer DNA. Analysis of the synthetic product demonstrates that the sequence of deoxynucleosides is the same as in the DNA primer which is used. The mechanism is illustrated in Figure 80.

The substrate must be a tri-, not a diphosphate, and only the deoxyribose compound is active. The DNA which is added acts more like a template than it does as a primer, such as we see when glycogen is synthesized (p. 270), since if one of the triphosphates is omitted the reaction proceeds only to a very limited extent. It is the capacity for base pairing (p. 125), by hydrogen-bonding between preexisting DNA and the nucleotides added as substrates, that accounts for the require-

$$\left.\begin{array}{l} n\ \text{TPPP} \\ n\ \text{dGPPP} \\ n\ \text{dAPPP} \\ n\ \text{dCPPP} \end{array}\right. + \text{DNA} \rightleftharpoons \text{DNA} - \begin{bmatrix} \text{TP} \\ \text{dGP} \\ \text{dAP} \\ \text{dCP} \end{bmatrix}_n + 4(n)\text{PP}$$

Figure 80. Equation for enzymatic synthesis of DNA. (From Kornberg: Science, *131:*1504, 1960.)

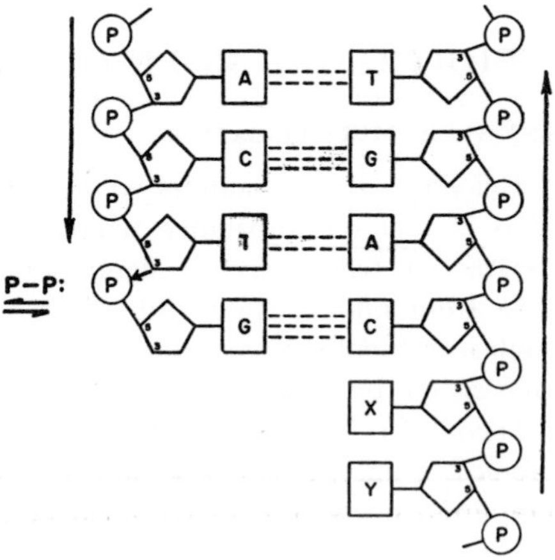

Figure 81. Mechanism for enzymatic DNA replication. (From Kornberg: Science, *131:*1504, 1960.)

ment for DNA. The DNA, therefore, acts as a coding machine, and adds the particular purine or pyrimidine substrate which will form a hydrogen-bonded pair with a base on the template. The enzymatic product is indistinguishable from high molecular weight, double-stranded DNA isolated from natural sources. It behaves like a long, stiff rod with a molecular weight of about six million. With purified enzyme, only single-stranded DNA is active but the double-stranded DNA shows no activity. Figure 81 illustrates the mechanism for enzymatic replication. Table 46 shows that the chemical composition of enzymatically prepared DNA is determined by the "primer" DNA which is used.

TABLE 46. CHEMICAL COMPOSITION OF ENZYMATICALLY SYNTHESIZED DNA, SYNTHESIZED WITH DIFFERENT PRIMERS. A, ADENINE; T, THYMINE; G, GUANINE; C, CYTOSINE.

DNA	A	T	G	C	$\dfrac{A+G}{T+C}$	$\dfrac{A+T}{G+C}$
Mycobacterium phlei						
Primer	0.65	0.66	1.35	1.34	1.01	0.49
Product	0.66	0.65	1.34	1.37	0.99	0.48
Escherichia coli						
Primer	1.00	0.97	0.98	1.05	0.98	0.97
Product	1.04	1.00	0.97	0.98	1.01	1.02
Calf thymus						
Primer	1.14	1.05	0.90	0.85	1.05	1.25
Product	1.12	1.08	0.85	0.85	1.02	1.29
Bacteriophage T2						
Primer	1.31	1.32	0.67	0.70	0.98	1.92
Product	1.33	1.29	0.69	0.70	1.02	1.90
A-T copolymer	1.99	1.93	<0.05	<0.05	1.03	40

(From Kornberg: Science, *131*:1503, 1960.)

BIOLOGICAL ROLE OF THE NUCLEIC ACIDS

PLANT VIRUS MULTIPLICATION

Evidence has accumulated which demonstrates that ribonucleic acid is in fact the substance which controls plant virus multiplication. By extraction from infected plants it is possible to obtain a protein that is free from nucleic acid and which is not infective to the plant, although it is identical with the protein portion of the virus nucleoprotein as measured by immunochemical methods. The tobacco mosaic virus has been split into protein and nucleic acid, and the two have been combined to reconstitute the original neucleoprotein. To prove that the plant virus needs the nucleic acid, inhibition of tobacco mosaic virus synthesis has been produced using chemical analogues (biological antagonists) of uracil, e.g., thiouracil. Reversal of inhibition occurs by the addition of uracil. Thus interference with nucleic acid synthesis interferes with virus multiplication.

EMBRYONIC GROWTH

The most important feature of experimental embryology is the phenomenon of morphogenesis—the development of form and structure in distinct stages. It has always been postulated that, in a vertebrate egg, development at a specific point in a structure is due to the presence of a hypothetical gradient—a regular increase in concentration of a substance to a maximum at that point. Such a gradient exists with respect to RNA distribution during the early stages of development. In amphibia there is a regular decrease in concentration of RNA from one pole (animal) to the other (vegetal) of the egg. After fertilization, when differentiation begins at the time of gastrulation, the dorsal lip of the blastopore (organizer) is the site of RNA synthesis. Later, every organ prior to differentiation is the site of RNA accumulation. Such gradients of RNA have also been found in the embryos of fishes, birds and mammals.

RNA AND PROTEIN SYNTHESIS

Caspersson and Brachet were among the first to suggest that RNA was involved in the synthesis of protein. We find RNA abundant in rapidly growing cells which synthesize relatively large quantities of protein; for example, cells of the gastric mucosa, which manufactures pepsin, and of the pancreas, which synthesizes other enzymes. Tissues which do not synthesize much protein (though their activity, physiologically, may be high) contain but small amounts of RNA; for example, heart, muscle and kidney. Microorganisms which are forced to synthesize their own proteins in a short time are very rich in RNA.

Of interest in this connection is the discovery that the silk gland in silkworms is very high in its content of RNA; and the only known function of this silk gland is to manufacture the protein of silk.

It may also be noted that during embryonic development the synthesis of RNA precedes the synthesis of protein.

Still further evidence is that if an animal is put on a low-protein diet, the RNA content of the liver drops sharply (although the content of DNA is *not* affected).

Using growing cultures of microorganisms, it can be shown that a close correspondence exists between the content of RNA and the synthesis of protein, especially if measurements are made during the logarithmic phase of growth.

The role of s-RNA of the liver cell in the transfer of activated amino acids to microsomal protein (p. 339) confirms the relationship between RNA and protein synthesis.

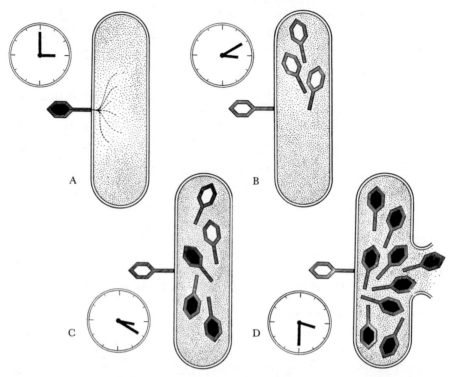

Figure 82. Reproduction of bacterial virus (coliphage T2) consists of four stages: A, infection, in which the virus attaches to the host bacterium by the "tail," and the nucleic acid core is emptied into the bacterial cell; B, the "dark" period during which virus nucleic acid begins to multiply and induces formation of new protein "coats;" C, the "rise" period when nucleic acid appears within the protein coats; and D, the burst, when some 200 new virus particles are released. The bacterium lyses and disappears. (From Stent: Scientific American, May 1953.)

RELATION OF DNA TO THE GENE

From a quantitative view the most important nucleic acid in the chromosome is of the DNA type. Historically this was associated with a positive Feulgen staining reaction.* The reaction is now known to be due to the instability of DNA in warm acid, resulting in the liberation of aldehyde groups which give a color with Schiff's reagent (a component of the Feulgen reagent). Actually, nearly all the DNA of the cell is in the nuclear chromatin. Removal of the DNA-protein from tissues (using strong salt solutions) results in a loss of definition and stainability of the nuclear material. Since Morgan showed the parallelism between organized chromosome movement and movements of genetic

* For the Feulgen reaction, see, for example, Frobisher's Microbiology, 1953, p. 116.

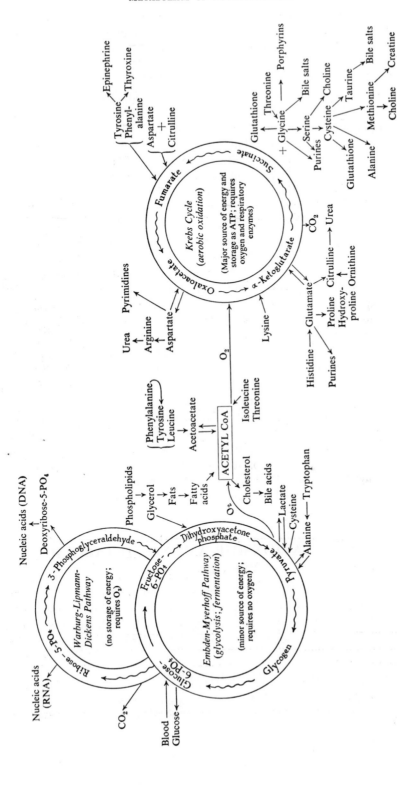

Figure 83. Interrelationships among carbohydrate, lipid, protein and nucleic acid metabolism.

determinants deduced from Mendelian genetics, the chromosome has been accepted as a carrier of the gene—the hereditary unit. It is now recognized that genes control the formation of enzymes and many proteins.

Evidence for the genetic function of DNA has been obtained from the results of treatment with agents which bring about mutational effects and at the same time affect DNA. Among these agents are ultraviolet and x-radiation, sulfur and nitrogen mustards, and methylated purines, such as caffeine and theophylline, which presumably interfere with normal incorporation of purines into the nucleic acids. Further evidence comes from the phenomenon of bacterial transformations, but such a discussion is outside the scope of this book.

ROLE OF DNA IN BACTERIOPHAGE

Growth of living matter apparently involves the duplication of structures containing DNA. One area of study which has yielded important evidence for a role of DNA in the duplication process is that concerned with the viruses which infect bacteria, the *bacteriophages*. Among these are the "T coliphages" which duplicate themselves within *Escherichia coli,* lyse the bacteria and pour the extra phage particles into the medium, ready to infect new bacteria. These phage particles appear as hexagonal or rounded bodies with tail-like projections and are composed of some 60 per cent protein and 40 per cent DNA.

When a phage is grown in a medium containing P^{32} or S^{35}, the P^{22} is incorporated into the nucleic acid and the S^{35} into the protein, thus providing a label for each moiety. The protein portion of the phage particle is the membrane which surrounds a mass of free or loosely bound DNA. Figure 82 illustrates the life cycle of the phage particle with particular reference to the protein and DNA portions of the phage as well as that of the host bacterial cell. Electron micrographs show these phage particles attached to the host bacterium as illustrated in the diagram on page 374.

INTERRELATIONSHIP AMONG METABOLIC PROCESSES

It is sometimes helpful to view the entire scheme of metabolic reactions in one picture. Figure 83 attempts to relate the metabolic pathways of carbohydrate, lipid, protein and nucleic acids. Many details covered in previous chapters are deleted for purposes of clarity.

REFERENCES

For an introduction, see *Davidson:* The Biochemistry of Nucleic Acids, 1950. A much more comprehensive treatise is The Nucleic Acids by *Chargaff* and *Davidson,* 1955.

Schmidt in *Chargaff* and *Davidson's* treatise (see above), Vol. II, p. 584, discusses the enzymes involved in the degradation of nucleic acids.

Moore, Hirs and *Stein:* Federation Proceedings, *15*:840, 1956, describe their work on the structure of ribonuclease, an enzyme which, like all enzymes so far investigated, is a protein.

The pentose phosphate pathway of carbohydrate metabolism is discussed by *Horecker* and *Mehler:* Ann. Rev. Biochem., *24*:229, 1955.

Carter's article (Ann. Rev. Biochem., *25*:130, 1956) describes the biosynthesis of purines. In the same article there is a discussion of the biosynthesis of pyrimidines. See also *Buchanan:* Harvey Lectures, series LIV, p. 104, 1958–9.

For the relationship of adenine to guanine, see *Bendich, Furst* and *Brown:* J. Biol. Chem., *185*:423, 1950; for the relationship of purine synthesis and nucleic acid metabolism, see *Brown* and *Roll* in *Chargaff* and *Davidson's* The Nucleic Acids, Vol. II, p. 381, 1955; *Brown:* Federation Proceedings, *15*:823, 1956.

The role of DNA in the bacteriophage is discussed by *Hotchkiss,* in *Chargaff* and *Davidson's* The Nucleic Acids, Vol. II, p. 462, 1955.

The synthesis of RNA is described by *Ochoa,* et al., in Science, *122*:907, 1955; the synthesis of DNA will be found in Science, *131*:1503, 1960.

See also *Khorana:* Federation Proceedings, *19*:931, 1960.

The interrelationship among the folic acid coenzymes is discussed by *Huennekena, Osborn* and *Whitely,* in Science, *128*:120, 1958.

Some miscellaneous papers are by *Buchanan, Sonne* and *Delluva:* J. Biol. Chem., *173*:69, 81, 1948 (uric acid synthesis); *Kalckar:* Harvey Lectures, 1949–1950, p. 11 (Biosynthesis of Purines and Pyrimidines); *Racker:* J. Biol. Chem., *196*: 347, 1952 (pentose metabolism); *Cohen, Doherty* and *Volken* in *McElroy* and *Glass's* Phosphorus Metabolism, Vol. II, p. 339, 1952 (enzymic degradation of nucleic acids); *Ochoa:* Federation Proceedings, *15*:832, 1956 (synthesis of acid-like polynucleotides).

For genes and enzymes see also *Hotchkiss* and *Evans:* Federation Proceedings, *19:* 912, 1960.

ENERGY METABOLISM

The energy required by the living cell must be present in a form which the cell can use. There is energy needed for muscular contraction, for keeping the body warm, for transmission of nerve impulses, etc.; such energy must be convertible to the specific needs of the body.

The complete oxidation of a food to CO_2 and H_2O at the moment when its energy is needed would be a wasteful process. Actually, by a series of intermediary processes, the energy originally incorporated into chemical bonds in foods (chemical compounds) is transferred in a form which can be released when needed.

ATP, for example, stores in its terminal phosphate bond the energy originally present in the chemical bonds of carbohydrates, fats and proteins. When needed for specific cell functions, ATP can transfer its energy to systems which bring about muscular contraction, the transmission of nerve impulses (Chap. 19), peptide synthesis, etc.

ATP, it should be emphasized at this point, is widely distributed; and it is constantly being built and rebuilt, largely during aerobic processes.

During the reactions involving metabolism, oxygen is consumed and most of the carbon and hydrogen are excreted as CO_2 and H_2O. Some of the carbon and hydrogen, as well as much of the nitrogen, is excreted as urea, uric acid, creatinine, etc. Elements such as sulfur and phosphorus are excreted in the form of inorganic ions, although some of the former are eliminated as "neutral" sulfur and "ethereal" sulfate (Chap. 20).

In any event, what should be stressed is that, except for nitrogen and sulfur, the elements which have been discussed can be oxidized as completely in the body as outside of it; and one result of such an oxidation is the production of heat—a very necessary result in so far as the activities of living matter are concerned.

378

It is no small tribute to the genius of Lavoisier that he connected his theory of oxidation with the general process of respiration in man.

THE TEMPERATURE OF THE BODY

The temperature of a normal person (measured by mouth) is in the neighborhood of 37° C. (98.6° F.).* This temperature varies imperceptibly, irrespective of weather. Not only is heat produced, but there must also be some heat-regulating mechanism whereby fluctuations in temperature are prevented.

Mammals and birds, the warm-blooded animals, show such constancy of temperature, irrespective of outside conditions. The reptiles, amphibia, and fishes, the cold-blooded animals, show temperature fluctuations dependent upon environmental conditions. Their heat-regulating mechanism is either less efficient, or, for more profound reasons, it may not be needed. Hibernating animals also show a temperature in accord with their surroundings; and during this period, their heat-regulating mechanism seems to function little.

The fact that the temperature of the body is 37° C. and that it remains so is a clear indication that heat is being produced. The *quantity* of such heat production can be measured, not by a thermometer, but by a calorimeter.

CALORIMETRY

Calorimeters are of two kinds: one measures the fuel value of coal or food, and the other measures the heat evolved by the body. We shall deal first with the former type.

THE "BOMB" CALORIMETER

The principle of the "bomb" calorimeter of Berthelot is easily understood. The fuel (or food) is in a steel cylinder filled with oxygen. The reaction is started by a platinum wire heated by an electric current. The heat evolved in the reaction is communicated to a weighed quantity of water surrounding the cylinder. Knowing the weight of the water and the increase in temperature, the heat evolved by the fuel (or food), measured in calories, can be readily calculated.

Heat is measured in calories. The *calorie* used in physics represents that amount of heat necessary to increase the temperature of 1 gm. of water 1° C. (from 15° to 16° C.). The calorie used in nutritional studies is the large *Calorie* (spelled with a capital *C*)—also written as kg. cal. and kcal.—representing the amount of heat necessary to increase the

---

* The normal range of body temperature (measured by mouth) is between 96.7° and 99° F. The rectal temperature is about 97.2 to 99.5° F. Rectal temperature is the more reliable.

temperature of 1 kg. of water 1° C. The Calorie, then, is equivalent to 1000 small calories. We shall use the Calorie (C) exclusively.

Returning to our calorimeter, if the quantity of water is represented by 1 kg., and the increase in temperature is 1° C., the heat produced by the burning of the foodstuff would be 1 C(alorie). Similarly,

> 4 kg. of water raised 1° C. corresponds to 4 C.
> 1 kg. of water raised 4° C. corresponds to 4 C.
> 2 kg. of water raised 2° C. corresponds to 4 C.

The calorific value, then, is obtained by multiplying the weight of the water (in kilograms, in our case) by the increase in temperature (in °C).

In this way we arrive at the following average values:

> 1 gm. of carbohydrate when burned yields 4.1 C.
> 1 gm. of fat when burned yields 9.4 C.
> 1 gm. of protein when burned yields 5.6 C.

These are the values obtained when such foodstuffs are burned in the calorimeter. Of the three foodstuffs, the absorbed carbohydrates and fats can be burned as completely in the body as in the calorimeter; but this is not true of the protein. Here its nitrogen is not eliminated as such, but in the form of urea and several other nitrogenous products. Making due allowance for such incomplete combustion in the body, the fuel value of 1 gm. of protein, so far as the body is concerned, is nearer 4.1 C. Or, after considering the average degrees of digestibility, the figures are approximately,

> 1 gm. of carbohydrate yields 4 C.
> 1 gm. of fat yields 9 C.
> 1 gm. of protein yields 4 C.

THE ANIMAL CALORIMETER

This apparatus, developed by Atwater, Rosa and Benedict, is adapted for measuring the heat evolved by an individual (*direct* calorimetry) and for measuring the oxygen intake and carbon dioxide and nitrogen output, from which the amount of protein, carbohydrate, and fat metabolized can be calculated; and these figures also supply data for calculating the heat produced (*indirect* calorimetry).

Several details of the calorimeter—known as a *respiration calorimeter* (see Fig. 84)—include a lighted and furnished room in which the individual (the subject) may remain in comparative comfort, with walls of metal and wood to prevent heat loss. In the room are pipes containing water—with the flow carefully regulated—which take up the heat given off by the body. The amount of heat can be calculated by knowing the temperature of the water as it enters the room, the temperature when it leaves it, and the rate of flow of the water.

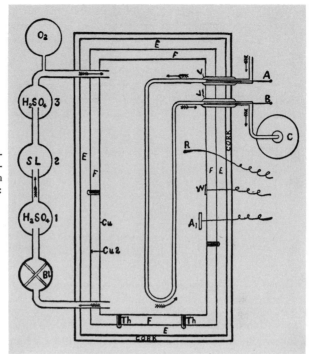

Figure 84. Schematic diagram of the Atwater-Rosa-Benedict respiration calorimeter. (From Lusk: Science of Nutrition.)

Ventilating System:
  O_2, Oxygen introduced as consumed by subject.
  3, H_2SO_4 to catch moisture given off by soda lime.
  2, Soda lime to remove CO_2.
  1, H_2SO_4 to remove moisture given off by patient.
  Bl, Blower to keep air in circulation.
Indirect Calorimetry:
  Increase in weight of H_2SO_4 (1) = water elimination of subject.
  Increase in weight of soda lime (2) + increase in weight of H_2SO_4(3) = CO_2 elimination.
  Decrease in weight of oxygen tank = oxygen consumption of subject.
Heat-absorbing System:
  A, Thermometer to record temperature of ingoing water.
  B, Thermometer to record temperature of outgoing water.

V, Vacuum jacket.
C, Tank for weighing water which has passed through calorimeter each hour.
W, Thermometer for measuring temperature of wall.
A_1, Thermometer for measuring temperature of the air.
R, Rectal thermometer for measuring temperature of subject.
Direct Calorimetry:
  Average difference of temperatures of A and B $\times$ liters of water + (gm. water eliminated $\times$ 0.586) $\pm$ (change in temperature of wall $\times$ hydrothermal equivalent of box) $\pm$ (change of temperature of body $\times$ hydrothermal equivalent of body) = total calories produced.
Th, thermocouple; Cu, inner copper wall; Cu2, outer copper wall; E, F, dead air spaces.

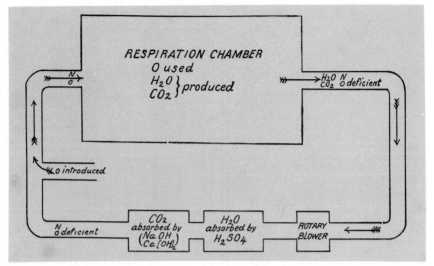

Figure 85. Diagram of circulation of air through respiration apparatus. (Atwater and Benedict.)

Using a closed circuit (see Fig. 85), a measured amount of air is drawn in by a pump, and the eliminated carbon dioxide and water are absorbed and weighed. Measured quantities of oxygen are added when needed. Provision is also made for the collection of urine and feces, with the main object of determining the amount of nitrogen eliminated.

OXYGEN

How and under what conditions the oxygen of the air reaches the cells of the body via the blood has already been discussed. Some abnormalities may be stressed at this point.

Hypoxia (oxygen deficiency) may develop at times. For example, at high altitudes "mountain sickness" may result, owing to diminished oxygen tension in the air and hence in the alveolar air and blood stream.

A common clinical form of anoxia is observed in diseases of the respiratory tract, as in pneumonia, for example. Here there is an interference with oxygen absorption.

Another common decrease is seen in cases of anemia; owing to a diminished amount of hemoglobin, not so much oxygen can combine with the blood pigment as under normal conditions.

Poisoning due to carbon monoxide interferes with respiration, because of the preferential combining capacity of hemoglobin with carbon monoxide rather than with oxygen.

Certain drugs will cause methemoglobinemia. Such substances oxidize hemoglobin to methemoglobin, which cannot combine with oxygen. The extent of active respiration will depend upon the amount of hemoglobin which has not been changed.

THE RESPIRATORY QUOTIENT

For reasons which will become apparent as we proceed, the value of the respiratory quotient (R. Q.) must be known. By the R. Q. is meant the volume of carbon dioxide evolved, divided by the volume of oxygen consumed.

When carbohydrates are oxidized, the reaction may be represented (using glucose as a type):

$$C_6H_{12}O_6 + 6\,O_2 \longrightarrow 6\,CO_2 + 6\,H_2O$$

Here the R. Q. $= \dfrac{6\,CO_2}{6\,O_2} = 1$

Fats contain less oxygen in their molecules than carbohydrates, and need, relatively, more oxygen from the outside for complete combustion:

$$\underset{\text{Triolein}}{C_{57}H_{104}O_6} + 80\,O_2 \longrightarrow 57\,CO_2 + 52\,H_2O$$

$$R.Q. = \dfrac{57\,CO_2}{80\,O_2} = 0.71$$

Since the formula of a protein is usually unknown, and therefore an equation such as the above cannot be written, the R. Q. must be determined in an indirect way.

According to Loewy, quoted by Lusk, the analysis of 100 gm. of meat protein gives the following figures (in grams):

	C	H	O	N	S
	52.38	7.27	22.68	16.65	1.02
of which is eliminated in the urine:	9.406	2.663	14.099	16.28	1.02
and in the feces:	1.47	0.212	0.889	0.37	
leaving for the respiratory process:	41.50	4.40	7.69		
deducting intramolecular water:		0.961	7.69		
leaving behind	41.50	3.439			

To oxidize 41.5 gm. of carbon and 3.439 gm. of hydrogen, we require 138.18 gm. of oxygen, and 152.17 gm. of carbon dioxide are produced.

The *weights* must now be converted into *volumes* in order to get the R. Q. of proteins. One gram of oxygen, at standard conditions, occupies a volume of 0.699 liter; and 1 gm. of carbon dioxide occupies a volume of 0.5087 liter.

For oxygen, then, $138.18 \times 0.699 = 96.63$ liters, and for carbon dioxide, $152.17 \times 0.5087 = 77.39$ liters.

The R. Q. of protein $= \dfrac{77.39}{96.63} = 0.801.$

When 1 gm. of nitrogen (in the form of urea, etc.) is eliminated, it means the following: 1 gm. of urinary nitrogen corresponds to 6.25 gm. of protein, and represents the absorption of 5.92 liters of oxygen, the elimination of 4.75 liters of carbon dioxide, and the production of 26.51 Calories (Lusk).

In severe diabetes, the R. Q., which normally on a mixed diet may be around 0.85, may reach a figure as low as 0.7, indicating that much of the combustion is derived from fats and that less carbohydrate is being metabolized. One of the many striking results of insulin treatment is that the R. Q. increases, showing that carbohydrates (and part of the protein molecule) are being better utilized for energy purposes.

INDIRECT CALORIMETRY

By knowing the oxygen consumption and the carbon dioxide output, and the amount of nitrogen (as urea, etc.) eliminated, it is possible

TABLE 47. THE SIGNIFICANCE OF THE NONPROTEIN RESPIRATORY QUOTIENT AS REGARDS THE HEAT VALUE OF 1 LITER OF OXYGEN, AND THE RELATIVE QUANTITY IN CALORIES OF CARBOHYDRATE AND FAT CONSUMED

One Liter of Oxygen is Equivalent to

Nonprotein respiratory quotient	Grams		Calories
	Carbohydrate	Fat	
0.707	0.000	0.502	4.686
0.71	0.016	0.497	4.690
0.72	0.055	0.482	4.702
0.73	0.094	0.465	4.714
0.74	0.134	0.450	4.727
0.75	0.173	0.433	4.739
0.76	0.213	0.417	4.751
0.77	0.254	0.400	4.764
0.78	0.294	0.384	4.776
0.79	0.334	0.368	4.788
0.80	0.375	0.350	4.801
0.81	0.415	0.334	4.813
0.82	0.456	0.317	4.825
0.83	0.498	0.301	4.838
0.84	0.539	0.284	4.850
0.85	0.580	0.267	4.862
0.86	0.622	0.249	4.875
0.87	0.666	0.232	4.887
0.88	0.708	0.215	4.899
0.89	0.741	0.197	4.911
0.90	0.793	0.180	4.924
0.91	0.836	0.162	4.936
0.92	0.878	0.145	4.948
0.93	0.922	0.127	4.961
0.94	0.966	0.109	4.973
0.95	1.010	0.091	4.985
0.96	1.053	0.073	4.998
0.97	1.098	0.055	5.010
0.98	1.142	0.036	5.022
0.99	1.185	0.018	5.035
1.00	1.232	0.000	5.047

(From Zuntz and Schumberg, modified by Tusk, modified by McClendon.)

to calculate the amount of carbohydrate, fat, and protein consumed, and the amount of heat (in Calories) produced. Here the heat is not measured directly and the apparatus employed is simple.

Bodansky* gives the following instructive example: During a twenty-four-hour period, the subject consumed 400 liters of oxygen, and eliminated 340 liters of carbon dioxide and 12 gm. of nitrogen.

The amount of protein represented by 1 gm. of nitrogen (1×6.25 gm. protein) requires for oxidation 5.92 liters of oxygen, and 4.75 liters of carbon dioxide are eliminated. Since 12 gm. of nitrogen were eliminated, this would mean $12 \times 5.92 = 71$ liters of oxygen (approximately), and $12 \times 4.75 = 57$ liters of carbon dioxide were derived from protein. The oxygen consumption owing to carbohydrate and fat is $400 - 71 = 329$ liters; and the production of carbon dioxide owing to carbohydrate and fat is $340 - 57 = 283$ liters.

The R. Q. of "nonprotein" (carbohydrate + fat) = 283/329 = 0.86.

From Table 47 we gather that when the R. Q. of "nonprotein" is 0.86, 1 liter of oxygen is equivalent to 0.622 gm. of carbohydrate and 0.249 gm. of fat. Therefore, 329 liters of oxygen mean

$$329 \times 0.622 = 204 \text{ gm. of carbohydrate}$$
$$\text{and } 329 \times 0.249 = 82 \text{ gm. of fat}$$
and 12 gm. of nitrogen eliminated mean $12 \times 6.25 = 75$ gm. of protein.

In other words, during this twenty-four-hour period, the subject utilized 204 gm. of carbohydrate, 82 gm. of fat, and 75 gm. of protein.

The heat value of these foodstuffs can now be calculated approximately:

$$75 \times 4 = 300 \text{ Calories from protein}$$
$$82 \times 9 = 738 \text{ " " fat}$$
$$204 \times 4 = \underline{816} \text{ " " carbohydrate}$$
$$1854 \text{ Calories†}$$

BASAL METABOLISM

The total energy output is the resultant of two factors. Under normal conditions one of these factors is a fairly constant one. It represents the energy needed in maintaining the temperature of the body (in warm-blooded animals), in maintaining the heart beat, etc. The other factor is a widely fluctuating one, depending upon the extent of exercise and upon the amount of food consumed. A subject who has fasted for some 12 hours before the experiment, and who is in a state of complete rest during the experiment, will give off an amount of heat which will tend

* Physiological Chemistry, 1938, p. 517.

† We can recalculate this in a different and more accurate way. Assume 26.51 Cal./gm. urinary N for protein and 4.875 Cal./liter of oxygen for carbohydrate and fat; then total heat = heat from protein ($26.51 \times 12 = 318.1$ Cal.) + heat from carbohydrate and fat ($329 \times 4.875 = 1603.9$ Cal.) = 1922 Cal. This is more nearly accurate than 1854 Cal. (Harold Goss).

to be constant. The heat output, under these conditions, is called the "basal metabolism," and it is measured in terms of the number of Calories produced per square meter of body surface per hour.

In one form of basal metabolic test the amount of oxygen consumed is measured. Under the conditions of the experiment, for each liter of oxygen consumed, 4.8 C. of heat is generated.

If, for example, the individual consumes 1 liter of oxygen in four minutes, or 15 liters in one hour, the heat generated would be 15×4.8, or 72 C. per hour.

If, depending upon the height and weight (Figure 86), the individual has a surface area of 2 square meters, each square meter will give off 36 C. of heat.

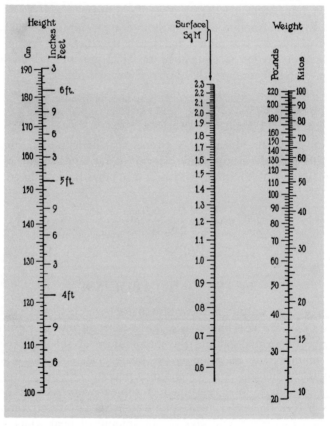

Figure 86. Nomogram permitting direct estimation of surface area from height and weight by DuBois' formula $A = H^{0.725} \times W^{0.425} \times 71.84$. A = surface area in square centimeters, H = height in centimeters, and W = weight in kg. (Sq. cm = sq. m. $\times$ 1/10,000.) The surface area is found at the point of intersection of the middle scale with a straight line drawn from the observed height on the left-hand scale to the observed weight on the right-hand scale. (From Peters and Van Slyke: Quantitative Clinical Chemistry.)

The number "36" represents Calories per square meter of surface per hour.

The importance of surface area was first emphasized by Rubner. The variations obtained by recording metabolic experiments per unit of weight are quite large.

DuBois has developed an empirical formula relating surface area, height and weight.

$$A = W^{0.425} \times H^{0.745} \times 71.84$$

where A = surface area in sq. cm., W = weight in kg., and H = height in centimeters. The nomogram makes the estimation of surface area very simple (Fig. 86).

The average basal metabolic rate for normal adults (between 30 and 40 years) is 39.5 C. for males and 36.5 C. for females.

To calculate the basal metabolic rate based on heat production, we shall take an example from Cantarow and Trumper.[*]

The individual is a male, aged 35, height 67 inches, weight 154 pounds. His surface area is 1.8 square meters.

The actual oxygen consumption is 200 cc. per minute, or 12 l per hour.

For every 1 l. of oxygen consumed, 4.825 Calories of heat are generated.

Therefore, the heat expenditure is $12 \times 4.825 = 57.9$ C. per hour.

Since the patient's surface area is 1.8 square meters, the Calories per square meter per hour $= \dfrac{57.9}{1.8} = 32.16$ C.

The normal value, according to DuBois, is 39.5 C. per square meter per hour.

Therefore, the basal metabolic rate =

$$\frac{39.5 - 32.16}{39.5} \times 100 = -18.5 \text{ per cent};$$

which is 18.5 per cent below normal.

VARIATIONS IN BASAL METABOLISM

Variations due to age are given in Table 48. The most striking variations are observed in thyroid disease. "It must be admitted," write DuBois and Chambers, "that the basal metabolism tests are seldom of great value except in the diagnosis and treatment of the thyroid gland. . . ."

In severe cases of hyperthyroidism, increases of 75 per cent (and more) above normal have been obtained; and in hypothyroidism (myxedema), figures representing 40 per cent below normal are not uncommon.

[*] See reference at the end of the chapter.

TABLE 48.   STANDARD VALUES FOR CALORIES PER SQUARE METER PER HOUR

Males		Females	
Age last birthday	Mean	Age last birthday	Mean
Years		Years	
6	53.00	6	50.62
7	52.45	6½	50.23
8	51.78	7	49.12
8½	51.20	7½	47.84
9	50.54	8	47.00
9½	49.42	8½	46.50
10	48.50	9–10	45.90
10½	47.71	11	45.26
11	47.18	11½	44.80
12	46.75	12	44.28
13–15	46.35	12½	45.58
16	45.72	13	42.90
16½	45.30	13½	42.10
17	44.80	14	41.45
17½	44.03	14½	40.74
18	43.25	15	40.10
18½	42.70	15½	39.40
19	42.32	16	38.85
19½	42.00	16½	38.30
20–21	41.43	17	37.82
22–23	40.82	17½	37.40
24–27	40.24	18–19	36.74
28–29	39.81	20–24	36.18
30–34	39.34	25–44	35.70
35–39	38.68	45–49	34.94
40–44	38.00	50–54	33.96
45–49	37.37	55–59	33.18
50–54	36.73	60–64	32.61
55–59	36.10	65–69	32.30
60–64	35.48		
65–69	34.80*		

* Obtained by extrapolation.
(From Boothby, Berkson, and Dunn: Am. J. Physiol., 116:468.)

In fevers (pneumonia, typhoid, etc.) the metabolic rate is increased by about 13 per cent for each 1° C.

In prolonged starvation, covering a period of some ten days or more, the metabolic rate is definitely reduced.

Of course, muscular work increases considerably the energy requirements above the basal metabolic level. In Table 49, prepared by Rubner, a comparison is made between the effect on heat production of (a) the addition of carbohydrate and protein, and (b) work. None of the heat production due to work is derived from the specific dynamic action of the foodstuffs.

The effect of certain drugs on the basal metabolic rate has been much investigated. This applies more particularly to phenol derivatives of the type of 2,4-dinitrophenol and 4,6-dinitro-o-cresol. The injection of

TABLE **49.** THE INFLUENCE OF DIET AND MECHANICAL WORK UPON THE METABOLISM OF A MAN **61** TO **63** KG. IN WEIGHT

	Heat produced			Heat lost		
Diet and conditions	Twenty-four hours	In-crease	In-crease due to work	Evap. H_2O	Rad. and cond.	Work
	Calories	Per cent	Calories	Calories	Calories	Calories
No food, rest.................	1976	.....	.....	380	1596	
Cane sugar + H_2O, taken during rest...................	2023	+ 2.4	.....	529	1494	
Same + work...............	2868	+45.2	845	907	1727	234
Protein, large amount of meat, rest......................	2515	+27.2	.....	614	1901	
Protein, same diet, + work.....	3370	+70.5	855	1235	1901	234

3 mg. per kilogram weight of the former substance increases the basal metabolic rate ten-fold. In this respect its effect is comparable to thyroxine. However, in myxedema, such phenols will restore the basal rate without influencing the other symptoms of the disease, which is in striking contrast to the effect of thyroxine.

SPECIFIC DYNAMIC ACTION

When protein equivalent to 100 C. is ingested, heat equivalent to 130 C. is produced. This action of protein in stimulating metabolism Rubner called the "specific dynamic action" (S.D.A.) of protein. The results are the same whether the protein is taken in as food or whether its constituent amino acids are injected. It is true that the kidney does work in excreting urea and ammonia derived from the protein (or amino acid) ingested; but Borsook asserts that this accounts for less than one-half the observed increase in metabolism. Nor can the result be due to increased gastrointestinal activity, for the feeding of bones and meat extract, which gives rise to much intestinal irritation, has no effect on S.D.A.

The individual amino acids all show powerful S.D.A. effects, although they vary among themselves.

In an experiment dealing with the effect of the ingestion of gelatin, Borsook showed that there was not only an increase in energy metabolism, but also an increase in the excretion of urinary nitrogen, sulfur, and uric acid.

That the liver may be concerned with the process is made probable by Wilhelmj's observation that after hepatectomy, glycine and alanine show no S.D.A.

Borsook expresses S.D.A. as the ratio of the Calories in excess of the basal to urinary nitrogen in excess of the basal. The variation in the S.D.A. of protein, he explains, can be interpreted on the basis of a new

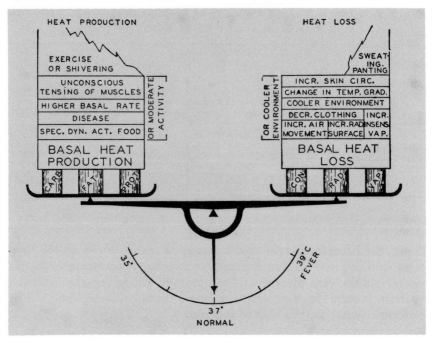

Figure 87. Balance between factors increasing heat production and heat loss. (From DuBois: Harvey Lectures, Ser. 34, p. 88.)

theory of specific dynamic action: the S.D.A. is a composite of two factors, the one nearly constant and represented by the increased energy production resulting from the metabolism and excretion of nitrogen (7 to 10 C. per gram of nitrogen); and the other a more variable and, usually, larger fraction, arising from the metabolism of carbon.

The effectiveness of the amino acids (in the form of ingested protein) as an energy producer is made more evident when we consider the relationship of the amino acids to members of the tricarboxylic acid cycle.

HEAT REGULATION

Under normal conditions there is, as it were, a balance of forces between the extent of heat produced and the extent of heat lost (Fig. 87). In order that the temperature may remain constant, the equilibrium will shift either to the right or to the left.*

---

* "The hypothalamus integrates the reactions responsible for thermal equilibrium. Through its influence on the somatic and visceral motor neurons, the hypothalamus functions as a physiologic thermostat and changes the rate of heat production and heat loss according to the thermal status and requirements of the body." (Wakim)

The manner in which heat is lost from the body, as well as its extent, is summarized by Vierordt (quoted by Howell):

Through urine and feces....................	1.3 per cent or	48 C.
By expired air: warming of air...............	3.5 " " "	84 C.
Vaporization of water from lungs.............	7.2 " " "	182 C.
Evaporation from skin.......................	14.5 " " "	364 C.
Radiation and conduction from skin...........	73.0 " " "	1792 C.

Total daily loss = 2470 C.

While such figures may change with changes in environmental conditions, in general it may be said that loss of heat is due chiefly to evaporation and radiation. To some extent, such heat loss is controlled by clothing. But the important regulatory mechanism is an automatic reflex control (through sweat nerves and vasomotor nerves).

The heat production, on the other hand, is dependent upon the extent of cellular oxidation; and this, in turn, is partly dependent upon the amount of muscular activity and upon the food eaten. But there is also an involuntary control, in the shape of an involuntary reflex on muscular metabolism. For example, as the outside temperature is lowered, the heat production is increased, although the temperature of the body does not change. This is termed "chemical regulation" by Rubner.

ENERGY REQUIREMENTS

Roughly speaking, the energy requirement is the resultant of two factors: a fairly constant factor, as represented by the basal metabolism; and a variable factor, depending upon physical activity. The effect due to S.D.A. must also be taken into account.

An exhaustive study of energy needs has been made by Stiebling and Ward. In preparing "adequate diets" they have constructed a standard table giving not only the calorific needs at various ages and varying activity, but also the amounts needed of protein, calcium, phosphorus, and iron.

Using this table, we get

8 hours of sleep at 65 C. per hour	=	520 C.
2 hours light work at 170 C.	=	340 C.
8 hours carpenter work at 240 C.	=	1902 C.
6 hours sitting at rest at 100 C.	=	600 C.

Total daily requirement 3380 C.

For a moderately active man, with a daily calorific requirement of 3000, the authors suggest 67 gm. of protein. The British Ministry of Health, using the same calorific requirement, is more liberal with its protein. It suggests 80 to 100 gm. per day, "of which not less than one third must be of animal origin."

DuBois and Chambers state that some 1200 of the 2000 to 3000 Calories needed per day should come from "protective foods" to supply the minimum necessary quantities of vitamins, calories and essential amino acids. These 1200 Calories are derived from 1 pint of milk, 1 egg,

TABLE 50. ENERGY EXPENDITURE PER HOUR UNDER DIFFERENT CONDITIONS OF MUSCULAR ACTIVITY

| | Calories per hour | | |
Form of activity	Per 70 kg. (average man)	Per kg.	Per pound
Sleeping	65	0.93	0.43
Awake lying still	77	1.10	0.50
Sitting at rest	100	1.43	0.65
Reading aloud	105	1.50	0.69
Standing relaxed	105	1.50	0.69
Hand sewing	111	1.59	0.72
Standing at attention	115	1.63	0.74
Knitting (23 stitches per minute on sweater)	116	1.66	0.75
Dressing and undressing	118	1.69	0.77
Singing	122	1.74	0.79
Tailoring	135	1.93	0.88
Typewriting rapidly	140	2.00	0.91
Ironing (with 5-pound iron)	144	2.06	0.93
Dishwashing (plates, bowls, cups, and saucers)	144	2.06	0.93
Sweeping bare floor (38 strokes per minute)	169	2.41	1.09
Bookbinding	170	2.43	1.10
"Light exercise"	170	2.43	1.10
Shoe making	180	2.57	1.17
Walking slowly (2.6 miles per hour)	200	2.86	1.30
Carpentry, metal working, industrial painting	240	3.43	1.56
"Active exercise"	290	4.14	1.88
Walking moderately fast (3.75 miles per hour)	300	4.28	1.95
Walking down stairs	364	5.20	2.36
Stoneworking	400	5.71	2.60
"Severe exercise"	450	6.43	2.92
Sawing wood	480	6.86	3.12
Swimming	500	7.14	3.25
Running (5.3 miles per hour)	570	8.14	3.70
"Very severe exercise"	600	8.57	3.90
Walking very fast (5.3 miles per hour)	650	9.28	4.22
Walking up stairs	1100	15.8	7.18

(From Sherman: Chemistry of Food and Nutrition. By permission of The Macmillan Company, Publishers.)

1 serving (3–4 ounces) of meat, 3 teaspoons (15 gm.) of butter, 4 servings of whole grain bread or cereal, 2 vegetables, other than potato, one of which is raw, and 2 fruits, one of which is raw.

The energy expenditures (per hour) under different conditions of muscular activity are given by Sherman in Table 50.

OBESITY

The problem of obesity is, in most cases, the problem of overeating. The consequences in terms of life expectancy are serious. Newburgh refers to Dublin's study involving some 200,000 men and concludes that "the penalty of overweight is an increase in mortality." Fish has reported that 50 pounds overweight impose as much extra mortality as valvular heart disease.

Treatment involves a decrease in total fuel intake without omitting food essentials (such as minerals and vitamins, which are negligible so far as calorific effect is concerned). Protein allowance should remain normal—some 60 to 70 gm. per day. The main restrictions involve fat and certain sources rich in carbohydrates (sugar, breadstuffs). Based on these facts, a balanced diet can be planned to contain not more than 800 to 1000 Calories per day, which diet should be continued until normal weight is reached.

The substitution of drugs for a reduced calorific intake should be discouraged,* because of bad after-effects. For example, while thyroid preparations will cause reduction in weight, they also give rise very frequently to symptoms of hyperthyroidism; and drugs which decrease appetite—such as amphetamine sulfate (Benzedrine)—often cause restlessness, irritability, and insomnia.

* Unless under a doctor's care.

REFERENCES

One of the early accounts of the "human" calorimeter of Atwater and Rosa is to be found in Bulletin 63, U. S. Dept. of Agriculture, 1899. A later one, by Atwater and Benedict, is described in a publication of the Carnegie Institution, Washington, 1905. See also *Lusk:* The Science of Nutrition, 1928, Chap. 3.

A detailed account of energy metabolism will be found in *Peters* and *Van Slyke:* Quantitative Clinical Chemistry, Vol. I, p. 3, 1946.

In connection with the temperature of the body, see *Horvath, Menduke,* and *Piersol:* J. Am. Med. Assoc. *144:*1562, 1950 (oral and rectal temperatures).

For nitrogen metabolism, see *Kade, Phillips,* and *Phillips:* J. Nutrition, *36:*109, 1948 (nitrogen balance).

Practical details concerned with basal metabolism are given by *DuBois:* Basal Metabolism, 1936; *Cantarow* and *Trumper:* Clinical Biochemistry, 1955.

A critical discussion of the heat loss from the human body is to be found in the Harvey Lectures, Ser. 34, 1938–1939, p. 88, by *DuBois.*

The important study by *Stiebling* and *Ward* dealing with energy requirements is published as U. S. Dept. of Agriculture, Circular 296 (1933). See, further, *Keys:* J. Am. Med. Assoc., *142:*333, 1950; Federation Proceedings, *8:*523, 1949; *Taylor* and *Keys:* Science, *112:*215, 1950.

On the subject of obesity, see Nutr. Rev., *11:*144, 1953; *Mayer:* Scientific American, Nov., 1956, p. 108; Borden's Review of Nutrition Research, *19:*35, 1958; *Pollack:* Bull. N. Y. Acad. Med., June, 1960, p. 389; *Buskirk:* Ibid., June, 1960, p. 365; *Sebrell:* Ibid., June, 1960, p. 407.

INORGANIC
METABOLISM

The mineral elements which the body needs in what might be called substantial quantities are calcium, magnesium, sodium, potassium, phosphorus, sulfur, chlorine and iron. The body also needs, in smaller, or "trace" amounts, copper, iodine, manganese, cobalt, zinc, and probably magnesium, molybdenum, and some others. Such elements are sometimes associated with enzyme systems.

The general biological importance of calcium, phosphorus, iron, sodium, potassium, sulfur, and chlorine has been stressed from time to time in these pages. Their presence in the body has been known for some time, and some of their functions have been discovered. More recent work—in many cases involving spectroscopic examination—has revealed the presence of not less than 55 elements in plant or animal tissue. Many of them are present in traces only, and the temptation is strong to dismiss such elements by calling them "impurities." While such a conception may apply to some, it probably does not apply to a number of them. In any case, caution is necessary. We shall see presently how effective traces of copper are in the utilization of iron.

The "trace" elements are also known as "oligo" elements (from the Greek meaning "scanty"). Their concentration is usually in the neighborhood of 1×10^{-6} to less than 1×10^{-12} gm. per gram of wet tissue.

Sherman gives a list of a number of the more important elements (with their percentages), found in the human body (Table 51).

As showing how many more elements in traces there may be, the results of a spectrum analysis of milk ash by Drea may be cited. He has been able to detect the following elements in addition to common ones: aluminum, barium, boron, chromium, fluorine, lead, lithium, molybdenum, silver, rubidium, silicon, strontium, tin, titanium, van-

394

adium, and zinc. In other tissues—in plant as well as animal tissues—we find, in addition, cobalt, nickel, selenium, bromine, bismuth, arsenic, etc.

The functions of some of the mineral elements which have been studied are fairly clear. A number, such as calcium and phosphorus, are constituents of bone and teeth; some, such as iron, sulfur, and phosphorus, are necessary elements in important organic compounds found in the body; still others, such as sodium chloride, serve as electrolytes; and it is possible that some, like copper, play a role as catalysts.

TABLE 51. APPROXIMATE ELEMENTARY COMPOSITION OF THE BODY

Element	Percentage
Oxygen	65.
Carbon	18.
Hydrogen	10.
Nitrogen	3.
Calcium	2.[a]
Phosphorus	1.1[b]
Potassium	0.35
Sulfur	0.25
Sodium	0.15
Chlorine	0.15
Magnesium	0.05
Iron	0.004
Manganese	0.00013
Copper	0.00015
Iodine	0.00004
Cobalt	[c]
Zinc	[c]
Others of more doubtful status	

[a] Estimates vary widely.
[b] Percentage varies with that of calcium.
[c] Believed to be essential, but quantitative data are not yet at hand.
(From Sherman and Lanford: Essentials of Nutrition. By permission of The Macmillan Co.)

Not only are such elements in themselves important but also they are equally important in their relationship to one another. The relationship of calcium to phosphorus in rickets will be referred to (Chap. 18). Only brief mention may be made here of several other elements. When a frog's heart is immersed in solutions containing several salts at various concentrations, it has been found that the heart will beat normally, provided the ratio K^+/Ca^{++} is that found in frog's blood. In dealing with the effect of ionic concentrations upon the irritability of tissues, Holmes points out that the irritability depends very largely upon the ratio

$$\frac{Na^+ + K^+ + OH^-}{Ca^{++} + Mg^{++} + H^+}$$

and that when the concentration of the ions in the numerator is increased, there is an increase of irritability; whereas the reverse is true if the ionic concentration in the denominator is increased. Ringer's solution, so often used to retain the activities of tissues and tissue slices, is made up of a solution of chlorides of potassium, sodium, calcium, and magnesium in concentrations comparable to those in blood.

An interesting case of competitive antagonism was noticed by Snell working with certain types of lactic acid bacteria. These bacteria require potassium for growth. When the optimal amount of K^+ necessary for growth was present, the addition of Na^+ caused inhibition of growth; this inhibition was removed by the addition of K ions. Again, the addition of Na ion caused inhibition.[*]

CALCIUM†

This mineral element is present in greater abundance in the body than any other. An adult weighing some 70 kg. contains about 1200 gm. of calcium.

As the chief constituent of bone, calcium is present as a salt resembling minerals of the hydroxyapatite group [3 $Ca_3(PO_4)_2Ca(OH)_2$]; 99 per cent of the total amount of calcium in the body is found in the bones. Smaller amounts of calcium are found in the teeth (36 per cent in enamel), skin, and blood.

In the blood, calcium is found almost exclusively in the plasma, where it occurs to the extent of about 9 to 11.5 mg. per 100 ml. of serum or 4.5 to 5.5 milli-equivalents per liter. The relationship [Ca] $\times$ [P] = 36 (where [Ca] and [P] are expressed in milligrams per 100 ml.) holds fairly well. Some 60 per cent of the calcium in the blood is in a diffusible form, and the remainder is quite nondiffusible. The nondiffusible portion is probably attached to the serum albumin.

A concentration of ionic calcium below the normal amount, brought about by a deficiency of the parathyroid hormone, affects the central nervous system and produces an increased irritability of the peripheral nerves. At a later stage, muscle spasms (affecting the face, hands, and feet) and general convulsions make their appearance. We have here an example of tetany which can be cured by an extract of parathyroid glands (Chap. 21).

Hyperactivity of the parathyroids gives rise to an excess of calcium in the blood. At the same time, owing to calcium deposition, there

[*] Electrolytes in the body are usually expressed "milli-equivalents per liter."

$$\text{mEq. per liter} = \frac{\text{mg. per 100 ml.} \times 10 \times \text{valence}}{\text{atomic weight}}$$

The milli-equivalent per liter of sodium, for example, is

$$\frac{\text{mg. per 100 ml.} \times 10}{23}$$

† See Phosphorus, page 397.

occurs a hardening of various organs (heart, lungs, arteries, etc.). The excess calcium is derived from the bones, which, in turn, become soft and weak.

While the common form of rickets is one in which there is a deficiency of phosphorus, calcium may also be involved (Chap. 18). Vitamin D, possibly by stimulating the utilization of calcium from the intestine, influences the extent to which the body uses the element.

It appears that the absorption of calcium is increased by increasing the acidity of the intestinal contents, and it also seems that more calcium is absorbed from concentrated than from dilute solutions.

Apart from the importance of calcium in the structure of bone and teeth and in its influence upon the excitability of the motor system, it also plays a role in blood clotting.

Unlike sodium and potassium, much of the calcium is excreted by the bowel. As a rule, some 65 to 75 per cent of the element is found in the feces, and 25 to 35 per cent in the urine.

Sherman is of the opinion that not less than 0.70 gm. of calcium is the daily need of the adult. From 0.8 to 1.0 gm. represents an optimal rather than a minimal allowance. The National Research Council recommends 1.0 gm.

The ratio of calcium to phosphorus should be 1:1.5 or 2. An excessive amount of phosphorus will form insoluble salts with calcium and so create a deficiency of calcium.

Milk and cheese are particularly rich sources. Milk contains about 1.4 gm. of calcium per liter, and cheese, 5 to 10 gm. per kg.

The mere fact that a food is rich in calcium—or in any other element—does not necessarily mean that eating such a food will cause 100 per cent absorption and assimilation. Various studies have shown that from 20 to 30 per cent of the calcium in milk is utilized by the human organism. In the case of green vegetables and other foods, poor utilization of the element is perhaps due to the presence of oxalic acid, citrates, and phytic acid, which may interfere with the absorption of calcium owing to the insolubility of their salts.

Present-day consumption of large quantities of refined cereals, with much of the original calcium in the whole grain lost, and sugar which is devoid of minerals added, makes the problem of supplying mineral needs difficult.

PHOSPHORUS

This element is present in every cell of the body. Phosphorus is not only present in inorganic combinations (in bones, teeth, blood, etc.), but in many organic combinations. Among the latter may be mentioned phosphatides, nucleic acid, phosphoprotein (as casein), adenylic acid, coenzyme, yellow enzymes, thiamine phosphate, phosphocreatine, hexosephosphates, and triosephosphates. All of these substances have already been discussed in various sections of the book.

It has been estimated that there is some 700 gm. of phosphorus in the body, of which 600 gm. is found in the skeleton, 57 gm. in muscle, 5 gm. in brain, 2 gm. in blood, etc. About 80 per cent of the phosphorus in the body is in combination with calcium in bones and teeth. The daily needs have been calculated by Sherman to be some 1.32 gm. The normal level of phosphate in serum is 3.2 to 4.3 mg. per 100 ml. The foods particularly rich in this element are cheese, nuts, eggs, meat, and milk.

The functions of phosphorus are numerous; they involve the chemistry of the blood, the synthesis of deoxyribonucleic acid, the acid-base balance of the body, skeletal growth, tooth development, muscle metabolism, intermediary metabolism of carbohydrate, fat, protein, and brain, the activity of enzymes, etc. Fortunately for us, the element is widely distributed in foods. Indeed, foods rich in calcium and protein are excellent sources of phosphorus.

The use of isotopes has shown that what is true of the organic constituents is equally true of the inorganic ones: the body constituents are in dynamic equilibrium with each other and with ingested foods. This applies to what were considered as permanent structures, such as bones and teeth; here, too, the constituents exist in a dynamic state, undergoing continuous degradation and synthesis.

The pioneer work using radiophosphorus (P^{32}) was done by Hevesy, who indeed was the first to use radioactive tracers in investigating metabolic problems. Hevesy, in his earlier work, showed that an appreciable amount of the phosphorus from food proceeded rapidly to bones, teeth, muscle, etc. Later Hevesy showed that lecithin could be isolated from the brain of rats, mice, and rabbits which contained the radiophosphorus. Still another experiment on goats showed that the ingestion of sodium phosphate (containing P^{32}) resulted in the deposition of labeled phosphates in milk in from three to four hours. Since the casein in the milk also contained the isotope (P^{32}), the phosphorus used in the synthesis of casein in the mammary gland must have been derived from the inorganic phosphate in blood, which, in turn, was dependent upon the inorganic phosphate of the food.

MAGNESIUM

This element is an essential constituent of the chlorophyll molecule, and therefore is of importance to plant life. That it is also important to animal life has been shown by Kruse and by McCollum, among others, who found that a diet containing 0.18 mg. of magnesium per 100 gm. of food (but otherwise quite adequate) gives rise, in rats, to vasodilatation and hyperirritability of the nervous system, resembling in some ways, the tetany due to calcium deficiency. Under these conditions, while, of course, the amount of magnesium in the blood is subnormal, the amount of calcium remains at its normal level. Nor, in a reverse situation, with a low blood calcium, can tetany be prevented by the addition of magnesium. What is called "tetany" due to magnesium deficiency has characteristics which make it different from "tetany" due to calcium deficiency.

About 71 per cent of the total magnesium found in the body is located in the bones (in the form of phosphate and carbonate). In the blood we find 1 to 3 mg. per 100 ml. or 1.9 mEq. per liter. The serum contains less than half as much magnesium as the cells in contrast to calcium, which is found almost exclusively in serum.

While the total quantity of magnesium in the body is far less than that of calcium, more of the former is found in muscle than of the latter. On the average we find about 21 mg. of magnesium per 100 gm. of muscle tissue, as compared to 7 mg. of calcium.

Many enzymes require Mg^{++}—in addition to ATP—for their activity.

Like the corresponding salts of calcium and strontium, the magnesium salts of mineral acids produce acidosis. This is due to the fact that whereas much of the Mg^{++} is excreted with the feces, the acid ion is absorbed and finally excreted in the urine. Magnesium salts are diuretics and cathartics.

Tables 52, 53, and 54 deal with analyses of calcium, phosphorus, and magnesium.

As to the requirements for magnesium, little is known. The average intake per person (in the U. S.) is 0.27 gm. per day, which is probably sufficient.

TABLE 52. APPROXIMATE AMOUNTS OF CALCIUM, PHOSPHORUS, AND MAGNESIUM IN 100 GM. OF EDIBLE FOOD

	Calcium	Phosphorus	Magnesium
	Gm.	Gm.	Gm.
Beef (lean)	0.007	0.218	0.024
Eggs	0.067	0.180	0.011
Egg yolk	0.137	0.524	0.016
Milk	0.210	0.093	0.012
Cheese	0.931	0.680	0.037
Wheat	0.045	0.423	0.133
Potatoes	0.014	0.058	0.028
Corn meal	0.018	0.190	0.084
Oranges	0.045	0.021	0.012
Almonds	0.239	0.465	0.251
Spinach	0.067	0.068	0.037
Beans (dried)	0.160	0.470	0.156
Linseed meal	0.413	0.741	0.432
Cotton seed meal	0.265	1.193	0.462

(From Schmidt and Greenberg: Physiol. Rev., 15:300.)

TABLE **53.** DISTRIBUTION OF ELEMENTS IN THE BLOOD OF HUMAN SUBJECTS IN MILLIGRAMS PER 100 ML.

Substance	Normal (mean value)
Total serum calcium	10.3
Diffusible calcium	5.4
Nondiffusible calcium	4.9
Inorganic serum phosphorus	4.0
Whole blood magnesium	4.6
Red corpuscle magnesium	6.6
Plasma magnesium	2.7
Serum magnesium	2.5
Diffusible serum magnesium	1.9

(From Schmidt and Greenberg: Ibid.)

TABLE **54.** COMPOSITION OF BLOOD IN CERTAIN PATHOLOGICAL CONDITIONS

Disease	Substance	Mg. per 100 ml.
Rickets (human subjects)	Serum calcium	9.0
	Inorganic phosphate	3.0
	Serum magnesium	2.2
Parathyroid tetany (human subjects)	Serum calcium	7.9
	Inorganic phosphate	5.0
	Serum magnesium	2.0
Hyperparathyroidism (human subjects)	Serum calcium	15.9
	Inorganic Phosphate	2.2

(From Schmidt and Greenberg: Ibid.)

SODIUM

Sodium, as sodium chloride, has two important functions: to contribute toward the acid-base balance of the body, and to be responsible, in large measure, for the total osmotic pressure of the extracellular fluids.

Our main source of this element is the salt (sodium chloride) employed in cooking and seasoning, although some, of course, is derived from the foods we eat. The ordinary daily diet contains 10 to 20 gm. of sodium chloride.

Sodium (and this is also true of potassium) is very easily absorbed, some 90 to 95 per cent appearing in the urine. It has been claimed by Bunge, and generally accepted, that the addition of an excess of sodium to the diet causes an excessive excretion of potassium, and vice versa. The explanation offered as to why herbivorous animals so often have a craving for salt is that their food is particularly rich in potassium, thereby giving rise to an excessive excretion of sodium. Foods of vegetable origin are richer in potassium than in sodium.

Some 93 per cent of the total cations in blood serum is due to sodium (Table 55). Together with other salts, it maintains the osmotic pressure and equilibrium of the blood.

TABLE 55. APPROXIMATE CONCENTRATION OF CATIONS IN BLOOD AND MUSCLE

	Serum (mEq./liter)	Red Cells (mEq./liter)	Muscle (mEq./kg.)
Na^+	142	0 (?)	31
K^+	5	108	93
Ca^{++}	5	0 (?)	4
Mg^{++}	3	2	19

The extent of the excretion of sodium is dependent upon the amount of intake, and although an animal can maintain itself on surprisingly small quantities—in the rat, as little as 0.1 per cent of sodium chloride in the diet—a minimum amount is probably necessary. Below minimal quantities, there are loss of appetite, retarded growth, disturbance of the reproductive function, and ultimate death.

A relationship between the adrenals and the metabolism of sodium has been established. The removal of the adrenals is followed by a considerable loss of the element from the body (Chap. 21).

Extreme sweating due to high temperature or much exertion may cause so much loss of sodium chloride from the body as to cause the development of leg and abdominal cramps.

Salt (and water) intake may be suggested for the following: prolonged vomiting (chloride loss); diarrhea (sodium loss); adrenal cortex insufficiency (disturbance of salt metabolism); and shock, due to loss of blood volume (in surgery, wounds or severe burns).

A low salt diet has been suggested in the treatment of hypertension.

POTASSIUM

Although potassium resembles sodium in ease of absorption and general metabolism, each element has very specific functions, since they cannot replace one another. It has already been indicated that potassium is found very largely in the cells of the body, whereas sodium is widely distributed in the body fluids (see Table 50).

Using radioactive potassium, it can be shown that the element penetrates rapidly into most of the tissues of the body and only a small quantity is found in the plasma.

In Addison's disease, associated with an adrenal cortex deficiency, the potassium in the blood is definitely increased.

The actual requirement of potassium for the body is not known, but since the element is widely distributed in foods deficiencies are not apt to occur under normal conditions.

CHLORINE *✓

In the form of sodium chloride, the chloride ion plays a role in osmotic pressure relationships and in maintaining the water content of the body. The loss of salt by the body means loss of water.

The chloride concentration of normal serum is 340 to 370 mg. per 100 ml., or 97 to 105 milli-equivalents per liter. A solution of 9 gm. of sodium chloride per liter is isotonic with serum, which means that the chlorides are responsible for two thirds of the osmotic pressure of the blood.

The chloride shift is of importance in acid-base equilibria. It will be remembered in this connection that the chloride ion readily passes through the cell membrane, but that the sodium and potassium ions do not.

In tracing the origin of the hydrochloric acid of the stomach, we must ascribe it, to some extent at least, to the sodium chloride of the blood. Changes in gastric acidity involve changes in the composition of the blood and are not influenced by variations in chloride intake.

The metabolism of chlorine cannot be separated from the metabolism of sodium. As has been pointed out, some 10 to 20 gm. of sodium chloride are needed daily. The chlorine (as chloride) is as readily absorbed and metabolized as is the sodium (as sodium chloride); on a diet deficient in salt, the excretion of chlorine is reduced correspondingly. In one case (cited by Sherman), the excretion dropped from 4.60 gm. per day to 0.17 gm. during the course of 13 days.

IODINE ✓

Iodine is obtained largely from the supply of food and, to some extent, from salt and water. The amount of iodine found in drinking water is, at times, used to estimate the content of iodine in the soil nearby, as well as its fruits, grains, grasses, and vegetables.

A man weighing 70 kg. probably contains within his body some 25 mg. of iodine, of which some 15 mg. is found in the thyroid. Iodine is an important precursor in the formation of thyroxine.

The concentration of iodine in the thyroid gland is remarkable. Whereas in whole blood the iodine concentration is of the order of one part in 25 million, in the thyroid it is one part in 2500.

Using radioactive iodine it can be shown that the iodine from the blood stream is rapidly transported to the thyroid where it quickly be-

* See Sodium, page 400.

comes incorporated into organic molecules. Thyroid function is often assessed by administering radioiodine (I^{131}).

The blood may show values for iodine ranging from 3 to 20 micrograms per 100 ml. (1 microgram = 0.001 mg.); and about one fourth of this amount represents thyroxine.

The average excretion of urinary iodine by normal adults (in 24 hours) has been estimated at 50 micrograms.

A deficiency of iodine in food (and water) may lead to simple (endemic) goiter. In certain inland regions, such as the Great Lakes district in this country, or the Alpine regions in Europe, the water (and the food grown on the soil) may contain less iodine than is necessary for normal well-being. When that happens, goiter in its various stages makes its appearance. The simplest treatment—and a very effective one—is to incorporate a small quantity of iodine, in the form of sodium iodide, in the common table salt. Usually one part of sodium iodide in 100,000 parts of sodium chloride ("iodized salt") is sufficient.

It has been estimated that the average person needs from 100 to 200 micrograms per day. Although the concentration of iodine in sea water is low, sea life (algae, fish, oysters) concentrate this element so that such organisms are a good source of iodine.

BROMINE

That bromine is present in animal tissues is beyond question, but just what its function is, if it has any, is a mystery. The claims made at one time or another that the metabolism of bromine bears some relation to mental disease or that there is a bromine-containing hormone in the pituitary are questionable. It is true that what appear to be significant amounts of bromine have been detected in the brain (hypophysis); and it is also true that the bromine value of blood is markedly lowered in manic-depressive psychoses.

It has been estimated that the blood contains from 0.23 to 1.71 mg. per 100 ml. In ordinary salt, for every gram of chlorine there is about 1 mg. of bromine.

FLUORINE

This element is present in various tissues of the body, particularly in bone and teeth. It has been estimated that the normal bone contains from 0.01 to 0.03 per cent of fluorine, and dental enamel, 0.01 to 0.02 per cent.

Since no diet has so far been devised which is free from fluorine, it is difficult to investigate, at present, the function of the element. Mottled enamel, a defect in teeth, endemic in parts of this country and elsewhere, has been attributed to the fluorine in the drinking water.

The amount must be in excess of one part per million. Such teeth show chalky white patches, and the enamel is frequently pitted and corroded. Histological examination reveals imperfect calcification. The minimum quantity of fluorine in water to give rise to mottled enamel is believed to be from 1 to 2 mg. per liter. Fluorine (as fluoride), given in relatively large doses, is quite toxic. From 8 to 9 mg. of fluorine per kilo of body weight given to cattle produces loss of appetite, disturbed osseous metabolism, and fatty degeneration. Studies in oxygen uptake suggest interference with cellular metabolism.

Some startling facts have appeared linking dental caries with the lack of fluorine. It would seem that a certain amount of fluorine in the water—somewhere in the neighborhood of 1 part per million, and therefore less than what would give rise to mottled enamel—gives some protection against dental caries. Where the drinking water contains but a trace of the element, caries is more prevalent.

The suggestion has been made that when the enamel contains appreciable quantities of fluoroapatite, it becomes more resistant to attacks by acid.

IRON

A 70-kg. man contains some 4 to 5 gm. of total iron. Table 56 shows the distribution of this iron among the various iron compounds known to be present in the body.

Some 60 to 70 per cent of the total iron is present in the form of circulating hemoglobin, 3 to 5 per cent as myoglobin and small amounts

TABLE 56. APPROXIMATE COMPOSITION OF THE IRON-CONTAINING COMPOUNDS IN THE HUMAN (70-KILO MAN)

Compounds	gm.	Fe in gm.	% of Total Fe
Iron porphyrin (heme) compounds:			
Blood hemoglobin	900	3.0	60–70
Muscle hemoglobin (myoglobin)	40	0.13	3–5
Heme enzymes:			
cytochrome c	0.8	0.004	0.1
catalase	5.0	0.004	0.1
cytochrome, a, a_3, b	—	—	—
peroxidase	—	—	—
Non-iron porphyrin compounds:			
Transferrin (siderophilin)	10.0	0.004	0.1
Ferritin	2–4	0.4–0.8	15
Hemosiderin	—	—	—
Total available iron stores	—	1.2–1.5	—
Total Iron		4–5	100

(From Granick, S.: Bull. N. Y. Academy of Med., *30:*82, 1954.)

as the various heme-containing enzymes (catalase, peroxidase and the cytochromes). Thus almost 70 per cent of the total iron is present in the form of compounds involved in the processes of oxygen transfer or cellular respiration. The remainder of the iron is present in three forms. These are listed below.

Transferrin. Plasma contains about 120 micrograms (μg.) iron per 100 ml. This iron is bound to a plasma protein which is part of the beta-globulin fraction and is called, variously, transferrin, siderophilin, or, most simply, the plasma iron-binding globulin. This protein is capable of combining with a maximum of two iron atoms per molecule. The plasma is partially "unsaturated" with respect to iron. Addition of iron salts to plasma results in an uptake of this iron by the unsaturated iron-binding globulin until no more iron can be bound. This is the basis for a quantitative method of estimating the plasma "latent iron-binding capacity." Normal plasma has an iron-binding capacity equivalent to 200 μg. iron per 100 ml.; it is therefore about one-third saturated. The nature of the bond between the iron and protein in the complex is unknown, although we do know that oxygen and carbon dioxide are required for the reaction with ferrous iron. The bond which is formed is very strong but can be weakened and iron removed at acid pH in the presence of reducing agents, suggesting that the bond with ferrous iron is much weaker than with the ferric iron which forms when iron is added to the protein.

Ferritin. About 15 per cent of the nonporphyrin iron is represented by an unusual iron-protein complex called ferritin, which can be obtained in crystalline form containing from 17 to 25 per cent, by dry weight, of iron. It is found in the liver, spleen and bone marrow, as well as in other organs in smaller quantities (Table 57).

TABLE **57.** FERRITIN CONTENT OF TISSUES

Tissue	Ferritin N (μg. per gm. wet tissue)
Liver (dog)	97
Spleen (dog)	99
Marrow (dog)	15
Kidney cortex (dog)	18
Placenta (human)	10
Pancreas (dog)	6
Skeletal muscle (dog)	5

(From Mazur and Shorr: J. Biol. Chem., *182:*607, 1950.)

When tested in the ultracentrifuge, ferritin in solution behaves like a mixture of molecules of varying size. The smallest of these molecules has a molecular weight of 465,000 and is essentially devoid of iron.

Fractions containing molecules of greater size contain larger quantities of iron. However, when ferritin is treated with a reducing agent at acid pH, the iron can be completely removed by dialysis, leaving behind a colorless protein, apoferritin, which has a molecular weight of 465,000 and which behaves like a single molecular species (apoferritin) in the ultracentrifuge. Aggregation appears to be due to the iron in the molecules of ferritin. Evidence is available which indicates that the bulk of ferritin iron is internally situated in the protein molecule in the form of colloidal micelles of iron hydroxide–iron phosphate.

Although the bulk of ferritin iron exists in the ferric state and is nondialyzable at neutral pH, a small portion of its iron is present at or near the surface in the ferrous state. This ferrous iron can be removed at neutral pH in the presence of iron-binding agents such as transferrin. Recent experiments have shown that the reduction of "surface" ferric iron to the ferrous state can be accomplished by the enzyme xanthine dehydrogenase (xanthine oxidase). Its action may be illustrated by the following equations:

$$\text{Xanthine + enz. ox.} \longrightarrow \text{uric acid + enz. red.}$$
$$\text{Enz. red + ferritin.Fe}^{+++} \longrightarrow \text{enz. ox. + ferritin.Fe}^{++} + H^+$$

In this scheme the reduced flavoprotein enzyme is reduced by xanthine, which is oxidized to uric acid. The reduced enzyme is in turn oxidized by ferric-ferritin, which in turn is reduced to ferrous-ferritin. The ferrous iron of ferritin can now dissociate for combination with transferrin as follows:

$$\text{Ferritin.Fe}^{++} \rightleftharpoons \text{ferritin + Fe}^{++}$$
$$\text{Fe}^{++} + \text{transferrin} \longrightarrow \text{Fe}^{+++}.\text{transferrin}$$

Confirmation of this reaction in the intact animal was obtained by an increase in plasma iron in animals injected with hypoxanthine or xanthine. These results suggest that the action of xanthine dehydrogenase is the normal mechanism for the release of iron from tissue stores.

The mechanism of the reverse reaction, the movement of plasma-bound iron to the liver and spleen and its incorporation into ferritin, has also been clarified. In this reaction both ATP and ascorbic acid act to release iron bound to plasma transferrin. As a result the ferric iron of transferrin is converted to the ferrous state and is incorporated into ferritin protein. Free sulfhydryl groups of the ferritin molecules are involved since blocking of such groups inhibits the reaction. As a consequence, it may readily be seen that the rate of oxidative metabolism in the liver and spleen, by virtue of their ability to synthesize ATP from ADP and inorganic phosphate, will regulate the rate of transfer of plasma iron to tissue ferritin stores. In addition, there now appears a specific role for ascorbic acid since this is the only biochemical reducing agent which is capable of performing the "incorporation" reaction. Guinea pigs deficient in ascorbic acid show a markedly lowered rate of incorporation of plasma iron into ferritin of the liver and spleen.

As a result of these findings, we may summarize the mechanisms which regulate the movement of iron between the plasma and tissues as follows:

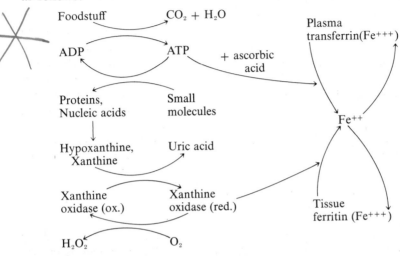

Hemosiderin. These are insoluble iron-protein granules seen in histological sections of liver and spleen. The chemical nature of these particles is obscure, although in the disease known as hemosiderosis, excessive deposits of these granules are found throughout the body. Some believe that these represent the storage form of excessive amounts of iron in equilibrium with ferritin.

ABSORPTION

Unlike other inorganic constituents of the body, very little iron is absorbed by the adult and very little is excreted from the tissues. Most of the iron ingested with the food is eliminated with the feces. Thus the iron which is present in the body must be used over again. There is evidence which indicates that before the iron of the food is absorbed, it must be reduced to the ferrous state. Normally less than 2 mg of iron per day is absorbed. Since little is excreted from the tissues, the body must have some mechanism for the regulation of its absorption. Experiments using radioactive iron compounds indicate that a "braking" mechanism exists in the intestinal mucosa which prevents iron absorption until such time as iron has been lost (hemorrhage). Following the loss of blood there is no immediate increase in absorption of iron. However, after some time, during which the iron stores (ferritin) have been partially depleted, the "mucosal block" is lifted, leading to increased absorption of iron. A clue to the nature of the mechanism responsible for the regulation of intestinal iron absorption is given by studies which have shown an increase in ferritin in the cells of the intestinal mucosa coincident with increased absorption of iron. Thus the appearance of apoferritin as an iron acceptor may be the regulating mechanism. Indeed, it has been demonstrated that the injection of iron salts stimulates the synthesis of apoferritin. Several workers have questioned this "block" mechanism.

THE METABOLIC CYCLE OF IRON

Our understanding of the movement of iron within the body has been aided in no small measure by the use of radioactive Fe^{59}. When injected in tracer doses it does not upset the normal concentration of iron in the body fluids, and its course can now be followed. When Fe^{59} is injected into the plasma, it combines with the iron-binding globulin and soon disappears at an exponential rate whose half-life in the normal

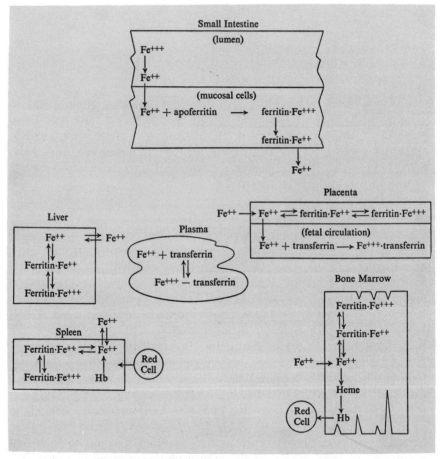

Figure 88. The transport of iron in the body.

human corresponds to 100 minutes. Most of this iron is taken up by the bone marrow; smaller amounts go to the liver and spleen. The iron incorporated into the bone marrow finds its way into the hemoglobin of newly born red cells which are soon found in the circulation. The tagged hemoglobin in the red cells will keep its iron intact for a period of time which corresponds to its life span, which in the normal human being is some 120 days.

The dying red cells are phagocytized by the reticuloendothelial cells of the liver, spleen and bone marrow; and the hemoglobin is degraded to amino acids, bile pigments and iron. Most of the iron which arises from dead red cells is incorporated in the marrow into new hemoglobin and some finds its way into ferritin. Thus the tissue ferritin (mostly the liver in terms of total amount per organ) represents a convenient storage form of iron, which takes care of excess iron not needed immediately for synthesis of hemoglobin, and which releases iron in order to maintain a plasma concentration suitable to the needs of the bone marrow. In addition to hemoglobin, other iron-proteins are also synthesized. These are catalase and the cytochromes. The "turnover" of these proteins in the body can be measured by following the incorporation and release of its radioactive iron.

The presence of ferritin in the human placenta suggests that the release of iron from this compound regulates the transfer of iron from the maternal plasma to fetal plasma in order to supply iron for hemoglobin (catalase and cytochromes) synthesis in the fetus.

The present concept of iron transfer reactions in the body is summarized in Figure 88.

ALTERATIONS IN IRON METABOLISM

The most common derangement of iron metabolism is represented by the anemias: abnormally low concentration of hemoglobin in the circulation. These anemias may be due to iron deficiency in the diet (nutritional anemia) or to a loss of blood (hemorrhage). In addition, there may also occur a loss of ability to absorb the vitamin B_{12} which is present in the diet. This is the case in pernicious anemia, in which the lack of B_{12} results in the loss of ability to utilize iron for hemoglobin synthesis. Anemia may be due also to chronic infectious diseases or to a deficiency of the vitamin, pyridoxine.

Anemia which is caused by the temporary loss of blood (red cells) is soon corrected by the release of iron from ferritin stores and the accelerated synthesis of red cells in the marrow. Anemia due to nutritional deficiency in the diet is common among young children and infants. In investigations in East Africa on the effect of different diets, it was shown that in a population where food consisted largely of cereals, 48 per cent of the boys were definitely anemic; whereas in an adjoining district, where food included relatively large percentages of meat, blood and milk (see Table 58), the anemic individuals among a corresponding group numbered less than 12 per cent. Anemias of this type respond well to the incorporation of iron salts in the diet, together with small amounts of copper and vitamins. The role of copper in hemoglobin synthesis is not known.

TABLE 58.   IRON IN TYPICAL FOOD MATERIALS

Food	Iron (in mg.) per 100 gm. fresh substance
Beans, dried	10.5
Egg yolk	8.6
Peas, dried	5.7
Wheat, entire grain	5.0
Oatmeal	4.8
Eggs	3.1
Beef	3.0
Prunes	2.8
Spinach	2.5
Beefsteak, medium fat	2.0
Cheese	1.3
Beans, string, fresh	1.1
Potatoes	1.1
White flour	1.0
Rice, polished	0.9
Beets	0.8
Carrots	0.6
Bananas	0.6
Turnips	0.5
Oranges	0.5
Tomatoes	0.4
Apples	0.3
Milk	0.2

(From Sherman: Chemistry of Food and Nutrition. By permission of The Macmillan Company.)

Anemias which accompany infectious disease do not respond to administration of iron orally or by injection. In fact the injected iron is removed from the circulation faster than from normal individuals. The injected iron is deposited in the tissues (liver and spleen).

The anemia which accompanies pyridoxine deficiency is alleviated by feeding the vitamin. Unlike the anemia of chronic infection, in pyridoxine deficiency the plasma iron is abnormally high. Little is known about the mechanisms of these two types of anemias.

Polycythemia, an increase in blood hemoglobin above normal levels, is accompanied by an overproduction of erythrocytes, although the life span of the red cell remains normal. It may be induced in animals and man by subjecting them to high altitudes or to an atmosphere low in oxygen content. It is believed that the anoxia stimulates the erythropoietic tissue of the bone marrow. This phenomenon can also be induced when cobalt salts are administered. Polycythemia also occurs in humans as an irreversible disease.

COPPER

Copper is present in all living matter, both plant and animal. In plants it may be associated with the formation of chlorophyll. In animals its association with hemoglobin formation has been stressed. The mechanism of this reaction is obscure. The largest amounts of the element are found in the liver, spleen, and kidneys.

Among naturally occurring organic substances, several contain copper. One of them, hemocyanin, a copper-protein complex, is found in the blood of certain invertebrates (Table 59). In the crab, spider,

TABLE 59. COPPER CONTENT OF BLOODS CONTAINING HEMOCYANIN

Group	Animal	Copper
		mg. per 100 ml.
Mollusca, Cephalopoda.................	Octopus vulgaris	23.5
	Sepia officinalis	23.7
Mollusca, Gastropoda....................	Helix pomatia	6.5–7.5
	Astacus fluviatilis	7.0
	Palinurus vulgaris	9.5
Crustacea, Decapoda....................	Homarus vulgaris	10.0
	Cancer pagurus	6.0
	Carcinus maenas	9.0
	Maia squinado	3.5
Crustacea, Stomatopoda.................	Squilla mantis	6.1

(From Elvehjem: Physiol. Rev., *15:*472.)

and snail, for example, the hemocyanin functions as an oxygen carrier similar to hemoglobin in man. Turacin is a pigment found in the feathers of the South African bird, turaco. Certain oxidizing enzymes, such as ascorbic acid oxidase, polyphenoloxidase, laccase, and tyrosinase are copper-protein complexes.

Other copper compounds were discovered by Keilin and Mann, who isolated a copper-protein compound from the red blood corpuscles of mammals, to which they gave the name *hemocuprein.* They isolated another copper-protein compound, *hepatocuprein,* from the liver. "It is certain," they write, "that some of the copper supplied . . . as food is utilized for building up hemo- and hepatocuprein. The formation of these compounds may therefore represent one of the steps in copper metabolism and may directly or indirectly be responsible for some of the physiological effects which are rightly ascribed to copper."

The copper content of several foods is summarized by Rose (from data by Elvehjem) (Table 60).

TABLE 60.   THE COPPER CONTENT OF FOODS (AVERAGE FIGURES)

Substance (per kg.)	Copper (in mg.)
Liver	44.1
Nuts	11.6
Legumes	9.0
Cereals	4.7
Fruits	4.2
Poultry	3.0
Fish	2.5
Green legumes	1.7
Leafy vegetables	1.2

Cow's milk contains from 0.09 to 0.17 mg. of copper per liter. Nelson has isolated a copper-protein compound from milk.

It has been estimated that the daily need for copper is in the neighborhood of 2 mg. per day. Much of its excretion is via the bowels.

Table 61 gives a number of copper-containing proteins and enzymes.

TABLE 61.   COPPER-CONTAINING PROTEINS AND ENZYMES IN MAMMALIAN TISSUES

Protein	Molecular wt.	% Copper	Substrate
Butyryl coenzyme A dehydrogenase	120,000– 220,000	0.35	Saturated acyl coenzyme A derivatives of fatty acids (C_3-C_8)
Uricase	110,000	0.06	Uric acid
Tyrosinase	100,000 *	0.25	Tyrosine, dopa
Ceruloplasmin	151,000	0.34	Paraphenylene-diamine
Hepatocuprein	35,000	0.34	?
Hemocuprein (erythrocuprein)	(35,000)	(0.34)	?
Milk copper protein	?	0.19	?

* Values are for plant tyrosinase.

SULFUR

Most of the sulfur is found in the protein molecule and is therefore part of an organic molecule. In fact, the metabolism of sulfur, just like the metabolism of nitrogen, is very intimately associated with the metabolism of protein itself.

The sulfur of the protein is centered in the groups containing cystine and methionine. The essential nature of the latter and the metabolism of both amino acids have already been discussed.

Sulfur is largely oxidized to sulfate in the body and excreted as inorganic and ethereal sulfates, both of which will be discussed under Urine (Chap. 20).

Organic compounds of sulfur found in the body are glutathione, coenzyme A, insulin, thiamine, ergothionine, taurocholic acid, sulfocyanide, ethereal sulfates (esters of phenols and sulfuric acid), chondroitin sulfuric acid (in cartilage, etc.), and melanins (pigments of the body). Small quantities of inorganic sulfates (mainly sodium and potassium) are found in the blood and various tissues of the body.

The average amount of sulfur in various foods is 1 per cent.

COBALT

Because it is a component of vitamin B_{12} (p. 470), which is essential for a large variety of animals and even microorganisms, it is probable that cobalt is essential for man as well as for all animals. However, the amount required is so small that neither in rabbits nor in rats could deficiency symptoms be developed.

A type of nutritional anemia ("pine disease") occurring in cattle or sheep has been successfully treated with cobalt.

Using radioactive cobalt it has been determined that most of the element is quickly eliminated via the kidneys. This is in contrast to manganese, which is excreted almost exclusively in the feces.

Salts of cobalt produce polycythemia (an excess in the number of red corpuscles in the blood) when fed or injected. As little as 0.04 to 0.05 mg. in the entire body (of the rat) is enough to develop polycythemia. When injected, cobalt also gives rise to a marked hyperglycemia.

MANGANESE

This element is found in plant and animal tissues and seems to belong to the essential group. When present in deficient amounts there is a marked retardation of growth in the rat. In the female estrous cycles are irregular; and in the male one finds testicular degeneration and sterility due to absence of spermatozoa.

Elvehjem and Hart, in some extensive experiments on rats, showed that on a synthetic diet which included but 5 γ of manganese per day the growth of the animals was impaired. The deficient rats had poorer bone formation and their serum phosphatase was increased two- or three-fold.

The kidney and the liver are the chief storage places for the element in the body. In 100 gm. of tissue, we find 0.17 mg. in the liver and 0.087 mg. in the kidney. The manganese content of blood varies from 0.004 to 0.020 mg. per 100 ml.

It was pointed out under Cobalt that manganese is very largely excreted with the feces. Greenberg, using the radioactive isotope of manganese, makes it clear that the bile plays an important role in the intestinal excretion of the element, for some 50 to 75 per cent of it is carried by the bile.

The amount of manganese in foods varies considerably. In terms of kilogram of dry material, those having from 100 to 200 mg. are beet tops, blueberries, lettuce, pineapple, and wheat bran; those from 35 to 100 mg., beets, blackberries, spinach, whole grain wheat. Fruits, as a rule, have less than 15 mg. per kilogram, and round of beef and the fish so far examined have little or none.

Chicks deficient in manganese reveal reduced levels of blood and bone phosphatase, and a condition of perosis, or "slipped tendon" (an anatomical deformity of the leg bones), may develop.

There is evidence to indicate that the element is involved in activating several enzymes (peptidases, phosphatases, arginase, cozymase, carboxylase, cholinesterase).

While it has not yet been established that manganese is an essential element for man, the suggestion has been made that from 0.02 to 0.03 gm. of the element per kilogram of body weight, incorporated in the diet (particularly for children), might be of value.

ZINC

The weight of evidence is in favor of the view that zinc is an essential element. Todd, Elvehjem, and Hart kept young rats in monel-metal cages and fed them a highly purified ration which included all of the known vitamins and essential mineral elements, together with 2 ml. of milk. The only probable deficiency of this diet was its low content of zinc—1.6 mg. per kilo of the food offered. These animals were compared with controls which received more zinc; the former were inferior to the latter in rate of growth and maximum weight attained. There is also, on this low zinc diet, some interference with the development of a normal fur coat.

Scott has shown that zinc is a constituent of crystalline insulin. Zinc is also a constituent of the enzyme, carbonic anhydrase.

The zinc content of the pancreas of diabetics is about one-half the normal amount, which suggests that the element may be concerned with the storage and utilization of insulin.

It has been estimated that the average daily diet contains 12 to 20 mg. of the element. Much of the excretion is by the intestinal tract. Radioactive zinc accumulates in the mucosa of the intestine and in the pancreas and the liver.

MOLYBDENUM

For a possible relationship of molybdenum to copper and other trace elements, see the reference at the end of the chapter. It is an essential constituent of xanthine oxidase.

ALUMINUM

The amount of aluminum in the diet varies from less than 10 mg. to 100 mg. per day. The absorption of aluminum is slight; its physiological role is not clear.

ENZYMES AND INORGANIC ELEMENTS

Many enzymes require small quantities of inorganic elements for their activity. Smith is of the opinion that the metal acts by forming a bond between the enzyme-protein groups, on the one hand, and the substrate, on the other.

Table 62 presents a list of the metal requirements of several enzymes:

TABLE 62. SOME ENZYMES AND THEIR METALS

Enzyme	Reaction	Metal
Carbonic anhydrase	$CO_2 + H_2O \leftrightarrows H_2CO_3$	Zn
Inorganic pyrophosphatase	Pyrophosphate $+ H_2O \rightarrow PO_4$	Mg
Catalase	$2H_2O_2 \rightarrow 2H_2O + O_2$	Fe
Cytochromes	Electron transport	Fe
Tyrosinase	Tyrosine $+ \frac{1}{2}O_2 \rightarrow$ Hallochrome	Cu
Laccase	Phenols $\rightarrow$ Ortho and paraquinones	Cu
Ascorbic acid oxidase	Ascorbic acid $\rightarrow$ Dehydroascorbic acid	Cu
Prolidase	Glycylproline $\rightarrow$ Proline	Mn
Carboxypeptidase	Chloroacetyl-tyrosine $\rightarrow$ Tyrosine	Mg
Glycylglycine dipeptidase	Glycylglycine $\rightarrow$ Glycine	Zn

(From McElroy and Swanson: Scientific American, Jan., 1953, p. 22.)

REFERENCES

For a discussion of "trace" elements, see *Underwood:* Trace Elements in Human and Animal Nutrition, 1956; *Wallace:* J. Royal Soc. Arts, May 24, 1957, p. 40; Nutr. Rev., 8:178, 1950; *McElroy* and *Swanson:* Scientific American, Jan., 1953, p. 22; *Koch, Smith, Shimp* and *Connor:* Cancer, 9:499, 1956.

The competitive antagonism between ions—using bacteria—is described in Nutr. Rev. 9:135, 1951.

MINERAL METABOLISM. *Underwood:* Ann. Rev. Biochem., 28:499, 1959.

CALCIUM AND PHOSPHORUS. *Wassermann:* Federation Proceedings, 19:636, 1960; Ibid., 18:1075, 1959; *Schofield* and *Morrell:* Ibid., 19:1014, 1960 (and magnesium).

MAGNESIUM. *O'Dell:* Federation Proceedings, 19:648, 1960.

MANGANESE. Nutr. Rev., *15*:80, 1957.

MOLYBDENUM. Nutr. Rev., *14*:315, 1957.

SODIUM AND POTASSIUM. *Overman:* Physiol. Rev., *31*:285, 1951 (Na, K and chloride alterations in disease); *Smith:* Nutr. Rev., *11*:33, 1953 (history and use of salt); Ibid., *9*:208, 1951 (influence of Na on K requirement); *Fenn:* Scientific American, Aug., 1949, p. 16 (review of potassium); *Hoffman:* J. Am. Med. Assoc., *144*:1157, 1950 (clinical physiology of K); Nutr. Rev., *10*:163, 1952 (K depletion in man); *Dahl:* Nutr. Rev., *18*:97, 1960 (salt, fat and hypertension).

IODINE. *Sebrell:* Nutr. Rev., *8*:129, 1950 (review); *Youmans:* J. Am. Med. Assoc., *143*:1256, 1950 (clinical review).

BROMINE. Nutr. Rev., *14*:349, 1956.

COBALT. *Davis* and *Loosli:* Ann. Rev. Biochem., *23*:468, 1954.

FLUORINE. Nutr. Rev., *9*:149, 1951 (fluorides and experimental tooth decay).

IRON. *Granick:* Bull. N. Y. Acad. Med., July, 1949, p. 403; Physiol. Rev., *31*:489, 1951; *Mazur, Litt,* and *Shorr:* J. Biol. Chem., *187*:473, 485, 497, 1950 (iron metabolism); *Granick:* Bull. N. Y. Acad. Med., *30*:81, 1954; *Green* and *Mazur:* J. Biol. Chem., August, 1957; *Mazur, Green, Saha* and *Carleton:* J. Clinical Investigation, *37*:1809, 1958; *Mazur, Green* and *Carleton:* J. Biol. Chem., *235*:595, 1960.

COPPER. *Darby:* J. Am. Med. Assoc., *142*:1294, 1950 (review); *Glass:* Copper metabolism (Johns Hopkins Univ., 1950) (review); *Matrone:* Federation Proceedings, *19*:859, 1960 (iron and copper); *Miller* and *Engel:* Ibid., *19*:666, 1960 (copper, molybdenum and sulfur); *Keilen:* Biochem. J., *49*:544, 1951 (turacin); *Chase, Gubler, Cartwright,* and *Wintrobe:* J. Biol. Chem., *199*: 757, 1952; *Wintrobe, Cartwright,* and *Gubler:* J. Nutrition, *50*:395, 1953 (function and metabolism); J. Am. Med. Assoc., *161*:530, 1956.

MANGANESE. *Hill, Holtkamp, Buchanan* and *Rutledge:* J. Nutrition, *41*:359, 1950 (Mn deficiency); *Cotzias:* Federation Proceedings, *19*:655, 1960.

ZINC. *Banks, Tupper,* and *Wormall:* Biochem. J., *47*:466, 1950 (Fate of Zn compounds in body); *Forbes:* Federation Proceedings, *19*:643, 1960 (zinc and calcium).

MOLYBDENUM. *Miller* and *Engel:* Federation Proceedings, *19*:666, 1960 (copper, molybdenum and sulfur).

ALUMINUM. Nutr. Rev., *16*:23, 1958.

NUTRITION

Our foods include proteins, fats (lipids), carbohydrates, mineral salts, vitamins, water, and oxygen. A separate chapter is devoted to vitamins; water is discussed in connection with the biochemistry of the kidneys; and the function of oxygen is discussed under blood and respiration. The changes which carbohydrates, fats, proteins, and mineral salts undergo in the body have already been discussed. At this stage we wish to refer to a few pertinent facts involving food and diet in general.

Over a considerable period of time the emphasis was laid on the calorific needs of the body. Calorimetric studies revealed that a normal person weighing 70 kg. expends, on an average, energy equivalent to about 3000 Calories per day.* The variations are considerable, depending upon age and depending upon the amount of physical labor expended. The first column in Table 63 deals with calorific requirements.

For many years foods have been analyzed for their "energy" content, and those foods high in calorific value have been preferred. While it is well recognized that the energy needs of the body must be fulfilled if health is to be maintained, the shift in emphasis has been, first, toward a better distribution within the diet of the three basic. foodstuffs (protein, fat, and carbohydrate), and secondly, toward a more careful consideration of the individual components of the diet (and this would also include the mineral salts and vitamins).

THE AMOUNT OF PROTEIN IN THE DIET

This problem has proved a difficult one. More than fifty years ago, Voit made an elaborate study of what the average German laborer consumes in the shape of protein. This led him to the view that the needs of the average man were in the neighborhood of 118 gm. of protein

---

* For the average individual in the white collar class in America, the figure is probably somewhat high. For a definition of the Calorie, see page 379.

TABLE 63. FOOD AND NUTRITION BOARD, NATIONAL RESEARCH COUNCIL, RECOMMENDED DAILY DIETARY ALLOWANCES,[1] REVISED 1958

DESIGNED FOR THE MAINTENANCE OF GOOD NUTRITION OF HEALTHY PERSONS IN THE U.S.A.

(Allowances are intended for persons normally active in a temperate climate)

	AGE YEARS	WEIGHT KG. (LB.)	HEIGHT CM. (IN.)	CALORIES	PROTEIN GM.	CALCIUM GM.	IRON MG.	VITAMIN A I.U.	THIAM. MG.	RIBO. MG.	NIACIN[2] MG. EQUIV.	ASC. ACID MG.	VITAMIN D I.U.
Men.............	25	70 (154)	175 (69)	3200[3]	70	0.8	10	5000	1.6	1.8	21	75	
	45	70 (154)	175 (69)	3000	70	0.8	10	5000	1.5	1.8	20	75	
	65	70 (154)	175 (69)	2550	70	0.8	10	5000	1.3	1.8	18	75	
Women.............	25	58 (128)	163 (64)	2300	58	0.8	12	5000	1.2	1.5	17	70	
	45	58 (128)	163 (64)	2200	58	0.8	12	5000	1.1	1.5	17	70	
	65	58 (128)	163 (64)	1800	58	0.8	12	5000	1.0	1.5	17	70	
	Pregnant (second half)			+300	+20	1.5	15	6000	1.3	2.0	+3	100	400
	Lactating (850 ml. daily)			+1000	+40	2.0	15	8000	1.7	2.5	+2	150	400
Infants[4].............	0–1/12[4]				See Footnote 4								
	2/12–6/12	6 (13)	60 (24)	kg. × 120		0.6	5	1500	0.4	0.5	6	30	400
	7/12–12/12	9 (20)	70 (28)	kg. × 100		0.8	7	1500	0.5	0.8	7	30	400
Children.............	1–3	12 (27)	87 (34)	1300	40	1.0	7	2000	0.7	1.0	8	35	400
	4–6	18 (40)	109 (43)	1700	50	1.0	8	2500	0.9	1.3	11	50	400
	7–9	27 (60)	129 (51)	2100	60	1.0	10	3500	1.1	1.5	14	60	400
	10–12	36 (79)	144 (57)	2500	70	1.2	12	4500	1.3	1.8	17	75	400
Boys.............	13–15	49 (108)	163 (64)	3100	85	1.4	15	5000	1.6	2.1	21	90	400
	16–19	63 (139)	175 (69)	3600	100	1.4	15	5000	1.8	2.5	25	100	400
Girls.............	13–15	49 (108)	160 (63)	2600	80	1.3	15	5000	1.3	2.0	17	80	400
	16–19	54 (120)	162 (64)	2400	75	1.3	15	5000	1.2	1.9	16	80	400

[1] The allowance levels are intended to cover individual variations among most normal persons as they live in the United States under usual environmental stresses. The recommended allowances can be attained with a variety of common foods, providing other nutrients for which human requirements have been less well defined.

[2] Niacin equivalents include dietary sources of the preformed vitamin and the precursor, tryptophan. 60 milligrams tryptophan equals 1 milligram niacin.

[3] Calorie allowances apply to individuals usually engaged in moderate physical activity. For office workers or others in sedentary occupations they are excessive. Adjustments must be made for variations in body size, age, physical activity, and environmental temperature.

[4] The Board recognizes that human milk is the natural food for infants and feels that breast feeding is the best and desired procedure for meeting nutrient requirements in the first months of life. No allowances are stated for the first month of life. Breast feeding is particularly indicated during the first month when infants show handicaps in homeostasis due to different rates of maturation of digestive, excretory and endocrine functions. Recommendations as listed pertain to nutrient intake as afforded by cows' milk formulas and supplementary foods given the infant when breast feeding is terminated. Allowances are not given for protein during infancy.

per day. Chittenden, working at Yale twenty years later, maintained nitrogen equilibrium (where the intake and the output of nitrogen are approximately equal) on as little as 45 gm. of protein per day. But the problem assumed an entirely new aspect as a result of the pioneer researches of Kossel and Fischer on the chemical constitution of the protein molecule. It became apparent that the emphasis must be placed on the amino acid content of the protein, rather than on the protein as a whole.

For example, it had been known for some time that gelatin is a "deficient" protein. That is to say, assuming the presence in the diet of optimal amounts of fat, carbohydrate, etc., the use of gelatin as the sole source of protein proved disastrous.* An analysis of gelatin showed that it was deficient in a number of important amino acids. Tryptophan, valine, and tyrosine are entirely missing; cystine is present in small amounts. A number of investigators next showed that growth and development—though probably not *normal* growth and development—are possible by the addition to the diet of the missing amino acids.

Economically, the problem of gelatin is of importance. It is a cheap protein and is easily obtained from tendon, cartilage, bone, and skin by boiling with water, thereby converting the collagen into gelatin.

OSBORNE AND MENDEL

We owe to Osborne and Mendel the fundamental work on the effect in the diet of various proteins viewed in the light of their content of amino acids. Casein, despite its deficiency in glycine, is an excellent protein (Fig. 89). Apparently glycine is an amino acid which can be synthesized by the body.† Gliadin (a protein in wheat and rye) and zein (in maize) are deficient (Fig. 89).

These experiments—and others later—established the indispensability of certain amino acids (such as lysine and tryptophan). It became clear that a diet devoid of such amino acids (or rather, a diet in which the proteins are deficient in such amino acids) is a deficient diet. Apparently, the synthetic abilities of the body are limited.

ROSE

The experimental method adopted by Osborne and Mendel was to feed carefully purified proteins and to supplement "deficient" proteins with the missing amino acids. Another method, which has been widely adopted, may be illustrated by an example. Casein is first completely hydrolyzed until a mixture of amino acids is obtained. From this mixture histidine is removed as completely as possible. The residue proves

---

* "Cadet de Vaux in Paris during the French Revolution tried to persuade the poor that gelatin soup was a satisfactory and nutritious diet. The poor refused and their attitude has since been amply justified. . . . " T. F. *Dixon:* Nature, March 4, 1944.

† This is true for the rat but not necessarily for other animals.

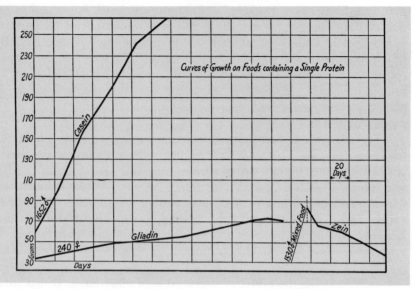

Figure 89. Showing typical curves of growth of rats maintained on diets containing a single protein. On the casein food (devoid of glycine) satisfactory growth is
obtained, on the gliadin food (deficient in lysine) little more than maintenance of
body weight is possible, on the zein food (devoid of glycine, lysine, and tryptophan) even maintenance of body weight is impossible. (From Osborne and Mendel:
Harvey Lectures, Ser. 10, Williams and Wilkins Co.)

deficient. Supplementing the residue with histidine causes recovery.
Histidine is, then, an essential, or indispensable, amino acid (Rose, and
Harrow and Sherwin).

The third method, adopted by Rose, is relatively costly, but it is
the most satisfactory method. It consists in feeding a mixture of purified amino acids, comparable in number and in relative amounts to
those found in casein (which is a biologically wholesome protein).
These highly purified amino acids (19 in number), added to a diet of
the necessary fat, carbohydrate, mineral salts, and vitamins, were quite
inadequate for the normal growth of young rats. This result was in
striking contrast to the use of hydrolyzed casein as the source of protein; here growth was obtained. Evidently, some unknown substance or
substances essential to growth were present in the hydrolyzed casein
and absent in the synthetic mixture of amino acids. The substitution of
part of the synthetic amino acid mixture with some native protein,
such as casein, improved the condition of the animals. Eventually, from
the monoamino-monocarboxylic acid fraction of the hydrolyzed protein, Rose isolated a new amino acid, threonine, or α-amino-β-hydroxy-
butyric acid (Fig. 90). This acid is found in casein, fibrin, serum albumin, and serum globulin, among others, but hemoglobin contains little,
if any.

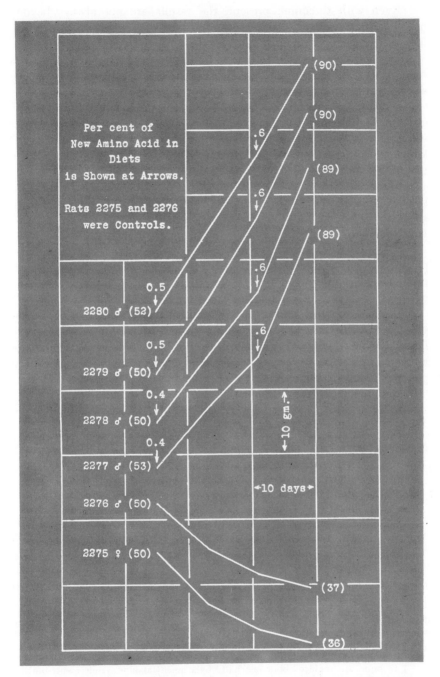

Figure 90. Rats 2275 and 2276 did not grow on a purified amino acid mixture. The addition of the amino acid threonine caused growth. (From McCoy, Meger and Rose: J. Biol. Chem., *112*:283.)

Even with threonine present, the results are not always beyond question. For instance, Elvehjem and his co-workers, using the chick, find casein as such superior to a synthetic diet (including threonine).

The introduction of protein hydrolysates in clinical medicine has brought out the fact that even hydrolysates may not always be the equal—nutritionally speaking—of unhydrolyzed proteins.

Woolley has shown that some "factor" in casein (and a number of other proteins) stimulates the growth of *Lactobacillus casei;* and that this factor is probably a peptide. The unknown substance was called *strepogenin.* It is present in casein, trypsinogen, insulin, and hemoglobin, but not in egg albumin and gelatin.

Mice and rats fed on hydrolyzed casein—a protein always considered high in the biological series—did not develop normally until strepogenin (in the form of a protein rich in the substance, like casein) was added to the diet.

It should be explained that "protein hydrolysates" are hydrolytic products of proteins brought about by the action of acid or the appropriate enzyme (pepsin or trypsin, for example). The proteins used are casein, lactalbumin, fibrin, etc.

The use of such protein hydrolysates—given parenterally—is important in disturbances of digestion and absorption of food, as in severe illness, or after surgical operations involving the digestive tract. The attempt is made to regain nitrogen equilibrium (Chap. 15) and even a positive nitrogen balance.

TABLE 64.   CLASSIFICATION OF AMINO ACIDS WITH RESPECT TO THEIR GROWTH EFFECTS IN THE RAT

Essential	Nonessential
Lysine	Glycine
Tryptophan	Alanine
Histidine	Serine
Phenylalanine	Cystine †
Leucine	Tyrosine ‡
Isoleucine	Aspartic acid
Threonine	Glutamic acid§
Valine	Proline§
Arginine*	Hydroxyproline§
Methionine	Citrulline

* Arginine can be synthesized by the rat, but not at a sufficiently rapid rate to meet the demands of maximum growth. Its classification, therefore, as essential or nonessential is purely a matter of definition.

† Cystine can replace about one sixth of the methionine requirement, but has no growth effect in the absence of methionine.

‡ Tyrosine can replace about one half of the phenylalanine requirement, but has no growth effect in the absence of phenylalanine.

§ Glutamic acid and proline can serve individually as rather effective substitutes for arginine in the diet. This property is not shared by hydroxyproline.

(From Rose, Oesterling, and Womack: J. Biol. Chem., *172:*753.)

A list of essential (indispensable) and nonessential (dispensable) amino acids (so far as these have been studied up to the present) is given in Table 64.

Rose defines an indispensable (essential) amino acid as one which cannot be synthesized by the organism out of materials ordinarily available at a speed commensurate with the demands for normal growth.

Another factor which has to be taken into consideration in dealing with these amino acids is their optical activity. Where the racemic synthetic product is used, Rose gives double the theoretical amount to ensure the presence of the active isomer at the desired level.

Rose finds that with the following amino acids, only the *natural* isomers promote growth: valine, leucine, isoleucine, lysine, and threonine; on the other hand, in dealing with tryptophan, histidine, phenylalanine, and methionine, it is found that both isomers promote growth.

The experiments of Rose dealing with essential and nonessential amino acids apply to the rat. He has also used dogs in place of rats and finds that in general the response is similar. These results, however, do not necessarily apply to all other animals. For example, Almquist, using chicks in the place of rats, showed that glycine and arginine were important.

Rose has extended his studies to man. Arginine, which is necessary for optimal growth in the rat, is not required for the maintenance of nitrogen equilibrium in normal human adults. Perhaps the most striking result is that here histidine is dispensable. This result is a surprising one, for the amino acid is essential for all species of animals so far tested.

The amino acids which have so far been found essential for man are given in Table 65.

The clinician is familiar with the results of an inadequate protein diet over an extended period. One such result is nutritional edema, also known as war or starvation edema—a condition produced in animals

TABLE 65.   MINIMUM AND RECOMMENDED INTAKES FOR NORMAL MAN
WHEN DIET FURNISHES SUFFICIENT NITROGEN FOR SYNTHESIS OF
NONESSENTIAL AMINO ACIDS (STRICTLY TENTATIVE VALUES)

Amino acid	Minimum Daily Rqt. (gm.)	Recommended Daily Intake (gm.)
L-Tryptophan	0.25	0.5
L-Phenylalanine	1.10	2.2
L-Lysine	0.80	1.6
L-Threonine	0.50	1.0
L-Valine	0.80	1.6
L-Methionine	1.10	2.2
L-Leucine	1.10	2.2
L-Isoleucine	0.70	1.4

(From Rose: J. Biol. Chem. *181*:307, 1949.)

when fed a low protein diet. In this condition, the plasma protein (the albumin fraction) is considerably below normal in amount (hypoproteinemia).

In order to show that these amino acids are the true precursors of protein in the body, Whipple restored the plasma protein in dogs which had previously been bled (reducing tissue and plasma protein) by feeding them protein hydrolysates.

It has been suggested that the biological efficiency of a protein may be determined by the regeneration of liver protein after a period of starvation. During starvation the weight of the liver decreases rapidly. Part of this decrease is due to the absence of protein. Using the rate of regeneration of liver protein as the basis, several authors have shown that casein and lactalbumin bring about such regeneration much more efficiently than, say, gelatin or zein.

Not only are amino acids needed for the building and repair of tissue proteins, but they are also needed for the synthesis in the body of enzymes, hormones and antibodies.

HIGH AND LOW PROTEIN

In the light of such work as that of Osborne and Mendel, and of Rose, the danger of incorporating too little protein in the diet becomes apparent. The problem must be attacked, first, from the point of view of including proteins which contain all the essential or indispensable amino acids, and, secondly, from the point of view of including enough of such proteins, so that the essential amino acids may be present in sufficient amounts. Dealing in dietetics for man, with complex natural foodstuffs rather than with artificial mixtures, the answer to the problem is not an easy one. Both Sherman and Rose are of the opinion that an allowance for the adult of 70 to 75 gm. per day of mixed proteins is within the region of safety. This is approximately 1 gm. of protein per kilogram of body weight. The British Ministry of Health advocates 50 gm. of "first class protein," meaning by that protein of animal origin (milk, eggs, cheese, meat, and fish).

It is worth noticing in this connection that meat is by no means the *only* source of animal protein. Nor, if meat it must be, is there evidence that, nutritionally speaking, expensive cuts are necessarily superior to portions less expensive. And some parts of the animal, such as blood, lungs, brain, and heart, richly nutritious, are often spurned.

At this stage a word should be said about the proteins in the soybean, of which *glycinin* is the most abundant. While, from the point of view of essential amino acids, animal proteins are to be preferred to vegetable proteins, the proteins of the soybean take their place somewhere in between—on the whole, better than other vegetable proteins, but probably not quite so good as animal proteins. Cooked soybean meal is superior to the raw variety. Heating seems to remove the effects of a trypsin inhibitor—a substance which interferes with the action of the digestive enzyme.

The proteins in yeast closely approximate, in biological value, those found in the soybean which means that, on the whole, they are superior to most of the proteins found in the vegetable world.

It may be added, in conclusion, that an abundance of protein in the diet of patients slowly recovering from disease or from wounds is of importance.

Kwashiorkor, a disease of infants due to chronic protein malnutrition, is "prevalent in many parts of the world where supplies of milk are limited and where infants are commonly fed diets consisting almost entirely of carbohydrate foods after weaning" (Nutr. Rev. Oct., 1956).

THE AMOUNTS OF FAT AND CARBOHYDRATE IN THE DIET

Fats and carbohydrates are essentially energy-yielding foods. The so-called "staple" foods, cereal grains, potatoes and rice often constitute one-half of the calorific intake, and famine is often associated with a decreased supply of these staple foods.

If the protein intake is equivalent to 75 gm., some 300 Calories can be attributed to protein (1 gm. of protein is equivalent to 4 Calories). If the total calorific requirement is about 3000 Calories, more than 2000 Calories must be derived from the burning of fat and carbohydrate in the body. This means that the calorific equivalent of the fat plus the carbohydrate must be between 2000 and 3000 Calories. Just what proportions of fat and carbohydrate should be included is probably not important, within broad limits. This much is definite: in the absence of carbohydrate, and when the fat alone supplies all the energy requirements, acidosis sets in. On the other hand, in the absence of fat from the diet, no matter how much carbohydrate is present, rats develop a deficiency disease. This deficiency is due to the absence from the diet of highly unsaturated fatty acids—acids present in various fats. These are known as "essential fatty acids."

Linoleic Acid, $CH_3(CH_2)_3(CH_2CH:CH)_2(CH_2)_7COOH$
Linolenic Acid, $CH_3(CH_2CH:CH)_3(CH_2)_7COOH$
Arachidonic Acid, $CH_3(CH_2)_3(CH_2CH:CH)_4(CH_2)_3COOH$

It should also not be overlooked that many fats are admixed with vitamins.

Fats almost always contain variable quantities of lipids such as lecithin. The choline present in the lecithin molecule prevents the development of fatty liver. Researches by Best, György and others have demonstrated the relationship of nutritional factors to liver injury.

Thus, on diets low in protein and moderately or distinctly high in fat, there is produced in the rat liver damage which is called nutritional cirrhosis. The early stages are characterized by a fatty deposition in the liver, followed by fibrotic changes in this tissue. The fatty infiltration and, to some extent, the fibrosis may be stopped and even reversed by incorporation into the diet of compounds called "lipotropic factors." These are choline, betaine and methionine, or a protein containing adequate amounts of methionine. Inositol, although once claimed as a potent lipotropic substance, seems to be of little value. In contrast to the action of methionine or choline, cystine, either in the form of the free amino acid or of a protein high in cystine and relatively low in methionine, promotes fat infiltration.

Not only is fat needed in the diet for the various reasons stated, but it should be fresh. A rancid fat is unpalatable and has a destructive action on other foods, particularly vitamins A and E (see next chapter). The fat in this condition may even be somewhat toxic. Sometimes the extent to which a food can be preserved will depend upon the condition of the fat present—the more rancid the fat the more rapid the deterioration of the food mixture.

Apparently both carbohydrate and fat must be incorporated in the diet. Usually from 20 to 25 per cent of the total calories represents fat in the diet. Many diets contain from four to five times as much carbohydrate as fat (by weight). A typical diet might be composed of 75 gm. of protein ($75 \times 4 = 300$ Calories*), 80 gm. of fat ($80 \times 9 = 720$ Calories), and 400 gm. of carbohydrate ($400 \times 4 = 1600$ Calories); with a total calorific value of 2620.

INORGANIC ELEMENTS

The common inorganic elements found in animal tissues include calcium, magnesium, sodium, potassium, sulfur, phosphorus, chlorine, iron, and iodine. The spectroscope has revealed traces of many other elements. Some of them, such as copper, seem as essential for the normal development of the animal as do the amino acids themselves. These inorganic elements play various roles: as components of skeletal structures, as cellular constituents, as regulators of body neutrality, etc.

ACID-BASE BALANCE OF FOODS

It may be mentioned that foods metabolized in the body may also influence the acid-base balance. For example, meat and eggs are foods which when oxidized in the body give rise to acids. On the other hand, many fruits and vegetables are potential base-formers. The sulfur and phos-

* These are large calories, or kilocalories.

phorus of proteins—abundant in meat and eggs—are oxidized to sulfuric and phosphoric acids. On the other hand, the organic acids of fruits are often, though not always, oxidized to carbonates.

The nutritive value of some common foods is given in the Appendix. *Vitamins* are treated in Chapter 18, and *water* is discussed in Chapter 20.

SOME CHARACTERISTICS OF VARIOUS FOODS

MILK

It is generally agreed that no other natural food compares with milk in its "protective" capacity. No other food so well protects the individual from possible deficiencies in the diet. For the past decade particularly, nutrition experts have been advocating a more liberal consumption of milk; and this applies not altogether to the poorer section of the community, though, of course, the need is most urgent among these people.

Aside from its protein, fat, and carbohydrate supply, milk is rich in calcium, phosphorus, and vitamin A. It also contains appreciable quantities of other vitamins and minerals.

One standard set by a state (New York) insists that milk must contain 11.5 per cent of solids, 3 per cent of fat, and not more than 88.5 per cent of water. As compared with this standard, the actual average composition of milk is as follows (in per cent): casein 3.0, fat 3.7, milk sugar 4.7, albumin 0.4, ash 0.7, other constituents 0.06, and water 87.3. Present in traces, and yet of extreme importance, are a number of the vitamins.

Milk Fat. The milk fat represents, for the most part, a mixture of a number of fats containing, as a rule, saturated fatty acids. Associated with these fats are vitamins A and (to a lesser extent) D. Commercially, the value of milk depends upon its fat ("butter-fat") content, for much of cream and butter and cheese represents fat.

The fats in milk and the quantities (in percentages) are as follows: butyrin, $C_3H_5(COOC_3H_7)_3$, 3.8; caproin, $C_3H_5(COOC_5H_{11})_3$, 3.6; caprylin, $C_3H_5(COOC_7H_{15})_3$, 0.5; caprin, $C_3H_5(COOC_9H_{19})_3$, 1.9; laurin, $C_3H_5(COOC_{11}H_{23})_3$, 7.4; myristin, $C_3H_5(COOC_{13}H_{27})_3$, 20.2; palmitin, $C_3H_5(COOC_{15}H_{31})_3$, 25.7; stearin, $C_3H_5(COOC_{17}H_{35})_3$, 1.8; olein, $C_3H_5(COOCH_{17}H_{33})_3$, 35.0. If by "fat" we mean "lipids," then small quantities of cholesterol, lecithin, etc., are also present.

The Proteins in Milk. The known proteins in milk are casein, lactalbumin, and lactoglobulin, the casein constituting 80 per cent of the total protein. Casein is rich in essential amino acids, and the other two proteins are also rich in these substances. Casein is the protein constituent in a synthetic diet for rats which has been used successfully by many investigators in many lands.

Casein is a phosphoprotein; it yields phosphoric acid and amino acids on hydrolysis. The isoelectric point of casein is at pH of about 4.6, but the pH of milk itself is in the neighborhood of 7. This means that casein in milk is in alkaline combination, probably in the form of calcium caseinate.

Casein itself is insoluble in water. The addition of acid to milk precipitates this protein. The same process is accomplished by allowing the milk to stand for some time, when the lactic acid bacteria convert the lactose to lactic acid, which, in turn, precipitates the protein. The casein precipitated under these conditions can be redissolved in alkali and reprecipitated by acids. This is, in fact, one method of purifying the protein.

Milk forms a clot upon the addition of rennin (commercial rennet). The composition of this clot has been the subject of much speculation. It is believed that the rennin first changes the casein to another compound, paracasein. Some are of the opinion that this change involves the splitting of one molecule of casein into two molecules of paracasein. At any rate, this changed casein, this paracasein, it is believed, forms the clot by combining with calcium. The calcium paracaseinate, unlike the calcium caseinate, is insoluble in water and insoluble in dilute acids and alkalis. It is quite different from the precipitate obtained by the addition of acid to milk or by the addition of ammonium sulfate to milk. One thing is certain: the clotting of milk does not take place in the absence of calcium.*

Casein, unlike lactalbumin and lactoglobulin, does not coagulate on heating. The skin which forms when milk is boiled is vaguely referred to as a mixture of the protein with the fat.†

Lactose. The carbohydrate in milk is lactose, or milk sugar. It is a rich source of energy, similar to cane sugar, and is often of value in aiding lactic acid bacteria to replace the undesirable putrefactive bacteria in the intestine.

The Inorganic Constituents of Milk. The inorganic constituents are many, but only a few are present in any quantity. Among the latter we can include calcium, phosphorus, potassium, sodium, chlorine, and magnesium. Iron is present but in small amounts. The demands for this element by the organism are such that additional iron must be obtained from other foods. Spectroscopic studies have revealed traces of many elements. Copper, for example, is present to the extent of perhaps 0.15 mg. per liter of milk, and yet this trace in conjunction with iron is of

---

* Compare the action of calcium in the clotting of milk with the action of the same element in blood coagulation.

† Casein in solution with certain compounds develops adhesive qualities and is used industrially in glues, coatings, and the like. With other combinations, it is used in plastics and paints.

importance in preventing anemia. The readiness with which "traces" and "impurities" have been dismissed as of no importance is giving place to a more cautious and critical attitude.

Human versus Cow's Milk. Human milk contains less protein (1.4 per cent) and more sugar (7.2 per cent) than cow's milk. Even when cow's milk is properly diluted and the correct amount of lactose added, it is not always a complete substitute for the natural milk when feeding the young. Whatever differences there are are obscure.

Types of Milk and Milk Products. *Certified milk* is raw milk of higher purity. It must not contain more than 10,000 bacteria per cubic centimeter of milk and must not be more than 36 hours old when delivered.

Grade A raw milk has an average bacterial count not exceeding 50,000 bacteria per cubic centimeter at the time of delivery to the customer.

Pasteurized milk is "milk that has been subjected to a temperature not lower than 145° F. for not less than thirty minutes."

The composition of milk (from several sources) and of milk products is given in Tables 66, 67, and 68.

TABLE 66. AVERAGE COMPOSITION OF MILK OF VARIOUS KINDS

Kind of milk	Water	Protein (N × 6.37)	Fat	Lactose (by difference)	Mineral matter (ash)	Fuel value per pound
	Per cent	Per cent	Per cent	Per cent	Per cent	Calories
Human.................	87.5	1.4	3.7	7.2	0.2	307
Cow....................	87.1	3.4	3.9	4.9	.7	310
Goat....................	87.0	3.3	4.2	4.8	.7	318
Sheep..................	82.6	5.5	6.5	4.5	.9	447
Reindeer...............	63.7	10.3	19.7	4.8	1.5	1078

(Compiled by Food Composition Section, Bureau of Home Economics.)

Cream usually contains about 20 per cent of fat, although in the "heavy" cream, fat may reach as high as 40 per cent.

Butter, as defined by Federal food laws, is "the clean sound product, made by gathering in any manner the fat of fresh or ripened milk or cream into a mass, which also contains a small portion of other milk constituents, with or without salt, and contains not less than 80 per cent of milk fat."

In the manufacture of butter, cream usually is pasteurized and then ripened. The ripening—an acid fermentation—is accomplished by inoculating with the desired organisms. The next process, that of churning, separates the fat globules, which can be drawn off and thereby separated from the butter milk.

Margarine, or *oleomargarine* as it is sometimes called, is coming into use more and more as a butter substitute. It must contain at least

80 per cent of fat by weight. Its fat content is made up of mixtures of vegetable fats, the basis usually being cottonseed and soybean oils. An agreeable flavor is given to the product by churning these fats and oils in specially cultured skim milk, and the nutritional value is enhanced by incorporating vitamin A.

TABLE 67. AVERAGE COMPOSITION OF MILK AND MILK PRODUCTS

Product	Water	Protein (N × 6.37)	Fat	Lactose,* etc. (by difference)	Mineral matter (ash)	Fuel value per pound
	Per cent	Per cent	Per cent	Per cent	Per cent	Calories
Whole milk...............	87.1	3.4	3.9	4.9	0.7	310
Cream:						
Single................	72.5	2.9	20.0	4.0	.6	942
Double...............	54.4	2.2	40.0	3.0	.4	1727
Skim milk..............	90.5	3.5	.2	5.0	.8	162
Buttermilk..............	90.7	3.5	.5	4.6	.7	167
Whey...................	93.0	1.0	.3	5.1	.6	123
Evaporated milk, un-						
sweetened.............	73.7	7.0	7.9	9.9	1.5	629
Condensed milk,						
sweetened.............	27.0	8.1	8.4	54.8†	1.7	1484
Dried whole milk........	3.5	25.8	26.7	38.0	6.0	2248
Dried skim milk.........	3.5	35.6	1.0	52.0	7.9	1630
Butter..................	15.5	.6	81.0	.4	2.5	3325
Cheese:						
American cheddar......	34.5	25.6	34.7	1.9	3.3	1916
Swiss.................	34.0	28.6	31.3	1.9	4.2	1831
Cottage (skim milk)....	74.0	19.2	.8	4.3	1.7	459
Cream................	42.7	14.5	39.9	1.0	1.9	1910

* Including lactic acid and other undetermined substances. The amount of sugar in some of the cheeses is probably negligible.

† Mainly added sucrose. Average percentage of added sugar is about 42 per cent of the condensed milk.

(Compiled by Food Composition Section, Bureau of Home Economics.)

"When margarine is fortified with vitamin A . . . it can be substituted for butter in the ordinary diet without any nutritional disadvantage" (Council on Food and Nutrition, A.M.A.).

Vegetable and animal fats, it seems, are absorbed and utilized equally well. The lack of vitamins—particularly vitamin A—in vegetable fats makes the animal fat more desirable; but such a deficiency can be easily overcome, as has just been pointed out.

Mineral oil (liquid petrolatum), sometimes used in the place of other oils and fats, is chemically not a fat at all but largely a mixture of hydrocarbons. It may be objectionable in foods because it may interfere with the absorption of a number of the vitamins, such as vitamins A, D, K, and carotene, the precursor of vitamin A (see the next chapter).

Skim milk is milk from which most of the fat has been removed,

TABLE 68. NUTRIENT VALUE OF DIFFERENT FORMS OF MILK

Type of milk	Quantity	Energy (calories)	Protein (grams)	Carbohydrate (grams)	Fat (grams)	Calcium (grams)	Phosphorus (grams)	Iron (grams)
Milk, whole...............	6 oz. (1 medium glass)	123	6.1	8.8	7.0	0.212	0.167	0.40
Milk, condensed............	1 tbsp., or 15 grams (to make 1 glass)	49	1.2	8.2	1.3	0.045	0.035	0.10
Milk, buttermilk...........	6 oz. (1 medium glass)	65	6.3	9.0	0.4	0.189	0.175	0.50
Milk, evaporated...........	1 tbsp., or 16 grams (to make 1 glass)	21	1.1	1.5	1.2	0.040	0.032	0.03
Milk, malted.............	1 tbsp., or 9 grams (to make 1 glass)	38	1.3	6.4	0.8	0.032	0.031	0.20
Milk powder, skim.........	28.35 grams (1 ounce)	102	10.1	14.7	0.3	0.346	0.272	0.90
Milk powder, whole........	28.35 grams (1 ounce)	141	7.3	10.8	7.6	0.261	0.201	0.40
Milk, skim...............	6 oz. (1 medium glass)	65	6.3	9.0	0.4	0.220	0.173	0.50

[From Bowes and Church: Food Values of Portions Commonly Used (Philadelphia Child Health Society).]

which means that its fuel value is low, and that its content of vitamin A is very small. From the standpoint of the manufacturer, skim milk is the most important by-product of milk. Casein, skim-milk powder, and condensed, cultured, and chocolate milks are prepared from it. A large amount is fed to farm animals.

Buttermilk is comparable to skim milk in composition. It is the product obtained after the removal of the fat of the milk during the course of buttermaking.

Homogenized milk is produced by forcing milk through minute openings under high pressure. The fat becomes more evenly distributed, and the fat globules are smaller than in milk.

Condensed milk is milk from which a certain amount of water has been removed and to which some sugar has been added. *Evaporated milk* is milk with less than its usual water content, but here no sugar has been added.

In the preparation of condensed milk, some 18 pounds of sugar are used for 100 pounds of milk, and the mixture is evaporated in vacuo at a temperature close to that of pasteurization. In the evaporated, or unsweetened, milk, much of the water from fresh milk is removed (in vacuo), the fat globules are broken up into smaller sizes by means of a "homogenizer," and the product, run into cans and sealed, is sterilized.

Dried milk is milk from which practically all the water has been removed. From 100 pounds of milk some 13 pounds of the white powder may be obtained.

Dried skim milk contains practically none of the fat of whole milk.

Fermented milk—buttermilk and acidophilus milk for example— is a milk which has been acted upon by desirable bacteria, in which the lactic acid bacteria are abundant. Buttermilk is the product left in the churn after the butter has been removed. The cream is usually churned when sour, and the buttermilk is therefore slightly acid.

Milk may be fortified with vitamin D. Few common foods contain vitamin D in any quantity. This is the reason why milk is at times enriched with the vitamin. The addition of other vitamins, or the addition of various minerals, is hardly necessary for an individual whose diet is varied.

*Cheese** is essentially a concentrate of the casein and fat of milk. (Cottage cheese is an exception; it is made from skim milk, rather than from whole milk, and therefore contains very little fat.) After the cheese has been removed, what is left is the "whey," and contains most of the lactose, some protein and some vitamins and mineral salts. What is known as "cream cheese"—made from cream—is richer in fat than cottage cheese. The hard cheeses—Cheddar, Swiss—are usually made from whole milk. The manufacture of cheese is based on the coagulation

* See U. S. Dept. Agriculture, Bull. No. 608, for varieties of cheese: descriptions and analyses.

process resulting from the action of rennin on casein. The variations in cheese depend upon the bacteria, the source of milk, the extent of ripening, and the temperature used.

Ice cream consists of cream or milk fat, sugar, flavoring matter, and binder (such as gelatin). The composition varies widely. The milk fat may range from 10 to 14 per cent, and the total solids, including protein and carbohydrate, from 20 to 30 per cent.

EGGS

Eggs are valuable in nutrition mainly for their content of protein and lipids. The protein, high in the biological scale, is found largely in egg white (ovalbumin and ovoglobulin), but also in the yolk (ovovitellin, a phosphoprotein). The lipids (fat, lecithin, cholesterol) are largely in the yolk. An approximate composition of the egg as a whole is (in per cent): protein 13.4, fat 10.5, ash 1.0, water 73.7. The egg is rich in a number of vitamins.

MEAT

According to Federal authorities, meat "is the properly dressed flesh derived from cattle, from swine, from sheep, or from goats . . . ," and flesh is "any clean, sound, edible part of the striated muscle of an animal." Like eggs, meat is of particular value for its content of protein and fat; and like eggs again, it has very little carbohydrate. Lean meat may contain (in per cent): protein 15 to 20, fat 8 to 14, ash 1, and water 65 to 75. The proteins are myogen, a water-soluble substance, and myosin, a globulin which is water-insoluble. A small quantity of glycogen (usually less than 1 per cent) is also found in muscle substance. "Extractives," which give rise to the flavor of meat, include creatine and such purine bodies as xanthine and hypoxanthine. The mineral salts are characterized by their relatively high percentage of potassium and phosphorus.

FISH

As a food fish is, to a considerable extent, similar to meat or to eggs. In fact, these three foods can largely replace one another in the diet. An approximate composition of fish (in per cent) is: protein 10.9, fat 2.4, ash 0.7 (including, in the case of marine fish and shellfish, appreciable quantities of iodine), water 44.6, refuse 41.6. The fat of mackerel may be as high as 16 per cent. Vitamins are also present.

CEREALS

Cereals are the edible portions (grains) of the grass family, *Gramineae*. The grain, according to Federal authorities, is "the fully matured, clean, sound, air-dry seed of wheat, maize (corn), rice, oats, rye, buckwheat, barley, sorghum, millet, or spelt." For Americans, wheat is the most important cereal, being used very largely in the form of bread. Twenty-five per cent of the average caloric intake in the United States is due to this cereal. Some of the other cereals are used for breakfast foods.

An approximate composition of wheat (in per cent) is: protein 11.9, fat 2.1, carbohydrate 71.9, fiber (cellulose, etc.) 1.8, ash 1.8, moisture 10.5. The two principal proteins are gliadin and glutenin, with smaller quantities of edestin. The "gluten" of flour consists very largely of gliadin and glutenin.

Most wheat flour milled in this country is converted into bread which is made from a mixture of flour and water, fermented with the production of carbon dioxide by an appropriate "leavening" agent, and subsequently baked. The nutritive value of bread depends upon the flour used in preparing it. The milling process has little effect on the protein and carbohydrate, but the fat and ash are reduced in quantity. In the manufacture of white flour, with the consequent removal of the bran and germ, one half of the calcium is lost, and there are definite losses in phosphorus and iron.

Whole wheat flour is milled to contain 100 per cent of the wheat kernel. White flour contains that part of the wheat kernel called the "endosperm." "Enriched flour" is white flour with various additions such as thiamine, nicotinic acid, iron, etc.

Whole wheat is a very good source of iron, but some four-fifths is lost when white flour is produced. The thiamine, riboflavin, and nicotinic acid present in the whole wheat are also largely lost in the milling process to produce white flour.

Wheat flour contains practically none of the vitamins C and D (see next chapter), and very little A, though it does contain an appreciable amount of the water-soluble B vitamins.

In the United States the various cereals contribute about one third of the calories to the diet; in Europe they very often contribute up to 50 per cent.

Macaroni is defined as the "shaped and dried doughs prepared by adding water to one or more of the following: farina, semolina, wheat flour."

The three main cereals are rice, wheat and corn. One half of the human race depends upon rice as its main food.

SUGAR

This is practically pure carbohydrate and, therefore, is rich in energy-yielding material. Before World War II, of the 7,000,000 tons used per year, 60 per cent was used by households and restaurants. Other uses were in industries connected with baking, canning, flavoring, soft drinks, dairying, tobacco, etc.

The common food sugars include cane sugar or sucrose, milk sugar or lactose, malt sugar or maltose, glucose or dextrose, and fructose or levulose.

The cane sugar is derived from sugar cane and the sugar beet. Malt sugar is made from the partial digestion of starch. The malt food for infants contains maltose and dextrins. Glucose is obtained from starch but occurs also as such in nature. Commercial corn syrup is a mixture of glucose and dextrins. Fructose is found in honey—which also contains glucose—and in many fruits.

Maple sugar and maple syrup represent the sap of the sugar maple. The mother liquor left after the removal of part of the cane sugar from the boiled juice is molasses.

On the whole, much too much sugar (in various forms) is used in this country. The quantities which are consumed lessen the desire for other—and more important—foods.

FRUITS AND VEGETABLES

These contribute relatively little as sources of energy, but they are nevertheless very important for their content of minerals and vitamins. Leafy, green, and yellow vegetables include asparagus, yellow sweet corn, beets, lettuce, parsley, spinach, water cress, etc. They are rich in provitamin A and, as a rule, in iron. Citrus fruits (orange, lemon, grapefruit, etc.) and tomatoes are splendid sources of vitamin C. The presence of moderate amounts of cellulose lends bulk to the food and aids in proper digestion. The average composition of a vegetable such as cabbage is (in per cent): protein 1.4, fat 0.2, carbohydrate (including fiber) 5.6, ash 1.8, water 77.7, refuse 15. The average composition of a number of fruits is (in per cent): protein 1, fat 0.7, carbohydrate (including fiber) 13, ash 0.6, water 63, waste 22.

The potato is a food of high energy value, rich in carbohydrates, relatively poor in protein, and relatively poor in minerals and vitamins. It is a cheap source of iron and vitamin C.*

COOKING

To a greater or less degree, cooking affects more particularly the vitamins and minerals of foods. So variable are the various factors—amount of water, length of cooking, temperature, etc.—that no one statement will cover all the possibilities.†

---

* Coffee, tea, chocolate, flavoring spices, add to the "spice of life" but are not in themselves necessary foods.

† The following, taken from the Manual of Industrial Nutrition (Government Printing Office, Washington, 1943), are several practical illustrations of things to bear in mind.

Use fresh vegetables and fruits as soon as possible after delivery. Handle very carefully, for bruising causes rapid losses of vitamins. Keep vegetables and fruits

PROCESSING OF FOODS

Various methods for preserving foods have been developed. These methods received a great impetus during World War II when urgent demands arose not only for foods which did not deteriorate with time, but also for those which occupied considerably less space than the untreated food (which contains varying quantities of water). The processes employed come under the following headings; drying or dehydration, sterilization (the canning process), low temperature chilling and freezing, pickling, smoking, spicing, fermentation, etc. The products obtained by these means are of the utmost value when fresh foods are unattainable.

The high-vacuum and low-temperature evaporator has made the frozen food industry possible. As to variety, fruits, vegetables, fish, meat, etc., are all obtainable.

Concentration of juices is a spectacular development in recent years. The basis for this achievement, as has been intimated, is the utilization of very high vacua without additional application of heat. Fruit juices—orange juice, particularly—are concentrated to one-fourth their volume. The product, a four-fold concentration, is packed in tin containers and kept in a frozen state.

If properly processed, as much as 98 per cent of the vitamin C (Chap. 18) content of the original orange juice may be retained.

There is, of course, always the danger that foods so prepared have lost some of their nutritional value. This applies more specifically to some minerals and to a number of vitamins of varying stability, such as carotene, vitamin A, thiamine, riboflavin, and ascorbic acid. The extent to which such foods are undamaged depends upon a number of factors: exposure to light; temperature and length of time of heating and of standing; the pH of the solution; the extent of loss of water-soluble material.

It would, of course, be to the advantage of the consumer if com-

---

crisp and cool until time to cook them. Shred or chop vegetables and fruits just before they are to be served or cooked.

Add vegetables or fruits to rapidly boiling water. Cook quickly and in as little water as possible. Do not add soda to vegetables or fruits to preserve their color because it destroys certain vitamins. Cook until just done with some of the original crispness left. Do not stir or expose to air and light any more than absolutely necessary. Do not let vegetables or fruits stand in water. Standing destroys vitamins. Use vegetable cooking water in gravies, soups, or sauces. Bring precooked canned fruits and vegetables quickly to a boil but do not continue boiling. Add frozen vegetables and fruits directly to boiling water. Do not defrost preliminary to cooking.

With meats, short methods of cooking such as sautéing or broiling are less destructive of vitamins than slower methods. Roasting at a low temperature is less destructive than at a high temperature. As with other foods, meats should be served as soon as possible after cooking. Standing in a warmer or on a steam table is accompanied by vitamin losses.

plete analyses—including vitamins and minerals—would appear on the labels of cans.

CHEMICALS IN FOODS

Some chemicals are accepted without question. They have undergone adequate investigation, they serve a useful purpose and, so far as rigorous testing provides evidence, they are not harmful. In this group we may include the addition of potassium iodide to salt to prevent goiter; the use of chlorine in drinking water; the use of baking powder; the addition of vitamins to various foods; the use of certified food colors. However, some chemicals, not adequately tested as to toxicity, may get into foods. For example, foods may become contaminated by substances added to the soil, or by the use of sprays for plants and animals, or by adding chemicals in the course of processing foods. Here, to prevent possible disaster, the nation's laws relating to nutrition must be made more rigorous.

AN ADEQUATE (NORMAL) DIET

This should include the equivalent of some 2600 to 3000 Calories (for the adult), about 70 gm. of protein, of which 50 gm. should be of animal origin, from 80 to 90 gm. of fat, and from 400 to 500 gm. of carbohydrate. Meat, milk, eggs, and fish supply "first-class proteins," that is, proteins rich in essential amino acids; cereals supply carbohydrates and proteins which are usually not "first-class"; and fruits and vegetables supply minerals and "roughage" (cellulose, etc.). A mixture of such foods contains the more important vitamins. To take care of possible deficiencies in the diet, even on so mixed a fare, it is advisable to consume from one to two glasses of milk a day.

SOCIAL PROBLEMS

MALNUTRITION

Bertram* tells us that the world's population increased from 545 million in 1650 to 2057 million in 1933. Of this total, 75 per cent are farmers and their dependents.

It has been estimated that some 75 per cent of Asia's population of over 1000 million live on a subnormal diet. It has been further estimated that even in the two most civilized countries of the world, the United States and Great Britain, from 20 to 30 per cent of the population suffer from malnutrition.

In a carefully controlled study entitled "Food, Health, and Income," by J. B. Orr, the author points out that the consumption of milk,

* Nature, March 22, 1947.

eggs, fruit, vegetables, meat, and fish rises with income. An examination of the composition of the diets shows that the degree of adequacy for health increases as income rises. As income increases, disease and death rate decrease, children grow more quickly, adult stature is greater, and general health and physique improve. Among the poorer children the improvement of the diet is accompanied by improvement in health and increased rate of growth. This improvement in diet means increased consumption of milk, eggs, butter, fruits, vegetables, and meat to the extent of from 12 to 25 per cent.

Where family income is limited the possibilities of varying the diet in sufficient amounts—so important in the attainment of a "wholesome" diet—become more restricted. The poor spend more on flour and cereals, potatoes and sugar, and less on butter and fats, meat, eggs, milk and fruits and vegetables than do the more prosperous members of the community.

In a study by Jolliffe, McLester, and Sherman, the conclusion is reached that dietary inadequacies and malnutrition are of frequent occurrence in the United States. They define "dietary inadequacy" as the failure to ingest an essential nutritional factor or factors in amounts sufficient to meet the existing requirement of the body, and "malnutrition" as a bodily condition, detectable by any method of examination, caused by a nutritional inadequacy.

To eat adequately—that is, to have a well-balanced diet—means that one must have a certain sum of money to spend and that one must be familiar with the elements of nutritional science. Assuming both these points, we may quote from an excellent pamphlet by Carpenter and Stiebeling, "Diets to Fit the Family Income."

A liberal diet, as its name implies, provides very generously for all of the food requirements. It contains an abundance of fruits and vegetables, eggs, and lean meat, as well as a generous allowance of milk, along with moderate quantities of cereals, fats, and sugars. This combination of foods allows for better-than-average nutrition because it provides more than amply for the items necessary for growth, health, and general well-being. At the same time, it offers an assortment pleasing to the eye and the palate, and allows for a great deal of variety from meal to meal.

Table 69 gives the nutritive value of a moderate-cost adequate diet.

It is interesting to compare this table with the one devised by a committee of the National Research Council. This committe first formulated a series of recommendations which is summarized on page 418. Compare these tables with Table 70, which deals with the approximate food value of the daily allowance of a man moderately active and weighing 70 kilograms. In Table 70 the foods are listed, the approximate measures given, and also the calorific equivalent of each food is listed.

It should not be overlooked that malnutrition may have its origin in factors other than a lack of dietary intake. Poor absorption or poor

TABLE 69. NUTRITIVE VALUE OF A MODERATE-COST DIET

Persons	Food energy	Protein	Calcium	Phosphorus	Iron	Vitamin A	Thiamine	Riboflavin	Ascorbic acid
	Calories	Grams	Grams	Grams	Milli-grams	Interna-tional units	Milli-grams	Milli-grams	Milli-grams
Children:									
9–12 months	970	38	1.1	1.0	6	4,400	0.8	1.9	60
1–3 years	1,300	55	1.3	1.3	7	5,700	1.1	2.4	65
4–6 years	1,710	65	1.3	1.4	9	6,200	1.4	2.6	80
7–9 years	2,130	79	1.4	1.6	12	8,000	1.7	3.0	100
10–12 years	2,670	91	1.4	1.8	14	9,200	2.1	3.3	115
Girls:									
13–15 years	2,980	102	1.5	1.9	16	9,700	2.4	3.5	115
16–20 years	2,590	94	1.4	1.8	15	9,800	2.1	3.3	125
Women:									
Moderately active	2,590	86	1.1	1.6	14	9,700	2.1	2.8	120
Very active	3,250	104	1.2	1.8	17	8,800	2.3	3.1	120
Sedentary	2,260	80	1.1	1.5	13	8,800	1.9	2.7	110
Pregnant	2,750	95	1.5	1.8	15	10,500	2.1	3.4	130
Nursing	3,240	114	2.1	2.3	17	12,100	2.6	4.4	170
Boys:									
13–15 years	3,420	112	1.5	2.0	18	9,600	2.6	3.7	130
16–20 years	4,020	122	1.5	2.2	20	10,200	3.0	4.0	140
Men:									
Moderately active	3,250	104	1.2	1.8	17	8,800	2.3	3.1	120
Very active	4,860	139	1.3	2.3	24	10,500	3.5	4.0	140
Sedentary	2,580	85	1.1	1.6	14	9,000	2.0	2.8	115

[From Family Nutrition. (Philadelphia Child Health Society.)]

TABLE 70. APPROXIMATE FOOD VALUE OF DAILY ALLOWANCE OF MAN, MODERATELY ACTIVE, AND WEIGHING 70 KG.

Foods	Amount	Approximate measure	Calories	Protein	Calcium	Iron	Vitamin A	Thiamine (B_1)	Riboflavin	Ascorbic acid
	Grams			Grams	Grams	Mg.	I.U.	Gamma*	Gamma*	Mg.
Milk	480	1 pint	336	15.8	0.58	0.15	528	244	1,000	6
Meat	100	¼ pound	150	21.0	.01	3.00	50	120	225	
Potatoes	350	3 medium	300	7.2	.05	3.66	144	432	162	12
Baked beans	200	1 cup	200	13.2	.09	4.00	110	235	130	
Cabbage, raw	100	1 cup	25	1.1	.04	.43	88	70	72	35
Carrots	100	½ cup	40	1.2	.04	.64	2,100	60	58	
Tomato	200	⅝ cup	50	2.4	.02	.80	2,000	182	122	48
Prunes, stewed	200	⅝ cup	250	1.4	.03	1.88	990	120	132	
Oleomargarine	66	5 tablespoons	500				2,600			
Oatmeal, cooked	300	1¼ cups	200	8.0	.03	2.40	....	270	60	
Bread, whole wheat or "enriched"	200	6 slices	500	19.0	.10	3.0	....	480	207	
Gingerbread	75	Large piece	200	3.5	.08	2.0	....	40	30	
Sugar, jam			250							
Totals	...	....	3,001	93.8	1.07	22.0	8,602	2,253* 2.25 mg.	2,234* 2.23 mg.	101
Compared with recommended allowances	...	....	3,000	70.0	.80	12.0	5,000	1.80 mg.	2.70 mg.	75

* 1 milligram (mg.) equals 1000 micrograms (gamma).
[From Proc. National Nutrition Conference for Defense. (Washington, 1941.)]

utilization may also bring about malnutrition. During pregnancy and lactation, in fever, and in cases of hyperthyroidism—to name some examples—the bodily needs are increased, and if such demands are not met, the results may be disastrous.

REFERENCES

Among the books covering the field of nutrition, we have *McLester* and *Darby:* Nutrition and Diet in Health and Disease, 1952; *Jolliffe, Tisdall* and *Cannon:* Clinical Nutrition, 1950.

The Ann. Rev. Biochem., *27:*403, 1958, has an article on protein requirements by *Schrimshaw, Arroyaye* and *Bressani.* See also *Olson.* Ibid., *28:*467, 1959 (essential fatty acids).

Nutritional Reviews, published monthly by the Nutrition Foundation, reviews advances in nutrition.

Many popular pamphlets on nutrition may be obtained from various Federal and other agencies; for example, Bureau of Home Economics, U. S. Dept. Agriculture; Children's Bureau, U. S. Dept. Labor; Office of Education, and Public Health Service, Federal Security Agency; Dept. Health, N. Y. City; Farmer's Bulletin, U. S. Dept. Agriculture.

A stimulating article by *Keys* dealing with the physiology of the individual as an approach to a more quantitative biology of man will be found in Federation Proceedings, *8:*523, 1949.

The pioneer work of *Osborne* and *Mendel* is described by the latter in an article on nutrition and growth, Harvey Lectures, Ser. 10, p. 1.

Rose's work on amino acids in nutrition is summarized in Chem. Eng. News, *30:* 2385, 1952.

For genetic factors in obesity, see *Mayer:* Bull. N. Y. Acad. Medicine, May, 1960, p. 323. See also the article on body fat by *Dole* in Scientific American, Dec., 1959, p. 71.

The age-old problem of human milk versus cow's milk is debated by *Jeans:* J. Am. Med. Assoc., *142:*806, 1950.

Barry: Scientific American, Oct., 1957, p. 121, is the author of an article which describes how the mammal makes milk out of blood.

See also A Century of Milk in Borden's Rev. Nutritional Research, *18:* July–August, 1957.

For a description of various cheeses, see U. S. Department of Agriculture Bull. No. 608.

The nutritional aspects of egg yolk are discussed by *Schjeide* in Nutr. Rev., *17:*1, 1959.

The food problem, with its many ramifications, is discussed by *Boyd-Orr:* Scientific American, *183:*11, 1950.

Kwashiorkor. Nutr. Rev., *14:*296, 1956; *Schrimshaw, Behar, Arroyaye, Viteri* and *Tejada:* Federation Proceedings, *15:*977, 1956; *Brock:* Ann. Rev. Biochem., *24:*532, 1955.

The problem of chemicals in foods (and food colors) is discussed in Chem. Eng. News, July 30, p. 3666, and Sept. 10, p. 4366, 1956; and by *Kaplan:* J. Chem. Educ., Feb., 1960, p. 82.

See Agricultural Information Bulletin No. 160, U. S. Dept. Agriculture for "Essentials of an Adequate Diet."

Adam: J. Royal Society of Arts, Feb., 1960, p. 167, is the author of an article on advances in food preservation.

Ebbs: Nutr. Rev., *17:*129, 1959, discusses nutrition in the space age.

See also *Engel:* Nutr. Rev., *17:*353, 1959 (food faddism), and *Spies:* J. Am. Med. Assoc., *167:*675, 1958 (advances in nutrition).

For a review of many aspects of nutrition see the account of the fifth congress of nutrition in Federation Proceedings, *20,* March, 1961.

VITAMINS

CHAPTER EIGHTEEN

WHAT IS A VITAMIN

In addition to carbohydrates, lipids, proteins, inorganic salts and water, normal growth and good health require the presence of additional compounds in the diet. These are organic in nature and are called vitamins. Not all living organisms require vitamins (some bacteria do not), nor do they necessarily need the same number or kind, since some vitamins can be synthesized by the organism. For example, the guinea pig, man and other primates cannot synthesize vitamin C (ascorbic acid) and are therefore susceptible to scurvy, whereas the rat can synthesize this vitamin from glucose and therefore does not require the vitamin in its diet. Although we do not know the biochemical functions of all the known vitamins, we have accumulated much information about many of them.

HISTORY

That disease can result from a food deficiency had been vaguely known for many years. Sailors discovered that scurvy could be prevented by incorporating fresh fruit or fresh vegetables in the diet. In 1882 Takaki eliminated beriberi from the Japanese navy by giving increased quantities of meat, barley and fruit to his sailors. To be sure, he was wrong in his explanation that a sufficient amount of protein prevented beriberi, but he was right in supposing that a food deficiency was a causal factor in its development. Toward the close of the nineteenth century, a number of physicians began to recognize the value of cod liver oil in curing rickets.

An impetus for further study was given by Eijkman, a Dutch physician, with his discovery that experimental beriberi could be induced in birds. This occurred in 1897. He found that hens developed the disease when fed with polished rice. Moreover, such hens could be cured by giving them the rice polishings. Still under the influence of Pasteur,

442

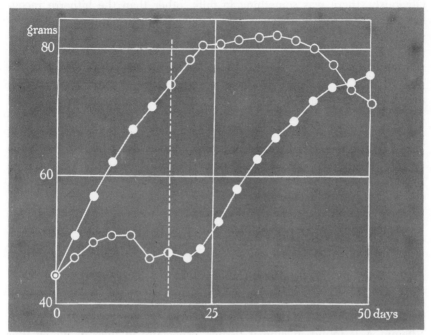

Figure 91. Growth curves of rats, with and without vitamins (Hopkins). ○ Artificial diet alone. ● Artificial diet plus milk.

Eijkman for a time believed that the rice polishings contained a "something" that neutralized the beriberi toxin in the polished rice.

An equally important advance we owe to the Norwegians, Holst and Frölich, who, in 1907, caused scurvy in guinea-pigs by feeding them a cereal diet deficient in "greens."

We owe to Funk the first clear evidence of the validity of the vitamin hypothesis. From the very first (1911), Funk regarded the Eijkman factor in beriberi as a definite chemical substance (present in whole rice in relatively small quantities), the absence of which, in polished rice, causes the disease. He boldly attacked the problem of its isolation from rice and from yeast, the latter of which he found to be rich in the antiberiberi factor. He obtained extremely active concentrates, isolating from his fractions nicotinic acid, which is now recognized as one of the vitamins of the B complex. Incidentally, we owe the name "vitamin" to Funk.

Shortly thereafter (in 1912), Hopkins in England published an important paper on the influence of small quantities of milk added to a synthetic diet. An artificial diet, consisting presumably of all the important constituents found in milk (protein, fat, carbohydrate, mineral salts and water), proved deficient; but when 2 ml.* of milk was added to the diet of each rat each day, the animals recovered (see Fig. 91).

* With a very pure synthetic diet, 2 ml. of milk is insufficient.

Obviously, there was something in milk, other than the hitherto recognized components, which was present in minute quantities and which was essential for the normal development of the animal. This "something" is a vitamin.

The suspicion that there might be more than one vitamin was strengthened by the work of McCollum and Davis in 1915. They showed that the substitution of lard for egg yolk in a synthetic diet prevented rats from growing, and that the substitution of highly purified lactose for ordinary lactose prevented growth and also gave rise to polyneuritis. The first factor, associated with fats, was named "fat-soluble A," and the second factor, associated with water-soluble material, was named "water-soluble B." These two substances were later renamed vitamin A and vitamin B, respectively.

The vitamins are usually divided into those which are fat-soluble and those which are water-soluble. The fat-soluble vitamins are A, D, E and K; the water-soluble vitamins are the B complex and C. For the sake of convenience they will be considered in alphabetical order.

VITAMIN A

Vitamin A is found in animal tissues, especially in liver in which it is stored. Fish liver oils are particularly rich in this vitamin. In plants the

TABLE 71. SOME CAROTENOIDS, THEIR SOURCES AND THEIR RELATION TO VITAMIN A

Compound	Sources	Formula	Relative physiological activity
β-carotene	Alfalfa, carrots, green leaves, red palm oil, butter	$C_{40}H_{56}$	100
α-carotene	Red palm oil, green chestnut leaves, mountain ash berries	$C_{40}H_{56}$	53
Cryptoxanthin (3-hydroxycarotene)	Yellow corn, egg yolk, green grass, butter	$C_{40}H_{56}O$	57
Aphanin (3-keto-β-carotene)	Blue-green algae	$C_{40}H_{54}O$	50
γ-carotene	*Gonocarium pyrifirme* (Dutch East Indies plant) lily-of-the valley leaves	$C_{40}H_{56}$	27

(From Sebrell and Harris: The Vitamins. Academic Press, 1954.)

vitamin occurs in a precursor form as *provitamin A*. These precursors belong to a family of pigmented hydrocarbons called *carotenoids*, and the conversion of hydrocarbon carotenoid to vitamin A alcohol is believed to take place in the intestinal tract of animals. *Carotenes* are a group of hydrocarbons with the formula $C_{40}H_{56}$ and consist of isoprene units strung together forming a series of alternating double bonds. In addition, the carotenes have ring structures (trimethylcyclohexenyl) called *β-ionone*. There are three carotenes: *α-*, *β-* and *γ-*, of which *β*-carotene is most active physiologically (Table 71).

STRUCTURE AND STEREOCHEMISTRY

Whereas the carotenes are hydrocarbons, vitamin A is an alcohol which is derived by cleavage of the hydrocarbon at the central double bond:

$$C_{40}H_{56} + 2\,H_2O \longrightarrow 2\,C_{20}H_{29}OH$$

The mechanism for this conversion is unknown.

Because of the system of alternating double bonds and the H and CH_3 groups attached to the carbon atoms in the chain, the carotenoids and vitamin A are subject to geometrical isomerism. When the substituent groups of the carbon atoms attached to each other by double bonds lie in the same plane, they bear a *cis* relationship. When they lie in opposite planes, they have a *trans* structure. The formulae for *β*-carotene and vitamin A$_1$ are shown below. Note that they have an all-*trans* configuration:

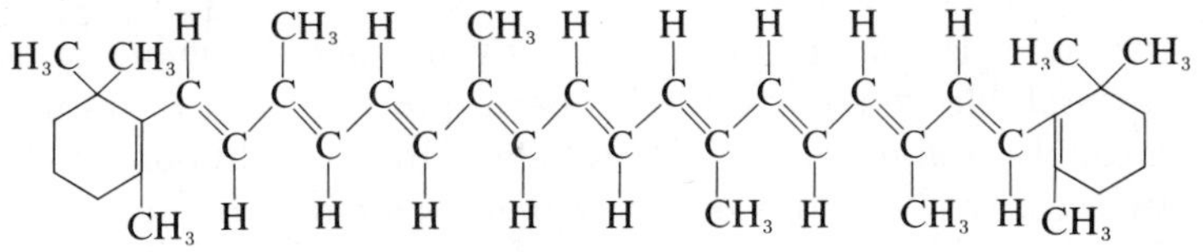

β-Carotene (all-*trans*)

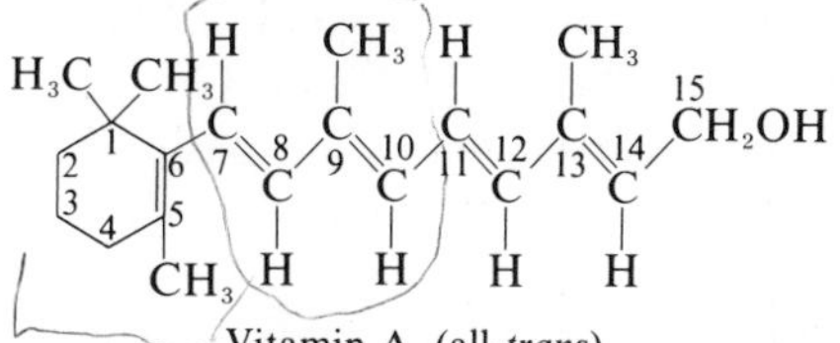

Vitamin A$_1$ (all-*trans*)

Vitamin A$_1$ is the most abundant of the vitamins of this group and is found in the liver and viscera of all land animals, sea- and fresh-water fishes. Vitamin A$_2$ is found in liver oils of some fresh-water fish. It differs from A$_1$ in the extra double bond of the ring:

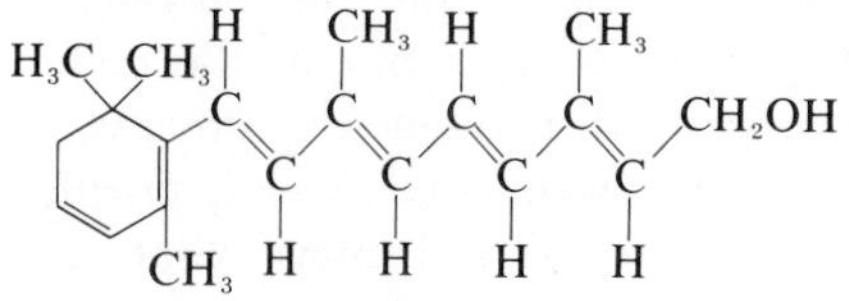

Vitamin A$_2$

Two additional isomers of vitamin A are known which involve the relationship of H and CH_3 groups at specific double bonds. These are: *neo-a vitamin* A_1, the 13-*cis* isomer which occurs in vitamin A concentrates prepared from liver, and which has a potency of 85 per cent of the all-*trans* vitamin; and *neo-b vitamin* A_1, the 11-*cis* isomer which is found in the retina and is concerned in the visual process. Their formulae are shown:

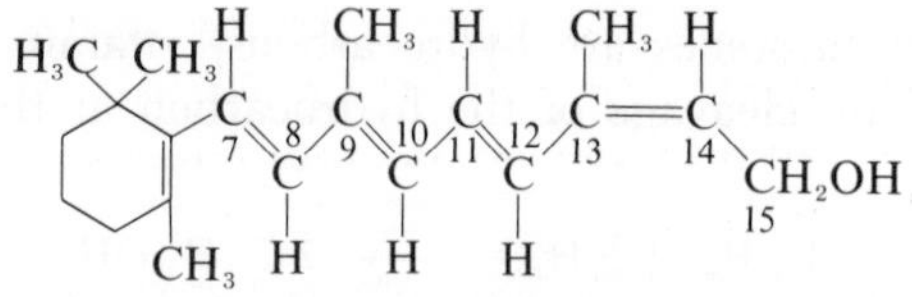

Neo-a Vitamin A_1 (13-*cis*)

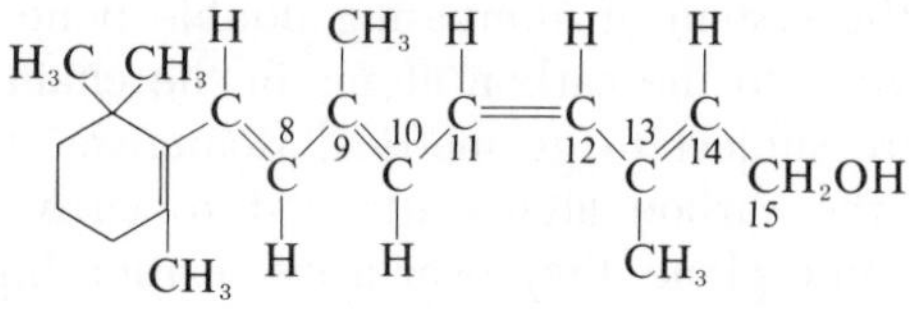

Neo-b Vitamin A_1 (11-*cis*)

PROPERTIES

Vitamin A is soluble in organic solvents and insoluble in water, but water-soluble derivatives have been prepared. It is unstable in air but can be stabilized against oxidation by the addition of antioxidants such as hydroquinone or α-tocopherol (vitamin E). Since it is an alcohol, vitamin A forms esters which are more stable than the free vitamin. The acetate is the international standard. The vitamin reacts with $SbCl_3$ in chloroform solution to yield a blue color which absorbs light with a maximum at 620 mμ. The color fades and gives a new maximum at 580 mμ. This has been made the basis of a quantitative assay. Both vitamins A_1 and A_2 have been synthesized.

VITAMIN A AND VISION

The retina in most vertebrates contains visual elements consisting of two kinds of light receptors: *rods* and *cones*. The rods are concerned with vision in dim light and the cones are the organs of vision in bright light and of color vision. The light sensitivity of these elements is due to the compound *rhodopsin* (or *porphyropsin* in some freshwater fishes) in the rods and *iodopsin* in the cones. These compounds are proteins conjugated with carotenoid pigments.

Rhodopsin, originally designated "visual purple," upon exposure to light is bleached, through a series of intermediate colored compounds, to a colorless compound. The end-products of this particular series of reactions are *retinene*₁ and the protein *opsin*. Retinene₁ is actually vitamin A₁ aldehyde and therefore has the all-*trans* configuration. Retinene₁ cannot recombine with opsin to form rhodopsin because the carotenoid moiety in rhodopsin is of the 11-*cis* structure. Also, retinene₁ is easily oxidized to vitamin A₁ which is sent out into the circulation, taken up by the liver and converted to neo-b vitamin A₁ which has the 11-*cis* configuration. The retina can absorb this compound and oxidize it to the corresponding aldehyde, neo-b retinene₁, which combines with opsin to form rhodopsin. Vitamin A appears to function as part of an external circuit which can refresh itself from the vitamin absorbed with the diet. Vitamin A appears in the retina of the rat within 3 hours after its oral administration. Vitamin A is present in the blood as the alcohol, whereas in the liver it is found as the ester.

The nature of the enzyme system which oxidizes retinene to vitamin A, and which can reduce the vitamin to the aldehyde, "retinene reductase," has been identified as alcohol dehydrogenase, which requires DPN as a coenzyme. It is of interest that only the dehydrogenase from liver is active; that from yeast is inactive. The reaction may be formulated as follows:

$$\text{Retinene} + 2 \text{ DPNH} + 2 \text{ H}^+ \rightleftharpoons \text{Vitamin A} + 2 \text{ DPN}^+$$
$$(\text{C}_{19}\text{H}_{27}\text{CHO}) \qquad\qquad\qquad (\text{C}_{19}\text{H}_{27}\text{CH}_2\text{OH})$$

This enzyme is also concerned in the interconversion of retinene₂ to vitamin A₂ in some fresh-water fish. Below is a scheme for the biochemical transformations which occur during vision in dim light in the rods of the retina.

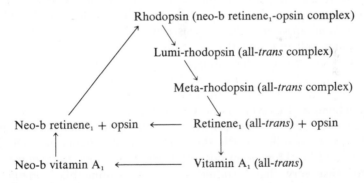

When one comes into a dimly lit room from the brightly illuminated outdoors, some time is required in order to adapt to the change in illumination and to be able to see objects in the room. This phenomenon of dark adaptation has been used to measure vitamin A deficiency. Night blindness (impaired dark adaptation) was recognized in Egyptian medicine as a disorder of the eyes curable by the ingestion of animal liver.

VITAMIN A ACID

This compound does not occur in nature but has been prepared synthetically. The alcohol group is replaced by a carboxyl group. It has a potency of two-thirds that of vitamin A when one uses the growth rate of young rats as a measure. However, this compound has no activity in the visual process. It has been suggested that there may be no relationship between the functions of vision and growth with which the vitamin is concerned. This may be illustrated in the following diagram:

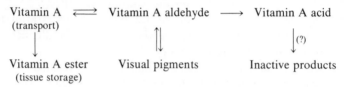

THE VITAMIN B COMPLEX

Originally, vitamin B referred to the vitamin the absence of which gives rise to beriberi in man and polyneuritis in birds. The work of Goldberger on pellagra led to the view that vitamin B consisted of at least two factors, the heat-labile antiberiberi factor, and the comparatively heat-stable antipellagra factor. Some called the former the true vitamin B, and others, vitamin B_1; some called the heat-stable factor vitamin G, and others, vitamin B_2.

In 1933, Kuhn, P. György and Wagner-Jauregg isolated what they supposed at the time was vitamin G (B_2) and found it to be a flavin. That this flavin—now known as riboflavin—was not the sole antipellagra factor became apparent when it was shown that the pigment does not cure human pellagra, and that a combination of vitamin B_1 plus riboflavin does not prevent dermatitis in rats. Riboflavin, then, had little, if anything, to do with pellagra, and it became obvious that the so-called vitamin B_2 consisted of more than one factor.

Elvehjem and co-workers next found that after removing the flavin from liver extract (a good source of much of the vitamin B complex) by adsorption on fuller's earth, the residue cured pellagra-like symptoms in chicks and blacktongue in dogs. But Elvehjem's arresting contribution was the discovery that nicotinic acid cures canine blacktongue (the analogue of pellagra in man); and he succeeded in isolating the amide of nicotinic acid from highly active concentrates of liver extract.

But the vitamin B complex, as represented by yeast, rice bran and liver extracts, contains still other factors. These substances have been discovered by showing that the isolated constituents are still not the equivalent in biological response to the yeast or liver or rice bran from which they were extracted.

THE SUBSTANCES COMPRISING THE VITAMIN B COMPLEX

They are:

a. *Thiamine* (vitamin B_1, antineuritic factor, aneurine, heat-labile factor)
b. *Riboflavin* (vitamin B_2, vitamin G), a growth factor
c. *Niacin* (nicotinic acid or nicotinic acid amide, P-P factor), pellagra preventive factor
d. *Vitamin B_6* (pyridoxine, etc.), antidermatitis factor
e. *Pantothenic acid* (filtrate factor), chick antidermatitis factor
f. *Biotin* (vitamin H, coenzyme R, anti-egg white injury factor), needed for the growth of yeasts, molds and bacteria
g. *Inositol* (mouse anti-alopecia* factor)
h. *Choline*, a growth factor. It also prevents perosis† in chicks and is needed for methylating compounds in the body (Chap. 12)
i. *Para-aminobenzoic acid*
j. *Folic acid*
k. *Vitamin B_{12}*, anti-pernicious anemia factor

These vitamins—the vitamin B complex—are not related to one another, either chemically or physiologically. If a relationship does exist, it is that most of them, if not all, are part of enzyme systems which play vital roles in metabolism.

The experimental difficulties in working with these vitamins are enhanced by the fact that a number of them can be synthesized by intestinal microorganisms (this is particularly true of ruminants), so that putting an animal on a diet devoid of pyridoxine, say, does not necessarily mean that some pyridoxine may not be formed within the body. To some extent the problem has been overcome by the use of sulfa compounds which tend to destroy such microorganisms.

THIAMINE (B_1)

A deficiency of thiamine primarily involves the nervous circulatory systems. In the absence of this vitamin, peripheral neuritis develops, resulting in paralysis. The beriberi of man has its corresponding analogue in the polyneuritis of the bird and the rat. Not only is there the typical paralysis, but cardiovascular symptoms, edema and loss of appetite are noticed.

CHEMISTRY

The vitamin was isolated in the crystalline state by Williams and has been synthesized. Its structure was elucidated by Williams, Clarke

* alopecia = baldness.
† perosis = a shortening and thickening of the bones.

and their co-workers. It is made up of a pyrimidine and thiazole structure:

$$\times \quad CH_3 \underset{N}{\overset{N}{\bigcirc}} NH_2 \quad —CH_2— \overset{+}{N} \underset{C-S}{\overset{}{\bigcirc}} \underset{CH_3}{\overset{CH_2.CH_2.OH}{}}$$

pyrimidine *pyrophosphate*

Thiamine is soluble in water, and in alcohol up to 70 per cent. It is insoluble in fat solvents. The pure substance is quite stable in acid solutions and can be sterilized for 30 minutes at 120° C. without appreciable loss of activity. In alkaline and neutral solutions, the vitamin is rapidly destroyed, because here it is hydrolyzed into its two main components, substances containing the pyrimidine and thiazole rings.

The vitamin can be assayed by chemical or by microbiological methods. The latter technique makes use of the fact that many microorganisms require the vitamin for their growth. Thiamine will also accelerate the alcoholic fermentation of baker's yeast. The compound is oxidized by ferricyanide to thiochrome which can be measured by its fluorescence. It can also be coupled with an aromatic amine such as sulfanilic acid by diazotization and the color of the resulting complex measured.

BIOSYNTHESIS

Microorganisms are capable of growth when supplemented with the pyrimidine and thiazole portions of the vitamin, which suggests that these are coupled by the organisms for the synthesis of the vitamin. The preparation of organisms which will require thiamine or any other vitamin for growth was discovered by Beadle and Tatum using the fungus *Neurospora*.

Beadle and Tatum based their studies on Muller's observation that exposure of organisms to x-rays increases greatly the frequency of mutations and that vitamins of the B complex are part of enzyme systems required by the red mold. In this way they were able to isolate mutant forms which required specific compounds in the medium in order to grow. The mold was first raised on a minimal diet of agar, inorganic salts, biotin and a disaccharide (medium A, Fig. 92). Just before spore formation, the fungus was irradiated with x-rays. Spores were isolated, cultured on a complete medium (medium B), including yeast (rich in amino acids and B vitamins), and then tested for their ability to grow on minimal medium (medium A). Those strains which did not grow were given vitamins (Fig. 92). In this way it could be shown that one strain had lost the ability to synthesize thiamine, and another had lost the ability to synthesize nicotinic acid.

Working with some 60,000 single spore cultures, Beadle and his co-workers have obtained forty different strains of neurospora, each strain deficient in the ability to synthesize some one substance.

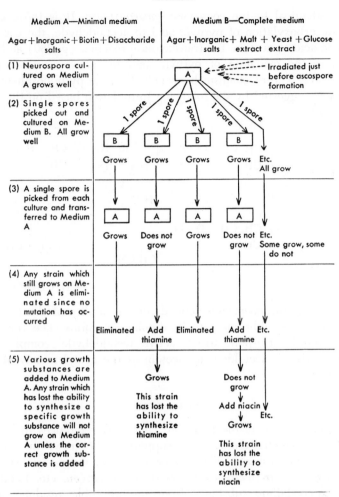

Figure 92. Diagrammatic explanation of the method used by Beadle and Tatum on *Neurospora*. (From Goldstein, P.: Wallerstein Communications.)

BIOCHEMICAL FUNCTION

Peters was able to demonstrate that thiamine was involved in carbohydrate metabolism, especially that of pyruvate. Oxygen consumption of brain tissue from polyneuritic pigeons was depressed and could be increased by addition of thiamine. It was later shown that thiamine occurs in fresh tissue, to a great extent, as a pyrophosphate derivative

Thiamine pyrophosphate

cocarboxylase

which is identical to the coenzyme *cocarboxylase*. It is the coenzyme for the decarboxylation of pyruvic acid to acetaldehyde, the conversion of pyruvic acid to acetoin, the transketolase reaction (p. 280) and is also involved in the oxidation of pyruvic acid to "active acetate" (acetyl coenzyme A). The mechanism by which thiamine pyrophosphate exerts its action is suggested by the following formulation based on the studies of Breslow:

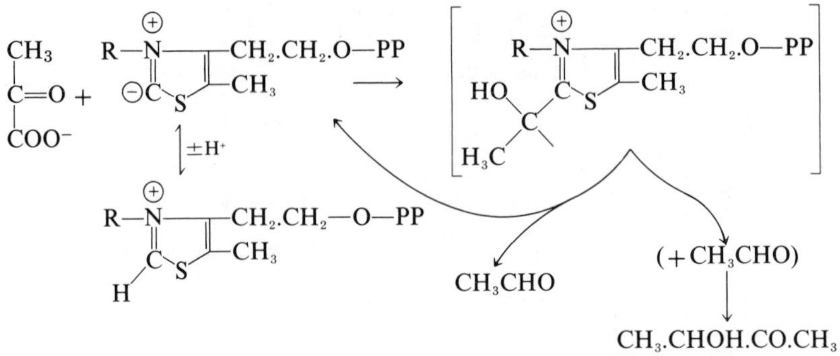

The activity of the coenzyme depends on the ability of the thiazolium salt to exist in equilibrium with its dipolar ion forms. The complex in brackets would correspond to an "active acetaldehyde" complex which would give rise to acetaldehyde, acetoin or the acetyl moiety of acetyl coenzyme A.

LIPOIC ACID

For a number of years the literature contained references to a variety of substances which were active in supporting the growth of a number of bacteria and protozoa. The unknown factors were variously called alpha-lipoic acid, pyruvate oxidation factor, protogen, etc. Reed et al. isolated a crystalline substance from the insoluble residues of liver which was identical in its activity with all of these factors. It has been identified as a cyclic disulfide derived from 6,8-dimercapto-n-caprylic acid, or more simply, 6,8-dithiooctanoic acid:

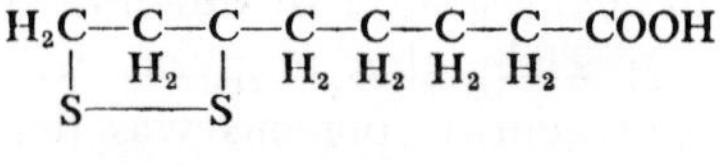

$$
\begin{array}{c}
\text{H} \\
\text{H}_2\text{C}-\text{C}-\text{C}-\text{C}-\text{C}-\text{C}-\text{C}-\text{COOH} \\
\mid\ \ \text{H}_2\ \mid\ \ \text{H}_2\ \text{H}_2\ \text{H}_2\ \text{H}_2 \\
\text{S}-\!\!-\!\!-\!\!-\text{S}
\end{array}
$$

Its action is that of a catalytic agent for the oxidative decarboxylation of pyruvic acid. This conversion involves the probable formation of an acetaldehyde complex with thiamine pyrophosphate (TPP) and the subsequent reaction of the acetaldehyde group with lipoic acid:

a. Pyruvate + TPP $\xrightarrow{\text{Mg}^{++}}$ Acetaldehyde.TPP + CO$_2$
b. Lipoic acid + Acetaldehyde.TPP $\longrightarrow$ S-Acetyldihydrolipoic acid
c. S-Acetyldihydrolipoic acid + CoA $\longrightarrow$ Dihydrolipoic acid + acetyl CoA

RIBOFLAVIN $\left(B_2\right)$

Riboflavin, also called *vitamin B_2*, has the formula

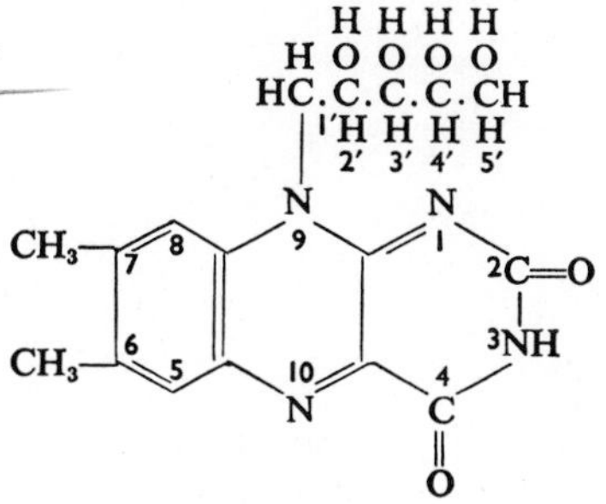

Riboflavin

Riboflavin, derived from isoalloxazine, is 6,7-dimethyl-9-D-1'-ribityl-isoalloxazine and has a structure which exhibits several groups: a pyrimidine (1,2,3,4), azine (9,10), benzene (5,6,7,8) and the alcohol (ribitol) derived from the sugar ribose attached at position 9.

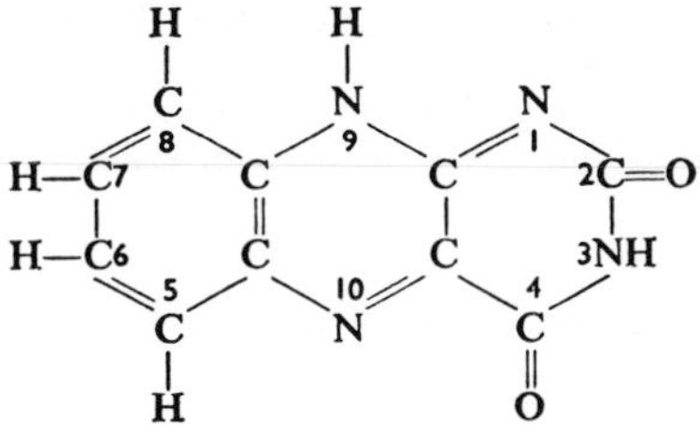

Isoalloxazine

The vitamin properties of the compound are apparently dependent upon these structural components. For instance, by substituting arabinose for ribose, the resulting compound is much less active.

The crystalline, orange-yellow, water-soluble material is fairly heat stable, and stable to air, but very photolabile, so that solutions are rapidly affected when exposed to light. The solutions are much more stable in acid than in alkaline media.

The solution, greenish-yellow in color, has a greenish-yellow fluorescence. Under ultraviolet rays the fluorescence becomes much more intense, and this is made the basis for an estimation of riboflavin.

BIOCHEMICAL FUNCTIONS

The function of riboflavin may be anticipated by inspecting the structures of flavin mononucleotide (FMN), also known as riboflavin-5'-phosphate, and of flavin adenine dinucleotide (FAD). These

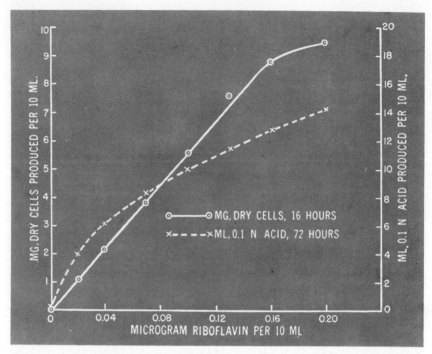

Figure 93. Growth and acid production of *Lactobacillus casei* as a function of riboflavin concentration. (From Snell: Wallerstein Labs.)

are coenzymes for a large number of enzymes involved in oxidation-reduction reactions: dehydrogenases and oxidases. Among these enzymes are the yellow enzyme of Warburg, the Haas enzyme, diaphorase, cytochrome *c* reductase, xanthine oxidase, aldehyde oxidase, D-amino acid oxidase, L-amino acid oxidase, glycine oxidase, fumaric hydrogenase, glucose oxidase and diaminooxidase (histaminase).

Figure 93 illustrates the response of a microorganism which requires riboflavin in addition to the basal medium. Note that growth of cells as well as lactic acid production may be used to follow the response of the organism to the vitamin.

BIOLOGICAL ANTAGONISM

The close chemical relationship between sulfanilamide and *p*-aminobenzoic acid, but the striking biological antagonism of these two substances, has led to much work on chemical constitution as related to biological action. Several examples will be given in this chapter, among other places.

By replacing the two methyl groups in riboflavin with chlorine atoms, we get dichlororiboflavin, which acts antagonistically toward the vitamin.

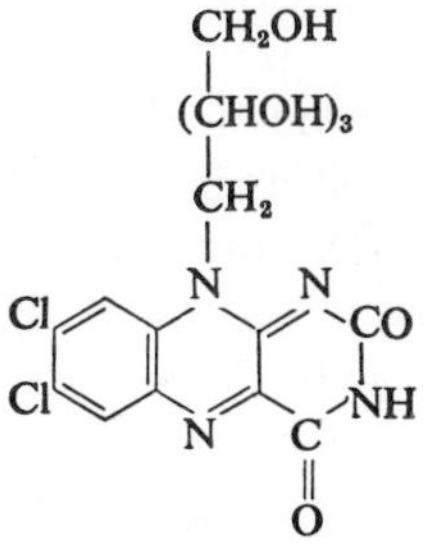

$$CH_2OH$$
$$|$$
$$(CHOH)_3$$
$$|$$
$$CH_2$$

Dichlororiboflavin

Isoriboflavin, a compound in which one of the CH_3 groups is shifted to another position in the benzene ring, also behaves antagonistically toward riboflavin. The growth of rats is arrested by isoriboflavin, and this effect is counteracted by riboflavin.

NICOTINIC ACID

Nicotinic acid, or niacin, and the corresponding amide, nicotinamide, are curative factors for canine blacktongue disease and for human pellagra. A deficiency of the vitamin results in the "three d" symptoms—dermatitis, diarrhea and dementia. The vitamin was first isolated by Funk in 1911 who demonstrated that it had no effect in curing polyneuritis in pigeons. The structures of the two compounds are shown:

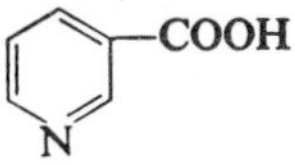

Nicotinic acid
(pyridine-3-carboxylic acid)

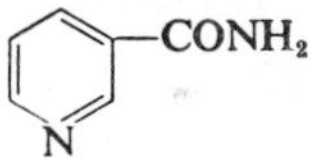

Nicotinamide

BIOCHEMICAL FUNCTION

The biochemical significance of nicotinic acid was made clear when it was shown that the amide was a part of the structures of DPN and TPN and that it took part in the oxidation-reduction reactions associated with dehydrogenases. By 1954 there were some 40 biochemical reactions which had been identified as dependent on these coenzymes. These reactions may be summarized as follows:

1. Synthesis of "high energy" bonds.
2. Pyruvate metabolism.
3. Pentose metabolism.
4. Lipid metabolism.

5. Glycolysis.

6. Nitrogen metabolism (amino acid oxidative deamination).

7. Photosynthesis.

The conversion of nicotinic acid to nicotinamide takes place in kidney and brain slices, as well as in liver slices if glutamine is present.

The biosynthesis of DPN and TPN may be illustrated by the following reactions which are suggested by Preiss and Handler from their studies of the erythrocyte:

a. Nicotinic acid + PRPP $\longrightarrow$ desamido-NMN + PP$_i$

b. ATP + desamido-NMN $\longrightarrow$ desamido-DPN + PP$_i$

c. Desamido-DPN + glutamine + ATP $\longrightarrow$ DPN + glutamate + AMP + PP$_i$

d. DPN + ATP $\longrightarrow$ TPN + ADP

In these equations PRPP stands for phosphoribosylpyrophosphate and desamido-NMN stands for nicotinamide mononucleotide in which the amino group of the adenine moiety has been replaced by a hydroxyl group.

METABOLISM

Nicotinic acid, in man and in a wide variety of species, is derived from the amino acid, tryptophan, which is also active in curing pellagra. It is clear that in the body the amino acid is converted to anthranilic acid and through a series of intermediates to nicotinic acid. These reactions are outlined below:

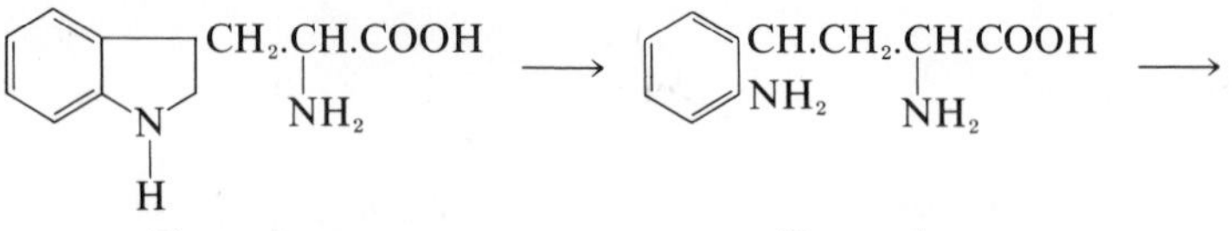

Tryptophan   Kynurenine

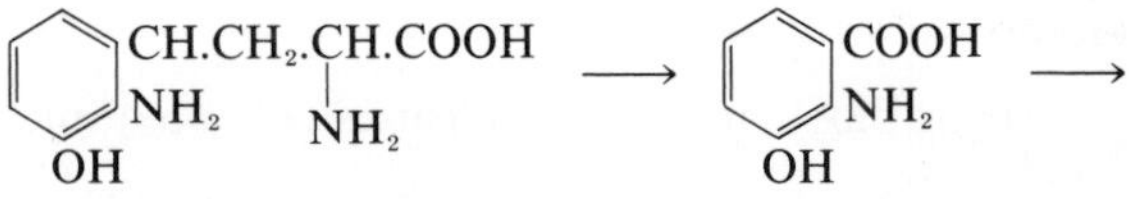

3-Hydroxykynurenine   3-Hydroxyanthranilic acid

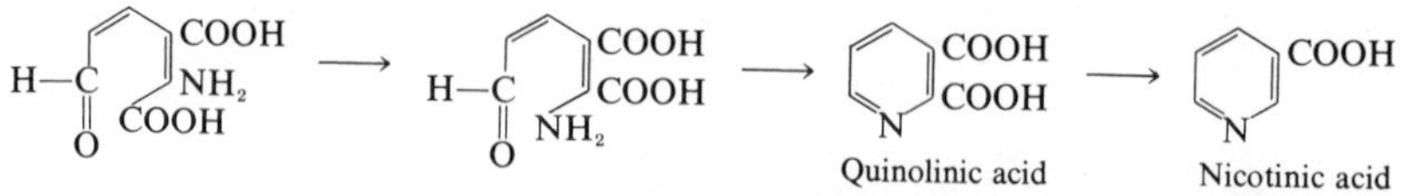

Quinolinic acid   Nicotinic acid

Administration of nicotinic acid or the amide to animals results in the excretion of a variety of derivatives. The following scheme suggests the pathways for their formation:

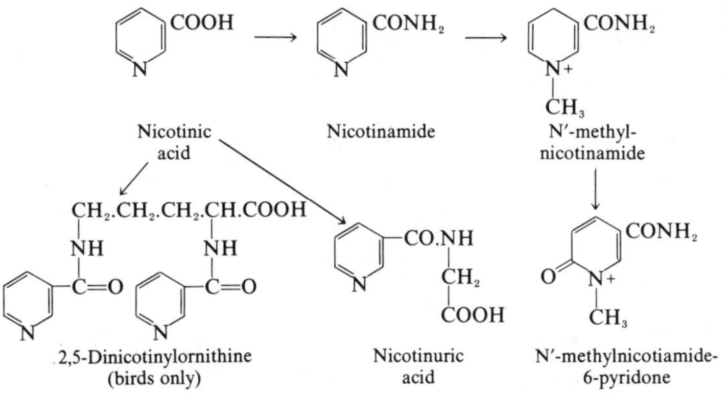

Nicotinic acid → Nicotinamide → N'-methyl-nicotinamide

2,5-Dinicotinylornithine (birds only) · Nicotinuric acid · N'-methylnicotiamide-6-pyridone

Nicotinic acid (or its amide) is necessary for the growth of various microorganisms; pyridine-3-sulfonic acid prevents such growth; and growth is resumed by the addition of sufficient niacin. Here the rela-

Pyridine-3-sulfonamide   Pyridine-3-sulfonic acid

tionship of these two substances is not altogether unlike the relationship of *p*-aminobenzoic acid and sulfanilamide. This fact is even more strikingly brought out by the discovery that pyridine-3-sulfonamide behaves very much the way pyridine-3-sulfonic acid does.

PYRIDOXINE GROUP (B_6)

Vitamin B_6 includes pyridoxine, which was the first to be isolated, and pyridoxal and pyridoxamine, which were discovered by microbiological assay. Their structures are shown below:

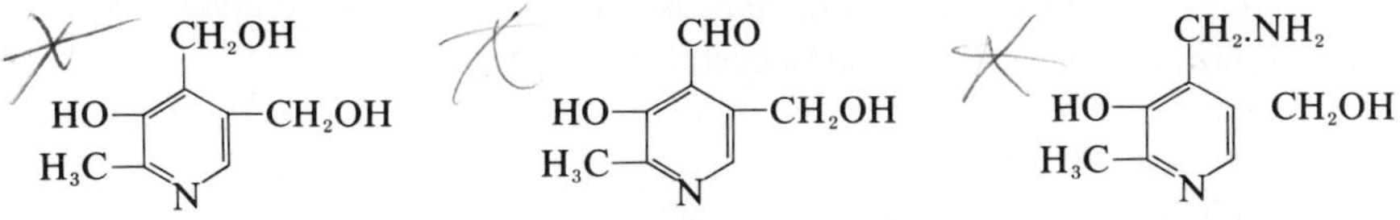

Pyridoxine   Pyridoxal   Pyridoxamine

A deficiency of this vitamin in young rats results in the development of dermatitis with swelling and edema. This skin disturbance, at first thought to resemble pellagra, cannot be cured with nicotinic acid. Any of the three members of this group are active biologically.

BIOCHEMICAL FUNCTION

The three members of the B_6 group are present in tissues as phosphate esters. The active coenzyme form is believed to be pyridoxal phosphate. Their interrelationships are summarized as follows:

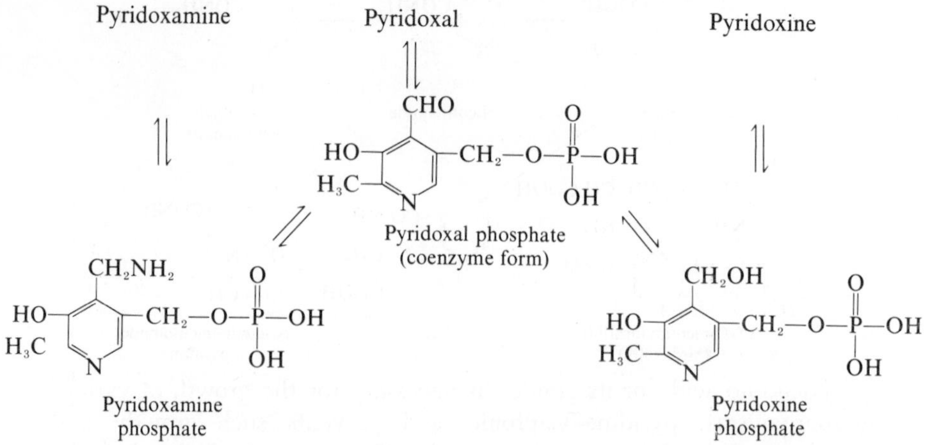

Pyridoxamine Pyridoxal Pyridoxine

Pyridoxal phosphate
(coenzyme form)

Pyridoxamine
phosphate

Pyridoxine
phosphate

It is likely that the enzymatically active form of the vitamin is pyridoxal phosphate, whereas the storage form is pyridoxamine phosphate. Among the enzymes which require pyridoxal phosphate as coenzyme are:

1. Amino acid decarboxylases.

2. Transaminases. Among the many transaminase reactions, only that between glutamate and pyruvate to form alanine, and between glutamate and oxalacetate to form aspartate, are reversible. In pyridoxine deficiency, transaminase activity in tissues is low.

3. Racemases. These are enzymes that catalyze the formation of an equilibrium mixture of DL-alanine from either D- or L-alanine.

4. Enzymes involved in tryptophan metabolism: (a) tryptophanase, which converts tryptophan to indole, pyruvate and ammonia, in bacteria, (b) enzyme which converts kynurenine to anthranilic acid and (c) the synthesis of tryptophan from indole and serine.

5. Cystathionase. This enzyme is involved in the conversion of cystathionine to serine and homocysteine.

Isonicotinyl hydrazide is a potent antagonist of B_6, and is used in the treatment of tuberculosis.

PANTOTHENIC ACID

Pantothenic acid was partially purified from a variety of sources but it was not recognized that it was the same factor in each case. The effects of deficiency are: growth failure in the chick, dermatitis in the chick, graying of the hair in rats and other animals, adrenal necrosis and hemorrhage in the rat. It has been variably known as the antidermatitis factor, the liver filtrate factor, the yeast factor and the chick antipellagra factor. A clue to its constitution came when Williams demonstrated that β-alanine was a growth stimulant for yeast and pantothenic acid was isolated from yeast. Its chemical structure is:

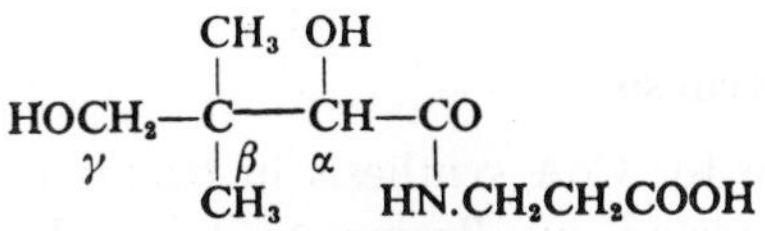

$$CH_3 \quad OH$$
$$HOCH_2-\underset{\gamma}{C}-\underset{\beta}{\overset{|}{C}}\underset{\alpha}{H}-CO$$
$$\underset{CH_3}{|} \qquad \underset{HN.CH_2CH_2COOH}{|}$$

Pantothenic acid
[N-(α,γ-dihydroxy-β,β-di-
methylbutyryl)-β-aminopropionic acid]

BIOCHEMICAL FUNCTION

Identification of pantothenic acid as part of the coenzyme A molecule has implicated pantothenic acid in a large number of important
biochemical reactions. This was made possible largely through the studies
of Lipmann who observed that the acetylation of sulfanilimide in cell-
free extracts of liver involved a cofactor of unknown structure. Independently, Nachmansohn discovered the need for a cofactor for the
acetylation of choline to form acetylcholine. These cofactors were found
to be identical and β-alanine was shown to be part of their structures.
The new cofactor was shown to be coenzyme A and pantothenic acid
was found as a part of its structure (see p. 286).

Coenzyme A is largely found in the liver with lesser quantities in
the adrenals and other tissues. There may be as much as up to 400 mg.
CoA per kg. of liver. Lipmann has summarized the many reactions in
which CoA is involved:

A. *Acetyl Transfer.*

    a. ATP-CoA-acetate:
       ATP + CoA + Ac $\longrightarrow$ Ac-CoA + AMP + PP
    b. Phosphotransacetylation:
       Ac-P + CoA $\longrightarrow$ Ac-CoA + P
    c. Formotransacetylation:
       Pyruvate + CoA $\longrightarrow$ Ac-CoA + formate
    d. Transacetylation:
       Ac-CoA + butyrate $\longrightarrow$ butyrylCoA + Ac
    e. Acetoacetate
    f. Citrate in reverse
    g. Acetaldehyde + CoA + DPN $\longrightarrow$ Ac-CoA
    h. Pyruvate + CoA + DPN $\longrightarrow$ Ac-CoA + DPNH + CO_2

The above reactions are examples of donor systems. As acceptor
systems we may list: acetokinases (for aromatic amines, choline, histamine, amino acids and glucosamine) and condensation reactions as for
acetoacetate, citrate and pyruvate.

B. *Succinyl Transfer.* As a donor system:

$$\alpha\text{-ketoglutarate} + DPN + CoA \rightarrow succinylCoA + DPNH$$

and as an acceptor system we can list the role of succinyl CoA in the
synthesis of heme.

C. *Benzoyl Transfer.* Hippuric acid synthesis is an example.

D. *Complex Systems.* Here we may list CoA involvement in fatty

acid synthesis, butyrate and fatty acid oxidation, and the systems for
steroid and fat synthesis.

COENZYME A BIOSYNTHESIS

The mechanism for CoA synthesis in bacteria and mammalian systems has been reported by Brown to take place in the following manner:

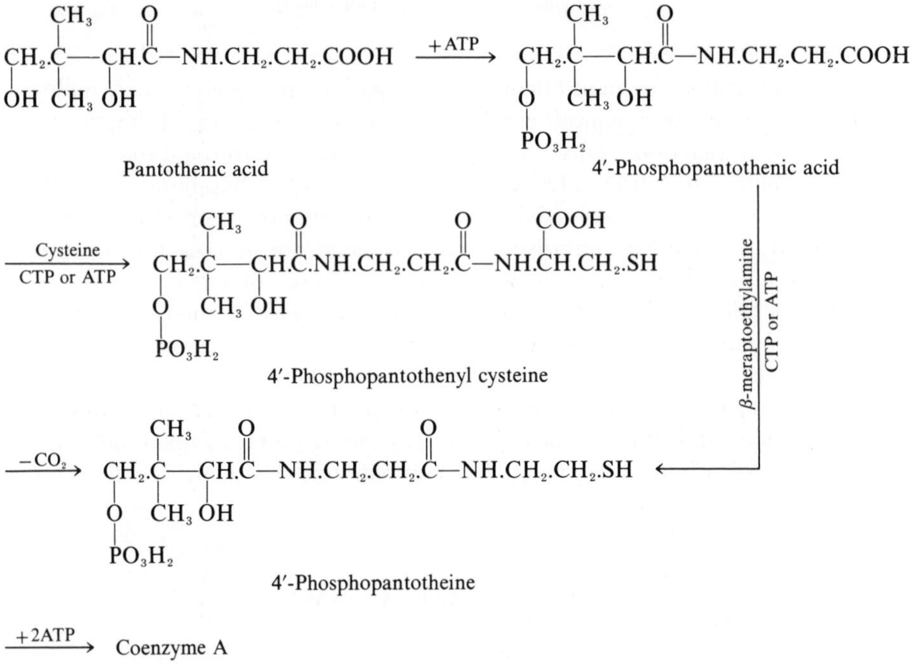

$$
\underset{\text{OH}}{\overset{\text{CH}_3}{\text{CH}_2.\text{C}}}\text{---}\underset{\text{CH}_3}{\text{CH}.}\overset{\text{O}}{\text{C}}\text{---NH.CH}_2.\text{CH}_2.\text{COOH} \quad \xrightarrow{+\text{ATP}} \quad \underset{\text{O}}{\overset{\text{CH}_3}{\text{CH}_2.\text{C}}}\text{---}\underset{\text{CH}_3}{\text{CH}.}\overset{\text{O}}{\text{C}}\text{---NH.CH}_2.\text{CH}_2.\text{COOH}
$$

OH CH₃ OH ... O CH₃ OH / PO₃H₂

Pantothenic acid   4'-Phosphopantothenic acid

$$
\xrightarrow[\text{CTP or ATP}]{\text{Cysteine}}
$$

CH₂.C—CH.C.NH.CH₂.CH₂.C—NH.CH.CH₂.SH

4'-Phosphopantothenyl cysteine

β-meraptoethylamine
CTP or ATP

$$
\xrightarrow{-\text{CO}_2}
$$

CH₂.C—CH.C—NH.CH₂.CH₂.C—NH.CH₂.CH₂.SH   ←

4'-Phosphopantotheine

$$
\xrightarrow{+2\text{ATP}} \quad \text{Coenzyme A}
$$

Pantoyltaurine, the sulfonic acid analogue of pantothenic acid, inhibits the growth of microorganisms which need the acid, whereas pantothenic acid causes resumption of growth upon addition to the medium in the presence of the inhibitor.

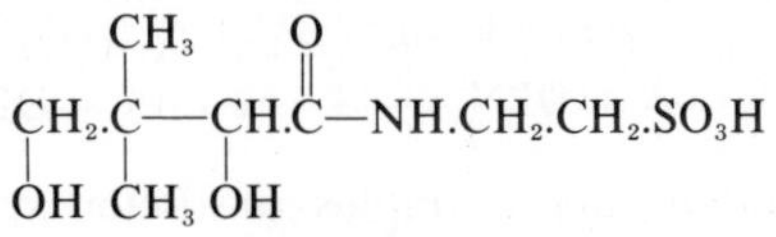

$$
\underset{\text{OH}}{\overset{\text{CH}_3}{\text{CH}_2.\text{C}}}\text{---}\underset{\text{CH}_3}{\text{CH}.}\overset{\text{O}}{\text{C}}\text{---NH.CH}_2.\text{CH}_2.\text{SO}_3\text{H}
$$

OH CH₃ OH

Pantoyltaurine

BIOTIN

As was the case with many vitamins, biotin was identified as a curative factor under many names. It was known as a growth factor for yeast and was isolated from egg yolk by Kögl and Tonnis. It was found to be the same as vitamin H, the curative factor for "egg white injury," caused by feeding raw egg white to rats receiving an otherwise balanced diet. The rats develop progressive emaciation and skin changes and eventually die. The protein-like material from egg white, *avidin*, is denatured as well as inactivated by heating. Avidin forms a stable complex with biotin which is inactive as a vitamin. The complex probably involves the imidazolidine ring of biotin, whose structure is shown below together with that of *biocytin*, which is a bound form of biotin linked as a peptide with the amino acid lysine found in tissues:

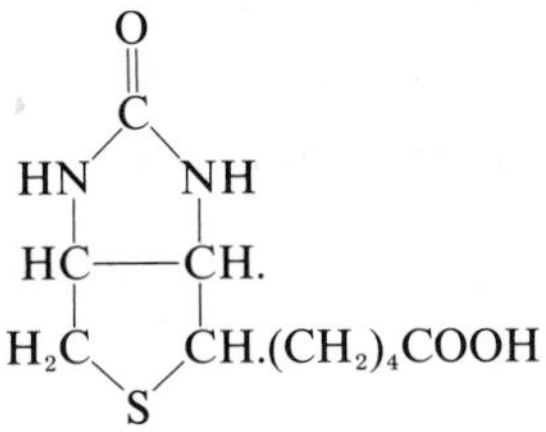

Biotin

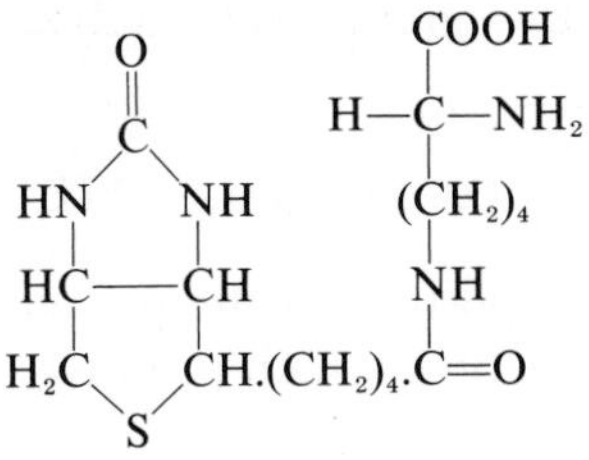

Biocytin

STEREOISOMERS AND ANALOGUES

Two forms of the vitamin can exist, *allobiotin* (and *epiallobiotin*) and *biotin* (and *epibiotin*). These are shown in the accompanying diagram:

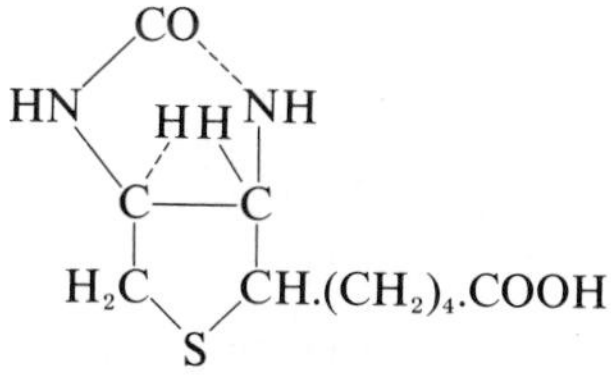

Allobiotin,
epiallobiotin

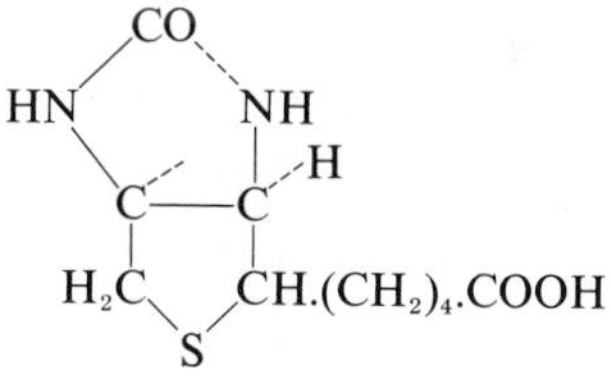

Biotin,
epibiotin

Only the (+) biotin is active; the dl-biotin is half as active as the naturally occurring biotin.

Oxybiotin, in which the S atom has been replaced with an oxygen atom, has some activity; the epi form is inactive. *Desthiobiotin*, a compound with its S atom removed and replaced by two H atoms, is as active as biotin when assayed in the *Saccharomyces cerevisiae* system, but is inactive with *Lactobacillus casei*. It has been suggested that some organisms can use desthiobiotin for the synthesis of biotin. Their structures are shown below:

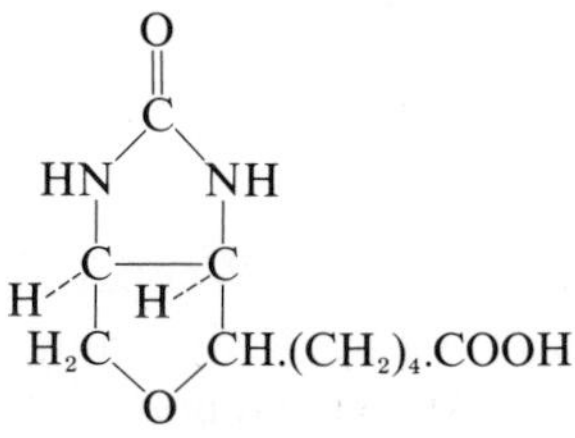

Oxybiotin (*cis-*)

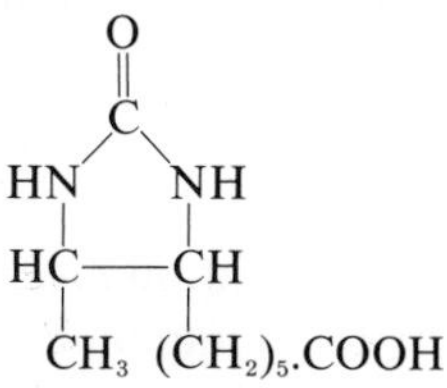

Desthiobiotin

BIOCHEMICAL FUNCTION

Biotin plays an important role in a variety of carboxylation and decarboxylation reactions. Two specific examples may be listed:

1. The enzyme, β-methylcrotonylCoA carboxylase contains biotin as an active group and catalyzes the following reaction:

$$\underset{\overset{|}{CH_3}}{CH_3.C}=CH.CO.CoA + CO_2 + ATP \;\rightleftharpoons\; \underset{\overset{|}{CH_3}}{HOOC.C}=CH.CO.CoA + ADP + P_i$$

Lynen has postulated the presence of an "active CO_2" intermediate during the reaction, which proceeds as follows:

a. $ATP + biotin.enzyme \;\underset{Mg^{++}}{\rightleftharpoons}\; ADP.biotin.enzyme + P_i$

b. $ADP.biotin.enzyme + CO_2 \;\underset{Mg^{++}}{\rightleftharpoons}\; CO_2.biotin.enzyme + ADP$

c. $CO_2.biotin.enzyme + \beta\text{-methylcrotonylCoA} \;\rightleftharpoons\; biotin.enzyme + \beta\text{-methylglutaconylCoA}$

Lynen has suggested the following structure for the biotin.CO_2 intermediate:

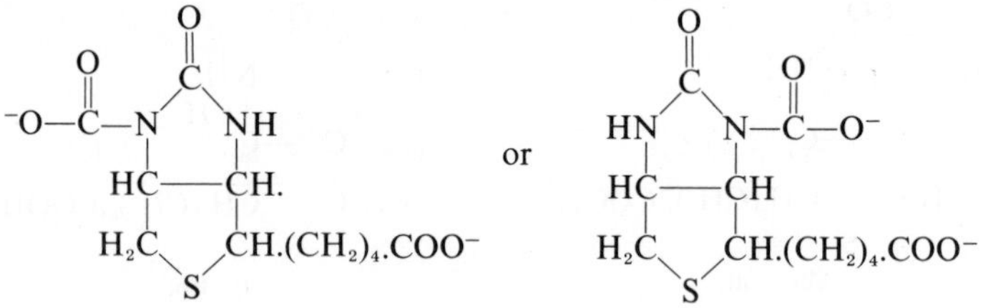

Biotin.CO_2 complex

2. There are enzymes in avian liver which catalyze the conversion of acetyl CoA to palmitic acid. There is evidence that a malonic acid derivative is involved as an intermediate. The first step in this reaction which leads to fatty acid synthesis requires biotin in a CO_2 fixation reaction:

$$CH_3.CO.CoA + CO_2 + ATP \xrightarrow{\text{biotin}} HOOC.CH_2.CO.CoA$$

The addition of malonyl CoA to acetyl CoA results in an increase in chain length via a series of intermediate steps.

INOSITOL

This is the mouse anti-alopecia factor. We owe to Woolley the addition of inositol to the vitamin B complex. Working with young mice, and using a synthetic diet containing all the known vitamins, Woolley discovered that his mice failed to grow and that their hair was affected.

The addition of pantothenic acid—the absence of which may also give rise to hair changes—proved useless. Neither was the addition of biotin or para-aminobenzoic acid any better. Cures were observed by the addition of phytin, obtained from cereal grain, or inositol,* isolated from liver.

Inositol is required by certain yeasts for normal growth. The mouse requires it, as Woolley has shown. Woolley isolated the vitamin from liver. Its formula is

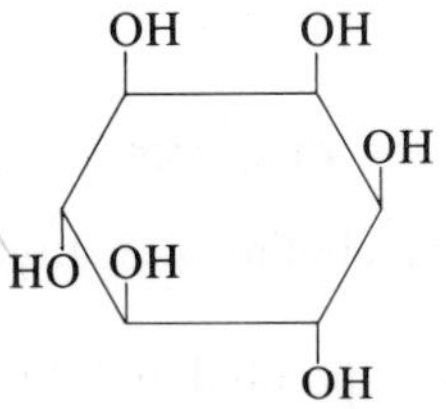

myo-Inositol

It has been claimed that the "spectacle eye" condition in rats can be cured with inositol. This claim has also been made for biotin. Some are of the opinion that an interrelationship exists between inositol and biotin.

The contradictory results occasionally obtained—with mice, for example—have been shown, here again, to be due to the ability of the microorganisms in the intestines to synthesize inositol, sometimes in amounts sufficient to prevent the development of alopecia.

OCCURRENCE

Inositol is found in muscles, liver, kidneys, brain and other animal tissues, and also in various fruits and vegetables.

Inositol has been isolated from the phosphatides of the tubercle bacillus and has been found in the cephalin fraction of the brain and spinal cord. It has also been found in the phosphatide of the soybean; Woolley has given the name "lipositol" to this phosphatide—a compound containing 16 per cent inositol, besides galactose, fatty acids, phosphoric acid and ethanolamine.

ASSAY

Inositol stimulates the growth of yeast cells (*Saccharomyces cerevisiae*) in a special medium.

Beadle has described a mutant of *Neurospora* which requires inositol for growth, and which he uses as the basis for a quantitative estimation of the vitamin. Mice showing deficiency symptoms can be cured

---

* In plants inositol is found in combination with phosphoric acid. Phytin is the calcium-magnesium salt of such a combination.

by feeding 10 mg. of inositol per 100 gm. of food. Whether inositol is needed for human nutrition is not certain.

Since inositol is isomeric with the hexoses, attempts have been made to show whether the vitamin can be converted into glucose in the body. Stetten fed inositol containing an excess of deuterium in the carbon-bound portions to a phlorhizined rat and isolated glucose containing significant concentrations of deuterium from the urine. An enzyme system is present in rat kidney which catalyzes the oxidation of inositol to glucuronic acid.

CHOLINE

As a constituent of lecithin, choline has already been discussed under the phosphatides.

Its role in nutrition was pointed out by Best, who presented evidence to show that choline prevented the development of fatty livers in depancreatized dogs. On a diet low in choline, many animals develop fatty livers and hemorrhagic renal changes, and if such a diet continues, cirrhosis of the liver appears. In the earlier stages of degeneration, the inclusion of choline in the diet is followed by marked improvement of the condition.

Choline may function in several ways: to stimulate the production of phospholipids, to produce acetylcholine, or to supply labile methyl groups.

Using mutations of *Neurospora* that have lost their ability to synthesize choline, Horowitz has shown that this deficiency is due to a deficiency in the formation of a necessary intermediate in the synthesis —N-monomethylaminoethanol. The steps in the synthetic process are:

$$
\begin{array}{ccc}
\underset{\text{NH}_2}{\overset{\text{CH}_2\text{CH}_2\text{OH}}{|}} & \longrightarrow & \underset{\text{H—N—CH}_3}{\overset{\text{CH}_2\text{CH}_2\text{OH}}{|}} & \longrightarrow \\
\text{Aminoethanol} & & \text{N-monomethylaminoethanol}
\end{array}
$$

$$
\begin{array}{ccc}
\underset{\text{N(CH}_3)_2}{\overset{\text{CH}_2\text{CH}_2\text{OH}}{|}} & \longrightarrow & \underset{+\,\text{N(CH}_3)_3}{\overset{\text{CH}_2\text{CH}_2\text{OH}}{|}} \\
\text{Dimethylaminoethanol} & & \text{Choline}
\end{array}
$$

Choline may be determined microbiologically by using a mutant of *Neurospora crassa* as a test organism.

OCCURRENCE

The richest source is egg yolk. Liver and kidney are other good sources. In cereal grains, the choline is found largely in the germ.

PARA-AMINOBENZOIC ACID (PABA)

Ansbacher demonstrated that mouse achromotrichia (lack of hair pigment) could be cured by feeding rice polishings or by the addition to the diet of p-aminobenzoic acid. It appeared to be essential for growth and for the maintenance of a normal fur coat for the rat.

Interest in PABA was greatly stimulated by the observation of Woods that the bacteriostatic properties of sulfanilamide could be offset by addition to the medium of PABA. Sulfanilamide appeared to act as a competitive inhibitor. The similarity in structures of the two compounds led to the concept that sulfanilamide attached itself to the surface of an enzyme which is normally involved in a reaction concerned with an important aspect of the growth process, thus preventing PABA from forming its normal linkage to that enzyme. This property of PABA could be duplicated by use of tissue extracts. Furthermore, the anti-sulfanilimide property of tissue extracts could be enhanced by allowing the tissue to autolyze or hydrolyze in the presence of acid. PABA occurs in conjugated form as a part of the important vitamin, folic acid and its derivatives and will be discussed together with this vitamin.

The formulae for PABA and sulfanilamide are shown:

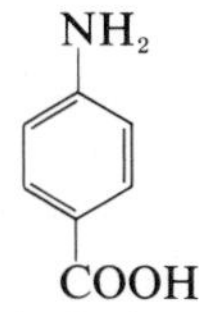

NH_2

COOH

p-Aminobenzoic
acid (PABA)

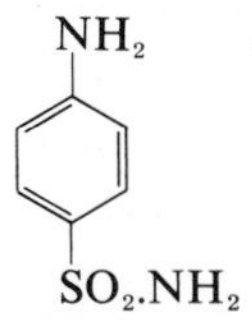

NH_2

$SO_2.NH_2$
Sulfanilamide
(p-aminobenzene-
sulfonamide)

FOLIC ACID

Some lactic acid bacteria require an essential factor which is found in liver extracts. Using *Streptococcus lactis* as a test organism, it has been shown that, in addition to liver, kidney, mushroom, yeast, and particularly green leaves and grass contain the factor. The name folic acid (folium = leaf) has been given to the substance. Folic acid has the formula

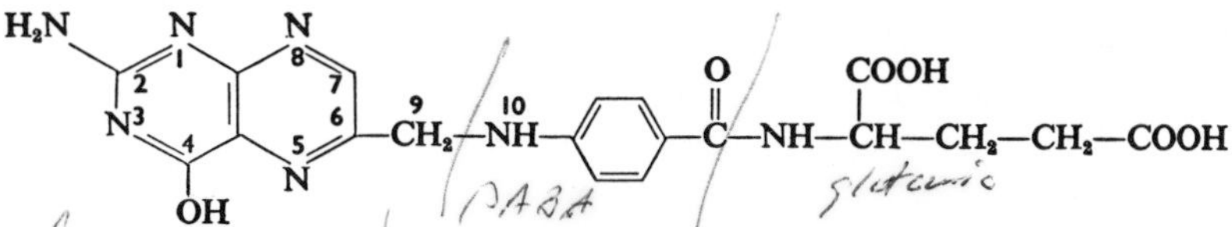

H_2N

Folic acid

It is a combination of glutamic acid, para-aminobenzoic acid and a pteridine nucleus. This pteridine nucleus together with para-amino-benzoic acid is known as pteroic acid, so that folic acid itself is also called pteroyl glutamic acid (PGA). In nature it is found either as folic acid itself or as compounds with additional glutamic acid—pteroyl tri-glutamic acid and pteroyl heptaglutamate.

Folic acid has been used with success in some macrocytic anemias,* such as those developed in sprue and the macrocytic anemias of pregnancy. However, the hope held out for a time that it would be of benefit to sufferers with pernicious anemia has not been borne out, because of its failure to cure the neurological lesions in the disease.

It is of interest to note that bacterial organisms which need para-aminobenzoic acid for growth utilize folic acid with almost equal facility.

Folic acid is needed for growth and blood formation by chicks and monkeys, among others. Rats and dogs, as a rule, do not need the vitamin, since sufficient quantities are synthesized by intestinal bacteria. This probably applies to man himself. At any rate, on the basis of analogy, some 0.1 to 0.2 mg. per day should prove ample.

FOLIC ACID ANALOGUES

A number of compounds similar in their structure to folic acid have been isolated. As an example, optimal growth of *Leuconostoc citrovorum* requires a substance originally called the "citrovorum factor" but which has been isolated and shown to have a structure similar to that of folic acid; its chemical name is *folinic acid*. The formulas for several such analogues are shown:

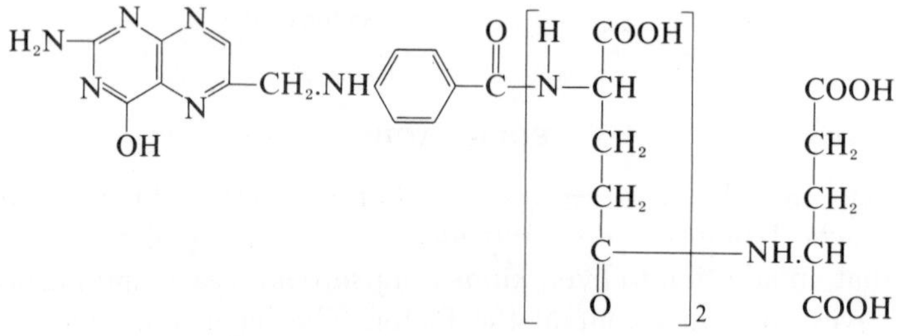

Fermentation *Lactobacillus casei* factor
(pteroyl-γ-glutamyl-γ-glutamylglutamic acid)

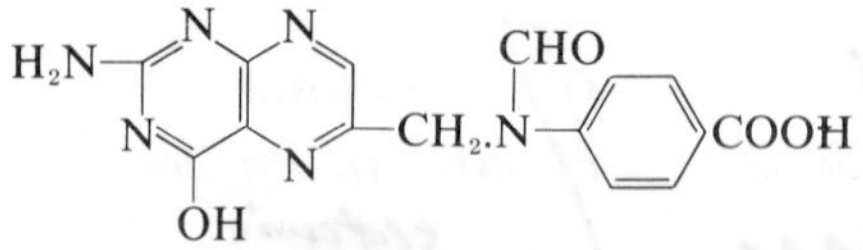

Rhizopterin
(*Streptococcus faecalis R* factor)

* Increase in average size of red corpuscles.

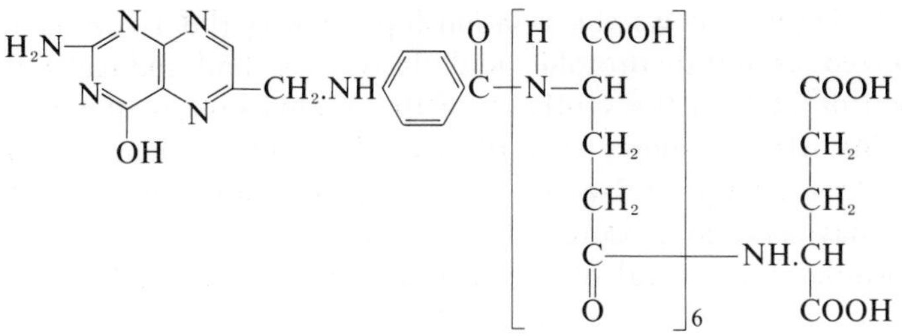

Bc conjugate
(pteroylhexaglutamylglutamic acid)

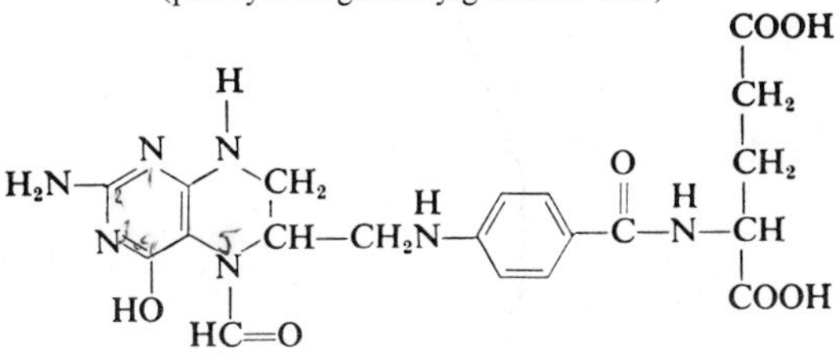

Folinic acid
(5-formyl-5,6,7,8-tetrahydropteroylglutamic acid)

BIOCHEMICAL FUNCTION

The primary role of folic acid and its derivatives is in the synthesis of purines, pyrimidines and certain amino acids which involve the incorporation of a single carbon fragment. It is well established that "active formate" and "active formaldehyde" consist of the formyl (—CHO) and hydroxymethyl (—CH$_2$OH) groups bound to tetrahydrofolic acid (THF). The origin of THF can be accounted for by the presence of enzymes which convert folic acid to the dihydrofolic and tetrahydrofolic acids:

$$\text{Folic acid} + \text{TPNH} + \text{H}^+ \rightleftarrows \text{7,8-dihydrofolate} + \text{TPN}^+$$
$$\text{7,8-DHF} + \text{TPNH} + \text{H}^+ \rightleftarrows \text{5,6,7,8-THF} + \text{TPN}^+$$

Formate can be "activated" by an enzyme which forms the 10-formyl-THF which then undergoes a series of reactions outlined in the accompanying diagram:

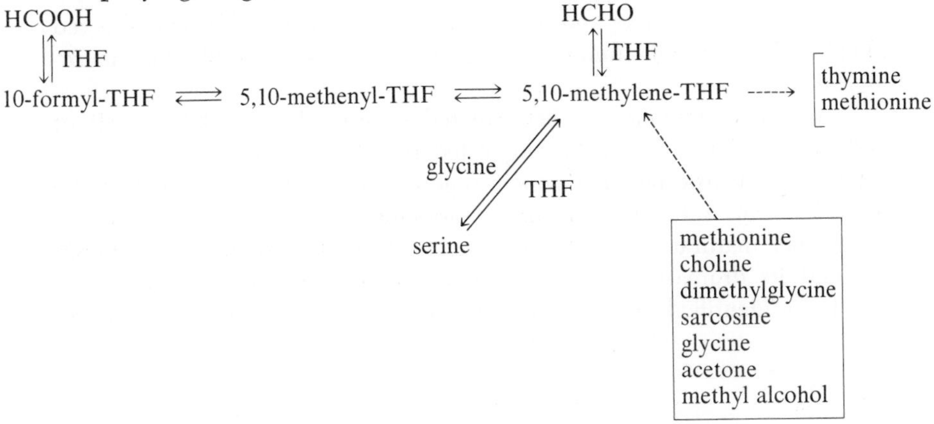

The diagram shows the relationships among the 1-carbon moieties metabolized as tetrahydrofolic acid derivatives and indicates the participation of THF in the synthesis of the methyl groups of thymine and methionine. It also shows that formate, formaldehyde and serine may be used as a source of 1-carbon unit, and the compounds enclosed in the box may serve as a source of methyl groups.

Formulas for several of the derivatives of THF are shown below:

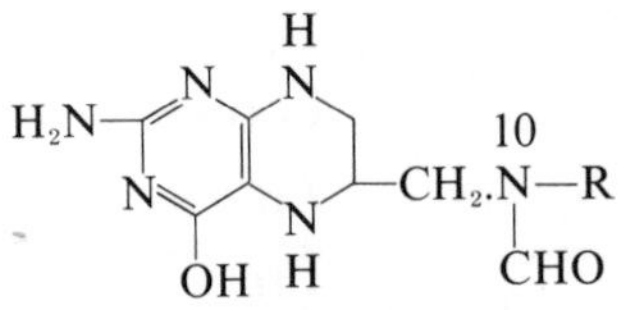

10-formyl-THF

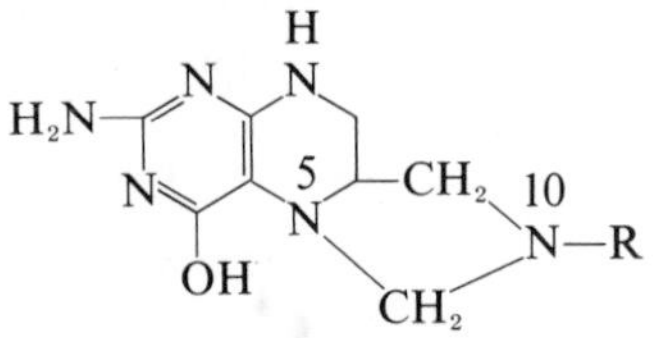

5,10-methylene-THF
(Hydroxymethyl-THF)

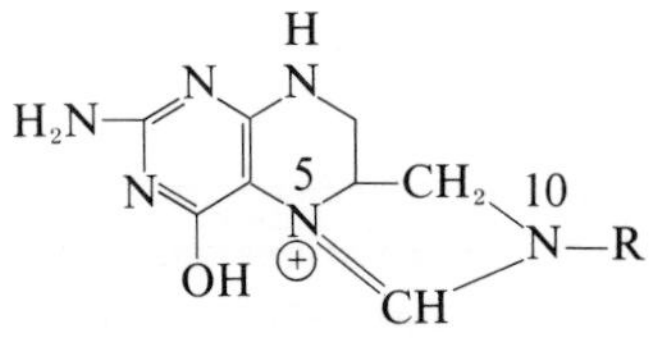

5,10-methenyl-THF

VITAMIN B_{12}

Making use of the observation by Shorb that there is a growth factor for *Lactobacillus lactis* which is present in purified liver extracts, and that the amounts of the growth factor are proportional to the anti-pernicious anemia activity of the extracts, Folkers, Smith and others isolated a factor from liver which is curative in pernicious anemia and is now termed vitamin B_{12}. It is found in animal tissues in the form of a conjugate with a polypeptide. The vitamin not only induces an increased reticulocyte rise and an increase in the hemoglobin and the red blood cell count but—unlike folic acid—it affects favorably the neurological symptoms.

Pernicious anemia was first treated successfully in 1926 by Minot and Murphy. In 1929 Castle suggested that the gastric juice contained a factor ("intrinsic factor") which, together with a factor present in the food ("extrinsic factor"), forms a principle which is responsible for the proper maturation of the erythrocyte. With the isolation of vitamin B_{12} and its dramatic action in pernicious anemia, the extrinsic factor has been identified. Vitamin B_{12}, when injected, restores the red cell count to normal and improves the central nervous system effects in pernicious anemia.

TABLE 72. VITAMIN B CONTENT OF A FEW TYPICAL FOODS

Foods *	Thia-mine †	Ribo-flavin †	Nia-cin †	Panto-thenic Acid † ‡	Vita-min B_6 † ‡	Bi-otin † ‡	Folic Acid † ‡
Apples	0.04	0.02	0.2	0.05	0.03	....	...
Bananas	0.09	0.06	0.6	0.18	0.30	....	0.01
Bread							
White (unfortified)	0.08	0.13	0.8	0.40	0.20	....	...
White (fortified)	0.24	0.15	2.2	0.40	0.20	....	...
Cabbage	0.07	0.06	0.3	0.18	0.29	....	0.01
Carrots	0.07	0.06	0.5	0.24	0.19	0.002	0.01
Cheese	0.04	0.50	0.1	0.35	0.20	0.002	...
Corn meal, degerminated	0.15	0.06	0.9	....	0.25	....	0.02
Eggs, whole fresh	0.12	0.34	0.1	2.70	...	0.025	0.01
Meat							
Beef	0.12	0.15	5.2	1.10	0.40	0.004	0.02
Pork loin	1.04	0.20	4.4	1.50	0.60	0.005	0.01
Poultry, chicken or turkey	0.10	0.18	8.0	0.90	0.20	0.01	...
Liver, pork or beef	0.27	2.80	16.1	5.20	0.80	0.1	0.08
Milk, whole fluid	0.04	0.17	0.1	0.30	0.07	0.005	...
Oatmeal	0.65	0.14	1.1	1.30	0.25	....	0.03
Oranges	0.08	0.03	0.2	0.12	...	....	0.01
Peas, fresh	0.36	0.18	2.1	0.60	0.05	0.002	0.03
Peanuts, roasted	0.30	0.16	16.2	2.5	0.30	....	...
Potatoes	0.11	0.04	1.2	0.40	0.16	....	0.01
Spinach	0.12	0.24	0.7	0.7	0.08	0.002	0.18
Tomatoes	0.06	0.04	0.6	0.37	0.07	0.002	0.01
Turnips	0.06	0.06	0.5	0.25	0.10	0.002	...
Yeast, brewer's dry	9.69	5.45	36.2	20.00	2.90	0.2	0.7
Wheat, whole	0.56	0.12	5.6	1.30	0.40	0.005	0.05

* Edible portion.

† Values are given in milligrams per hundred grams.

‡ Values for pantothenic acid, pyridoxine (vitamin B_6), biotin and folic acid are based on data from only a limited number of samples. Some of the values may be low because of incomplete liberation of the vitamin. (Elvehjem: J. Am. Med. Assoc., *138*:961.)

CHEMISTRY

Vitamin B_{12} is a dark red compound containing 1 atom of cobalt which is bound by coordinate linkages to the 4 nitrogen atoms of a partially hydrogenated tetrapyrrole, to a CN group and to a nucleotide: 5,6-dimethyl-1-(-D-ribofuranosyl)-benzimidazole-3'-phosphate. The structure follows:

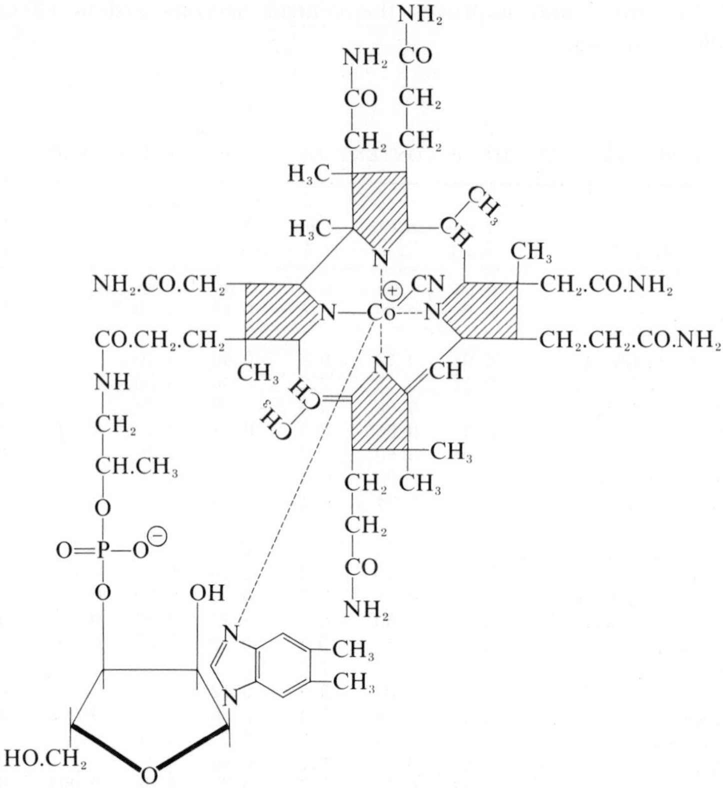

Vitamin B$_{12}$ (Cyanocobalamin)

Because there are a variety of compounds closely related both in structure and in activity to B$_{12}$, the general term *cobalamin* (or *cobamide*) is used to describe this group. Vitamin B$_{12}$ is therefore called *cyanocobalamin,* and vitamin B$_{12a}$, isolated from *Streptomyces griseus,* which has an OH group in place of the CN group, is called *hydroxocobalamin.* The latter compound is converted to cyanocobalamin by treatment with cyanide. In addition there is also *pseudovitamin* B$_{12}$ which contains the purine base adenine instead of 5,6-dimethyl-benzimidazole.

Barker and Weissbach have recently isolated a group of cobamide compounds with coenzyme activities. One of these is *adenylcobamide coenzyme* (Fig. 94) which differs from pseudovitamin B$_{12}$ by containing not one but two adenine moieties. The first of these adenine groups is attached to ribose as in pseudovitamin B$_{12}$ but the second is attached to the Co atom in place of the CN. This adenine also appears to have a sugar residue, a pentose but not ribose.

Two additional cobamide coenzymes have been isolated. By growing *Clostridium tetanomorphum* in the presence of benzimidazole, a corresponding *benzimidazole cobamide coenzyme* is produced. Addition

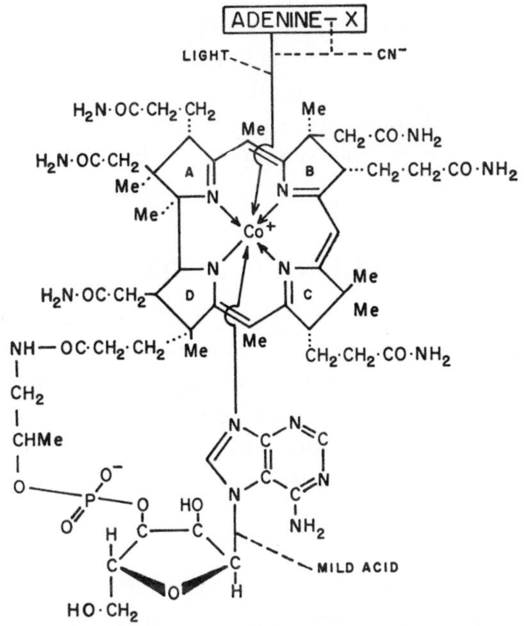

ADENINE—X

LIGHT------------CN⁻

$H_2N \cdot OC \cdot CH_2 \cdot CH_2$
$H_2N \cdot OC \cdot CH_2$
Me
Me
Me
Me
$CH_2 \cdot CO \cdot NH_2$
$CH_2 \cdot CH_2 \cdot CO \cdot NH_2$

A B

N N

Co^+

N N

C D

$H_2N \cdot OC \cdot CH_2$
Me
Me
Me
$CH_2 \cdot CH_2 \cdot CO \cdot NH_2$

$NH-OC \cdot CH_2 \cdot CH_2$ Me Me
CH_2
$CHMe$

N—C—N
N—C—C—N
NH_2

O^-
$O=P-O$
O
H O HO
C—C
C C
$HO \cdot CH_2$ O H

MILD ACID

Figure 94. Postulated structure of the AC (adenylcobamide) coenzyme, showing bonds cleaved by cyanide ion, mild acid hydrolysis, and light.

to the medium of 5,6-dimethyl-benzimidazole yields a corresponding coenzyme. The *5,6-dimethyl-benzimidazole coenzyme* has been found in rabbit liver and accounts for a considerable fraction of the total cobalamin. Of special interest is the fact that treatment of the adenine-cobamide coenzyme with CN⁻ and exposure to light results in the formation of the corresponding vitamin form.

BIOCHEMICAL FUNCTION

Vitamin B_{12} and its family of compounds appear to be involved in a large number of biochemical reactions, although little is known of the mechanism of their action. One example of the action of the cobamide coenzymes is their specificity for the conversion of glutamic acid to β-methylaspartic acid in microorganisms:

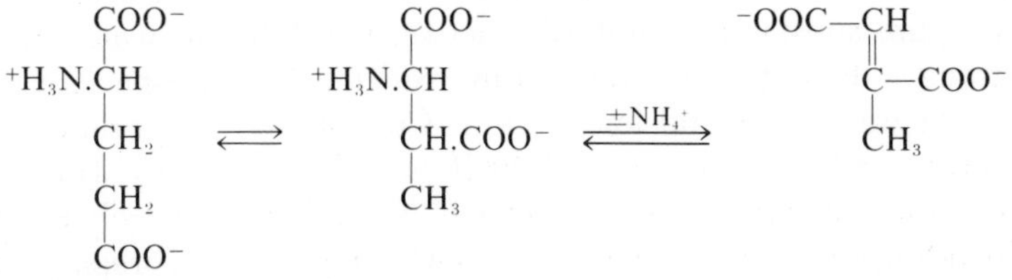

COO^-
$^+H_3N.CH$
CH_2
CH_2
COO^-
Glutamate

$\rightleftharpoons$

COO^-
$^+H_3N.CH$
$CH.COO^-$
CH_3
β-Methylaspartate

$\xrightarrow{\pm NH_4^+}$

$^-OOC-CH$
$C-COO^-$
CH_3
Mesaconate

The vitamin is required for the biosynthesis of methyl groups from one-carbon precursors and for the synthesis of thymidine and other deoxyribosides. Its action on red cell maturation is unknown. It has also been implicated in protein synthesis, in the activation of SH enzymes, and for the adequate storage of folic acid. Vitamin B_{12} affects myelin formation; one of the symptoms of B_{12} deficiency is demyelinization.

ASCORBIC ACID

Ascorbic acid, also known as *vitamin C*, is the vitamin whose absence gives rise to scurvy. This disease, so common among sailors at one time, is characterized by a tendency to bleeding, with, among other things, pathological changes in the teeth and gums. In guinea pigs, in which experimental scurvy can be induced by a diet lacking in "greens," the joints become enlarged and painful.

SOURCE

It has been known for a long time that fresh fruits and vegetables constitute excellent antiscorbutic sources. Dried cereals and legumes contain practically no vitamin C. Dry seeds, in general, are devoid of the vitamin, but as a result of sprouting (by moistening and warming the seeds) the vitamin appears.

Very good sources of vitamin C are citrus fruits (orange, grapefruit, lemon), berries, melons, tomatoes, green peppers, raw cabbage, and salad greens. Leafy green vegetables contain appreciable quantities, though losses are incurred in cooking. Especially among the poor, potatoes are an important source, since relatively large quantities are consumed.

CHEMISTRY

The isolation and characterization of ascorbic acid involved many workers over a long period. A pure and very active form of the vitamin was prepared by Zilva, which was, however, noncrystalline. Szent-Györgi isolated the crystalline compound from the paprika plant and named it "hexuronic acid." It was then isolated by King from lemon juice. The West Indian cherry is the richest fruit source of ascorbic acid.

The pure substance is optically active, is soluble in water and is a very strong reducing agent. It is easily oxidized in air, especially in the presence of traces of metal ions such as Cu^{++} or Fe^{+++}. Several syntheses of ascorbic acid are known, of which one developed by Haworth is shown. It starts with L-xylosone which is made by hydrolysis of the corresponding osazone, a compound which may be prepared from D-galactose or D-glucose:

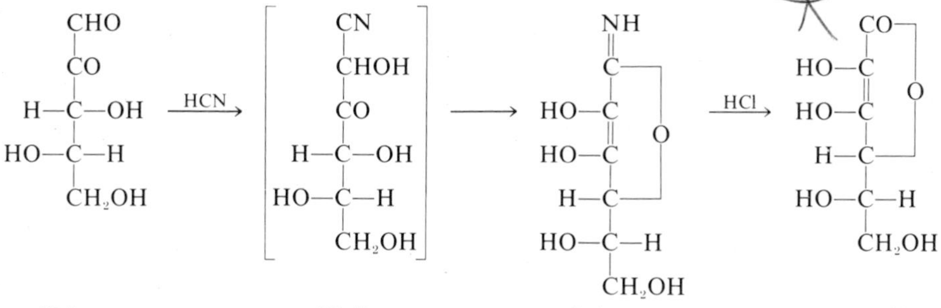

$$\text{L-Xylosone} \xrightarrow{\text{HCN}} \text{Nitrile} \longrightarrow \text{Imino-L-ascorbic acid} \xrightarrow{\text{HCl}} \text{L-Ascorbic acid}$$

ANALOGUES OF ASCORBIC ACID

Following are the structures of several analogues of ascorbic acid and their corresponding antiscorbutic activities. Although the enediol structure appears to be necessary for vitamin activity it is not sufficient:

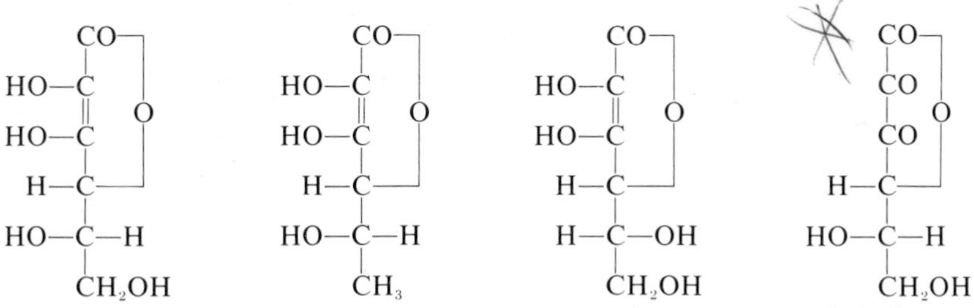

L-Ascorbic acid (100) 6-Deoxy-L-ascorbic acid (33) D-Arabo-ascorbic acid (5) Dehydro-L-ascorbic acid (100)

The biological activity of dehydroascorbic acid is due to its conversion to ascorbic acid; dehydroascorbic acid is known to be the oxidation product of the vitamin.

BIOSYNTHESIS OF ASCORBIC ACID

Plants and all animals except pigs, man and other primates have the ability to synthesize ascorbic acid. The rat, for example, is resistant to scurvy. In animals, the liver and adrenals (cortex) are probably the main sites of synthesis. In plants, all tissues contain the vitamin except for woody tissues or seeds, although it can be shown to be present in early stages of germination.

Early experiments showed that administration of D-glucose caused the formation of L-ascorbic acid. In the rat, the administration of hypnotic drugs stimulates the excretion of ascorbic acid as well as of D-glucuronides, suggesting that these two compounds may have a common intermediate. By use of C^{14}-labeled sugars, King demonstrated that uniformly labeled glucose is converted to uniformly labeled ascorbic acid, showing that the carbon chain was not broken during its conversion to the vitamin. On the basis of many studies in recent years the following scheme is presented for the biosynthesis of ascorbic acid, which probably applies as well to plants:

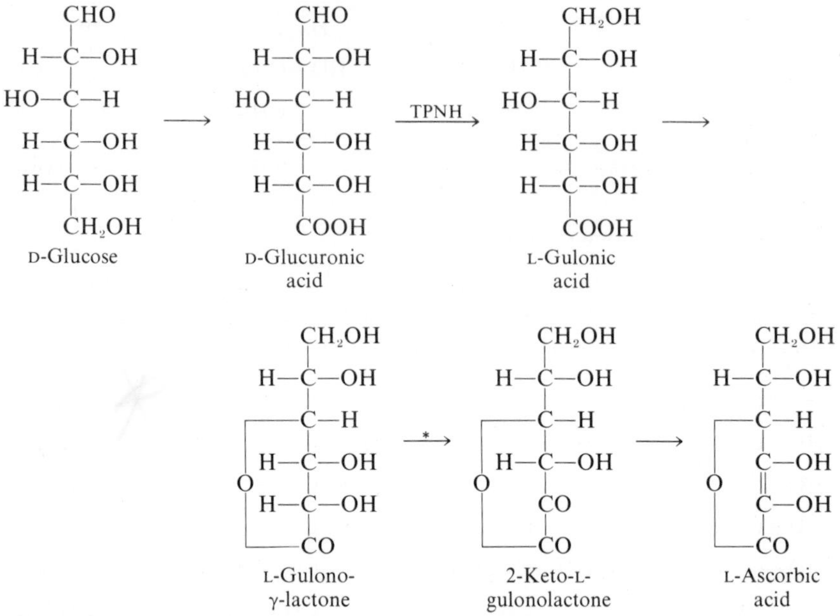

D-Glucose   D-Glucuronic acid   L-Gulonic acid

L-Gulono-γ-lactone   2-Keto-L-gulonolactone   L-Ascorbic acid

Ascorbic acid can also arise from D-galactose via D-galacturonic acid, L-galactonic acid, L-galactono-γ-lactone, and 2-keto-L-galactonolactone. The defect in man which prevents the synthesis of ascorbic acid is the absence of the enzyme, L-gulono-oxidase, present in the microsomes.

METABOLISM OF ASCORBIC ACID

The following sequence of reactions is believed to represent the catabolic breakdown of ascorbic acid in rat kidney:

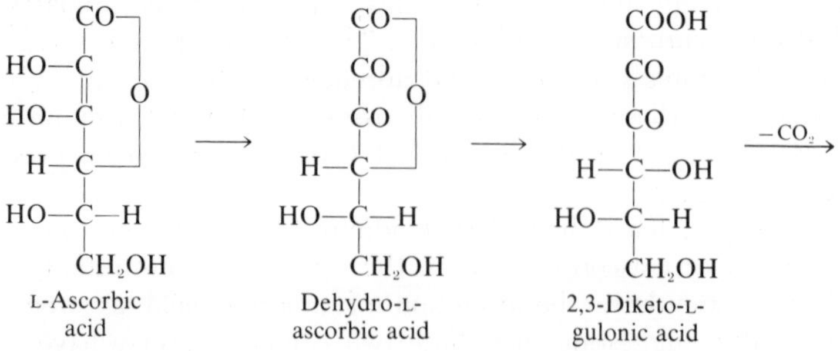

L-Ascorbic acid   Dehydro-L-ascorbic acid   2,3-Diketo-L-gulonic acid

° L-gulono-oxidase.

$$
\begin{array}{cc}
\begin{array}{l}
\text{COOH} \\
\text{HO—C—H} \\
\text{H—C—OH} \\
\text{HO—C—H} \\
\text{CH}_2\text{OH}
\end{array}
&
\begin{array}{l}
\text{COOH} \\
\text{H—C—OH} \\
\text{H—C—OH} \\
\text{HO—C—H} \\
\text{CH}_2\text{OH}
\end{array}
\end{array}
$$

L-Xylonic   L-Lyxonic
acid   acid

Plants contain an enzyme, *ascorbic acid oxidase,* which oxidizes the vitamin to dehydroascorbic acid. The pure enzyme is blue and contains 0.26 per cent Cu; its molecular weight is 150,000. It is conveniently prepared from summer crookneck squash. During the course of the reaction 1 atom of oxygen is consumed per mole of ascorbic acid oxidized and water is formed. This reaction is different from that catalyzed by inorganic Cu^{++}, which requires 2 atoms of oxygen, and during which H_2O_2 is formed. The activity of the enzyme, however, is concerned with its Cu, since removal of the metal leads to inactivation of the enzyme.

BIOCHEMICAL FUNCTION

The primary defect of scurvy involves the connective tissue; and it is now certain that the formation and maintenance of normal collagen depends on ascorbic acid. In vitamin C deficiencies a nonfibrous collagen precursor accumulates, and there are apparent abnormalities of the mucopolysaccharides of the cellular ground substance. The accumulation of mucopolysaccharides leads to a disaggregation of the collagen fibers. Because of the unusual presence of the amino acid, hydroxyproline, in collagen, it has been suggested that ascorbic acid is required for the conversion of proline to hydroxyproline.

Ascorbic acid plays an important role in tyrosine metabolism, specifically in the step involving the oxidation of p-hydroxyphenylpyruvic acid to homogentisic acid (see p. 352). It does not appear to be required as a cofactor but it protects the enzyme, p-hydroxyphenylpyruvic acid oxidase, from inhibition by excess substrate.

Ascorbic acid is involved in hydroxylation reactions and in electron transport in the microsome. A DPNH oxidase is present in this cellular fraction which requires ascorbic acid for its activity. During the course of this reaction ascorbic acid is oxidized to monodehydroascorbic acid, which is the semi-oxidized form of ascorbic acid, having lost one of its H atoms, that is, one electron. Indirect evidence for the presence of such a radical-like compound has been obtained. The sequence of events is as follows:

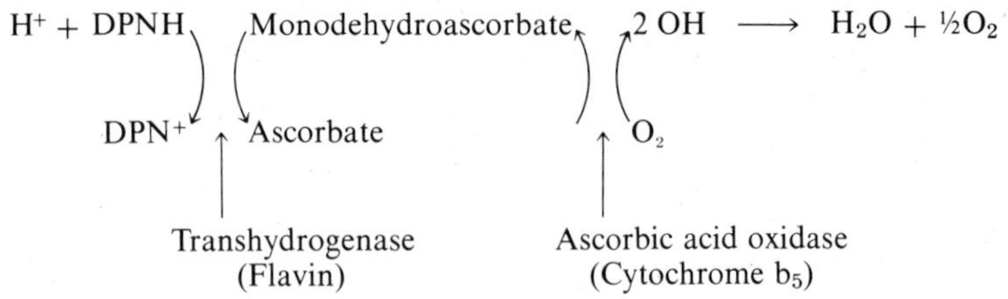

$$H^+ + DPNH \diagdown \diagup Monodehydroascorbate \diagdown \diagup 2\,OH \longrightarrow H_2O + \tfrac{1}{2}O_2$$

$$DPN^+ \diagup \uparrow \diagdown Ascorbate \diagup \diagdown \uparrow O_2$$

Transhydrogenase
(Flavin)

Ascorbic acid oxidase
(Cytochrome b_5)

The monodehydroascorbate acts as a carrier between reduced nucleotide and oxygen. It has been suggested that cytochrome b_5, which is present in microsomes, might act as the natural form of ascorbic acid oxidase. It can also be seen that the final step, the conversion of 2 OH to water might be replaced by the hydroxylation of some organic compound.

Ascorbic acid and ATP (p. 406) are required in the reaction concerned with the removal of tightly bound Fe^{+++} of plasma transferrin and the incorporation of this iron into tissue ferritin.

ASSAY

Ascorbic acid can be determined quantitatively by two procedures. The first depends on the strong reducing properties of the vitamin. It is allowed to react with oxidizing dyes such as 2,6-dichlorophenolindophenol to produce a colorless compound. This titration must be done on an extract from which non-ascorbic acid reducing compounds have been removed. The other method is based on the coupling of ascorbic acid with 2,4-dinitrophenylhydrazine to form a chromogenic compound. The reaction with oxidizing dye is shown in the following:

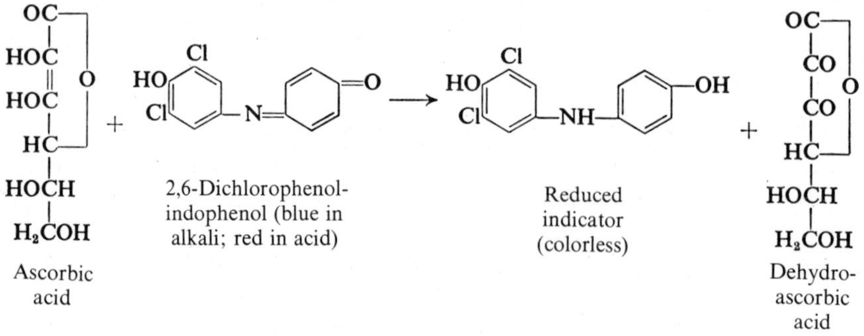

| Ascorbic acid | + | 2,6-Dichlorophenol-indophenol (blue in alkali; red in acid) | → | Reduced indicator (colorless) | + | Dehydro-ascorbic acid |

VITAMIN D

The term vitamin D is used to describe a number of compounds with antirachitic properties which are chemically related to the sterols. In

1921 Mellanby recognized the need for a factor in food (cod liver oil) which could prevent rickets. McCollum demonstrated that this vitamin was not the same as vitamin A and in 1924 Steenbock and Hess were able to show that many foods acquire vitamin D activity after exposure to ultraviolet irradiation.

In the absence of this vitamin, or in its presence in insufficient amounts, rickets in varying degree of severity develops. In the child the disease is associated with bowlegs, knock knees, enlarged joints, etc. The growing parts of the bone—particularly the ends of the long bones of arms and legs—are affected. An x-ray examination makes diagnosis relatively simple. In experimental animals an analysis of the bone ash is also of diagnostic significance. In rickets the ends of the bones show incomplete calcification; as healing advances the material becomes more dense. Two other diagnostic tests of value are the decrease of the inorganic phosphorus content of the blood in rickets* (normal amounts are obtained upon healing), and an increase of the enzyme phosphatase in blood during the disease (with a decrease of phosphatase upon healing).

Phosphatase can decompose organic phosphorus compounds— hexose phosphate, for example—into inorganic phosphate. There are several phosphatases. The particular one of importance here is known as the alkaline phosphatase with an optimum pH action of about 9. This one, in contradistinction to the acid phosphatase (about pH 5), is widely distributed in ossifying cartilage, bone, kidneys, intestinal mucosa, and liver. It is found, in relatively smaller amounts, in blood serum. In rickets of infancy and early childhood, the serum alkaline phosphatase may be high.†

* As a rule, it is the inorganic phosphorus, rather than the calcium, which shows low values. The normal phosphorus values for an infant are 4 to 6 mg. per 100 ml. of blood. Values below 3.5 mg. are of diagnostic significance. Sometimes, however, there is a decreased concentration of calcium, and sometimes a decreased concentration of both elements. In any case, we may regard the situation as involving a lowering of the ion product—a factor which regulates the precipitation of calcium phosphate from the blood into the cartilage and bone.

When the concentrations of calcium and phosphate ions are decreased, and therefore the product of their concentration is decreased below the solubility product of the bone salt, "lime salt deposition in bone and cartilage becomes irregular and, if the value is low enough, deposition stops altogether. The failure in lime salt deposition is responsible for the weakness of the bones. This, in turn, results in the development of the well-known deformities of the disease and at the same time is the cause of almost, if not all, the histological changes. The first demonstrative pathological change in rickets is the failure of lime salt deposition in the proliferative cartilage of the epiphysis and in newly forming bone" (Park).

A large part of the serum calcium is combined with protein. Out of a total of 10 mg. of calcium in 100 ml. of serum, about 4.5 mg. is ionized.

† The estimation is based upon the amount of phosphorus liberated as PO_4 ions by serum incubated with sodium β-glycerophosphate and buffered at pH 8.6. The "unit" represents the number of milligrams of phosphorus which 100 ml. of the serum can liberate in one hour as phosphate ions.

CHEMISTRY

The active vitamin which was isolated from irradiated food materials proved to be calciferol, which was formed from its provitamin, ergosterol, a plant sterol. However, it soon turned out that irradiated ergosterol was much less effective than cod liver oil, on a rat unit basis, in the prevention of rickets in chicks. Calciferol was therefore called vitamin D_2. The provitamin in animals was shown to be 7-dehydrocholesterol which, upon irradiation, gave rise to vitamin D_3, the vitamin in cod liver oil and other fish liver oils.

In plants, ergosterol is the predominant provitamin D. The transformation of ergosterol to the vitamin involves a series of intermediates shown below:

$$\text{Ergosterol }(C_{28}H_{44}O) \longrightarrow \text{Lumisterol} \longrightarrow \text{Protachysterol} \longrightarrow$$

$$\text{Tachysterol} \longrightarrow \text{Precalciferol} \longrightarrow \text{Calciferol}$$

$$\swarrow \qquad \searrow$$

$$\text{Toxisterol} \qquad \text{Suprasterols}$$

Irradiation products of ergosterol of known structure are:

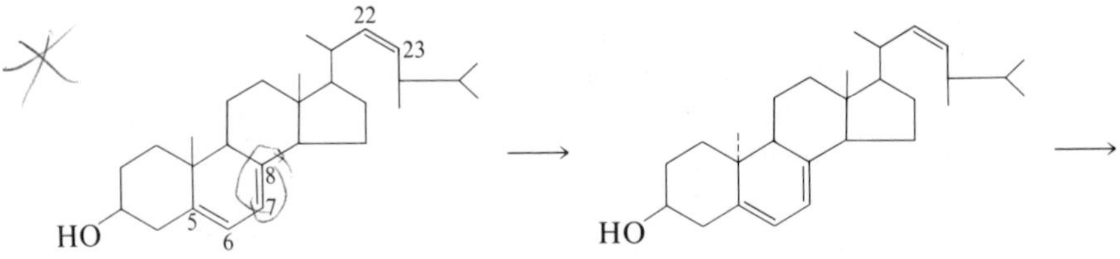

Ergosterol   Lumisterol

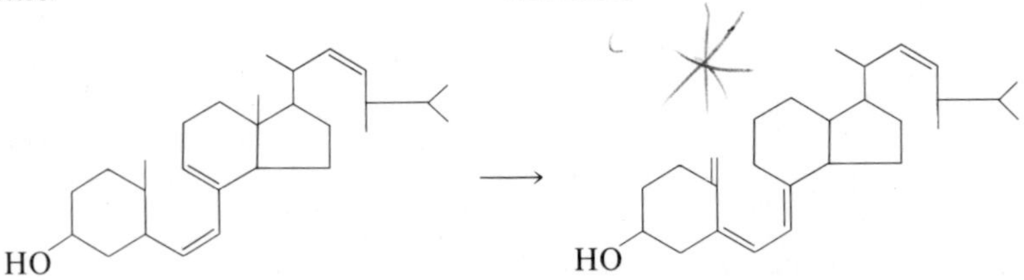

Tachysterol   Calciferol
(Vitamin D_2)

Irradiation of 7-dehydrocholesterol also produces a series of intermediates: lumisterol$_3$, tachysterol$_3$ and precalciferol$_3$. The formation of vitamin D_3 is shown below:

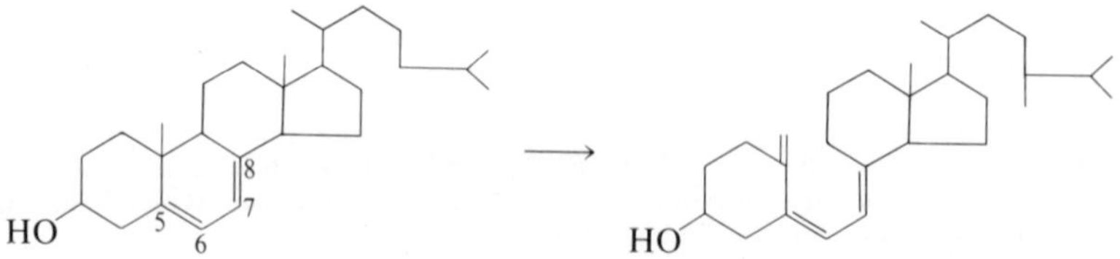

7-Dehydrocholesterol   Vitamin D_3

Other forms of vitamin D may be obtained by the irradiation of other sterols. Vitamin D_4 is made by irradiation of 22-dihydroergosterol; it has an activity of 50 to 75 per cent of that of D_2.

FUNCTION

It is believed that the primary function of vitamin D is to regulate the absorption and utilization of calcium and phosphorus. As evidence of this, a relatively large quantity of calcium and phosphorus is lost in the feces in rickets.

That increased absorption alone is not sufficient to account for the function of the vitamin is brought out by the work of Greenberg. Using radiophosphorus (P^{32}) this author studied the influence of vitamin D on the phosphorus metabolism of rachitic rats. The increase in the absorption of phosphate (administered by stomach tube) was from 10 to 15 per cent. However, the more striking changes occurred in the phosphorus fractions of the bone. The lipid phosphorus (alcohol-ether-soluble P) was not altered, but the labeled phosphorus of the inorganic fraction increased by 40 per cent.

VITAMIN E

Until 1922 it was supposed that a syntheic diet for rats could be used which would allow normal growth and reproduction. Such a diet included casein, starch or sucrose, lard, salts, cod liver oil and yeast. Evans and Bishop, and then Sure, showed that while this diet allowed for apparently normal growth, there was some interference with reproduction. Only by incorporating in this diet small quantities of certain natural foods—cereal grains, green leaves, legumes, nuts and particularly the oil from wheat germ—could reproductive disturbances be avoided. The necessary factor is known as vitamin E. It is also known as the "antisterility" vitamin. In the absence of vitamin E the germinal epithelium of the testes of rats is destroyed. In the female rat, ovulation and fertilization take place, but also there is death and resorption of the fetus. This situation can be repaired by incorporating vitamin E in the diet.

PROPERTIES

Vitamin E, like vitamins A and D, is soluble in fat solvents and insoluble in water. It is resistant to heat (up to 200° C.) but is fairly easily oxidized and is destroyed by ultraviolet rays. Like vitamins A and D, it is found in the nonsaponifiable fraction of fats and oils. Out of the nonsaponifiable fraction of wheat germ oil, Emerson and Evans succeeded in isolating and crystallizing two substances, to which the names α-tocopherol and β-tocopherol were given (*tokos* = childbirth, *phero* = to bear, *ol* = alcohol). The α-form was biologically much the more active of the two: as little as from 1 to 3 mg. proved effective. Somewhat later, α-tocopherol was also isolated from cottonseed oil. A γ-modification has also been obtained.

Since the α-form is biologically the most potent and is now readily available as a synthetic product, this modification is the one that is almost invariably used.

Vitamin E is easily absorbed from the intestinal tract and stored, to some extent, in body fats, muscles, etc.

CHEMICAL STRUCTURE

The three tocopherols are derivatives of chromane:

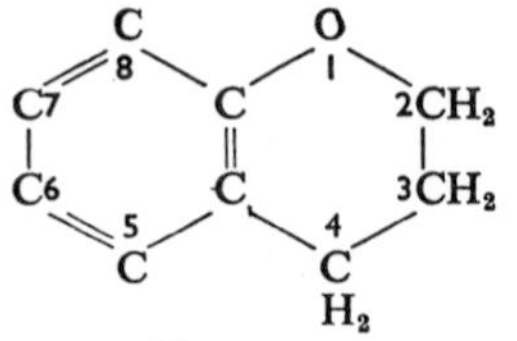

Chromane

and their formulas are:

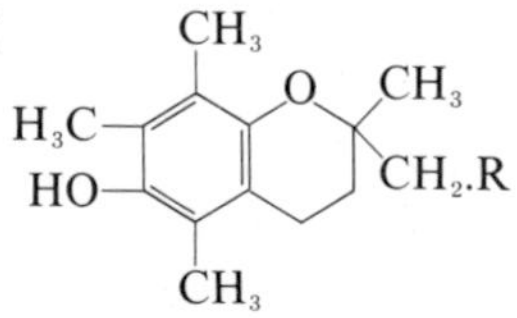

α-Tocopherol β-Tocopherol γ-Tocopherol

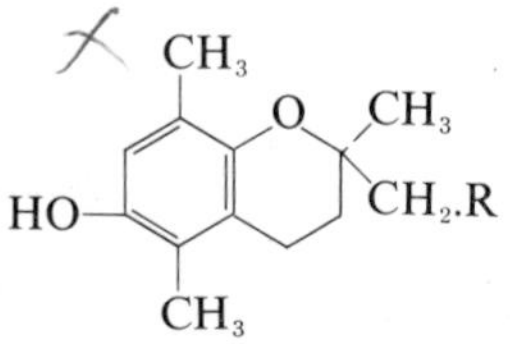

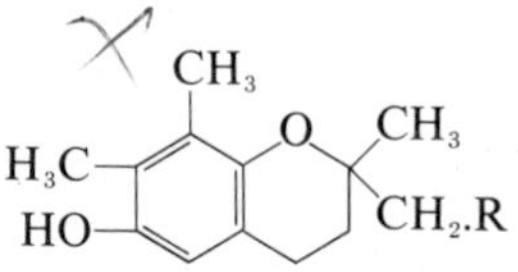

$$\left[R = CH_2.CH_2.\underset{\underset{CH_3}{|}}{CH}.CH_2.CH_2.CH_2.\underset{\underset{CH_3}{|}}{CH}.CH_2.CH_2.CH_2.\underset{\underset{CH_3}{|}}{\overset{\overset{CH_3}{|}}{CH}} \right]$$

The relative biological potencies of these tocopherols are:

α-tocopherol = 100
β-tocopherol = 25
γ-tocopherol = 19

The presence of all three methyl groups attached to the benzene ring is necessary for full activity. Still another analogue of vitamin E, δ-tocopherol has been isolated from soybean oil. It has but one methyl group and is practically without activity.

The structural similarity of α-tocopherol to coenzyme Q_{10} (ubiquinone) and to vitamin K_1 can be seen from their formulas:

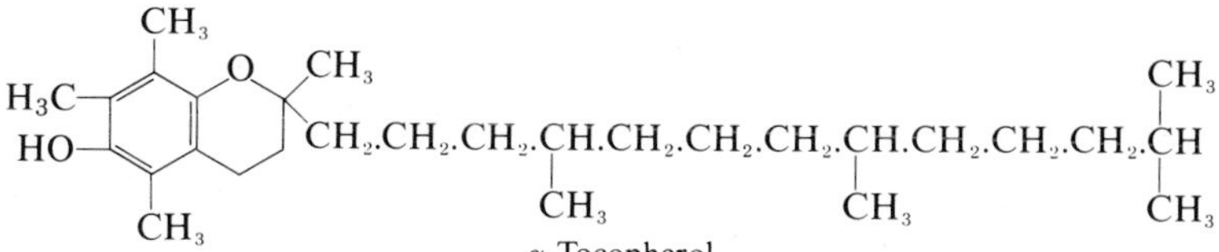

CH₃

H₃C—
HO—

$CH_2.CH_2.CH_2.CH.CH_2.CH_2.CH_2.CH.CH_2.CH_2.CH_2.CH$

CH₃ CH₃ CH₃ CH₃

α-Tocopherol

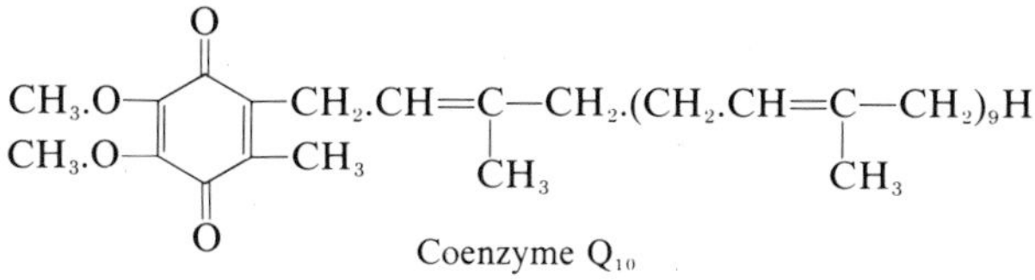

$CH_3.O—$
$CH_3.O—$ —CH_3 —$CH_2.CH=C—CH_2.(CH_2.CH=C—CH_2)_9H$

CH₃ CH₃

Coenzyme Q₁₀

—$CH_2.CH=C—CH.(CH_2.CH_2.CH.CH_2)_3H$
—CH_3 CH₃ CH₃

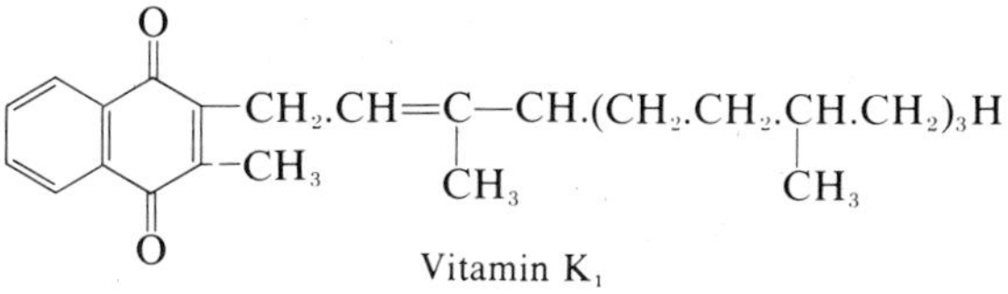

Vitamin K₁

FUNCTION

The biochemical function of vitamin E is still not clear. Although it is required by the rat for normal reproductive function, it appears to have no such action in the human. It has also been associated with normal physiology of the muscular and vascular system; rabbits made deficient in vitamin E exhibit physiological signs similar to that of muscular dystrophy.

Among the observations which have been made in animals deficient in this vitamin we may list the following:

1. Loss of integrity of membranes.
2. Hemolysis of red cells.
3. Depressed oxidative phosphorylation.
4. Decreased lipogenesis.
5. Decline in respiration.
6. Altered DNA:RNA ratio.
7. Decreased storage of vitamin A.
8. Involved in electron transport in mitochondria, just prior to cytochrome *c*.

VITAMIN K

Dam, and later Almquist, described a hemorrhagic disease in chickens due to a food deficiency. The disease is associated with a decrease in the amount of prothrombin in the blood. The factor missing from such a diet, which is associated with the fat-soluble fraction, has been given the name *vitamin K* (after Dam, who named it "Koagulations vitamin").

VITAMIN K AND THE CLOTTING PROCESS

The theory of the blood clotting process as at present understood is that thromboplastin, liberated from wounded tissue cells or from disintegrated blood platelets, together with calcium ions, converts prothrombin into thrombin, and once the thrombin is formed, it converts the fibrinogen of the plasma into insoluble fibrin (blood clot). Vitamin K is necessary for the formation of prothrombin, a process which occurs in the liver.

CHEMISTRY

The vitamin isolated from alfalfa and from putrified fish meal is called vitamin K_1 (see p. 481). Another compound with antihemolytic properties was isolated from *Bacillus brevis* and called vitamin K_2. Vitamin K_2 is also a derivative of 2-methyl-1,4-naphthoquinone, but with a side chain at position 3 other than phytyl.

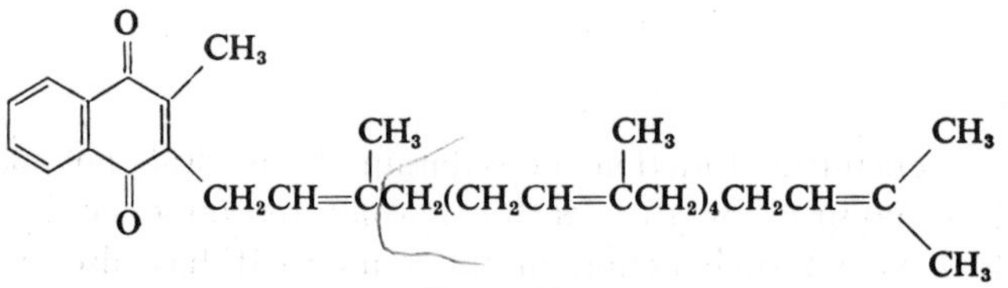

Vitamin K₂

1,4-Naphthoquinone itself shows vitamin K activity. It is also of interest that phthiocol, isolated by Anderson and associates as the pigment in human tubercle bacilli, and a 1,4-naphthoquinone derivative, shows slight antihemorrhagic properties.

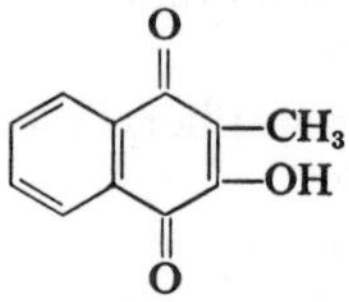

Phthiocol
(2-methyl-3-hydroxy-1,4-naphthoquinone)

However, 2-methyl-1,4-naphthoquinone (known as *menadione*) shows a biological activity which is higher than vitamin K_1 itself and is the one commonly used for treatment. Because of its insolubility in water, it is given together with bile salts.

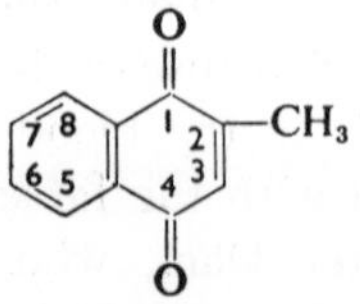

2-Methyl-1,4-naphthoquinone (Menadione)

COMPARATIVE ACTIVITIES OF SOME ANTIHEMORRHAGIC COMPOUNDS

Table 73 points to the fact that menadione is twice as potent as vitamin K_1 or K_2.

TABLE 73. COMPARATIVE ACTIVITIES OF THE MORE IMPORTANT ANTIHEMORRHAGIC COMPOUNDS BASED ON RECENT CHICK 5-DAY ASSAYS AN EXPRESSED IN 2-METHYL-1,4-NAPHTHOQUINONE UNITS PER MILLIGRAM

	Units per milligram
2-methyl-1,4-naphthoquinone (menadione)	1000
2-methyl-1,4-naphthoquinone diacetate	450
2-methyl-4-amino-1-naphthol .HCl	500
2-methyl-1,4-naphthoquinone diphosphoric acid ester (Na_4 salt, .$6H_2O$)	500
2,3-dimethyl-1,4-naphthoquinone	25
2-methyl-3-phytyl-1,4-naphthoquinone (vitamin K_1)	500
2-methyl-3-difarnesyl-1,4-naphthoquinone (vitamin K_2)	400
2-methyl-3-phytyl-1,4-naphthohydroquinone	170

(From Almquist, The Vitamins. Academic Press, 1954.)

In many cases the activity seems to be associated with the ease with which each compound can be converted to menadione in the body.

Cattle sometimes suffer from a deficiency of vitamin K due to eating spoiled sweet clover hay, which contains the hemorrhagic substance *bishydroxycoumarin.*

BIOCHEMICAL FUNCTION

Vitamin K, as is the case with vitamin E and coenzyme Q, has been implicated in electron transport and oxidative phosphorylation in the mitochondria. Vitamins K_1 and K_2 activate electron transport in the succinate oxidase of heart muscle preparations which had been inactivated by treatment with isooctane. The role of vitamin K in oxidative phosphorylation is suggested by the fact that bacterial extracts or liver mitochondria, when irradiated, have a specific requirement for vitamin K for oxidative phosphorylation. Menadione or vitamin E is inactive. The specific site of action of vitamin K is believed to occur between DPNH and cytochrome *b*. It has been suggested that a phosphate ester of vitamin K (reduced form), on oxidation, transfers phosphate to ADP to form ATP. Vitamin K is also required for the photosynthetic phosphorylation in particles of some microorganisms and a variety of plants.

ESSENTIAL FATTY ACIDS

Absence of several unsaturated fatty acids in the rat produces a variety of symptoms which can be reversed by addition of these compounds to the diet. Among the effects noted in the rat, are: growth failure, scaliness of the skin, necrosis of the tail, testicular tubular degeneration, hematuria, and reproductive failure. These effects can be offset by addition of 20 to 100 mg. of linoleic acid per day. Among the essential fatty acids are a group of polyunsaturated compounds of which the following three are probably the most important:

> linoleic acid (9,12-octadecadienoic acid)
> arachidonic acid (5,8,11,14-eicosatetraenoic acid)
> γ-linolenic acid (6,9,12-octadecatrienoic acid)

The metabolism of these compounds has been discussed elsewhere (p. 307).

REFERENCES

General Reviews: *Harris:* Vitamins, 1955; *Sebrell* and *Harris:* Vitamins, 3 vols., 1954; *Harris, Marrian* and *Thimann:* Vitamins and Hormones, Vol. 13, 1955. The Ann. Rev. Biochem. 1958, 1959, 1960 should be consulted for current reviews on vitamins. See also Food, the Yearbook of Agriculture, 1959, p. 130–161.
Among some special articles are *Wald:* Ann. Rev. Biochem., 22:496, 1953 (biochemistry of vision); *Pfiffner* and *Bird:* Ibid., 25:397, 1956 (vitamin B₁₂ and related substances); *Wilson* and *Henderson:* J. Biol. Chem., 235:2009, 1960 (niacin and tryptophan relationship); Nutr. Rev., 14:345, 1956 (function of essential fatty acids); *Stanier:* Harvey Lectures, 1958–59, p. 219 (carotenoid pigments); *Hubbard, Brown,* and *Knopf:* Nature, 183:442, 1959 (action of light on visual pigments); *Horwitt:* Borden's Rev. of Nutrition Research, 22: Jan.– March, 1961 (vitamin E).

CHEMISTRY OF THE TISSUES

An examination of the head, the trunk, and the limbs of the body reveals certain similar types of substances in each of them, such as bone, cartilage, muscle, nerve. These similar types, composed as they are of groups of similar cells, are called *tissues*. In this chapter we shall discuss the chemical composition of these tissues.

MUSCLE TISSUE

This tissue consists of three varieties: striped or striated muscle (voluntary), such as is found in the skeletal muscles of the body and which forms almost one half of the total weight of the body; smooth or nonstriated muscle (involuntary), such as we see in the walls of the bladder, skin, arteries, and veins; and cardiac muscle, which forms the main part of the wall of the heart.

Chemical examination of muscle reveals it to be composed of 75 per cent water and 25 per cent solids. Twenty per cent of the solids consists of proteins; the rest includes carbohydrates, salts, and nitrogenous compounds (also called "extractives"). Among the latter are creatine, phosphocreatine, purine bases, uric acid, adenylic acid and its derivatives (such as ADP and ATP), carnosine and anserine. The last two are peptides; little is known about them physiologically.

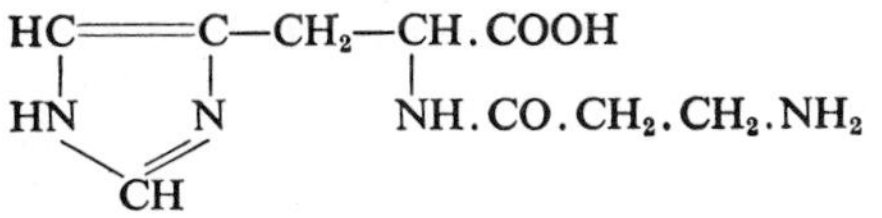

$$HC \!\!=\!\!\!=\!\! C - CH_2 - CH.COOH$$
$$HN \qquad N \qquad NH.CO.CH_2.CH_2.NH_2$$
$$CH$$

Carnosine (dipeptide of histidine and β-alanine)

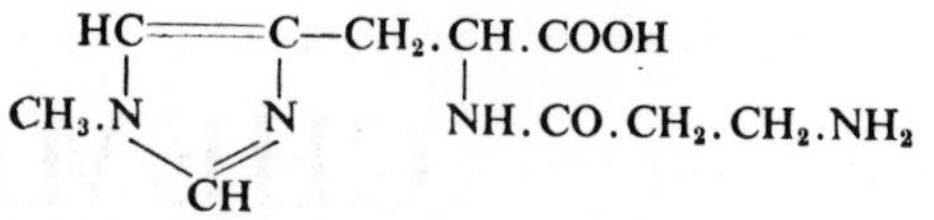

$$HC \!=\!\!=\!\! C \!-\! CH_2.CH.COOH$$

$$CH_3.N \qquad N \qquad NH.CO.CH_2.CH_2.NH_2$$

$$CH$$

Anserine (dipeptide of methyl histidine and β-alanine)

CREATINE

Creatine, largely in the form of phosphocreatine, is found in muscle (Table 74), brain and blood. Its role in muscular contraction and carbo-

TABLE 74. DISTRIBUTION OF PHOSPHOCREATINE AND ATP IN MUSCLE (IN MOLES PER GRAM OF TISSUE)

	Skeletal	Cardiac	Smooth
ATP	5×10^{-6}	1.5×10^{-6}	2×10^{-6}
Phosphocreatine	20×10^{-6}	2×10^{-6}	0.7×10^{-6}

(From Mommaerts, in McElroy and Glass: Phosphorus Metabolism, 1951, Vol. I, p. 551.)

hydrate metabolism has already been mentioned and its functions will be further discussed.

Creatine appears to be confined to vertebrates; in invertebrates, arginine plays a similar role.

In the urine of vertebrates we find creatinine, the anhydride of creatine. Creatinine is the stronger base.

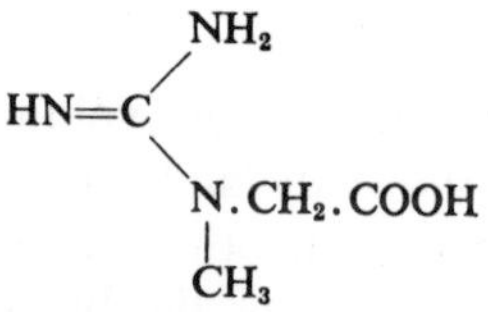

$$HN\!=\!\!C\!\!\begin{array}{c} NH_2 \\ \\ N.CH_2.COOH \\ | \\ CH_3 \end{array}$$

Creatine

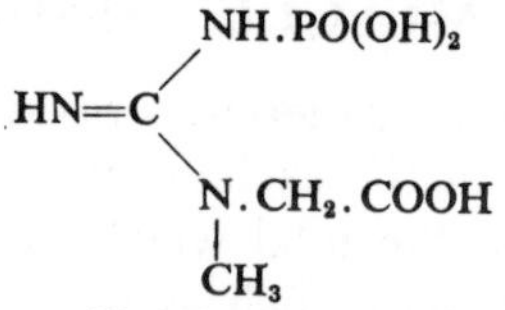

$$HN\!=\!\!C\!\!\begin{array}{c} NH.PO(OH)_2 \\ \\ N.CH_2.COOH \\ | \\ CH_3 \end{array}$$

Phosphocreatine

$$HN\!=\!\!C\!\!\begin{array}{c} NH \\ \\ N.CH_2.CO \\ | \\ CH_3 \end{array}$$

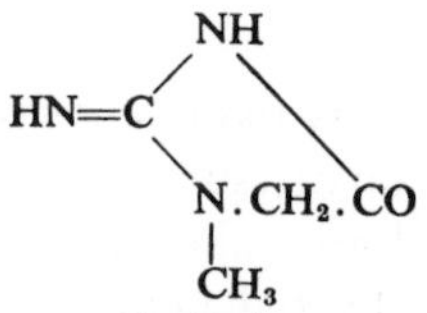

Creatinine

When creatine is treated with acid, it is converted to creatinine. In an alkaline medium a partial reversal of the process takes place, resulting in an equilibrium mixture. In N/2 HCl, at a temperature of 117° C., the change from creatine to creatinine is practically complete in 15 minutes.

Biosynthesis of Creatine. When isotopic guanidoacetic acid (glycocyamine) is fed to rats, both isotopic creatine and creatinine are formed. Creatine is formed in two steps: (a) the production of guanidoacetic acid, and (b) the methylation of the compound produced.

Borsook, working with liver slices, showed that guanidoacetic acid is converted into creatine, but at a very slow pace. However, the addition of methionine, supplying additional methyl groups, accelerated the process a great deal.

Using isotopic compounds Bloch and Schoenheimer found that among various compounds arginine and glycine were the most effective creatine formers. By degrading the creatine so formed, the particular nitrogen supplied to creatine could be located:

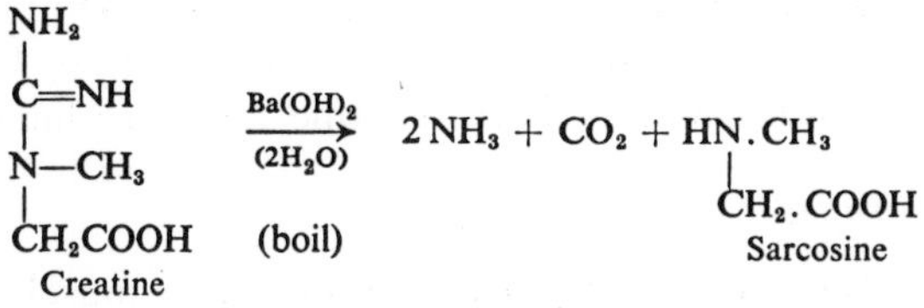

$$
\begin{array}{l}
NH_2 \\
| \\
C\!=\!NH \\
| \\
N\!-\!CH_3 \\
| \\
CH_2COOH
\end{array}
\xrightarrow[\substack{(2H_2O)\\(boil)}]{Ba(OH)_2}
2\,NH_3 + CO_2 +
\begin{array}{l}
HN.CH_3 \\
| \\
CH_2.COOH
\end{array}
$$

Creatine   Sarcosine

All of the N in the amidine group of creatine is recovered as NH_3, and the remaining N as sarcosine.

When isotopic glycine was fed, the isotope was located in the sarcosine fraction of creatine. On the other hand, the feeding of isotopic arginine concentrated the isotope in the ammonia fraction obtained from creatine.

In this way it could be shown that the amidine group in creatine is derived from arginine, and the sarcosine portion, from glycine.

The origin, then, of creatine, can be summarized as follows:

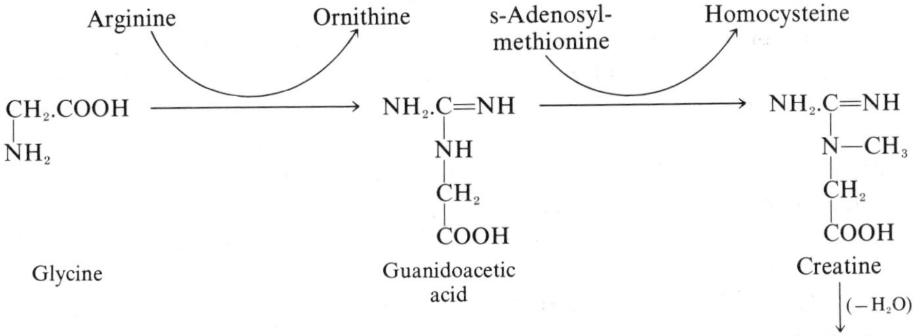

Arginine   Ornithine   s-Adenosyl-methionine   Homocysteine

$$
\begin{array}{l}
CH_2.COOH \\
| \\
NH_2
\end{array}
\longrightarrow
\begin{array}{l}
NH_2.C\!=\!NH \\
| \\
NH \\
| \\
CH_2 \\
| \\
COOH
\end{array}
\longrightarrow
\begin{array}{l}
NH_2.C\!=\!NH \\
| \\
N\!-\!CH_3 \\
| \\
CH_2 \\
| \\
COOH
\end{array}
$$

Glycine   Guanidoacetic acid   Creatine

$\Big\downarrow (-H_2O)$

Creatinine

While the methyl group of methionine is used for the building of the creatine of muscle, neither creatine, nor creatinine, nor sarcosine can supply its methyl group to convert homocystine to methionine.

Creatine-Creatinine Relationships. The feeding of labeled creatine leads to the isolation from the urine of labeled creatinine. It can be assumed, therefore, that creatinine arises from creatine. However, the feeding of isotopic creatinine does not result in the formation of isotopic creatine, but in the elimination of unchanged creatinine.

Folin was among the first to show that the amount of creatinine excreted in the urine of a normal individual remains remarkably constant. What happens to the creatine other than that which is excreted as creatinine is still a question. There may, indeed, be other pathways for the metabolism of creatine.

The normal male adult excretes no creatine. However, the base does appear in the urine in periods of starvation, fever, and when muscle atrophies. In the female adult, one meets with intermittent creatinuria. During pregnancy, creatine appears in the urine. Until puberty children of both sexes excrete both creatine and creatinine.

PROTEINS IN MUSCLE

Table 75 gives the percentages of proteins in muscle.

TABLE 75. PROTEIN FRACTIONS OF WHITE MUSCLE

Protein	Per cent of total protein
Myogen	9
Globulin X	18
Myosin	57
Stroma	16

(From Mommaerts: Muscular Contraction, 1950.)

Myogen is the so-called albumin fraction of muscle which is soluble in the absence of salts. It represents a mixture of several proteins; two of them, myogen A and myogen B, have been isolated in crystalline form.

This myogen fraction contains a number of enzymes; isomerase, aldolase, triosephosphate dehydrogenase and phosphorylase constitute some 16 per cent of this fraction.

Little is known about globulin X. The substance precipitates when the salts are removed by dialysis.

"Stroma" is the protein fraction of muscle which remains after several extractions with salt solutions. It is believed to be the source of actin which, in combination with myosin, yields actomyosin, the contractile protein.

MUSCLE CONTRACTION

Our present knowledge of the chemistry of the contractile proteins in muscle is based largely on the work of Szent-Györgyi.

Inside the muscle there are present bundles of small fibers called myofibrils; a series of these make up a muscle fiber, which contracts under the influence of a nerve impulse (Plates 7 and 8).

If ground muscle is extracted for short periods of time with salt

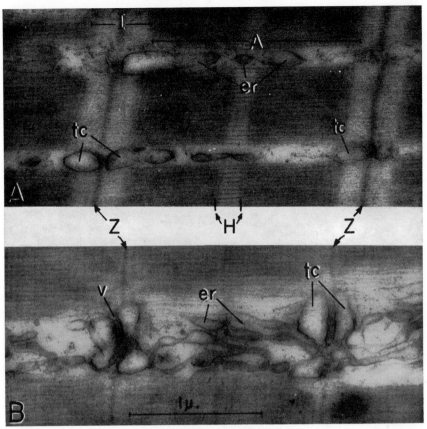

Plate 7

Electron micrographs of the sarcoplasmic reticulum (*er*) in skeletal muscle. *A*, Section through the myofibril and, *B*, section tangential to the surface of the myofibril. *tc*, Terminal cisternae, showing small vesicles between (V) and at the level of the Z line; 40,000×. (Courtesy of K. R. Porter; from De Robertis, Nowinski and Saez: General Cytology.)

solutions, the extract contains myosin; or, as we now know, a mixture of myosin and actin. If, however, the muscle is extracted for a longer period with concentrated salt solutions, a complex protein, actomyosin, is obtained. This actomyosin is presumably the result of the reaction between myosin and actin.

Actomyosin is a viscous substance and displays, in solution, the property of birefringence (double refraction). When a salt solution of actomyosin is extruded into a more dilute salt solution, threads of actomyosin precipitate. These threads contract in the presence of ATP and K and Mg ions.

The contraction is similar to that which occurs in muscle *in vivo*. By comparing the *in vitro* contraction of actomyosin threads with the

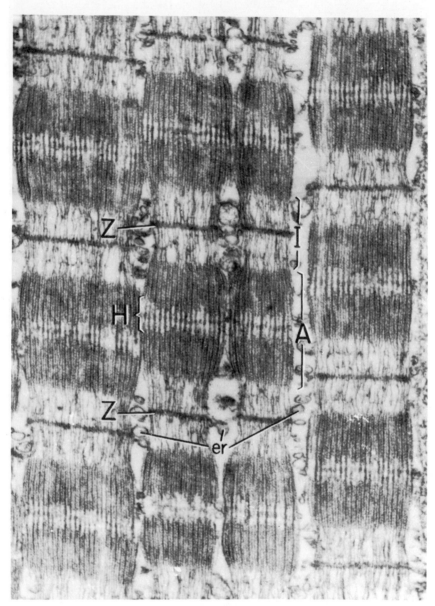

Plate 8

Electron micrograph of four myofibrils, showing the alternating sarcomeres with the Z lines and the H, A and I bands. *er*, Sarcoplasmic reticulum situated between the myofibrils. The finer structure of the myofibril represented by the thin and thick myofilaments is also observed; 60,000×. (Courtesy of H. Huxley; from De Robertis, Nowinski and Saez: General Cytology.)

optical properties of the myofibrils in the intact muscle fiber, it appears fairly certain that the shortening during contraction is due to the actomyosin in the myofibril.

Myosin has been crystallized and found to have a molecular weight of 900,000. Actin can exist in two forms: globular actin (G-actin), which is converted to fibrillar actin (F-actin), which is highly polymerized. This conversion needs ATP:

$$\text{G-Actin} + \text{ATP} \longrightarrow \text{F-actin} + \text{ADP} + \text{PO}_4^=$$

Agents which block sulfhydryl groups (such as p-chloromercuribenzoate), inhibit both fibril contraction and polymerization, which probably means that the contractile protein requires free —SH groups for its activity.

Mommaerts has proposed the following sequence of events during muscle contraction: Muscle at rest contains G-actomyosin which reacts with ATP to form F-actin. The latter polymerizes and combines with myosin to yield F-actomyosin, which then contracts and liberates ADP. During the relaxation of muscle, ADP is reconverted to ATP via the action of phosphocreatine, or other energy-rich phosphate compounds.

MYOSIN AND ADENOSINETRIPHOSPHATASE (ATPASE)

The discovery associating the enzyme ATPase with myosin we owe to Engelhardt and Lyubimova. They believe the enzyme to be myosin itself. As evidence it is pointed out that the enzymic properties of myosin are unchanged throughout a series of mild reactions—reprecipitation, dilution, and salting out. No protein fraction other than myosin itself shows these enzyme properties to anywhere near such an extent. Any reaction, however mild, which denatures myosin also destroys the properties of the enzyme.

Subsequent work by Meyerhof, Cori, and others has thrown some doubt on these views. While it is agreed that the enzyme ATPase is closely associated with myosin, yet the latter is not the enzyme itself. Meyerhof completely separated a second ATPase, activated by magnesium, from myosin. He claimed that this magnesium-activated enzyme is mainly responsible for the ATPase activity of fresh myosin.

Mommaerts has shown that with a highly purified preparation of myosin, the ATPase activity remains low within the physiological range of pH, and that it accounts for but 1 per cent of the dephosphorylation of ATP during muscle contraction.

Myosin has also been digested by trypsin, and as a result of such treatment it no longer reacts typically with actin. The ATPase activity, however, remains unchanged. It is possible, therefore, that myosin may form a complex with ATPase, and that the enzyme is liberated by the action of trypsin.

MYOGLOBIN

In muscle we also find a compound similar to hemoglobin: myoglobin. It may appear in the urine after injury to the limbs. It has been obtained in crystalline form and has an iron content of 0.34 per cent, similar to human hemoglobin.

NERVE TISSUE

The nerve tissue includes the brain, spinal cord, peripheral nerves, ganglia, and plexuses. Its importance lies in its ability to respond to stimuli and to conduct impulses. The biochemistry of the nervous system is now discussed under the heading of "neurochemistry."

COMPOSITION

The gray matter of the brain may contain as much as 80 per cent —and even more—of water. Of the solids present in nerve tissues, some 50 per cent may be due to proteins, of which collagen and neurokeratin are the most abundant, according to Block. Neurokeratin itself, though possibly different from the keratin found in epidermal tissue, is similar to the latter in so far as its general insolubility and its resistance to peptic and tryptic digestion are concerned. Block believes that neurokeratin is possibly the protein in the neurofibrils, the filaments in the nerve cells, and their axons.

Relatively small quantities of alkaline phosphates, phosphocreatine, adenosinetriphosphate, hexosephosphate and chlorides, carbohydrates, extractives (creatine, etc.), and inositol are also present. Aside from the proteins, the materials present in largest quantity (in nerve fibers, at least), and in many ways the most characteristic materials, are the lipids.

The brain of a rat embryo contains 10 per cent of fatty acids; so does the liver. When the rat is thirty days old, the fatty acids of the liver still remain 10 per cent, but those of the brain have increased to 20 per cent.

The turnover of these lipids in the brain is a slow process by comparison with other tissues of the body. Using deuterium as the tracer, it can be shown that in the adult brain, some 20 per cent of the fatty acids are replaced in a week. In the liver, on the other hand, the turnover is as high as 50 per cent in one day.

The chemistry of these lipids has already been discussed (Chap. 3). These substances include lecithin, cephalin, sphingomyelin, cerebrosides, and sterols (particularly cholesterol), besides the true fats. While not peculiar to nervous tissue, some, like the cerebrosides, are rarely found in any other part of the body; and they are certainly present in abundance. Furthermore, Thannhauser has found that the fatty acids of the sphingomyelin in brain differ from those present in the sphingomyelin of other organs (lung and spleen).

A disease of childhood, known as *Niemann-Pick disease,* is characterized by an increase in the sphingomyelin of the brain.

The "cephalin" in brain is not a definite compound, as was supposed, but apparently a mixture of several compounds. Folch has shown that it is a mixture of three different phosphatides: one contains ethanolamine, another serine, and a third inositol.

The principal constituent of the sheath, "myelin," is a mixture of substances. The principal lipid constituents are free cholesterol, cerebroside and sphingomyelin, rather than cephalin and lecithin, as was thought at one time.

The distribution of lipids in the peripheral nerves resembles that of the lipids in the white matter of the brain rather than that of the gray matter.

Both brain white matter and peripheral nerves contain more cerebroside, free cholesterol, and sphingomyelin than brain gray matter does.

When a peripheral nerve is cut, the portion of the nerve distal to the point of section soon loses its ability to transmit a nerve impulse. This is associated with histological changes known as *Wallerian degeneration.*

With the degeneration of the nerve, the myelin, rich in lipids, which surrounds the axon of the nerve, is ultimately completely destroyed.

THE METABOLISM OF NERVES

The unit of the nervous system, the neuron, consists of the cell, the dendrites, and the axon (Fig. 95). The axon (or axis-cylinder) is the central core of a nerve fiber. The nervous impulse is propagated along the nerve with a velocity of 27 meters per second in the frog, and more rapidly in the mammal. There is a change in electric potential: the portion of the nerve in action is electrically negative, as compared with "resting" portions, in front and behind. The fatigue of the nerve comes only after relatively long periods of activity.

It is possible, particularly when working with cold-blooded animals, to excise a nerve and keep it "in action" for some time, assuming a temperature which is low enough, and provided, also, that the moisture is suitable. Under such conditions, it is possible, by the use of delicate instruments, to measure the production of heat generated during the course of the activity of the nerve and to examine a number of electrical properties.

The fact that heat is produced during the conduction of an impulse is evidence of a metabolic process. Such a condition is not merely a physical, but also a chemical, phenomenon. Although the amount of heat produced is small, it has been measured; it amounts to 141×10^{-5}

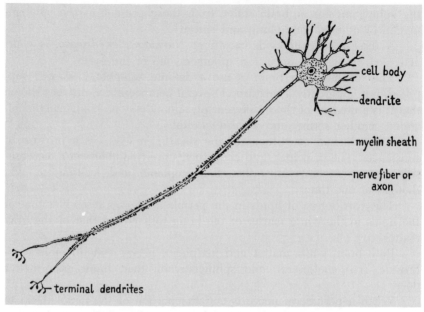

Figure 95.   A nerve cell or neuron. (Dawson.)

calories per gram of nerve for a stimulus lasting ten seconds. The heat is evolved in two stages; a small amount of heat—from 2 to 3 per cent of the total—is produced immediately; and the remainder is evolved over a period which may last half an hour or so after the stimulation.

Oxygen is absorbed by the nerve at rest, but during and following stimulation much more is absorbed. The Q_{O_2} of resting frog nerve at 15° is −0.08, and of stimulated frog's nerve, −0.3. The nerve, it is known, will conduct for a comparatively long time in an atmosphere of nitrogen. Upon the admission of oxygen, however, this gas is consumed in larger quantities than would have taken place without the preliminary treatment with nitrogen. This process is spoken of as "going into oxygen debt."

The nerve can produce lactic acid from carbohydrate in the absence of oxygen. The lactic acid is oxidized very slowly. It is still uncertain whether the stimulation of a nerve involves a glycogen–lactic acid metabolism at all comparable to what takes place in muscle. One would expect that under the stimulation of oxygen an increased amount of lactic acid would disappear, but the results do not support this view.

A somewhat mysterious effect is the production of ammonia when the nerve is stimulated. The significance of this ammonia is not clear; nor has the origin of this compound been settled. There are two substances present in brain tissue which might give rise to ammonia: one is adenylic acid and the other is glutamine. Adenylic acid may lose ammonia, yielding inosinic acid. Here the change involved is a change

of the adenine (in adenylic acid) to hypoxanthine (in inosinic acid).
Glutamine, also, may break down to glutamic acid and ammonia:

$$CONH_2.CH_2.CH_2.CHNH_2.COOH \longrightarrow NH_3 + COOH.CH_2.CH_2.CHNH_2.COOH$$

There is reason to believe that glutamine itself is first formed by the reverse process: the combination of glutamic acid and ammonia. In any case, gray cortex can "bind" large quantities of ammonia, provided glutamic acid is present; and, what is very significant, no other amino acid can take the place of glutamic acid.

As a result of stimulation in oxygen, this gas is consumed and carbon dioxide, ammonia, and inorganic phosphate are liberated.

It is believed that potassium ions are involved in the electrical phenomena of nerve. Bathing a nerve in oxygenated sea water does not change the content of potassium in the nerve, despite the fact that the concentration of the element inside is ten times that of the element outside. Such a difference in concentration would give rise to a difference in electrical potential. But should the nerve be stimulated, or should it be deprived of oxygen, it begins to lose its potassium. It is of interest to find that so long as the potassium ions are retained by the tissue, so long can a potential difference be noted between the inside and the outside of the fiber. But the loss of potassium, resulting from stimulation or oxygen deprivation, causes the potential difference to disappear.

BRAIN

The brain—and all nervous tissue—is characterized by a high lipid content. Table 76 compares the distribution of various lipids among a number of tissues:

TABLE 76. LIPIDS IN OX TISSUES AS PERCENTAGE OF DRY WEIGHT

	Brain	Liver	Kidney	Heart	Muscle	Lung
Total lipid	51.60	23.99	17.25	16.45	11.99	14.83
Neutral fat	2.97	5.81	4.45	4.06	7.57	2.41
Phospholipin	26.38	16.22	10.32	9.83	3.24	9.79
Sphingomyelin	4.97	0.76	1.67	0.53	0.20	2.28
Cerebroside	12.01	0	0.71	2.00	0.95	0.44
Cholesterol, free	10.00	0.44	1.44	0.34	0.18	1.34
Cholesterol, esters	0.25	0.53	0.34	0.23	0.07	0.89

(From Kaucher, Galbraith, Button, and Williams: Arch. Biochem., 3:203, 1943.)

The gross composition of human (whole) brain is: water (per cent fresh weight), 76.9; protein (per cent dry weight), 37.7; lipid, 54.4; extractives, 7.9.

The brain gets its energy practically exclusively from the oxidation of carbohydrate; its R.Q. is 1. It does not store glycogen though it needs glucose (and oxygen). Glycolysis occurs in brain tissue and many of the enzymes and phosphorylated intermediates active in glycolysis are known to be present, though it is not certain that the pathway of carbohydrate metabolism here is altogether comparable to what happens in muscle or liver.

Gamma aminobutyric acid has been shown to be a constituent of the brain, and it exists largely in the free form. The suggestion has been made that this compound is formed by the decarboxylation of glutamic acid.

THE MEMBRANE THEORY OF CONDUCTION

This theory assumes that the nerve is surrounded by a polarized membrane, the outside of which carries a positive charge and the inside a negative charge, owing to the fact that the concentration of potassium ions is higher inside than outside the membrane. This selective permeability to potassium ions, and the leakage of potassium ions during nerve activity, is the basis for the membrane theory of nerve conduction. When a stimulus is applied to the surface membrane, a reversal of charge takes place and the outside surface becomes negative to an ad-

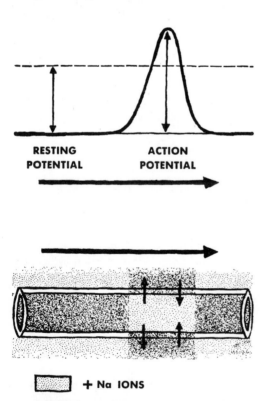

RESTING POTENTIAL **ACTION POTENTIAL**

+ Na IONS

− K IONS

Figure 96. Action potential wave (top) spreads along the surface of a nerve fiber (bottom). During the rise of the action potential, sodium ions (Na) enter the fiber and make it positive; during the resting state of the nerve, the outward pressure of potassium ions (K) keeps the interior of the fiber negative. (From Katz, Bernhard: The Physics and Chemistry of Life. Copyright 1955, Scientific American, Inc. Published by Simon and Schuster, New York.)

jacent point on the membrane. In this way a flow of current results which stimulates an adjacent point. There is, apparently, an exchange of potassium ions across the nerve membrane even during the resting stage, thus establishing a dynamic concentration gradient with respect to this ion, as well as to sodium ions, which are more concentrated outside than inside the membrane. The flow of current in an isolated nerve after a suitable stimulus has been applied can be seen and measured with the aid of the cathode ray oscilloscope. The current which is produced is called the "action potential" (Fig. 96).

ROLE OF ACETYLCHOLINE AND ACH-ESTERASE IN NERVE TRANSMISSION

Of the two types of nerve endings, the sympathetic release epinephrine (adrenalin) and norepinephrine, whereas the parasympathetic release acetylcholine. We owe to Hunt and Dale our knowledge of the relationship of acetylcholine to the parasympathetic nerves. The first clear-cut observation that acetylcholine could be a mediator of nerve impulse transmission was that of Otto Loewi in 1921, who found that following stimulation of the vagus nerve of an isolated frog heart, a substance appeared in the perfusion fluid which, when applied to a second frog heart, had the same effect as vagal stimulation. This "Vagus-stoff" was soon identified as acetylcholine.

The work of the earlier nerve physiologists was largely confined to the study of the electrical signs of nerve activity. Nachmansohn and his group are responsible for the biochemical studies involving the enzymes which synthesize and split acetylcholine.

The biosynthesis of acetylcholine is associated with oxidative metabolism and requires an enzyme, choline acetylase, together with coenzyme A. In addition, a source of ATP is also required and can be furnished by those metabolic reactions in the cell which incorporate the high energy phosphate bond to form ATP, e.g., phosphocreatine breakdown. In the electric eel the chemical energy released by the breakdown of phosphocreatine is adequate to account for the electrical energy released by the action potential.

Nachmansohn assumes that acetylcholine is present in the cell in an inactive form bound to protein or lipoprotein and is thus protected from the action of acetylcholine esterase (ACh-esterase). When, during the flow of current, a stimulus reaches this point, acetylcholine is released. Having produced its effect it is then hydrolyzed by ACh-esterase to form acetate and choline. During the recovery phase more acetylcholine would be synthesized.

One of the most important criteria for chemical mediation of nerve impulse transmission is the exceedingly great speeds involved, since we are dealing with electrical currents. Nachmansohn states that such a chemical reaction would have to take place within less than 100 microseconds. ACh-esterase does, in fact, split acetylcholine at speeds which satisfy this requirement. Thus, the enzyme from the electric tissue of the electric eel has been purified to the extent that 1 mg. portein splits 75 gm. acetylcholine per hour. An approximate molecular weight of such material is 3,000,000, according to sedimentation rate studies with the ultracentrifuge. It can be calculated that one molecule of enzyme would split one molecule of acetylcholine in 3 to 4 microseconds.

ACh-esterase is localized in nerve tissue and in the muscle at the motor end plate. In the electric eel there is a parallel relationship between the action potential and ACh-esterase concentration in the electric tissue, as well as a correlation between voltage and ACh-esterase concentration.

One of the most fruitful studies of ACh-esterase has centered around its inhibition by a variety of chemical agents. The administration of such highly specific ACh-esterase inhibitors results in the accumulation of acetylcholine and block nerve conduction. The death of an animal treated *in vivo* with such agents is associated with a complete inhibition of its brain ACh-esterase. *In vitro* the addition of such an inhibitor to the medium bathing the nerve results in an alteration of the action potential. Physostigmine (eserine) and neostigmine are reversible inhibitors, so that they may be removed from the nerve by washing, with a restoration of conduction. Diisopropyl fluorophosphate, an irreversible inhibitor, if used for a sufficient period of time, causes an irreversible abolition of nerve conduction. *In vivo* the latter compound is a powerful nerve poison.

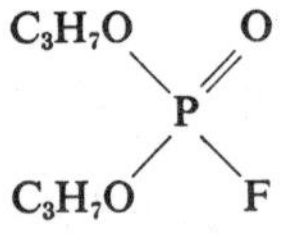

Diisopropyl fluorophosphate

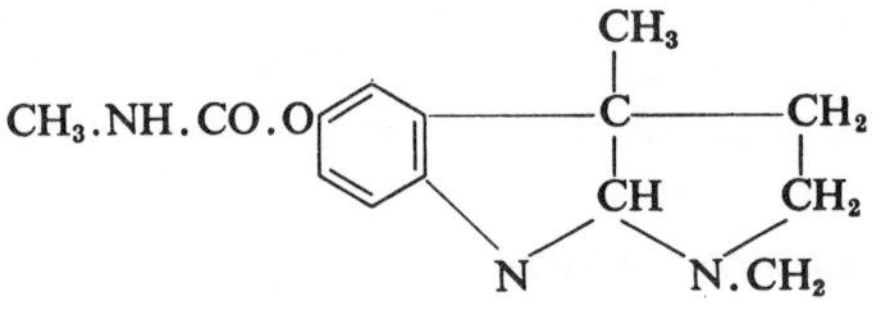

Physostigmine

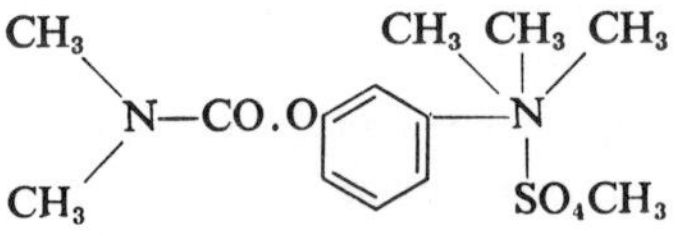

Neostigmine

VITAMINS

A number of vitamins are necessary for the prevention of degenerative changes in the central nervous system; they belong almost exclusively to the vitamin B complex. Of this group, the one which has received most attention so far is vitamin B_1, or thiamine.

The brain oxidizes carbohydrate almost exclusively; and for this purpose, does not require insulin—unlike other organs, such as muscle, heart, kidney, and liver. Then, too, the path of carbohydrate metabolism may follow the path outlined in Chapter 11, or it may take some other form; or, at different times, it may take several forms.

The metabolic defects on a vitamin B_1-deficient diet—which also appear elsewhere (heart and kidney) besides the nervous system— appear before there is any degeneration of tissue, which means that a fairly prompt supply of the missing factor restores the animal to normal health.

The development of beriberi is accompanied by an increase in the amount of pyruvate present in the brain and also by a decrease in the amount of oxygen consumed (Peters). It is assumed that the oxidation of glucose in the brain may follow the path: glucose → lactic acid → pyruvic acid → carbon dioxide; and it is believed that vitamin B_1 (thiamine) as well as CoA and α-lipoic acid are concerned with the change of pyruvic acid to acetic acid and CO_2 by a process of oxidative decarboxylation:

$$CH_3CO.COOH \xrightarrow[+O]{-CO_2} CH_3.COOH + CO_2$$

A cocarboxylase, as well as carboxylase itself, is necessary for the proper functioning of this system. This coenzyme is none other than a pyro-phosphoric ester of vitamin B_1 (Lohmann).

From the work of Peters and his associates it seems clear that not only is carboxylase active in the oxidation of pyruvic acid in brain, but that the C_4 acids (succinic, fumaric, malic, oxaloacetic) play an essential role in this transformation. In others words, the C_4 acids are important whether we deal with oxidations in muscle or oxidations in brain.

HORMONES

We will presently (Chap. 21) touch upon the subject of insulin in hypoglycemic shock, and we have referred to the probability that nerves themselves liberate substances which may be regarded as hormones. A study of one or two hormones, generated in other parts of the body, in their possible effect on the activity of the brain has been made. Thyroxine, for example, increases the respiration of both nerve and brain. This is presumably brought about by inducing an increased production of dehydrogenases, the enzymes involved in processes of oxidation.

Extracts from the adrenal cortex have a profound effect on the metabolism of sodium in the body, and it is not surprising to find that they influence the potassium and sodium balance in the brain.

EFFECT OF DRUGS

It has been emphasized that, from the point of view of metabolism, the brain is not a homogeneous tissue. Neither is it homogeneous in its anatomical or chemical structure. The multiplicity of results obtained by the use of different chemicals is not surprising.

To cite a few examples: cocaine paralyzes sensory nerve endings; atropine paralyzes the nerve endings of the parasympathetic system only; morphine depresses the centers dealing with pain perception; analgesics and antipyretics (salicylates, aspirin, etc.) depress the pain-perceiving and temperature-regulating mechanisms; alcohol depresses the power of judgment and releases inhibitions.

Serotonin, or 5-hydroxytryptamine,

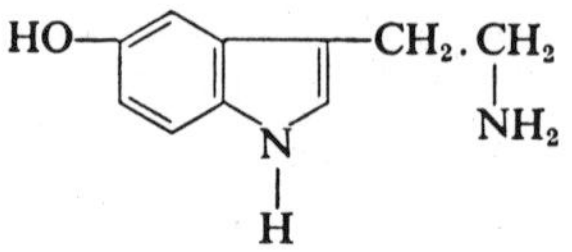

though found in many tissues of the body, is concentrated in the brain. Tryptophan is probably its precursor, being converted by oxidation to 5-hydroxytryptophan, which then undergoes decarboxylation to yield serotonin. It is an intense local vasoconstrictor.

"Tranquilizing" substances for the treatment of hypertensive, nervous and mental disorders have come into use. One such substance is the alkaloid, reserpine, which Woodward has synthesized.

EPITHELIAL TISSUE

Epithelial tissue is found in the covering of the surface of the body (the skin), in the lining of the respiratory tract, as an essential part of glandular organs, and as hair and nails. Melanin (p. 353) is the characteristic pigment of the skin and hair. (In an abnormal condition (albinism), it is completely absent.) The melanins, in general, are brown or black pigments that have their origin in the oxidation products of tyrosine or chemically related compounds.

KERATIN

The characteristic substance present in this tissue is the albuminoid keratin. Among proteins it is the most resistant to chemical action. It is insoluble in any of the solvents which dissolve other proteins and is not attacked by gastric or pancreatic juice. Human hair contains from 16 to 21 per cent of cystine.

Though normally resistant to chemical and enzymic action, by exhaustive grinding, keratin becomes more digestible. For example, if wool fibers (rich in keratin) are first ground in a ball mill, they can be digested by both pepsin and trypsin. Significantly enough, after grinding, these wool fibers, if extracted with water, show larger quantities of nitrogen and sulfur constituents in solution than before grinding. Similar results are obtained with keratins from human hair, turkey feathers, duck feathers, chicken feathers, and porcupine quills.

That such mechanical grinding, aside from increasing surface area and so enabling the proteolytic enzymes to come into more intimate contact with substrate, is accompanied by some chemical change is made probable by the fact that, after the operation, there is a decrease in cystine sulfur, and one half to one fourth of the water-soluble sulfur is in the form of inorganic sulfates, a change which suggests some oxidation.

Suggestive, too, are experiments with animals which lead to the conclusion that such finely ground keratin can be utilized to some degree as the protein constituent in the diet of animals. Supplementing the diet with tryptophan, methionine, and histidine—amino acids present in very small quantities—improved the condition of the animals. To convert what has always been considered a purely waste product from the point of view of food—keratin—into a useful animal "feed" would be an important practical achievement.

Male hair, it seems, contains more cystine than female hair; and dark hair contains more cystine than light hair.

According to Edwards and Duntley, the color of normal skin is due to several pigments: melanin, a closely related substance which the authors call "melanoid," carotene, reduced hemoglobin, and oxyhemoglobin. "Our studies confirm the idea that the colored races owe their characteristic color only to variations in the amount of melanin present. . . . No pigments other than those found in the whites are encountered in the dark races. . . ."

Human red hair yields a red iron pigment of unknown constitution. This pigment cannot be obtained from human hair unless it is bright red in color.

CONNECTIVE TISSUE

Under this heading we shall discuss collagen (white fibrous tissue), elastin (yellow elastic tissue), chondromucoid (mucoprotein of cartilage) and the variety of substances which make up the "ground substances" of the cell (Fig. 97).

COLLAGEN

The main organic constituent of white fibrous tissue is the albuminoid *collagen,* which, like keratin, is chemically resistant, but not to the same degree. Collagen is also found in bone, skin, and the walls of blood vessels. In the calcified tissues, bones and teeth, collagen is the major component of the matrix (Piez and Likins). It is formed from precollagenous material in maturing connective tissue—a process which ceases to some extent in scurvy.

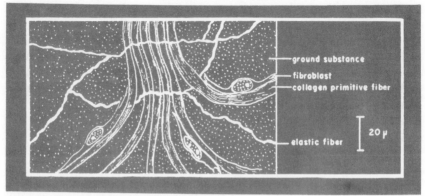

Figure 97. The distinctive components of connective tissue. (From Bear, in Anson and Edsall: Advances in Protein Chemistry, 7:69, 1952.)

Collagen is fairly well digested by pepsin, but only slightly by trypsin. Preliminary treatment with alkali makes the albuminoid more digestible by trypsin. It contains much less sulfur (in the form of cystine or methionine) than does keratin. By boiling with water, the collagen is converted to *gelatin,* a much more easily digestible protein. The chemical nature of this interconversion is still not clear; the tendency is to regard the change in the nature of an intramolecular rearrangement. Both gelatin and collagen are unusual proteins because of their content of hydroxyproline.

Radioactive studies show a low turnover for collagen, unlike the proteins in liver and muscle.

In rheumatoid diseases there develop degenerative changes in the collagen.

An analysis by Gies of the tendo achillis of the ox—an example of white fibrous tissue—reveals that the solids constitute from 35 to 40 per cent, only a fraction of a per cent of which is inorganic matter. The organic matter is composed of the following (in per cent): collagen, 31.6; elastin, 1.6; mucoid, 1.2; fatty substance, 1.0; and extractives, 0.9.

The elastin is referred to in the next section. The mucoid (tendomucoid) resembles the mucin of the saliva, which means that it is a glucoprotein.

ELASTIN

It has been suggested that elastin is a lipoprotein and that it is fairly active metabolically. According to Gies, the analysis of ligamentum nuchae—an example of yellow elastic tissue—yields some 40 per cent of solids, composed of the following (in per cent): elastin, 31.6; collagen, 7.2; fatty substance, 1.1; mucoid, 0.5; inorganic matter, 0.4; and extractives, 0.8.

The elastin, like keratin and like collagen, belongs to the class of proteins known as albuminoids; which means that it is, relatively speaking, a chemically resistant protein. In general, it resembles collagen in its properties, although, unlike the latter, it is not changed to gelatin when boiled with water.

Elastin is that which is left over when everything else is hydrolyzed by dilute acid or alkali. Lowry hydrolyzes tissue with 0.1 N NaOH at 95° C. for 20 minutes, obtaining an insoluble material which is the elastin.

An enzyme (elastase) has been isolated from the pancreas which has the ability to dissolve elastin.

Elastin is slowly digested by pepsin and trypsin.

Table 77 gives the amino acid composition of collagen and elastin.

TABLE 77. AMINO ACID COMPOSITION OF BOVINE COLLAGEN AND ELASTIN (GM. IN 100 GM. PROTEIN)

Amino Acid	Collagen	Elastin
Glycine	19.9	22.5
Alanine	7.6	15.1
Phenylalanine	3.7	4.4
Leucine(s)	4.8	10.1
Valine	2.9	12.5
Proline	12.7	13.4
Hydroxyproline	12.1	1.7
Glutamic acid	10.0	2.4
Aspartic acid	5.5	0.35
Arginine	7.9	0.88
Lysine	4.0	0.39
Hydroxylysine	1.1	....
Histidine	0.7	0.04
Serine	2.7	0.68
Threonine	2.0	0.87
Methionine	0.7	0.18
Cystine	0.0	0.28
Tyrosine	1.3	1.4
Tryptophan	0.0	0.0
Total	99.6	87.2
Total N	18.6	16.9
Amide N	0.65	0.04

(From Bowes and Kenton: Biochem. J., *43*:358, 1948 [collagen]; Graham, Waitkoff, and Hier: J. Biol. Chem., *177*:529, 1949 [elastin].)

Collagen is characterized by an unusually high concentration of hydroxyproline.

CARTILAGE

This rather tough and firm material, popularly known as "gristle," is composed almost exclusively of collagen and chondromucoid.

If we define, with Meyer, a mucopolysaccharide as a hexosamine-containing polysaccharide which occurs either free or loosely combined with protein, then chondroitin sulfate, mucoitin sulfate, hyaluronic acid, and heparin are examples.

Chondroitin sulfate, which, in addition to cartilage, can also be isolated from umbilical cord tissue, spongy bone, and skin, is made up of equimolar parts of acetyl galactosamine, ester sulfate, and glucuronic acid.

Mucoitin sulfate is a monosulfuric acid ester of hyaluronic acid.

HEPARIN

This substance in liver which prolongs the clotting time of blood is also a mucopolysaccharide containing more than one ester sulfate group.

HYALURONIC ACID

The hyaluronic acids, in general, are nonbranched polymers formed by alternating β 1-3 glucuronidic and 1-4 glucosaminidic bonds. They are found, among other places, in synovial fluid (viscid fluid of a joint cavity), vitreous humor (fluid between the retina and lens of the eye) and umbilical cord. When prepared under suitable conditions they have a high viscosity.

Hyaluronidase is an enzyme which can break down hyaluronic acid, a process which leads to a decrease in viscosity of the acid (a depolymerization) and to its hydrolysis. In the native state hyaluronic acid is present as a gel. When made acid, the hyaluronic acid precipitates (together with protein in the extract) to form a clot.

The importance of the hyaluronic acid–hyaluronidase system is evident from a list of reactions with which it has been associated:

A. The "spreading reaction" of hyaluronidase, which brings about a decrease in viscosity of tissue fluids and allows for the invasion or "spreading" of chemical substances throughout the tissue.

B. Decapsulation of mucoid strains of streptococci.

C. During fertilization it is believed that hyaluronidase disperses the viscous substance cementing the cumulus cells of the ova, facilitating the process of fertilization. Only mature spermatozoa contain relatively large amounts of the enzyme.

D. Capillary permeability.

BONE* (OSSEOUS TISSUE)

Bone is a living structure. It participates in the body metabolism and may act as a storehouse for minerals. It is not merely a rigid anatomic structure. It plays a role in maintaining the level of calcium in the blood.

* Compare this section with the section devoted to teeth (p. 508).

The organic matrix is similar to that found in cartilage and connective tissues in general. We find collagen, a glycoprotein, and an osseo-albuminoid. The normal mature bone contains nearly one-half its weight of water, and sometimes as much as 24 per cent of fat. Using the dry, fat-free material, some 30 to 40 per cent of this substance is organic in nature. The chief inorganic constituents are calcium, phosphate, and carbonate (Table 78).

TABLE 78. COMPOSITION OF BONE

Animal	Condition	Calcium	Magnesium	Phosphorus	CO_2
		In per cent of total bone ash			
Dog........................	Normal	35.7	0.46	15.8	5.6
Cow........................	Normal	36.1	0.74	16.4	4.6
Rabbit.....................	Normal	36.3	0.53	16.0	5.7
Hen........................	Normal	37.2	0.51	16.4	5.5
Rat........................	Normal	37.5	0.85	18.5	

(From Morgulis: J. Biol. Chem., *93:*455; Hammet: *Ibid.*, *64:*693.)

Among the organic constituents is citric acid, a substance which was overlooked for a long time, probably because in the ordinary analysis of bone as "bone ash" the citrate had been converted into carbonate and recorded as such.

Dickens has found citric acid—probably as the calcium salt—in bone to the extent of about 1 per cent. In fact, more than 90 per cent of the citric acid in the body is located in bony structure. It may be of use to the organism in two ways: as a reserve supply of citrate in the course of the metabolism of carbohydrate, and to form soluble calcium salts, probably as a preliminary step in the active metabolism of bone.

INORGANIC SALTS

The principal inorganic constituents of bone are calcium, phosphate, and carbonate, with lesser quantities of magnesium and sodium. The x-ray diffraction pattern of bone is similar to that of the mineral apatite, known as hydroxyapatite, $Ca_{10}(PO_4)_6(OH)_2$, which is sometimes written as $Ca_{10}(PO_4)_6F_2$. Substitutions of F^- for OH^- and Mg^{++} for Ca^{++} occur with only minor changes in the diffraction pattern.

In any case, the composition of the inorganic constituents of bone is by no means constant. Changes occur with age, in rickets, in acidosis and alkalosis, as a result of change in diet, etc. The most frequent changes occur in the percentage of carbonate.

Sobel and Kramer have shown that the calcium and phosphorus content, and the vitamin D content of the diet, influence the $CO_3:Ca$ ratio of bone.

That there is active metabolism in bone was shown by Hevesy who used labeled (radioactive) phosphorus and found that some of the phosphorus atoms of the mineral constituents of the bone exchange rapidly with those present in the plasma. Within fifty days 29 per cent of the mineral constituents of the femur and tibia epiphyses was found to be renewed.

ABSORPTION OF CALCIUM AND PHOSPHORUS

The normal adult absorbs only one half of the calcium ingested with his food, and about two-thirds of his ingested phosphate. Only the water-soluble form of calcium will be absorbed and inasmuch as neutral or alkaline pH favors the formation of insoluble calcium compounds, the pH of the intestinal contents plays an important role in calcium absorption. The absorption of calcium is aided by the presence of amino acids, fats, bile salts and by vitamin D.

The absorption of inorganic phosphate is intimately connected with that of calcium. Most of the excreted calcium is in the form of the insoluble calcium phosphate.

FACTORS AFFECTING CALCIFICATION

a. *The Calcium and Phosphorus of the Blood.* The concentration of the calcium and phosphorus is important since it affects the composition of fluid in immediate contact with tissues undergoing calcification. More specifically, we are here interested in the ion product which determines precipitation of mineral material.

Of the 9 to 11 mg. per cent calcium in the plasma, 4 mg. is ionizable, and from 3 to 5 mg. is associated with the plasma proteins and is nondiffusible; the remainder, the nature of which is in dispute, is nonionized but diffusible. Even the 2 mg. per cent of ionizable calcium is theoretically enough to yield a supersaturated solution.

Intermediate carbohydrate metabolism plays its role here since it makes available organic phosphorus compounds from which phosphorus ions are liberated by action of alkaline phosphatase.

Of the total phosphorus in the blood, 2 to 5 mg. per cent is inorganic phosphate, and together with the organic ester phosphorus (14 to 29 mg. per cent) makes up the "acid-soluble" phosphorus. The remainder includes the phospholipid P (8 to 18 mg. per cent) together with a small quantity of nucleic acid P. The inorganic P is equally distributed between the plasma and corpuscles; the ester P is mostly in the corpuscles and the lipid P is higher in the corpuscles than in the plasma.

From the work of Robison and others it seems clear that an important factor in the process of calcification is the presence of the enzyme *phosphatase*. This enzyme, present in bones, teeth, and ossifying cartilage of young animals, hydrolyzes hexosemonophosphoric ester and glycerophosphoric ester, liberating inorganic phosphate. A rachitic bone, cut longitudinally and placed in a solution of calcium hexosemonophosphate or calcium glycerophosphate, absorbs calcium phosphate and deposits the salt in the zones prepared for calcification. The conclusion has been drawn from this work that the bone phosphatase acts on the organic phosphorus ester liberating inorganic phosphate which, in turn, affects the product of the calcium and phosphate ions in solution to such a degree that the solubility product is exceeded, and the excess calcium phosphate is deposited.

Gutman has accumulated evidence which makes it likely that glycolysis, the utilization of glycogen in hypertrophic cartilage cells, plays an important role in calcification. Thus, enzyme inhibitors block the calcification of bone slices *in vitro*. Marks and Shorr inhibited calcification by the use of iodoacetamide, which interferes with the enzyme 1,3-diphosphoglyceric aldehyde dehydrogenase, and also showed that the removal of glycogen from cartilage slices markedly impaired the calcification process when inorganic phosphate was used but not when glucose-1-phosphate was used. It has also been demonstrated that a number of enzymes and their substrates of the glycolytic cycle are present in cartilage. The process of calcification appears to be anything but a simple precipitation of calcium phosphate.

b. The Calcium and Phosphorus in Food. The diet should include the following daily amounts (in grams):

	Ca	P
Children (3–13 years of age)	1.0	1.16–1.46
Adults	1.0	1.5
Pregnancy	1.5	1.5
Lactation	2.0	2.0

c. Vitamin D. See page 478.

d. Reaction of the Intestinal Tract. Dogs fed a normal diet show a pH in the small intestine varying from 5.7 to 6.6. When these animals are fed a rickets-producing diet, the pH of the intestine is changed to 6.4 to 7.4. The addition of cod-liver oil, or irradiation of the animal, lowers the pH more to the acid side (Grayzel and Miller). Apparently, in a more acid medium, the calcium salts are more soluble, and, therefore, more easily absorbed.

e. Potential Acidity and Alkalinity of the Diet. This may be a factor in pH changes in calcifying tissues. Also, a large excess of acid-forming food may be a drain on the fixed base of the body, including calcium.

f. Endocrine Glands. (The relation of calcium and the parathyroid hormone is discussed on page 542). Especially important are the parathyroids, thyroid, anterior pituitary, and sex glands.

These factors may affect calcification by their influence, directly or indirectly, on one or more of the following: by acting directly on the calcifying cells, thereby altering the rate of deposition or solution of the inorganic or organic substances; by varying the absorption of calcium and phosphorus from the intestinal tract; by regulating the excretion of calcium and phosphorus; and by altering the composition of the fluid in contact with the calcifying tissues.

The tooth consists of three calcified parts: the dentin, the chief substance of the tooth surrounding the tooth pulp; the cementum, covering the root of the tooth; and the enamel, the hardest of the three, covering the dentin (Fig. 98). These three, the dentin, the cementum, and the enamel, contain both inorganic and organic matter.

Organic Matter. The approximate percentages of organic matter are enamel, 1; dentin, 18; cementum, 23. The main constituent in enamel is keratin, with smaller quantities of cholesterol and phospholipids. In dentin we find mainly collagen and small quantities of lipids. Collagen is found in cementum.

The Inorganic Matter. The inorganic matter (in percentage, and on a dry basis) is approximately 96 for enamel, 70 for dentin, and 65 for cementum. The water content (in percentage) is approximately 3, 12, and 27 for enamel, dentin, and cementum, respectively. The following figures give the average results of analysis of human enamel and dentin (Karshan), and for comparison, an analysis of human bone (Gabriel).

	Enamel	Dentin	Bone
Calcium	35.8	26.5	23.84
Magnesium	0.38	0.79	0.30
Phosphorus	17.4	12.7	10.41
Carbon dioxide (from carbonate)	2.9	3.1	3.81

Enamel also contains (in per cent) 0.7 of sodium, 0.3 of potassium, 0.3 of chlorine, 0.0112 of fluorine and 0.0218 of iron; and dentin (in per

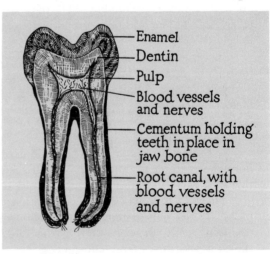

Figure 98. Molar tooth cut lengthwise. (U. S. Dept. Agriculture.)

Enamel
Dentin
Pulp
Blood vessels and nerves
Cementum holding teeth in place in jaw bone
Root canal, with blood vessels and nerves

cent) 0.19 of sodium, 0.07 of potassium, 0.03 of chlorine, 0.0204 of fluorine, and 0.0072 of iron.

Analyses of whole, sound teeth (human) give the following figures (in percentages and on a dry basis): Ca, 29.7; Mg, 0.6; P, 14.2; CO_2 (from carbonate), 2.9 (Lefevre and Hodge). The average of inorganic and organic matter in whole human teeth is 85 and 15 per cent, respectively.

As in the case of bone, the exact nature of the main mineral substance in teeth has not as yet been completely clarified. In general, what was stated for bone holds for teeth. With regard to tooth enamel, it may be noted that the x-ray diffraction patterns of this tissue and of hydroxyapatite are strikingly similar.

The view held at one time that enamel is a "lifeless, inert, mostly inorganic substance" has undergone modification. This has become possible because of the application of radioactive isotopes for the study of mineral metabolism.

A contribution to the metabolism of teeth was made by Hevesy who showed that when compounds of radioactive phosphorus were injected into animals, radioactive phosphorus was found in the whole teeth. The enamel contained about 10 per cent of the radioactive element present in dentin.

For the teeth to calcify properly the diet must i..clude enough calcium and phosphorus and some of the vitamins (A, C, D). Some of the hormones are also important.

Fluorine and Dental Caries. It has been maintained that fluorine is related to resistance to dental caries. This conclusion is based mainly on the fact that there is less dental decay in localities where the drinking water contains about one part (or a little more) per million of fluorine. Ordinarily the amount of fluorine in water is much less than one part per million. It has also been found that topical application of sodium or potassium fluoride solution to the teeth may reduce caries by as much as 40 per cent.

Another important fact is that treatment of enamel with fluoride solutions reduces the solubility of enamel in acid.

The fluorine content of the water is relatively high in areas of endemic mottled tooth enamel. Further, the teeth of rats develop fewer caries when fluorine is added to the diet, either during the time of development of the teeth or after the teeth are mature.

REFERENCES

MUSCLE TISSUE. W. F. H. M. *Mommaerts:* Ann. Rev. Biochem., 23:381, 1954; *Weber:* Ibid., 26:667, 1957; *Szent-Györgyi:* Chemistry of Muscular Contraction, 1951; Chemical Physiology of Contraction in Body and Heart Muscle, 1953; Science, 124:873, 1956 (energetics of myosin); *Katchalsky* and *Lifson;* Scientific American, March, 1954, p. 72 (muscle as a machine); *Huxley:*

Endeavour, *15*:177, 1956 (muscular contraction); *Kendrew:* Federation Proceedings, *18*:740, 1959 (myoglobin).

CONNECTIVE TISSUE. *Tunbridge:* Annals of Rheumatic Diseases, *16*:6, 1957; *Piez* and *Gross:* J. Biol. Chem., *235*:995, 1960 (collagen).

CREATINE. *Ratner* and *Rochovansky:* Arch. Biochem., *63*:277, 296, 1956; *Cantoni* and *Vignos:* J. Biol. Chem., *209*:647, 1954 (biosynthesis); *Walker:* J. Biol. Chem., *235*:2357, 1960 (biosynthesis).

NERVE TISSUE. *Nachmansohn:* Harvey Lectures, 1953–1954, p. 57 (metabolism and function of the nerve cell); *McIlwain:* Biochemistry of the Central Nervous System, 1955; *Waelsch:* Biochemistry of the Developing Nervous System, 1955; *Le Baron:* Ann. Rev. Biochem., *28*:579, 1959 (neurochemistry).

BRAIN. *Page:* Science, *125*:721, 1957 (chemistry); *Sprinson* and *Coulon:* J. Biol. Chem., *207*:585, 1954 (precursors of sphingosine); *Roberts* and *Frankel:* J. Biol. Chem., *187*:55, 1950 (γ-aminobutyric acid); *Udenfriend:* Recent Progress in Hormone Research, *13*:1, 1957; *Wilkins:* New England J. Medicine, July 19, 1956, p. 115 (serotonin, etc.); Chem. Eng. News, May 7, 1956, p. 2240 (reserpine); *Pennes:* Bull. N. Y. Acad. Med., *33*:81, 1957.

EPITHELIAL TISSUE. *Lorinz:* J. Society Cosmetic Chemists, *9*:197, 1958.

ELASTIN. *Lewis, Williams* and *Brink:* J. Biol. Chem., *22*:705, 1956 (elastase); *Labella:* Nature, *180*:1360, 1957 (elastin).

HYALURONIC ACID, ETC. *Meyer:* Harvey Lectures, 1955–1956, p. 88; Federation Proceedings, *17*:1075, 1958.

BONE. *Bourne:* Biochemistry and Physiology of Bone, 1956; *Stein:* Surgical Clinics of N. America, *33*:1745, 1953; *McLean:* Scientific American, Feb., 1955, p. 84; *Neuman:* Borden's Rev. Nutrition Research, *21*:37, 1960; *Seifter:* Bull. N. Y. Acad. Med., *3*:156, 1961.

TEETH. *Leicester:* Ann. Rev. Biochem., *22*:341, 1953; *Sognnaes:* Scientific American, June, 1953, p. 39 (enamel); Chem. Eng. News, *32*:1658, 1954 (dental caries); *Leicester:* J. Chem. Educ., Feb., 1957, p. 96 (dental caries); Nutr. Rev., *18*:139, 1960 (trace elements); Ibid., *17*:13, 1959 (fluoride concentration).

BIOCHEMISTRY
OF THE
KIDNEYS—URINE

CHAPTER TWENTY

THE KIDNEYS; FORMATION OF URINE

The kidney is the chief organ of the body for the elimination of water and a number of compounds in blood of relatively low molecular weight. The chief functions of this organ might be said to be the maintenance of electrolyte composition of the body and the regulation of its acid-base balance.

In a very general way, the kidney serves the function of maintaining the composition of the fluids of the body at a certain level. This function is shared with the respiratory system, the skin, and the gastrointestinal tract. To maintain a fluid of constant composition within the body, the kidney eliminates urine which, from time to time, varies very much as to composition, and which also varies as to rate of production. A constituent such as urea is found in far higher concentration in urine than in blood; and, under normal conditions, not more than a trace of glucose is found in the urine, although there are appreciable quantities in the blood.

The kidney represents a complex organ made up of innumerable small tubes, the uriniferous tubules. From each kidney a tube, the ureter, carries urine to the bladder (Fig. 99), and by means of another tube, the urethra, the urine is voided.

At the beginning of the uriniferous tubule is a capsule, known as "Bowman's capsule," which surrounds a tuft of capillaries, the glomerulus. What is known as a "malpighian corpuscle" is made up of such a glomerulus and a Bowman's capsule.

511

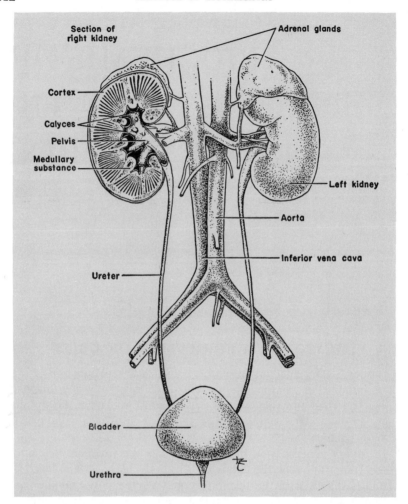

Figure 99. The human urinary system, seen from the ventral side. The right kidney is cut open to reveal the internal structures. (Villee: Biology, 3rd Edition.)

To each capsule is attached a long tubule including a convoluted tubule terminating in the loop of Henle, and an ascending loop, which ultimately connects with a main collecting tube opening into the renal pelvis (Fig. 100).

There have been many theories to explain the process by which urine is formed. It is generally agreed that at least two processes are involved: one includes a filtration process through Bowman's capsule; and the other, a process of concentration as the liquid passes along the tubules, until what is known as "urine" is formed. Richards emphasizes these facts as follows: the kidney, first of all, has to separate a filtrate from the blood so enormous in volume as to contain the waste products

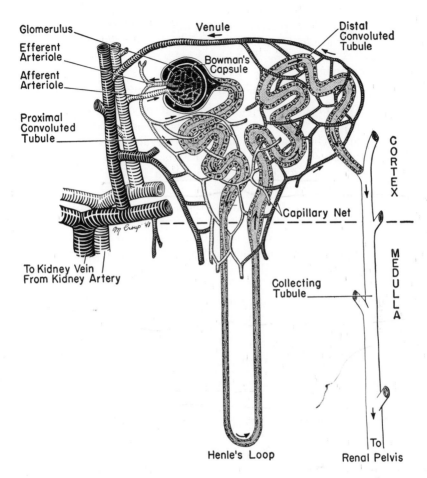

Figure 100. Diagram of a single kidney tubule and its blood vessels. (Villee: Biology, 3rd Edition.)

of metabolism and the unneeded salts and water. But were the activities of the kidney to stop here, death would result from dehydration and loss of Na+. This is prevented by a process of reabsorption along the different segments of the tubules. In this way the water, salts and other diffusible compounds are maintained at a constant level of concentration in the plasma.

GLOMERULAR FILTRATION

The first step in the formation of urine is filtration of the non-protein substances across the glomerulus. Richards, using microtechniques, showed this to represent an ultrafiltration of plasma, with a composition similar to plasma except for its proteins. This filtration process occurs when the blood pressure in the glomeruli is greater than the sum of the osmotic pressure of the plasma proteins and the pressure in Bowman's capsule. This is referred to as the "filtration pressure."

TUBULAR REABSORPTION

If the glomerular filtrate is of a composition similar to the non-protein portion of blood, it is obvious that much of the water and dissolved substances must be returned to the blood before urine as such can be formed. This reabsorption takes place along the renal tubules. The glomeruli (both kidneys) filter 170 liters of solution per day. Since the volume of urine excreted in a day is about 1.5 liters, 168.5 liters, or 99 per cent of the glomerular filtrate, is reabsorbed.

Some 80 to 87 per cent is reabsorbed along the upper (proximal) portion of the tubule; this fraction is referred to as "obligatory" reabsorption. Along this section of the tubule the urine remains isosmotic with blood plasma. Concentration of urine takes place along the lower (distal) portion of the tubule; this is known as "facultative" absorption. This fraction amounts to 13 to 20 per cent of the total filtrate. It is reabsorbed against the osmotic pressure of urine, and it requires energy. This energy is provided by the metabolic activity of the renal tubular cells.

ENERGY EXPENDITURE BY THE KIDNEY

Table 79 shows the energy expended.

TABLE 79. THE TOTAL WORK PERFORMED BY THE HUMAN KIDNEY IN THE PRODUCTION OF THE 24-HOUR URINE

Kind of Work Performed	Quantity of Work ($-\Delta F$)
	(gm. calories)
Concentration	−1126
Transport of water	+267
Formation of ammonia from urea	+155
	−704

(From Borsook and Winegarden: Proc. Nat. Acad. Sci., U. S., *17*:3, 13, 1931.)

The kidney must expend 704 calories in order to form 1 to 1.5 liters of urine. This corresponds to 70 gm. calories per gram of nitrogen, or 0.7 gm. calories per milliliter of urine. A further calculation showed that the energy consumed by the kidney in the production of this urine is equal to 6 to 11 calories per gram of nitrogen excreted. Calculating the ratio of work performed and energy used, we get an efficiency of 1 to 2 per cent—a very low figure, considering that we are dealing with a healthy kidney.

TUBULAR EXCRETION

In addition to a flow of substances from the plasma across the glomeruli and a flow of substances across the tubular cells back into the plasma, there is also a flow from the plasma directly across the tubular cells into the lumen of the tubule. Figure 101 shows that glucose, under normal conditions, is completely reabsorbed along the proximal length of the tubules, whereas creatinine is filtered both via the glomerulus and also via the proximal tubules to join the urine.

ACID-BASE REGULATION

Table 80 illustrates the substances of the plasma which constitute its ionic constituents. Except for carbonic acid, which is regulated by

TABLE **80.**   IONIC COMPOSITION OF BLOOD PLASMA*

Cations		Anions	
(milliequivalents per liter of plasma)			
Na^+	142	HCO_3^-	27
K^+	5	Cl^-	103
Ca^{++}	5	HPO_4^-	2
Mg^{++}	3	SO_4^-	1
	155	Org. acids	6
		Protein	16
			155

* Cations are often referred to as "fixed base," and anions as "fixed acid." (From Gamble: Extracellular Fluid, 1950.)

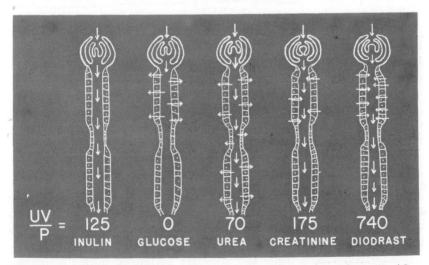

$$\frac{UV}{P} = \quad 125 \qquad 0 \qquad 70 \qquad 175 \qquad 740$$

INULIN   GLUCOSE   UREA   CREATININE   DIODRAST

Figure 101.   Results of clearance studies with five different test substances. (Gamble: Extracellular Fluid, 1950.)

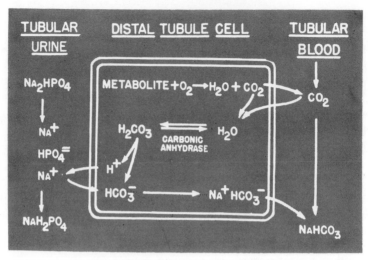

Figure 102. Nature of the cellular mechanism for acidification of the urine. (Pitts and Alexander: Federation Proceedings, 7:422, 1948.)

the respiration, and the plasma proteins, all the other constituents are regulated by the kidney.

The acidity of the urine can be expressed either in terms of pH, or concentration of H^+, or as titratable acidity, which expresses the total free acid present.

The pH of normal urine varies from 5.0 to 7.0, with a mean of 6.0. This pH is maintained largely by the relative amounts of NaH_2PO_4 and Na_2HPO_4 present. The change from a pH of 7.4 in the plasma to a pH of 6.0 in the urine is accomplished by a change in the proportion of these phosphates. In the plasma, $Na_2HPO_4:Na_2HPO_4 = 1:5$, whereas in the urine the ratio is 9:1. In this way a large quantity of Na^+ of the body is conserved at the time when pH changes take place during the passage of the urine through the distal tubules.

Among the theories suggested to explain this change in pH, there is one by Pitts, who suggests that the secretion of acid by the tubules is due to an ionic exchange: the H^+ in the plasma, derived from H_2CO_3, is exchanged for Na^+ across the cell wall (Fig. 102).

KIDNEY FUNCTION TESTS

Methods for the determination of renal function are important for two reasons: in the first place, they help to locate the site of impairment of renal function; secondly, they add to our information concerning the normal biochemical function of the cells of the kidney.

Analyses of both blood and urine are performed during a specified time and under controlled conditions. The substance to be determined in blood and urine may be one normally present, such as urea, or it may be one which is foreign to the body and is intravenously injected. The result is expressed in terms of amount of substance found in urine (over a unit of time) to the volume of plasma which it would occupy at the existing plasma concentration.

Figure 101 illustrates five such "test" substances used in these "clearance" studies. In the calculation—"urea clearance"—a comparison is made between the concentration of urea in the blood and the rate of its excretion in the urine.

$$C = \frac{UV}{P}$$

where C is the volume of plasma cleared per minute, U is the concentration of substance in urine, V is the volume of urine excreted per minute, and P is the concentration of substance in blood.

Inulin, a polysaccharide which yields fructose on hydrolysis and has a molecular weight of 5000, is completely filtered by the glomerulus. It is not reabsorbed or excreted by the tubules and is, therefore, an index of glomerular filtration. Diodrast, 3,5-diiodo-4-pyridone-N-acetic acid,

$$CH_2.COOH$$

is excreted by the tubules as well as by the glomerulus. Its clearance rate is high, as Figure 101 indicates.

RENIN

One of the commonest diseases suffered by man is arterial hypertension. Goldblatt discovered that persistent hypertension could be induced in the dog by constriction of both main renal arteries, or by the constriction of one renal artery and the excision of the opposite kidney. That some active substance was discharged by the kidney into the blood was made probable by several experiments. One of these consisted in transplanting a kidney to the neck, with no nervous connections with the rest of the body; a rise of blood pressure still occurred when the main artery to the kidney was constricted. This indicated that some active substance is released by the kidney into the systemic circulation.*

The substance responsible for this rise in blood pressure has been given the name *renin.* It is believed that renin (which acts like an

---

* "Although the kidney is not generally looked upon as an endocrine organ, there is no reason to deny the possibility of its performing such a function; for the elaboration of humoral substances is not limited to specifically endocrine organs" (Grollman, Harrison, and Williams, Jr.).

enzyme) decomposes a serum globulin (hypertensinogen) to produce hypertensin, a polypeptide. Hypertensin is present in the blood of individuals with malignant hypertension. Hypertensin—there are probably two modifications—has been shown to be a polypeptide. Hypertensin is also known as "angiotensin." Page emphasizes that "stress on the kidney stimulates the release of renin into the veins, where it acts on renin substrate (made in the liver) to release angiotensin I." A converting enzyme changes angiotensin I to angiotensin II. Arteries carry angiotensin II to the capillary beds where arterioles are constricted.

The "converting enzyme," a normal constituent of the blood, converts angiotensin from an inactive decapeptide to an active octapeptide.

COMPOSITION OF URINE

A diagram representing comparative concentrations of substances in blood plasma and urine is instructive (Fig. 103).

The kidney is the main organ of regulation of extracellular fluid, which, it may be remembered, consists of plasma and interstitial fluid, including lymph. A substance like urea is in far higher concentration in urine than in blood. Substances like protein and glucose are not found in normal urine to any appreciable extent. Ammonia (in the form of ammonium salt) is present in urine and probably absent in blood.

Using very rough figures, and on the basis of a 24-hour sample of urine, we may say that the average amount of urine voided during this period would be about 1500 ml. In this 1500 ml. of fluid would be found some 60 gm. of solids. Roughly one-half (or 30 gm.) is due to urea and one-quarter (or 15 gm.) is due to sodium chloride. The remaining 15 gm. includes the various organic and inorganic constituents (uric acid, creatinine, amino acids, ammonia, hormones, enzymes, vitamins, sulfates, phosphates, etc.).

Under pathological conditions substances appear in the urine which are normally absent, or, if anything, present in traces; these include proteins, sugar, acetone bodies, bile, hemoglobin, etc.

QUANTITY

As has already been stated, the quantity of urine voided in 24 hours may be some 1500 ml. Of course this figure varies considerably with different individuals. The fluctuations for a normal adult are probably from 800 to 2300 ml. Increases beyond the normal amount (polyuria) occur in a number of diseases—chronic nephritis, diabetes insipidus, etc. The reversed condition, the elimination of a decreased quantity of urine (oliguria), occurs in diarrhea, fevers, etc.

The renal excretion of water is in part under the control of the antidiuretic hormone of the pituitary.

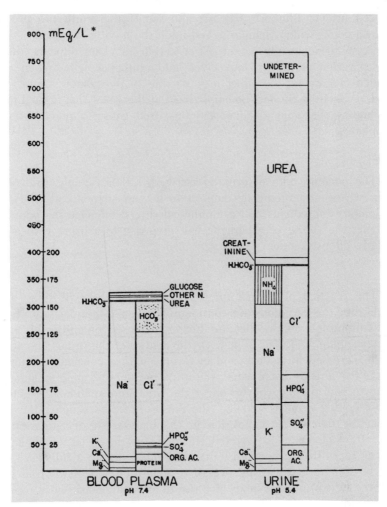

Figure 103. Comparison of composition of blood plasma and urine. (Gamble: Extracellular Fluid, 1950.)

* mEq/L = milliequivalents per liter. For sodium ion, for example, milliequivalents per liter is obtained by multiplying the mg. per 100 ml. by 10 and dividing by 23.

COLOR

The color of the urine, usually from yellow to reddish yellow, will vary with the amount of urine voided. The chief pigment is urochrome (yellow in color). Small quantities of urobilin and hematoporphyrin are also present. Where there are abnormal constituents, the color may change considerably. The presence of hemoglobin will give rise to a brown to red color. Bile in the urine may produce a yellow foam when the sample is shaken, and the color of the urine may become a pronounced brown. Rhubarb, cascara, and some other cathartics produce a brown color, which changes to red upon the addition of alkali.

Fresh urine is transparent. After a time, a cloud appears, due to the separation of mucus, leukocytes, and epithelial cells. When there is much cloudiness, the effect may be due to phosphates, urates, pus, blood, or bacteria. It must be emphasized at this point that normal urine, on standing, becomes alkaline, and this itself causes a precipitation of phosphates.

ODOR

The peculiar odor of urine is ascribed, rather vaguely, to "volatile acids." Urine undergoing decomposition has an ammoniacal odor. Certain dietary ingredients and a number of drugs influence the odor. For example, the eating of asparagus will give rise to a urine with a particularly offensive odor.

PH

The reaction of normal urine is usually on the acid side (about pH 6), but the variations are considerable, even in normal samples. An excess of protein in the diet, producing increased quantities of sulfate and phosphate, will tend to increase the acidity of the urine. The acidity is also increased in acidosis and in fevers (with a concentrated urine).

As has already been stated, the urine becomes alkaline on standing, owing to the gradual conversion of the urea into ammonia. When the freshly voided urine is alkaline, the reason must be sought elsewhere. It may be due to decomposition in the bladder—a decomposition of urea after the urine is secreted. It may, on the other hand, signify nothing more than a temporary "alkaline tide," due to a full meal, or it may be the result of eating excessive quantities of fruit. In the latter case, the salts of organic acids give rise to an alkaline ash when oxidized in the body.

The ingestion of from 3 to 5 gm. of sodium bicarbonate is enough, in a normal individual, to produce an alkaline urine.

SPECIFIC GRAVITY

The usual range is from 1.010 to 1.030. It varies, in general, inversely with the quantity of urine voided.

The specific gravity is low in chronic nephritis and in diabetes insipidus, and it is high in fevers and in diabetes mellitus.

SOME GENERAL CONSIDERATIONS

The organic substances present undergo decomposition rapidly when the urine is left standing. For example, urea is changed to ammonia. It is important, therefore, in examining urine with a view to a quantitative analysis of its constituents, to work with fresh urine; or, since that is usually difficult, to use urine to which a preservative has been added. Such preservatives include boric acid, Formalin, thymol, toluene, chloroform, etc. All of them are objectionable. The objection is usually due to some interference with a chemical test. Thymol and toluene are probably the most widely used.

NORMAL CONSTITUENTS

The variations within normal limits are given in Table 81.

TABLE 81. COMPOSITION OF NORMAL URINE

Color: slightly yellow to amber	Uric Acid: 0.3 to 0.8 gm./24 hrs.
Quantity: 1000 to 1500 ml./24 hrs.	Hippuric Acid: 0.7 gm./24 hrs.
Specific Gravity: 1.008 to 1.030$^{15°}$	Chlorides (NaCl): 10 to 15 gm./24 hrs.
pH: 5.5 to 7.5	Phosphorus (P): 1.2 gm./24 hrs.
Sugar: 0.015%	Sulfur (S) {Total: 1.2 gm./24 hrs. / Inorganic: 1.0 gm./24 hrs. / Ethereal: 0.1 gm./23 hrs.
Nitrogen {Total: 7 to 20 gm./24 hrs. / Amino acid: 0.15 to 0.30 gm./24 hrs.	Sodium (Na): 2.5 to 4.0 gm./24 hrs.
Urea: 12 to 35 gm./24 hrs.	Calcium (Ca): 0.1 to 0.3 gm./24 hrs.
Ammonia: 0.6 to 1.2 gm./24 hrs.	Potassium (K): 1.5 to 2.0 gm./24 hrs.
Creatinine: 0.8 to 2.0 gm./24 hrs.	Magnesium (Mg): 0.1 to 0.2 gm./24 hrs.
Creatinine Coefficient: 22 to 30 mg. creatinine per kg. per day.	

(From Lang: Handbook of Chemistry, 1949.)

A brief description of a number of these constituents will now be given.

Urea. This substance represents the principal nitrogenous end product. This is not true of all animals, as Baldwin has once again emphasized (Table 82).

TABLE 82. NITROGEN END PRODUCT OF VARIOUS ANIMALS

Animal	*Nitrogen end-product*
Sharks, dog-fishes	Urea
Bony fishes (teleostei)	Ammonia
Frogs, newts	Urea
Turtles	Urea
Snakes, lizards	Uric acid
Birds	Uric acid
Mammals	Urea

(From Baldwin: Comparative Biochemistry, Cambridge Univ. Press, London.)

However, in man, for example, the output of urea varies directly with the protein intake, and usually constitutes from 80 to 90 per cent of the total nitrogen excretion. On a low protein diet, this ratio (80 to 90 per cent) is lowered (Table 83).

TABLE 83.   SHOWING THE AVERAGE AMOUNT OF DIFFERENT FORMS OF NITROGEN EXCRETED WHEN LOW, NORMAL AND HIGH PROTEIN DIETS WERE INGESTED

	Normal diet			High protein diet			Low protein diet		
Volume of urine Specific gravity	1364 ml. 1.022			1472 ml. 1.023			1408 ml. 1.019		
Substance	Amount	Nitrogen content	Per cent of total N	Amount	Nitrogen content	Per cent of total N	Amount	Nitrogen content	Per cent of total N
	gm.	gm.		gm.	gm.		gm.	gm.	
Total nitrogen...............	....	11.16	....	....	15.28	....	....	7.97	....
Urea......................	20.38	9.51	85.21	28.29	13.20	86.36	13.20	6.16	77.29
Ammonia..................	0.66	0.54	4.83	0.83	0.68	4.45	0.52	0.43	5.39
Uric acid.................	0.57	0.19	1.70	0.63	0.21	1.37	0.54	0.18	2.26
Creatinine................	1.70	0.63	5.64	1.78	0.66	4.32	1.67	0.62	7.78
Undetermined nitrogen } by difference }	....	0.29	2.62	....	0.53	3.50	....	0.58	7.28

(From Beard.)

The formation of urea in the body has already been discussed (p. 329).

Urea is soluble in water and alcohol and insoluble in ether and chloroform. It forms biuret when heated.

It is oxidized by hypobromite in alkaline solution:

$$CO(NH_2)_2 + 3\,NaOBr \longrightarrow 3\,NaBr + N_2 + CO_2 + 2\,H_2O$$

which forms the basis for a rough quantitative estimation of urea by measuring the volume of nitrogen eliminated. A much more accurate method for estimating this substance is based on the action of the enzyme _urease_ (found in soy and jack beans), which quantitatively converts urea into ammonia.

Characteristic crystals of urea nitrate, $CO(NH_2)_2.HNO_3$, and urea oxalate, $CO(NH_2)_2.H_2C_2O_4$, are easily obtained by mixing urea with the respective acids; these salts are valuable for identification.

The amount of urea excreted is increased in fevers, diabetes (with little acidosis), etc. In diseases of the liver (acute yellow atrophy, cirrhosis, etc.), with a decreased formation of urea, there is less excreted. This is also true in cases of acidosis, where some of the nitrogen which would be normally converted into urea is eliminated as a salt of ammonia.

Aside from a decreased formation of urea with a subsequent decreased output, a retention of urea (as in nephritis) also leads to a smaller output. Here, for diagnostic purposes, the estimation of urea in the blood is of great importance.

Creatinine. This substance—and its relationship to creatine—has already been discussed (p. 487). Creatinine is a normal constituent of urine; it is, according to Folin, relatively independent of the amount of protein ingested. Its amount, however, is decreased in many pathological conditions.

Creatinine is soluble in water and alcohol and forms a characteristic double salt with zinc chloride, $(C_4H_7N_3O)_2.ZnCl_2$, which is used for the purpose of isolating the base. With picric acid in an alkaline solution it forms a red color which is the basis for a colorimetric determination (Jaffe, Folin). Greenwald is of the opinion that the reaction is due to the formation of a red tautomer of creatinine picrate. In addition to this test, originally due to Jaffe, there is the test in which the urine (containing creatinine) is mixed with alkali and sodium nitroprusside, yielding a red color which turns yellow (Weyl); and if acetic acid is now added to the yellow solution and heated, a green, and finally a blue color (Prussian blue) is obtained (Salkowski).*

Uric Acid. This substance represents one of the final stages in the oxidation of the purines in the body and is the chief nitrogenous end-product in birds, snakes, and lizards (Table 82). It is derived from the nucleoproteins of the food and from the breakdown of nucleoprotein within the cells of the body.

Uric acid forms salts with sodium and potassium to give the corresponding urates. It is these urates, very largely, which are found in the urine, the highly insoluble free acid being obtained on strong acidification. The acid itself, however, is probably also present to some degree. The urates—the acid salts particularly—are precipitated from solution when urine is concentrated, giving the sediment of "amorphous urates."

In leukemia, with destruction of leukocytes, the uric acid output is very much increased. This is also true in diseases associated with the liver, an organ rich in nucleoprotein. Gout has long been popularly associated with a disturbed metabolism of uric acid; but the connection is not altogether clear. Before an attack, the output is somewhat decreased, and for several days after the attack the output is definitely increased.

A characteristic test for uric acid is the *murexide reaction*. This is obtained by evaporating the uric acid with nitric acid and treating the residue with ammonia; a reddish violet product (murexide, or ammonium purpurate) is obtained. The nitric acid oxidizes uric acid to dialuric acid and alloxan, which then condense:

---

* Creatine, to the extent of about 6 per cent of the total creatinine output, is also present.

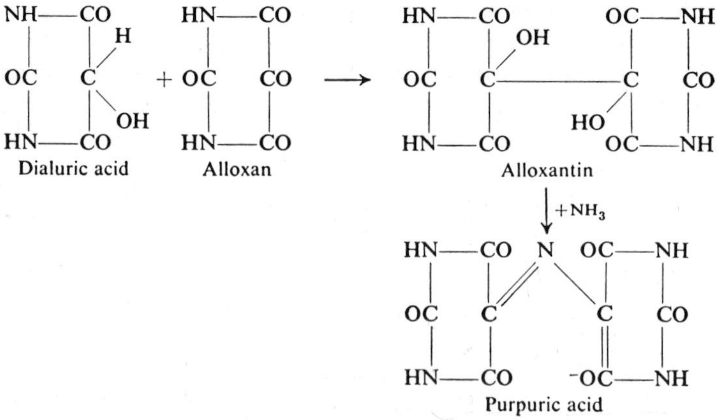

NH——CO   HN——CO   HN——CO   OC——NH

| | H | | | OH | |

OC   C   + OC   CO ⟶ OC   C————————C   CO

| \OH | | | | HO | |

HN——CO   HN——CO   HN——CO   OC——NH

Dialuric acid   Alloxan   Alloxantin

$\downarrow +NH_3$

HN——CO N OC——NH

| | \\// | |

OC   C   C   CO

| | || |

HN——CO   ⁻OC——NH

Purpuric acid

Uric acid also reduces silver solutions in an alkaline medium (Schiff test) and gives a blue color with phosphotungstic acid (Folin), which serves as the basis for one quantitative procedure.

Amino Acids. The small quantity normally in urine (about 1 gm. daily) is much increased in impairment of hepatic function (as in yellow atrophy of the liver), eclampsia, and in certain types of poisoning (such as that due to chloroform, phosphorus, arsenic, or carbon tetrachloride).

The use of protein hydrolysates in nutritional disturbances has made the study of amino acid excretion important. Methods based on microbiological technique or paper chromatography are used extensively.

Normal urine is usually considered protein-free. However, very small quantities are present. On an average, some 15 mg. of albumin and 26 mg. of globulin (per 24 hours) are found (Rigas and Heller).

Chlorides. Next to urea, chlorides are the most abundant substances. The chlorides, mainly as sodium chloride, are derived chiefly from the food; and the output, therefore, fluctuates depending upon the intake. During starvation the output may be almost abolished, yet the chlorides in the blood will maintain for a time their normal concentration.

There is a decrease in the elimination of chlorides in several forms of nephritis and in fevers.

Sulfates. Most of the sulfur has its origin in protein. Much of it is derived from the protein in the food, and some of it has its source in cellular activity.

The sulfur appears in the urine in three forms: inorganic sulfate, ethereal sulfate, and neutral sulfur.

Inorganic Sulfates. Roughly speaking, the output of sulfate is proportional to the output of total nitrogen; the ratio $N:SO_3$ is about $5:1$. Since the amount of nitrogen eliminated (as urea, etc.) is a measure of the amount of protein metabolized, estimations of inorganic sulfate as well as of nitrogen are valuable in studies dealing with protein metabolism.

Ethereal Sulfates. Of the total preformed sulfates present in urine, about nine-tenths is in the inorganic form (combined with Na, K, Ca, and Mg). About one-tenth, however, is in the form of an ester: a combination of sulfuric acid with phenols:

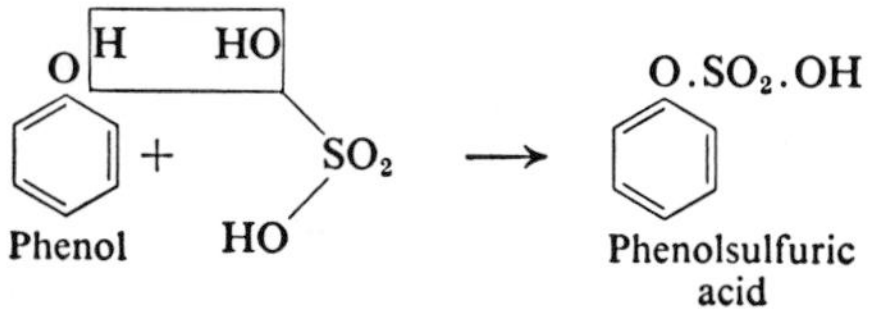

Phenol   +   Phenolsulfuric acid

Other substances combined with the acid are p-cresol, indole (as indoxyl) and skatole (as skatoxyl). All these are included under the name "ethereal sulfates."

The mechanism of formation of ethereal sulfates has been clarified by the studies of Lipmann, who has demonstrated the enzymatic formation of an "active sulfate" compound from ATP. The formation of phenolsulfuric acid ester is shown below:

$$\text{ATP} + {}^-\text{O}-\overset{\text{O}}{\underset{\text{O}}{\overset{\|}{\underset{\|}{\text{S}}}}}-\text{OH} \longrightarrow \text{Pyrophosphate} + \text{Adenine-ribose}-\text{O}-\overset{\text{O}}{\underset{\text{OH}}{\overset{\|}{\text{P}}}}-\text{O}-\overset{\text{O}}{\underset{\text{O}}{\overset{\|}{\underset{\|}{\text{S}}}}}-\text{OH}$$

Adenosine-5′-phosphosulfate

Adenosine-5′-phosphosulfate $\xrightarrow{\text{ATP}}$

$$\text{Adenine}-\overset{\text{OH}}{\underset{}{\text{CH}}}-\overset{\text{OPO}_3\text{H}_2}{\underset{}{\text{CH}}}-\text{CH}-\text{CH}-\text{CH}_2-\text{O}-\overset{\text{O}}{\underset{\text{OH}}{\overset{\|}{\text{P}}}}-\text{O}-\overset{\text{O}}{\underset{\text{O}}{\overset{\|}{\underset{\|}{\text{S}}}}}-\text{OH}$$

Adenosine-3′-phosphate-5′-phosphosulfate

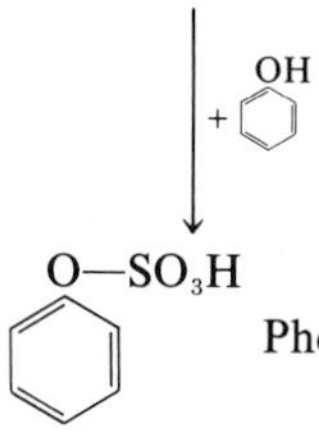

O—SO$_3$H   Phenolsulfuric acid

The ethereal sulfates represent, to some extent, the putrefactive products in the intestine which are detoxified in the liver and then eliminated. To a large extent these substances are the result of normal protein metabolism in the body. The exception, according to Folin, is indican, which really represents putrefactive activity. Indican is the potassium salt of indoxyl sulfuric acid (Chap. 22).

Indicanuria (a substantial increase in the output of indican) is common in diseases of the small intestine (intestinal obstruction, for example), and in intestinal indigestion ("biliousness"). Simple constipation of the large intestine is not, as a rule, followed by indicanuria. Increases in indican are also noted in diseases of the stomach in which there is a subnormal amount of hydrochloric acid (gastritis, cancer).

The tests used in detecting indican in the urine depend upon its decomposition and oxidation to indigo-blue (Jaffe, Obermayer):

| Indoxyl | Indigo-blue |

In the Obermayer method, the urine is mixed with the reagent (ferric chloride and concentrated hydrochloric acid), chloroform is added, and the mixture is shaken. The chloroform turns blue, the intensity depending upon the amount of indican present.

Acidification of urine with hydrochloric acid and addition of barium chloride precipitates inorganic sulfates. This precipitate is filtered off, and the filtrate is heated. If an excess of barium chloride has been added, a second precipitate will be formed. The hot acid hydrolyzes the ethereal sulfates, and the sulfate ion combines with the barium ion. This method is used not only qualitatively for the detection of the two types of sulfur, but also as the basis for a quantitative determination.

Neutral Sulfur. This represents sulfur in an incomplete state of oxidation, possibly in the form of cystine, taurine, sulfides, thiocyanates, etc. Its amount seems to be independent of the amount of protein ingested, and in this sense it resembles creatinine.

This type of sulfur can be tested for by adding zinc and hydrochloric acid to a sample of urine. The hydrogen combines with the sulfur, and the hydrogen sulfide which is liberated is identified with a strip of paper soaked in a solution of lead acetate. Black lead sulfide is formed.

The quantitative determination of neutral sulfur is carried out by evaporating a sample of urine to dryness, heating the residue with an oxidizing mixture (a mixture of copper nitrate and potassium chlorate, or just sodium peroxide alone), thereby converting all the sulfur to sulfate. By precipitating with barium chloride, the total sulfate can be determined. If we now subtract the inorganic and ethereal sulfates from the total sulfate, the difference represents the neutral sulfur.

Phosphates. These substances are very largely derived from the foods we eat, though a small quantity has its origin in cellular metabolism. There are two types of phosphates, the alkaline and the earthy phosphates. The alkaline phosphates, which make up some two thirds of the whole, are salts of sodium and potassium, and the earthy phosphates are combinations of calcium and magnesium. In alkaline urines the "amorphous" phosphate precipitates are due to the alkaline earth variety. The ammonia formed when urine is exposed for a time combines with the magnesium and the phosphate to form ammonium magnesium phosphate, or "triple phosphate," which is an insoluble and characteristically crystalline product.

From the clinical point of view variations in the phosphate content of urine are not very important; here studies in blood chemistry yield results of greater significance. But it should be mentioned that in bone diseases (rickets, osteomalacia) there is an increased excretion of phosphorus. Sometimes a decreased output has been noted in infectious diseases and in diseases of the kidneys.

The two types of phosphates can be detected by first precipitating the earthy phosphates by the addition of ammonium hydroxide, filtering, adding magnesia mixture (magnesium sulfate + ammonium chloride + ammonium hydroxide) to the filtrate, and warming; the white precipitate so obtained represents the alkaline phosphates.

Several methods are available for the determination of phosphate. One method depends upon the addition of molybdate solution (sodium molybdate in sulfuric acid) to form phosphomolybdate, which is then reduced to a blue compound by means of stannous chloride; the intensity of the blue color can be estimated colorimetrically.

Ammonia. Ammonia is excreted as ammonium salts in amounts which tend to adjust the acid-base balance of the body. Unless ammonia (as ammonium ion) were available, acids might use too much of the basic ions of the blood and so endanger blood neutrality. This adjustment comes admirably into play when acids or foods yielding acids in the body are fed; the amount of ammonia excreted is increased. On the other hand, when alkali or foods yielding bases in the body are ingested, the excretion of ammonia is decreased.

The origin of this ammonia was explained in this way: normally amino acids are deaminated and most of the ammonia which results is converted into urea, a small portion escaping as ammonia. The danger of acidosis diverts some of the ammonia, which normally would be used to form urea, into combination with acid radicals, resulting in increased ammonia and decreased urea output.

The discovery that the kidneys as well as the liver could deaminate amino acids suggested that the source of urinary ammonia could be traced to amino acids in general.

The work of Van Slyke and his associates suggests further and newer possibilities. Using explanted kidneys, they determined the amounts of materials removed from the blood per unit of time. All of the urea in the blood found its way into the urine; there was apparently no conversion into ammonia. The small amount of α-amino acids removed from the blood failed to account for the amount of ammonia in the urine.

However, one amino acid in the form of its amide, glutamine, is apparently one source of urinary ammonia. The amount of glutamine in the blood is enough to account for much of the ammonia in the urine (conversion of glutamine to glutamic acid plus ammonia); the remainder is derived from the amino acids of plasma.

The enzyme glutaminase, present in the kidney, catalyzes the conversion of glutamine to glutamic acid and ammonia. Under suitable conditions, this process is also reversible. The hydrolytic process is prevalent in the kidney, whereas the synthetic process is dominant in other tissues.

When glutamine or various amino acids were administered to a dog suffering from experimentally induced acidosis (with HCl), the amount of ammonia excreted was increased. On the other hand, in a dog suffering from alkalosis—induced with sodium bicarbonate—the amount of glutamine removed from renal blood decreased.

The deamination of amino acids can also occur in the kidney because three deaminating enzymes are present here: glycine oxidase and D- and L-amino acid oxidases.

One method of estimating the ammonia in the urine is to liberate it from its ammonium salt (by the addition of alkali) and to aerate the ammonia so liberated into an excess of standard acid. The acid left unneutralized is titrated with standard alkali.

Allantoin. This is a partial oxidation product of uric acid. It is present in very small quantities in human urine, but in other mammals (except the anthropoid ape) it is the chief end-product of the metabolism of purines. It will be remembered that in the human being the chief end-product of purine metabolism is uric acid.

The efficacy of the rather ancient treatment of healing wounds with maggots is now attributed to the formation of allantoin.

Oxalic Acid (COOH)$_2$. This acid is found in the form of insoluble calcium oxalate and is kept in solution by the presence of the acid phosphate. The source of the acid is believed to reside in the food we eat. Cabbage, grapes, lettuce, tomatoes, etc., contain oxalates.

Citric Acid. Though easily oxidized by the body, citric acid is nevertheless found in the urine. The excretion increases in cases of alkalosis (Östberg).

Purine Bases. Several purine bases, representing substances which have not been oxidized to uric acid, are found. Some of them are derived from the caffeine and theobromine found in coffee and tea.

ABNORMAL CONSTITUENTS

In pathological conditions, a number of substances are found in the urine which, normally, are hardly found at all. Among such substances are glucose, protein, acetone bodies, etc. Brief descriptions of some of these will now be given.

Proteins. What is known as the "albumin" of the urine is really a mixture of serum albumin and serum globulin. "Albuminuria" is commonly attributed to damaged kidneys (nephrosis), such as an inflamed organ (nephritis). As much as 20 gm. of protein may be eliminated in 24 hours.

Addis and Longcope speak of hemorrhagic, degenerative, and vascular nephritis as several forms of what is commonly called "Bright's disease."

The first, hemorrhagic (glomerular) nephritis, is the most common. It usually results from an infection due to a hemolytic streptococcus, such as in scarlet fever.

The degenerative form, a complication of the hemorrhagic variety, has an obscure origin.

The vascular form (nephrosclerosis) is related to the problem of arterial hypertension. Patients suffering from arterial hypertension sometimes succumb to uremia (the toxic condition produced by urinary constituents in the blood).

The albumin may be detected by heating the urine, then adding a little dilute acetic acid: a white cloud (or precipitate) is formed. The several methods of estimating the protein depend upon a preliminary precipitation of the protein with trichloracetic acid or some other "alkaloidal" reagent. In one such method (Van Slyke), the protein is precipitated with trichloracetic acid, dissolved in sodium hydroxide, and copper sulfate added. The intensity of the color formed ("biuret") is estimated colorimetrically.

Bence Jones proteinuria, often associated with multiple myeloma (tumorlike hyperplasia of the bone marrow), is due to a peculiar protein in urine which precipitates at a low temperature (50 to 60° C.) and is dissolved—to a greater or lesser extent—when heated above 80° C., the precipitate forming once again upon cooling.

An analysis of the hydrolytic products of the protein—by paper chromatography—reveals the presence of the common amino acids except for methionine. Since all the main fractions of plasma protein— from which, presumably, the Bence Jones variety is derived—contain some methionine, the abnormal character of the Bence Jones variety becomes more pronounced. Dent suggests that multiple myelomatosis may be due to an infection by a virus "which stimulates the plasma cells to reproduce rapidly, as in the case of the white cells in fowl leukemia." Possibly the Bence Jones protein is the protein which, when attached to a nucleic acid, is the virus itself.

It may be significant too, in this connection, to recall that virus proteins are usually free of methionine.

Glucose. Appreciable quantities of this sugar in the urine indicate glycosuria. What is known as "renal glycosuria" is due to a lowered renal threshold, which means that although sugar appears in the urine, there is no increase of sugar in the blood. An increase of sugar in the blood (hyperglycemia), with a corresponding elimination of sugar in the urine, is found in diabetes. In most instances glycosuria is indicative of diabetes. In this condition, the sugar will vary from 3 to 5 per cent, although sometimes it is even higher.

Benedict's test for glucose has already been discussed (Chap. 2). This is also the basis for a quantitative estimation.

Acetone Bodies. These have been discussed in connection with fat metabolism. While these substances are present in normal urine in traces, in pathological conditions they may increase from 0.02 to 6 gm., of which β-hydroxybutyric acid often forms a large percentage. This last substance, together with acetoacetic acid, is eliminated as a salt thus depleting the alkali reserve of the body and giving rise to an acidosis. To meet the crisis more ammonia is formed in the kidney.

The qualitative tests for acetone bodies are, as a rule, tests for acetone, and as acetoacetic acid very easily decomposes into acetone, the tests also include this acid. One such test is based on the transformation of acetone into iodoform; the urine is heated with sodium hydroxide and iodine and a precipitate of iodoform is formed.

If the urine is fresh, the presence of acetoacetic acid may be shown by obtaining a reddish-colored solution with ferric chloride. The test for β-hydroxybutyric acid is seldom carried out, since it is somewhat involved, necessitating, first, the removal of the other two acetone bodies.

One method of determining these substances quantitatively is to convert the two acids to acetone and precipitate the latter as a basic mercuric sulfate (Van Slyke). Given a mixture containing acetone, acetoacetic acid, and β-hydroxybutyric acid, the mere heating of such a mixture will convert acetoacetic acid into acetone; and if, in addition to the heating, an oxidizing agent is present (such as dichromate), β-hydroxybutyric acid is also converted to acetone. This procedure, then, gives "total acetone bodies." If we wish to determine acetone and acetoacetic acid alone, the dichromate is omitted. On the other hand, by making use of the relative volatility of acetone and acetoacetic acid —they may be removed by heating the acidified urine—β-hydroxybutyric acid itself may be determined.

Bile. An obstruction in the bile duct, preventing the normal outflow of bile and forcing it back into the general circulation, gives rise to jaundice, or icterus. The yellowness of the skin is due to the bile pigments, which also appear in the urine. The pigments may be detected by the play of colors obtained on the addition of concentrated nitric acid (Gmelin), the various colored products representing stages of oxidation of bilirubin.

Another test is based upon the green color obtained when methylene blue is added to urine containing bile. The bilirubin (of the bile) and the methylene blue react to form a green compound.

The pigment related chemically to bilirubin and normally found in urine is urobilin.

Blood. Blood in the urine (hematuria) may result from a lesion in the kidney or the urinary tract. This is more common than "hemoglobinuria," in which hemoglobin without the red corpuscles is recognized. Where the destruction of red blood cells is very great (as in bad burns), the liver cannot change all of the hemoglobin into bile pigments, and some of the blood pigment appears in the urine. The tests for hemoglobin have already been given (Chap. 8).

Porphyrins. These iron-free pyrrole substances, under normal conditions, build hemoglobin and various oxidizing enzymes (cytochromes, for example). In the plant world, together with magnesium, they form the building blocks for chlorophyll. There are several varieties of these porphyrins. Under normal conditions, the daily output of one of them —called coproporphyrin—is from 14 to 99 micrograms in the urine and from 100 to 200 micrograms in the feces.

PORPHYRIA. This metabolic disturbance, involving the excretion of abnormal amounts of porphyrins, may occur in cirrhosis, obstructive jaundice, etc.

Hans Fischer, who has done much of the chemical work on these substances, was able to isolate two of these porphyrins, known as copro- and uroporphyrin, from cases of congenital porphyria, and he showed that these two differed in chemical structure from those found in the urine and feces of normal subjects.

WATER

Of all compounds in the body, water is the most abundant. It constitutes (roughly) 70 per cent of the total weight of the body. A loss of 10 per cent of the water content (in man) results in illness, and a loss of 20 per cent may cause death. We find water in cellular and vascular spaces. Small portions are also deposited in conjunction with protein and carbohydrate. Fat in storage, however, is accompanied by little water.

Water is present in every tissue, but the amounts vary considerably.

The following data, collected by Rowntree, give some figures (in percentages): saliva, 99.5; cerebrospinal fluid, 99; vitreous humor, 98.5; embryonic brain, 91; milk, 88; brain (gray matter), 86; kidney, 83; thyroid, 82; thymus, 81; adrenals, 80; blood, 79; pancreas, 78; muscle, 75; spleen, 76; liver, 70; skin, 72; brain (white matter), 68 to 70; tendon, 68; cartilage, 67; elastic tissue, 50; bones, 50; fat, 20; dentin, 10.

FUNCTION

A very large percentage of the water is of the utmost importance physiologically—as solvent, as a carrier in transporting foods to tissues and wastes from tissues, and as a regulator of body temperature.

Water helps to maintain the electrolyte balance of the body. A state of health is possible only so long as the osmotic pressure exerted by solutes remains in equilibrium.

Within the body we have intracellular and extracellular compartments. The latter may be further divided into intravascular and interstitial compartments. The fluid representing the intravascular part circulates through blood vessels and lymphatics; the interstitial fluid surrounds the cells representing the tissues of the body.

Of the total content of body water, the extracellular fluid represents 20 per cent of the body weight. Of this amount, 25 per cent represents plasma, and the rest is interstitial fluid.

Heat is gained by the oxidation of foodstuffs in the body. Heat is lost through the following channels (in percentages); urine and feces, 1.8; warming of expired air, 3.5; vaporization from lungs, 7.2; evaporation from skin, 14.2; radiation and conduction from skin, 73.0.

AMOUNT NEEDED

The needs of the body for water are met in two ways: by direct intake, and by the oxidation of the foodstuffs in the body. By "direct intake" we mean water as such and water present in foods. Roughly speaking, on a diet equivalent to 3000 Calories, probably 2000 ml. of water is derived from the water in foods and from the products of the oxidation of foodstuffs in the body. Since the requirement may be some 3000 ml. per day, another liter of water must be supplied.

The amount of water liberated as a result of the oxidation of foodstuffs is approximately 10 to 14 gm. per 100 Calories. For example, 100 gm. of fat, when oxidized, produces 107 ml. of water. The 100 gm. of fat is equivalent to 930 Calories, which means that fat equivalent to 100 Calories will produce 11.5 ml. of water. Similarly, carbohydrate and protein equivalent to 100 Calories each will produce 13.5 and 10.1 ml. of water, respectively.

REGULATION

Since the amount of water in the body tends to vary but little, the regulation of the water balance in the body is a very important matter. Not only is water taken into the system in the manner already referred to, but it also leaves the body through several channels—urine, sweat, expired air, feces, and, in much smaller quantities, tears.

Reference has already been made to the reabsorption of water and dissolved compounds. This phase of water reabsorption is regulated by a hormone of the posterior lobe of the pituitary, the antidiuretic hormone (p. 549). This hormone (vasopressin) is believed to act directly on the distal tubular cells, increasing the rate of water reabsorption. When the hypophyseal stalk is cut or the neurohypophysis removed, the hormone is no longer secreted and the animal develops polyuria, an excessive excretion of urine (diabetes insipidus). A similar condition is observed in man when the posterior pituitary fails to secrete vasopressin.

Diuresis, the excretion of excessive amounts of water, occurs after the ingestion of large quantities of water or of concentrated salt solutions. A transitory, though marked, diuresis is caused by drugs such as caffeine, mercurial compounds, and phloridzin. The last substance also produces a glycosuria and probably acts largely on the proximal tubular cells.

The intake and output of water is summarized in the following:

	Intake		Output	
Drink	1200 ml.	Urine		1400 ml.
Water in food	1000 ml.	Stool		200 ml.
Water of oxidation	300 ml.	Insensible water *		900 ml.
Totals	2500 ml.			2500 ml.

* Vaporized through skin and lungs.

The water loss through the lungs is quite constant, but the loss through the sweat glands is associated with their function as regulators of body heat.

DEHYDRATION

This term is applied to the loss of fluid from the body. When water is lost, electrolytes (Na^+, K^+, etc.) are also lost. If sufficient water is consumed, some electrolyte must be eliminated in order to maintain the ionic concentrations of the body fluids. From this it also follows that the removal or loss of electrolyte requires the removal of some water.

The removal of sweat and the loss of gastrointestinal secretions removes not only water but electrolyte. "Dehydration," writes Gamble, "is an incomplete term since it does not indicate the accompanying loss of electrolyte." The treatment of "dehydration," then, means not only replacing the water lost but also the electrolyte lost.

As showing fine internal adjustments, some 10 per cent of the body's weight may be lost owing to depriving the individual of water without any appreciable reduction in blood volume.

REFERENCES

For a general discussion see *Smith:* The Kidney, Scientific American, Jan., 1953, p. 40.

For kidney function tests see New and Nonofficial Drugs, 1960, p. 449.

For practical handbooks dealing with the analysis of urine, see *Todd, Sanford,* and *Wells:* Clinical Diagnosis by Laboratory Methods, 1953, Chap. 3; *Hawk, Oser,* and *Summerson:* Practical Physiological Chemistry, 1947, Chaps. 28–32.

Theories dealing with the secretion of urine are reviewed by *Richards:* Harvey Lectures, Ser. 30, 1934–1935, p. 93; Bull. N. Y. Acad. Med., Jan., 1938; Proc. R. S. (London), Series B, 126:398, 1938; *Smith:* Scientific American, Jan., 1953, p. 40.

For the story of angiotensin see *Page, Bumpus* and *Schwarz:* Scientific American, March, 1959, p. 54.

EXCRETION OF WATER. *Smith:* Bull. N. Y. Acad. Med., April, 1947, p. 127; *Gamble:* Extracellular Fluid (Harvard Medical School, 1950); *Robinson:* Biological Reviews, 28:158, 1953 (water transport in living systems); *Mazur:* Biological Review (City College), *14:* No. 1, 1952; *Wolf:* Scientific American, Nov., 1958, p. 125 (body water).

ACIDITY OF URINE. *Pitts:* Federation Proceedings, 7:418, 1948 (review); *Menaker:* Am. J. Physiol., *154:*174, 1948.

RENIN. *Haas, Lamfrom* and *Goldblatt:* Arch. Biochem., 42:368, 1953; 48:256, 1954.

For the possible origin of Bence Jones protein see *Putnam* and *Hardy:* J. Biol. Chem., *212:*361, 371, 1955.

HORMONES

Most of the glands of the body have ducts. The secretions which these glands manufacture are poured out through such ducts. Typical examples are the salivary and gastric glands. Another group of glands (the endocrine organs, Fig. 104) discharge their secretions directly into the blood (ductless glands); these secretions usually contain hormones. *Hormones* are chemical substances which are carried by the blood to various organs of the body to influence the activities of such organs. They are the "chemical messengers" of the body. We have reasons for believing that the hormones act by influencing enzyme systems and membrane permeability.

Some of the hormones are proteins (insulin, for example), others are related to the steroids (sex and adrenal hormones), and still others are relatively simple compounds (epinephrine and thyroxine).

We shall discuss these hormones in connection with the glands which manufacture them.

THE THYROID*

The thyroid gland is made up of two lobes, one on each side of the trachea and the larynx. It weighs, on an average, about 25 gm. in the adult and contains about 10 mg. iodine—about one fifth of the total in the body. Through its hormone it regulates, among other things, the rate of metabolism within the body. It also has other profound effects, as is seen in cases of cretinism, where we have individuals who are mentally and physically retarded, and who suffer from a deficiency of the hormone. Thyroxine, the hormone used, will cause remarkable cures. An enlargement of the gland, known as a *goiter*, may be of two kinds: "endemic goiter," due to insufficient iodine; or one due to an abnormally high activity of the thyroid gland, as in exophthalmic goiter

* See also Iodine, page 402.

535

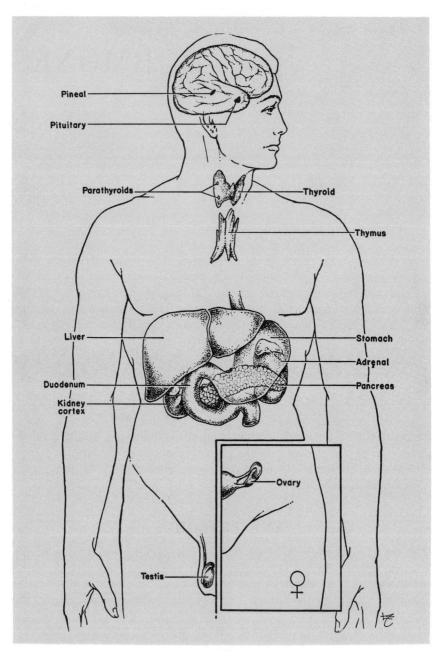

Figure 104. The approximate locations of the endocrine glands in man. Although the pineal body, thymus and stomach are shown, they are not definitely known to secrete hormones. (Villee: Biology, 3rd Edition.)

and Graves' disease. The endemic goiter lends itself to treatment with iodine. Both hypo- and hyperactivities of the thyroid affect the basal metabolism.

The treatment of endemic goiter—endemic because it occurs in places where the soil or water is deficient in iodine—with sodium iodide has been markedly successful. Marine and Kimball, pioneers in this field, discovered that in the Akron-Cleveland district about 45 per cent of the school girls from the fifth to twelfth grades and about 18 per cent of the boys showed goiter symptoms in various degrees. Treatment which involved the use of 2 gm. of sodium iodide, given in doses of 0.2 gm., and distributed over two weeks, caused complete cures. Iodized salt—sodium chloride containing 0.01 per cent of potassium iodide—is used quite extensively.

As early as 1895 Baumann made the discovery that the thyroid contains iodine—an element which until then was not suspected as one of the elements of the body. An active substance present in the thyroid gland is thyroxine, which was first isolated by Kendall and later by Harington. We owe to Harington its correct formula, as well as its synthesis.

Thyroxine
β-[3,5-diiodo-4-(3',5'-diiodo-4'-hydroxy-phenoxy)-phenyl]-α-amino-propionic acid

IODINE IN THE BODY

Iodine circulates in the body in two forms: as iodide and as thyroid hormone. The inorganic iodide in plasma is largely trapped and utilized by the thyroid gland to build up the hormone. The concentration of iodide in the thyroid gland is several hundred times that in circulating blood. Iodide is evenly distributed throughout the body fluids (including the brain); the hormonal iodine is associated with the plasma proteins.

Most of the iodine in the thyroid is in organic combination as thyroxine, triiodothyronine and diiodotyrosine. These organic compounds are bound to protein and can be freed (and isolated) by first hydrolyzing the tissue.

Using the radioisotope of iodine, I^{131}, Chaikoff showed that 15 minutes after the injection, some 95 per cent of the radioactivity present in the thyroid could be precipitated with trichloracetic acid, which meant that 95 per cent of the substance containing this iodine was in organic combination. At this stage, some 80 per cent of the activity was in the diiodotyrosine fraction, and 10 to 15 per cent in the thyroxine fraction.

The amount of iodine in the blood may prove to be of diagnostic value. Normally, the total iodine in blood may vary from 3 to 20 micrograms per 100 ml. of blood. This blood iodine is increased in exophthalmic goiter and also in several diseases not caused by thyroid dysfunction. In hypothyroidism, the iodine in the blood may show normal values, but the acetone-insoluble fraction (containing the circulating hormone) is about one-half the normal amount.

The urinary excretion of iodine may vary as much as 72 to 340 micrograms per day in nongoitrogenous regions, and from 27 to 64 micrograms in goitrogenous regions. In hypothyroidism (and in several diseases not caused by thyroid dysfunction) there is a tendency to increase the amount of iodine lost in the urine.

THYROXINE

Thyroxine is not found as such in the thyroid gland, but in the form of a protein, *thyroglobulin*. Iodine is a precursor of the thyroid hormone and is accumulated by the thyroid gland as inorganic iodide. Presumably the first step involves the oxidation of iodide to free iodine, or more probably, to hypoiodate (IO^-). This oxidized form of iodine reacts quickly to form organically bound iodine. It is postulated that the enzymes involved in the oxidation of iodide are cytochrome oxidase and peroxidase. The organically bound form of iodine would involve a reaction with tyrosine to form the intermediate, 3,5-diiodotyrosine, and then a condensation between two moles of the latter to form thyroxine.

In 1951 a new thyroxine-like compound was isolated from the thyroid and plasma and shown to be five times as potent as thyroxine in preventing the goiter produced by feeding thiouracil. It also produces a more rapid elevation in oxygen consumption in hypothyroid animals and in man than does thyroxine. This compound is 3,5,3,'-triiodothyronine. It is considered by some to be the active thyroid hormone. The relationships are shown in the following scheme, although the exact sequence of reactions is still in some doubt:

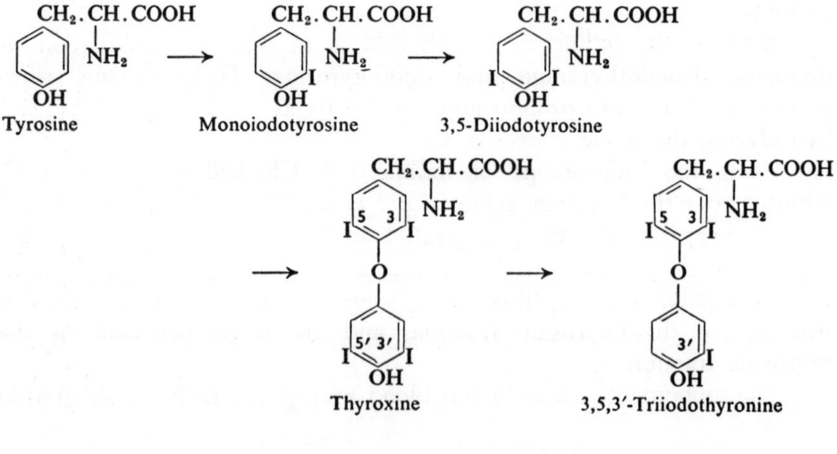

Tyrosine   Monoiodotyrosine   3,5-Diiodotyrosine

Thyroxine   3,5,3'-Triiodothyronine

Thyroglobulin is not found in the circulation, although thyroxine and triiodothyronine are present in the plasma. Since precipitation of plasma proteins also precipitates most of the organic iodine, it is believed that the thyroid hormone exists in a protein-bound form. Although most of the plasma iodine is associated with the albumin fraction, the highest concentration of iodine is found in the alpha-globulin fraction.

Thyroxine from Iodinated Proteins. If casein (or some other protein) is "iodized"—if, in other words, it is treated in an alkaline solution with iodine—the product shows definite thyroid activity. When this iodized protein is hydrolyzed and fractionated, diiodotyrosine and thyroxine can be separated.

As might be anticipated, casein is not the only protein which by iodination and subsequent treatment yields thyroxine. Soybean protein serves equally well. Apparently the value of the protein for this purpose lies in its content of tyrosine.

One of the hormones of the anterior pituitary, the *thyrotropic hormone* (TSH) (p. 545), influences the activity of the thyroid gland. An injection of the thyrotropic hormone into a normal animal gives rise to hypertrophy and hyperactivity of the thyroid.

Therapeutic Use. In cases of hypothyroidism, as in cretinism and myxedema, thyroxine or desiccated thyroid can be administered. These materials can be given orally, though, of the two, the thyroid is the more easily absorbed and utilized. With the probable exception of one or two of the sex hormones, thyroxine is the only hormone which is so readily active when given orally, for insulin and other hormones have to be given parenterally.

Where there is hyperfunction of the thyroid, an increased elimination (in the urine) of iodine results. Sometimes the increase is from three to four times the normal amount. Estimations of iodine in blood and in urine may therefore be of value. The treatment is often surgical. Some four-fifths of the gland is removed.

Radioactive iodine is also used. "As the radioactive atoms disintegrate within the thyroid, they emit beta and gamma rays, producing the same kind of tissue reaction as x-rays, but the irradiation is largely confined to the gland itself" (Werner, Quimby, and Schmidt). The normal uptake is 20 to 30 per cent of the administered tracer dose. Above 40 per cent is regarded as hyperthyroid; below 20 per cent, as hypothyroid.

Mechanism of Action of Thyroxine. It has been found that thyroxine or triiodothyronine, when incubated with isolated mitochondria, is capable of uncoupling oxidative phosphorylation. However, Lehninger has shown that the thyroid hormones do not seem to act directly on the enzyme systems themselves, but produce an osmotic effect on the mitochondria by causing them to swell. In this respect, the thyroid hormones uncouple oxidative phosphorylation by a mechanism different from that brought about by a compound such as dinitrophenol.

Antithyroid Compounds. Thiouracil and several other compounds possess the property of inhibiting the production of thyroxine. This is explained on the ground that these compounds prevent the oxidation of iodide, which means that the iodine cannot be used for the synthesis of thyroxine. This property has led to the use of such compounds in hyperthyroidism.

$$
\begin{array}{cc}
\text{HN} & \text{CO} \\
| & | \\
\text{S=C} & \text{CH} \\
| & \| \\
\text{HN} & \text{CH}
\end{array}
$$

Thiouracil

Thiouracil itself is relatively toxic; less so are propylthiouracil, thiourea,

$$
\text{S=C} \underset{\diagdown \text{NH}_2}{\overset{\diagup \text{NH}_2}{}}
$$

Thiourea

and methylthiouracil. Among these, propylthiouracil has been used most extensively. It is three times more active than thiouracil and much less toxic.

These substances and their uses have an interesting history. In the attempt to prevent the synthesis of some vitamins by intestinal flora, several investigators used sulfaguanidine. After several weeks a hypertrophy of the thyroid gland was noticed. The glands were several times larger than those of animals which had not received sulfaguanidine. There was at the same time a lowering of the basal metabolism. Administering iodine had no effect, but thyroxine reversed the process: the gland approached normality again and the basal metabolic rate was restored. Many compounds were now tried in the attempt to duplicate the action of sulfaguanidine. Thiourea and thiouracil were picked as the most promising at the time.

It is possible that the antithyroid action of a compound is related to its reducing power and preferential reactivity with iodine, thereby inhibiting the formation of diiodotyrosine and thence thyroxine (Pitt-Rivers).

Another inhibitor of the thyroid is iodide itself, which is used in the treatment of hyperthyroidism (Graves' disease). It brings about an involution (return to normal size) of the thyroid, thus differing from the action of thiouracil. The reason for the therapeutic effect of iodide is in doubt.

Analogues of Thyroxine. With the view of relating structure to physiological action, several compounds closely related chemically to thyroxine have been prepared, and the biological action of such compounds has been tested. The diiodo compound, 3′,5′-diiodothyronine (I)

I $HO{-}\overset{I}{\underset{I}{\langle\rangle}}{-}O{-}\langle\rangle{-}CH_2.\underset{NH_2}{CH}.COOH$

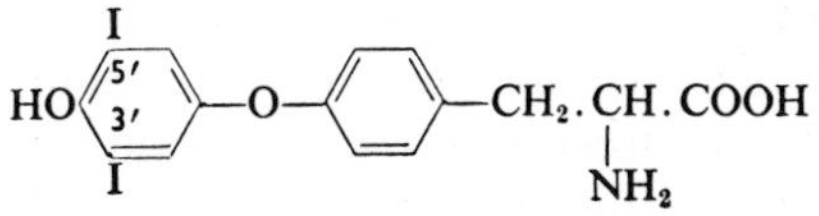

(thyronine is the name given to thyroxine without its iodine atoms) is but one-fourth as active as thyroxine. 3,5,3′-triiodothyronine is said to be more active than thyroxine itself.

Of two isomers of thyroxine, the one with the OH group in the meta position (II) was inactive, and the other with the OH group in the ortho position (III) showed slight activity.

II $I\overset{H}{\underset{O}{\langle\rangle}}{-}O{-}\overset{I}{\underset{I}{\langle\rangle}}{-}CH_2.\underset{NH_2}{CH}.COOH$

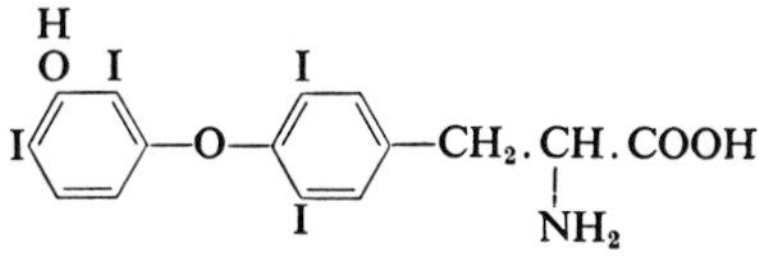

III $\overset{H}{\underset{I}{\langle\rangle}}{-}O{-}\overset{I}{\underset{I}{\langle\rangle}}CH_2\underset{NH_2}{CH}.COOH$

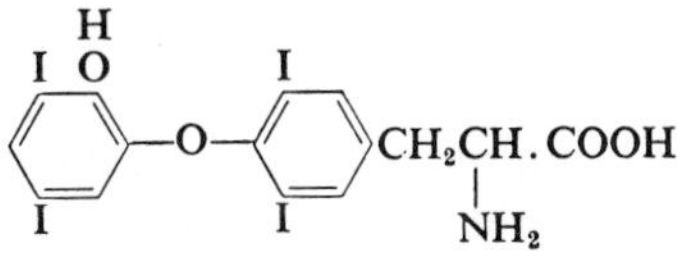

Niemann suggests the necessity of a potential quinoid structure for the compound to show physiological activity (IV):

IV $O{=}\overset{I}{\underset{I}{\langle\rangle}}{=}\overset{+}{O}{-}\overset{I}{\underset{I}{\langle\rangle}}CH_2\underset{NH_2}{CH}.COOH.$

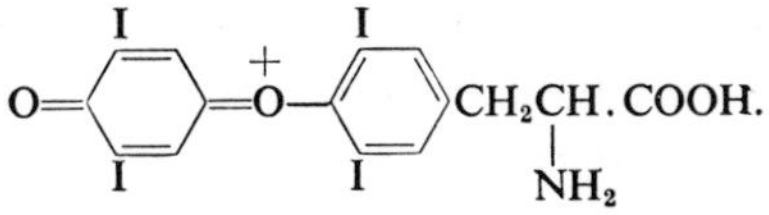

As in the case of vitamins, some attempts have been made to show that certain structural analogues of hormones exhibit physiological antagonism. In one such experiment, Woolley synthesized several ethers of N-acetyldiiodotyrosine. As a test method, he made use of the fact that thyroxine is a lethal agent for tadpoles (though minute quantities of the hormone accelerate metamorphosis). Relatively large amounts of the hormone cause rapid metamorphosis and ultimate death. The derivatives of diiodotyrosine were able to protect tadpoles against the lethal action of thyroxine.

THE PARATHYROIDS

Attached to the thyroid are four small organs, the parathyroids, which for a long time were confused with the thyroid itself. The combined weight of the glands varies from 0.05 to 0.3 gm.

The removal of the parathyroids gives rise to two types of change: neuromuscular and chemical. There develop muscular twitchings (tetany) leading to convulsions. The calcium in the plasma steadily decreases. The tetany can be relieved by the administration of a soluble calcium salt.

Tetany develops when the calcium in plasma falls from 10 mg. per 100 ml. (normal) to 7 mg. per 100 ml.; convulsions occur when the calcium is further decreased to 3.5 to 5 mg. per 100 ml. plasma.

As the calcium declines in the blood there is a decrease in the urine; however, during this period the phosphorus in plasma increases from a normal of 5 mg. per 100 ml. to 9 mg. per 100 ml., and even higher.

Collip and Hanson prepared an extract, obtained by the acid hydrolysis of the gland, which when injected into a parathyroidectomized animal restored its health and, at the same time, raised the percentage of calcium in the blood. It was shown subsequently that the injection of a potent extract into a normal dog doubled the amount of blood calcium normally present (the normal amount being about 10 mg. per 100 ml.). The plasma calcium shows the first signs of an increase in about four hours and then reaches a maximum in from 12 to 18 hours; from then on a decrease sets in until the normal level is reached in from 20 to 24 hours.

The increase in plasma calcium is followed by an increased urinary excretion of calcium and inorganic phosphate and a decrease in blood phosphate.

It is believed that this extra calcium is derived from the bones by a withdrawal of the element. Under such conditions of hypercalcemia, the kidney undergoes pathological changes and abnormal deposits of calcium salts accumulate in soft tissues.

Parathyroid preparations have been used successfully in the treatment of tetania parathyreopriva (tetany caused by removal of parathyroids) and of infantile tetany. Occasionally, in operations on the thyroid gland, tetany may develop due to removal of or injury to the parathyroid glands or their blood supply.

The hormone has been isolated in a chemically pure state (Craig and Rasmussen). It is a protein with a molecular weight of 9,500—somewhat larger than insulin. The most potent preparations show an ultraviolet absorption spectrum almost identical with that of many simple proteins. Further, the action of pepsin or trypsin completely inactivates the material.

THE PITUITARY (HYPOPHYSIS)

This gland, no larger than the end of the little finger, situated at the base of the skull, seems to have a multiplicity of functions. There are three distinct portions to this gland, the anterior, the pars intermedia, and the posterior; and while all three may be important enough, it is the anterior portion which seems to be actually essential to life.

Clinically, types of gigantism and acromegaly (examples of hyperpituitarism) and dwarfism (a possible example of hypopituitarism) have been known for some time. But more recently, extracts have been obtained which show a multiplicity of actions. Since the active substances show the properties of proteins, the difficulties of separating them are great.

ANTERIOR PITUITARY

We shall first take up the question of the anterior pituitary, which is responsible for the following hormones:

a. Growth hormone (GH).
b. Gonadotropic hormones:
 1. Interstitial cell–stimulating hormone (ICSH).
 2. Follicle-stimulating hormone (FSH).
c. Lactogenic hormone (prolactin).
d. Thyrotropic hormone (TSH).
e. Adrenocorticotropic hormone (ACTH).

After hypophysectomy the thyroids, the adrenal cortex, and the gonads are much affected and their functional activity is greatly lessened. Lactation ceases. In general, atrophy of many of the endocrine glands and a deficient output of glandular secretions are evident.

While survival for a time is possible without the anterior lobe of the hypophysis, a normal life span is probably not possible.

In rats retention of as little as 10 per cent of the original gland will prevent the various deficiencies.

GROWTH HORMONE

Hypophysectomy in young animals gives rise to dwarfism and sexual infantilism. Cretinic dwarfs may also be the result of a depression of the pituitary function. Evans succeeded in preparing active material which when injected into rats produced definite gigantism.

Such growth appears to resemble normal growth and is not the result, for example, of an accumulation of water and fat. The hormone influences chiefly skeletal growth by stimulating the epiphyseal cartilages, but it also affects the soft tissues, etc. It promotes the synthesis of tissue protein from the circulating amino acids.

Production of growth hormone after normal growth is completed results in acromegaly.

The extracts originally used by Evans were essentially dilute aqueous alkaline solutions which, in addition to containing the active growth hormone, retained varying quantities of a number of other hormones present in the anterior portion of the pituitary; but such extracts have been very much purified since then. In fact, Evans, Li, and Simpson obtained the hormone as a chemically pure protein. Assays were made on female rats hypophysectomized when 27 days old. Injections were begun 14 days later, once daily for ten days. They found that

0.010 mg. of the purified product gave an increase of 10 gm. in body weight.

As evidence of the purity of the product, the injection of as much as 5 gm. of the product failed to show the presence of any of the other hormones in the anterior portion of the pituitary (such as those dealing with lactogenic, thyrotropic, adrenotropic and follicle-stimulating properties).

The purified hormone has a molecular weight of about 44,000 and an isoelectric point of 6.9. Incubation with the enzyme carboxypeptidase does not destroy its activity, although the hormone releases a number of amino acids. This would suggest a certain sequence of amino acids which is required for biological activity. It will be seen that this has been shown to be true for several hormones of the pituitary.

The activity of the hormone is destroyed by peptic or tryptic digestion. It is unstable at the temperature of boiling water and is more stable in alkaline than in acid solutions. Iodination of the hormone destroys its biological activity, which is an indication that tyrosine groups are essential.

It should be pointed out that several investigators object to this conception of a "growth hormone"; for, as Smith points out, "growth is such a complex process, that it is difficult to conceive of its being due to a single hormone." However, that there is some "principle" or hormone in the hypophysis which is essential for general body growth seems well established.

GONADOTROPIC (GONAD-STIMULATING) HORMONES

P. E. Smith and Aschheim and Zondek discovered that when a piece of anterior pituitary tissue is implanted under the skin of an immature rat, the ovaries develop within a few days. Zondek later postulated that the growth of the ovarian follicles is due to a "follicle-stimulating hormone" ("prolan A"), and the development of lutein tissue, to a luteinizing hormone.

In 1931 Hisaw and Leonard separated the pituitary gonadotropic fractions into two components: ICSH (interstitial cell–stimulating hormone) and FSH (follicle-stimulating hormone). ICSH increases the ovarian weight of the normal immature female rat, stimulates the repair of ovarian interstitial tissues of hypophysectomized rats, increases the weight of the seminal vesicles of the normal immature male rat and increases the weight of the ventral lobe of the prostate in hypophysectomized male rats.

ICSH has been prepared in a pure state and is a protein which remains homogeneous when tested electrophoretically, by the ultracentrifuge and by solubility tests. The hormone (in sheep) has a molecular weight of 40,000 and contains 4.5 per cent of mannose and 5.8 per cent of hexoseamine.

FSH stimulates follicular growth, thereby increasing ovarian weight, and causes the enlargement of ovarian follicles in the hypophysectomized rat. It also behaves as a single protein in experiments involving electrophoresis, diffusion and ultracentrifugation. It contains 1.2 per cent hexose and 1.51 per cent hexoseamine.

Gonadotropins other than those obtained from the pituitary are known. These substances may be classified as follows: (1) Human chorionic* gonadotropin (present in blood, urine, and tissues of pregnant women); (2) human nonchorionic gonadotropin (present in blood and urine of ovariectomized and post-menopausal women); and (3) equine gonadotropin (present in blood and placental tissue of the pregnant mare). There is evidence which indicates that extracts of human placenta, pregnancy blood, and pregnancy urine contain gonadotropic substances which are not the same as those in the pituitary. However, pregnant mare's serum contains a substance more comparable to the gonadotropins in the pituitary and different from human placental gonadotropic hormones.

Zondek and Aschheim originally discovered a gonadotropic hormone in the urine of pregnancy, which led them to their pregnancy test. The principle involved in the pregnancy test is to inject immature mice with the suspected urine, kill the animals on the fourth day, and examine the ovaries for hemorrhagic spots and yellowish protrusions (developed corpora lutea).

During pregnancy we find a relative abundance of an estrogenic (female) hormone and the gonadotropic hormone in the urine. The latter appears in recognizable quantity by the first missed period (the Aschheim-Zondek test), and reaches its maximum between the second and third months of pregnancy; the former appears somewhat later, but lasts until birth, and then decreases very rapidly.

LACTOGENIC HORMONE

Riddle was among the first to prepare an extract of the pituitary which stimulates the enlargement and functioning (formation of "crop milk") of the crop glands in pigeons. This hormone, which initiates lactation, is known as *prolactin.*

It is believed that a female hormone produced by the placenta during pregnancy stimulates the growth of the mammary gland and at the same time inhibits the secretion of prolactin. At parturition, the inhibiting influence of the placenta is removed, the prolactin is released, and the secretion of milk is fostered.

Crystalline products have been obtained by Evans, White, and Riddle.

THYROTROPIC HORMONE

This is also called the *thyroid-stimulating hormone* (TSH). An appropriate extract of the pituitary injected into normal animals re-

* Pertaining to the more external of the two fetal membranes.

sults in the enlargement and hyperplasia of the thyroid. There is an increase in the metabolism and in the heart rate and the development of an exophthalmos resembling Graves' disease. Smith was among the first to show that the extirpation of the pituitary results in the atrophy of the thyroid. This condition can be improved by implanting fresh pituitary into a hypophysectomized animal.

Active extracts injected into rabbits or guinea-pigs—rats are more immune—result in symptoms of exophthalmic goiter: the thyroid is increased in size, the iodine is decreased, there is a loss of colloid and the cells are enlarged, or hypertrophied. There is also a rapid rise in basal metabolism.

The relation between the pituitary and the thyroid is regarded as reciprocal. When thyroxine is administered, there results a reduction of TSH in the pituitary; and when TSH is administered, the content of thyroid hormone is increased.

The hormone, a protein, contains 3.5 per cent hexose, 2.5 per cent glucosamine and 1.0 per cent sulfur. It has a molecular weight of approximately 10,000. The purity of the isolated product is still in question.

ADRENOCORTICOTROPIC HORMONE (ACTH)

Hypophysectomy results in the atrophy of the adrenal cortex. Improvement is possible by using pituitary implants or by injecting appropriate pituitary extracts; but no improvement results when the adrenal cortical hormone is injected. The injection of ACTH results in an enlargement of the adrenals of both normal as well as hypophysectomized animals.

The active hormone was originally isolated as a protein fraction with an approximate molecular weight of 20,000. Since that time smaller polypeptides have been prepared from this material and shown to retain all of its biological activity. Among these polypeptides are α-corticotropin and β-corticotropin; treatment of the α-hormone with pepsin produces the β-hormone with all of its activity intact. Each polypeptide exists in the form of a single chain. The polypeptides differ among the various animal species in the sequence of amino acid residues along one end of the chain. Partial hydrolysis showed that one could prepare a peptide containing the first 24 amino acid residues and still retain activity. These amino acid sequences were identical for human and various animal species. Recently, Hoffman and associates have synthesized a polypeptide containing 23 amino acid residues corresponding to the sequence of the natural peptide and have found the synthetic material to be entirely active. Prior to this study, a synthetic peptide containing 19 amino acids was found to have 30 per cent of the activity of the natural hormone. The synthetic hormone with 23 amino acid residues has a molecular weight of 3200 and represents the largest synthetic polypeptide yet prepared.

Administration of ACTH to an animal with intact adrenals produces effects similar to those obtained when the adrenal cortical steroids are given. ACTH probably acts by stimulating the adrenals to release their hormones although some of its effects may be independent of the adrenals. In large doses, ACTH produces a liberation of free fatty acids.

OTHER ANTERIOR PITUITARY HORMONES

Particularly since the discovery of insulin, it has been believed that blood sugar is regulated primarily, if not exclusively, by the pancreas. It has already been pointed out that the removal of the pancreas leads to diabetes. However, Houssay showed that if the pituitary is also removed, the rise in blood sugar can be prevented. Both Houssay and Evans have since shown that the injection of anterior pituitary extracts into normal animals produces hyperglycemia and glycosuria.

Largely through the work of Young it has been established that the anterior pituitary contains a "diabetogenic hormone" which causes a rise in blood-sugar level. But even more arresting is the observation that by increasing the daily dose of the pituitary extract (equivalent to 25 gm. of fresh ox anterior lobe), and then stopping the injections, the diabetic condition continues and presumably becomes permanent. This is true—in many cases but not in all—of the dog, but it apparently does not apply to the cat.

Dogs made permanently diabetic with the diabetogenic hormone exhibit injury of the islands of Langerhans in the pancreas (the place where insulin is manufactured); and it is possible that some cases of diabetes in man may be due to an overactivity of the hypophysis.

In addition to affecting carbohydrate metabolism, Funk and others are of the opinion that the pituitary harbors a "fat-metabolism" hormone. Extracts have been obtained which, when injected, cause a very marked increase in the acetone body production.

Extracts from urine have been obtained which have a hyperglycemic function and which can also give rise to acetone bodies. It is not clear whether such active material has its origin in the pituitary (Harrow).

POSTERIOR LOBE OF THE PITUITARY

Aqueous extracts of this portion of the gland (pituitrin) have long been used in the labor of childbirth. Two substances have been separated by Kamm and others: one, *vasopressin* (Pitressin), raises blood pressure and decreases the secretion of urine (antidiuretic); the other, *oxytocin* (Pitocin), contracts the muscles of the uterus and perhaps functions during parturition to remove the products of conception.

Vasopressin stimulates the peripheral blood vessels and causes a rise in blood pressure. It has been used to combat the low blood pressure of shock following surgery. The claim has been made that, under certain conditions, vasopressin has the advantage over epinephrine in that the former gives rise to a more gradual increase in blood pressure, and that this pressure is of longer duration.

It has been shown that the injection of vasopressin in cases of diabetes insipidus—a disease characterized by the elimination of large quantities of urine—checks the flow of urine; it is an antidiuretic substance.

By means of electrophoretic studies, using the principle of electrical transport and the relative migration velocities of different molecules, Du Vigneaud and his associates have shown that, starting with the juice of the posterior gland, "the pressor activity travelled at a faster rate than the oxytocic activity, thus demonstrating that the activities . . . were manifestations of different chemical entities."

Du Vigneaud has isolated both the oxytocic and vasopressor materials, each free of the other. Both preparations contain but eight amino acids; six of these are common to both: tyrosine, proline, glutamic acid, aspartic acid, glycine, cystine and three equivalents of ammonia. Oxytocin also contains leucine and isoleucine, while vasopressin contains arginine and phenylalanine (beef).

Further work by Du Vigneaud and co-workers has enabled them to synthesize an octapeptide amide, with a molecular weight of approximately 1000, which shows the hormonal activity of oxytocin.

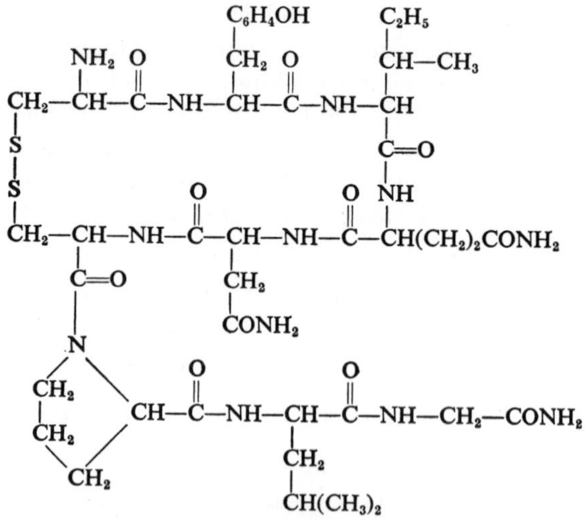

Oxytocin

Vasopressin (arginine vasopressin) has the following structure:

$$C_6H_4OH \qquad C_6H_5$$
$$\qquad\qquad | \qquad\qquad |$$
$$NH_2 \ O \qquad CH_2 \ O \qquad CH_2$$
$$| \qquad || \qquad\quad | \qquad || \qquad\quad |$$
$$CH_2-CH-C-NH-CH-C-NH-CH$$
$$|\qquad\qquad\qquad\qquad\qquad\qquad\qquad |$$
$$S \qquad\qquad\qquad\qquad\qquad\qquad C=O$$
$$|\qquad\qquad\qquad\qquad\qquad\qquad\qquad |$$
$$S \qquad\qquad\qquad O \qquad\qquad\quad O \ \ NH$$
$$|\qquad\qquad\qquad || \qquad\qquad\quad || \quad |$$
$$CH_2-CH-NH-C-CH-NH-C-CH-CH_2-CH_2-CONH_2$$
$$|\qquad\qquad\qquad\qquad CH_2$$
$$C=O \qquad\qquad\qquad | $$
$$|\qquad\qquad\qquad\qquad CONH_2$$
$$CH_2-N$$
$$| \qquad\qquad\quad \backslash \qquad O \qquad\qquad O$$
$$\qquad\qquad\qquad\quad CH-C-NH-CH-C-NH-CH_2-CONH_2$$
$$CH_2-CH_2 \qquad\qquad\qquad | $$
$$\qquad\qquad\qquad\qquad\qquad CH_2$$
$$\qquad\qquad\qquad\qquad\qquad |$$
$$\qquad\qquad\qquad CH_2-CH_2-NH-C-NH_2$$
$$\qquad\qquad\qquad\qquad\qquad\qquad\quad ||$$
$$\qquad\qquad\qquad\qquad\qquad\qquad\quad NH$$

Vasopressin

PARS INTERMEDIA

This lobe of the pituitary manufactures a hormone which can be recognized by its effect on the pigment cells of the skin of lower vertebrates. The injection of an extract into a minnow (*Phoxinus laevis*) causes a red color at the point of attachment of the thoracic, abdominal, and anal fins. Beyond its exerting an influence on the chromatophores of cold-blooded animals, the significance of this hormone, called *Intermedin*, is not clear.

Intermedin has been isolated in pure form and is a polypeptide. It is also called MSH (melanocyte stimulating hormone).

The sequence of amino acids in this hormone contains one portion which is identical with that found for ACTH. ACTH has 1 per cent of the pigmentation activity of MSH, which has but 18 amino acids and no adrenal activity. It is believed that the identical sequences of amino acids which appear in both hormones are responsible for their pigmentation activity.

MSH: Asp.Glu.Gly.Pro.	Tyr. Lys.	Met.Glu.His.Phe.Arg.Try.Gly.	Ser. Pro.	Pro.Lys.Asp.
ACTH: Ser.	Tyr. Ser.	Met.Glu.His.Phe.Arg.Try.Gly.	Lys. Pro.	.... Phe.

THE PANCREAS*

INSULIN

As has already been stated, the pancreas has two distinct functions: it secretes a juice (pancreatic juice) which flows into the intes-

* See also page 181.

tine and which contains digestive enzymes, and it secretes at least two hormones which find their way into the blood and which play an important role in the regulation of carbohydrate metabolism.

The removal of the pancreas results in the following: (a) hyperglycemia (rise in blood sugar) and glycosuria (increase in urinary sugar); (b) depletion of the glycogen stores of liver and muscle; (c) lowering of the respiratory quotient; (d) increased NPN excretion; (e) increased formation of acetone bodies. Death results in about three weeks. Banting, Macleod, Best, and Collip prepared an acid alcoholic extract of the pancreas which prevented these symptoms in a pancreatectomized animal and which could be used to relieve diabetic sufferers among human beings. The hormone is called *insulin*. (See Fig. 105.)

When injected into normal animals, insulin lowers the blood sugar. This discovery led to a method for standardizing the hormone.

The effects attributed to the administration of insulin are (a) acceleration of glucose oxidation in the tissues; (b) increased rate of conversion of glucose to glycogen or fat in the tissues; (c) inhibition of carbohydrate formation in the liver from noncarbohydrate sources; (d) inhibition of excessive formation of ketone bodies.

Starting with highly active commercial fractions, Abel and his coworkers obtained crystalline insulin. Crystalline preparations of insulin

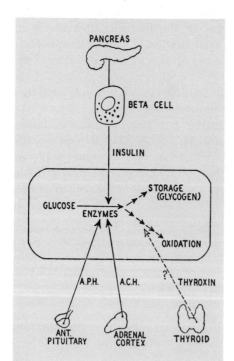

Figure 105. Endocrine factors in diabetes. (From Lazarow, Physiol. Rev., 29:48, 1949.)

contain zinc.* In any case, apart from the zinc, the hydrolysis of insulin yields nothing but amino acids. Tryptophan, methionine and cysteine have not been detected.

Proteolytic enzymes attack insulin and, indeed, the hormone has to be injected rather than be given by mouth. It has been claimed that during peptic hydrolysis of insulin, the decrease in its activity runs parallel with a decrease in its tyrosine content.

Insulin is easily destroyed by alkali but is relatively stable in slightly acid solutions.

Stern and White acetylated insulin with ketene, $CH_2{=}C{=}O$. They found that when ketene acted on insulin for five minutes at room temperature and at pH 5.7, only free amino groups were acetylated. If the reaction is continued beyond this time, the hydroxyl groups of tyrosine are slowly acetylated. In this way, it could be shown that acetylating the free amino groups of insulin has no appreciable effect on its activity; on the other hand, when the hydroxyl groups on tyrosine were acetylated, there was marked reduction in the activity of the hormone.

These results are of special interest, since Northrop and Herriott showed that the tyrosine group plays an analogous role in so far as the activity of pepsin is concerned.

Insulin contains its sulfur (cystine) in the —S—S— form; if reduced to the —SH modification, it loses its activity.

Thanks largely to the work of Sanger, the structure of insulin has now been determined (see p. 107).

INSULIN THERAPY

A notable advance in insulin therapy was made by Hagedorn and Jensen, who by combining insulin with protamine (one of the basic proteins) prepared a product which, when injected, is absorbed more slowly than insulin itself, and whose effects are therefore more lasting. Instead of two and three injections a day, often but one suffices. The addition of zinc to protamine insulin was suggested by Scott and Fischer. This "protamine zinc insulin" prolongs the effective action of insulin; it lowers the blood sugar for more than 24 hours. A further modification, "NPH insulin," differs from protamine zinc insulin by containing less protamine and less zinc and by being crystalline. The blood sugar–lowering action is intermediate between globin insulin and protamine zinc insulin.

Globin insulin with zinc has also come into use. The globin is the protein derived from hemoglobin. The action time is intermediate between that of insulin alone and protamine zinc insulin. This globin insulin with zinc is a "twelve-to-fifteen-hour insulin" (the action lasts that long) and in certain cases, involving careful regulation of diet, is preferred.

* It may be significant that normal pancreatic tissue is relatively rich in zinc.

In the use of protamine zinc insulin a drop in blood sugar begins in four to six hours; with insulin alone, the action is immediate; with globin insulin and zinc, the lowering occurs within two hours.

MECHANISM OF DIABETIC ACTIVITY

Two theories have been advanced:

a. One is sometimes called the "nonutilization theory." It states that in the absence of insulin, the capacity of the peripheral tissue to metabolize glucose is greatly decreased. Several of the hormones from the anterior pituitary and the adrenal cortex depress the utilization of glucose and also stimulate glucose production in the liver from protein.

b. The other is sometimes called the "overproduction theory." It states that the utilization of glucose in the tissues is not affected to any great extent by insulin or by hormones of the pituitary or adrenals. In the absence of insulin, excess glucose is due to a stimulation of glucose production, not only from amino acids but also from fatty acids in the liver, and this stimulation develops from the activity of hormones in the pituitary and the adrenals.

INSULIN SHOCK

Another advance we owe to Sakel, who finds that insulin injections almost up to the point of shock often have a beneficial effect in certain mental disorders (schizophrenia or dementia praecox).

INSULIN AND THE PITUITARY

The pituitary and possibly the adrenals are involved in the activity of insulin. As has been pointed out elsewhere, Cori and his co-workers have claimed that the enzyme hexokinase, which promotes the formation of glucose-6-phosphate (in the carbohydrate cycle), is inhibited by certain fractions from the anterior pituitary, and that the inhibition is removed by insulin. This has been challenged by Mirsky.

ALLOXAN DIABETES

Alloxan, a substance structurally related to pyrimidine, produces diabetes in various animals. A single injection will often produce the disease in 24 to 28 hours.

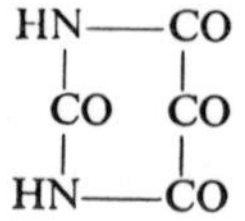

$$
\begin{array}{cc}
HN\!\!-\!\!\!-\!\!CO \\
| \quad\ | \\
CO \quad CO \\
| \quad\ | \\
HN\!\!-\!\!\!-\!\!CO
\end{array}
$$

Alloxan

The disease is brought about by the destruction of pancreatic tissue (selective necrosis of the islets of Langerhans) with a lessening production of insulin.

While it is also possible to produce experimental diabetes in the animal by the injection of the diabetogenic hormone from the pituitary or by partial pancreatectomy, the diabetes so obtained is considered as due to overwork of the beta cells; alloxan diabetes brings about their actual destruction. As evidence for this view, in the early stages of the disease, starvation or treatment with insulin will prevent the diabetes due to surgical operation or the injection of the anterior pituitary extract; but this is not true of diabetes due to alloxan.

Lazarow showed that the injection of large amounts of glutathione immediately preceding a dose of alloxan protects rats from diabetes. While substances other than glutathione are known to do this, glutathione is a natural constituent of cells. It is known that glutathione reacts with alloxan to change it to a compound which is not diabetogenic.

GLUCAGON

It was noted quite frequently in the past that when crude insulin preparations were injected into animals, a transient *hyper*glycemia was produced; but this was soon followed by the *hypo*glycemia characteristic of the effects of purified insulin. The material responsible for the hyperglycemic effect was called the hyperglycemic-glycogenolytic factor and is now known as glucagon. It has since been isolated in crystalline form and is believed to be manufactured by the alpha cells of the pancreas. One tenth of a microgram per kilogram produces a rise of 25 mg. of glucose per 100 ml. of cat blood. It has a molecular weight of 3482 and is almost lacking in cystine. It thus differs considerably from insulin. Furthermore, glucagon contains methionine and tryptophan, which are absent in insulin.

There appears to be a relationship between the biological activities of glucagon and insulin. The insulin requirement of alloxan-diabetic dogs is reduced after removal of the pancreas. The activity of glucagon resembles that of epinephrine, and the site of its action is the liver. The three important reactions which are involved in the production of blood glucose from liver glycogen are:

1. Glycogen + $PO_4^{\equiv}$ $\xrightarrow{\text{phosphorylase}}$ glucose-1-PO_4
2. Glucose-1-PO_4 $\xrightarrow{\text{phosphoglucomutase}}$ glucose-6-PO_4
3. Glucose-6-PO_4 $\xrightarrow{\text{phosphatase}}$ glucose + $PO_4^{\equiv}$

Since phosphoglucomutase and phosphatase are present in liver in excess as compared with phosphorylase, reaction 1 is the rate-limiting step in the production of glucose in the blood. In the presence of glucagon, glucose-1-PO_4 and glucose-6-PO_4 concentration in liver slices shows an increase. Pre-incubation of the liver slices with glucagon results in an enhancement of phosphorylase activity. Glucagon also protects phosphorylase (liver) against the inactivation which otherwise takes place. Again, its action appears to be similar to that of epinephrine, although not by the same mechanism: epinephrine favors the conversion of inactive muscle phosphorylase b to active phosphorylase a, but this is not so for glucagon.

THE ADRENALS

There are two distinct parts to the adrenals, the medulla and the cortex. The medulla, related to the sympathetic nervous system, contains the hormone epinephrine; and the cortex, essential to life, contains several hormones which have been isolated.

THE ADRENAL MEDULLA

Epinephrine (Adrenalin). This was first isolated by Abel and Takamine. The method employed by Takamine in isolating the hormone was to extract it from the glands with warm acidulated water, filter, concentrate the filtrate, precipitate inert material with an excess of alcohol, and finally precipitate the epinephrine with ammonia. Its formula is:

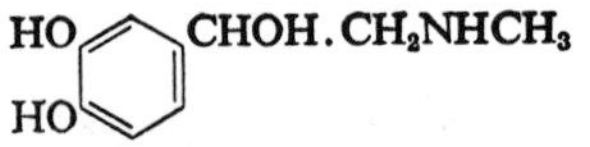

$$HO \underset{HO}{\bigcirc} CHOH . CH_2NHCH_3$$

Epinephrine (Adrenalin)

which means that it is catechol to which a hydroxyethylmethylamine group is attached.

Using methyl-labeled epinephrine one can show that in the body (the rat) some 50 per cent is inactivated by the loss of methylamine (probably through the action of an amine oxidase). The methylamine is partially oxidized to CO_2 but some 10 per cent is excreted in the urine in various forms.

Norepinephrine (Noradrenalin). Besides epinephrine the adrenals also contain norepinephrine,

$$HO \underset{HO}{\bigcirc} CHOH . CH_2NH_2$$

which is epinephrine minus the N-methyl group. In the adrenals of cattle both are found in the proportion of one part of norepinephrine to 4 parts epinephrine. In fact, most commercial preparations of epinephrine contain from 10 to 20 per cent of norepinephrine. The hyperglycemic effect of norepinephrine is 1/20 that of epinephrine, but the former is more active on arterial blood pressure.

It is believed that in the body norepinephrine can be converted to epinephrine by a methylation reaction involving enzymes of the adrenal and methionine, and requiring ATP.

Epinephrine constricts the splanchnic and cutaneous blood vessels, causing a rise in blood pressure; it accelerates the heart rate; it causes a temporary increase in blood sugar and blood lactic acid.

The L-form is fifteen times more effective than the D-form.

Epinephrine is used in shock and collapse, in asthmatic attacks (also as the isopropyl derivative), and in combination with local anesthetics (to prevent bleeding).

Epinephrine is the most powerful vasoconstrictor known. It is this property which makes it so useful as an adjunct in local anesthesia. The anesthetic effects are prolonged by adding epinephrine to the solution of the local anesthetic to be used. Not only does the hormone prolong the anesthetic effect but less of the anesthetic is needed.

Cannon is of the opinion that one function of epinephrine is to act in emergencies (in cold, fatigue, shock, etc.).*

It has already been mentioned that epinephrine plays a role in the metabolism of carbohydrates. Its effect is to increase the conversion of liver glycogen to blood sugar and to increase the conversion of muscle glycogen to lactic acid (which may be ultimately converted to liver glycogen).

THE ADRENAL CORTEX

The adrenal medulla produces epinephrine and norepinephrine. The cortex produces a mixture of many steroids, several of which act as hormones. Histologically the cortex is made up of three layers: zona glomerulosa (outside), zona fasciculata, and the zona reticularis (inside). These three layers are responsible for the elaboration of a number of hormones which, in the form of a crude extract of the cortex, are called *cortin*. The glomerulosa is believed to produce the hormones responsible for electrolyte and water balance, and the fasciculata, those affecting carbohydrate and protein metabolism.

The zona glomerulosa is stimulated after sodium deprivation or potassium administration and is depressed by potassium deprivation or administration of deoxycorticosterone (see p. 557). The zona fasciculata is the source of the steroids which have an oxygen atom at position 11. It is stimulated by the administration of ACTH, or by induced hy-

* "The adrenal medulla cooperates with sympathetic impulses in producing adrenalin. This sympathico-adrenal system is brought prominently and usefully into action in emotional excitement, in vigorous muscular work, in asphyxia, low blood pressure, chilling surroundings, and hypoglycemia—in brief, it serves effectively in emergencies; furthermore, this service can be given a general expression in stating that the system guards the constancy of the internal environment of the organism; and finally that secreted adrenalin itself acts to prolong the effects of nerve impulses, to accelerate metabolism, to shorten coagulation time, and to release glucose from the liver. There is no evidence that secreted adrenalin is an important agent in maintaining a high blood pressure" (Cannon).

perthyroidism or by alarm stimuli. It is depressed in hypothyroidism and after administration of the O-11 steroids. In man ACTH stimulates all three zones of the adrenal cortex.

When an animal is adrenalectomized, it dies soon afterward unless supported by injections of cortin. The important chemical findings after bilateral adrenalectomy are:

1. Decreased Na^+, Cl^-, bicarbonate and glucose in the serum.
2. Increased K^+ and NPN in the serum.
3. Decreased Na^+ in the muscle.
4. Increased K^+ and water in the muscle.
5. Decreased glycogen in the liver and muscle after fasting.
6. Increased excretion of Na^+, Cl^- and bicarbonate.
7. Decreased excretion of K^+ and total N.
8. Inability to excrete ingested water.

These findings are quite similar to those observed in *Addison's disease* in man. Addison's disease is characterized by the loss of function of the adrenals. The chemical alterations are very similar to those which take place in the adrenalectomized animal. It has been successfully treated with extracts from the cortex of the adrenals, and with 11-deoxycorticosterone (p. 557).

Adrenal Corticosteroids. As a result of work by many investigators over a period of 25 years, some 28 steroids have been isolated from the adrenal glands, and many from the urine, which appear to be related to adrenal metabolism, especially when associated with diseases of the adrenals. Only six of these steroids from the adrenals possess biological activity; the others probably represent metabolic intermediates. Of special interest is an amorphous fraction, still uncharacterized, which has considerable activity.

Figure 106 gives the formulas for the more important of the adrenal steroids. They are characterized by the fact that they contain 19 or 21 carbon atoms and in all instances C-11 is either unsubstituted (11-deoxy series) or bears a ketonic or alcoholic function (11-oxygenated series). Several are active with respect to only one metabolic dysfunction produced by adrenalectomy. Thus 11-deoxycorticosterone causes a retention of Na^+ and water but is without effect in maintaining normal carbohydrate metabolism. On the other hand, 17-hydroxycorticosterone is active in its effect on carbohydrate metabolism but has no effect on sodium retention. The following illustrates the importance of the various steroid hormones of the adrenal in a series of tests designed to show the repair of function in the adrenalectomized animal:

1. Recovery of fatigued muscle in the adrenalectomized rat: The most potent is 11-deoxycorticosterone.
2. Survival of adrenalectomized rats: All are active, but the most active is 11-deoxycorticosterone.
3. Na^+ and Cl^- retention in the dog: Again 11-deoxycorticosterone

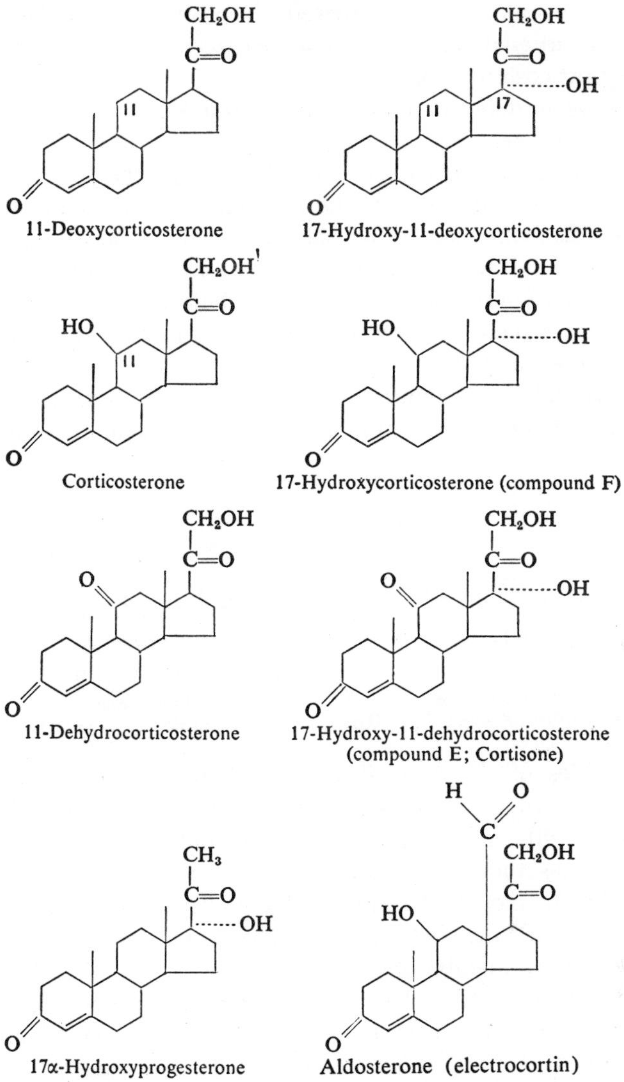

Figure 106. Biologically active adrenal steroids.

(DCA, as the acetate) is active; corticosterone is about one-half as active. 17-Hydroxycorticosterone and 17-hydroxy-11-dehydrocorticosterone are inactive.

4. Work performance under the influence of repeated electrical stimuli in the adrenalectomized rat: The most active are the 17-hydroxy steroids.

5. Prevention of insulin convulsions in the intact rat: Both of the 17-hydroxy compounds are most active, whereas the corticosterone and 11-dehydrocorticosterone are less active. 11-Deoxycorticosterone is inactive.

6. Diabetogenic action: Increased glycosuria in partially depancreatized and in adrenalectomized-depancreatized rats. Corticosterone and 17-hydroxycorticosterone are the most active.

7. Glycogen deposition in fasted adrenalectomized rats: The 17-hydroxy steroids are most active.

On the basis of such experimental findings, the following conclusions may be drawn in terms of the relationship of structure to activity:

1. For life maintenance and salt and water balance, one needs an α,β-unsaturated 3-ketone with a reducing α-keto grouping in the side-chain and a stable orientation of the side-chain at C-17.

2. For glycogenic potency, it is necessary to have a ketonic oxygen atom substituted at C-11.

Two synthetic compounds which have structures similar to that of cortisone and which are useful in clinical treatment are listed below:

Fluorocortisone
(Fluorohydrocortisone; C_{11} = OH)

Prednisone
(Prednisolone; C_{11} = OH)

Metabolites of the adrenal steroids appear in the urine. In man two groups of urinary steroids are associated with adrenal metabolism: the 17-ketosteroids and the glycogenic corticoids. Analysis of 17-ketosteroids determines the adrenal and testicular steroids of androgenic activity and their metabolic end products. These are concerned with nitrogen (protein) metabolism. The glycogenic steroids are concerned with carbohydrate metabolism.

The function of ACTH of the pituitary is believed to be one of stimulation of the adrenals to secrete 17-hydroxy-11-dehydrocorticosterone. Both ACTH and this adrenal steroid have been used with some success in the treatment of rheumatoid arthritis.

Origin of the Cortical Hormones. Based on some experimental evidence, the suggestion has been made that cholesterol may eventually prove to be the mother substance. Bloch has shown that when cholesterol (tagged with deuterium) is fed to pregnant women, pregnanediol containing the isotope could be recovered from the urine. Now pregnanediol is the normal urinary excretory product of progesterone, one of the female hormones, and this progesterone has even been isolated from the adrenals by Reichstein.

Also, in this connection, it may be noticed that when the adrenocorticotropic hormone of the pituitary (which controls the secretory activity of the adrenals) is injected, the cholesterol (and, incidentally, the ascorbic acid) is decreased; at the same time, there is an increased rate of secretion of the adrenal cortical hormones. All this suggests that the adrenal cholesterol is a direct precursor of the adrenal cortical steroids (Long).

The metabolic interrelationships of the biologically active adrenal steroids are shown below:

Corticosterone → Compound F
↑ ↑
Deoxycorticosterone → 11-Deoxycortisol
↑ ↑
Progesterone → 17-Hydroxyprogesterone

Deoxycorticosterone → Aldosterone

Adrenals and Sex. The cortex of the adrenals also elaborates substances belonging to the group of sex hormones.* Abnormal changes in sex may sometimes be due to disturbances in the adrenal cortex involving sex hormones. The female assumes male secondary sex characteristics and at the same time certain female characteristics become repressed. This is a type of masculinity or virilism known as "adrenal virilism." The cases are less frequent in the male; but when they do occur, the tendency is towards feminization—enlargement of the breasts, genital atrophy, etc.

These developments are due, first, to the fact that the adrenals manufacture androgens and estrogens, male and female hormones (which is, apparently, a perfectly normal function); but, second, that owing to some unknown cause, the hormones may be produced in excessive amounts, or their normal metabolism may be disturbed—in any case, giving rise to these sex changes.

Reichstein and others have isolated several compounds from beef adrenals which are androgens, or male hormones. One of them, adrenosterone, shows a capon comb test equivalent to one-fifth that of androsterone. Adrenosterone has been obtained artificially from 11-dehydro-17-hydroxycorticosterone, a compound which has already been included among the cortical hormones and which is effective to some extent in maintaining life after adrenalectomy.

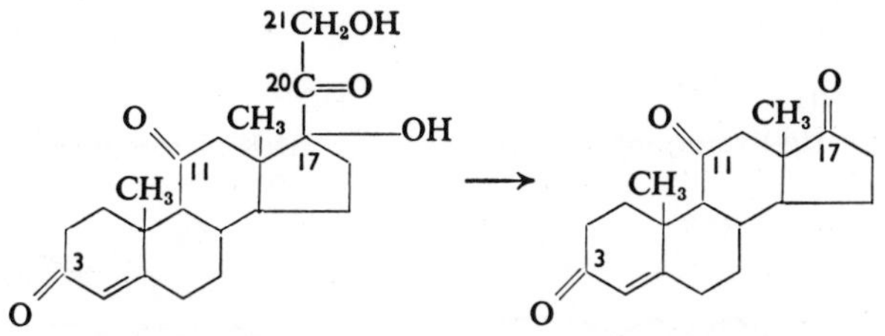

11-Dehydro-17-hydroxycorticosterone Adrenosterone

* The following paragraphs might be read in conjunction with the section dealing with the sex hormones.

It is also of interest to note that often malignant cortical tumors (adrenal carcinoma, for example) give rise to the excretion in excessive quantities of androgens; and this irrespective of the sex of the patient.

One of a number of these androgens isolated from the urine is de-hydroisoandrosterone, a compound which is excreted in small amounts by normal men and women and which probably means that its source is in the adrenals rather than in the reproductive organs.

From such observations it seems reasonable to conclude that not all of the androgens excreted by normal subjects have their source in the gonads, but some of them, at least, are derived from the adrenal cortex. It is significant that the urine of eunuchs and of ovariectomized women still shows the presence of androgens.

Large amounts of estrogens, or female hormones, are sometimes excreted in cases of virilism. Here, too, it may be noted that the urine of male and female castrates shows some estrogenic activity, suggesting the adrenal cortex as the origin of such substances. The typical estrogen, estrone, has actually been isolated from adrenal glands.

Are the compounds in the adrenals which are related to the sex compounds merely by-products of truly cortical substances manufactured by the gland? Or are they specifically manufactured by the adrenal cortex to help regulate normal sex functions?

The following two androgenic (male) hormones produced by the adrenal gland are metabolized as follows:

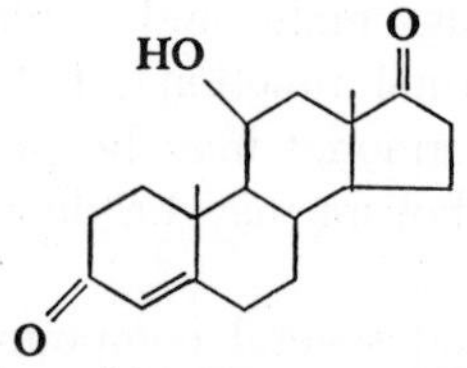

11β-Hydroxy-Δ⁴-androstene-3,17-dione 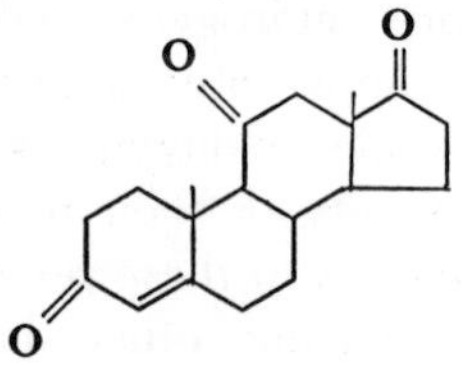   Adrenosterone

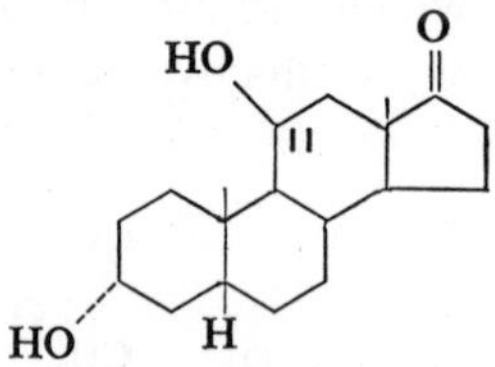

11β-Hydroxyandrosterone 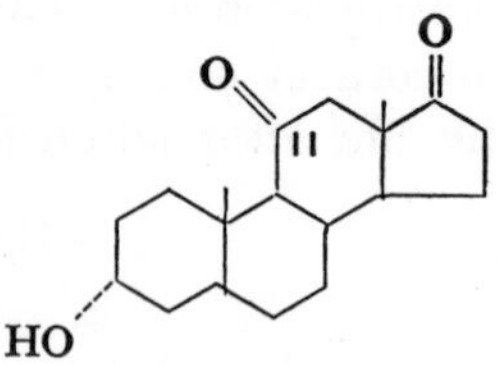   11-Ketoandrosterone

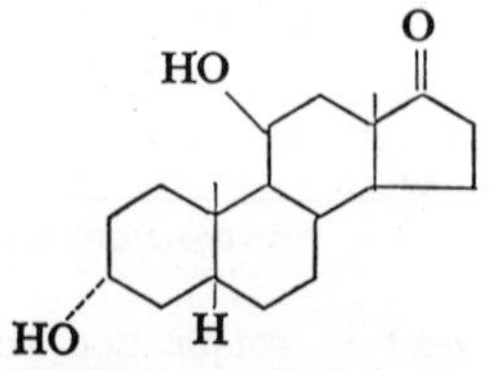

3α,11β-Dihydroxyetiocholan-17-one 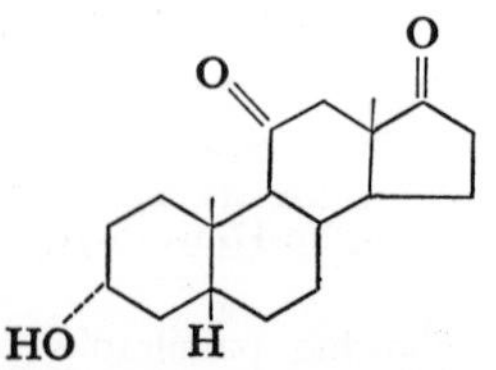   3α-Hydroxyetiocholane-3,17-dione

THE SEX HORMONES

Under the stimulation of hormones from the anterior pituitary (gona-dotropic hormones), the sex hormones in the testes and in the ovary are secreted.

The genital tract and the accessory male organs are influenced by the male hormones. One method of detecting the presence of an active extract is to observe its effect on the growth of comb and wattles in a capon. The cocks are castrated; this is followed by a shriveling of the comb and wattles. The injection of a potent extract causes a renewal of growth of these secondary sex organs (Funk and Harrow; Koch and Gallagher).

In the female two types of hormones are found to function. One type, as represented by estradiol, is a product of the ovary; the other, progesterone (progestin), is derived from the corpus luteum, which is formed after the ovum is ruptured and expelled. Both hormones control the uterine cycle.

Under the influence of the hormones from the anterior pituitary (the sex-stimulating hormones, or gonadotropins), the ovary elaborates female hormone (estradiol) which causes the endometrium—the membrane that lines the uterus—to grow; and it also elaborates progesterone, or corpus luteum hormone, which causes the endometrial glands to secrete and transforms connective tissue (stroma) into decidua-like cells. These changes are necessary for the implantation of the fertilized ovum.

The normal menstrual cycle occurs only when conception has not taken place. Here the hormones involved ultimately decrease in concentration and the endometrium degenerates.

Where impregnation has occurred, the corpus luteum increases in size and continues to function until nearly the end of pregnancy.

Figure 107 shows the comparative concentration of three of the hormones eliminated (in the urine) during pregnancy. One of them, a gonadotropic hormone found in pregnancy urine, is used as the basis for the Aschheim-Zondek test for pregnancy. One method is to inject the urine into immature mice. On the fourth day the animals are killed and the ovaries examined for hemorrhagic spots (blutpunkte) and yellowish protrusions (developed corpora lutea).

The Friedman test for pregnancy, a modification of the Aschheim-Zondek test, makes use of the rabbit. The urine under examination is injected into the marginal ear vein of a mature female rabbit. The ovaries are examined 24 hours later. The presence of ruptured or hemorrhagic follicles is an indication of pregnancy.

The hormones of the estrin type, of which estradiol, found in the ovary, is the most potent, are detected by the Allen and Doisy test: the production of estrus (with complete cornification of the vaginal mucosa as judged from a smear) in ovariectomized sexually mature rats. The

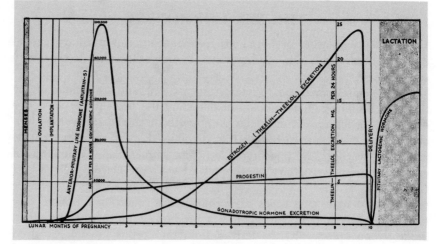

Figure 107. Hormone excretion in pregnancy. Three important hormones, which profoundly influence physiologic conditions in pregnancy, are excreted by the kidneys. Chorionic gonadotropin appears in the urine; 24-hour excretion rises from less than 20,000 rat units to about 200,000 rat units during the first two lunar months. After a rapid decrease in excretion a level of approximately 10,000 rat units is reached at the sixth lunar month and maintained until delivery.

Combined estrogen excretion in 24 hours does not rise beyond 5 mg. during the first half of pregnancy; it increases rapidly during subsequent months, reaching a peak of more than 20 mg. during the tenth lunar month. Precipitous decline occurs during the last week, values reaching the nonpregnant normal at or shortly after parturition.

Corpus luteum hormone is essential to early pregnancy and plays a vital role in the pregravid phase of each menstrual cycle; it is excreted as pregnanediol. After the second lunar month, the level of progesterone mounts slowly until parturition, after which it drops sharply. (From Therapeutic Notes, July, 1938, p. 197, courtesy of Parke, Davis & Co.)

basis of the test for progesterone (progestin), as developed by Corner and Hisaw, is that it exerts a specific proliferative action on the uterine endometrium.

One method of obtaining active extracts from pregnancy urine involves, first, the fact that the active factors are soluble in fat solvents; second, that the hormones can be saponified without destruction; and third, that they can be recovered after saponification by first acidifying and extracting with ether.

In an alcohol-benzene mixture most of the estriol (see below) is taken up by alcohol and almost all the estrone by benzene.

Doisy and also Butenandt, in 1929, isolated the follicular hormone (estrone) from pregnancy urine. In 1931, Butenandt obtained a hormone from male urine (androsterone). In 1934, W. Allen, Wintersteiner, Butenandt, and others obtained a crystalline corpus luteum hormone (progesterone) from swine ovaries.

OVARIAN HORMONES (ESTROGENS)

The following substances of the estrone group have been isolated: (1) estrone (pregnancy urine, stallion urine, mare urine, and palm kernels); (2) estradiol (ovaries and mare urine); (3) estriol (placenta, pregnancy urine); (4) equilin (mare urine); (5) equilenin (mare urine).

The principal hormone produced by the ovary is estradiol. Estriol

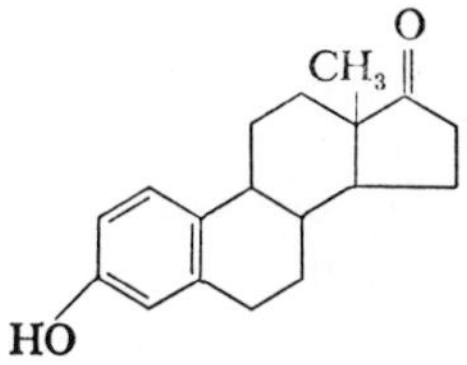

Estrone, $C_{18}H_{22}O_2$
(Theelin)
(3-hydroxy-17-keto-Δ1,-3,5-estratriene)

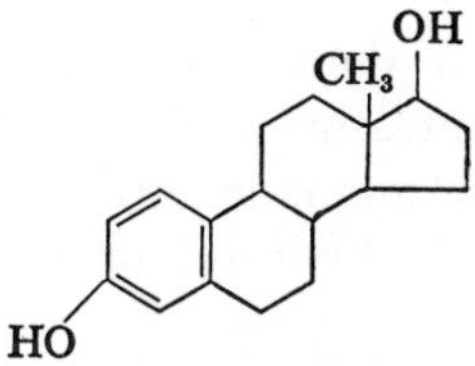

Estradiol, $C_{18}H_{24}O_2$
(Dihydrotheelin)
(3,17-dihydroxy-Δ1,3,5-estratriene)

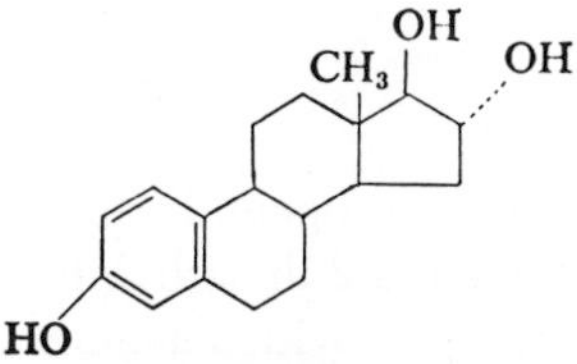

Estriol, $C_{18}H_{24}O_3$
(Theelol)
(3,16,17-trihydroxy-Δ1,3,5-estratriene)

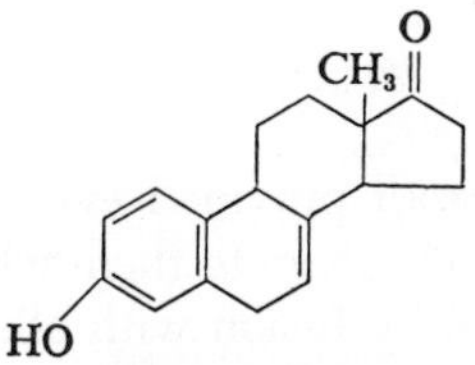

Equilin, $C_{18}H_{20}O_2$
(3-hydroxy-17-keto-Δ1,3,-5,7-estratetraene)

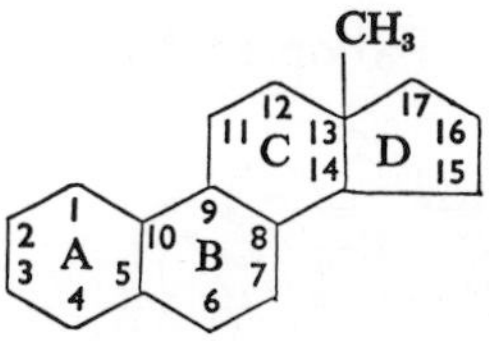

Estrane, $C_{18}H_{30}$
(parent hydrocarbon)

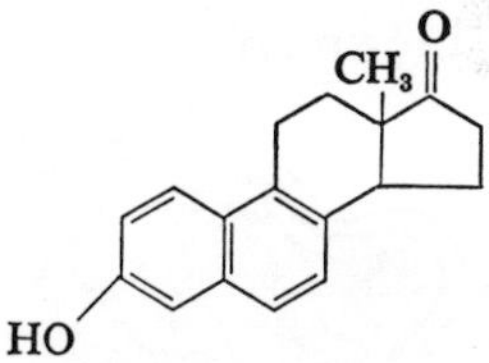

Equilenin, $C_{18}H_{18}O_2$
(3-hydroxy-17-keto-Δ1,3,-5,6,8-estrapentaene)

is the chief hormone found in human pregnancy urine and in human placenta. (For a drawing of the uterus, etc., see Fig. 108.)

Since some of the rings in the compounds are true benzene rings and others are hydrogenated, one of them, estrone, is rewritten as follows:

The chemical structure diagram:

$$
\begin{array}{c}
\text{H}_2\text{C} \quad \text{CH}_3 \quad \overset{\text{O}}{\overset{\|}{\text{C}}} \\
\text{H}_2\text{C} \quad \text{C} \quad \text{CH}_2 \\
\text{H—C} \quad \text{C—CH}_2 \\
\text{H—C} \quad \text{C} \quad \text{C—H} \quad \text{H} \\
\text{HO—C} \quad \text{C} \quad \text{CH}_2 \\
\text{C} \quad \text{C} \\
\text{H} \quad \text{H}_2
\end{array}
$$

In all of these compounds the first ring is a truly aromatic one, and the OH represents a phenolic hydroxyl group. In equilenin, the second ring is also aromatic. At the other end of the molecule, we find (*a*) carbonyl, (*b*) hydroxyl, or (*c*) glycol arrangements:

$$
\begin{array}{ccc}
\overset{\text{O}}{\underset{\displaystyle C}{\|}} & \overset{\text{H} \quad \text{OH}}{\underset{\displaystyle C}{\diagdown\diagup}} & \overset{\text{H} \quad \text{OH}}{\underset{\displaystyle C}{\diagdown\diagup}} \\
(a) & (b) & (c)
\end{array}
$$

Butenandt provided evidence that these compounds have the four-ring structure given to them when he obtained 1,2-dimethylphenanthrene from estriol by fusion with alkali and reduction with selenium and zinc dust. Further confirmation came from the work of Cook, who converted

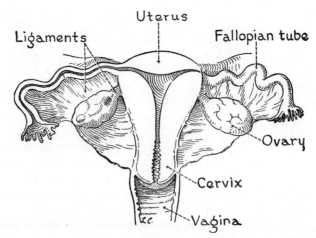

Figure 108. Vertical section of the uterus and its appendages. (Etheredge: Health Facts.)

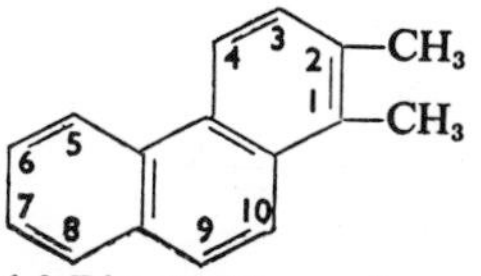

1,2-Dimethylphenanthrene

estrone into a derivative of cyclopentanophenanthrene (A), the structure of which was proved by synthesis:

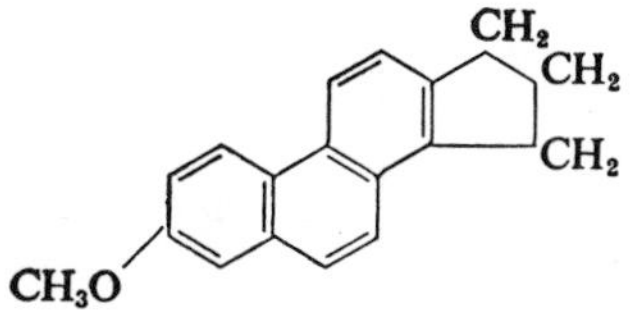

7-Methoxyl-1,2-cyclopentanoperhydrophenanthrene (A)

(Notice that phenanthrene compounds are numbered differently from compounds derived from estrone.)

This chemical work made it clear that the female hormones belonged to the steroid group, of which cholesterol is so prominent a member. This also means that these estrogens are chemically related to androgens (p. 572), to hormones in the adrenal cortex, to progesterone (p. 569), and to bile acids.

Estradiol. As has been pointed out, estradiol is found mainly in the ovaries, and it is believed to be the mother substance of estrone and estriol.

Estradiol can occur in two stereochemical forms with respect to the position of the hydroxyl group on C-17. These are called alpha and beta. In the older literature the more active form was called "alpha." However, it is now called beta-estradiol. The alpha-estradiol form is excreted in the urine when the beta form is administered to animals.

Metabolism. There is much that is conflicting in this field. The simplest hypothesis is to suggest that estradiol, the main product of the ovary, and the most potent of the various estrogenic substances, is changed and ultimately eliminated as estrone and estriol. However, there is evidence to show that the conversion of estradiol to estrone is a reversible process in the human body. Furthermore, the administration of estrone (in large doses, to be sure) enables one to extract estriol from the urine. These and other reactions have suggested the pathways shown on page 566. Of these compounds, all but the two compounds enclosed in brackets have been isolated from tissues and/or urine. The reactions listed with question marks have not been experimentally confirmed.

That the liver is involved in several of these metabolic changes was demonstrated when estradiol was perfused through the liver, and was converted—partly, at least—to estrone and estriol. When, however, estrone was perfused through the liver, it was partly converted into estradiol and estriol. Repetition of the experiment, using estriol as the starting material, did not lead to the production of any more active product. Finally, continued perfusion of these estrogens destroyed all estrogenic activity (Schiller).

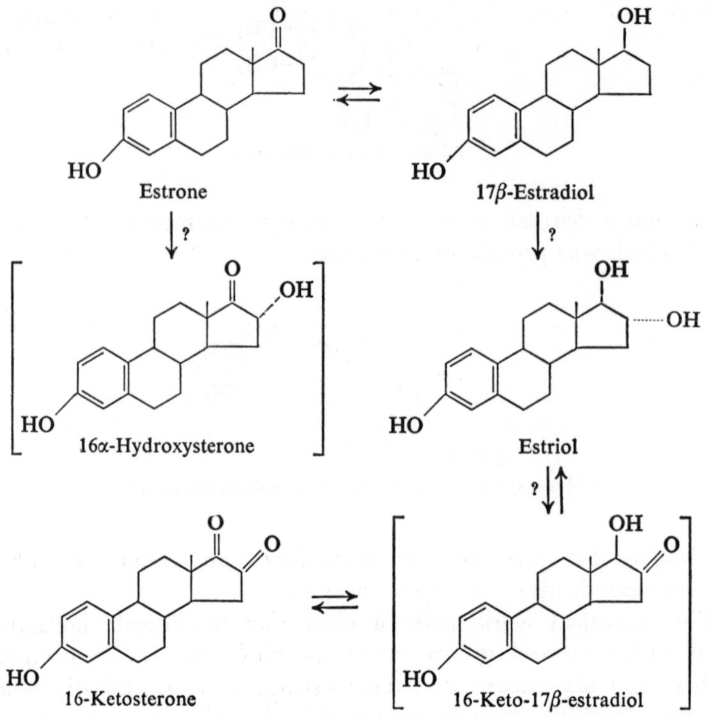

It has also been possible to show that an enzyme system in the liver catalyzes the conversion of estradiol to estrone.

Some two-thirds of the estrogen transported by the blood to the tissues is said to be bound to protein, and as such is biologically inactive. This protein-estrogen combination is in equilibrium with free estrogen or estrogen-glucuronide, which when removed by tissues causes a partial dissociation of the protein-estrogen complex to create a new equilibrium. It is suggested that the liver is involved in the formation of this complex.

The estrogens are largely excreted in a combined form with glucuronic acid. The combined form is more water-soluble and less biologically active than the original estrogen. There is evidence, too, that the estrogens may be partly eliminated in combination with sulfuric acid.

As in most conjugations of this kind, the reaction probably occurs in the liver.

Stilbestrol. Several derivatives containing the *p*-hydroxyphenyl group have shown potent estrogenic activity. The best known of these compounds is stilbestrol

$$HO\langle\!\!\!\bigcirc\!\!\!\rangle\!-\!\underset{\underset{C_2H_5}{|}}{C}\!=\!\underset{\underset{C_2H_5}{|}}{C}\!-\!\langle\!\!\!\bigcirc\!\!\!\rangle OH$$

a substance which can be synthesized at relatively low cost, and which, if given in sufficient dosage, is potent orally. Its possible disadvantage is that it may prove somewhat toxic.

Stilbestrol is eliminated, at least partly, as the glucuronide, and, to a much smaller extent, as the ethereal sulfate.

Stilbestrol has also proved of some value in the treatment of cancer of the prostate. Colston and Brendler claim that 75 per cent of patients under this treatment will shcw "objective regression of the primary growth." The malignant cells require androgen (male hormone) "for their viability"; and it is possible that the stilbestrol neutralizes the effect of the androgen.

Whether we are dealing with the natural or with the synthetic estrogens, the compounds are often administered in the form of their esters (as benzoates or propionates) to allow for a more prolonged action.

CORPUS LUTEUM HORMONE (PROGESTERONE)

This hormone is found in the female during the second stage of the monthly cycle. It makes its appearance in the cavity of the ruptured follicle after the egg has developed and continues the action of the female hormone in the development of the mucous membrane of the uterus. It acts on the uterus so that this organ may receive and nourish the fertilized ovum. "When an ovum begins its journey through the fallopian tube, the follicle from which it took origin gives place to the corpus luteum, and this organ thereupon delivers into the blood stream a substance, progesterone, that has the property of causing extensive development of the endometrium, preparing the uterus for the reception and nutrition of the embryo." (Corner.)

Isolation. The hormone has been prepared in crystalline form from ovarian extracts by a number of workers (among them, Butenandt, W. Allen, Wintersteiner, Slotta). Its formula is $C_{21}H_{30}O_2$ and it is a tetracyclic diketone. It has been prepared artificially from several substances: from cholesterol, from pregnanediol (Marrian) found in pregnancy urine, and from stigmasterol, a plant sterol.

Metabolism. Pregnanediol is the chief product of excretion of the corpus luteum hormone. During the latter half of the menstrual cycle, from 1 to 10 mg. daily of sodium pregnanediol glucuronidate may be recovered from the urine. The presence of pregnanediol in the urine indicates a progestational endometrium, and its absence, a follicular endometrium.

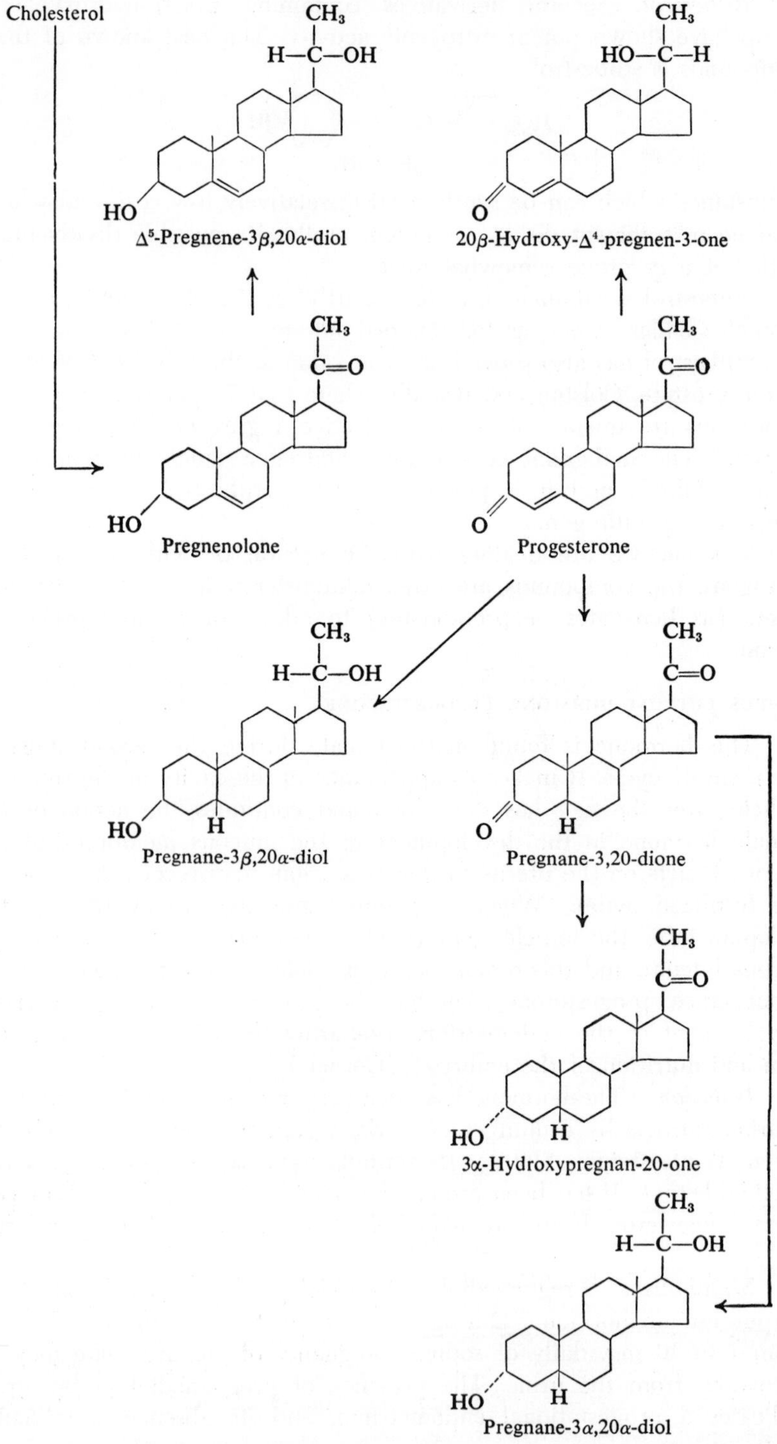
Cholesterol
CH3
H—C—OH
HO
Δ5-Pregnene-3β,20α-diol
CH3
HO—C—H
O
20β-Hydroxy-Δ4-pregnen-3-one
CH3
C=O
HO
Pregnenolone
CH3
C=O
O
Progesterone
CH3
H—C—OH
HO
H
Pregnane-3β,20α-diol
CH3
C=O
O
H
Pregnane-3,20-dione
CH3
C=O
HO
H
3α-Hydroxypregnan-20-one
CH3
H—C—OH
HO
H
Pregnane-3α,20α-diol

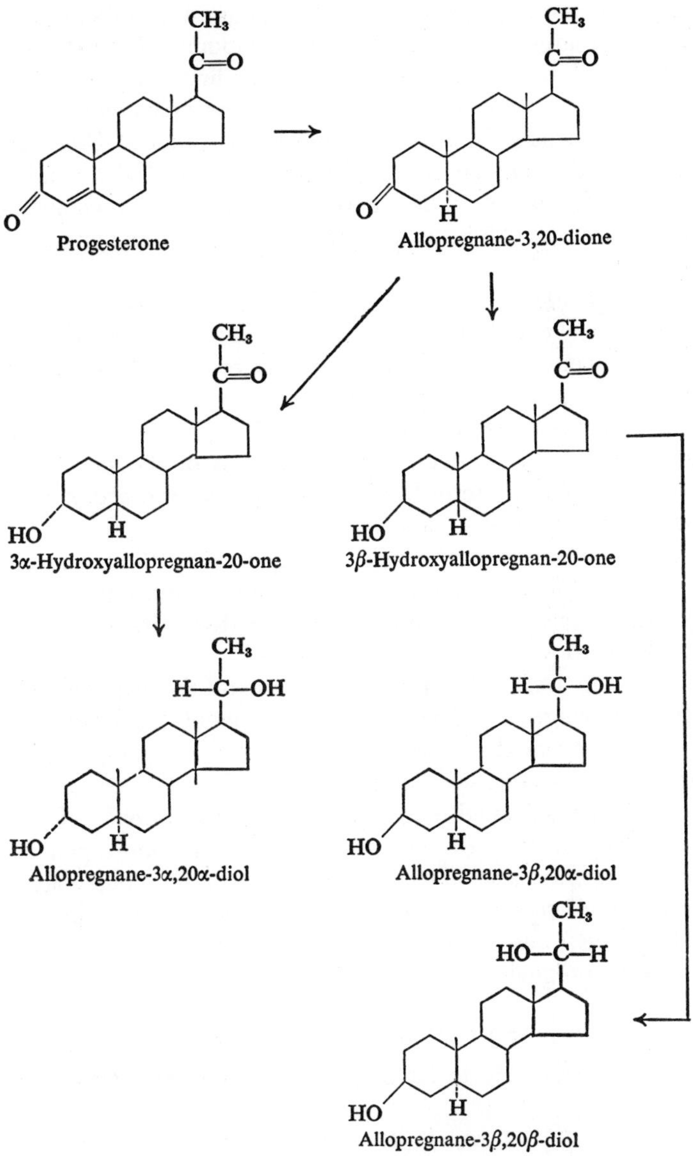

An important contribution to the metabolism of progesterone was made by Bloch. Cholesterol, containing deuterium in the side-chain and in the nucleus, was fed to a woman in the eighth month of pregnancy. At this stage enough pregnanediol glucuronidate was excreted in a day for a deuterium analysis. The glucuronidate was isolated and found to contain significant concentrations of the isotope.

Since pregnanediol, in this instance, is a metabolic product of progesterone, this experiment implies that cholesterol can be transformed in the body into progesterone.

The schemes on pages 568 and 569 suggest metabolic pathways. They are based largely on the isolation of compounds from the urine and on changes which take place in the tissues. The first scheme illustrates the formation of the pregnane series, in which pregnanediol is the compound called pregnane-3α-20α-diol. Here the H atom at C-5 bears a *cis* relationship to the angular methyl group at C-10. The second scheme illustrates the formation of the allopregnane series of compounds, in which the H atom at C-5 bears a *trans* relationship to the angular methyl group at C-10.

Cholesterol, then, may perhaps be regarded as a precursor of steroid hormones and bile acids, though the quantities of cholesterol used for such conversions are negligible as compared to those present in animal tissues.

These metabolic activities of cholesterol apply to tissues other than the brain, for though relatively large quantities of the sterol are found in the brain, such cholesterol has been shown to be metabolically inert: "it is not regenerated at a detectable rate."

The female secretes not only estrogens (female hormones) and progesterone, but also a considerable amount of androgens (male hormones). Androgens are probably formed by the adrenal cortex rather than by the ovaries.

Therapeutic Use. The therapeutic use of the estrogens is based upon the following: (*a*) developmental action of the reproductive organs (e.g. hypogenitalism, or sexual infantilism); (*b*) inhibition of pituitary hormones (e.g., excessive lactation after delivery and in treatment of menopausal syndrome); and (*c*) constitutional effects (e.g., increase in muscle strength, etc.). This last one is more open to doubt.

The therapeutic use of the corpus luteum hormone may include the production of secretory endometrium (often indicated by functional uterine bleeding), and inhibition of uterine motility (as a possible protection during pregnancy).

STEROID STRUCTURES AND NOMENCLATURE

Just as it is possible to have *cis* and *trans* forms of the compound 2-butene,

$$CH_3—C—H \qquad CH_3—C—H$$
$$CH_3—C—H \qquad H—C—CH_3$$

Cis-2-butene   *Trans*-2-butene

so it is possible to have a similar type of stereoisomerism in ring structures, as in the decalins:

Cis-decalin   *Trans*-decalin

The dotted line indicates that the H atom is related to the upper H atom in a different space relationship than when there is a solid line.

Among the steroids, isomerism is possible in a number of places, since there are many asymmetric carbon atoms. Thus, isomerism around C-3 concerns the relationship of the OH group at this position to the angular methyl group attached to C-10. If the OH group among the androgens is *cis* to this methyl group, it is called a member of the β series; if it is *trans*, it is called a member of the α series. The same holds for the OH group at position 17.

MALE HORMONES (ANDROGENS)

"The testicle," writes Moore, "exercises two principal functions; it produces spermatozoa, which are necessary for fertilization, and it secretes a substance or substances (hormone) that play an important role in the organism. This hormone regulates the function of numerous special accessory reproductive organs: epididymis, vas deferens, prostate, seminal vesicles, penis, etc., that make possible the delivery of spermatozoa to the place where fertilization can occur; and at least in subprimate vertebrates the hormone initiates the sexual drive, or inclinations to mate with females. The sex urge in man is not so clearly or exclusively dependent upon hormone action since imitation, custom, and psychology play such a great role in human conduct." (See Fig. 109.)

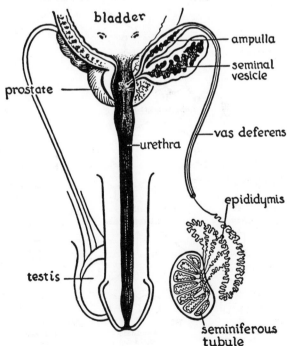

Figure 109. The male reproductive system. (Gerard: The Body Functions. John Wiley & Sons.)

A number of extracts bring response in the male hormone tests (comb growth in the capon, for example). An active extract, responding in the comb test, may be prepared from the urine of males by extracting an acidified portion with an organic solvent, such as chloroform, evaporating the chloroform from the extract, heating the residue with sodium hydroxide, extracting the active material with ether, evaporating the ether, and incorporating the residue with oil (Funk, Harrow, and Lejwa).

A potent extract injected into a castrated cock over a period of 18 days will produce well developed comb and wattles.

Androgens represent the active products of the testes, ovaries, adrenal cortex and possibly the placenta. The most active of these androgens is testosterone. Its biosynthesis is controlled, in part, by the gonadotropic hormones.

The steroid androgens which are found in the blood are dehydroepiandrosterone (adrenals), Δ^4-androstene-3,17-dione (testes, adrenals), testosterone (testes), 11β-hydroxy-Δ^4-androstene-3,17-dione (adrenals) and adrenosterone (adrenals).

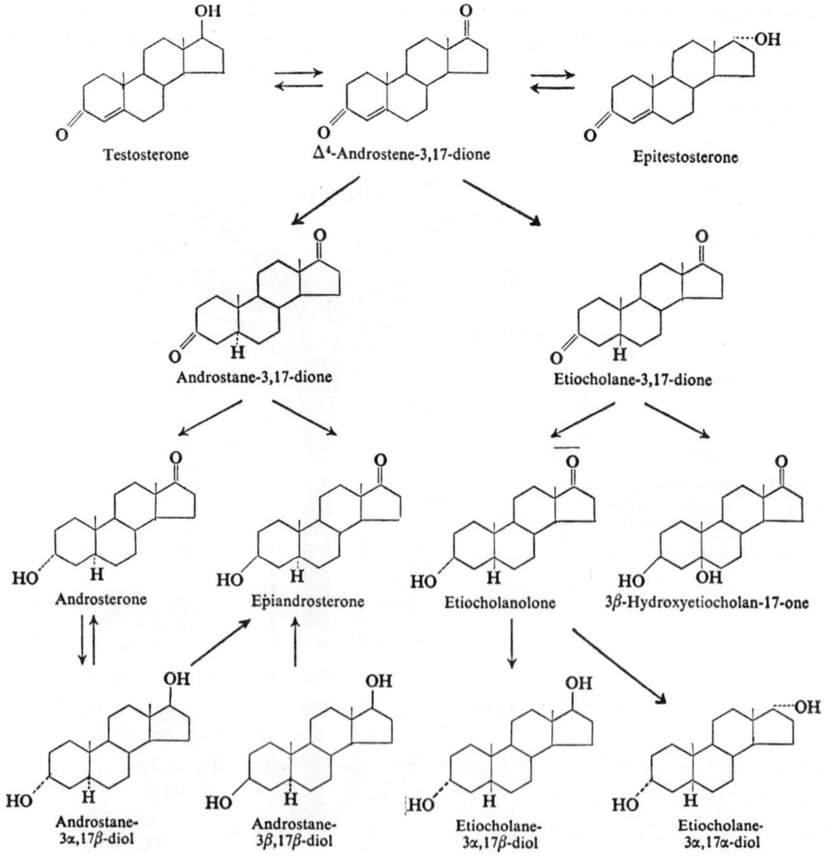

Testosterone　　　Δ^4-Androstene-3,17-dione　　　Epitestosterone

Androstane-3,17-dione　　　Etiocholane-3,17-dione

Androsterone　　　Epiandrosterone　　　Etiocholanolone　　　3β-Hydroxyetiocholan-17-one

Androstane-3α,17β-diol　　　Androstane-3β,17β-diol　　　Etiocholane-3α,17β-diol　　　Etiocholane-3α,17α-diol

In addition the following relationships exist:

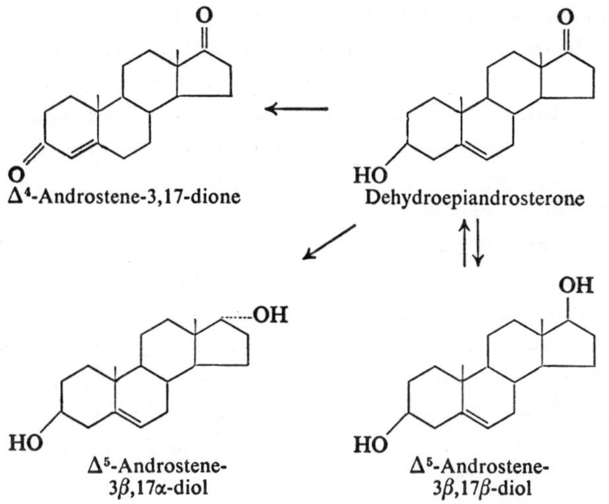

Δ^4-Androstene-3,17-dione

Dehydroepiandrosterone

Δ^5-Androstene-
3β,17α-diol

Δ^5-Androstene-
3β,17β-diol

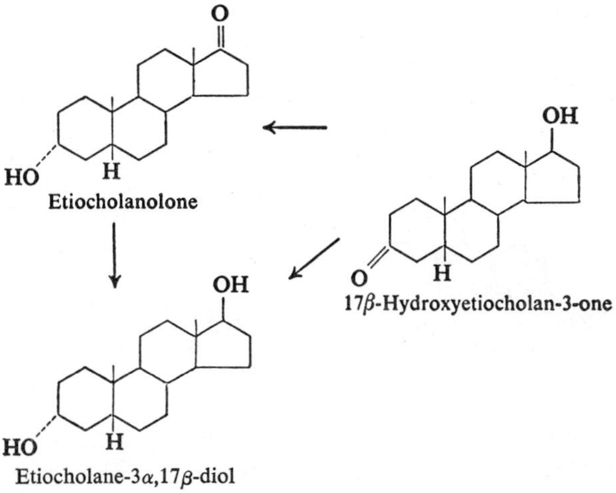

Etiocholanolone

17β-Hydroxyetiocholan-3-one

Etiocholane-3α,17β-diol

The metabolic interrelationships among the androgens are shown in the accompanying schemes. Evidence for the existence of these steroids is based on isolation and identification of the products from tissues and from urine. In these schemes the catabolism of the three principal tissue androgens—testosterone, Δ^4-androstene-3,17-dione, and dehydroepiandrosterone—is considered. In man the most important products (from a quantitative standpoint) are androsterone and etiocholanolone; dehydroepiandrosterone is, to a large extent, excreted unchanged.

Of these substances testosterone is physiologically the most powerful and is considered the parent hormone in the testes.

Metabolism and Elimination. A number of products of the metabolism of testosterone are found in the urine. The principal product is androsterone, which has a very marked physiological potency, though not so powerful as testosterone. Androsterone and some five other chemically closely related substances belong to the group known as the 17-ketosteroids (because of a ketone group in position 17) and are all metabolic products of testosterone.

The estrogens, it has been seen, are eliminated, at least partly, as glucuronides and as sulfate. This is also true of the androgens.

Androsterone and other 17-ketosteroids are found in both male and female urines. Since these substances have been isolated from the urine of eunuchs and from the urine of ovariectomized women, the genital glands are not always necessarily the originators of such compounds. There is reason to believe that under certain conditions the adrenal glands manufacture these substances.

Chemistry. Based on chemical work somewhat analogous with that on the female hormones, it was possible for Butenandt to predict the tetracyclic nature of these substances. This view was further strengthened by the successful reduction of estrone into octahydroestrone (absorption of eight hydrogen atoms), giving a product which responded to male hormone tests:

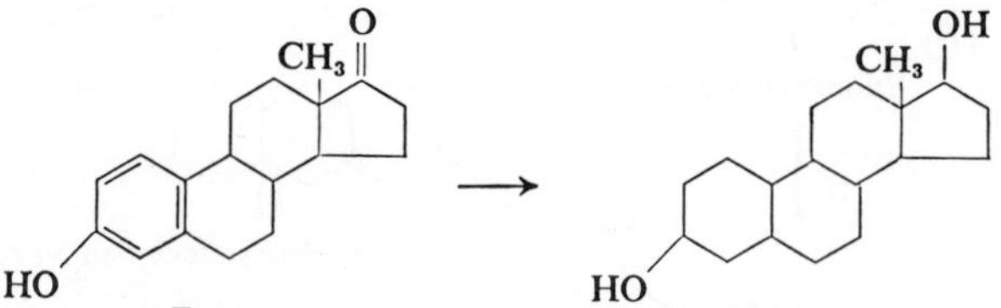

Estrone   Octahydroestrone

A very important advance in our knowledge of these structures was the success attained by Ruzicka in converting a cholesterol derivative into androsterone, one of the male hormones.

Testosterone has also been prepared artificially, starting with dehydroandrosterone.

The biosynthesis of testosterone has been accomplished by showing that testicular tissue slices can convert labeled acetate to the hormone.

Therapeutic Use. Clinically, the androgen favored is testosterone in the form of the propionate (in which form, absorption and elimination are delayed). Here, as in the case of the natural estrogens, injections are much more effective than when the hormone is given orally.

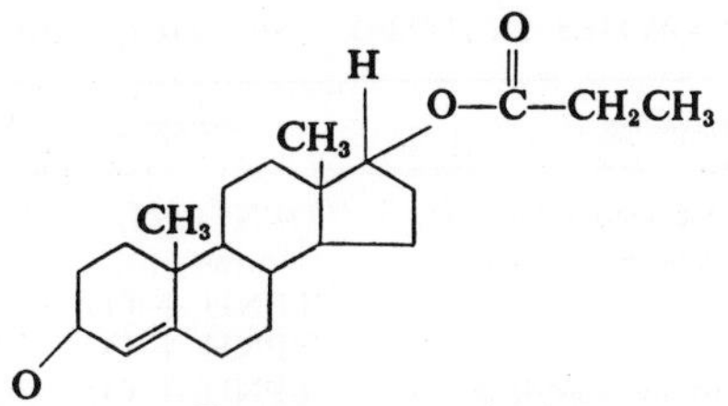

Testosterone propionate

In this connection, methyl testosterone (where the H at C-17 in testosterone is replaced by CH_3) is said to be much more active than the mother substance.

The testosterone in use is derived from cholesterol. This is in contrast to estradiol which, so far, cannot be made cheaply enough by any synthetic process.

Testosterone propionate is of value in eunuchoidism, serving as replacement therapy, but many other claims are hardly warranted. It has practically no effect in psychic impotence or as an aphrodisiac.

Testosterone has been shown to be active in stimulating protein synthesis (its anabolic activity). This is reflected by an increase in body weight (skeletal muscle) and a decrease in nitrogen excretion in the urine.

The formulas for two synthetic substances which resemble testosterone are shown below.

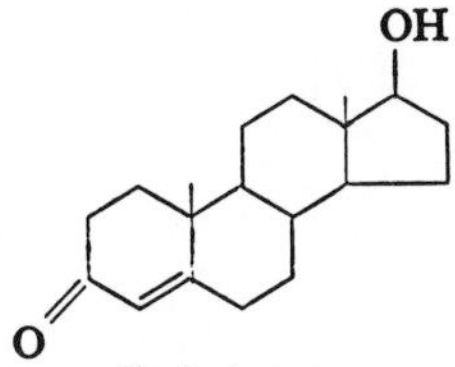

Testosterone

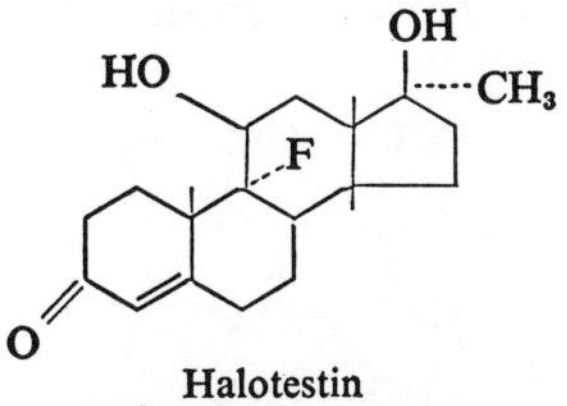

Halotestin
($11\beta,17\beta$-dihydroxy-
9α-fluoro, 17-methyl-
4-androstene-3 one)

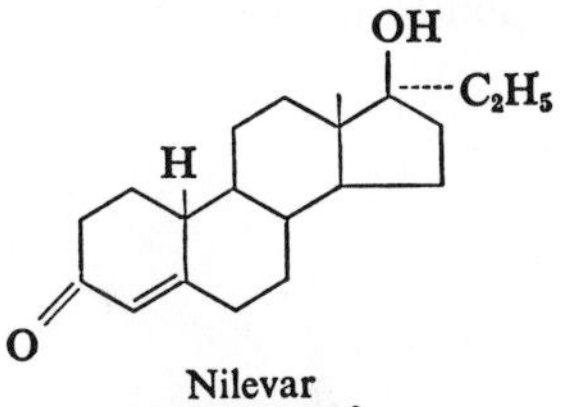

Nilevar
(17α-ethyl,17β-
hydroxy-norandrosterone

Halotestin has 10 times the androgenic activity of methyl testosterone and 20 times its anabolic activity, whereas Nilevar has one-sixteenth the androgenic activity but a high anabolic effect.

For hormone units, see Table 85, page 578.

ENZYMES IN STEROID HORMONE METABOLISM

Table 84 presents a summary of the enzymes which have been identified in biosynthetic reactions of the steroid hormones. They are found in those tissues associated with the synthesis of the hormone and will be found to be associated with different parts of the cell structure.

TABLE 84.   ENZYMES IN STEROID HORMONE METABOLISM

Enzyme System	Coenzyme	Cell fraction
3β-Hydroxysteroid dehydrogenase	DPN(TPN)	Microsomes
Δ⁴-Δ⁵ Steroid isomerase	none	Supernatant
17α-Hydroxylase	TPNH + O₂	Microsomes
21-Hydroxylase	TPNH + O₂	Microsomes
17α-Hydroxysteroid hydroxylase (side-chain-splitting)	TPNH + O₂	Microsomes
11β-Hydroxylase	TPNH + O₂	Mitochondria
18-Hydroxylase	TPNH + O₂	
17β-Hydroxysteroid dehydrogenase	TPN, (DPN)	Microsomes
17β-Estradiol dehydrogenase	DPN, (TPN)	Supernatant
20α-Hydroxysteroid dehydrogenase	TPN(DPN)	Supernatant
19-Hydroxylase	TPNH + O₂	
Aromatizing system	TPNH + O₂	Microsomes

(From Samuels, in Metabolic Pathways, edited by Greenberg, Vol. 1, Academic Press, 1960.)

SYNTHETIC SUBSTANCES SHOWING PHYSIOLOGICAL PROPERTIES

Slight modifications in structure—the change of a carbonyl group to a secondary alcoholic group—may markedly change the physiological activity of a compound. Many compounds have been made which can produce estrus; some are but distantly related to the original estrane structure. For example, a derivative of dibenzanthracene (A) corresponds in its activity to the natural estriol.

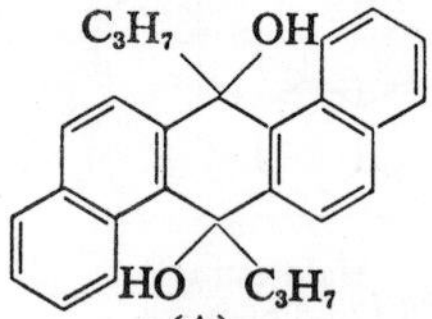

(A)

This substance (A), incidentally, shows not only estrogenic properties but also cancer-producing activities; for, when applied continuously to the skin of a mouse over a period of time, there develops a malignant tumor. The same is true of a compound, methylcholanthrene, which may be obtained artificially from deoxycholic acid, one of the acids of the bile (Fieser).

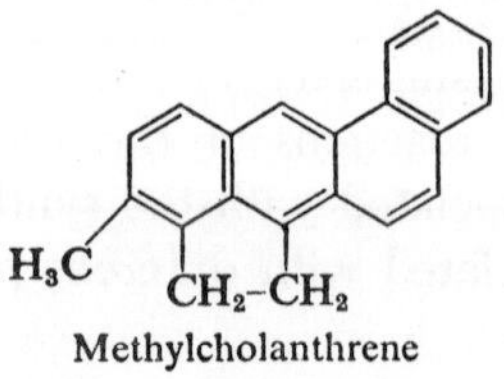

Methylcholanthrene

We have already discussed stilbestrol, a synthetic compound with powerful estrogenic properties.

Butenandt has prepared compounds to bring about a reversal in physiological action. For example, 6-oxo-testosterone, derived from testosterone, shows no testicular action but a very definite follicular action.

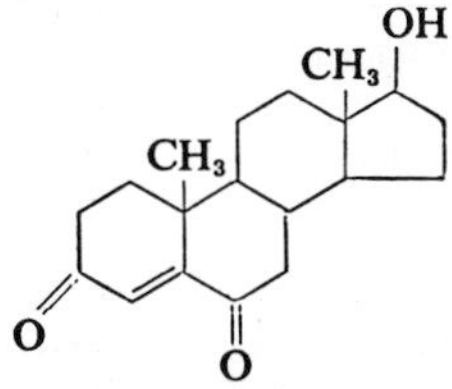

6-Oxo-testosterone

This change from male hormone to female hormone activity is also illustrated by the conversion of androstanedione to $\Delta^{1,2}$-androstenedione, which produces complete estrus in a castrated female mouse when in-

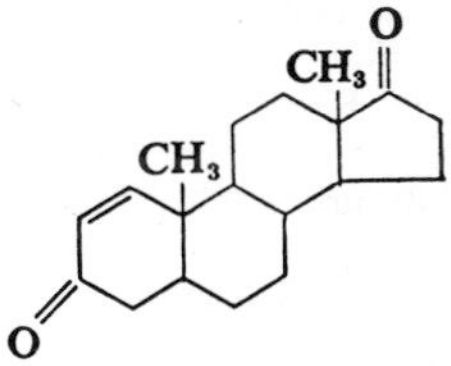

$\Delta^{1,2}$-Androstenedione

jected; but even 4 mg. of the material still fails to cause growth of the comb of the capon. "In this example," as Butenandt says, "the difference between a male and female substance is merely the position of the double bond in ring I." But he has even gone one step further. He has obtained a substance, androstenediol, from dehydroandrosterone, which shows both male and female properties.

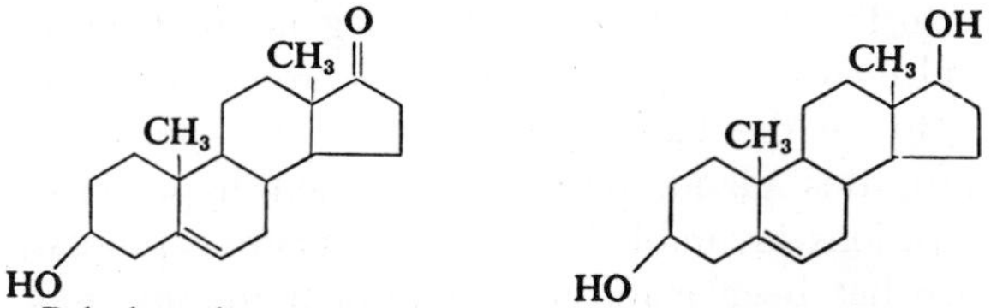

Dehydroandrosterone   Androstenediol
♂   ♂ ♀

HORMONES AND CARCINOGENESIS

It has already been pointed out that derivatives of dibenzanthracene and methylcholanthrene exhibit cancer-producing activities. It has also been observed that in adrenal cortical tumor, resulting in adrenal virilism, large amounts of male hormones are excreted.

TABLE 85.   HORMONE UNITS IN TERMS OF 1 MG. QUANTITIES

Hormone	Units		Hormone	Units	
Androsterone	10 CU	(a; j)	Estrone	10,000 IU	(b; j)
Benzestrol	25,000 IU	(b)	Estrone	2,666 RU	(c; p)
Benzestrol	1,250 RU	(c)	Estrone	1,000 RU	(c; k; q)
Estradiol	70,000 to 120,000 IU	(b; k)	Estrone		
Estradiol	12,000 RU	(c; m)	benzoate	10,000 IBU	(d)
Estradiol			Insulin	22 IU	(e)
benzoate	70,000 to 120,000 IBU	(d; k)	Progesterone	1 IU	(f)
Estradiol			Progesterone	1 CAU	(g)
benzoate	6,000 RU	(c; m)	Progesterone	2 CIU	(h; q)
Estradiol,			Progesterone	4 to 6 ECU	(i; q)
ethinyl	100,000 IU	(c; n)	Testosterone	70 to 75 CU	(a; m)
Estradiol			Testosterone		
ethinyl	20,000 IU	(b; n)	propionate	50 CU	(a; m)
Estriol	16,000 IU	(b; n; q)	Testosterone		
Estriol	1,600 RU	(c; k; q)	methyl	15 CU	(a; m; n)

(a) Capon Units of androgenic potency; (b) International Units of estrogenic potency or Estrone Units; (c) Rat Units of estrogenic potency by Allen-Doisy method; (d) International Benzoate Units of estrogenic potency; (e) International Units of insulin activity; (f) International Units of progestational activity; (g) Corner-Allen Units; (h) Clauberg Rabbit Units; (i) European Clinical Units; (j) by definition; (k) by calculation; (m) by experimental finding; (n) for oral use only; (p) chemical determination, J. Biol. Chem. *116*: 415 (1936); (q) conversion data unreliable. (From Lange's Handbook of Chemistry, 1949.)

In one case Fieser points out that the amount of dehydroandrosterone excreted was 100 times as much as in the normal. Fieser is of the opinion that in abnormal metabolism—such as the example just cited—a sterol compound (represented by one of the sex hormones or cholesterol) may, perhaps, be transformed into a "carcinogen," or cancer-producing product, of the cholanthrene type.

"An abnormal process leading to the formation of a carcinogen may be only slightly differentiated from normal sex hormone metabolism. Suspicion as to the point of origin of a 'degenerated biocatalyst' centers around the adrenal cortex partly because steroids of the adrenal cortical type appear to be the likely precursors of all the sex hormones and partly because this gland, particularly when hyperactive, appears to maintain conditions favorable for dehydrogenative processes." (Fieser.)

Reference has been made to a treatment in cancer of the prostate with estrogens. Some work has also been done on the use of testosterone in the treatment of cancer of the breast; the results have been conflicting. At best, there is temporary relief. Cortisone and ACTH have been used in leukemia with some success, if only temporary.

Studying the inciting factors which play a role in the genesis of spontaneous mammary cancer in mice, Bittner lists them as three: inherited susceptibility, hormonal stimulation, and the mammary tumor milk agent (the agent transferred in the mothers' milk); the last represents Bittner's discovery of a substance—probably a virus—which is normally transmitted by nursing.

The study of neoplastic cells—cells showing abnormal growth, such as a tumor—has been pushed very vigorously (see references at the end of the chapter).

$$CH_3-N\begin{matrix} \nearrow CH_2CH_2Cl \\ \searrow CH_2CH_2Cl \end{matrix}$$

Nitrogen mustard
Methyl-bis (β-chloroethyl) amine

The toxic effect of "nitrogen mustard" compound on neoplastic tissue of the hematopoietic system is the basis for the treatment of Hodgkins' disease and leukemia; though, to be sure, the relief afforded is but temporary.

In studying the effect of nitrogen mustard on neoplastic tissue, the discovery was made that it arrests mitosis and causes mutations (in *Drosophila* and *Neurospora*). In low concentrations the nitrogen mustard inhibits the synthesis of cellular nucleic acid (which is needed for the synthesis of tissue proteins and, presumably, enzymes).

GASTROINTESTINAL HORMONES*

In so far as the secretion of saliva is concerned, a hormone mechanism seems to play no part. A humoral mechanism may, in part, be involved in gastric secretion. The injection of an acid extract of the pyloric mucosa stimulates secretion. This stimulation is attributed to a hormone, *gastrin*.

Komarov obtained histamine-free extracts from the pyloric mucosa which contains two active materials: one of these stimulates the gastric glands (gastrin), and the other stimulates the external secretion of the pancreas (similar to secretin).

Enterogastrone, a substance which inhibits gastric secretion, has been obtained in concentrated form from the upper intestinal mucosa. A probable excretory product, showing some of the properties of the mother substance, is *urogastrone*.

The mucosa of the upper part of the intestine is responsible for two hormones, *secretin* and *cholecystokinin*. Bayliss and Starling obtained an acid extract of the mucosa, which, when injected, caused a flow of pancreatic juice. The active material in this acid extract was named "secretin," and substances of the type represented by secretin were called "hormones" (from the Greek, "to excite").

Crystalline products of secretin have been obtained by Hammarsten and Ågren. The substance is probably a basic polypeptide.

* Refer to Chapter 7.

Extracts from the mucosa of the upper part of the intestine (freed from histamine and choline) give, when injected, a prolonged contraction of the gallbladder with evacuation. The substance which stimulates this contraction of the gallbladder is called "cholecystokinin" (Ivy) which, chemically, resembles secretin, although it is not identical with it. There is also said to be still another hormone, *pancreozymin,* released by the upper intestinal mucosa, which stimulates the secretion of enzymes by the pancreas.

PLANT HORMONES*

While plant hormones belong, more specifically, to plant biochemistry and not to animal biochemistry, plant and animal hormones may be related. At any rate, plant hormones have been obtained from the urine of human beings and a "female hormone" has been obtained from plant extracts.

In plants the hormones do not originate in certain glands (as in the animal kingdom), but in buds or other growing centers. These plant hormones—or growth-promoting substances—stimulate root cuttings, induce production of seedless fruits in tomatoes and cucumbers, prevent potatoes from sprouting during storage, control the pre-harvest fall of apples, and act on selective weed-killers.

The "growth substance" to be tested—which, for example, is found in the tips of the coleoptile of oats—is placed in contact with cubes of agar-agar, which allow the active material to diffuse into it. If such cubes are placed on the cut area of the coleoptile, curvature results, and the extent of such curvature is proportional to the concentration of active material produced (Fig. 110).

While the name "auxin" has been used indiscriminately for any growth-promoting substance, probably the true or "native" auxin is indole-3-acetic acid, which is the "only true growth-promoting hormone definitely known to occur naturally" (Thimann). Its origin can be traced, probably, to tryptophan.

Indole-3-acetic acid

Hitchcock and Zimmerman have tried many substances for their growth-promoting properties and find them very widely distributed—

* One finds various names in the literature: Auxins, growth hormones, growth regulators, phytohormones, growth substances. These include true hormones, like indole-3-acetic acid, and many substances which affect growth (positively and negatively), but which are not necessarily part of the plant structure.

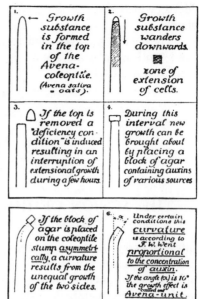

Figure 110. Estimation of plant hormone. (From Kögl: Chemistry and Industry, 57: 49.)

from such a simple substance as ethylene to indole, benzene, naphthalene, and even anthracene derivatives. They found effective root-forming substances to be α-naphthalene acetic acid and indole-3-butyric acid, although they were not as effective as indole-3-acetic acid for epinastic* response of leaves.

α-Naphthalene acetic acid   Indole-3-butyric acid

(This property of accelerating root growth is, incidentally, a property possessed by ethylene, which, in addition, can accelerate the ripening of fruit.)

In studying the relation between chemical structure and growth-promoting activity, the following conclusions have been drawn: that the essential groups are an unsaturated or an aromatic ring, a carboxyl group, or one converted to a carboxyl by the plant; and that the carboxyl group must be separated from the ring by one carbon (or oxygen) atom. It is believed that energy-rich phosphate bonds are involved in the growth-promoting effects.

Recently, a group of substances, the gibberellins, have been intro-

* Downward curvature of a plant member induced by a more active growth on its upper side.

duced, which show striking effects on the growth and development of plants.

The auxins are also used to prevent premature drop of apples and pears; and a particular auxin, 2,4-D(2,4-dichlorophenoxyacetic acid), is used as a weed-killer.

OCH$_2$.COOH

2,4-D

THE ACTION OF HORMONES ON METABOLIC REACTIONS: A SUMMARY

Little is known, even at present, regarding the direct effect of specific hormones on specific enzymes. However, in a more general, somewhat indirect way, much is known about the relationship of many hormones to the general metabolic cycle. Figure 111 constructed by Engel, illustrates the probable sites at which the hormones of the anterior pitui-

SUMMARY OF ENDOCRINE FACTORS IN METABOLISM (DIRECT & INDIRECT EFFECTS)

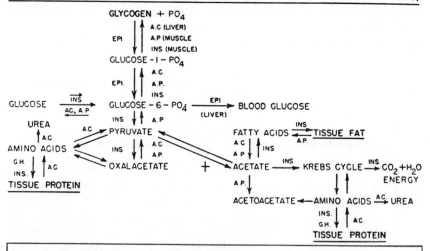

A.C. — ADRENAL CORTEX   INS. — INSULIN
A.P. — ANTERIOR PITUITARY   EPI. — EPINEPHRINE
G.H.— GROWTH HORMONE

NOTE: ONLY THE GENERAL DIRECTIONS IN WHICH METABOLIC REACTIONS ARE INFLUENCED BY HORMONES ARE INDICATED. THESE SHOULD NOT BE INTERPRETED AS SPECIFIC SITES OF ACTION OF HORMONES.

Figure 111. Diagram showing over-all directions in which metabolic reactions are influenced by hormones. (From Engel, F. L.: Bull. N. Y. Acad. Med., 29:199, March, 1953.)

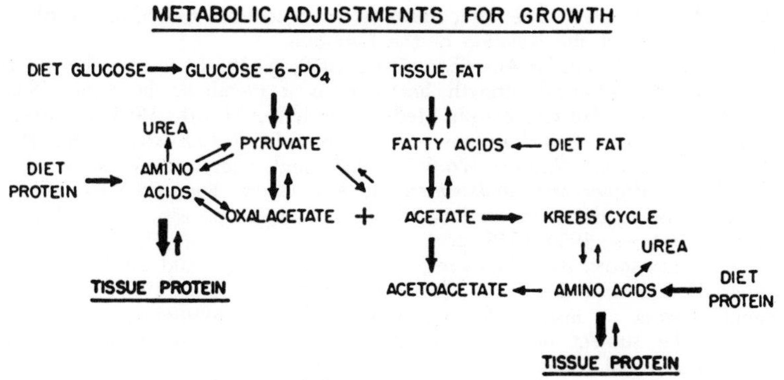

METABOLIC ADJUSTMENTS FOR GROWTH

Figure 112. (From Engel, F. L.: Bull. N. Y. Acad. Med., *29*:196, March, 1953.)

tary, adrenals and the pancreas act on carbohydrate, fat and protein metabolism.

Figure 112 by Engel, shows the relationship of a number of hormones to the process of normal growth.

REFERENCES

GENERAL. For an introduction see *Turner:* General Endocrinology, 1960. See also New and Nonofficial Drugs, 528, 1960; *Zuckerman:* Scientific American, March, 1957, p. 77; *Pincus* and *Thimann:* Hormones, 3 vols. (1948–1955); *Pincus:* Progress in Hormone Research, Vol. 11, 1955; *Dorfman* and *Shipley:* Androgens, 1955; *Harris, Marrian* and *Thimann:* Vitamins and Hormones, Vol. 13, 1955.

The Ann. Rev. of Biochem. has reviews. See, for example, *Shoppe:* 22:261, 1953 (chemistry of cortisone); *Stack-Dunne* and *Young:* 23:405, 1954 (biochemistry of pituitary and adrenals); *Roche* and *Michel:* 23:481, 1954 (thyroid hormone and iodine metabolism); *Dorfman:* 26:523, 1957 (steroid hormones); *Acher:* 29:541, 1960 (protein hormones).

THYROID. A book by the foremost authority is *Harington's:* The Thyroid Gland, 1933. *Kendall,* himself a pioneer in the field, is the author of Thyroxine, 1929.

The formation of diiodotyrosine and thyroxine from iodine, using the radioactive isotope, and with the help of thyroid tissue, is described by *Morton* and *Chaikoff:* J. Biol. Chem., *147*:1, 1943.

The thyroxine-like activity of some thyroxine analogues are described by *Bruice, Winzler* and *Kharasch:* J. Biol. Chem., *210*:1, 1954.

For thyronine, see *Gross* and *LeBlond:* Proc. Soc. Exp. Biol. Med., *76*:688, 1951, *Gross* and *Pitt-Rivers:* Lancet, 1:439, 593, 1952.

PARATHYROIDS. The review by *Thompson* and *Collip:* Physiol. Rev. *12*:309, 1932, should be consulted. See also, *Rasmussen:* Scientific American, April, 1961, for an account of the isolation of the hormone.

PITUITARY. See *Li:* Scientific American, Oct., 1950, p. 18. *Li* is also the author of article on the pituitary growth hormone as a metabolic hormone (Science, *123:*617, 1956). *Morris:* British Medical Bulletin, *11:*101, 1955, discusses the chemistry of the gonadotropins. (See, also, *Li, Geschwind, Cole, Raacke, Harris* and *Dixon:* Nature, *176:*687, 1955; and *Shepherd, Willson, Howard, Bell, Davis, Eigner* and *Shakespeare:* J. Am. Chem. Soc., 78:5067, 1956.)

For the hormones of the posterior lobe, oxytocin and vasopressin, see *du Vigneaud:* Harvey Lectures, 1954–1955, p. 1.

INSULIN AND GLUCAGON. *Best:* Diabetes, *1:*257, 1952; *Sanger* and *Smith:* Endeavour, Imperial Chemical Industries, Vol. *16*, No. 61, Jan., 1957, review their chemical work on insulin; *Beaser:* New England J. Medicine, *251:*698, 1954, reviews the subject of diabetes. On the subject of glucagon, see *Pincus:* Archives Internal Medicine, 92:666, 1953; *Staub, Sinn* and *Behrens:* Science, *117:*628, 1953 (crystallization); *Bromer, Sinn, Staub* and *Behrens:* J. Am. Chem. Soc., 78:3858, 1956 (amino acid sequence).

ADRENALS. *Shepherd* and *Best:* J. Physiol., *120:*15, 1953 (adrenal medulla); *Burn:* Irish J. Medical Science, 1951, No. 308, p. 345 (noradrenaline). For a review of adrenocortical steroids, see *Roberts* and *Szego:* Ann. Rev. Biochem., 24:544, 1955.

17-KETOSTEROIDS, ETC. *Mason* and *Engstrom:* Physiol. Rev., 30:321, 1950.

SEX HORMONES. For a general review, see *Allen:* Sex and Internal Secretions, 1943 (articles by specialists), in which the biological aspect is stressed. See also *Dorfman,* in *Pincus* and *Thimann's* Hormones, Vol. 3, 1955 (steroid hormone metabolism); *Callow:* British Medical Bulletin, *11:*126, 1955; *Roberts* and *Szego:* Ann. Rev. Biochem., 24:553, 1955; *Wotiz, Lemon* and *Voulgaropoulos:* J. Biol. Chem., *206:*525, 1954; *209:*437, 1954 (steroid metabolism-testosterone).

GASTROINTESTINAL HORMONES. *Grossman:* Physiol. Rev., 30:33, 1950.

PLANT HORMONES. *Went* and *Thimann:* Phytohormones, 1937; *Kögl:* J. Society of Chemical Industry, 57:49, 1938. *Salisbury:* Scientific American, April, 1957, p. 125; *Kraus:* American Scientist, July, 1954, p. 439; *Thimann:* Ibid., Oct., 1954, p. 589; *Grodon:* Ann. Rev. Plant Physiol., 5:341, 1954.

For the influence of the endocrines on metabolism, see *Engel:* Bull. N. Y. Acad. Med., *29:*175, 1953.

For additions to the literature, see Annals N. Y. Acad. Sciences, 70:1–152, 1957 (I¹³¹-labeled proteins); *Soffer, Gutman, Geller* and *Gabrilove:* Bull. N. Y. Acad. Med., *33:*665, 1957 (adrenal steroids and electrolyte metabolism); *Goodall* and *Kirshner:* J. Biol. Chem., 226:213, 1957 (epinephrine and norepinephrine); *Li:* Federation Proceedings, *16:*775, 1957 (growth hormones); *West:* J. Chem. Educ., Jan., 1958, p. 42 (gibberellins and plant growth); *Behrens:* 17th Biology Colloquium, p. 46, 1956 (glucagon).

METABOLISM
OF FOREIGN
ORGANIC COMPOUNDS

This chapter, originally entitled "detoxication," really deals with the chemical changes which foreign organic compounds undergo in the animal body.

That detoxication is not always a conversion of a toxic to a nontoxic body is made clear by one or two examples. For instance, the female sex hormone is eliminated (to some extent, at least) as a glucuronide and the male sex hormone (also to some extent) as the sulfate. Obviously, neither of these hormones, of importance to the body, can be considered a toxic substance. Again, as Quick points out, the formation of taurocholic acid from cholic acid and glycine—a normal metabolic process—cannot, in reality, be distinguished from a detoxication involving glycine in other reactions.

Peters points out that fluoroacetate—the acid is $CH_2.F.COOH$—itself innocuous, becomes toxic because enzymes convert it into a toxic substance (fluorocitrate); this is precisely the opposite of the detoxication mechanism by which the body commonly attempts to eliminate poisonous substances.

The toxic substances produced in the large intestine and discussed in Chapter 7 are largely eliminated in the stool; those which are not, are detoxified—that is, absorbed, combined in the liver or kidney with perhaps sulfuric or glucuronic acid, and then eliminated through the kidneys into the urine.

In a general way, it may be said that in the attempt to detoxify a substance introduced into the body several methods are employed; toxic material may be oxidized or the toxic substance may combine

585

with glucuronic acid, sulfuric acid, one of the amino acids, etc., and thereby bring about a detoxified product.

In Chapter 7 we discussed the production of indole from tryptophan, a bacterial change brought about in the large intestine. Much of the indole is eliminated in the feces. Some of it is absorbed, partially oxidized, and combined with sulfuric acid to form indican, which is eliminated in the urine.

The amount of indican in the urine may be indicative of the extent of putrefaction in the large intestine.

Indole   Indoxyl   Indican

The changes which some substances undergo in the body will now be discussed. Such changes are usually studied in experiments on animals. The usual procedure is to feed or inject the substance under investigation into the animal (dog, rabbit, etc.), collect the urine over a given period of time, and recover from it changed and unchanged material. The practical difficulties are often very great, and much of the information at present is in an incomplete state.

The tissue slice technique developed by Warburg is also employed.

ENZYMES

It should be emphasized at the very outset that the chemical changes which the substances described in this chapter undergo in the body are brought about by the action of enzymes. If no mention is made of such enzymes, it is merely because few enzymic studies have been undertaken. Until recently investigators were content with studying the chemical changes involved, and this important phase of the work is still being pursued, but a more complete answer will be obtained when, together with the chemical work, enzymic studies are made of such reactions.

In connection with such enzyme studies, the question at once arises whether these catalysts are specific for the many *un*physiological compounds which are discussed in this chapter. Two possibilities exist, which are not mutually exclusive. One possibility is that the enzyme which catalyzes a reaction involving a foreign compound also carries out a similar function with physiological compounds, provided both the foreign and the physiological compound contain similar chemical groupings. One such example is the enzyme which brings about the acetylation of sulfanilamide—a "foreign" compound, in so far as the body is concerned—and requires coenzyme A for the transfer of the acetyl group and acetylations involved in such cases as the formation of acetylcholine.

Another possibility is that the enzyme which acts on the "foreign" compound is normally not an enzyme at all but merely some protein; and the "foreign" substance fits in certain groupings of the protein. A possible example is the discovery in the liver and kidney of rabbits of an enzyme which is capable of catalyzing the hydrolytic cleavage of the phosphorus-fluorine linkage in diisopropyl fluorophosphate.

OXIDATION

In a general way, it may be said that aliphatic compounds are more easily oxidized than aromatic ones. It is true that this does not apply to α-amino acids attached to aromatic nuclei. These are, of course, foods and not poisonous products. For example, so far as we know, phenylalanine and tyrosine, both containing the benzene nucleus, are quite readily oxidized in the animal organism. On the other hand, the fate of benzene itself is still a matter of some dispute. Many years ago Jaffe claimed to have isolated muconic acid as a result of feeding benzene; this was confirmed by Drummond and others.

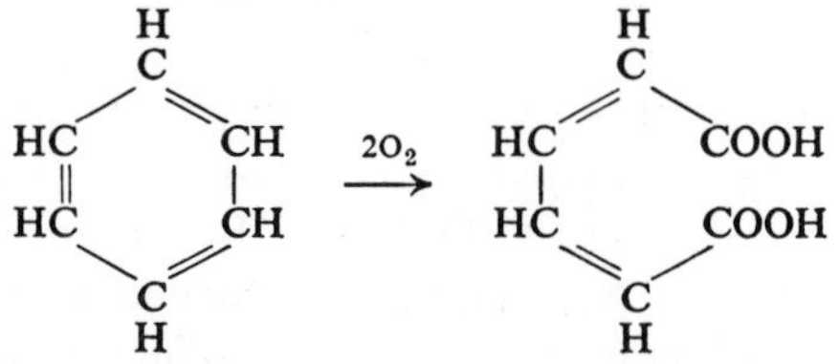

Benzene   Muconic acid

However, some of this benzene is converted into phenol by both man and the dog. Some of the phenol, in turn, is excreted in conjugated form, partly with sulfuric acid and partly with glucuronic acid and with cystine.

Using benzene labeled with C^{14}, Williams has shown that 45 per cent of the dose is eliminated in expired air: 43 per cent as unchanged benzene, and some of the rest as CO_2. At the same time, 35 per cent of the benzene appears in the urine as the following end-products (in per cent of dose): phenol, 23; quinol, 5; catechol, 2; hydroxyquinol, 0.3; phenylmercapturic acid, 0.5; and muconic acid, 1.3.

Toluene and ethylbenzene are oxidized to some extent to benzoic acid. With m-xylene, $C_6H_4(CH_3)_2$, containing two methyl groups, one methyl group is oxidized to a carboxylic acid group. This is also true of mesitylene, the symmetrical trimethylbenzene, $C_6H_3(CH_3)_3$, which, when ingested, has but one of its CH_3 groups converted to COOH.

Among the aliphatic alcohols, methyl alcohol is oxidized in the body to formaldehyde and then to formic acid. It is a highly toxic substance and often gives rise to incurable blindness.

A large part of ethyl alcohol is first oxidized to acetaldehyde and then to acetic acid; this takes place largely in the liver. The ultimate oxidation products are carbon dioxide and water. Ninety per cent of the radioactive carbon-14 in ethyl alcohol, for example, is excreted as radioactive CO_2 in the expired breath in the course of ten hours.

In the oxidation of alcohol to acetaldehyde, alcohol dehydrogenase and DPN are involved.

Primary aromatic alcohols are often oxidized to the corresponding carboxylic acids. For example, benzyl alcohol, $C_6H_5.CH_2.OH$, is converted to benzoic acid, C_6H_5COOH; and phenylethyl alcohol, $C_6H_5.CH_2.CH_2.OH$, to phenylacetic acid, $C_6H_5.CH_2.COOH$.

Aromatic aldehydes are usually oxidized to the corresponding carboxylic acids. Benzaldehyde, $C_6H_5.CHO$, for example, is converted into benzoic acid. Vanillin is oxidized to vanillic acid:

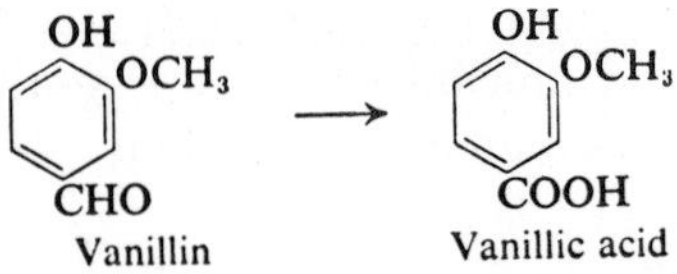

Vanillin   Vanillic acid

Whereas aliphatic amines—like aliphatic compounds, in general—are destroyed by the body, aromatic amines are sometimes converted to carboxylic acids. Benzylamine, $C_6H_5.CH_2NH_2$, is oxidized to benzoic acid. Where, however, the NH_2 group is attached to the benzene nucleus, the results are different. For example, aniline, $C_6H_5.NH_2$, itself, is oxidized to p-aminophenol

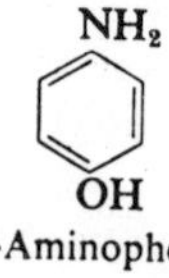

p-Aminophenol

though it is finally excreted in combination with sulfuric acid and possibly glucuronic acid.

Histamine, the important pharmacological base derived from the amino acid histidine, has been studied using the base labeled with C^{14} in the imidazol ring. The major excretory products appear to be compounds whose imidazol ring has been modified.

Acetanilid, $C_6H_5.NH.CO.CH_3$, is oxidized to p-acetylaminophenol, $HO.C_6H_4.NH.CO.CH_3$, and is excreted as the glucuronide and ethereal sulfate.

Naphthalene, phenanthrene and anthracene

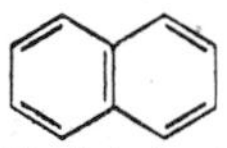

Naphthalene 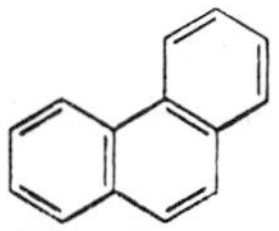   Phenanthrene 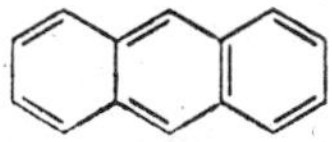   Anthracene

are partially oxidized to dihydroxy compounds:

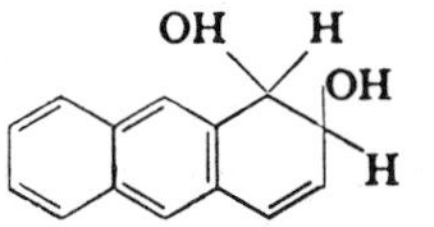

1,2-Dihydroxy-1,2-dihydroanthracene

although a part also combines with glucuronic acid.

REDUCTION

Though less common than oxidation, reduction of substances in the animal body does occur. (We exclude here reactions in the large intestine, where reducing bacteria are very active.) A classic example of this type of reaction is the conversion of picric acid into picramic acid:

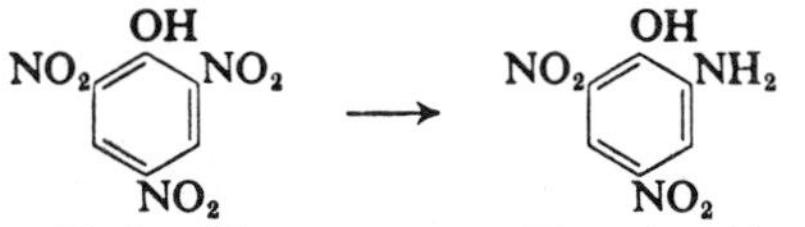

Picric acid   Picramic acid

Sometimes a simultaneous reduction and oxidation within the same compound will occur; for example, when rabbits are fed p-nitrobenzaldehyde they excrete appreciable quantities of p-aminobenzoic acid:

p-Nitrobenzaldehyde p-Aminobenzoic acid

Nitro compounds are converted to the corresponding amino compounds. The simplest aromatic nitro derivative, nitrobenzene, $C_6H_5NO_2$, reacts similarly to p-nitrobenzaldehyde because reduction and oxidation occur to give rise to p-aminophenol.

It is interesting to note that both aniline and p-nitrophenol, $HO.C_6H_4.NO_2$, also form p-aminophenol.

2,4-Dinitrophenol, one of a number of nitrophenols which affect basal metabolism, yields a mixture of compounds.

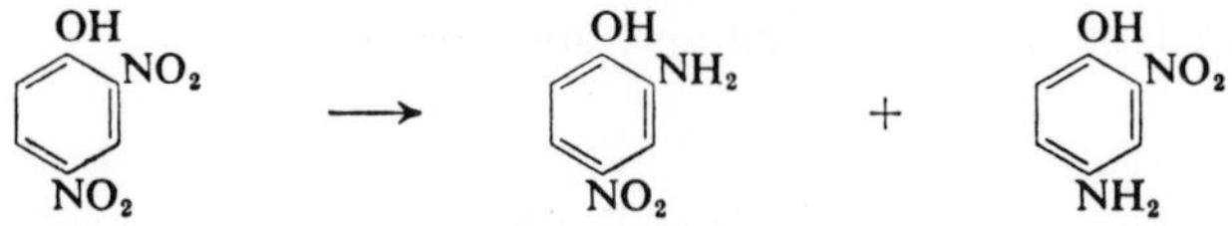

2,4-Dinitrophenol　　　2-Amino-4-nitrophenol　　　2-Nitro-4-aminophenol

2,4,6-Trinitrotoluene (T.N.T.) is partially reduced to 2,6-dinitro-4-aminotoluene:

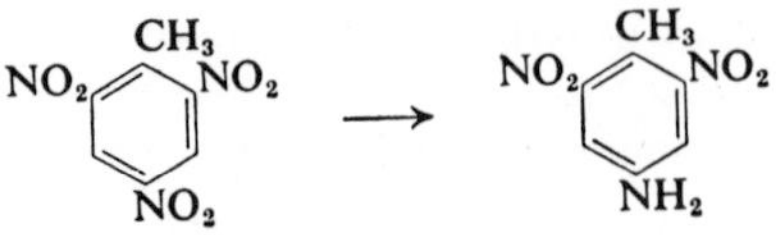

and also partially excreted as the glucuronide.

CONJUGATION

Where oxidation fails, conjugation becomes an alternate (or added) procedure. (As we have seen, a substance like anthracene can be partly oxidized and partly conjugated.) Conjugation involves the combination of the toxic product with some substance available to the body to form a detoxified product which is then eliminated. The substances known to be used by the body for detoxifying purposes are glycine, glutamine, ornithine, cysteine, sulfuric acid, glucuronic acid, acetic acid, and the methyl group.

GLYCINE

This amino acid seems to attach itself to acids in particular. The well-known example is the production of hippuric acid by feeding benzoic acid:

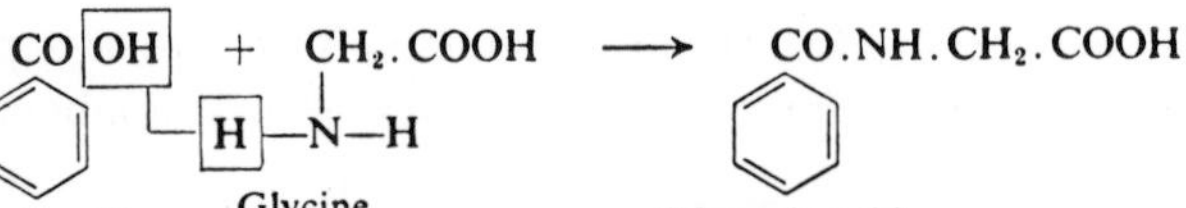

Benzoic acid　　　Glycine　　　　Hippuric acid

However, combination of acids with glucuronic acid is also common.

It might be expected that o-hydroxybenzoic acid, which is the compound of pharmacological importance known as salicylic acid, would also be detoxified in the body by combining with glycine; and, in fact, the main product in man is salicyluric acid,

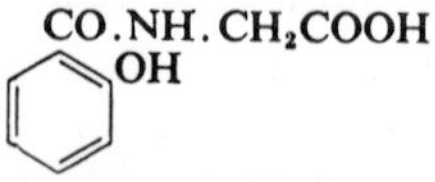

Salicyluric acid

(the combination of salicylic acid and glycine). Some gentisic acid,

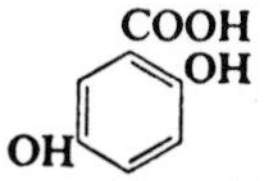

Gentisic acid

is also formed.

p-Hydroxybenzoic acid is excreted partly uncombined and partly conjugated with glycine.

In dealing with detoxifying agents it should be pointed out that because the horse forms hippuric acid when it is fed benzoic acid, one cannot necessarily conclude that hippuric acid will always be formed, irrespective of the animal used. As a matter of fact, in this instance, with one exception, every vertebrate so far tried forms hippuric acid. The one exception is the fowl, in which benzoic acid is combined with ornithine instead of with glycine.

Niacin is partly conjugated with glycine in the body to form nicotinuric acid:

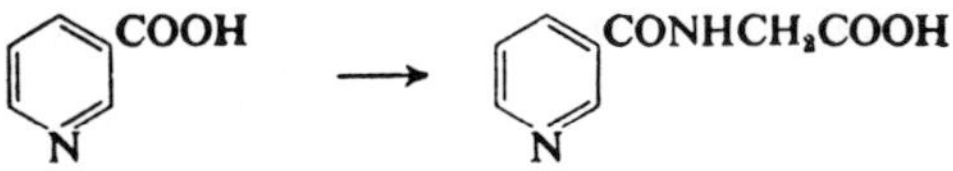

Niacin   Nicotinuric acid

GLUTAMINE

This amide of glutamic acid is an active detoxifying agent only in human beings and in the chimpanzee. The ingestion of phenylacetic acid by a human being gives rise to phenylacetylglutamine, a product which can be isolated from the urine:

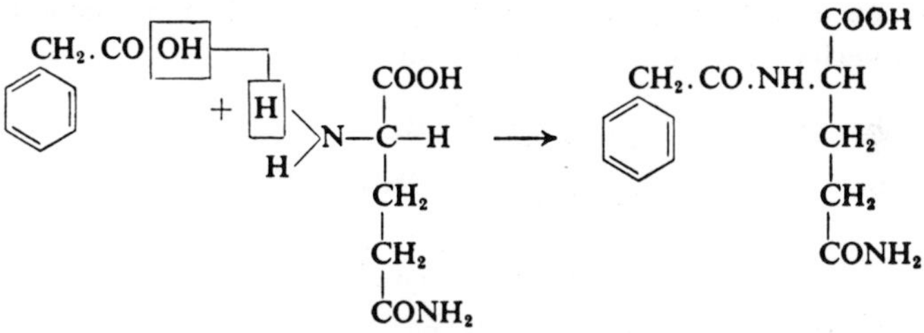

Phenylacetic acid   Glutamine   Phenylacetylglutamine

Illustrating once again the difference in behavior depending upon the animal used, in the fowl, phenylacetic acid combines with ornithine, and in most other animals, phenylacetic acid combines partly with glycine and partly with glucuronic acid.

ORNITHINE

As has already been indicated, the fowl is the one animal that utilizes ornithine for detoxifying purposes. With phenylacetic acid the reaction is as follows:

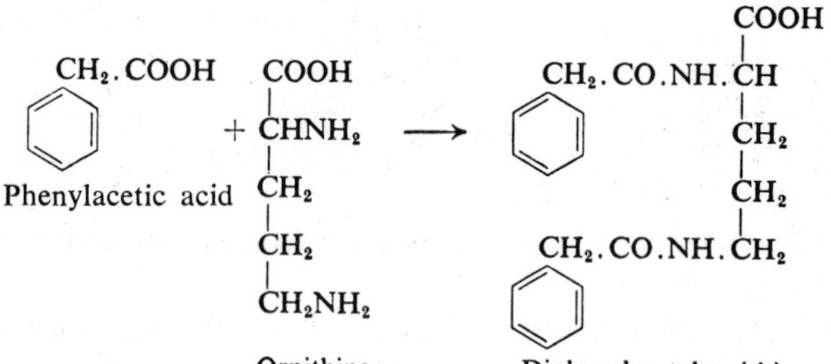

$$\text{Phenylacetic acid} \quad CH_2.COOH \quad + \quad \begin{array}{c} COOH \\ | \\ CHNH_2 \\ | \\ CH_2 \\ | \\ CH_2 \\ | \\ CH_2NH_2 \end{array} \quad \longrightarrow \quad \begin{array}{c} COOH \\ | \\ CH_2.CO.NH.CH \\ | \\ CH_2 \\ | \\ CH_2 \\ | \\ CH_2.CO.NH.CH_2 \end{array}$$

Phenylacetic acid   Ornithine   Diphenylacetylornithine

CYSTEINE

The feeding of bromobenzene to dogs results in the formation of a mercapturic acid; which means that cysteine is used for detoxifying purposes. (The amino group of the cysteine is acetylated at the same time.)

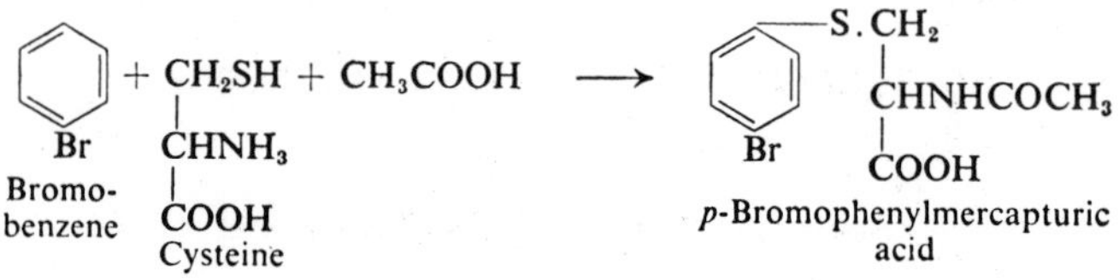

$$\underset{\substack{\text{Bromo-}\\\text{benzene}}}{\overset{Br}{\bigcirc}} + \underset{\substack{\text{Cysteine}}}{\begin{array}{c} CH_2SH \\ | \\ CHNH_3 \\ | \\ COOH \end{array}} + CH_3COOH \longrightarrow \underset{\substack{\text{p-Bromophenylmercapturic}\\\text{acid}}}{\overset{Br}{\bigcirc}} \begin{array}{c} -S.CH_2 \\ | \\ CHNHCOCH_3 \\ | \\ COOH \end{array}$$

Some of the bromobenzene is oxidized to p-bromophenol, and the latter is excreted partly in combination with sulfuric acid and partly in combination with glucuronic acid.

Chlorobenzene, iodobenzene, and fluorobenzene are converted into the corresponding mercapturic acid derivatives.

Bourne and Young discovered that in rabbits naphthalene is partially converted into its mercapturic acid:[*]

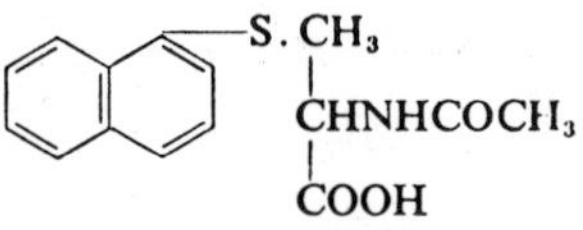

$$\begin{array}{c} -S.CH_3 \\ | \\ CHNHCOCH_3 \\ | \\ COOH \end{array}$$

Naphthylmercapturic acid

Some of the naphthalene is also excreted in combination with glucuronic and sulfuric acids.

There is evidence at hand that anthracene is detoxicated in a similar manner; and some claim this to be true also of phenanthrene.

Small quantities of phenylmercapturic acid have been isolated by Young after administering benzene to rats.

The evidence for the formation of mercapturic acid with benzene and phenanthrene is an increased neutral sulfur excretion when they

---

[*] When naphthalene is repeatedly administered to rabbits, the crystalline lens of the eye undergoes degeneration—a process which resembles that observed in human senile cataract.

are administered. Further evidence is afforded by the fact that on certain synthetic diets the growth of rats is inhibited when phenanthrene (or naphthalene or bromobenzene) is added to the diet. Probably the explanation is that phenanthrene attaches itself to cystine (or other sulfur-containing compounds), thereby making the latter unavailable to the animal. If phenanthrene and cystine (or methionine) are simultaneously added to the diet, no deficiency occurs.

ETHEREAL SULFATES

The well-known example of the formation of indican from indole (p. 586) is an instance of this type of detoxication. Phenol behaves similarly:

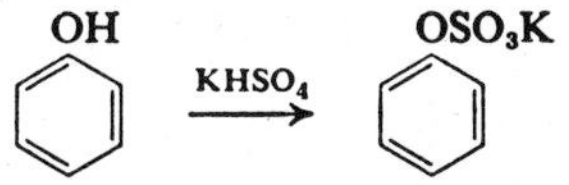

Phenol   Phenylpotassium sulfate

The enzymic mechanism for sulfate ester formation is as follows:

$$SO_4^{=} + ATP \longrightarrow \text{``active sulfate''}$$
$$\text{Phenol} + \text{``active sulfate''} \longrightarrow \text{phenol sulfate}$$

In general phenolic hydroxy compounds have a tendency to form such sulfate combinations, although androsterone, one of the male hormones and a secondary alcohol, combines with sulfuric acid.

Not only is part of the phenol conjugated (with sulfuric and glucuronic acids) but part of it is oxidized and part of it excreted unchanged. (In many of these detoxication experiments one finds very appreciable quantities of the ingested material in the urine.)

In the case of a methyl substituted phenol, such as p-cresol, $HO.C_6H_4.CH_3$, this substance when ingested is first converted to p-hydroxybenzoic acid, $HO.C_6H_4.COOH$, and then probably converted to the corresponding sulfate or glucuronide salts.

Alpha naphthol and β-naphthol, like phenol itself, are excreted in combination with sulfuric and glucuronic acids.

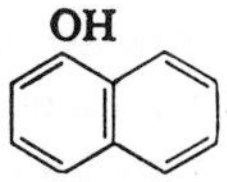

α-Naphthol   β-Naphthol

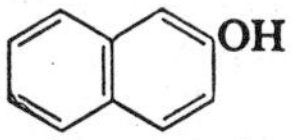

Acetanilid is first oxidized to p-acetaminophenol and finally excreted in combination with sulfuric and glucuronic acids.

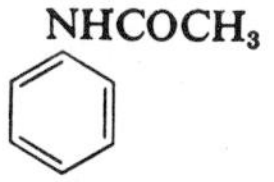

Acetanilid 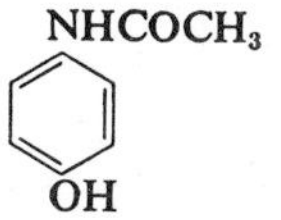 p-Acetaminophenol

It would seem that the administration of epinephrine markedly increases the elimination of ethereal sulfates. This suggests that the inactivation of epinephrine in the body is not necessarily accomplished by oxidative destruction, but by coupling it with sulfuric acid.

GLUCURONIC ACID

Combinations with this acid are extremely common. Many compounds containing hydroxyl or carboxyl groups—or compounds which are first changed in the body to such derivatives—form conjugates with glucuronic acid.

Benzoic acid combines not only with glycine but also with glucuronic acid to form 1-benzoylglucuronic acid:

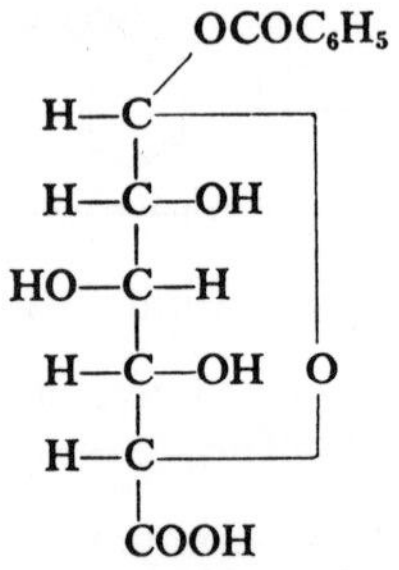

$$OCOC_6H_5$$

$$
\begin{array}{l}
H-C \\
H-C-OH \\
HO-C-H \\
H-C-OH \quad O \\
H-C \\
COOH
\end{array}
$$

1-Benzoylglucuronic acid

The same is true of phenol; it also combines with glucuronic acid (as well as with sulfuric acid) to form phenolglucuronic acid:

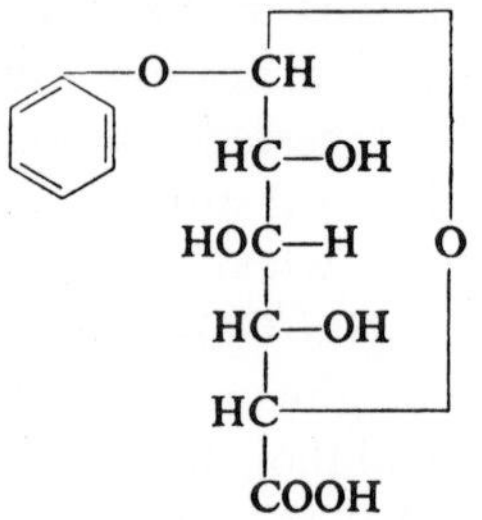

$$
\begin{array}{l}
O-CH \\
HC-OH \\
HOC-H \quad O \\
HC-OH \\
HC \\
COOH
\end{array}
$$

Phenolglucuronic acid

The combination of benzoic acid with glucuronic acid can be shown in the pig, the dog, the sheep, and in man. In man some 5 per cent may be eliminated as the glucuronide. The maximum excretion occurs in the first three hours and detoxication is complete in 9 to 15 hours, depending on the amount of benzoic acid ingested.

Phenylacetic acid, the first homologue of benzoic acid, is also eliminated as a glucuronide to the extent of about 7.5 per cent.

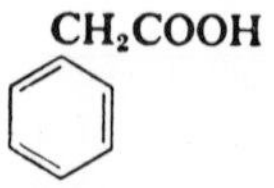

$$CH_2COOH$$

Phenylacetic acid

The synthetic female hormone, stilbestrol, is partly converted into the monoglycuronide:

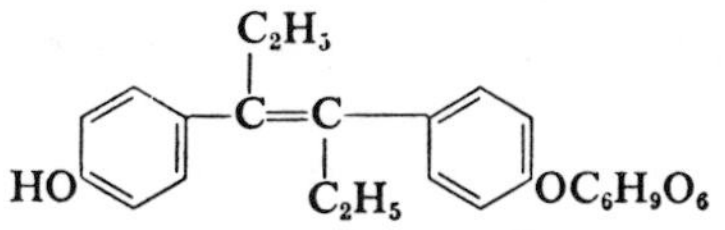

Stilbestrol glycuronide

The indicator (and drug) phenolphthalein is detoxified, to some extent at least, as its glucuronide.

Anthracene is not only partially oxidized, as we have seen, but combines to some extent with cysteine to form a mercapturic acid, and combines to some extent with glucuronic acid to form a glucuronide.

Marrian has shown that the female sex hormones are partially eliminated as glucuronides.

Borneol, the secondary alcohol obtained from camphor when the latter is reduced, combines almost exclusively with glucuronic acid. In

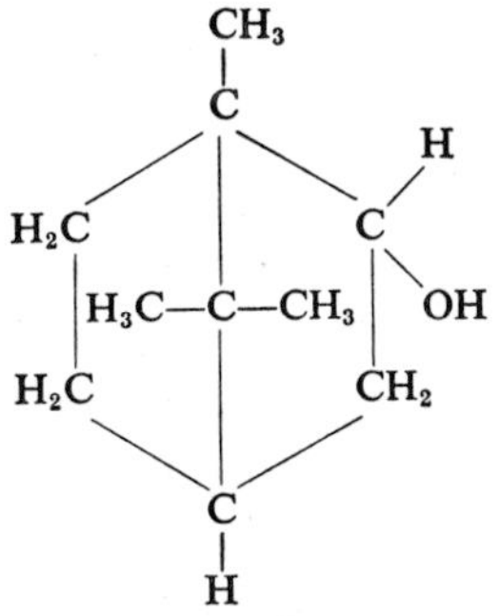

Borneol

man the ingestion of borneol results in the excretion in 24 hours of some 90 per cent or more in the form of its glucuronide. The maximum excretion occurs in from three to six hours, and the detoxication is complete in about 15 hours.

The combination of borneol (and menthol or phenol) with glucuronic acid may also be shown by using liver slices in a saline medium (at pH 7.4), to which borneol is added, and shaking the mixture in a Warburg apparatus.

Sulfapyridine is eliminated, to some extent, as a glucuronide of a hydroxysulfapyridine.

Glycoside formation in plants might correspond to the formation of glucuronides in animals, in the sense that, as a rule, less toxic substances are produced.

The mechanism of the biosynthesis of glucuronic acid really involves two problems: the mechanism of the synthesis of glucuronic acid itself, and the mode of conjugation. Glucuronic acid is synthesized in the organism directly from glucose. The labeled carbons of glucose can be detected in the carbon chain of glucuronic acid in borneol and menthol glucuronides isolated from rabbit urine (King, Gurin).

An enzyme, β-glucuronidase, hydrolyzes glucuronides, and some claim has been made that it can also act in the reverse direction by causing "coupling" of glucuronic acid with various substances.

Glucuronidase is present in animal tissues, mostly in the spleen and liver. Interest in this enzyme has centered around its ability to hydrolyze glucuronides of the estrogens (female sex hormones) which are normally present in the animal organism. In fact, it has been shown that there is a correlation between the tissue glucuronidase activity and the process of cell proliferation.

ACETIC ACID

This acid (in the form of acetyl CoA) is used by the organism for the detoxication of amino groups. One such example has already been given in the formation of the mercapturic acids. Another well known example is the acetylation of p-aminobenzoic acid:

p-Aminobenzoic acid → p-Acetylaminobenzoic acid

Insulin markedly increases the output of p-acetylaminobenzoic acid. That this is a result of a stimulating effect on carbohydrate metabolism seems probable.

Reduced glutathione alone has no effect upon the acetylation process. But the simultaneous injections of insulin and glutathione very definitely inhibit the output of p-acetylaminobenzoic acid. Such a result is probably due to the inactivation of insulin by glutathione.

Approximately 25 per cent of the p-aminobenzoic acid can be accounted for as the acetylated product. Some of the acid is also eliminated in the form of the glucuronate.

Sulfanilamide is largely excreted in the form of the acetylated derivative (in man, rabbit, etc., but not in the dog):

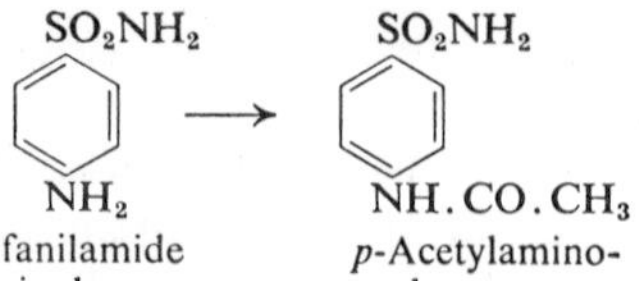

Sulfanilamide (p-aminobenzene sulfonamide) → p-Acetylamino-benzene-sulfonamide

From 50 to 90 per cent of the sulfanilamide administered can be accounted for by the acetylated and the free drug which is eliminated in the urine. However, there is an increase in the output of ethereal sulfate, and this suggests that some of the sulfanilamide is changed in the body to a hydroxy compound, possibly a phenol (*p*-aminophenol?), which is then eliminated in the combined form with sulfate.

Lipmann has shown that the acetylation of sulfanilamide—and acetylations in general—is brought about by an enzyme system which includes coenzyme A, a derivative of pantothenic acid.

The derivatives of sulfanilamide, such as sulfapyridine and sulfathiazole, are also eliminated to some extent as their acetylated compounds, though—like sulfanilamide itself—they are partly oxidized to phenolic compounds which then combine with sulfuric and glucuronic acids.

The acetylation process is carried out not only by animals but even by a mold, *Neurospora crassa*.

METHYLATION

It was supposed for a time that this type of detoxication was not common. One of the few examples quoted was the conversion of pyridine to a methyl derivative:

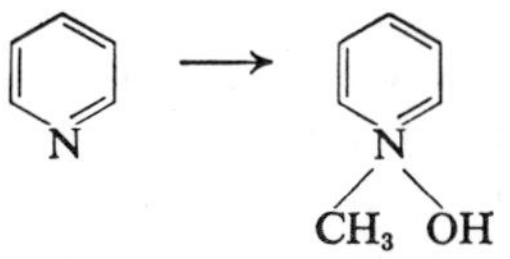

| Pyridine | Methyl hydroxypyridine |

However, it has now been shown that methylation in the body is very common. Both choline and methionine, for example, can supply their methyl groups for various needs.

In this connection it may be mentioned that a compound closely related to pyridine, namely niacin, is methylated to some extent in the body, forming N'-methylnicotinamide:

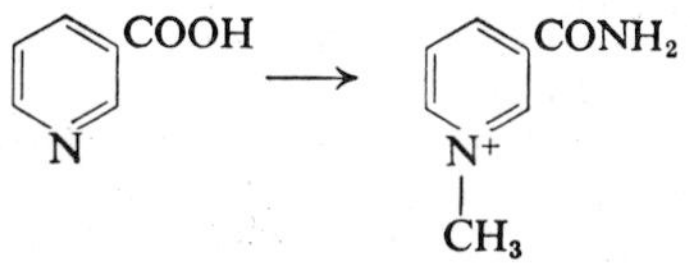

The methyl group required for this reaction is probably derived from methionine.

THIOCYANATE

The thiocyanate found in saliva, etc., is derived from cyanides (which are derived from fruits, the breakdown of proteins, and tobacco smoke). Since the cyanides are toxic whereas the thiocyanates are not, this is indeed a detoxication process.

The conversion of cyanide to thiocyanate is brought about by an enzyme (rhodanase) in the presence of a suitable compound of sulfur.

THE LIVER AND DETOXICATION

The liver seems to be the major seat for the detoxicating process, although experiments are not wanting to prove that often the kidney and other organs also function in this capacity.

Using the tissue slice technique, Borsook has found that in the guinea pig, rabbit, and rat, hippuric acid synthesis (conjugation of benzoic acid and glycine) can occur in both kidney and the liver, whereas in the dog it occurs in the kidney but not in the liver.

It is interesting to note that when the tissue cell structure is destroyed by maceration or poisoned with toluene or cyanide, no synthesis takes place.

Detoxicating reactions have been suggested at various times for testing the function of organs.

GLUTATHIONE

Aside from a possible role which glutathione plays in oxidative mechanisms, the suggestion has been advanced that it may be of importance as a detoxifying agent. It is, to say the least, extremely likely that this polypeptide consists of three amino acids (glycine, cysteine, glutamic acid), each one of which is known to act as a detoxifying agent. Evidence in favor of this view has been presented.

REFERENCES

An introduction to the subject is by *Williams:* Detoxication Mechanisms, 1947.

A review will be found in the article by *Fishman:* Ann. Rev. Biochem., 25:659, 1956.

References to the metabolism of benzene and other aromatic hydrocarbons are *Williams:* Ann. Rev. Biochem., 20:453, 1951. See also *Parke* and *Williams:* Ibid., 46:236, 1950, 54:231, 1953.

For a discussion of the metabolism of aniline, see *Williams:* Ann. Rev. Biochem., 20:455, 1951; for histamine, see *Schayer:* J. Biol. Chem., 196:469, 1952; for acetanilide, see *Williams:* Ann. Rev. Biochem., 20:444, 1951.

Young: Biochemical Society Symposia, No. 5, p. 27, 1950, discusses the oxidation of polycyclic hydrocarbons in the animal body. See also *Young:* Biochem. J., 41:417, 1947 (metabolism of naphthalene); *Boyland* and *Wolf:* Ibid., 47:64, 1950 (metabolism of phenanthrene).

The synthesis of hippuric acid from benzoic acid and glycine is discussed by *Simkin* and *White:* Biochem. J., 65:574, 1957.

The conjugation of phenol in the body is described by *Meio* and *Tkacz:* J. Biol. Chem., 195:175, 1952, and by *Segal:* Ibid., 213:161, 1955.

For the formation of mercapturic acids, see *Barnes, James* and *Wood:* Biochem. J., 71:680, 1959.

References to glucuronic acid as a detoxicating agent are many. See, for example,

Wagreich, Bernstein, Pader, and *Harrow:* Proc. Soc. Exp. Biol. Med., *46:*582, 1941; *Ottenberg, Wagreich, Bernstein,* and *Harrow:* Arch. Biochem., *2:*63, 1943; *Bray, Humphries, Thorpe, White,* and *Wood:* Biochem. J., *52:*416, 1952; *Baldwin, Robinson* and *Williams:* Biochem. J., *71:*638, 1959 (excretion of glucuronides and sulfates in hens).

The origin of glucuronic acid is discussed by the following: *Eisenberg* and *Gurin:* J. Am. Chem. Soc., 73:4440, 1951; *Mosbach* and *King:* J. Biol. Chem., *185:* 491, 1950; *Doerschuk:* Ibid., *195:*855, 1952; *Bidder:* J. Am. Chem. Soc., 74:1616, 1952; *Packham* and *Butler:* J. Biol. Chem., *194:*349, 1952; *Douglas* and *King:* Ibid., *198:*187, 1952.

Articles dealing with the enzyme glucuronidase are by *Mills:* Biochem. J., *40:*283, 1946; *Graham:* Ibid., *40:*603, 1946; *Levy:* Ibid., *42:*2, 1948; *Fishman:* J. Biol. Chem., *169:*7, 1947; *Fishman* and *Fishman:* J. Biol. Chem., *152:*487, 1944; *Levy, Kerr* and *Campbell:* Biochem. J., *42:*462, 1948.

The problems of acetylation are discussed from various angles in the following articles: *Bloch* and *Rittenberg:* J. Biol. Chem., *155:*243, 1944; *159:*45, 1945; *Lipmann:* Ibid., *160:*173, 1945; *Lipmann:* Harvey Lectures (1948–1949), p. 104; *Marshall:* J. Biol. Chem., *211:*499, 1954.

The toxicity of fluoroacetate is discussed by *Peters:* Endeavour, Imperial Chem. Industries, July, 1954, p. 147.

The metabolism of ethyl alcohol in the body is discussed by *Jacobsen:* Nature, *169:* 645, 1952.

For an article on the metabolism of phenylhydrazine see *McIsaac, Parke* and *Williams:* Biochem. J., *70:*688, 1958.

IMMUNOCHEMISTRY
AND
CHEMOTHERAPY

▰▰▰▰▰▰▰▰▰▰▰▰

CHAPTER TWENTY-THREE

MICROORGANISMS WHICH CAUSE DISEASE

These may be divided into three groups; animal parasites, such as protozoa; vegetable parasites, such as bacteria and fungi; and filter-passing viruses.

Amebic dysentery, malaria, and sleeping sickness—all three common in tropical countries—are caused by protozoa. Since the spirochetes are usually classed as protozoa, syphilis would be included here.

In temperate climates, the chief diseases are caused by bacteria. Some of these bacteria and the diseases they give rise to are the following:

Streptococcus pyrogenes, or β-hemolytic streptococcus, includes some thirteen different strains of bacteria which give rise to septic wounds, blood poisoning, erysipelas, scarlet fever, etc.

Diplococcus pneumoniae, or pneumococcus, includes some 34 strains which are the common cause of pneumonia.

Staphylococcus aureus, commonly found in the skin, usually causes boils.

Neisseria gonorrhoeae, or gonococcus, gives rise to gonorrhea.

Neisseria intracellularis, or meningococcus, causes cerebrospinal meningitis.

Various bacteria also cause diphtheria, tuberculosis, cholera, plague, lockjaw, anthrax etc.

Bacteria are grouped under gram-positive (those that are not de-

600

colorized by alcohol in Gram's method of staining) and gram-negative (those that are decolorized by alcohol in Gram's stain).

Diseases due to viruses—particles which were once thought to be invisible bacteria but which are now known to be large protein molecules of the type of nucleoproteins—are smallpox, infantile paralysis, typhus fever, common colds, and probably measles, mumps, influenza, etc.

So far, greater success has attended the treatment of protozoal and bacterial diseases than the virus diseases.

DEFENSES SET UP BY THE BODY

The skin and the acid of the stomach are among these defenses—the skin by preventing entrance of bacteria and the hydrochloric acid by destroying them. But many bacteria do get into the body. The large intestine (and the eliminated feces) is full of bacteria, but these cannot penetrate the intestinal wall to enter the body proper.

However, whether through the nose, through the throat or through a cut, or as a result of lessened resistance, bacteria do penetrate the blood and tissues. To counter this menace, certain cells, macrophages, engulf the bacteria and are usually strong enough to destroy them. The macrophages are found lining the blood vessels of the liver, bone marrow, etc. (reticuloendothelial system), and some wander and may even circulate in the blood. The white cells (leukocytes) of the blood have a function similar to the macrophages.

IMMUNOCHEMISTRY

This is a branch of the general subject of immunology; it deals with the chemistry of antigens and antibodies and the chemical basis underlying immunity and resistance to disease.

ANTIGENS AND ANTIBODIES

We have seen how the body handles certain toxic substances by detoxicating them and then eliminating the detoxified products. When, however, the toxic substance which enters the blood stream is chemically of a sufficiently complex nature—approaching, say, that of a protein—the body tries to resist the effects of such toxicity by building up for its defense antibodies (proteins related to serum gamma globulin), which tend to combine with, and so nullify the effects of, the toxic substance.

The substances which give rise to these antibodies are called "antigens." The antigens include bacteria, protozoa, molds, and "foreign" proteins.

haptenes — smaller than antigen but does act like one

In general proteins which are "foreign" to the body—that is to say, proteins which are not normally found in the animal—give rise to antibodies. Certain polysaccharides may also stimulate antibody production.

When a suspension of living or dead bacteria (pneumococci, for example) is injected into an animal in increasing doses, an immunity to further infection by subsequent injection of bacteria may be acquired, and the serum of the animal reacts characteristically when mixed with an extract of the bacteria. The characteristic reaction resulting from the mixing of the serum with the bacteria originally used for the injection may give rise to a clumping, or agglutination; to a dissolving, or lysis; or to a precipitate, or precipitin, depending upon conditions. The agglutinins, lysins, and precipitins are all antibodies.

Heidelberger, and also Marrack, consider specific immune precipitation and specific agglutination of bacteria as due to the combination of antigen and antibody in such a way that molecules of antigen may become attached to molecules of antibody through one or more linkages.

As this concept postulates several reactive groupings in the molecules, an antigen-antibody complex may combine with other antigen or antibody molecules, or with preformed antigen-antibody combinations to build up large aggregates which separate from solution (or, in the case of bacteria, clump together and settle).

The process of immune combination is a reversible one. Aggregates may dissociate into uncombined antigen and antibody molecules. This dissociation, however, is relatively small.

The antigenic properties of the bacteria are usually ascribed to the proteins which they contain. Proteins, in general, with the notable exception of gelatin, give rise to antibodies. These substances are removed from the serum with the fraction containing the gamma globulins—a fact which is used as evidence that the antibodies resemble the serum gamma globulins.

These antibodies, then, are globulins, but differ from the ordinary serum globulins in one important respect: their reactivity with the antigen—which means that the antibody molecule differs in some structural way from the serum globulins.

COMPLEMENT

For lysis, or solution, of bacteria to occur the serum must be fresh. The use of old serum, or serum which has been heated to 56° C. for one-half hour, prevents this lysis. This lytic action can be restored by the addition of fresh serum. The factor so easily destroyed by heating or on standing is known as "complement," and the action of antigen and antibody in the presence of complement is called "complement fixation."

ESTIMATING ANTIBODY

A method of estimating the amount of antibody is based on the specificity of immunological reactions and on the fact that antibodies are proteins. The precipitate of antigen-antibody is analyzed for its total nitrogen content. By subtracting the nitrogen content of the antigen from that of antigen-antibody, the nitrogen content of antibody is obtained.

In a specific example, the antibody prepared against horse ferritin was treated with increasing quantities of this ferritin (antigen) and the precipitates analyzed for nitrogen (Fig. 113). Reactions of a similar kind were done, but apoferritin—differing from ferritin by being free of iron—was substituted for ferritin as the antigen. It will be noticed that the values both for ferritin and apoferritin fall on the same curve, which is an indication that, immunologically, the two are identical, and that the iron does not interfere in the reaction of antigen with antibody.

On the other hand, when the same antibody is reacted with *dog* ferritin as the antigen, a different curve is obtained.

It is true that the antibody to horse ferritin did react to some extent with dog ferritin—a "cross reaction"—but the extent of this reaction was much less than with the homologous antigen-antibody pair. The "cross reaction" actually indicates immunochemical similarity but not identity, a conclusion borne out by differences in the electrophoretic behavior of these two species of ferritins.

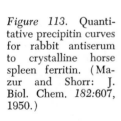

Figure 113. Quantitative precipitin curves for rabbit antiserum to crystalline horse spleen ferritin. (Mazur and Shorr: J. Biol. Chem. *182*:607, 1950.)

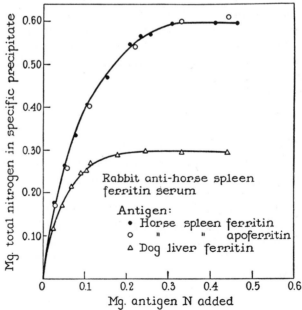

Many are the theories which have been advanced to explain the formation of antibodies in response to injection of antigen. Porter writes: "All accept the principle that combination of antibody with antigen depends on the configuration of parts of the antibody molecule being complementary to parts of the antigen molecule."

SPECIFICITY

Some idea of the specificity of these reactions may be obtained by using chemically altered antigens. For example, azo proteins may be formed by coupling the diazotized product of sulfanilic acid with the tyrosine groups of crystallized egg albumin:

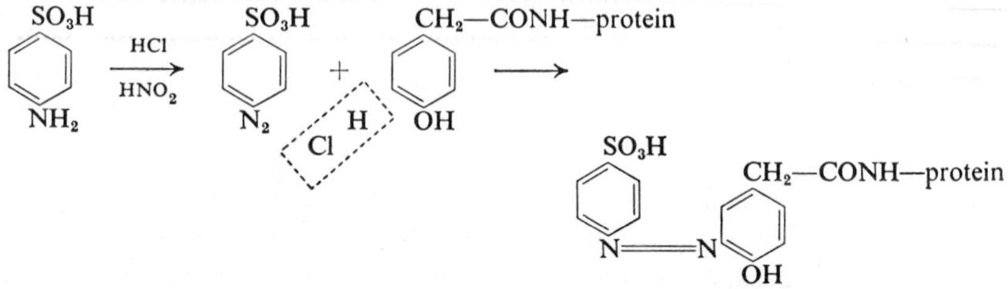

Rabbits immunized with this azo protein form antibodies which react, with sulfanilic acid joined to some other protein and react but slightly with egg albumin alone.

The specificity of these immunological reactions is remarkable. The immunological test for human blood has already been given. Here is another example: if crystallized egg albumin is injected, the antibodies produced, present in the serum, will not precipitate solutions of another albumin, such as crystalline horse serum albumin.

TOXINS

Certain bacteria—those causing diphtheria and tetanus, for example —produce toxic proteins, or toxins. Injection of such toxins in relatively small quantities, or injection of the *toxoid* (the detoxified product made by treating the toxin with formaldehyde), gives rise to antitoxins in the serum. These antitoxins when mixed with their respective toxins tend to neutralize the toxic effects of the latter. These toxins, then, are antigenic poisons.

Botulinal and tetanal toxins and several toxoids have been isolated in crystalline form.

ANAPHYLAXIS

In contradistinction to prophylaxis, anaphylaxis is the lack of protective effects, and the term was coined by Richet in 1902 to describe this experiment: Using toxic extracts of certain sea anemones, but in sublethal doses, and working with dogs, Richet found that the first injection produced no obvious symptoms; a second injection, however, given sometime after the first, caused illness and often death of the animal.

Subsequently it was shown that the substance causing this anaphylaxis need not be a toxic substance. Similar results could be produced by the use of normal serum from a different species or by the use of such a food as egg white.

This anaphylaxis also represents an antibody-antigen reaction.

In the attempt to explain the phenomenon, some investigators believe that a toxic substance is liberated as a result of the antigen-antibody combination, which produces the "shock." The toxic substance, it has been suggested, might be histamine or some histamine-like compound.

ALLERGY

This word, meaning "changed or altered reactivity," was coined by Von Pirquet to indicate "any acquired specific alteration in the capacity to react, which occurs in living organisms or tissues upon exposure to living agents or inanimate substances." The sufferer is "hypersensitive" upon exposure to certain substances; he is "allergic."

Some believe that a hereditary factor is involved, though contact with the allergen is necessary.

The fact that the allergy may be due to a relatively simple compound e.g., drug allergy, seems to show that the antigen need not necessarily be complex. However, Landsteiner showed that comparatively simple chemical substances may become antigenic ("haptenic") provided they are attached to proteins; and it is possible that allergenic drugs combine with the individual's own proteins.

In a somewhat narrow (and popular) sense, the word "allergy" refers to the clinical conditions of hay fever, asthma, eczema, and urticaria.*

An allergy to foods is not uncommon, particularly in infants and young children.

HISTAMINE AND ANTIHISTAMINIC AGENTS

It had been noticed that anaphylactic reactions in the guinea pig showed certain similarities to reactions seen in asthma and hay fever. As far back as 1910, Dale and Laidlaw pointed out that the effects of histamine and the manifestations in anaphylactic shock have points of resemblance.

* In a general way, it may be stated that when the phenomena of sensitivity appear in lower animals, the reference is to "anaphylaxis"; when the sensitivity refers to humans, then we speak of an "allergy."

Histamine is the amine of the amino acid histidine:

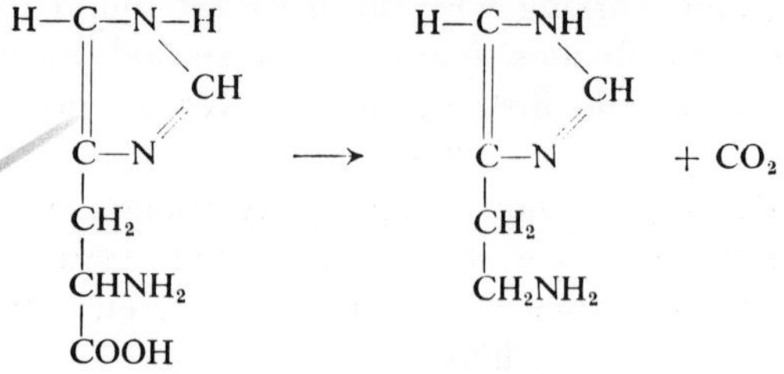

$$
\begin{array}{ccc}
\text{H—C—N—H} & & \text{H—C—NH} \\
\quad\quad\text{CH} & \longrightarrow & \quad\quad\text{CH} \\
\text{C—N} & & \text{C—N} \quad\quad + CO_2 \\
\text{CH}_2 & & \text{CH}_2 \\
\text{CHNH}_2 & & \text{CH}_2\text{NH}_2 \\
\text{COOH} & & \\
\text{Histidine} & & \text{Histamine}
\end{array}
$$

and like the other amines of the amino acids from proteins, it is a highly potent toxicological product.

The discovery by Best in 1929 that tissues contain an enzyme, histaminase, which is capable of decomposing histamine, led to the hope that the enzyme could be used in counteracting anaphylactic reactions. The results proved disappointing.

More encouraging results have been obtained by applying the theory of metabolic antagonists. This, in turn, is based on a theory of the action of histamine which may be stated as follows: histamine is a normal constituent of the body but present in an inactive form—perhaps bound to certain amino acid components within the cell. In the anaphylactic reaction the cell is injured in some mysterious way, following the union of antigen and antibody, and histamine is set free.

Here substances—somewhat analogous in structure to histamine—are used which can compete with histamine. These substances "supposedly prevent histamine from reaching those cells or enzymes to which histamine normally becomes anchored," writes Mayer, "and they are capable of occupying those places which histamine normally would occupy. In other words, antihistaminic substances compete with histamine for the normal histamine-receptive sites. For this reason, no histamine effects appear."

Among the first of these antihistaminic drugs was a phenolic ether prepared by Fourneau in 1933 and shown to have the property of counteracting the action of histamine *in vivo* as well as *in vitro*. It has the following structure:

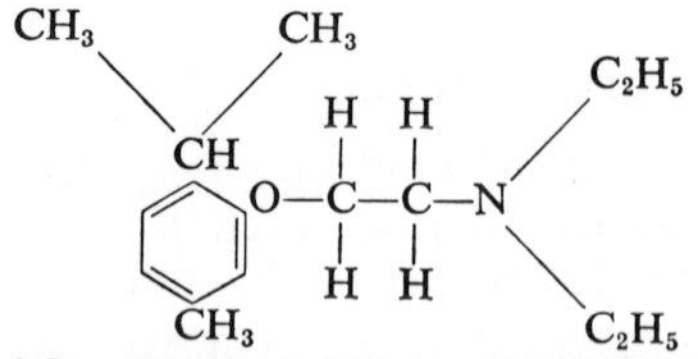

$$
\begin{array}{c}
\text{CH}_3 \quad\quad \text{CH}_3 \quad\quad\quad\quad\quad \text{C}_2\text{H}_5 \\
\text{CH} \quad\quad \text{H} \quad \text{H} \\
\text{O—C—C—N} \\
\text{CH}_3 \quad\quad \text{H} \quad \text{H} \quad\quad \text{C}_2\text{H}_5
\end{array}
$$

2-Isopropyl-5-methylphenoxyethydiethylamine

However, the toxicity of this substance led to a number of modifications in the structure. Two such products, of some practical value in clinical medicine, are diphenhydramine hydrochloride (Benadryl):

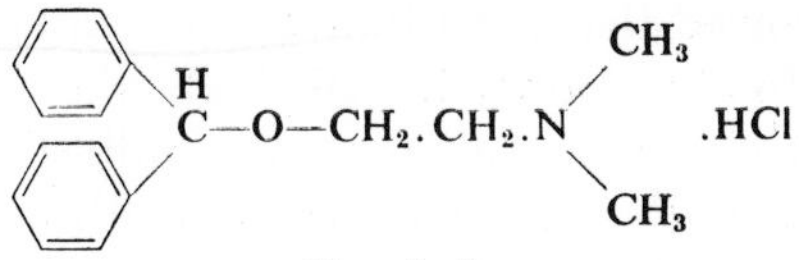

$$C-O-CH_2.CH_2.N\begin{matrix}CH_3\\\\CH_3\end{matrix}\quad .HCl$$

Benadryl

and tripelennamine hydrochloride (Pyribenzamine):

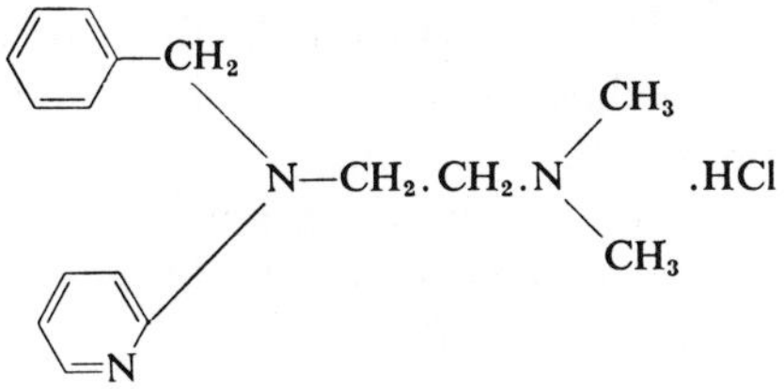

$$N-CH_2.CH_2.N\begin{matrix}CH_3\\\\CH_3\end{matrix}\quad .HCl$$

Pyribenzamine

Both of these compounds have been relatively more successful in the treatment of the patient suffering from hay fever than in the treatment of asthma.

"Both drugs," writes Feinberg, "give a high incidence of side reactions, among which sedation and drowsiness are most commonly observed." A cure cannot be expected. At best, the results are a temporary alleviation of the allergenic conditions. As for the use of "antihistamines" in curing colds, the evidence is negative.

BLOOD GROUP SUBSTANCES

There are four main blood groups, referred to as A, B, AB (a mixture of A and B) and O. Red cells containing these substances are agglutinated by certain agglutinins present in the serum of various individuals. This agglutination is the cause of the sometimes fatal reactions which occur when blood of a "foreign" type is used for transfusion.

The blood group substances are also found in saliva, commercial peptone and hog gastric mucin. They are glycoproteins or glycopeptides containing both carbohydrates and amino acids. Some of the carbohydrates are D-galactose, D-mannose and D-glucosamine.

THE RH FACTOR

Landsteiner immunized rabbits by injections with the blood of the rhesus monkey. The serum of such rabbits agglutinized about 85 per cent of human bloods. These human bloods acted as if they possessed the same immunizing or antigenic substance as the blood of the monkey; hence, the human factor was given the name rhesus or Rh factor.

Blood (red blood cells) containing the Rh factor was called Rh+ and blood not containing it (about 15 per cent), Rh—. The Rh— cells showed no agglutination.

Landsteiner showed that the Rh factor is transmitted as a dominant trait in heredity. "In the normal human body the Rh antigen is harmless; and its presence is important only in childbirth, blood transfusion, and paternity disputes. For example, when an Rh— woman, wedded to an Rh+ man, has an Rh+ infant, there is a possibility that the Rh factor may exert its malignant influence on the mother and child. This is accomplished by the flow of Rh+ antigenic substances through the placental barrier, from the fetus to the mother. In the mother's body the production of antibodies to Rh is thereby stimulated. When these antibodies return through the placenta to the fetus, they react with the blood cells of the fetus, destroying them and giving rise to a hemolytic disease of the fetus or newborn (erythroblastosis fetalis)." [*What's New* (Abbott Labs.), March, 1946.]

CHEMOTHERAPY

Aside from the defense mechanisms of the body for protecting itself against the effects of bacterial invasion, other possibilities suggest themselves. One method is to employ heat. Sufficient heat destroys bacteria. The same applies to the action of many chemicals. Phenol, formaldehyde, iodine, mercuric chloride, chloride of lime, and many other chemicals are excellent disinfectants. However, they have a serious disadvantage in that they are also effective destroyers of protoplasm.

The problem, then, is to find chemicals, drugs, which will destroy the organisms without materially harming the tissues. This is the problem of chemotherapy.

A partial answer to this problem was obtained when it was shown that malaria could be cured, to some extent, at least, with quinine, and syphilis with mercury compounds. This work also suggested that a definite chemical substance was specific in its attack on a definite organism.

The triumph of chemotherapy may be said to date back to 1910 when Ehrlich made his great discovery of "606," or salvarsan, as a cure for syphilis.

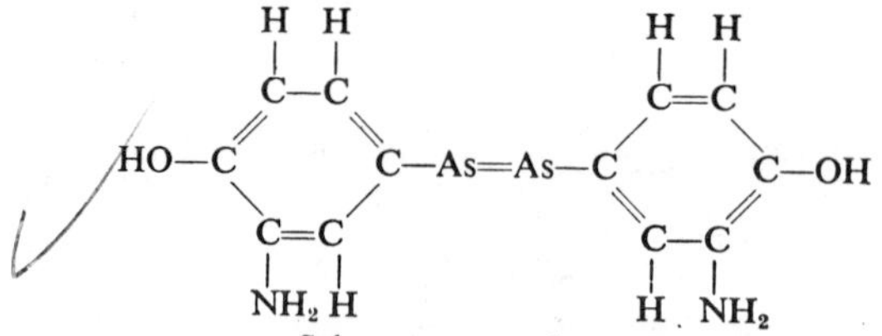

Salvarsan or arsphenamine
(3,3'-diamino-4,4'-dihydroxyarsenobenzene)

Until 1935 practically all of the successful chemical substances in use were remedies for tropical diseases caused by protozoa.

For example, one of the most striking of these diseases for which chemotherapy found an answer was malaria, a disease caused by the protozoan, *Plasmodium*, transmitted by the female *Anopheles* mosquito to man. It had been known for a long time that the bark of the cinchona tree was a remedy for malaria, but it took years to isolate quinine (one of twenty-odd alkaloids present in the bark).

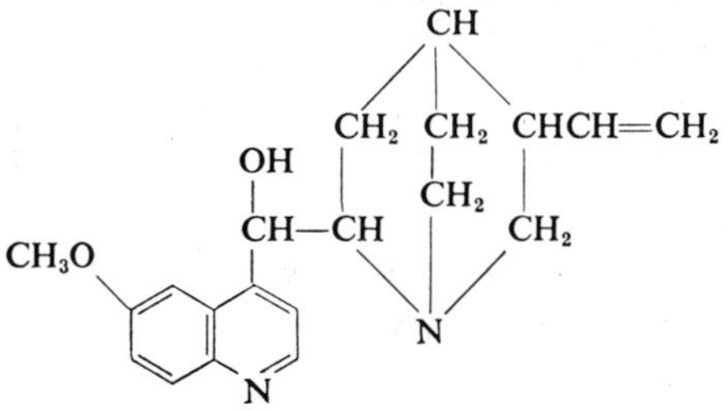

Quinine

This valuable drug is obtained largely from the Dutch East Indies. During the Second World War the occupation of these islands by the Japanese made it difficult for American health authorities to supply our troops with the needed quinine. Synthetic substitutes, such as Plasmochin (a quinoline derivative), and Atabrine (an acridine derivative) came into use. The synthesis of quinine, for years a stumbling block to organic chemists, was accomplished by Woodward and Doering in 1944.

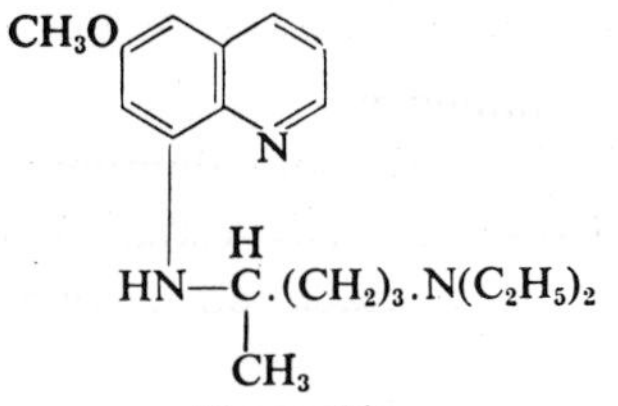

Plasmochin

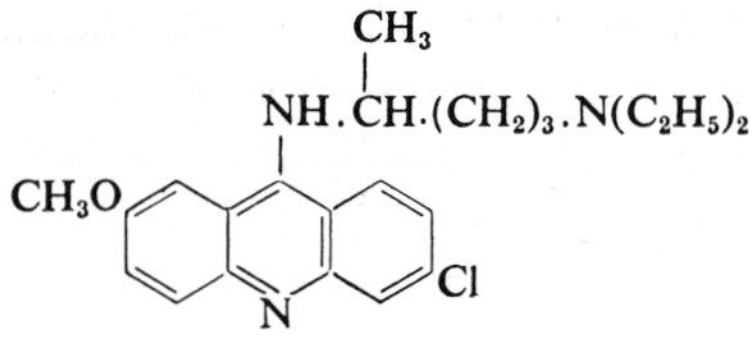

Atabrine

Chloroquine, another quinoline derivative, has also been used.

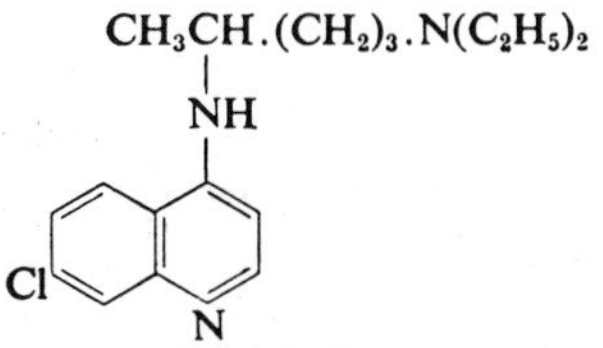

Chloroquine

The first fairly satisfactory drug for the cure of sleeping sickness was prepared by Jacobs and Heidelberger in 1919. It is known as tryparsamide and is an arsenical derivative of phenylglycineamide:

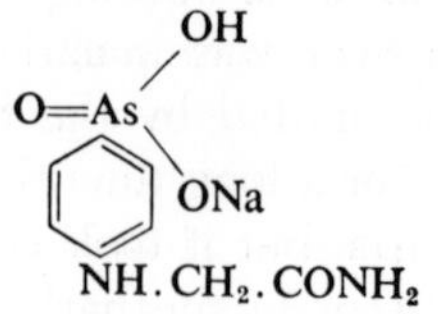

$$O=As \overset{OH}{\underset{ONa}{\big<}}$$

NH.CH$_2$.CONH$_2$
Tryparsamide

SULFONAMIDE COMPOUNDS

It was not until 1935, with the use of sulfanilamide, that the first of a series of substances was used which was effective against bacteria —the bacteria which give rise to the commonest diseases. Domagk, in an extension of the application of dyes to chemotherapy, discovered that Prontosil injected into mice infected with streptococci had a definitely curative effect.

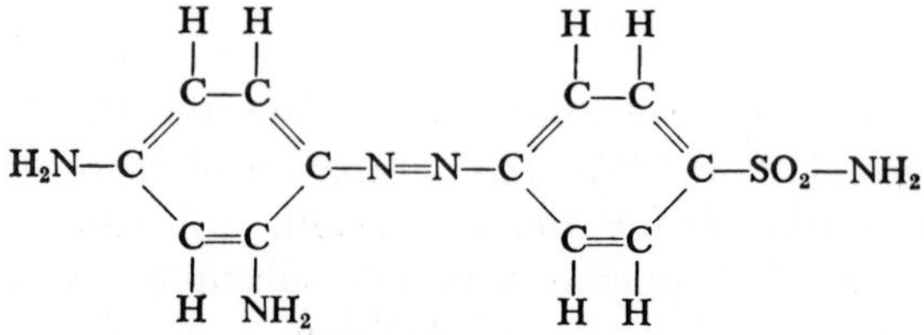

Prontosil
(4-sulfonamido-2′,4′-diaminoazobenzene)

Further work made clear that in man, Prontosil was an effective therapeutic agent against the β-hemolytic streptococcus, an agent which destroys red blood cells or which gives rise to red rashes on the skin (erysipelas and scarlet fever).

It was next shown that Prontosil was converted in the body into *sulfanilamide*, a very well known organic substance, and that sulfanilamide itself was most potent.

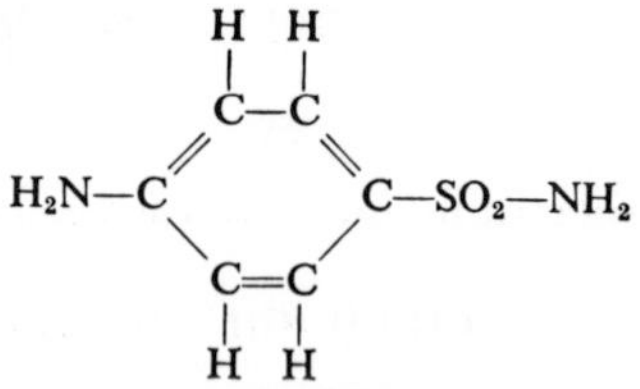

Sulfanilamide (*p*-aminobenzenesulfonamide)

Writing the skeletal form of sulfanilamide thus:

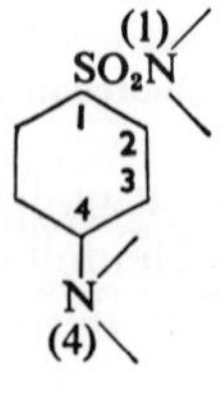

where the N in the *p* position is in position 4, and the other N would therefore be in position 1, we may say that the best results so far obtained are from substitution of hydrogen on the N (1) group.

Extremely effective compounds were obtained by replacing the hydrogen on N (1) with pyridine, thiazole, and other groups.

The steps in the synthesis of some of these sulfonamides are graphically shown in Figure 114.

Clinical Use. The sulfonamide drugs are administered by mouth and in fairly large quantities.

One or more of the drugs have been used, sometimes with amazing success, in septic wounds and blood poisoning, puerperal fever (disease of childbirth), erysipelas, meningitis, malignant endocarditis (infection of the heart), pneumonia, gonorrhea, certain kidney infections, etc.

But quite a number of bacterial diseases exist which, apparently, are not influenced by the "sulfa drugs." Among them are tuberculosis, typhoid, paratyphoid, cholera, bacillary dysentery, and whooping cough.

Also the main body of virus diseases are not influenced by treatment with the sulfonamides. These include smallpox, measles, infantile paralysis, colds, and influenza.

Mode of Action. An antisulfanilamide factor, obtained from an extract of yeast, was traced to *p*-aminobenzoic acid. Woods showed that a concentration as low as 1:10,000 was active in partially inhibiting the bacteriostatic effect of sulfanilamide at a concentration of 1:20,000.

This suggested to Woods and to Fildes a possible mechanism for the action of sulfonamide compounds. *p*-Aminobenzoic acid is regarded as an essential compound synthesized by the bacterial cells from amino acids, or obtained by the cells from their environment. To be properly utilized by the cell, the *p*-aminobenzoic acid is acted upon by an enzyme. If sulfanilamide is present, it attaches itself to the enzyme and thereby prevents the normal metabolism of the bacterial cell. The bacteria fail to get their proper nutrition and are ultimately destroyed.

Excretion. The sulfonamides are detoxicated in various ways in the body, presumably in the liver. They are excreted through the kidneys and appear in the urine in one or more of the following modifications: as an N_4-acetyl derivative, as a monohydroxyl derivative, as a glucuronide, as an ethereal sulfate.

Intestinal Antiseptics. Sulfaguanidine and succinylsulfathiazole are very poorly absorbed; they have therefore been used as intestinal antiseptics.

Experiments on animals have shown that these sulfa compounds, by destroying organisms in the intestine, often prevent, to a large extent, the synthesis of a number of vitamins which are normally brought about with the help of these organisms. Some of these vitamins are vitamin K and a few belonging to the vitamin B complex (biotin, folic and *p*-aminobenzoic acid).

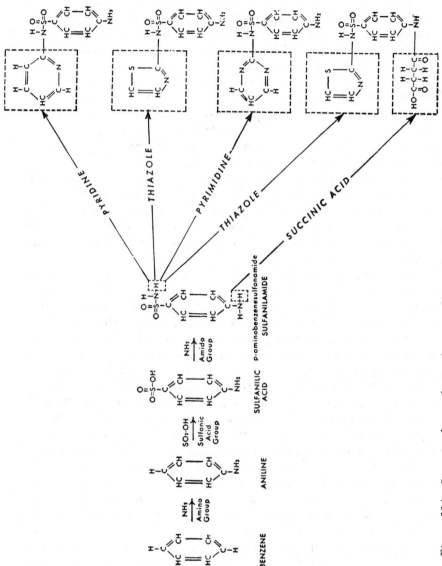

Figure 114. Steps in the synthesis of some sulfonamides. (Courtesy of Sharp & Dohme Seminar.)

ANTIBIOTIC SUBSTANCES

Florey records that as far back as 1877 Pasteur noticed that the growth of one type of bacteria may be stopped by the simultaneous growth of another adjacent to it. Later this phenomenon was shown to be due to the production of some definite chemical substance by the antagonistic microorganism. These chemical inhibitors were called *antibiotic*.

These substances, antimicrobial in action, are produced by molds, soil organisms (actinomycetes) and bacteria. They inhibit the growth of bacteria—they are bacteriostatic—though they may also, and to a lesser extent, show bactericidal properties. These substances show a certain specificity in their action. Some act on gram-positive bacteria and show little action upon gram-negative ones. Others show selective action on some of each group.

Representative members of this group of substances are penicillin, streptomycin, gramicidin, tyrocidine, bacitracin, polymyxin (formerly called aerosporin), Aureomycin, Terramycin and Chloromycetin. Several of these antibiotic substances have found wide clinical use.

Some of the antibiotics, such as Aureomycin, bacitracin, penicillin and Terramycin, are being incorporated in the food supplied to poultry, hogs, etc. on the ground that they act as growth stimulants.

Penicillin. In 1929 Fleming made his great discovery while studying the growth and properties of staphylococcus. He grew the organism on a solid medium containing agar. He noticed that "in a large colony of a contaminating mold the staphylococcus colonies became transparent and were obviously undergoing lysis." This observation, due to the accidental contamination of the media by molds from the air, was the key to the discovery.

The contamination, in Fleming's case, was due to a mold colony. He cultivated the mold in liquid broth and noticed that during growth something appeared which inhibited the growth of some organisms.

Fleming called this "something" *penicillin,* for the mold was identified (somewhat later) as *Penicillium notatum*—a mold not at all common and not the one found on bread.

Fleming made the important observation that his extract containing penicillin was not poisonous to animals and did not harm white blood cells.

It was not until 1938 that this work of Fleming's was actively pursued, this time by Florey, Chain, and their associates. This group developed a quick assay method and uncovered several chemical properties of penicillin, such as that it exhibited acidic properties, was unstable in acid and alkaline media and more stable in a neutral medium.

Florey, Chain and their associates found that the penicillin brew, after acidification, could be extracted with ether, and that the ether extract (containing much of the penicillin) when mixed with some water and the right amount of alkali yielded a more stable alkaline salt.

The properties of penicillin which made it so valuable a remedy for man were also largely uncovered by the Florey group. They confirmed Fleming's observation that the substance was nontoxic to animals and to white blood cells and tissue cultures (body cells grown outside of the body). They further found that the activity of penicillin was not affected by pus, blood or breakdown products of dead tissue (which is not true of the sulfonamides), and that it was little affected by the number of bacteria present (also not true of the sulfonamides).

Florey was of the opinion at the time that penicillin could not be given orally. While it is true that the antibiotic is partially inactivated by gastric juice, by making due allowance for this and giving a sufficient amount (about four to five times as much as for injection) the oral route is effective.

It has also been observed that penicillin was rapidly excreted, which meant that comparatively large and repeated doses were necessary. It has since been shown that 60 per cent of an injected dose is excreted within one hour, and in each succeeding hour 70 per cent of the remaining penicillin is excreted.

To retard this rapid excretion, penicillin is often incorporated with peanut or sesame oil and white wax, or is used as suspensions of procaine penicillin. Sometimes substances which inhibit tubular excretion—such as p-aminohippurate or caronamide, p-benzylsulfoneamidobenzoic acid —can be used.

Florey relates one of the early tests of the substance on mice, in preparation for its application to man. Mice were inoculated with germs which normally would kill them. "We sat up all night injecting penicillin every three hours into the treated group; and I must confess it was one of the more exciting moments when we found in the morning that all the untreated mice were dead and all the penicillin-treated ones were alive."

"The discovery of penicillin," concludes Florey, "was one of the luckiest accidents . . . for, without exception, all other mold antibiotics so far examined are poisonous."*

Assay. The "cup method," devised by Florey and associates, is widely used. An agar plate is seeded with cultures of the test organisms. Cylinders of glass, short and open at both ends, are placed on the agar, and the solutions which are to be tested are placed in the cylinders. After incubation, where the penicillin has diffused out and

* Many others have been examined since, and some are not so poisonous.

inhibited growth there appears a circular and clear zone around each cylinder. The diameter of the zone is related to the concentration of the penicillin.

The "Florey," or "Oxford," unit, widely used, is defined as "that amount of penicillin which, when dissolved in 50 cc. of meat extract broth, just inhibits completely the growth of the test strain of *Staphylococcus aureus*."

The International Unit, based on the activity of the crystalline sodium penicillin G, is 0.6 micrograms (mcg.) of this salt.

Chemistry. About fifty types of penicillin are known, but only types F, G, X, and K have been produced in quantity.

The penicillins all have the empirical formula $C_9H_{11}O_4SN_2.R$.

The formula for the penicillins is

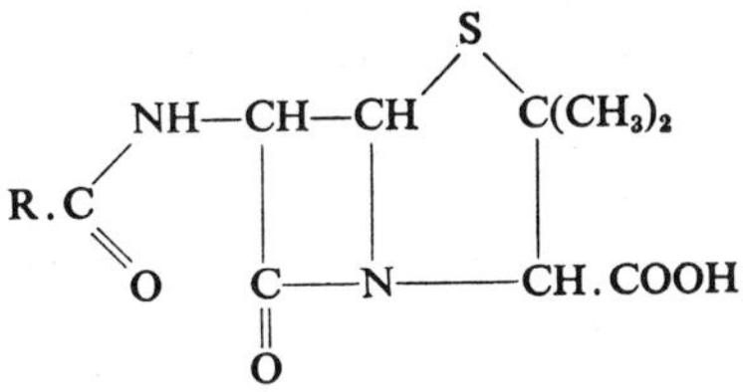

In F-penicillin, $R = \Delta^2$—pentenyl, $-CH_2.CH = CH.CH_2.CH_3$.

In G-penicillin, R is benzyl, $C_6H_5CH_2$.

In X-penicillin, R is *p*-hydroxybenzyl, $pHOC_6H_4CH_2$.

In K-penicillin, R is *n*-heptyl, $CH_3(CH_2)_6$.

The penicillins are strong monobasic acids with a pK of about 2.8, and they contain a thiazolidine ring (attached to a carboxyl and two methyl groups) joined to a β-lactam ring attached to a side-chain.

One form of penicillin has been synthesized by Sheehan.

Clinical Use. Blake, in comparing the action of penicillin with sulfonamides, divides the results into three groups:

1. Those in which both the sulfonamides and penicillin are more or less effective, though not necessarily equally so; namely certain gram-positive and gram-negative coccic infections: hemolytic streptococcus, pneumococcus, staphylococcus, *Streptococcus viridans*, meningococcus, and gonococcus.

2. Those in which the sulfonamides are of value but not penicillin; namely gram-negative bacillary infections such as those caused by *Escherichia coli*, *Shigella dysenteriae*, *Hemophilus influenzae*, *Klebsiella pneumonia*, and *Hemophilus ducreyi*.

3. Those in which penicillin is of value but not the sulfonamides; namely syphilis, yaws, and possibly other spirochetal infections and those due to *Clostridia*—gas gangrene.

How Does Penicillin Function? Penicillin does not affect the resting bacterial cell but gradually inhibits the respiration of rapidly growing bacteria. Labeled with S^{35}, penicillin has been shown to attach itself to the growing bacteria.

Bacteria contain a cell wall, a rigid structure which gives shape to the bacterium and protects the fragile protoplast. This is to be differentiated from the bacterial cell membrane. Growth of the cell wall during multiplication is always external to the cytoplasmic membrane.

Bacterial cell walls contain amino acids in rather high concentration, among them being alanine, glutamic acid and lysine. In some bacteria, diaminopimelic acid is present instead of lysine.

$$
\begin{array}{c}
\text{COOH} \\
| \\
\text{H.C.NH}_2 \\
| \\
(\text{CH}_2)_3 \\
| \\
\text{H.C.NH}_2 \\
| \\
\text{COOH}
\end{array}
$$

Diaminopimelic acid

In addition a peptide has been isolated from the cell wall which contains an amino sugar, 3-O-carboxyethyl hexosamine.

In 1949 Park and Johnson showed that uridine nucleotides accumulated in *Staphylococcus aureus* inhibited by penicillin. Later this nucleotide was isolated in combination with an amino sugar and a peptide composed of D-glutamic acid, L-lysine and DL-alanine. The time sequence of accumulation after addition of penicillin, the relationship of accumulation to the threshold bacteriostatic concentration of penicillin, and the conditions under which accumulation could be demonstrated, have suggested that this phenomenon is a very early and specific effect of penicillin and is closely related to the point of attack of penicillin within the bacterial cell.

Figure 115 shows the structure of the uridine nucleotide peptide.

It is suggested that the uridine pyrophosphate N-acetylamino sugar peptide is a biosynthetic precursor of the bacterial cell wall, and that the accumulation of this compound in penicillin-treated S. *aureus* is the consequence of the interference by penicillin with the biosynthesis of the cell wall—a loss of integrity of the cell wall following interruption of cell wall synthesis.

In addition, Lederberg has shown that samples of *Escherichia coli* in the presence of penicillin (and sucrose) are quantitatively converted to protoplasts: the cell walls are stripped. If penicillin is removed, the protoplasts revert to bacilli: they then make new cell walls.

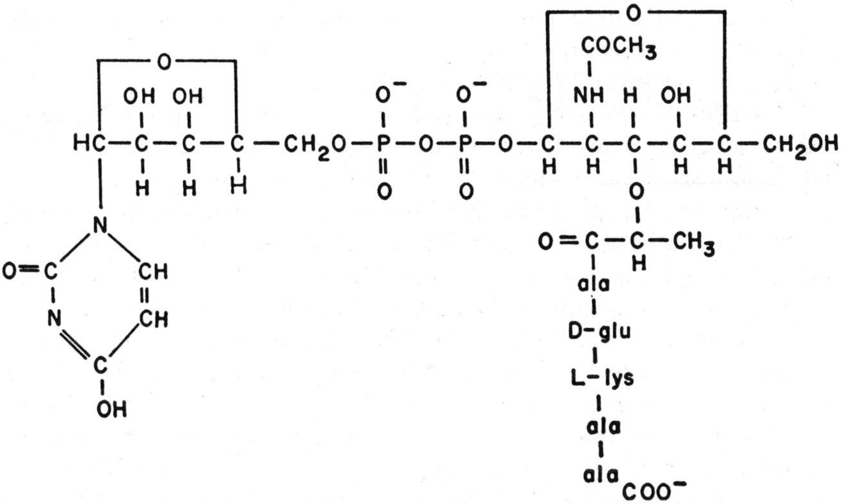

Figure 115. Proposed structure of the principal nucleotide that accumulates in penicillin-treated *Staphylococcus aureus*. In addition to the original structural determination of Park, this structure incorporates a structure proposed for the amino sugar by Strange. The sequence of amino acids in the peptide is one of the possible sequences indicated by Strominger. (From Park, J. T., and Strominger, J. L.: Science, *125*:100.)

Tyrothricin. Dubos isolated from the soil a sporulating bacillus which produces a soluble principle toxic for gram-positive bacteria. The substance so obtained was named tyrothricin, but this was later found to be a mixture of two crystalline compounds. The neutral, alcohol-soluble one was given the name *gramicidin* and the other basic one was called *tyrocidine*. Gramicidin has a molecular weight of about 2000. It is a polypeptide made up of the amino acids glycine, alanine, valine (D- and L-), tryptophan, and D-leucine, as well as ethanolamine.

A dose of 0.005 mg. of gramicidin will kill 10^9 pneumococci or group A streptococci in two hours at 30° C. One dose of 0.002 mg. of the substance injected into a mouse protects such an animal against 10,000 fatal doses of pneumococci or hemolytic streptococcus.

The mixture of gramicidin and tyrocidine—and possibly other substances—is known as *tyrothricin,* and while it is highly toxic when injected—and so cannot be considered in the same light as penicillin—

it has come to be used locally in restricted cases; for example, superficial indolent ulcers, empyema (accumulation of pus in the chest or some cavity of the body), mastoiditis, and several wound infections.

D-*Amino Acids.* L-Amino acids are found almost exclusively in nature. It may be significant that a number of antibiotics are derivatives of D-amino acids. In the penicillins we find D-penicillamine; in gramicidin, D-leucine and D-valine; in tyrocidine and bacitracin, D-phenylalanine; in polymyxin, D-leucine.

Significant, too, is that the L-analogue corresponding to the D-amino acid residue in penicillin is without activity; and that D-amino acids have been shown experimentally to inhibit bacterial growth.

Streptomycin. Penicillin has little effect on gram-negative bacteria. Among the latter are the colon bacilli, organisms of the dysentery and typhoid group, others causing undulant fever, etc. The bacillus of tuberculosis, it is true, is gram-positive, but penicillin has no effect.

Streptomycin was isolated by Waksman from a medium growing *Streptomyces griseus*, which is an inhabitant of garden soil,* river muds, and peat and compost heaps.

Streptomycin inhibits the growth of a number of gram-negative bacteria which are not affected by penicillin, for example, *Escherichia coli, Hemophilus influenzae, Proteus vulgaris, Eberthella typhosa*, etc. It is not sufficiently absorbed when given by mouth and the best results are obtained by parenteral injection.

This antibiotic has been successfully used in the treatment of certain urinary tract infections, tularemia (a disease of rodents resembling plague), influenzal meningitis (due to *Hemophilus* organisms), certain wound infections, etc. Its use in the treatment of undulant fever, bacillary dysentery, and typhoid fever has not shown much promise.

Since the work by Hinshaw and Feldman on the use of streptomycin in the treatment of tuberculosis, by which it was found that the antibiotic exerts a suppressive action on the disease process, streptomycin has become a drug of extreme usefulness in the therapy of tuberculosis. In addition to the inhibition of respiration, streptomycin exposure results in a failure of pyruvate to condense with oxalacetate, leading to an accumulation of acetate in the bacterial cell.

Chemistry. The chemistry of streptomycin has been elucidated. It consists of a base, streptidine (a diguanido derivative of cyclohexane),

---

* "Soil should not be regarded as a nonliving substratum suitable for supporting the growth of plants. In addition to its particles of weathered rock and partially decomposed plant and animal remains, it contains a dense and varied population of microorganisms. Bacteria are most abundant, fungi and actinomycetes usually somewhat less so, but a gram of fertile soil may contain hundreds or thousands of millions of viable units of each. They are not evenly distributed in the soil. They are most abundant in the surface layers, decreasing in abundance rapidly to a comparatively small number at a depth of two to three feet." (From Brian, London Times Science Review, 1955.)

linked to a nitrogen-containing disaccharide, streptobiosamine. The latter consists of streptose and N-methylglucosamine:

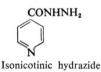

Streptidine   Streptose   N-Methyl-L-glucosamine

Streptomycin

Dihydrostreptomycin, a reduction product of the parent substance, has properties similar to streptomycin. Its toxic effects develop more slowly than do those of streptomycin, which means that sometimes it can be used for longer periods and in higher dosage than streptomycin.

Isoniazid, the hydrazide of isonicotinic acid, is used, in conjunction with streptomycin, for the treatment of tuberculosis.

CONHNH₂

Isonicotinic hydrazide

Erythromycin is produced by a strain of *Streptomyces erythreus* isolated from a soil sample collected in the Philippines. It has a low degree of toxicity and is effective in the treatment of infectious diseases caused by some gram-positive and gram-negative bacteria, including strains resistant to penicillin.

Neomycin. In attempts to get an agent active against streptomycin-resistant bacteria, Waksman isolated an antibiotic produced by a species of *Streptomyces Fradiae,* present in the soil, to which the name "neomycin" has been given. The treatment of clinical infections, particularly those of the urinary tract, has yielded encouraging results. Neomycin is a mixture of closely related compounds.

Tetracyclines. These antibiotics are derived from a mold belonging to the Streptomyces group and have proved effective against bacterial diseases such as undulant fever, peritonitis, urinary tract infections, gonorrhea, and pneumococcal pneumonia. They are active against rickettsial diseases (Rocky Mountain spotted fever, typhus) and some virus diseases (primary atypical pneumonia), and the venereal disease lymphogranuloma venereum. Bacteria do not seem to become resistant to the attacks of these antibiotics, as they do to penicillin and strepto-

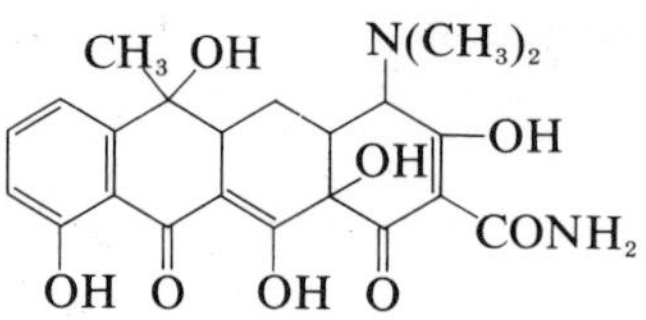

Tetracycline
(Achromycin)

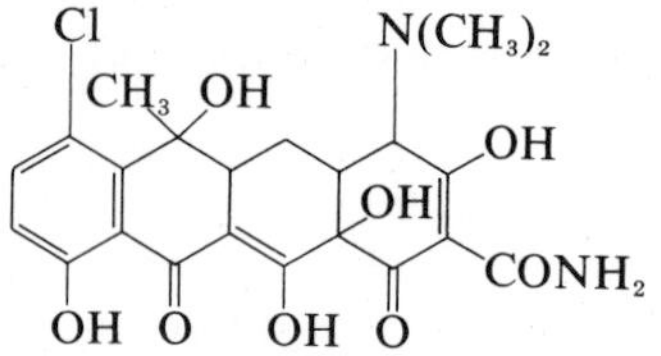

Chlortetracycline
(Aureomycin)

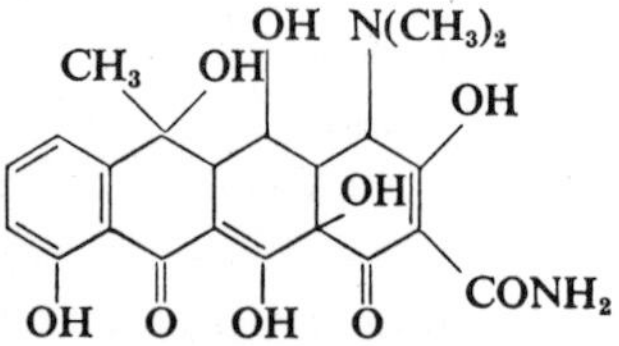

Oxytetracycline
(Terramycin)

mycin. The tetracyclines inhibit respiration, carbohydrate oxidation (glycolysis and the Krebs cycle), and protein synthesis in cells.

Chloramphenicol (Chloromycetin). This antibiotic is a product of *Streptomyces venezuelae,* isolated from soil near Caracas, Venezuela. It has been effective in treating mice experimentally infected with a number of rickettsia and viruses (rickettsialpox and the viruses of psittacosis and lymphogranuloma venereum). Clinically, it has proved effective in epidemic typhus, scrub typhus, and Rocky Mountain spotted fever. Its structure is

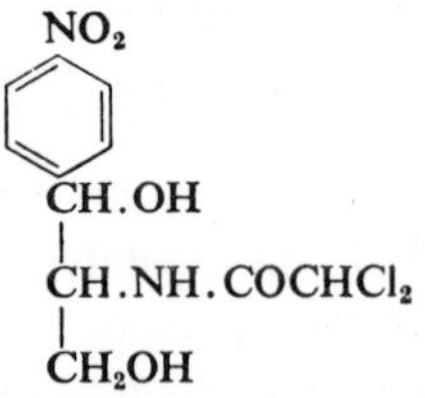

Chloramphenicol (Chloromycetin)

which means that it is 1-*p*-nitrophenyl-2-dichloroacetamidopropane-1,3-diol. It inhibits protein synthesis.

Bacitracin is produced from a strain of *Bacillus subtilis.* It inhibits the growth of more gram-positive than gram-negative organisms and is effective against rickettsiae and some viruses. This antibiotic is a polypeptide and is used locally.

Bacterial Resistance to Antibiotics. This problem has become one of common experience. When an antibiotic is applied frequently, bac-

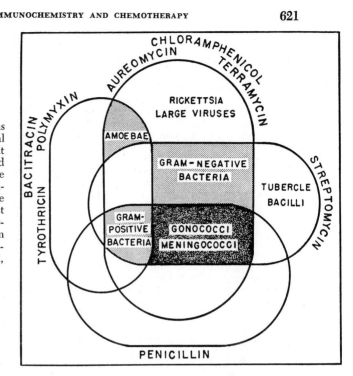

Figure 116. Domains of the five principal antibiotics and three that are less frequently used (*left*) overlap. The three "broad-spectrum" antibiotics at the top of the page are effective against the largest group of organisms. Adapted from Raper: Scientific American, *186*:49, April, 1952.)

teria often develop a "resistance" to it. Long suggests several possible mechanisms: (*a*) The bacteria may produce during growth a substance which antagonizes the antibacterial effect of the antibiotic; (*b*) previously sensitive bacteria become "adapted"; (*c*) certain cells among bacteria arise by spontaneous mutation which are resistant to the antibiotic; being resistant, they multiply freely.

Figure 116 gives a summary of the antibiotics and the organisms on which they act.

Antibiotics in Animal Feeding. Antibiotics produce growth response in a number of species of animals and are used on a commercial scale in the feeding of poultry, pigs, etc.

REFERENCES

IMMUNOCHEMISTRY. *Kabat* and *Mayer:* Experimental Immunochemistry, 1948; also *Kabat:* Blood Group Substances, 1956; *Heidelberger:* Lectures in Immunochemistry, 1956; Ann. Rev. Biochem., 25:641, 1956; *Tomcsik:* Ibid., 22:351, 1953 (immunopolysaccharides); and various chapters in *Green:* Main Currents in Biochemical Research, 1956; and *Graff:* Essays in Biochemistry, 1956; *Haurowitz:* Ann. Rev. Biochem., 29:609, 1960.

Stacy: Proc. R. S. (London), Series B, *133*:391, 1946, discusses the histochemistry of the Gram-staining reaction for microorganisms.

The theories dealing with antibody-antigen formation are summarized by *Porter:* Biochem. J., *46*:31, 1950. See also *Pauling:* Baskerville Chemical Journal (City

College N. Y.), 1950, p. 4; *Pardee* and *Pauling:* J. Am. Chem. Soc., *71*:143, 1949; *Singer:* Scientific American, Oct., 1957, p. 99 (specificity of antibodies).
For a discussion of "complement," see *Heidelberger:* American Scientist, *34*:597, 1947.
Dragstedt: Physiol. Rev. *21*:563, 1941, reviews the subject of anaphylaxis.
For the Rh factor, see What's New, Abbott Lab., March, 1946; *Boyd:* Merck Report, April, 1946, p. 16; *Fisher:* American Scientist, *35*:95, 1947.
CHEMOTHERAPY. See *Work* and *Work:* The Basis of Chemotherapy, 1948; *Albert:* Selective Toxicity with Special Reference to Chemotherapy, 1951, pp. 129, 153.
For the scientific work of *Ehrlich,* see *Aron:* J. Am. Med. Assoc., *154*:969, 1954; and *Burger:* Chem. Eng. News, *32*:4172, 1954.
The literature on the sulfonamides is enormous. Here are a few references: *Crossley:* Science, *91*:369, 1940; Ind. Eng. Chem., News Edition, *18*:385, 1940; *Marshall:* Bull. N. Y. Acad. Med., Dec., 1940, p. 723; *Blake:* Ibid., April, 1940, p. 197.
Urinary excretion products of the sulfonamides are discussed by *Scudi* and *Silber:* J. Biol. Chem., *156*:343, 1944.
For a discussion of the antagonism of p-aminobenzoic acid to sulfonamides, see Nutr. Rev., *3*:152, 1945; See also *Roblin:* Ann. Rev. Biochem., *23*:501, 1954 (metabolic antagonists).
Evans, Jr.: Federation Proceedings, *3*:390, 1946, describes the enzyme systems operating within the malarial parasite.
Northey is the author of the book: Sulfonamides and Allied Compounds, 1948.
ANTIBIOTICS. *Binkley:* Ann. Rev. Biochem., *24*:597, 1955; *Duggan* and *Singleton:* Ibid., *22*:459, 1953; *Hobby:* Bull. N. Y. Acad. Med., *31*:181, 1955; Annals N. Y. Acad. Sciences, *55*:967–1284, 1952 (antibiotics in tropical diseases); *Raper:* Scientific American, April, 1952, p. 49 (progress); *Finland:* Bull. N. Y. Acad. Med., *27*:199, 1951 (review); New and Nonofficial Drugs, 1960, p. 70. *Goldberg:* Antibiotics, Their Chemistry and Non-Medical Uses, D. Van Nostrand, 1959.
PENICILLIN. *Peck* and *Lyons:* Ann. Rev. Biochem., *20*:382, 1951 (chemistry); *Smith:* Analyst, *73*:197, 1948 (chemistry); *Gale:* Ibid., *3*:127, 1949 (how penicillin functions); *Park* and *Strominger:* Science, *125*:99, 1957 (mode of action).
STREPTOMYCIN. *Waksman:* Science, *118*:259, 1953 relates the story of the antibiotic; *Umbreit:* Trans. N. Y. Acad. Sciences, *15*:8, 1952 (mode of action); *Fox:* J. Chem. Educ., *29*:29, 1952 (chemotherapy of tuberculosis); *Dubos:* Scientific American, Oct., 1949, p. 31 (tuberculosis); *Selikoff, Robitzek,* and *Ornstein:* Ibid., *150*:973, 1952 (hydrazide therapy of tuberculosis).
ERYTHROMYCIN is described by *McGuire* and *Flynn:* Encyclopedia of Chemical Technology, *13*:94, 1954; Chem. Eng. News, Oct. 22, 1956, p. 5138.
AUREOMYCIN, TERRAMYCIN, AND CHLOROMYCETIN. See *Duggar* and *Singleton:* Ann. Rev. Biochem., *22*:460, 1953; *Rane:* Scientific American, April, 1949, p. 18 (Aureomycin); Annals N. Y. Acad. Sciences, *51*:175–342 (1948) (Aureomycin); Annals N. Y. Acad. Sciences, *53*:221–460, 1950 (Terramycin); *Hochstein, Stephens, Conover, Regna, Pasternack, Brunings,* and *Woodword:* J. Am. Chem. Soc., *74*:3708, 1952 (chemistry of Terramycin).
BACITRACIN. *Lockhart* and *Abraham:* Biochem. J., *62*:645, 1956.
A review of Antiviral Chemotherapy, by *Tamin,* may be found in the Yale J. Biol. and Medicine, *29*:33, 1956.
For growth-promoting properties of antibiotics, see *Stokstad* and *Jukes:* Proc. Soc. Exp. Biol. Med., *73*:523, 1950; *Elam, Jacobs, Tidwell, Gee,* and *Couch:* J. Nutrition, *49*:307, 1953; *Stokstad:* Food Technology, *9*:405, 1955.

ABBREVIATIONS
OF COMPOUNDS

The following abbreviations have become a part of the nomenclature of modern biochemistry and are listed as a useful reference:

Amino acid residues in polypeptides

Ala—alanyl
Arg—arginyl
Asp—aspartyl
Asp.NH$_2$—asparaginyl
Cy—cystine
CyS—half cystyl
CySH—cysteinyl
Glu—glutamyl
Glu.NH$_2$—glutaminyl
Gly.NH$_2$—glycaminyl
His—histidyl
Hylys—hydroxylysyl

Hypro—hydroxyprolyl
Ileu—isoleucyl
Leu—leucyl
Lys—lysyl
Phe—phenylalanyl
Pro—prolyl
Ser—seryl
Tyr—tyrosyl
Try—tryptophanyl
Thr—threonyl
Val—valyl

Nucleosides, Nucleotides and Nucleic acids

ADP—adenosine diphosphate
AMP—adenosine monophosphate (adenylic acid)
d AMP—5'-phosphate of 2'-deoxyribosyl adenine
ATP—adenosine triphosphate
CDP—cytosine diphosphate
CoA—coenzyme A
CMP—cytosine monophosphate (cytidylic acid)
CTP—cytosine triphosphate
DNA—deoxyribonucleic acid
DPN—diphosphopyridine nucleotide (*see* NAD)
FAD—flavin adenine dinucleotide
FMN—flavin mononucleotide
GDP—guanosine diphosphate
GMP—guanosine monophosphate (guanylic acid)
GTP—guanosine triphosphate
IMP—inosine monophosphate (inosinic acid)
NAD—nicotinamide-adenine dinucleotide (*see* DPN)
NADP—nicotinamide-adenine dinucleotide phosphate (*see* TPN)
NMN—nicotinamide mononucleotide
PNA—pentose nucleic acid
PRPP—phosphoribosyl pyrophosphate
RNA—ribonucleic acid
TPN—triphosphopyridine nucleotide (*see* NADP)
UDP—uridine diphosphate
UDPG—uridine diphosphoglucose
UMP—uridine monophosphate (uridylic acid)
UTP—uridine triphosphate

Hormones

ACTH—adrenocorticotropic hormone
DCA—deoxycorticosterone (also DOCA)
FSH—follicle-stimulating hormone
GH—growth hormone
IAA—indolyl acetic acid
LH—luteinizing hormone
MSH—melanocyte-stimulating hormone
TPP—thiamin pyrophosphate (cocarboxylase)
TSH—thyroid-stimulating hormone

Miscellaneous

Ac.CoA—acetyl coenzyme A
ACh—acetylcholine
DNFB—dinitrofluorobenzene
DNP—dinitrophenyl
G-1-P—glucose-1-phosphate
P_i—inorganic phosphate
PP_i—pyrophosphate
Hb—hemoglobin
IEP—isoelectric point
Nefa—non-esterified fatty acids
NPN—non-protein nitrogen
R.Q.—respiratory quotient
PGA—pteroyl glutamic acid
GSH—glutathione (reduced)
GSSG—glutathione (oxidized)
PROTO—Protoporphyrin

APPENDIX

TABLE 86. NUTRITIVE VALUE OF 100 GRAMS OF SELECTED FOODS, EDIBLE PORTION (ADAPTED FROM U. S. DEPARTMENT OF AGRICULTURE MISC. PUBL. NO. 572.)

Food item	Water	Food energy	Protein	Fat	Carbohydrate	Calcium	Phosphorus	Iron	Vitamin A value	Thiamine	Riboflavin	Niacin	Ascorbic acid
	Per cent	Calories	Grams	Grams	Grams	Milligrams	Milligrams	Milligrams	International Units	Milligrams	Milligrams	Milligrams	Milligrams
MILK, CREAM, ICE CREAM, CHEESE													
Milk:													
Buttermilk; cultured	90.5	35	3.5	0.1	5.1	(118)	(93)	(0.07)	(Trace)	(0.04)	(0.18)	(0.1)	(1)
Chocolate flavored [1]	83.0	75	3.2	2.2	10.6	109	91	.07	90	.03	.16	.1	0
Condensed; sweetened	27.0	327	8.1	8.4	54.8	273	228	(.20)	(430)	(.05)	(.39)	(.2)	(1)
Dry skim	3.5	359	35.6	1.0	52.0	1,300	1,030	.58	(40)	.35	1.96	1.1	7
Dry whole	3.5	496	25.8	26.7	38.0	949	728	.58	1,400	.30	1.46	.7	6
Evaporated; unsweetened	73.7	139	7.0	7.9	9.9	243	195	.17	400	.05	.36	.2	1
Fresh skim	90.5	35	3.5	.1	5.1	(118)	(93)	(.07)	(Trace)	.04	(.18)	(.1)	(1)
Fresh whole	87.0	69	3.5	3.9	4.9	118	93	.07	(160)	.04	.17	.1	1
Cream; ice cream:													
Cream (20 per cent); sweet or sour	72.5	208	2.9	20.0	4.0	(97)	(77)	(.06)	(830)	(.03)	(.14)	(.1)	(1)
Ice cream; plain [1]	62.0	210	4.0	12.3	20.8	132	104	.10	540	.04	.19	.1	Trace
Cheese:													
Cheddar type	39	393	23.9	32.3	1.7	873	610	(.57)	1,740	.04	.50	(.2)	(0)
Cottage	74.0	101	19.2	.8	4.3	82	263	(.46)	(30)	.02	.29	(.1)	(0)
Cream	53.3	367	7.1	36.9	1.7	(298)	(208)	(.17)	2,210	(.01)	.14	.1	(0)
Processed; canned [2]	37.5	382	21.9	31.8	2.0	716	831	.76	1,260	.03	.43	.1	(0)
FATS, OILS													
Bacon, medium fat	20	626	9.1	65	(1.1)	13	108	.8	(0)	(.42)	(.10)	(2.1)	0
Butter	15.5	733	.6	81	.4	16	16	.2	[3]3,300	Trace	.01	.1	0
French dressing	38.3	423	.8	39	17.3	(5)	(5)	.1	0	0	0	0	0
Lard, other shortening	0	900	0	100	0	0	0	0	0	(0)	(0)	(0)	0
Margarine with vitamin A added	15.5	733	.6	81	.4	(2)	(15)	(.2)	[4](1,980)	(0)	(0)	(0)	0
Mayonnaise	16	720	1.5	78	3.0	(19)	(60)	(1.0)	(210)	(.04)	(.04)	(0)	(0)
Salad dressing	44.7	391	1.1	36.8	13.9	(9)	(30)	(.4)	(140)	(.02)	(.03)	(0)	(0)
Salad or cooking oil	0	900	0	100	0	0	0	0	0	0	0	0	0
Salt pork; fat	8	781	3.9	85	0	2	42	.6	(0)	(.18)	(.04)	(.9)	0
EGGS													
Egg yolk; fresh	49.4	355	16.3	31.9	.7	147	586	7.2	3,210	.32	.52		0
Eggs; whole; dried	2	593	(48.2)	(43.3)	(2.6)	187	800	8.7	4,460	.35	1.23	.2	0
Eggs; whole; fresh	74.0	158	12.8	11.5	.7	54	210	2.7	1,140	.12	.34	.1	0

MEAT, POULTRY, FISH

Beef:													
Chuck roast (wholesale chuck)	65	218	18.6	16	0	11	200	2.8	(0)	.12	.15	5.0	0
Corned beef, canned	57.3	232	24.4	15	0	29	113	4.0	(0)	.02	.19	2.7	0
Corned beef, medium	54.2	288	15.8	25	0	9	170	2.4	(0)	.05	.10	1.7	0
Dried or chipped	47.7	194	34.3	6.3	0	20	370	5.1	(0)	.11	.22	3.7	0
Hamburger	55	316	16	28	0	10	172	2.4	(0)	.10	.13	4.3	0
Loin steaks (wholesale loin)	57	293	16.9	25	0	10	182	2.5	(0)	.10	.13	4.6	0
Rib roast or steak (wholesale rib)	59	277	17.4	23	0	10	188	2.6	(0)	.11	.14	4.7	0
Roast, canned	60.0	217	25	13	0	9	164	2.2	(0)	.02	.24	4.5	0
Round steak (wholesale round)	67	194	19.3	13	0	11	205	2.9	(0)	.12	.15	5.2	0
Rump roast (wholesale rump)	53	341	15.5	31	0	9	167	2.3	(0)	.10	.12	4.2	0
Soup meat (wholesale shanks)	70	162	20.3	9	0	12	219	3.0	(0)	.13	.16	5.5	0
Stew meat (73 per cent lean)	53	333	15.8	30	0	9	170	2.4	(0)	.10	.12	4.3	0
Lamb:													
Leg roast (wholesale leg)	63.7	230	18.0	17.5	0	10	194	2.7	(0)	.21	.26	5.9	0
Shoulder roast (wholesale 3-rib shoulder)	58.3	290	15.6	25.3	0	9	168	2.3	(0)	.18	.23	5.2	0
Sirloin chop (wholesale leg)	63.7	230	18.0	17.5	0	10	194	2.7	(0)	.21	.26	5.9	0
Pork:													
Bacon. See Fats, Oils.													
Ham, fresh	53	340	15.2	31	0	9	164	2.3	(0)	.96	.19	4.1	0
Ham, smoked	42	384	16.9	35	(.3)	10	182	2.5	(0)	.78	.19	3.8	(.3)
Loin	58	291	16.4	25	0	10	177	2.5	(0)	1.04	.20	4.4	0
Pork links; sausage	41.9	446	10.8	44.8	0	6	116	1.6	(0)	.22	.15	2.3	0
Salt pork. See Fats, Oils.													
Spareribs	53	346	14.6	32	0	8	157	2.2	(0)	.92	.18	3.9	0
Veal:													
Chops (wholesale loin)	69	176	19.2	11	0	11	207	2.9	(0)	.18	.27	6.3	0
Cutlet (wholesale round)	70	159	19.5	9	0	11	210	2.9	(0)	.18	.28	6.4	0
Leg roast or steak (wholesale leg)	(68)	186	(19.1)	(12.2)	0	11	206	2.9	(0)	.17	.27	6.3	0
Stew meat (74 per cent lean)	64	226	18.3	17	0	11	197	2.7	(0)	.17	.26	6.0	0
Variety meats; meat mixtures:													
Beef and gravy, canned [5]	65.3	188	19.4	11.7	1.3	19	122	2.7	(30)	.09	.19	2.7	0
Bologna	62.4	217	14.8	15.9	3.6	9	160	2.2	(0)	.31	.30	3.0	0
Chile con carne, without beans, canned [6]	66.3	198	10.2	14.6	6.4	21	152	.7	160	.01	.10	2.1	0
Frankfurters	64.3	201	15.2	14.1	3.3	9	164	2.3	(0)	.19	.23	2.4	0

Note: Parentheses indicate imputed value.

[1] Calculated from ingredients.

[2] Cheddar type.

[3] Year-round average.

[4] Plain margarine is considered to have no vitamin A value.

[5] 90 per cent beef, 10 per cent tomato gravy.

[6] Not less than 60 per cent meat, not more than 8 per cent cereals, seasonings.

TABLE 86.   NUTRITIVE VALUE OF 100 GRAMS OF SELECTED FOODS, EDIBLE PORTION (Continued)

Food item	Water	Food energy	Protein	Fat	Carbo-hydrate	Calcium	Phos-phorus	Iron	Vitamin A value	Thiamine	Ribo-flavin	Niacin	Ascorbic acid
	Per cent	Calo-ries	Grams	Grams	Grams	Milli-grams	Milli-grams	Milli-grams	Inter-national Units	Milli-grams	Milli-grams	Milli-grams	Milli-grams
MEAT, POULTRY, FISH—Continued													
Variety meats: meat mixtures—Continued:													
Ham and eggs, canned [7]	63.9	227	14.4	18.3	1.2	43	166	2.2	500	.16	.24	1.7	0
Hash, corned beef, canned [8]	69.4	143	15.1	6.1	7.0	26	(90)	1.3	(0)	.02	.13	2.4	0
Hash, meat and vegetable, canned [9]	73.3	122	10.0	5.0	9.3	14	(66)	1.2	(0)	.04	.11	2.5	6
Heart, fresh	75.4	126	(16.5)	(6.3)	(.7)	10	236	6.2	(0)	.54	.90	6.8	14
Liver, fresh	70.9	131	(19.8)	(4.2)	(3.6)	8	373	12.1	19,200	.27	2.80	16.1	31
Liver sausage	59.0	258	16.7	20.6	1.5	9	238	5.4	(5,750)	.17	1.12	4.6	(0)
Luncheon meat, canned [10]	56.3	270	15.2	22.5	1.7	21	170	1.4	(0)	.29	.21	2.7	0
Pork and gravy, canned [11]	64.9	206	15.4	15.2	1.9	16	162	1.6	(0)	.19	.24	2.7	0
Pork sausage, bulk, canned	57.0	280	16.0	24.0	0	17	131	2.2	(0)	.19	.21	2.8	0
Spaghetti with meat, canned [12]	71.0	142	9.8	6.9	10.2	38	97	1.8	480	.02	.12	2.2	...
Stew, meat and vegetable, canned [13]	72.9	127	11.6	5.5	7.8	36	(136)	1.4	1,780	.04	.12	2.4	4
Tongue, fresh, medium fat	68	202	16.4	15	.4	30	119	6.9	(0)	.22	.27	5.0	0
Vienna sausage, canned	64.1	210	16.0	16.2	0	19	(164)	.6	(0)	.07	.14	3.1	0
Poultry:													
Chicken, boned, canned	67.1	175	21.8	9.8	0	32	(218)	(1.9)	Trace	.01	.15	3.7	2
Chicken, roasters [14]	66.0	194	20.2	12.6	0	16	218	1.9	Trace	.11	.18	8.6	(2)
Turkey, medium fat [14]	58.3	262	20.1	20.2	0	23	320	3.8	Trace	.12	.19	7.9	...
Fish and shellfish:													
Cod	82.6	70	16.5	.4	0	18	189	.9	...	.04	.05	2.3	2
Fish, miscellaneous, medium fat	77.2	98	19.0	2.5	0	21	218	1.0	...	.07	.07	4.2	(2)
Oysters, solids and liquor	87.1	50	6.0	1.2	3.7	68	172	7.1	...	.18	.23	1.2	...
Salmon, canned	67.4	169	20.6	9.6	0	67	286	1.3	[15]80	.03	.18	6.5	0
Sardines, canned in oil, drained solids	57.4	207	25.7	11.0	1.2	35	365	1.8	290	.06	.12	5.2	0
Sardines, canned in oil, total contents of can	47.1	331	21.1	27	1.0	29	299	1.5	710	.05	.10	4.3	0
Shrimp, canned	78.3	82	17.8	.8	.8	(75)	(210)	(2.0)	60	.01	.03	1.9	0
Tuna fish, canned, drained solids	57.7	217	27.7	11.8	0	34	290	1.7	70	.04	.13	10.6	0
Tuna fish, canned, total contents of can	51.4	294	23.9	22.1	0	30	252	1.5	130	.04	.11	9.2	0
DRY BEANS AND PEAS, NUTS													
Dry beans and peas:													
Bean soup, navy, dehydrated [16]	7.2	332	17.6	1.2	62.7	(148)	(463)	(10.3)	(0)	.46	.22	2.4	1
Beans, canned, baked	71.0	117	5.7	2.0	19.0	(49)	(154)	(3.4)	[17]70	.05	.05	.8	[17]4
Beans, common or kidney, dry seed	10.5	350	22.0	1.5	62.1	148	463	10.3	0	.60	.24	2.1	2

Beans, lima, dry seed	12.6	341	20.7	1.3	61.6	68	381	7.5	0	.60	.24	2.1	2
Chickpeas	10.6	369	20.8	4.7	60.9	92	375	7.1	Trace	.35	.15	1.4	(2)
Cowpeas	10.6	351	22.9	1.4	61.6	80	450	7.8	0	.83	.23	2.2	2
Pea soup, dehydrated [18]	7.2	336	20.4	1.2	60.8	(73)	(397)	(6.0)	220	.62	.21	3.1	2
Peas, split	10.0	354	24.5	1.0	61.7	73	397	6.0	370	.87	.29	3.0	2
Soybeans, whole, mature	7.5	351	34.9	18.1	[19](12.0)	227	586	8.0	110	1.14	.31	2.1	Trace
Nuts:													
Almonds	4.7	640	18.6	54.1	19.6	254	475	4.4	0	0.25	0.67	4.6	Trace
Peanut butter	1.7	619	26.1	47.8	21.0	74	393	1.9	0	.20	.16	16.2	(0)
Peanuts, roasted	2.6	600	26.9	44.2	23.6	74	393	1.9	0	[20].30	.16	16.2	(0)
Pecans	3.0	747	9.4	73.0	13.0	74	324	2.4	50	.72	.11	.9	2
Walnuts, English	3.3	702	15.0	64.4	15.6	83	380	2.1	30	.48	.13	1.2	3
VEGETABLES													
Fresh:													
Asparagus	93.0	26	2.2	.2	3.9	21	62	.9	1,000	.16	.17	1.2	33
Beans, lima, green	66.5	131	7.5	.8	23.5	63	158	2.3	280	.25	.14	.9	32
Beans, snap	88.9	42	2.4	.2	7.7	65	44	1.1	630	.08	.10	.6	19
Beet greens	90.4	33	2.0	.3	5.6	21	45	3.2	6,700	.05	.17	.3	34
Beets	87.6	46	1.6	.1	9.6	27	43	1.0	20	.03	.05	.4	10
Broccoli	89.9	37	3.3	.2	5.5	130	76	1.3	3,500	.09	.21	.9	118
Brussels sprouts	84.9	58	4.4	.5	8.9	34	78	1.3	400	.11	(.06)	(.3)	94
Cabbage	92.4	29	1.4	.2	5.3	46	31	.5	80	.07	.06	.3	52
Carrots	88.2	45	1.2	.3	9.3	39	37	.8	12,000	.07	.06	.5	6
Cauliflower	91.7	31	2.4	.2	4.9	22	72	1.1	90	.10	.11	.6	69
Celery	93.7	22	1.3	.2	3.7	50	40	.5	0	.03	.04	.3	7
Chard	91.8	25	1.4	.2	4.4	[21]22	36	4.0	2,800	.06	.13	.2	38
Collards	86.6	50	3.9	.6	7.2	249	58	1.6	6,870	.22	(.20)	(.8)	100
Corn, sweet, white or yellow	73.9	108	3.7	1.2	20.5	9	120	.5	[23]390	.15	.14	1.4	12

Note: Parentheses indicate imputed value.

[7] 50 per cent ham, 50 per cent whole eggs.
[8] 72 per cent beef, 28 per cent potatoes.
[9] 50 per cent meat, 48 per cent potatoes, 2 per cent onions.
[10] Pork.
[11] 90 per cent pork, 10 per cent gravy.
[12] 50 per cent meat, 10 per cent dry spaghetti, 30 per cent tomato puree, 5 per cent cheese, 5 per cent onions.
[13] 50 per cent meat, 15 per cent potatoes, 15 per cent carrots, 8 per cent dry beans, 12 per cent tomato puree.

[14] Vitamin values based on muscle meat only.
[15] Based on pink salmon. Canned red salmon may have a value several times higher.
[16] Navy bean meal, farinaceous flour up to 15 per cent.
[17] Contributed by tomatoes.
[18] Pea meal, farinaceous flour up to 15 per cent.
[19] "Available" carbohydrate.
[20] Based on peanuts without skins; when skins are included the thiamine value is higher.
[21] 118 mg.; may not be available because of presence of oxalic acid.
[22] 105 mg.; may not be available because of presence of oxalic acid.
[23] Based on yellow corn; white corn contains only a trace.

TABLE 86. NUTRITIVE VALUE OF 100 GRAMS OF SELECTED FOODS, EDIBLE PORTION (*Continued*)

Food item	Water	Food energy	Protein	Fat	Carbohydrate	Calcium	Phosphorus	Iron	Vitamin A value	Thiamine	Riboflavin	Niacin	Ascorbic acid
	Per cent	Calories	Grams	Grams	Grams	Milligrams	Milligrams	Milligrams	International Units	Milligrams	Milligrams	Milligrams	Milligrams
VEGETABLES—Continued													
Fresh—Continued:													
Cucumbers	96.1	14	.7	.1	2.7	10	21	.3	[24] 0	.04	.09	.2	8
Dandelion greens	85.8	52	2.7	.7	8.8	187	70	3.1	13,650	.19	.14	(.8)	36
Eggplant	92.7	28	1.1	.2	5.5	15	37	.4	30	.07	.06	.8	5
Kale	86.6	50	3.9	.6	7.2	225	62	2.2	7,540	.12	.35	(.8)	115
Lettuce, headed	94.8	18	1.2	.2	2.9	22	25	.5	540	.06	.07	.2	8
Lettuce, all other	94.8	18	1.2	.2	2.9	62	20	1.1	1,620	.06	.07	.2	18
Mustard greens	92.2	28	2.3	.3	4.0	220	38	2.9	6,460	.09	.20	.8	102
Okra	89.8	39	1.8	.2	7.4	82	62	.7	740	.12	.10	.7	30
Onions, mature	87.5	49	1.4	.2	10.3	32	44	.5	50	.03	.02	.1	[25] 9
Parsnips	78.6	83	1.5	.5	18.2	57	80	.7	0	.11	.09	.2	18
Peas, green	74.3	101	6.7	.4	17.7	22	122	1.9	680	.36	.18	2.1	26
Peppers, green	92.4	29	1.2	.2	5.7	11	25	.4	630	.07	.04	.4	120
Potatoes	77.8	85	2.0	.1	19.1	11	56	.7	20	.11	.04	1.2	17
Pumpkin	90.5	36	1.2	.2	7.3	21	44	.8	(3,400)	(.05)	(.08)	(.6)	8
Radishes	93.6	22	1.2	.1	4.2	37	31	1.0	30	.04	.04	.1	24
Rutabagas	89.1	41	1.1	.1	8.9	55	41	.4	330	.06	.06	.5	36
Spinach	92.7	25	2.3	.3	3.2	[26]	55	3.0	9,420	.12	.24	.7	59
Squash, summer	95.0	19	.6	.1	3.9	15	15	.4	260	.04	.05	1.1	17
Squash, winter	88.6	44	1.5	.3	8.8	19	28	.6	4,950	.05	.08	.6	8
Sweetpotatoes	68.5	125	1.8	.7	27.9	30	49	.7	[27] 7,700	.10	.06	.7	22
Tomatoes	94.1	23	1.0	.3	4.0	11	27	.6	1,100	.06	.04	.6	23
Turnip greens	89.5	37	2.9	.4	5.4	259	50	2.4	9,540	.10	.56	.8	136
Turnips	90.9	35	1.1	.2	7.1	40	34	.5	Trace	.06	.06	.5	28
Canned:													
Asparagus	93.6	21	1.6	.3	3.0	20	34	1.0	[28] 600	.06	.09	.8	15
Beans, lima	80.9	72	3.8	.3	13.5	27	73	1.7	130	.03	.05	.5	8
Beans, snap	94.0	19	1.0	0	3.8	27	19	1.4	410	.03	.05	.3	4
Beets	89.4	39	1.0	0	8.7	15	29	.6	20	.01	.03	.1	5
Carrots	92.2	30	.5	.4	6.1	22	24	.6	12,000	.03	.02	.3	2
Corn, white or yellow	80.5	77	2.0	.5	16.1	4	51	.5	[28] 200	.02	.05	.8	5
Peas, green	82.3	69	3.4	.4	12.9	25	67	1.8	[29] 540	.11	.06	.9	8
Pumpkin	90.2	38	1.0	.3	7.9	(20)	(36)	(.7)	3,400	.02	.06	.5	(0)

Sauerkraut	93.2	20	1.1	.2	3.4	(46)	(31)	(.5)	Trace	.03	.20	.2	[29]18
Spinach	92.3	25	2.3	.4	3.0	[30]30	33	1.6	6,790	.02	.08	.3	14
Tomato catsup	69.5	110	2.0	0.4	24.5	12	18	0.8	(1,880)	0.09	0.07	2.2	11
Tomato juice	93.5	23	1.0	.2	4.3	(7)	(15)	(.4)	1,050	.05	.03	.7	16
Tomato puree	89.2	40	1.8	.5	7.2	(11)	(37)	(1.1)	1,880	.09	(.07)	1.8	28
Tomatoes	94.2	21	1.0	.2	3.9	(11)	(27)	(.6)	1,050	.05	.03	.7	16
FRUIT													
Fresh:													
Apples	84.1	64	.3	.4	14.9	6	10	.3	90	.04	.02	.2	5
Apricots	85.4	56	1.0	.1	12.9	16	23	.5	2,790	.03	.04	.7	4
Avocadoes	65.4	265	1.7	26.4	5.1	10	38	.6	290	.12	.15	1.1	16
Bananas	74.8	99	1.2	.2	23	8	28	.6	430	.09	.06	.6	10
Berries:													
Blueberries	83.4	68	.6	.6	15.1	16	13	.8	280	(.03)	(.07)	(.3)	16
Strawberries	90.0	41	.8	.6	8.1	28	27	.8	60	.03	.07	.3	60
Other berries	84.4	65	1.2	.8	13.2	36	34	.9	320	.03	(.07)	(.3)	23
Cantaloups	94.0	23	.6	.2	4.6	17	16	.4	[31]3,420	.06	.04	.8	33
Grapefruit	88.8	40	.5	.2	10.1	17	18	.3	Trace	.04	.02	.2	40
Grapes	81.6	74	.8	.4	16.7	17	21	.6	80	.05	.03	.4	4
Lemons	89.3	44	.9	.6	8.7	(14)	(10)	(.1)	0	.04	Trace	.1	45
Limes	86.0	53	.8	.1	12.3	(14)	(10)	(.1)	0	(.04)	(Trace)	(.1)	27
Oranges	87.2	50	.9	.2	11.2	33	23	.4	(190)	.08	.03	.2	49
Peaches	86.9	51	.5	.1	12.0	8	22	.6	880	.02	.05	.9	8
Pears	82.7	70	.7	.4	15.8	13	16	.3	20	.02	.04	.1	4
Pineapples	85.3	58	.4	.2	13.7	16	11	.3	130	.08	(.02)	(.2)	24
Plums	85.7	56	.7	.1	12.9	17	20	.5	350	.08	(.03)	.6	5
Rhubarb	94.9	18	.5	.1	3.8	[32]33	25	.5	30	.01		.1	9
Tangerines; other mandarin type oranges	87.3	50	.8	.3	10.9	(33)	(23)	(.4)	(420)	.07	(.03)	(.2)	31
Watermelons	92.1	31	.5	.2	6.9	7	12	.2	590	.05	.05	.2	6
Canned:													
Apples; applesauce	79.8	80	.2	.1	19.7	(4)	(6)	(.2)	(60)	.01	.01	Trace	1
Apricots	77.3	89	.6	.1	21.4	(10)	(15)	(.3)	1,350	.02	.02	.3	4
Cherries	78.1	86	.6	.1	20.8	(11)	(14)	(.3)	(430)	.03	.02	.2	3
Cranberry sauce	48.1	209	.1	.3	51.4	(8)	(7)	(.3)	(30)		(.04)		2
Fruit cocktail	(80.6)	78	(.4)	(.2)	(18.6)	(9)	(12)	(.4)	160	.01	.01	.4	2

Note: Parentheses indicate imputed value.

[24] Based on pared cucumber; unpared contains about 260 I. U. vitamin A per 100 gm.
[25] Green bunching onions contain about 23 mg. ascorbic acid per 100 gm.
[26] 81 mg.; may not be available because of presence of oxalic acid.
[27] If pale varieties only were used, value would be very much lower.

[28] Based on green products; bleached products contain only a trace.
[29] 90 mg.; may not be available because of presence of oxalic acid.
[30] Drained solids only.
[31] Based on deeply colored varieties.
[32] 51 mg.; may not be available because of presence of oxalic acid.

TABLE 86. NUTRITIVE VALUE OF 100 GRAMS OF SELECTED FOODS, EDIBLE PORTION (*Continued*)

Food item	Water	Food energy	Protein	Fat	Carbohydrate	Calcium	Phosphorus	Iron	Vitamin A value	Thiamine	Riboflavin	Niacin	Ascorbic acid
	Per cent	Calories	Grams	Grams	Grams	Milligrams	Milligrams	Milligrams	International Units	Milligrams	Milligrams	Milligrams	Milligrams
FRUIT—Continued													
Canned—Continued													
Grapefruit juice	89.4	41	.5	.2	9.4	8	12	.4	Trace	.03	.02	.2	35
Grapefruit segments	79.8	81	.6	.2	19.1	13	14	.3	Trace	.03	.02	.2	30
Orange juice	86	55	.6	.1	12.9	(33)	(23)	(.4)	(100)	.07	.02	.2	42
Peaches	80.9	75	.4	.1	18.2	(5)	(14)	(.4)	450	.01	.02	.7	4
Pears	81.1	75	.2	.1	18.4	(8)	(10)	(.2)	Trace	.01	.02	.1	2
Pineapple juice	86.2	54	.3	.1	13.0	15	8	.5	80	.05	.02	.2	9
Pineapples	78.0	87	.4	.1	21.1	29	7	.6	80	.07	.02	.2	9
Plums; Italian prunes	78.6	84	.4	.1	20.4	8	12	1.1	(230)	.03	.03	.4	1
Dried:													
Apple nuggets	1.6	390	1.4	1.0	93.9	24	42	4.1	(0)	.05	.08	.5	11
Apricots [33]	24	292	5.2	.4	66.9	86	119	4.9	7,430	.01	.16	3.3	12
Cranberries	4.9	409	2.9	6.6	84.4	82	22	3.4	660	.19	.18	.9	33
Peaches [33]	24	295	3.0	.6	69.4	44	126	6.9	3,250	.01	.20	5.4	19
Prunes [34]	24	299	2.3	.6	71.0	54	85	3.9	1,890	.10	.16	1.7	3
Raisins [34]	24	298	2.3	.5	71.2	78	129	3.3	50	.15	.08	.5	Trace
GRAIN PRODUCTS													
Baked goods:													
Bread:													
Rye, light	37.6	263	(6.4)	(3.4)	(51.7)	(22)	(96)	(.8)	(0)	.16	(.04)	(1.1)	0
White, enriched	35.9	261	8.5	2.0	52.3	(56)	(100)	(1.8)	(0)	(.24)	(.15)	(2.2)	0
Whole wheat	37	262	9.5	3.5	48.0	(60)	370	2.6	(0)	.28	.15	3.5	0
Cake, light batter type	26.8	327	6.4	8.2	57.0	62	(126)	2.0		.03	.10	.7	0
Cookies, assorted, plain	4.8	438	6.0	12.7	75.0	(22)	(65)	(.6)	(0)	(.04)	(.04)	(.5)	0
Cracker meal; crackers, assorted	4.5	422	9.5	10.3	72.7	22	102	1.5	(0)	(.07)	(0)	(.6)	0
Crackers, graham	5.5	419	8.0	10.0	74.3	20	203	1.9	(0)	.30	.12	1.5	0
Fig bars	13.8	363	4.2	4.8	75.8	(69)	(69)	(1.3)	(0)	.02	(.06)	(.9)	0
Pie, apple		266	(2.9)	(9.6)	(42.0)	(11)	(22)	1.9	(0)	(.05)	(.04)	.4	(0)
Pie, cream		223	(2.8)	(9.8)	(31.0)	20	(38)	.5	(0)	.03	.08	.2	(0)
Rolls, plain, enriched	29.4	304	8.2	6.1	54.1	(56)	(100)	(1.8)	(0)	(.24)	(.15)	(2.2)	0
Rolls, sweet, unenriched	29.6	304	7.8	5.4	56.0	(56)	(100)	.5	(0)	.08	.13	.8	0
Breakfast cereals:													
Corn flakes	9.3	359	7.9	.7	80.3	(10)	56	(1.0)	(0)	(.16)	.08	1.6	0
Corn flakes, restored													
Oatmeal	8.3	396	14.2	7.4	68.2	54	365	5.2	(0)	.55	.14	1.1	0

Rice flakes; puffed rice.	8.8	363	7.2	.4	82.6	(9)	(92)	.9	(0)	(.05)	(.03)	(1.4)	0
Rice flakes; puffed rice, restored.													
Wheat cereals:													
Farina.	11	359	11.5	1.0	76.1	21	125	.8	(0)	.06	.06	1.0	0
Farina, enriched.	11	359	11.5	1.0	76.1	21	125	(1.3)	(0)	(.37)	(.26)	(1.3)	0
Flakes; puffed wheat.	6.2	372	11.9	1.5	77.7	33	353	3.7	(0)	.15	.12	4.2	0
Flakes; puffed wheat, restored.													
Shredded wheat.	7.7	369	10.4	1.4	78.7	(38)	(385)	(3.8)	(0)	.20	.14	4.2	0
Whole-grain, uncooked.	8.7	368	11.7	2.0	75.8	38	385	3.8	(0)	.45	.13	4.6	0
Other cereals:													
Barley, pearled, light.	11.1	357	8.2	1.0	78.8	16	189	(2.0)	(0)	.12	.08	3.1	0
Hominy.	11.4	357	8.5	.8	78.9	11	70	1.0	(0)	.15	.05	(.9)	0
Macaroni; spaghetti	11	360	13	1.4	73.9	22	144	1.2	(0)	.13	.08	2.1	0
Noodles.	9.1	385	14.3	5.0	70.6	24	156	1.9	(200)	(.13)	(.12)	(2.1)	0
Rice:													
Brown.	12.0	356	7.5	1.7	77.7	39	303	5.5	(0)	.29	.05	4.6	0
Converted.	(12.3)	351	(7.6)	(.3)	(79.4)	(9)	(92)	(.7)	(0)	.23	.04	3.8	0
White.	12.3	351	7.6	.2	79.4	9	92	.7	(0)	.05	.03	1.4	0
Tapioca.	12.6	350	.6	.2	86.4	12	12	(1.0)	(0)	0	(0)	(0)	0
SUGARS, SWEETS													
Honey.	20	319	.3	0	79.5	5	16	.9	(0)	Trace	.04	.2	4
Jams; marmalades.	28	288	.5	.3	70.8	12	12	(.3)	(10)	.02	.02	.2	6
Jellies.	34.5	261	.2	0	65.0	(12)	(12)	(.3)	(10)	(.02)	(.02)	(.2)	4
Molasses, cane.	24	240	(0)	(0)	(60)	273	51	6.7	(0)	.08	.16	2.8	(0)
Sirup, table blends.	25	296	(0)	(0)	(74)	46	16	4.1	0	0	.01	.1	(0)
Sugar, brown.	3	382	(0)	(0)	(95.5)	[35] 76	[35] 37	2.6	(0)	(0)	(0)	(0)	(0)
Sugar, granulated or powdered.	.5	398	(0)	(0)	99.5	(0)	(0)	.1	(0)	(0)	(0)	(0)	0
MISCELLANEOUS													
Bouillon cubes.	(3)	259	17.7	0	47.0	40	510	9.2	(0)	0.03	0.83	[36] .6	(0)
Chocolate, unsweetened.	2.3	570	(5.5)	52.9	(18)	[37]	343	2.5	(0)	Trace	.24	1.1	(0)
Cocoa.	4.3	329	(9.0)	18.8	(31.0)	[38]	709	2.7	(0)	Trace	(.39)	(2.3)	(0)
Cocoanut, dry, shredded.	3.3	579	3.6	39.1	53.2	43	191	3.6	0	Trace	Trace	Trace	(0)
Gelatin dessert powder.	1.6	392	9.4	0	88.7	(0)	(0)	(0)	(0)	(0)	(0)	(0)	(0)
Olives, green.	75.2	144	1.5	13.5	4.0	101	15	2.0	420	Trace			(0)
Pickles, cucumber.	95.2	11	.5	.2	1.9	24	22	.9	190	2.05	.02	Trace	.7
Wheat germ.	11.0	389	25.2	10.0	49.5	84	1,096	8.1	(0)	.45	.80	4.6	(0)
Yeast, compressed, baker's.	70.9	109	13.3	.4	13.0	25	605	4.9	(0)	.45	2.07	28.2	(0)
Yeast, dried, brewer's.	7.0	348	46.1	1.6	37.4	106	1,893	18.2	(0)	9.69	5.45	36.2	(0)

Note: Parentheses indicate imputed value.

[33] Sulfured.
[34] Unsulfured.
[35] Based on dark brown sugar; lower values for light brown sugar.
[36] Based on vegetable extract type; meat extract type may have up to 27.0 mg. of niacin per 100 gm.
[37] 95 mg.; may not be available because of presence of oxalic acid.
[38] 160 mg.; may not be available because of presence of oxalic acid.

INDEX

Abbreviations, 623
Absorption, 170, 193
p-Acetaminophenol, 593
Acetanilid, 588, 593
Acetic acid, 45
  detoxicating agent, 596
Acetoacetic acid, 303, 345, 353
Acetoacetyl CoA, 304, 335, 345
Acetone bodies, 303
  in urine, 530
Acetyl adenylate, 335
Acetyl coenzyme A, 167. See also Co-
  enzyme A
Acetyl glucosamine, 21
Acetyl number, 51
Acetyl phosphate, 168
Acetyl sphingosine, 313
Acetyl transfer, 459
p-Acetylaminobenzene sulfonamide, 596
p-Acetylaminobenzoic acid, 596
Acetylcholine, 61
  nerve conduction and, 497
Acetylcholinesterase, 130, 139, 156, 497,
  498
Acetylmalonyl CoA, 305
Acetylneuraminic acid, 21
Acetylsulfanilamide, 335
Ac-globulin, 220
Achrodextrin, 35
Achromycin, 620
Acid(s). See also specific compounds
  bases and, 88–91
Acid albuminate, 73
Acid-base balance, 244, 245, 426
Acid-metaprotein, 73
Acidosis, 240, 244, 399
Aconitase, 133, 284
cis-Aconitic acid, 285

Acromegaly, 542
Actin, 489
Activation energy, 161, 162
Actomyosin, 489
Acyl dehydrogenase, 302
Adenase, 131, 361
Adenine, 116, 118
  metabolism, 367
Adenosine, 118, 362
Adenosine deaminase, 131
Adenosine diphosphate (ADP), 120
Adenosine phosphates, 121
Adenosine triphosphate (ATP), 120, 167,
  169, 275, 378
Adenosine-2-phosphate, 121
Adenosine-3-phosphate, 121
Adenosine-5'-phosphate, 120
Adenosinetriphosphatase (ATP-ase), 131,
  166, 491
s-Adenosylmethionine, 312, 350
Adenylate deaminase, 361
Adenylcobamide, 471
Adenylic acid(s), 120, 121, 272, 362
3',5'-Adenylic acid, 272
Adenylic acid deaminase, 361
ADP, 120
Adrenalin, 554. See also Epinephrine
Adrenal(s), 554
  cortex, 555
  corticosteroids, 556
  medulla, 554
  sex and, 559
  steroids in, 546
Adrenocorticotropin, 310, 546
Adrenosterone, 559
Aerobic dehydrogenases, 256
Aerobic glycolysis, 282
Aerobic oxidation, 283

Aerobic phosphorylation, 289–291
Agar, 30, 37
Air, analyses, 231
Alanine, 74, 86, 344
β-Alanine, 77
D-Alanine, 79
Albinism, 353
Albumins, 71, 101, 214, 528
Alcaptonuria, 353
Alcohol(s), oxidation, 588
Alcohol dehydrogenase, 150, 277
Aldehyde(s), oxidation, 588
Aldehyde oxidase, 153
Aldolase, 135, 277, 293
Aldosterone, 557, 559
Alkali albuminate, 73
Alkali metaprotein, 73
Alkalosis, 240, 244
Allantoic acid, 363
Allantoin, 329, 363
  in urine, 528
Allergy, 605
Allobiotin, 461
Allocholanic acid, 57
Allose, 12
Alloxan, 524
Alloxan diabetes, 552
Alloxantin, 524
Alpha-lipoic acid. See Lipoic acid
Altrose, 12
Aluminum, 415
Amandin, 71
Amidases, 131
Amines, acetylation, 335
  oxidation, 588
Amino acid(s), 74–79
  acids and bases, 92
  activation, 338
  C-terminal, 84
  chromatographic analysis, 83
  colorimetric methods for estimating, 81
  D-, 618
  decarboxylation, 327
  dissociation constants, 91–94
  essential, 422, 423
  formol titration, 94–96
  in urine, 524
  incorporation, 334
  isoelectric points, 94
  isolation, 79
  isotope dilution method for estimating,
    82
  microbiological estimation, 81
  N-terminal, 84
  ninhydrin and, 81
  nonessential, 422
  oxidative deamination, 326
  pool, 325
  quantitative estimation, 81–83
  synthesis, 86

Amino acid adenylate, 338–341
Amino acid decarboxylase, 135
Amino acid oxidases, 327
Amino sugars, 21
α-Aminoadipic acid, 348, 349
p-Aminobenzoic acid, 465
  relation to sulfanilamide, 596
γ-Aminobutyric acid, 78, 496
Aminoethanol. See Ethanolamine
Aminoethyl mercaptan, 192
p-Amino-hippuric acid, 335
4-Amino-5-imidazole carboxamide, 366
α-Amino-β-ketoadipic acid, 209
δ-Aminolevulinic acid, 209
2-Amino-4-nitrophenol, 590
Aminopeptidase, 132, 133
p-Aminophenol, 588
Ammonia, 329, 527
Amphoteric substances, 89
Amygdalin, 22
Amylase, 33, 131, 150
  pancreatic, 183
α-Amylase, 139
β-Amylase, 33, 139
Amylo-1,6-glucosidase, 34, 131, 269
Amylopectin, 31, 32
Amylose, 31, 32
Anaerobic dehydrogenases, 256, 257
Anaphylaxis, 604
Androgens, 571
Androstenediol, 577
Δ⁴-Androstene-3,17-dione, 572
Δ¹,²-Androstenedione, 577
Androsterone, 572
Anemia, 210, 382
  forms, 409
  nutritional, 409
  pernicious, 468
Aniline, metabolism, 588
Animal starch. See Glycogen
Anoxia, 382
Anserine, 346, 485
Anthracene, metabolism, 589
Anthrone test, 25
Antibiotic substances, 613, 620, 621
Antibodies, 601
  estimating, 603
Anticoagulants, 221
Anti-egg white injury factor, 460. See
  also Biotin
Antigens, 601
Antihemorrhagic compounds, comparative
  activities, 483
Anti-lewisite, 155
Antiprothrombin, 222
Antithrombin, 220, 222
Antithyroid compounds, 540
Apoenzyme, 155
D-Arabinoascorbic acid, 473
Arabinose, 12, 21, 36, 37

Arachidic acid, 45
Arachidonic acid, 45, 307, 425, 484
Arginase, 131
Arginine, 76, 193, 330, 342, 345, 346
  in urea formation, 330
  metabolism, 345
Arginosuccinic acid, 331
Arsenate, 290
Arsphenamine, 608
Artichoke, 36
Ascites tumor cells, 282
Ascorbic acid, 353, 472, 473
  biosynthesis, 474
  chemistry, 473
  function, 475
  in biological oxidations, 256, 258
Ascorbic acid oxidase, 134, 153, 255, 475
Asparagine, 75
Aspartic acid, 75, 305, 344
Aspartic-β-semialdehyde, 344
β-Aspartyl phosphate, 344
Atabrine, 609
ATP. See Adenosine triphosphate
ATP-ase. See Adenosinetriphosphatase
Aureomycin, 620
Auxin, 580
Azelaic acid, 48

BACITRACIN, 620
Bacterial polysaccharides, 21
Bacteriochlorophylls, 9
Bacteriophage, 376
BAL (2,3-dimercaptopropanol), 155
Barcroft-Warburg respirometer, 136
Barfoed's reagent, 26
Basal metabolism, 385, 387
Base pairing, 123, 124
Batyl alcohol, 54
Beeswax, 54
Benadryl, 607
Bence Jones proteinuria, 529
Benedict's solution, 26
Benzene, metabolism, 587
Benzimidazole cobamide, 471
Benzoic acid, 590
Benzoyl adenylate, 335
Benzoyl CoA, 335
Benzoyl transfer, 459
1-Benzoylglucuronic acid, 594
Beriberi, 449
Betaine, 312, 342, 426
Bile, 184
  in urine, 530
  tests for, 189, 190
Bile acids, 317–319
Bile pigments, 187
Bile salts, 185
Bilirubin, 187

Biliverdin, 187
Biochemistry, 1
Biocytin, 461
Biological antagonism, 452, 457, 460, 465
Biological oxidations, 250
Biotin, 303, 306, 460, 461
Biotin–carbon dioxide complex, 306, 462
Biuret, 80
Biuret reaction, 80
Blood, 200
  buffers, 240–242
  circulation, 201
  clot, 219
  coagulation, 219, 221
  composition, 201–204, 223
  function, 200
  in urine, 531
  proteins, 176
  tests for, 223
Blood chemistry, normal and abnormal
  findings, 202, 203
Blood gases, 232
  measurement, 229
Blood group substances, 607
Body, defenses set up by, 601
  elementary composition, 395
Bond energies, 70
Bone, 504
  analysis, 505, 508
  composition, 505
  metabolism, 506
Borneol, metabolism, 595
Boyle's law, 227
Brain, chemistry, 495–500
Bread, 434
Bromine, function, 403
Bromobenzene, metabolism, 592
p-Bromophenylmercapturic acid, 592
Buffer(s), 92
  of blood, 240–242
Bufotenin, 356
Butter, 429, 430
Buttermilk, 430
Butyric acid, 45
Butyryl CoA, 305

CADAVERINE, 193
Calciferol, 478
Calcification, factors affecting, 506
Calcium, absorption, 397
  amount, in foods, 397
  blood clotting and, 219
  in blood, 396
  in bone, 396
  parathyroids and, 542
Calorie, 163, 379
Calorimeter, 379, 380
Calorimetry, 379, 384

Canavanine, 79
Cane sugar. *See* Sucrose
Capric acid, 45
Caproic acid, 45
Caproyl CoA, 305
Caprylic acid, 45
Carbamyl phosphate, 331
Carbohydrases, 131
Carbohydrate(s), 5
    absorption, 196
    amount in diet, 425
    classification, 10
    configuration, 12
    conversion into fat, 309
    metabolism, 266
        hormones involved in, 272
    oxidation, 279
Carbon dioxide, 365
    forms, in blood, 238
    passage, from tissues to erythrocytes, 239
Carbonic anhydrase, 133, 153, 240
Carboxydismutase, 293
Carboxyhemoglobin, 206
Carboxylase, 277, 284, 499
Carboxypeptidase, 132, 133, 153
Caries, dental, 174, 404, 509
Carnauba wax, 54
Carnaubic acid, 45
Carnosine, 346, 485
Carotene(s), 455. *See also* Vitamin A
β-Carotene, 445
Carotenoids, 444
Carrier(s), coenzyme as, 263
Cartilage, 503
Casein, 72, 419, 427
Catalase, 134, 139, 150, 152, 153, 162, 255
Catalysts, 128
Cathepsins, 132, 133
CDP-choline, 313
CDP-diglyceride, 313
CDP-ethanolamine, 313
Cell fluid, 218
Cell structure, 142, 143
Cellobiose, 131
Cellulase, 131
Cellulose, 35, 36
Cephalin, 61, 66, 313
Ceramide, 313
Cerasin, 64
Cereals, 433
Cerebrogalactosides, 64
Cerebron, 64
Cerebronic acid, 45, 64
Cerebrosidase, 300
Cerebrosides, 64
Cerotic acid, 45
Ceryl alcohol, 55
Cetyl alcohol, 55

CF. *See* Citrovorum factor
Charles' law, 227
Chaulmoogric acid, 45
Cheese, 432
Chemotherapy, 608
Chenodeoxycholic acid, 319
Chimyl alcohol, 54
Chinese wax, 54
Chitin, 21, 36
Chloramphenicol, 620
Chloride(s), 524
Chloride shift, 239, 402
Chlorocruorin, 232
Chloromycetin, 620
Chlorophyll, 6, 7
Chlorophyll *a*, 6
Chlorophyll *b*, 6
Chloroplast, 8
Chloroquine, 609
Chlortetracycline, 620
Cholanic acid, 57
Cholecystitis, 190
Cholecystokinin, 579
Choleglobin, 187
Cholelithiasis, 190
Cholestenone, 58
Cholesterol, 55, 187
    absorption, 197
    converted into bile acids, 319
    metabolism, 315–317
    preparation, 56
    synthesis, 315
    tests for, 56
Cholesterol ester(s), 65
Cholesterol esterases, 130, 300
Cholic acid, 186, 319
Choline, 61, 141, 191, 342, 426, 464
    assay, 464
    fat metabolism and, 311
    prevention of fatty livers, 312
    synthesis, 312
Chondroitin, 504
Chromatography, 38–40, 50, 82, 83, 125–127
    liquid-gas, 50
    silica gel, 50
Chromoproteins, 72
Chylomicrons, 65, 299
Chymosin, 179
Chymotrypsin, 132, 133, 183
Chymotrypsinogen, 132, 181
Cirrhosis, of liver, 311
Citric acid, 285
    in urine, 528
iso-Citric acid, 284
Citric acid cycle, 284
Citrovorum factor (CF), 343, 370
Citrulline, 77, 78, 330
Clearing factor, 300
Clot, blood, 219

Clupein, 72
CoA. *See* Coenzyme A
Coagulation, blood, 219, 221
    proteins, 102
Cobalt, vitamin B_{12} and, 413, 468, 470
Cocarboxylase, 499. *See also* Thiamine pyrophosphate
Coenzyme, 152
Coenzyme A (CoA), 122, 285, 286, 459, 460
Coenzyme F, 370
Coenzyme I. *See* Diphosphopyridine nucleotide
Coenzyme II. *See* Triphosphopyridine nucleotide
Coenzyme Q, 291, 481
Collagen, 108, 501, 503
Complement, 602
Complement fixation, 602
Condensing enzyme, 286
Conduction, nerve, 496
Connective tissue, 501
Cooking, 435
Copper, 411, 412
Coprosterol, 57
Corpus luteum hormone. *See* Progesterone
Cortical hormones, 556. *See also names of specific compounds*
Corticosteroids, adrenal, 556. *See also names of specific compounds*
Corticosterone, 57
Cortisone, 557
Countercurrent distribution, 49, 50
Coupling of reactions, 167
Cream, 429, 430
Creatine, 342, 486, 487
Creatine phosphate. *See* Phosphocreatine
Creatinine, 486, 523
Cyanide poisoning, 248, 249
Cyanmethemoglobin, 206
Cyanocobalamin, 470
Cyclopentanoperhydrophenanthrene, 55
Cyprenine, 72
Cystathionine, 349, 350
Cysteic acid, 351
Cysteine, 76, 192, 349, 350
    detoxicating agent, 592
Cysteine desulfhydrase, 135
Cysteine disulfoxide, 351
Cysteine sulfenic acid, 351
Cysteine sulfinic acid, 351
Cystine, 76, 186, 311, 426
    action on, in intestine, 192
    metabolism, 349–351
Cytidine, 119
Cytidine deaminase, 361
Cytidine diphosphate, 312
Cytidine triphosphate, 169, 312, 339
Cytochrome a, 253
Cytochrome b, 253

Cytochrome b_5, 476
Cytochrome c, 253, 254
Cytochrome c reductase, 134, 153, 257
Cytochrome oxidase, 134, 253
Cytosine, 116, 118
Cytosine deaminase, 361

D- (Dee) and L- (Ell), versus dextro (+) and levo (−), 13
Dalmatian dog, 363
Dalton's law of partial pressures, 227
Deamination, oxidative, 326
Debranching enzyme, 269
Decarboxylation, 327
Dehydroandrosterone, 577
Dehydroascorbic acid, 256, 473, 474
7-Dehydrocholesterol, 478
11-Dehydrocorticosterone, 57
Dehydroepiandrosterone, 573
Dehydrogenases, 134, 256
Dehydropeptidase, 153
Denaturation, 102–104
Dental caries, 174, 404, 509
Deoxyadenosine, 119
6-Deoxy-L-ascorbic acid, 473
Deoxycholic acid, 186, 319
Deoxycytosine, 119
Deoxyribonuclease, 123, 360
Deoxyribonucleic acid, 115, 117, 123, 124, 339, 371, 372
D-2-Deoxyribose, 20, 26
Deoxyribose-5′-phosphate, 364
Desmolases, 135
Desmosterol, 317
Desthiobiotin, 461
Detoxication, 585
Dextran, 35
Dextrin, 33, 35
Dextrose. *See* Glucose
DFP. *See* Diisopropylfluorophosphate
Diabetes, 552
Dialuric acid, 524
2,6-Diamino purine, 367
Diaminopimelic acid, 616
Diastase. *See* Amylase
3,5-Dibromotyrosine, 78
Dichlorophenoxyacetic acid, 582
Dichlororiboflavin, 455
Dicumarol, 221, 290
Diesterase, 361
Diet, 437, 438
Digestion, 170
    gastric, 175
    intestinal, 181
    salivary, 170
Digestive tract, 171
Digitalis, 22
Digitogenin, 22

Digitonin, 22, 56, 57
D-α,β-Diglyceride, 43, 308
Dihydrocholesterol, 57
Dihydrofolic acid, 467
Dihydroorotic acid, 368
Dihydrosphingosine, 63, 313
Dihydrostreptomycin, 619
Dihydroxyacetone phosphate, 277, 308
1,2-Dihydroxy-1,2-dihydroanthracene, 589
5,6-Dihydroxyindole, 353
5,6-Dihydroxyindole-2-carboxylic acid, 353
3,4-Dihydroxyphenylalanine ("dopa"), 79, 255, 353
Dihydroxystearic acid, 48
3,5-Diiodotyrosine, 78
    transformed into thyroxine, 538
Diisopropylfluorophosphate (DFP), cholinesterase and, 498
2,3-Diketo-L-gulonic acid, 474
2,3-Dimercaptopropanol, 155
Dimethylbenzimidazole B_{12}, 303
Dimethylethanolamine, 312, 464
Dimethylglycine, 342
1,2-Dimethylphenanthrene, 565
Dinicotinyl ornithine, 457
2,6-Dinitro-4-aminotoluene, 590
2,4-Dinitrofluorobenzene, 84
2,4-Dinitrophenol, 290
Dinitrophenyl amino acids, 84
Diodrast, 517
Dipeptidase, 133, 153
Diphenylacetylornithine, 592
1,3-Diphosphoglyceric acid, 277
Diphosphoinositide, 63
Diphosphopyridine nucleotide (DPN), 121, 154, 258
Disaccharides, 10, 22–24
Dithiopropanol, 155
Djenkolic acid, 79
Donnan's theory, 104, 105
"Dopa." See 3,4-Dihydroxyphenylalanine
Dopaquinone, 255, 353
DPN. See Diphosphopyridine nucleotide
Drugs, 499
Dyes, 261

EDEMA, 212, 423
Edestan, 73
Edestin, 71
Eggs, 433
Eicosatetraenoic acid, 484
Eicosatrienoic acid, 307
Elastase, 503
Elastin, 502, 503
Electron transport, 264
Electrophoresis, 98

Embden-Meyerhof pathway, 276
Embryonic growth, 373
Enamel, 508
    mottled, 403, 509
End groups in proteins, 84, 85
Endergonic, 165
Endocrine glands. See Hormone(s) and names of specific glands
Endopeptidases, 131
Endothermic, 164
Energetics, 162
Energy, 162, 163
Energy coupling, 291
Energy metabolism, 378
Energy requirements, 391
"Energy-rich" bonds, 168
Enol hydrase, 302
Enol-pyruvic acid, 277
Enolase, 133, 277
Enterogastrone, 579
Enterokinase, 132, 181
Enthalpy, 163
Entropy, 164
Enzyme(s), 128. See also names of specific enzymes
    catalytic power, 161
    chemical nature, 129
    classification, 130
    co-factors for, 151
    distribution, 145
    hydrogen ion concentration and, 149
    inhibitors, 158, 159
    intermediate compound formation, 150
    isoelectric point, 145
    mechanisms, 151
    metals in, 153
    molecular weight, 145
    pH optimum of, 150
    proteolytic, 131
    purification, 145
    specificity, 129
    temperature and, 150
Enzyme activity, demonstration, 137–139
    distribution, in cell, 141–145
    kinetics, 145–148
Epiallobiotin, 461
Epibiotin, 461
Epicoprosterol, 57
Epidihydrocholesterol, 57
Epinephrine, 272, 310, 311, 353, 554
Epithelial tissue, 500
Equilenin, 563
Equilibrium constant, 165
Equilin, 563
Ergosterol, 58, 478
Ergothioneine, 77, 346
Erucic acid, 45
Erythrocytes, 204
    life span, 208

Erythrodextrin, 35
Erythromycin, 619
Erythrose, 12
Erythrose-4-PO$_4$, 280, 281
Esterases, 130
Estradiol, 561, 563, 566
  metabolism, 565
Estrane, 563
Estriol, 58, 563, 566
Estrogens, 570
Estrone, 563, 566
Ethanolamine, 312, 341, 464
Ethereal sulfates, 593
Ethyl benzene, oxidation, 587
Ethyl mercaptan, 192
Etiocholanic acid, 57
Etiocholanolone, 573
Excelsin, 71
Exergonic, 165
Exopeptidases, 133
Extracellular fluid, 215

FAD. See Flavin adenine dinucleotide
Farnesyl pyrophosphate, 316
Fat(s), 42
  absorption, 197, 298
  amount, in diet, 425
  analysis, 50
  blood, 299
  butter, 44
  fatty acid content, 44
  human, 46
  metabolism, 298
    choline and, 311
    liver and, 304
  neutral, 42–54
  storage, 299
Fatty acid(s), 45, 52, 53
  biosynthesis, 304, 305
  blood, 299
  chemical properties, 47
  desaturation, 306–308
  determination, 49
  effects of hormones, 309
  essential, 483, 425
  non-esterified, 299
  oxidation, 48, 300
Fatty acid adenylate, 308
Fatty acyl CoA, 308
Fehling's solution, 26
Female hormones, 563
Fermentation, 37, 138
Ferritin, 73, 405, 406
Fibrin, 219
Fibrinogen, 108, 214, 219
Fibrinolysin, 220
Filtrate factor. See Pantothenic acid
Fish, 433

Flavin adenine dinucleotide (FAD), 122, 258
Flavin mononucleotide (FMN), 122, 258
Floridorubin, 7
Flour, 434
Fluorine, distribution, 403
  effects of excessive quantities, 404
  mottled enamel and, 403, 509
FMN. See Flavin mononucleotide
Folic acid, 343, 369, 465. See also Citrovorum factor
Folinic acid, 370, 467
Food(s), 436, 626
Formaldehyde, 343, 467
Formamidino-L-glutamic acid, 347
Formic acid, 343, 347, 365, 467
Formol titration, 94–96
Formyl glycinamidine ribotide, 366
Formyl kynurenine, 355
Formyl tetrahydrofolic acid, 343, 370
Formylacetoacetic acid, 353
Formyl-L-glutamic acid, 347
Formylglycineamide ribotide, 366
Free energy, 164, 165, 263
Fructofuranose, 24
Fructokinase, 268
α-Fructopyranose, 20
Fructose, 19, 20, 29, 30
Fructose-1-6-diphosphate, 38, 293
Fructose-6-phosphate, 38, 280, 281
Fructosidase, 131
Fruit sugar. See Fructose
Fruits, 435
Fucosterol, 58
Fumarase, 133, 139, 166, 284
Fumaric acid, 285, 353
Furan, 18
Furfural, 25

GALACTANS, 37
Galactokinase, 269
Galactolipids, 64
Galactopyranose, 20
Galactosamine, 21
Galactose, 12, 20, 26, 30, 37, 65
Galactosidase, 131, 300
Galactowaldenase, 269
Galacturonic acid, 37
Gallstones, 190
Gas(es), blood, 232
  measurement, 229
Gas laws, 227
Gastric analysis, 180
Gastric digestion, 175
Gastric juice, 176
Gastrin, 176
Gastrointestinal hormone, 579
Gaucher's disease, 64

Gelatin, composition, 101
Gene(s), 374
Gentisic acid, 591
Gliadins, 71, 419
Globin, 72
Globulin(s), 71, 214
Glomerular filtration, 513
Glucagon, 272, 273, 553
Gluconic acid, 26
Glucopyranose, 16
Glucosamine, 36, 21
Glucosan phosphorylase, 157
Glucosazone, 29
Glucose, 10, 11, 12, 29
  blood, 270
  cyclic structure, 14
  in urine, 529
  isomers, 11–15
  methylation, 17
  oxidation in body, 274, 279
  oxygen bridge (1:4), 18
  spatial arrangement of isomers, 13
  structure, 10
α-Glucose, 15
β-Glucose, 15
Glucose-1,6-diphosphate, 154, 155
Glucose-1-phosphate, 33, 38, 294
Glucose-6-phosphate, 38, 294
Glucose-6-phosphate dehydrogenase, 257, 280
Glucosidase, 131
Glucosulfatase, 131
Glucuronic acid, 26, 27, 293, 294, 474, 594
Glucuronidase, 131, 596
Glutamic acid, 75, 345–347, 471
D-Glutamic acid, 79
Glutamic dehydrogenase, 150, 329
Glutamic-γ-semialdehyde, 346
Glutaminase, 520
Glutamine, 75, 365, 495, 527
  detoxicating agent, 591
Glutamyl transferase, 337
Glutathione, 154, 258
  biosynthesis, 336
  detoxicating agent, 598
Glutathione reductase, 259
Glutelins, 71
Glutenin, 71
Glyceraldehyde, 12
Glyceraldehyde-3-phosphate, 364. See also 3-Phosphoglyceraldehyde
Glycerin. See Glycerol
Glycerol, 44, 308
L-Glycerophosphate, 168, 308
Glycerophosphatase, 130
Glycerophosphorylcholine, 60
Glycerose, 12
Glyceryl ethers, 54

Glycine, 74, 86, 209, 341, 349, 350, 365, 366
  metabolism, 312
Glycineamide ribotide, 366
Glycinin, 424
Glycocholic acid, 186
Glycocoll. See Glycine
Glycocyamine, 342, 486
Glycogen, 34
  in liver, 268
  in muscle, 35, 271
  synthesis, 270
Glycogenesis, 268
Glycolaldehyde, 341
Glycolic acid, 341
Glycolipids, 64
Glycolysis, 37, 138, 145, 275
  aerobic, 282
Glycoproteins, 72
Glycosides, cardiac, 22
Glycosuria, 550
Glycylalanine, 87
Glycylglycine, 88
Glycylglycylalanine, 88
Glyoxalase, 154
Glyoxylic acid, 341, 363
Gmelin's test, 190
Goiter, 535
Gonadotropic hormones, 544
Gramicidin, 290
Grana, 8
Grape sugar. See Glucose
Growth, metabolism and, 583
Growth hormone, 310, 543
Growth substances, 580
Guanase, 361
Guanidoacetic acid, 486
Guanine, 116, 118
Guanosine, 118
Guanosine triphosphate, 122, 169
L-Gulonic acid, 294, 474
Gulono-γ-lactone, 294, 474
Gulose, 12
Gum, 10
Gum arabic, 36

HALLACHROME, 353
Halotestin, 575
Hanus method, 52
Heat, of combustion, 164
  regulation, 390
Heat content. See Enthalpy
Helix, 109, 110
Heme, 205, 208, 209
Hemin, 189
Hemocuprein, 411
Hemocyanins, 232, 411

Hemoglobin, 205, 232
  combination with carbon monoxide, 206, 248
  composition, 101
  kinds, 207, 208
Hemolysis, 204
Hemophilia, 222
Hemosiderin, 407
Henry's law, 229
Heparin, 21, 221, 222, 504
Hepatocuprein, 590
Heptose, 10
Hexadecenoic acid, 46
Hexapyranose, 16
Hexokinase, 134, 268, 277
Hexose(s), 10
Hexosemonophosphate shunt, 279
High altitude, 247
High-energy bond, 168
Hippuric acid, 301, 335, 590
Hirudin, 222
Histaminase, 606
Histamine, 193, 347, 588
  antihistaminic substances and, 605, 606
Histidine, 76, 346
  metabolism, 346
  related to histamine, 193, 606
Histone(s), 71, 72
Homocysteic acid, 351
Homocysteine, 78, 349, 350
Homogenates, 136
Homogentisic acid, 352
Homo-γ-linolenic acid, 307
Homoserine, 344, 350
Hopkins-Cole reaction, 80
Hordein, 71
Hormone(s), 272, 535, 579
  adrenocorticotropic, 310, 546
  carbohydrate metabolism, 272
  carcinogenesis and, 577
  corpus luteum. See Progesterone
  cortical, 556
  fatty acid metabolism, 309
  female, 563
  gastrointestinal, 579
  gonadotropic, 544
  growth, 310, 543
  lactogenic, 545
  male, 571
  metabolic reactions and, 582
  ovarian, 563
  parathyroid, 541
  pituitary, 543, 547
  plant, 580
  sex, 561
  somatotropic, 310, 543
  thyroid, 535
  thyrotropic, 310, 545
  units of, 578

Hyaluronic acid, 21, 36, 131, 504
Hyaluronidase, 131, 504
Hydrases, 133
Hydrochloric acid, 177
Hydrogen bond, 70, 125
Hydrogen carriers, 263
Hydrogen ion concentration. See pH
Hydrogen sulfide, 192, 351
Hydrogenase, 134
Hydrolases, 130
Hydroperoxidases, 254
β-Hydroxyacyl dehydrogenase, 302
3-Hydroxyanthranilic acid, 355, 456
p-Hydroxybenzoic acid, 591
β-Hydroxybutyric acid, 304
β-Hydroxybutyryl CoA, 305
17-Hydroxycorticosterone, 557
17-Hydroxy-11-deoxycorticosterone, 557
β-Hydroxyisovaleryl CoA, 345
3-Hydroxykynurenine, 355, 456
Hydroxylysine, 77
β-Hydroxy-β-methyl glutaryl CoA, 303, 313, 345
5-Hydroxymethyl tetrahydrofolic acid, 343
5-Hydroxymethylcytosine, 117
Hydroxymethylfurfural, 25
p-Hydroxyphenylpyruvic acid, 352
17α-Hydroxyprogesterone, 557
Hydroxyproline, 76, 77, 345, 346
5-Hydroxytryptamine. See Serotonin
5-Hydroxytryptophan, 356
Hyperglycemia, 550
Hypertensin, 518
Hypophysis, 542
Hypoproteinemia, 424
Hypoxanthine, 118, 362
Hypoxia, 382

ICE CREAM, 433
Icterus, 190
Idose, 12
Imidazole acetic acid, 347
Immunochemistry, 601
Indican, 525, 586
Indigo-blue, 526
Indole, 192, 586
Indole ethylamine, 192
Indoleacetaldehyde, 356
Indoleacetic acid, 192, 356, 580
Indole-3-butyric acid, 581
Indolepropionic acid, 192
Indolepyruvic acid, 356
Indophenol oxidase. See Cytochrome oxidase
Indoxyl, 586
Infraproteins, 73
Inhibitors, 158, 277, 284

Inorganic elements, 394, 426
Inosine, 362
Inosinic acid, 121, 362, 366
myo-Inositol, 63, 463
Inositol phosphatides, 313
Insulin, 101, 107, 273, 309, 310, 517, 550, 552
Intermedin, 549
Interstitial fluid, 216, 218
Intestinal digestion, 181
Intestinal flora, 191
Intestinal juice, 183
Intracellular fluid, 218
Inulin, 36
Invertase, 131, 150, 162
Iodine, 51, 54, 402, 403, 537
Iodoacetic acid, 275, 278
Iodogorgoic acid. *See* Diiodotyrosine
Iodopsin, 446
3-Iodotyrosine, 78
Ion-exchange resins, 127
β-Ionone, 445
Iron, 404, 408
Isoalloxazine, 453
Isocitric acid, 285
Isocitric dehydrogenase, 284
Isoelectric point, 94, 99
Isoleucine, 74, 345
Isonicotinyl hydrazide, 619
Isopentenyl pyrophosphate, 316
Isoprene, 315
Isotopes, 82, 139–141
Isovaleric acid, 315
Isovaleryl CoA, 345

JAUNDICE, 190

KEPHALIN. *See* Cephalin
Kerasin. *See* Cerasin
Keratin, 101, 108
β-Ketoacyl thiolase, 303
α-Ketoadipic acid, 349
α-Ketobutyric acid, 344, 350
α-Ketoglutaric acid, 285
3-Keto-L-gulonic acid, 294, 474
α-Keto-isocaproic acid, 345
3-Keto-6-phosphogluconic acid, 280, 281
Ketone bodies. *See* Acetone bodies
Ketosis, 246
Kidney(s), 511
  acid-base regulation, 515
  energy expenditure, 514
  function, 511, 516
  glomerular filtration, 513
  tubular excretion, 515
  tubular reabsorption, 514
Kilocalorie, 163, 379

Knoop theory, 300
Krebs cycle, 284
Krebs solution, 136
Kwashiorkor, 425
Kynurenic acid, 357
Kynurenine, 355, 456

LACCASE, 153
Lactalbumin, 71
Lactase, 131
Lactic acid, 277
  formed in muscle contraction, 274
Lactic dehydrogenase, 150, 257, 277
Lactobacillus arabinosus, 79
Lactogenic hormone, 545
β-Lactoglobulin, 101
Lactose, 23, 30, 428
14-*nor*-Lanosterol, 317
Lauric acid, 45
Laurin, 354
Lecithin, 52, 59, 60, 66
  absorption, 197
  metabolism, 312
Lecithinases, 130
Legumin, 71
Leucine, 74, 345
  metabolism, 344, 345
D-Leucine, 79
Leucine aminopeptidase, 132
Leucosin, 71
Leucovorin, 370. *See also* Citrovorum factor
Leukocytes, 210
Levulose. *See* Fructose
Lewisite, 155
Liebermann-Burchard test, 56
Light, 9
Lignoceric acid, 45, 64
Linoleic acid, 45, 307, 484, 425
Linolenic acid, 45, 307, 484, 425
Lipase, 131, 150, 175, 180, 300
  pancreatic, 52, 131, 162, 183
Lipid(s), 42, 66
  metabolism, 298
Lipidosis, 63
Lipoic acid, 287, 452
Lipolytic enzymes, 300
Lipoproteins, 65, 72
Lipotropic action, 311, 426
Lithocholic acid, 186
Liver, 267, 268, 598
  fat metabolism and, 304
Luciferase, 134
Lumi-rhodopsin, 447
Lumisterol, 478
Lymph, 217, 299
Lysine, 75
  converted into α-aminoadipic acid, 348

Lysine, in large intestine, 193
   metabolism, 348
Lysolecithin, 60, 66
Lysophosphatidase, 300
Lysozyme, 131
L-Lyxonic acid, 475
Lyxose, 12

MANGANESE, 413
Magnesium, 398, 399
Male hormones, 571
Malic acid, 285
Malic dehydrogenase, 284
Malnutrition, 437
Malonyl CoA, 305
Malt sugar. See Maltose
Maltase, 131, 150
Maltose, 22, 23, 30
Mandelonitrile, 22
Manganese, 413
Mannan, 30
Mannitol, 27
Mannose, 12, 28, 30
Margarine, 429
Meat, 433
Melanin, 255, 353, 500
Menadione, 482
Menthol glucuronide, 294
Mesaconic acid, 471
Mesobilirubinogen, 187
Messenger RNA, 339
Metabolism, basal, 385
   energy, 378
   inorganic, 394
   interrelationships, 375
Metaphosphatase, 131
Metaproteins, 73
Methane, 192
Methemoglobin, 206, 382
Methionine, 76, 311, 349, 350, 426
Methyl alcohol, oxidation, 588
Methyl glucosides, 15
Methyl hydroxypyridine, 597
Methyl mercaptan, 192
Methyl nicotinamide, 355
Methylamine, 192
β-Methylaspartic acid, 471
Methylation, in detoxication, 597
Methylcholanthrene, 58
5-Methylcytosine, 115, 117
Methylene blue, 290
Methylmalonyl CoA, 303
2-Methyl-1,4-naphthoquinone, 482
N-Methylnicotinamide, 457
N-Methylnicotamide-6-pyridone, 457
Mevalonic acid, 316
Mevalonic acid pyrophosphate, 316
Michaelis-Menten formulation, 150, 151

Microorganisms, 600
Microsomes, 65, 142–144, 340
Milk, 427, 430, 431, 443
Milk sugar. See Lactose
Millon's reaction, 80
Mitochondria, 65, 142–144, 290, 340
Molisch test, 25
Molybdenum, 415
Monodehydroascorbic acid, 476
Monoiodotyrosine, 538
Monomethylaminoethanol, 464
Monomethylethanolamine, 312, 464
Monomethylglycine, 342
Monophosphoinositide, 63
Monosaccharides, 10–22, 24–29
Mucic acid, 26
Mucilage, 10
Mucin(s), 174
Muconic acid, 587
Mucopolysaccharides, 21, 131
Murexide test for uric acid, 523
Muscarine, 191
Muscle, carbohydrate metabolism and, 274
   contraction, 488
   glycogen, 271
   proteins, 488
Muscle adenylic acid, 120
Muscle inosinic acid, 121
Muscle tissue, 485
   contraction, 271
Mutarotation, 14
Mycosterols, 58
Myelin sheath, composition, 494
Myofibril, 489, 490
Myogen, 488
Myoglobin, 238
Myoglobulin, 492
Myoinositol, 63, 463
Myosan, 73
Myosin, 108, 488, 491
   ATP-ase and, 491
Myosinogen, 71
Myricyl alcohol, 55
Myristic acid, 45

NAPHTHALENE, 589, 592
α-Naphthalene acetic acid, 581
α-Naphthol, 591
Naphthylmercapturic acid, 592
Nefa, 299
Neomycin, 619
Neostigmine, 498
Nephritis, 529
Nephrosis, 529
Nerve(s), composition, 492
   conduction, 496

Nerve(s), metabolism, 493
  potential (action), 497
  tissue, 492
Nervone, 64
Nervonic acid, 64
Neurine, 191
Neurospora, 451
Niacin. *See* Nicotinamide
Nicotinamide (niacin), 355, 455–457, 591
Nicotinic acid. *See* Nicotinamide
Nicotinuric acid, 457, 591
Niemann-Pick disease, 493
Nilevar, 575
Ninhydrin reaction, 81
Nitrate reductase, 153
2-Nitro-4-aminophenol, 590
p-Nitrobenzaldehyde, change in body, 589
Nitrogen mustard, 579
Nitrogen pool, 325
Nitrophenols, 589
Non-esterified fatty acids (Nefa), 299
Nonprotein nitrogen (NPN), 204
Noradrenalin, 554
Norepinephrine, 554
NPN, 204
Nuclease, 131
Nucleic acid(s), 115, 123, 125–127, 372, 373
  helical structure, 124
  metabolism, 363, 364
Nuclein deaminases, 131, 361
Nucleodepolymerase, 359
Nucleophosphatase. *See* Nucleotidase
Nucleoprotein(s), 72, 112, 359
Nucleosidase, 131, 361, 362
Nucleoside(s), 118
Nucleoside phosphorylase, 362
Nucleotidase, 131, 361
Nucleotide(s), 120
Nucleus, 142–144
Number, acetyl, 51
  iodine, 51
  Reichert-Meissl, 51
  saponification, 51
  turnover, 139
Nutrition, 417

O¹⁸ ISOTOPE, 157
Obesity, 393
Octadecadienoic acid, 484
Octadecatrienoic acid, 484
Octanoicoxidase, 145
Octanoyl CoA, 305
Octopine, 79
Oleic acid, 45, 48, 307
Oleomargarine, 429

Oleyl alcohol. *See* Selachyl alcohol
Oligosaccharides, 25, 26
Orcinol, 25, 26
Organic compounds, metabolism, 585
Ornithine, 77, 330, 345, 346, 591, 592
Orotic acid, 118, 368
Orotodine-5′-phosphate, 368
Oryzenin, 71
Osazones, 28
Osseomucoid, 72
Osseous tissue, 504
Ovarian hormones, 563
Ovoglobulin, 71
Oxalacetic decarboxylase, 145
Oxalic acid, in urine, 528
Oxaloacetic acid, 285
Oxalosuccinic acid, 285
Oxalosuccinic decarboxylase, 284
Oxidase(s), 134, 253
Oxidation(s), biological, 250, 251
β-Oxidation, 300
Oxidation-reduction potential, 259, 260, 261
Oxidative decarboxylation enzyme, 284
6-Oxotestosterone, 577
Oxybiotin, 461
Oxygen, 230–232, 382
Oxygen capacities, 232, 237
Oxygen consumption (Qo₂), 137
Oxygen dissociation curve, 233–236
Oxyhemoglobin, 206
Oxynervone, 64
Oxynervonic acid, 64
Oxytetracycline, 620
Oxytocin (Pitocin), 69, 548

PABA. *See* *p*-Aminobenzoic acid
Palmitic acid, 45, 313
Palmitic aldehyde, 313
Palmitoleic acid, 46
Palmityl alcohol. *See* Chimyl alcohol
Palmityl CoA, 313
Pancreas, 181, 273, 549, 550
Pancreatic amylase, 183
Pancreatic juice, 181
Pancreatic lipase, 52, 131, 162, 183
Pancreozymin, 183
Pantothenic acid, 458, 459, 460
Pantoyltaurine, 460
Papain, 132, 133
Parathyroid(s), 541, 542
Parathyroid hormone, 541
Pars intermedia, 549
Partition coefficient, 49, 50
Pectins, 37
Pelargonic acid, 48
Pellagra, 456
Penicillin, 613

Penicillium notatum, 613
Pentachlorophenol, 290
Pentosans, 36
Pentose(s), 10
  metabolism, 364
Pentosenucleic acids (PNA), 115
Pentosuria, 281
Pepsin, 101, 131–133, 150, 178
Pepsinogen, 131, 178
Peptic hydrolysis, products, 179
Peptide(s), 65, 69, 73
Peptide bond synthesis, 334–337
Peptones, 73
Pernicious anemia, 468
Peroxidase(s), 134, 153, 255
Pettenköfer's test, 190
PGA, 466
pH, meaning of, 89
Phenanthrene, 589
Phenol, metabolism, 591
Phenol potassium sulfate, 593
Phenolglucuronic acid, 594
Phenolphthalein, change, in body, 595
Phenolsulfatase, 131
Phenylacetic acid, 301, 591, 592, 594
Phenylaceturic acid, 301
Phenylacetylglutamine, 591
Phenylalanine, 74, 86
  metabolism, 352
D-Phenylalanine, 79
Phenylketonuria, 353
Phenylpyruvic acid, 354
Phlorhizin, 22
Phloroglucinol, 25, 26
Phosphatase(s), 131, 157, 293, 361
Phosphate(s), 526
Phosphatid(s), 58. See also Phospholipids
Phosphatidases, 52, 59, 61, 300
L-α-Phosphatidic acid, 60, 308
Phosphatidyl ethanolamine, 61, 62, 313
Phosphatidyl serine, 62, 313
Phosphocreatine, 167, 274, 275
  ATP and, 167
  in muscle, 274, 486
Phosphodiesterase, 131
Phosphodihydroxyacetone, 276, 277, 308
Phospho-enol pyruvic acid, 277
Phosphoglucomutase, 134, 154, 155, 268, 277
6-Phosphogluconic acid, 280
6-Phosphogluconic dehydrogenase, 280
6-Phosphogluconolactonase, 280
6-Phosphogluconolactone, 280
3-Phosphoglyceraldehyde, 277, 280, 281
3-Phosphoglycerate kinase, 277
2-Phosphoglyceric acid, 277
3-Phosphoglyceric acid, 277, 312
Phosphoglyceromutase, 277
Phosphohexokinase, 277

Phosphohexose isomerase, 135, 269, 277, 280
Phosphoinositide, 62, 63
Phospholipase, 130
Phospholipids, 58, 141
  in blood, 65, 66
  metabolism, 311–314
Phosphomonoesterase, 131
Phosphomutase, 134
Phosphopentokinase, 293
Phosphopentose isomerase, 280
Phosphoproteins, 72
5'-Phosphoribosyl pyrophosphate, 369
Phosphorolysis, 33
Phosphorus, 397
  isotopes, 141
Phosphorus-oxygen bond, 157
Phosphorylase(s), 33, 34, 134, 269, 271, 272, 277
Phosphorylated intermediates, 278
Phosphorylation, aerobic, 289–291
Phosphorylcholine, 60, 312
Phosphoserine, 77, 312
Phosphotriose isomerase, 293
Photon, 9
Photosynthesis, 5–9, 292, 293
Phrenosin, 64
Phthiocol, 482
Phycobilin, 7
Physostigmine, 498
Phytosphingosine, 64
Phytosterols, 58
Picramic acid, 589
Picric acid, reduction, in body, 589
Pipecolic acid, 349
Pitocin. See Oxytocin
Pitressin. See Vasopressin
Pituitary, 542
  anterior, 543, 547
  intermediate, 549
  posterior, 547
Pituitary hormones, 543, 547
pK, 91–94, 118
Plant hormones, 580
Plasma, 211, 217, 218
Plasma protein(s), 66, 98, 211–215, 332, 333
Plasmalogens, 62, 313
Plasmochin, 609
Platelet factor, 220
PNA. See Pentosenucleic acids
Polynucleotide phosphorylase, 370
Polypeptides, 87, 88
Polysaccharides, 10, 31–37
Porphin, 7
Porphobilinogen, 210
Porphyria, 531
Porphyrins, 205, 531
Porphyropsin, 446
Potassium, 401

Potato, 435
P-P factor, 455
Precalciferol, 478
Prednisone, 558
Pregnancy, hormones excreted in, 561
Pregnane, 58
Progesterone, 561, 567, 568, 569
Progestin. *See* Progesterone
Prolactin, 545
Prolamins, 71
Prolidase, 153
Proline, 76, 345, 346
D-Proline, 79
Prontosil, 610
Propionic acid, 303
Propionyl CoA, 303
Prosthetic groups, 130
Protachysterol, 478
Protamines, 72
Proteans, 73
Protein(s), 68
  absorption, 198
  acids and bases, 96
  amino acid content, 101
  amount, in diet, 417
  biosynthesis, 338
  classification, 71–73
  coagulation, 102
  color reactions, 80
  composition, 101
  conjugated, 72
  constant solubility, 99
  cross linkages, 85, 104
  deficient, 419
  denaturation, 102–104
  derived, 72
  dynamic state of body, 322–326
  electrophoresis, 98
  end-groups, 84, 85
  fibrous, 71
  globular, 71
  helix, 109
  high and low, 424
  hydrolysis, 79
  in diet, 417
  in urine, 528
  isoelectric point, 99
  metabolism, 321–326
  molecular weights, 99
  native, 72
  plasma, 66, 98, 211–215, 332, 333
  precipitation reactions, 100, 101
  purity, 97–100
  structure, 106–110
  turnover, 326, 332
Proteoses, 73
Prothrombin, 219
Prothrombinogen, 220
Protoporphyrin, 205, 209
Provitamin A. *See* Carotene

Pteroyl glutamic acid (PGA), 466
Ptomaines, 192
Ptyalin, 170, 172, 173
Purine(s), 116, 118
  interconversion, 366, 367
  metabolism, 365
Purine bases, in urine, 528
Purpuric acid, 524
Putrefaction, 190
Putrescine, 193
Pyran, 16
Pyranose, 16
Pyribenzamine, 607
Pyridine, change, in body, 597
Pyridine nucleotides, 121
Pyridine-3-sulfonamide, 457
Pyridine-3-sulfonic acid, 457
Pyridoxal, 457, 458
Pyridoxal phosphate, 272, 328, 457, 458
Pyridoxamine, 457, 458
Pyridoxamine phosphate, 328, 458
Pyridoxine, 457, 458
Pyridoxine phosphate, 458
Pyrimidine(s), 116–118, 367–369
Pyrimidine nucleotide dehydrogenase, 134
Pyrophosphatase, 131, 150
Pyrophosphothiamine, 287
Pyrrole, 205
Δ'-Pyrroline-5-carboxylic acid, 346
Pyruvate phosphokinase, 277
Pyruvic acid, 277
Pyruvic acid oxidase, 284.

Q_{O_2}, 137
Q_{10}, 456
Q values, definition, 137
Q-enzyme, 33
Quinine, 609
Quinolinic acid, 456
5,6-Quinone. *See* Hallachrome

RAFFINOSE, 10
Reduced hemoglobin, 206
Reichert-Meissl number, 51
Renin, hypertension and, 517
Rennet, 179
Rennin, 179
Reserpine, 500
Resins, ion-exchange, 127
Respiration, chemistry, 226
  control, 246
Respiratory enzyme, 252. *See also* Cytochrome oxidase
Respiratory quotient (R.Q.), 137, 383

Retinene, 447
neo-b-Retinene, 447
Retinene reductase, 447
Rh factors, 607
Rhizopterin, 466
Rhodanase, 135
Rhodopsin, 447
Riboflavin, 453–455
Riboflavin dehydrogenase, 134
Riboflavin-5′-phosphate, 122
Ribonuclease, 101, 123, 360
Ribonucleic acid (RNA), 115, 123, 339, 370, 373
  messenger, 339
  soluble, 338
  template, 339
Ribonucleoprotein granules, 142–144, 340
Ribose, 12, 20
D-Ribose-1-phosphate, 364
D-Ribose-5-phosphate, 38, 280, 281, 364
Ribulose, 21
D-Ribulose-5-phosphate, 280, 281
Rice, 434
Ricinoleic acid, 45
Rickets, 397
RNA. See Ribonucleic acid
R.Q. See Respiratory quotient

S (entropy), 164
Saccharic acid, 26
Saccharose. See Sucrose
Salicylic acid, metabolism, 590
Salicyluric acid, 590
Saliva, 170–173
Salivary amylase. See Ptyalin
Salivary calculus, 175
Salivary digestion, 170
Salkowski test, 56
Salmine, 72, 101
Salts, absorption, 198
Salvarsan, 608
Saponification, 44
Saponification number, 51
Sarcosine, 342, 486
Schweitzer's reagent, 35
Scombrine, 72
Scombrone, 72
Scurvy, 472
Sea water, 218
Secretin, 182, 579
Sedoheptulose, 21
Sedoheptulose-7-phosphate, 280, 281
Selachyl alcohol, 54
Seliwanoff test, 25
Senecioyl CoA, 345
Serine, 75, 312, 341, 342, 349, 350

Serotonin, 356, 500
Serum, mammalian, 136
Serum albumin, 71, 101, 214
Serum globulin, 71, 214
Sex hormones, 561
Shikimic acid, 352
Shock, 215
Sialic acid, 22
Sitosterols, 58
Skatole, 192
Soap, 45
Sodium, 400, 401
Soluble RNA, 338
Somatotropic hormone, 310, 543
Sorbitol, 27
Specific activity, 333
Specific dynamic action, 389
Specificity, 604
Spectrophotometry, 138
Sperm oil, 54
Spermaceti, 54
Sphingolipids, 63
Sphingomyelin, 64, 66, 313
Sphingosine, 64, 313
Spinal fluid, 203
Squalene, 317
S-RNA, 338
Starch, 31–33
Stearic acid, 45
Stearin, 44
Stearyl alcohol. See Batyl alcohol
Stercobilin, 188
Stercobilinogen, 188
Steroids, 56, 570
  metabolism, enzymes, 575
Sterols, 56
Stigmasterol, 58
Stilbestrol, 567, 595
Strepogenin, 422
Streptidine, 619
Streptobiosamine, 619
Streptomycin, 618
Streptose, 619
Sturine, 72
Succinic acid, 285
Succinic dehydrogenase, 134, 150, 284
Succinyl CoA, 303, 209
Succinyl transfer, 459
Succinylsulfathiazole, 612
Sucrase, 184
Sucrose, 23, 24, 30
Sugar, 434. See also Glucose
Sulfa drugs, 610, 612. See also names of specific compounds
Sulfanilamide, 465, 596, 610, 612
Sulfapyridine, 612
Sulfatases, 131
Sulfates, 351, 524, 525
Sulfathiazole, 612

Sulfhydryl groups, enzymes and, 155
Sulfonamide compounds, 610, 612. *See also names of specific compounds*
Sulfur, forms, 351, 412
 neutral, 526

TACHYSTEROL, 478
Talose, 12
Taurine, 186, 351
Taurocholic acid, 186
Temperature, of body, 379
Template RNA, 339
Tendomucoid, 72
Terramycin, 620
Testosterone, 572
 metabolism, 574
Testosterone propionate, 575
Tetracycline(s), 619, 620
Tetradecenoic acid, 46
Tetrahydrofolic acid, 467
Tetrose, 10
Theelin. *See* Estrone
Thermodynamics, 162
Thiamine, 449–452
Thiamine pyrophosphate, 287, 451, 452
Thiocyanate, in body, 597
Thiokinase, 302
Thiopropionic acid, 192
Thiouracil, 540
Thiourea, 540
D-β-Thiovaline, 79
Threonine, 75, 342, 344, 420
Threose, 12
Thrombin, 219
Thrombocytes, 211
Thromboplastin, 219
Thunberg method, 138
Thymidine, 119
Thymine, 116, 118
Thymus histone, 72
Thyroglobulin, 538
Thyroid, 535, 539
Thyroid hormone, 535
Thyrotropic hormone (TSH), 310, 545
Thyroxine, 78, 290, 535, 537, 538, 539, 540
Tissue(s), 485
 connective, 501
 epithelial, 500
 muscle, 485
  contraction, 271
 nerve, 492
 osseous, 504
Tissue slices, 136
Tocopherols, 480, 481. *See also* Vitamin E
Toluene, oxidation, 587
Tooth (Teeth), 508

Tooth (Teeth), decay, 174, 404, 509
Toxins, 604
Toxisterol, 478
TPN. *See* Triphosphopyridine nucleotide
Transacetylase, 135
Transaldolase, 280
Transaminases, 134
Transamination, 327–329
Transferase, 134
Transferrin, 405
Transglucosidase, 34
Transglucosylase, 157
Transketolase, 280, 293
Transmethylase, 135
Transmethylation, 135, 350
Transphosphorylase, 134
Tributyrin, 51
Tricaprin, 51
Tricarboxylic acid cycle, 284
Triglycerides, 43, 65, 308, 309
3,5,3'-Triiodothyronine, 78, 537, 538
Triketohydrindene reaction, 81
2,4,6-Trinitrotoluene, metabolism, 590
Triolein, 51
Triose, 10
Triose phosphate dehydrogenase, 156, 277, 293
Triosephosphate isomerase, 277
Tripalmitin, 44, 51
Tripeptidases, 132, 133
Triphosphopyridine nucleotide (TPN), 121, 281, 306
Trisaccharides, 10
Tristearin, 43, 51
Tritium, 318
Tryparsamide, 610
Trypsin, 132, 133, 150, 162, 182
Trypsinogen, 132, 181
Tryptamine, 356
Tryptophan, 75, 456
 in large intestine, 192
 metabolism, 355
TSH. *See* Thyrotropic hormone
Turacin, 411
Turnover number, 139
Tyramine, 193
Tyrocidine, 65, 527
Tyrosinase, 134, 153, 255
Tyrosine, 74
 in large intestine, 193
 metabolism, 352
 oxidation, 255
Tyrosinosis, 353
Tyrothricin, 617

UDP-GALACTOSE, 294
UDP-glucuronide, 293, 294

Ultracentrifuge, 98
Uncouplers, 290
Unsaturated fatty acids, 306–308
Uracil, 117, 118
Urea, 363, 521
  formation, 329, 330
  in urine, 521
Urea clearance test, for kidney function, 517
Urease, 131, 150
Ureidosuccinic acid, 368
Uric acid, 118, 329, 362
  in urine, 523
  murexide test for, 523
Uricase, 153, 363
Uridine, 119
Uridine diphosphate glucose, 122, 269, 293, 294
Uridine triphosphate, 122, 169, 294
Uridine-5-phosphate, 368
Uridyl transferase, 269
Urine, 518
  abnormal constituents, 528
Urobilin, 188
Urocanic acid, 347
Urogastrone, 529

Valine, 74, 345
d-Valine, 79
Van den Bergh reaction, 190
Vanillin, oxidation, in body, 588
Vasopressin (Pitressin), 548
Vegetables, 435
Verdoglobin, 187
Viosterol. See Vitamin D
Viruses, 113, 114, 372, 374
Vision, 446
Vitamin(s), 442–444. See also names of specific compounds
Vitamin A, 444–448. See also Carotene
neo-a-Vitamin A, 446
neo-b-Vitamin A, 446, 447
Vitamin A acid, 448
Vitamin A aldehyde, 448
Vitamin A ester, 448
Vitamin A esterase, 300
Vitamin A₁, 445
Vitamin A₂, 445
Vitamin B complex, 448–472
  content, in foods, 469
Vitamin B₁. See Thiamine

Vitamin B₂. See Riboflavin
Vitamin B₆. See Pyridoxine
Vitamin B₁₂, 370, 468, 470
Vitamin B₁₂ coenzyme, 303
Vitamin C. See Ascorbic acid
Vitamin D, 476
Vitamin D₂, 478
Vitamin D₃, 478
Vitamin E, 479, 480
Vitamin G. See Riboflavin
Vitamin K, 481–483
Vitamin K₁, 481
Vitamin K₂, 482
Vitellin, 72

Warburg-Barcroft respirometer, 136
Warburg-Lipmann-Dickens pathway, 279
Water, absorption, 198, 531, 532, 533
  sea, 218
Water balance, regulation, 532
Waxes, 37
Wheat, 434
Wool wax, 54
Wys method, 52

Xanthine, 118, 362
Xanthine dehydrogenase, 256
Xanthine oxidase, 153, 256, 362
Xanthoproteic reaction, 81
Xanthosine, 120
Xanthurenic acid, 357
Xanthylic acid, 364
Xylene, oxidation, 587
Xylitol, 281, 294
Xylose, 12, 21, 36
d-Xylose-5-phosphate, 294
d-Xylulose, 294
Xylulose-5-phosphate, 280, 281

Yellow enzyme(s), Warburg's, 454

Zein, 71, 419
Zinc, 414, 551
Zwitterions, 92
Zymase, 37, 129
Zymosterol, 317

Laurie
merriwether